Mechanisms of Inorganic Reactions

Mechanisms of Inorganic Reactions

A Study of Metal Complexes in Solution

Fred Basolo and Ralph G. Pearson

Professors of Chemistry
Northwestern University

Second Edition

John Wiley and Sons, Inc.
New York · London · Sydney

FIRST CORRECTED PRINTING, MAY, 1968

Sophus Mads Jørgensen (1837–1914)
Professor of Chemistry in Copenhagen (1871–1908)

Alfred Werner (1866–1919)
Professor of Chemistry in Zurich (1893-1919)
Nobel Prize in Chemistry 1913

This book is dedicated to S. M. Jørgensen and A. Werner, whose pioneering work laid the foundation for the subject of coordination chemistry. Since these two great adversaries met only once, briefly, during their lifetime, it is our pleasure to bring them together here and to acknowledge the debt owed them by all who are interested in the class of compounds dealt with in this book.

Preface

It has been more than nine years since we completed the first edition of this book. During this time, the number of publications in chemistry per month has doubled, the number in inorganic chemistry has roughly tripled, and the number in the kinetics and mechanisms of inorganic systems has nearly quadrupled. Clearly, contrary to the situation in 1957, there is no lack of results to document a treatise of this kind. Our problem has been to sort through this wealth of information and to try to choose particularly informative examples.

The results available now permit a much more detailed picture of the reaction mechanisms prevailing for complexes in solution than was possible earlier. We have been gratified to note in our revision that it has not been necessary to modify greatly the ideas that were presented in the first edition. The difference is that now our concepts are clearer and our understanding greater. We hope that we have conveyed this more complete treatment and understanding to our readers.

In contrast to the first edition, we have made less use of crystal field theory and other ionic models. By now crystal field theory has been discussed in several complete books, and its virtues and shortcomings have been documented. This was not the case in 1957. We have tried to make as much use of molecular orbital theory as possible. Unfortunately the applications are still limited because bond energies are not easily calculated. For this reason we have retained some calculations of crystal field activation energies, though these must certainly be used with caution.

The two other important changes have been the adding of a chapter on the reactions of the transition metal organometallics, and the inclusion of many results obtained as a result of the recent proliferation of rapid reaction techniques. Again it has been pleasing to note that the mechanistic interpretations of these systems agree with, and complement very well, the conclusions reached earlier from investigations of the more conventional systems.

Because of the large amount of literature available, we have been forced to select our examples and references for various reasons that seemed important to us. One significant factor has been our obvious preference for the more available (and to us more readable) American and English journals. To all of our readers we extend our apologies if we appear to have slighted work which they regard as particularly significant. It should also be mentioned that several books on inorganic reaction mechanisms have recently appeared. Worthy of note are *Inorganic Reaction Mechanisms* by J. O. Edwards and *Ligand Substitution Reactions* by C. H. Langford and H. B. Gray.

We wish to thank all of our colleagues who supplied us with reprints and kept us informed of their work. In particular we express our appreciation to Professor R. L. Burwell, Jr., for his cogent comments, to Professor D. J. Cram, for advice concerning three-dimensional drawings, and to Miss Dorothy Ann Caproni, a jewel among secretaries.

Fred Basolo
Ralph G. Pearson

Evanston, Illinois
February 1967

Contents

Mechanisms of Inorganic Reactions

1

Introduction

The subject of this treatise is the mechanism of reactions of certain inorganic compounds, usually in homogeneous solution. By *mechanism* is meant all the individual collisional or other elementary processes involving molecules (atoms, radicals, and ions included) that take place simultaneously or consecutively in producing the observed overall reaction. It is also understood that the mechanism of a reaction should give a detailed stereochemical picture of each step as it occurs. This implies a knowledge of the so-called *activated complex* or *transition state*[1] not only in terms of the constituent molecules but also in terms of the geometry, such as interatomic distances and angles.

Kinetic studies and stereochemical studies provide the most powerful methods of investigating detailed reaction mechanisms. However, it is generally not possible to get absolute information. Thus postulated mechanisms are essentially theories devised to explain the facts obtained by experiments. Like other theories, mechanisms are subject to change as new information is uncovered, or as new concepts are developed in related areas of science. Nevertheless, the postulation of reaction mechanisms is of the greatest help in understanding and systematizing the study of an area of chemistry.

The area of chemistry concerned in this case is that of *coordination or complex compounds*.[2] Such compounds contain a central atom or ion, usually a metal, and a cluster of ions or molecules surrounding it. It is characteristic of the complex that it retains its identity, more or less, even in solution, though partial dissociation may occur. The complex may be non-ionic or a cation or anion, depending on the charges carried by the central atom and the coordinated groups. These groups are called *ligands*, and the total number of attachments to the central atom is termed the *coordination number*. Other common names for these compounds include complex ions (if electrically charged), Werner complexes, coordination complexes, or, simply, complexes.

The historical development of the chemistry of coordination compounds dates back approximately to the end of the eighteenth century. Since the existing valency theory during the early stages of this development could not adequately account for such materials, they were commonly referred to as complex compounds, a term still in common usage but no longer for the same reason. Much of this time the compounds were formulated by writing the generators side by side, e.g., $2KCl \cdot HgCl_2$ and $2KCl \cdot MgCl_2$, as if they were all of the same type. After some investigation it became apparent that these two compounds are not similar. Aqueous solutions of the two both contain potassium ions, but the former yields only a total of three compared to seven ions per mole for the latter. It is now realized that the first one is a coordination compound with the four chloride ions firmly attached to the mercury, as indicated by the formulation $K_2[HgCl_4]$, whereas the other is a *double salt* and is correctly formulated as written. It is often not possible to distinguish between double salts and coordination compounds on the basis of their behavior in aqueous solution. For example, x-ray data conclusively show[3] that the four chloride ions are tetrahedrally distributed about the Co(II) ion in the salt $K_2[CoCl_4]$ and therefore that it is a coordination compound rather than a double salt. However, this complex is labile and immediately reacts with water to yield a pink solution,

$$K_2[CoCl_4] + 6H_2O \rightarrow 2K^+ + Co(H_2O)_6^{2+} + 4Cl^- \qquad (1)$$

so that its behavior in solution does in fact resemble that of a double salt.

One other class of coordination compounds consists of the *metal ammines*. Tassaert[4] reported in 1798 that ammoniacal solutions of Co(II) chloride allowed to stand overnight yield an orange-colored crystalline product containing six molecules of ammonia. It was assumed that these compounds were analogous to salt hydrates, and they were designated as ammoniates, $CoCl_3 \cdot 6NH_3$. This analogy is essentially correct, for in hydrates, except for interstitial and anion water, the water is coordinated to the central metal ion. However, such information on the structure of salt hydrates became known only after extensive investigations of the properties of metal ammines The ammonia was found to be very firmly bound in $CoCl_3 \cdot 6NH_3$. This compound shows no loss of ammonia even at 150°C, and a solution of it in dilute sulfuric acid can be refluxed for several hours without the formation of appreciable amounts of ammonium sulfate. Other compounds of Co(III) chloride containing fewer than six ammonia molecules per complex were also prepared as shown in Table 1.1. Observations of the firmness with which the ammonia molecules are bound, the wide variations in color, the variations in the numbers of ionic chloride, and the existence of a green and a violet salt of the compound containing four molecules of ammonia suggested that the ammonia must in some way be a definite part of the compound instead of just loosely held in the crystal lattice. Experimental facts of this type were collected on many different systems and were finally correctly interpreted by Werner[5] in 1893.

Werner introduced the concept that, in addition to having a *normal* or *primary* valence, elements may also possess a *residual* or *secondary* valence. Thus Co(III) has a normal valence of three but in addition an affinity for six groups, that is, a residual valence or coordination number of six. This concept led to the formulations shown in Table 1.1, which adequately account for the properties of these compounds. Werner also proposed that the secondary valence bonds are directed in space, and thus that the *praseo*

Table 1.1   Cobalt(III) ammine chlorides

Compound	Color	Class Name	No. of Ionic Chlorides	Werner's Formulation
$CoCl_3 \cdot 6NH_3$	orange	*luteo* salt	3	$[Co(NH_3)_6]^{3+}3Cl^-$
$CoCl_3 \cdot 5NH_3$	purple	*purpureo* salt	2	$[Co(NH_3)_5Cl]^{2+}2Cl^-$
$CoCl_3 \cdot 4NH_3$	green	*praseo* salt	1	*trans*-$[Co(NH_3)_4Cl_2]^+Cl^-$
$CoCl_3 \cdot 4NH_3$	violet	*violeo* salt	1	*cis*-$[Co(NH_3)_4Cl_2]^+Cl^-$
$CoCl_3 \cdot 3NH_3$	blue green	...	0	$[Co(NH_3)_3Cl_3]$

and *violeo* compounds are geometrical isomers. This postulate of directed valence bonds has been of extreme importance in connection with the stereochemistry of these compounds.

G. N. Lewis[6] later expressed Werner's views of secondary valence or coordination in terms of electrons. Thus the bond between the central ion and each of the attached groups involves a pair of electrons and is represented as a *coordinate* or *dative* bond, $M \leftarrow L$ or $M^{\delta-}:L^{\delta+}$. The electronic configuration of metal ions is often such that they can accommodate as many as twelve electrons, or more, which in turn means that coordination numbers of six and greater are entirely possible. It has been suggested that ions tend to add a sufficient number of electrons by coordination so that the ion in the resulting complex has an *effective atomic number* (E.A.N.)[7] of the next noble gas,

$$Co^{3+} \quad \text{contains} \quad 24 \text{ electrons}$$
$$6NH_3 \quad \text{donate} \quad 12 \text{ electrons}$$
$$\overline{}$$

E.A.N. of Co^{3+} in $Co(NH_3)_6^{3+} = 36$ electrons (the same as Kr)

This rule can be given only qualitative significance because there are a very large number of exceptions. Furthermore the coordination number of a metal ion may differ depending on the nature of the coordinated groups: Ni(II) forms compounds in which it has coordination numbers of either four, five (Table 1.2), or six; Fe(III) forms FeF_6^{3-} and $Fe(CN)_6^{3-}$ but only $FeCl_4^-$. The polarizability, size, and ability to π-bond of a ligand all seem to play an important role in fixing the coordination number of a metal ion (Chapter 2). Some metal ions are also known to coordinate to a certain number of ligands readily and to an additional number of the same ligand with greater difficulty. For example, Hg(II) forms four-coordinated complexes, but two of the ligands are much more readily bound than the other two. Thus, the stepwise formation constants (p. 21) for $HgCl_4^{2-}$ are $\log K_1 = 7.15$, $\log K_2 = 6.9$, $\log K_3 = 1.0$, and $\log K_4 = 0.7$. Bjerrum[8] suggests therefore that Hg(II) be said to have a *characteristic coordination number* of two and a *maximum coordination number* of four. In spite of this, the four chloride ions in $HgCl_4^{2-}$ are probably equivalent.

Much the same behavior is observed with Cu(II), which is usually assigned a coordination number of four but which can coordinate to six groups with the formation of a distorted octahedron.[9] Similarly Ag(I) has a marked affinity for two ligands but can also exhibit a coordination number of three (Table 1.2) and four.[10] In fact, for certain ligands Ag(I) does not exhibit a marked affinity for only two groups but instead coordinates readily with either three or four groups.[11] It is apparent, then, that the assignment of a definite coordination number to a given metal ion must often be done with some reservation.

Stereochemistry

The early classical approach to the determination of the structure of coordinated entities was to deduce the structure on the basis of the known geometrical and optical isomers. Square planar, tetrahedral, and octahedral structures assigned on this basis have since been verified by modern physicochemical methods, the most reliable being x-ray analysis.[12] Although the coordination number of the central ion for most compounds is either six or four, examples of compounds are known which exhibit each of the other numbers up to ten (Table 1.2).

The four ligands in four-coordinated complexes may be positioned either at the corners of a tetrahedron, as is true of carbon compounds, or at the corners of a square plane. For a discussion of other possible structures and a much more complete treatment of square complexes, the reader is referred to a review on the subject by Mellor.[13] The first suggestion that coordination compounds may have a square structure was made by Werner[5] in an attempt to account for the existence of α and β forms of $Pt(NH_3)_2Cl_2$. He pointed out that, since there can only be one form for tetrahedral compounds of this type, MA_2B_2 (individual letters A, B, C, L, X, Y, etc., are used to designate unidentate ligands), the isolation of two isomers is an indication of a planar structure. For $Pt(NH_3)_2Cl_2$ the isomers can be represented as

$$
\begin{array}{ccc}
& Cl & \\
& | & \\
Cl-&Pt&-NH_3 \\
& | & \\
& NH_3 & \\
& cis &
\end{array}
\qquad
\begin{array}{ccc}
& NH_3 & \\
& | & \\
Cl-&Pt&-Cl \\
& | & \\
& NH_3 & \\
& trans &
\end{array}
$$

where Pt(II) and the coordinated ligand atoms are all five in the plane of the paper.* The same view using sphere and stick models is shown by

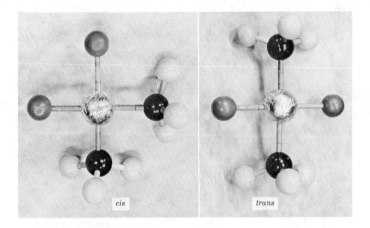

cis   trans

* These structural diagrams correspond to

$$
\begin{array}{ccc}
Cl- & \text{---} & NH_3 \\
/ & \searrow\!\!\!\nearrow & | \\
& Pt & \\
/ & \nearrow\!\!\!\searrow & | \\
Cl- & \text{---} & NH_3
\end{array}
\quad \text{or} \quad
\begin{array}{ccc}
Cl & \text{-------} & NH_3 \\
/ & Pt & / \\
Cl & \text{-------} & NH_3
\end{array}
$$

which are in common use by coordination chemists. Departure at this time from the more traditional representations is prompted by the fact that modern undergraduate textbooks use the solid-wedge/dashed-line representation. Students are rapidly becoming familar with projection diagrams of this type. We older chemists will require a little practice in order to visualize the stereochemistry easily. This method of representation is preferable because lines between atoms mean that there is a chemical bond, whereas in the traditional method some lines are used to designate structure and others to show bonding (in some cases the bonding lines are even omitted).

and for molecular models by

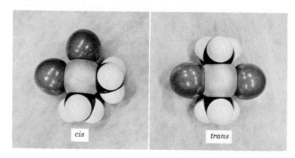

cis   trans

This arbitrary choice of placing all five of the coordinated atoms in the plane of the paper is convenient because it readily permits the visual expansion of coordination number to give a trigonal bipyramidal structure:

$$
\begin{array}{ccc}
NH_3 & NH_3Cl & NH_3 \\
| & | & | \\
Cl-Pt-Cl \xrightarrow{+I^-} & Cl-Pt \xrightarrow{-Cl} & Cl-Pt-I \\
| & | & | \\
NH_3 & NH_3 I & NH_3
\end{array}
$$

Alternative representations are available, and these can all be used interchangeably as the particular circumstances demand.

$$
\begin{array}{ccc}
NH_3 \quad Cl & NH_3 \quad Cl & NH_3 \\
\diagdown \quad \diagup & \diagdown \quad \diagup & \\
Pt & Pt & Cl-Pt-Cl \\
\diagup \quad \diagdown & \diagup \quad \diagdown & \diagdown \\
Cl \quad NH_3 & Cl \quad NH_3 & H_3N
\end{array}
$$

Same as the above representation with Pt(II) and all ligand atoms in the plane of the paper

The xy plane $\perp$ to the paper with vertical z axis in the plane of the paper

The x axis in the plane of the paper and y axis $\perp$ to it; vertical z axis in the plane of the paper

This assignment of a square planar structure to Pt(II) complexes seemed justified because of the large number of such isomers that had been isolated, e.g., $Pt(NH_3)_2(NO_2)_2$, $Pt(py)_2(NH_3)_2^{2+}$, and $Pt(py)_2Cl_2$.† Additional chemical evidence in support of this is afforded by the synthesis of two geometrical isomers of compounds such as $Pt(gly)_2$.[14] Planar compounds of this type, $M(AB)_2$ [a combination of letters in parentheses is used to designate multidentate ligands; for example, (AA) is a symmetrical bidentate group such as ethylenediamine, (AB) is an unsymmetrical bidentate group such as glycinate or benzylmethylglyoximate

---

† The meanings of symbols for some of the common ligands such as py and gly are given in Table 1.12.

ions, and (AABBAA) is a sexadentate group such as ethylenediaminetetra-acetate ion], can exist in *cis* and *trans* forms, neither of which is optically active:

$$
\begin{array}{cc}
\text{A—M—B} & \text{A—M—A} \\
\textit{cis} & \textit{trans}
\end{array}
$$

However, the tetrahedral structure gives rise to mirror image isomers,

$$
\textit{dextro} \qquad\qquad \textit{levo}
$$

Chernyaev[15] by an application of the phenomenon of the "*trans* effect" (Chapter 5) was able to prepare three isomeric forms of Pt(NH$_2$OH)(py)-(NH$_3$)NO$_2^+$. More recently three isomers have also been obtained of the compounds Pt(C$_2$H$_4$)(NH$_3$)ClBr[16] and Pt(py)(NH$_3$)ClBr.[17] A tetrahedral configuration for such compounds, MABCD, would result in an asymmetric central ion and optical activity, but a planar structure predicts the existence of three geometrical isomers:

$$
\begin{array}{ccc}
\text{D—M—B} & \text{D—M—C} & \text{C—M—B} \\
\end{array}
$$

Finally, a very elegant chemical approach to this problem was that of Mills and Quibell,[18] who prepared and resolved isobutylenediamine-*meso*-stilbenediamineplatinum(II) chloride. If the arrangement of the Pt(II) valences is tetrahedral, the complex has a median plane of symmetry and thus cannot be optically active. However, a coplanar arrangement of the two chelate rings does give a dissymmetric cation which can form mirror image isomers. The structure of four-coordinated Pt(II) compounds has now been determined by many different methods, and there can be no doubt that it is square planar.[12] The square planar structure has also been established for a number of complexes of Pd(II), Ni(II), Ag(II), Cu(II), Au(III), Rh(I), and Ir(I).

Optically active compounds of the type $M(AB)_2$ have been cited as evidence for the tetrahedral structures of B(III), Be(II), Zn(II), and Cu(II) (Table 4.9). These compounds racemize rapidly, so that generally the optical activity of the complex was attributed to the observed mutarotation in the presence of either an optically active resolving agent or ligand. This assignment of tetrahedral structure seems justified for complexes of B(III) and Be(II), but may not be correct for complexes of Zn(II) and Cu(II). These complexes can have a coordination number of six, which might also account for the observed mutarotations. However, on the basis of available physicochemical evidence, it is possible to assign a tetrahedral configuration to some metal complexes[12] of Cu(I), Ag(I), Au(I), Be(II), Zn(II), Cd(II), Hg(II), B(III), Al(III), Fe(III), Mn(II), Co(II), Ni(II), Cr(II) and Ni(O). Further investigations[19] show that transition metals form tetrahedral complexes more commonly than was initially expected on the basis of crystal field theory. This subject is discussed in the next chapter.

Except for a few special cases,[20] substances which contain six groups around a central ion have an octahedral configuration. Werner concluded that the octahedral distribution of groups was correct for six-coordinated compounds because in no case had more than two isomers of either MA_4B_2 or MA_3B_3 been isolated. He pointed out that, if such compounds had either a planar or a trigonal prismatic structure, three isomeric forms were possible. However, the geometrical isomers expected for the octahedral structure of complexes of the type MA_4B_2, such as $Co(NH_3)_4Cl_2{}^+$, are‡

cis   trans

‡ The representations that have been in more common use are

The stick-sphere models of this view are

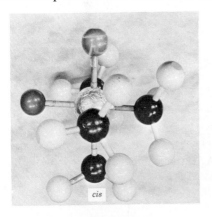

and the molecular models are

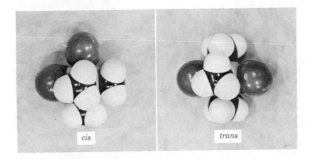

This choice of having four of the ligand atoms in the plane of the paper with one ligand in front and one behind the plane is made because it corresponds to the usual representation of the three cartesian axes. Such a representation can be readily simplified as follows:

$$x-Cl-\overset{\overset{\displaystyle Cl}{|}}{\underset{\underset{\displaystyle z}{|}}{Co}}-NH_3 \quad \text{or} \quad Cl-\overset{\overset{\displaystyle Cl}{|}}{\underset{\underset{\displaystyle NH_3 \ NH_3}{}}{\nearrow}}-NH_3$$

Thus, for the projection diagrams shown above of *cis*- and *trans*-$Co(NH_3)_4Cl_2^+$ the wedged-dashed line is the y axis. This type of representation is usual with authors interested in the application of group theory to chemical bonding in metal complexes. Again alternative representations are possible and in certain cases may be more desirable.

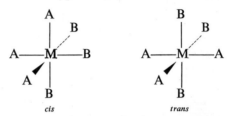

For compounds of the type MA_3B_3 the isomers are

A plane ⊥ to the paper with the two ligands in the plane of the paper in vertical positions

A plane in the paper and two ligands ⊥ to this plane, one in front and one in back of the plane of the paper

Three ligands in front of the plane of the paper and three behind in staggered positions

cis

trans

That complexes such as $Co(NH_3)_4(NO_2)_2^+$, $Co(NH_3)_4Cl_2^+$, and $Co(NH_3)_3(NO_2)_3$ had only been isolated in two different forms can only be cited as an indication of an octahedral structure. That neither the planar nor the trigonal prismatic structure is correct for these systems was finally established by the resolution of complexes of the type $M(AA)_3$, which would not be optically active for either of these two structures. The existence of such optically active complexes is, however, consistent with an octahedral structure. Since optical activity was originally associated with only organic compounds, it was necessary for Werner[21] to resolve

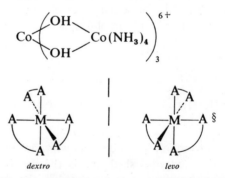

dextro

levo

§ Generally the chelate ring will be partly in back and/or in front of the plane of the paper. No attempt will be made to show this in the diagrams. A simple curved line will always indicate a chelate ring.

Only two other completely inorganic complexes have been resolved, *cis*-Rh(NHSO$_2$NH)$_2$(H$_2$O)$_2^-$ [22] and Cr(HPO$_3$)$_3^{3-}$.[23] The resolution of six-coordinated complexes of the metal ions Al(III), As(V), Cd(II), Cr(III), Ga(III), Ge(IV), Ir(III), Fe(II), (III), Ni(II), Os(II), (III), Pt(IV), Rh(III), Ru(II), Ru(III), Ti(IV), and Zn(II) has been reported, and examples of some of these are listed in Table 4.4. The octahedral structure has now been amply verified by x-ray analysis and is accepted for most six-coordinated compounds. Trigonal prismatic structures have long been known[20a] to exist in the infinitely extended systems of MoS$_2$ and WS$_2$. Recent investigations[20b] show that trigonal prismatic coordination occurs in molecular complexes of certain transition metals containing bidentate sulfur ligands.

Coordination compounds in which the coordination number of the central ion is different from either four or six are less common. Some examples of other coordination numbers are summarized in Table 1.2. In certain cases the structures have been determined by either x-ray analysis or electron diffraction measurements. However, for several of the complexes the coordination number is known only from data on the stoichiometry of the compounds and their molecular weights. Stoichiometric data alone are usually not sufficient to establish the coordination number of a compound. Thus, compounds of the composition (NH$_4$)$_3$ZnCl$_5$ and (NH$_4$)$_2$FeCl$_5$·H$_2$O, believed to have a coordination number of five, were shown by x-ray studies to have coordination numbers of four,[56] NH$_4$Cl·(NH$_4$)$_2$ [ZnCl$_4$], and of six,[58] (NH$_4$)$_2$[Fe(H$_2$O)Cl$_5$].

A discussion of the stereochemistry of coordination compounds is not complete without a summary of the different types of isomerism (Table 1.3). The synthesis, separation, and characterization of these isomers generally follow no set of fixed rules. However, the *trans*-effect phenomenon (Chapter 5) has been applied with some success to the synthesis of geometrical isomers of Pt(II) complexes. A general method has also been described[59] for the synthesis of geometric isomers of the types Pt(PR$_3$)$_2$Cl$_2$ and Pt(AsR$_3$)$_2$Cl$_2$. It depends upon the fact that the *cis* isomer is less soluble than the *trans* in benzene and that catalytic amounts of PR$_3$ or AsR$_3$ permit rapid *cis-trans* equilibration in solution. Thus, upon concentration of the solution in the presence of a catalyst, crystals of the less soluble *cis* isomer are obtained. At equilibrium in solution the mixture is largely the *trans* isomer. If the catalyst is removed by the addition of the dimer [Pt(PR$_3$)$_2$Cl$_2$]$_2$ or [Pt(AsR$_3$)$_2$Cl$_2$]$_2$ and the solution is evaporated, the product obtained is largely the *trans* isomer. The small amount of *cis* form which also separates is readily removed by extraction with ether (see also p. 424).

Likewise, a method for the preparation of *trans*-Pt(IV) ammines involves

Table 1.2 Some metal complexes of coordination numbers other than four or six

C.N.	Complex[a]	Structure[12]
2	$Ag(NH_3)_2^+$, $Au(CN)_2^-$, $Hg(NH_3)_2^{2+}$	linear
3	$M(PR_3)_2I$;[24] $M(I) = Cu$, Ag, Au	probably planar
	$Ag(PR_3)_3^+$, $Ag(SR_2)_3^+$,[25] $Ag(tu)_3^+$ [26]	,, ,,
5[27]	$Fe(CO)_5$,[28] $Pt(SnCl_3)_5^{3-}$,[29] $Mn(CO)_5^-$ [30]	trigonal pyramidal
	$Ir(PPh_3)_2CoCl$,[31] $Rh(PPh_3)_3(CO)H$ [32]	,, ,,
	$M(terpy)Cl_2$; $M(II) = Cu$, Zn, Cd[33]	,, ,,
	$M(QAS)X^+$; [34a] $M(II) = Ni$, Pd, Pt	,, ,,
	$Ni(TAP)_2X^+$,[34b] $NiTSPX^+$ [34c]	,, ,,
	$Ni(CN)_5^{3-}$,[34d] $Ni(PEt_3)_2Br_3$,[35] $Ni(triars)Br_2$ [36]	tetragonal pyramidal
	$MNO(S_2CN(CH_3)_2)_2$;[37] $M = V$, Fe, Co	,, ,,
	$[Co(MNT)_2py]^-$, $[Co(MNT)_2PPh_3]^-$ [38]	,, ,,
	$Co(CNR)_5^+$ [39]	,, ,,
	$Ni(X\text{-}SALen\text{-}NR_2)_2$,[40a] $M(R_5dien)X^+$ [40b]	distorted structure
7[41]	ZrF_7^{3-},[42] $[Fe(EDTA)H_2O]^-$ [43]	pentagonal bipyramidal
	NbF_7^{2-}, TaF_7^{2-},[44] $[Mn(EDTA)H_2O]^{2-}$ [45]	face-centered trigonal prism
8[46,47]	$Mo(CN)_8^{4-}$,[48] $Mo(CNBF_3)_8^{4-}$,[49]	triangular-faced
	$Zr(C_2O_4)_4^{4-}$ [50]	dodecahedral
	$M(N(CH_2COO)_3)_2^{2-}$; $M(IV) = Zr$, Hf[51]	,,
	$M(diars)_2Cl_4$; $M(IV) = Ti$, Zr, Hf, V, Nb, Tc, Re[46]	,,
	TaF_8^{3-},[52] $M(acac)_4$; $M(IV) = Zr$[53], Th, U[54]	square antiprismatic
9[41]	$Nd(H_2O)_9^{3+}$,[55] ReH_9^{2-} [56a]	face-centered trigonal prism
10	$La(H_2O)_4EDTA^-$ [56b]	see reference 56b

[a] The symbols used are: tu = thiourea; Ph = phenyl; terpy = 2,2′,2″-terpyridine; QAS = tris(o-diphenylarsinophenyl)arsine; TAP = tris(3-dimethylarsinopropyl)phosphine; TSP = tris(o-methylthiophenyl)phosphine; triars = $(CH_3)_2AS(CH_2)_3As(CH_3)(CH_2)_3As(CH_3)_2$; py = pyridine; MNT = 1,2-dicyanoethylene-1,2-dithiolate ion; X-SALen-NR$_2$ = Schiff bases formed from salicylaldehydes and N,N-substituted ethylenediamines; R$_5$dien = $R_2NC_2H_4NRC_2H_4NR_2$; EDTA = ethylenediaminetetraacetate ion; diars = o-phenylene-bis(dimethylarsine); acac = acetylacetonate ion.

Table 1.3 Types of isomerism for coordination compounds[2]

Isomerism	Examples
Geometrical	cis- and trans-Pt(NH$_3$)$_2$Cl$_2$ cis- and trans-[Co(NH$_3$)$_4$Cl$_2$]Cl
Optical	(+)- and (−)-bis(benzoylacetonato)beryllium(II) (+)- and (−)-[Cr(en)$_3$]Cl$_3$
Polymerization	Pt(NH$_3$)$_2$Cl$_2$, [Pt(NH$_3$)$_4$][PtCl$_4$], [Pt(NH$_3$)$_4$][Pt(NH$_3$)Cl$_3$]$_2$, and [Pt(NH$_3$)$_3$Cl]$_2$[PtCl$_4$]
Coordination	[Co(NH$_3$)$_6$][Cr(C$_2$O$_4$)$_3$] and [Cr(NH$_3$)$_6$][Co(C$_2$O$_4$)$_3$] [Cr(NH$_3$)$_6$][Cr(NCS)$_6$] and $\quad$[Cr(NH$_3$)$_4$(NCS)$_2$][Cr(NH$_3$)$_2$(NCS)$_4$] [Pt$^{(II)}$(en)$_2$][Pt$^{(IV)}$Cl$_6$] and [Pt$^{(IV)}$(en)$_2$Cl$_2$][Pt$^{(II)}$Cl$_4$]
Ionization	[Pt(NH$_3$)$_3$Cl]I and [Pt(NH$_3$)$_3$I]Cl [Co(en)$_2$(NCS)Cl]NCS and [Co(en)$_2$(NCS)$_2$]Cl
Hydrate	[Cr(H$_2$O)$_6$]Cl$_3$, [Cr(H$_2$O)$_5$Cl]Cl$_2$·H$_2$O, and [Cr(H$_2$O)$_4$Cl$_2$]Cl·H$_2$O [Co(NH$_3$)$_5$H$_2$O](NO$_3$)$_3$ and [Co(NH$_3$)$_5$NO$_3$](NO$_3$)$_2$·H$_2$O
Linkage	[(NH$_3$)$_5$Co—NO$_2$](NO$_3$)$_2$ and [(NH$_3$)$_5$Co—ONO](NO$_3$)$_2$ [(NH$_3$)$_5$Rh—NO$_2$]Br$_2$ and [(NH$_3$)$_5$Rh—ONO]Br$_2$ [60] (bipy)$_2$Pd—(NCS)$_2$ and (bipy)$_2$Pd—(SCN)$_2$ [61a] (OC)$_5$Mn—NCS and (OC)$_5$M—SCN [61b] (H$_2$O)$_5$Cr—NCS^{3+} and (H$_2$O)$_5$Cr—SCN [61c] (NC)$_5$Co—CN^{3-} and (NC)$_5$Co—NC^{3-} [62a] (H$_2$O)$_5$Cr—CN^{2+} and (H$_2$O)$_5$Cr—NC^{2+} [62b] (H$_3$N)$_5$Co—OSO$_2$S$^+$ and (H$_3$N)$_5$Co—SSO$_3^+$ [62c] (H$_3$N)$_5$Rh—NCS^{2+} and (H$_3$N)$_5$Rh—SCN^{2+} [62d]

Coordination
position

$$
(R_3P)_2Pt\begin{array}{c}\text{Cl}\\ \diagup\ \diagdown\\ \ \ \ \ \ \ \ \ \ \text{PtCl}_2\\ \diagdown\ \diagup\\ \text{Cl}\end{array}\ \text{and}\ ClR_3PPt\begin{array}{c}\text{Cl}\\ \diagup\ \diagdown\\ \ \ \ \ \ \ \ \text{PtPR}_3Cl\\ \diagdown\ \diagup\\ \text{Cl}\end{array}
$$

$$
\left[(NH_3)_4Co\begin{array}{c}\text{OH}\\ \diagup\ \diagdown\\ \ \ \ \ \ \ \ \ \ \text{Co(NH}_3)_2Cl_2\\ \diagdown\ \diagup\\ \text{OH}\end{array}\right]SO_4
$$

$$
\text{and}\ \left[Cl(NH_3)_3Co\begin{array}{c}\text{OH}\\ \diagup\ \diagdown\\ \ \ \ \ \ \ \ \ \ \text{Co(NH}_3)_3Cl\\ \diagdown\ \diagup\\ \text{OH}\end{array}\right]SO_4
$$

Conformation

$$
\begin{array}{c}
\text{Ph}_2\text{PCH}_2\text{C}_6\text{H}_5\\
|\\
\text{X—Ni—X}\quad\text{and}\\
|\\
\text{Ph}_2\text{PCH}_2\text{C}_6\text{H}_5
\end{array}
\qquad
\begin{array}{c}
\quad\quad\text{X}\\
\text{X} \quad\text{Ph}_2\ ^{63}\\
\quad|\\
\text{Ni—PCH}_2\text{C}_6\text{H}_5\\
\diagup\\
\text{Ph}_2\text{PCH}_2\text{C}_6\text{H}_5
\end{array}
$$

also planar and tetrahedral bis(R—N-salicylaldimino)nickel(II)
$\quad$complexes[64]

the oxidation of the appropriate Pt(II) compound. This results in an expansion of the coordination number from four to six, with the two ligands entering the *trans* positions.[65]

$$
\begin{array}{c}
NH_3 \\
| \\
H_3N\overset{II}{\underset{|}{-\!\!-Pt-\!\!-}}NH_3 \\
| \\
NH_3
\end{array}
\quad\xrightarrow[HCl]{Cl_2}\quad
\begin{array}{c}
NH_3 \\
| \ Cl \\
H_3N\overset{IV}{-\!\!-Pt-\!\!-}NH_3 \\
Cl \ | \\
NH_3
\end{array}
\tag{2}
$$

Such a method of converting a square planar complex to an octahedral complex does not always yield the *trans* isomer. Thus, the reaction of *trans*-Pt^{II}(PEt$_3$)$_2$(C$_6$H$_5$)$_2$ with I$_2$ yields Pt^{IV}(PEt$_3$)$_2$(C$_6$H$_5$)$_2$I$_2$, in which the PEt$_3$ groups remain *trans* to each other, but the phenyls become *cis* to one another and the iodide ions also occupy adjacent positions.[66] This *cis* addition of the oxidant to square planar phosphine complexes of Rh(I) and Ir(I) to give the corresponding trivalent metal octahedral complexes appears to be the general rule in these systems. Such reactions have been the subject of extensive investigations by Vaska.[67] He has reported the discovery of a synthetic oxygen carrier that undergoes the reversible equilibrium shown by

$$
\begin{array}{c}
P(C_6H_5)_3 \\
| \\
Cl\!\!-\!\!-Ir\!\!-\!\!-CO + O_2 \\
| \\
P(C_6H_5)_3
\end{array}
\rightleftharpoons
\begin{array}{c}
P(C_6H_5)_3 \\
| \ Cl \\
O\!\!-\!\!-Ir\!\!-\!\!-CO \\
O \ | \\
P(C_6H_5)_3
\end{array}
\tag{3}
$$

Ibers and La Placa[68] have determined the structure of this oxygen compound by means of x-ray diffraction and find that the O-O bond length (1.30 A) is longer than that for O$_2$ (1.20 A) but shorter than that for O$_2$$^{2-}$ (1.48 A). This structure supports one view[69] for the bonding of oxygen in oxyhemaglobin (see discussion of oxygen-carrier starting on page 641). It has also been found[70] that hydrogen adds readily to give a *cis* Ir(I) compound:

$$
\begin{array}{c}
P(C_6H_5)_3 \\
| \\
Cl\!\!-\!\!-Ir\!\!-\!\!-CO + H_2 \\
| \\
P(C_6H_5)_3
\end{array}
\xrightarrow{25°}
\begin{array}{c}
P(C_6H_5)_3 \\
| \ Cl \\
H\!\!-\!\!-Ir\!\!-\!\!-CO \\
H \ | \\
P(C_6H_5)_3
\end{array}
\tag{4}
$$

It should be made perfectly clear that stereospecific reactions, as cited above, are not often available for the synthesis of *cis* or *trans* isomers. Much more frequently the preparations employed yield a mixture of geometrical isomers which then must be separated by whatever technique is applicable to the particular system. This may require the proper choice of a counterion and/or solvent so that the isomeric salts differ sufficiently in solubility to permit their separation. Methods of chromatography are also useful in the separation of geometrical isomers.[71]

A reaction often used to prepare *cis* isomers, although not always entirely reliable, is one in which a bidentate group is replaced under mild experimental conditions:[72]

$$\tag{5}$$

(where ⌒ = en)

Since substitution reactions of six-coordination compounds may be accompanied by rearrangements (Chapter 4), there is no assurance that reactions of this type will yield exclusively the *cis* isomer, regardless of experimental conditions. Reactions such as these have also been used in reverse in attempts to establish the *cis* configuration of a given isomer, but this method suffers from the same criticism. The only reliable chemical approach to the assignment of *cis* and *trans* structures to geometrical isomers of the type $M(AA)_2B_2$ is the resolution of one form, which establishes that it is the *cis* isomer, since the *trans* form is symmetrical and cannot be optically active.

trans (symmetrical)   *cis* (mirror images)

Reactions of Pt(II) complexes usually take place without rearrangement; therefore chemical techniques can often serve to differentiate between *cis* and *trans* isomers of these compounds. A large variety of physicochemical methods, e.g., x-ray analysis, dipole moment measurements, and absorption spectra, can also be used to establish the configuration of geometrical isomers.

Optical isomerism is common among coordination compounds. The methods generally employed for the resolution of inorganic complexes are analogous to those used for organic compounds. The most common procedure is that of converting the racemic mixture into diastereoisomers by means of an optically active resolving agent and the separation of the diastereoisomers by fractional crystallization. Cationic complexes are often resolved by way of d-tartrate, antimonyl d-tartrate, d-camphor-π-sulfonate, of α-bromo-d-camphor-π-sulfonate salts, whereas anionic complexes are converted to salts of optically active bases such as brucine, cinchonidine, quinine, strychnine, or d-phenylethylamine. Subsequent removal of the resolving agent from the desired antipode is then accomplished by either precipitation or extraction, depending upon the property of the individual complex as well as the resolving agent. Dwyer and his students have used metal complexes to resolve other coordination compounds[73] as well as certain amino acids.[74] For example, it is possible to start with $(+)$-Co(en)$_2$(NO$_2$)$_2^+$ and to resolve these complexes:

$$(+)\text{-Co(EDTA)}^- \rightarrow (+)\text{-Co(en)}_2\text{C}_2\text{O}_4^+ \rightarrow (+)\text{Co(gly) (C}_2\text{O}_4)_2{}^{2-}$$

$$(+)\text{-Co(en)}_2(\text{NO}_2)_2{}^+$$

$$(+)\text{-Co(en)(C}_2\text{O}_4)_2{}^- \rightarrow (+)\text{-Co(en)}_2\text{CO}_3{}^+ \rightarrow (+)\text{Co(en)}_2\text{-H}_2\text{OCl}^{2+}$$

(6)

It appears that the best results are obtained by using salts in which the cation and the anion have the same numerical charge.

Non-ionic complexes, for which the method of fractional crystallization of diastereoisomers is not applicable, have been resolved by preferential adsorption on optically active solids. This method generally does not give the optically pure isomer, but rather only partial resolution. The more common solids used are optically active quartz,[75] starch,[76] and lactose.[77] The partial resolution of bis(acetylacetonate)-beryllium(II) on *dextro* crystals of sodium chlorate has been reported.[78] Zone melting techniques have also been applied[79] to the resolution of metal complexes.

Excellent reviews[80,81] have been written on the phenomenon of optical activity in metal complexes. For colored coordination compounds, the magnitude and sign of optical rotation in the visible region are largely dependent on the wavelength of the light used. This variation in optical rotation with wavelength is referred to as *optical rotatory dispersion* (O.R.D.) $(n_l - n_r)$, and its relationship to *elliptical polarization*, more often called *circular dichroism* (C.D.) or Cotton effect $(\epsilon_l - \epsilon_r)$, and absorption, ϵ, for an isolated absorption band in *dextro* and *levo* isomers is shown in Fig. 1.1. The rotatory dispersion curves are mirror images, and the shape of each curve is diagnostic of a particular configuration. Similarly the sign of the Cotton effect associated with each optically active transition may also be used as a criterion for the configuration of the asymmetric center. This is particularly valuable for systems where the rotatory dispersion curve is complicated by a number of overlapping absorption bands.

en

—Co—

en   en

D*(+)-Co(en)$_3$$^{3+}$,
Determined by x-ray
analysis[83]

en

—Co—NH$_3$

en   NH$_3$

D*(+)-Co(en)$_2$(NH$_3$)$_2$$^{3+}$,
Determined by comparison of
O.R.D. with D*(+)-Co(en)$_3$$^{3+}$

For analogous compounds it has been possible to correlate the generic configurations of optically active complexes by the relationship between their rotatory dispersion curves or Cotton effects.[82] For example the O.R.D.

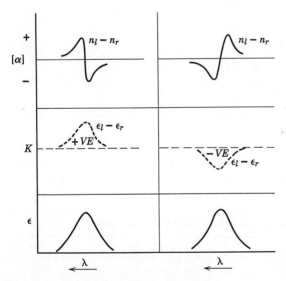

Fig. 1.1 The relationship between optical rotation ($n_l - n_r$) and circular dichroism ($\epsilon_l - \epsilon_r$) for an isolated absorption band (ϵ). From reference 81.

curves given in Fig. 1.2 show that all of these complexes have the same absolute configuration as that known for D*(+)-Co(en)$_3$$^{3+}$. This method has now been used to designate the absolute configurations of several optical isomers of metal complexes (Table 1.4).

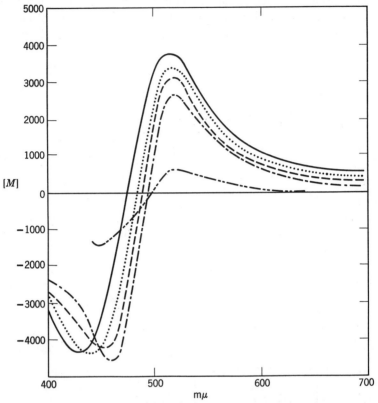

Fig. 1.2 The rotatory dispersion curves of the D* isomers of the following ions: [Co(en)₃]³⁺ — · — ·; [Co(en)₂(NH₃)₂]³⁺ — · · — · · —; [Co(en)₂(−)(pn)]³⁺ — — —; [Co(en)(−)(pn)₂]³⁺ · · · ·; and [Co(−)(pn)₃]³⁺ ——————. From reference 81.

Table 1.4[a] Absolute configuration of some optical isomers

D*(+)-Co(en)₃³⁺	D*(+)-Co(en)₂NH₃Cl²⁺	D*(+)-Co(en)₂(NO₂)₂⁺
D*(+)-Cr(en)₃³⁺	D*(+)-Co(en)₂NH₃Br²⁺	D*(+)-Co(en)₂CO₃⁺
D*(−)-Rh(en)₃³⁺	D*(+)-Co(en)₂NH₃NCS²⁺	D*(+)-Co(en)₂C₂O₄⁺
D*(−)-Ir(en)₃³⁺	D*(−)-Co(en)₂NH₃NO₂²⁺	D*(−)₅₄₆₁-Co(en)(C₂O₄)₂⁻
D*(+)-Co(+pn)₃³⁺	D*(+)-Co(en)₂H₂OCl²⁺	D*(−)₅₄₆₁-Co(C₂O₄)₃³⁻
D*(−)-Co(+chxn)₃³⁺	D*(+)-Co(en)₂H₂ONO₂²⁺	D*(+)-Cr(C₂O₄)₃³⁻
D*(+)-Co(−cptn)₃³⁺	D*(+)-Co(en)₂Cl₂⁺	D*(+)₅₄₆₁-Rh(C₂O₄)₃³⁻
D*(+)-Co(en)₂(NH₃)₂³⁺	D*(+)₅₄₆₁-Co(en)₂NCSCl⁺	D*(+)₅₄₆₁-Ir(C₂O₄)₃³⁻
D*(+)-Co(en)₂NH₃H₂O³⁺	D*(+)-Co(en)₂NO₂Cl	

Examples from reference 82.

[a] See nomenclature rule 10 (p. 43) for the meaning of D* and L* and of (+) and (−).

It is clear from this discussion that the wavelength of the measurement must be reported with the optical activity of the compound. Furthermore, zero optical rotation observed at one wavelength cannot be taken as proof that the compound is optically inactive; for example,

$$[Os(phen)_3](ClO_4)_2 \cdot H_2O \text{ has } [\alpha]_{5896} = 0$$

whereas its $[\alpha]_{5461} = 3670$.[84] The optical rotation of coordination compounds at the wavelength of the maximum rotation is generally much greater than that of organic compounds. Some metal complexes are optically stable, whereas others racemize rapidly. The kinetics and mechanisms of racemization are discussed in Chapter 4. Table 4.15 contains a listing of many of the known optically active metal complexes.

The other types of isomerism listed in Table 1.3 require no additional comment, except perhaps linkage isomerism and the newly discovered conformational isomerism. For a long time the only known examples of linkage isomers in metal complexes were those of the type M—ONO (nitrito) and M—NO$_2$ (nitro) for Co(III), provided by the discovery of Jørgensen[85] just before the turn of the century. Investigations of the mechanism of formation and rearrangement (see pp. 231, 291) of these systems have made possible the preparation of analogous linkage isomers of Rh(III), Ir(III), and Pt(IV).[60] Ligands such as NO$_2^-$ with two or more possible sites for attachment to the metal are known as *ambident ligands*. Generally, the metal has enough preference for one of the ligand sites so that only this stable form of the complex is isolated. Sometimes the unstable isomer can be formed and isolated before its rearrangement to the stable form.

Many other ambident ligands are known, such as SCN$^-$, CO, CN$^-$, S$_2$O$_3^{2-}$, SO$_3^{2-}$, (NH$_2$)$_2$CO, (NH$_2$)$_2$CS, and (CH$_3$)$_2$SO. Except for SCN$^-$, CN$^-$, and S$_2$O$_3^{2-}$ none of these has as yet yielded linkage isomers. It is well known that SCN$^-$ forms both M—SCN (thiocyanato) and M—NCS (isothiocyanato) metal complexes, depending on the metal. Several authors[86] have pointed out that the change from M—NCS to M—SCN bonding coincides approximately, for different metals, to the change in halogeno-metal complex stabilities from F$^-$ > Cl$^-$ > Br$^-$ > I$^-$ to I$^-$ > Br$^-$ > Cl$^-$ > F$^-$. This is discussed in the following section on stability. The significant observation was made[87] that for a given M the bonding site to SCN$^-$ depends on the other ligands in the complex. For example, M—SCN bonding is found in M(SCN)$_4^{2-}$ and M(NH$_3$)$_2$(SCN)$_2$, where M = Pd(II) or Pt(II), and M—NCS occurs in the phosphine complexes M(PR$_3$)$_2$(NCS)$_2$ and 2,2'-bipyridine complexes M(bipy) (NCS)$_2$. By using this information it was possible to design an experiment[61a] to permit the isolation of the unstable M—SCN species before it had time to rearrange to the stable M—NCS isomer:

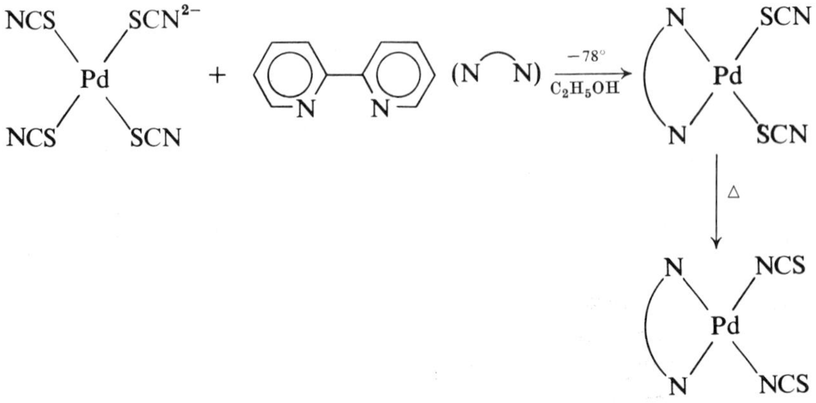

The success of this method for the isolation of the kinetic product depends on the fact that substitution reactions of Pd(II) are very fast and that the non-ionic product is insoluble and rapidly separates from the reaction mixture. Since there are metals that bond M—SCN and others that bond M—NCS, it follows that some borderline metal may produce an equilibrium mixture of the two types of species. This has in fact been observed by means of spectroscopic investigations of solutions of Cd(II)—SCN⁻.[88] Cadmium(II) gives both types of bonding, whereas the bonding for Zn(II) is Zn—NCS and that for Hg(II) is Hg—SCN. It may be mentioned that these linkage isomers, as well as the nitrito-nitro isomers, are readily distinguished by means of their i.r. spectra.[89]

Conformational isomerism is well known in organic compounds such as the boat and chair forms of cyclohexane and isomers containing like groups in either axial or equatorial positions. Similar conformational isomers are known for certain metal chelates.[81] However, unique pairs of conformational isomers have been isolated for certain Ni(II) complexes.[63] One example is provided by the green and brown forms of $Ni(PEtPh_2)_2Br_2$, which are readily interconvertible:

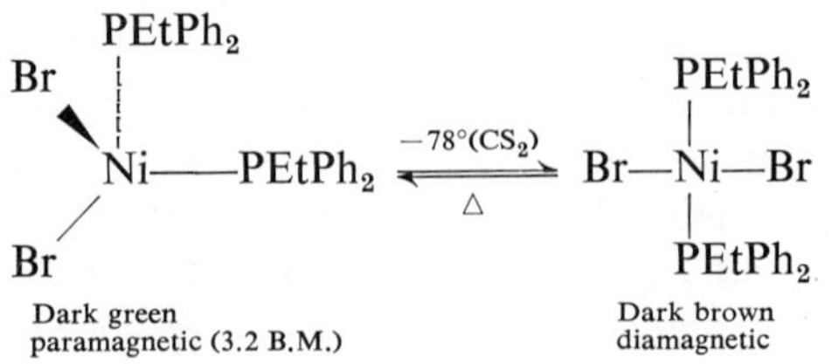

This type of square planar-tetrahedral isomerism has also been demonstrated in solution for the complexes bis(N-*sec*-alkylsalicylaldimino)-nickel(II)[64] and bis(N,N-disubstituted-aminotroponeiminato)nickel(II).[90] Detailed studies are reported on some of these systems, and they are discussed in Chapter 5. It may be mentioned that the coordination chemistry of nickel is most fascinating because of the ease with which it exhibits various oxidation states, different coordination numbers, and different structures.[91]

Stability

The electronic concept of coordination compounds indicates that they are formed as a result of Lewis acid-base reactions in which the metal ion is the acid (or *acceptor*) and the ligand is the base (or *donor*).[||] It therefore follows that all metal ions will tend to form coordination compounds; this tendency in general increases with rising electron affinity of the metal ion. It is also true that almost all molecules and ions with at least one free pair of electrons will tend to form complexes with metal ions. The different types of ligands known are summarized in Table 1.5.

The formation and dissociation of complex compounds, like that of polybasic acids, involve the successive equilibria

$$M + A \rightleftharpoons MA \qquad K_1 = \frac{[MA]}{[M][A]} \qquad (9)$$

$$MA + A \rightleftharpoons MA_2 \qquad K_2 = \frac{[MA_2]}{[MA][A]} \qquad (10)$$

$$MA_{n-1} + A \rightleftharpoons MA_n \qquad K_n = \frac{[MA_n]}{[MA_{n-1}][A]} \qquad (11)$$

Constants $K_1, K_2, \ldots, K_n$ are designated as *stepwise formation constants*. Another symbol, β, is used to represent the *overall formation constants*

|| Transition metals in many complexes are potential Lewis bases in that they contain non-bonding electron pairs. It is well known that protons add to the metal in $Co(CO)_4^-$ and $Fe(CO)_4^{2-}$ to form $HCo(CO)_4$ and $H_2F(CO)_4$, respectively. Many other metal carbonyls and organometallic compounds have now been protonated in strong acid.[92] Shriver[93] reports the formation of $(C_5H_5)_2WH_2 \cdot BF_3$, which is believed to contain a $W \rightarrow B$ coordinate bond. Parshall[94] has investigated the reaction of diborane with various metal carbonyl anions and obtained compounds such as $(C_2H_5)_4N[H_3B \leftarrow Mn(CO)_5]$.

Table 1.5   Types of ligands

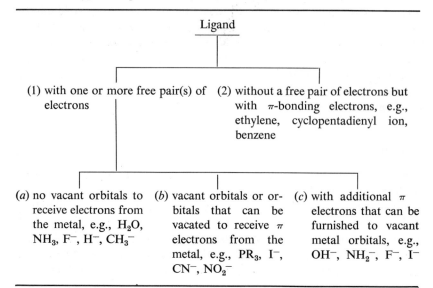

as follows:

$$M + A \rightleftharpoons MA \qquad \beta_1 = \frac{[MA]}{[M][A]} \qquad (12)$$

$$M + 2A \rightleftharpoons MA_2 \qquad \beta_2 = \frac{[MA_2]}{[M][A]^2} \qquad (13)$$

$$M + 3A \rightleftharpoons MA_3 \qquad \beta_3 = \frac{[MA_3]}{[M][A]^3} \qquad (14)$$

$$M + nA \rightleftharpoons MA_n \qquad \beta_n = \frac{[MA_n]}{[M][A]^n} \qquad (15)$$

From the above definitions of K and β it is clear that the overall β is the product of the stepwise K's:

$$\beta_4 = K_1 K_2 K_3 K_4 \quad \text{and} \quad \beta_n = K_1 K_2 K_3 \ldots K_n$$

The analysis of systems with successive equilibria and the method of evaluating the measurements are described in detail.[95] There is now a great deal of quantitative information on the stability of coordination compounds. Much of this has been summarized and discussed elsewhere,[96] so that only some of the more general trends will be mentioned.

The results of numerous investigations for the first transition series show that, regardless of the nature of the donor group, the so-called *natural order*[97] of the stability of complexes of bivalent transition metals is Mn < Fe < Co < Ni < Cu > Zn. Only in a very few cases have deviations from this order been observed. It has been found, for example, that the stability of $Fe(phen)_3^{2+}$ is greater than expected and, furthermore, that the value of K_3 for the addition of the third group is larger than that of either K_1 or K_2.[98] This is attributed to an electronic rearrangement, for it was shown[99] that the bis complex, $Fe(phen)_2X_2$, is paramagnetic, whereas the tris complex, $Fe(phen)_3^{2+}$, is diamagnetic.

If we attempt to list the other metal ions in the order of increasing stability of their complexes, this turns out to be impossible unless the ligand is specified. In the same way, it is not possible to put the common ligands into an order of complexing ability unless a reference metal ion is specified.

Hard and Soft Acids and Bases[100]

Various metal ions fall into two categories: (1) those binding strongly to bases which bind strongly to the proton, that is, basic in the usual sense; (2) those binding strongly to highly polarizable or unsaturated bases, which often have negligible proton basicity. Division into these two categories is not absolute and intermediate cases occur, but the classification is reasonably sharp and appears to be quite useful. It is convenient to divide bases also into two categories, those that are polarizable or "soft," and those that are non-polarizable or "hard." It is possible for a base to be both soft and strongly binding toward the proton, e.g., sulfide ion. Still it is generally true that hardness is associated with good proton binding. For example, for the bases in which the coordinating atom is from Groups V, VI, and VII (the great majority of all bases), the atoms fluorine, oxygen, and nitrogen are the hardest in each group and also the most basic to the proton.

It has long been recognized[101] that metal ions can be divided into two classes depending on whether they form their most stable complexes with the first ligand atom of each group, class (a), or whether they form their most stable complexes with the second or a subsequent member of each group, class (b). Thus, for class (a) metal ions the order of stability is as follows:

$$F^- > Cl^- > Br^- > I^-$$

$$O \gg S > Se > Te$$

$$N \gg P > As > Sb > Bi$$

Whereas for class (b) the order of stability is

$$F^- < Cl^- < Br^- < I^-$$
$$O \ll S \sim Se \sim Te$$
$$N \ll P > As > Sb > Bi$$

Class (a) metal ions bind best to the least polarizable (hardest) atom of a family, whereas class (b) metal ions bind best to a more polarizable (softer) atom of the same family. Notice that it is not always the most polarizable (softest) atom which forms the most stable complexes with a class (b) metal ion. The reason for this is that many bases, such as the stibines, are weak bases toward all metal ions. Their complexes with class (b) metals will usually be much more stable than their complexes with class (a) acids, however.

Other Lewis acids can be examined to see whether the stability of their acid-base adducts corresponds to class (a) or class (b) behavior. The acid-base or donor-acceptor[102] adducts which they form may be inorganic or organic molecules, complex ions, or charge-transfer complexes.

Table 1.6 contains a list of all generalized acids for which sufficient information can be found in the literature to enable a choice between class (a) and class (b) to be made. In classifying Lewis acids, the criterion previously used[101] was followed whenever possible, that is, to compare the stabilities of fluorine versus iodine, oxygen versus sulfur, and nitrogen versus phosphorus type complexes. When such comparisons are not feasible, other criteria may be used.[100] One is that class (b) acids will complex readily with a variety of soft bases that are of negligible proton basicity. These include CO, olefins, aromatic hydrocarbons, and the like.

The common characteristics of the two classes of Lewis acids are easily discernible from Table 1.6. The features which bring out class (a) behavior are small size, high positive oxidation state, and no easily distorted outer electrons. Class (b) behavior is associated with a low or zero oxidation state, with large size, and with easily distorted outer electrons. Both metals and non-metals can be either (a) or (b) type acids, depending or their charge and size. Since the features which promote class (a) behavior are those leading to low polarizability, and those which create type (b) behavior lead to high polarizability, it is convenient to call class (a) acids "hard" and class (b) acids "soft." We then have the useful generalization that *hard acids prefer to associate with hard bases, and soft acids prefer soft bases.*¶

¶ It is not implied that complexes of hard acids and soft bases, or vice versa, cannot exist and be quite stable. For example, CH_3^- is a soft base yet compounds such as $Mg(CH_3)_2$ can easily be made. Nevertheless this compound is thermodynamically unstable to hydrolysis, whereas $Hg(CH_3)_2$ is thermodynamically stable to hydrolysis.

Polarizability is simply a convenient property to use as a classification. It may well be that other properties which are roughly proportional to polarizability are more responsible for the typical behavior of the two classes of acids. For example, a low ionization potential is usually linked to a high polarizability, and a high ionization potential to a low polarizability. Hence, ionization potential or the related electronegativity might be the important property. Unsaturation, with the possibility of acceptor

Table 1.6   Classification of Lewis acids

Hard	Soft
H^+, Li^+, Na^+, K^+	Cu^+, Ag^+, Au^+, Tl^+, Hg^+
Be^{2+}, Mg^{2+}, Ca^{2+}, Sr^{2+}, Mn^{2+}	Pd^{2+}, Cd^{2+}, Pt^{2+}, Hg^{2+}, CH_3Hg^+,
	$Co(CN)_5^{2-}$, Pt^{4+}, Te^{4+}
Al^{3+}, Sc^{3+}, Ga^{3+}, In^{3+}, La^{3+}	Tl^{3+}, $Tl(CH_3)_3$, BH_3, $Ga(CH_3)_3$, $GaCl_3$,
N^{3+}, Gd^{3+}, Lu^{3+}	GaI_3, $InCl_3$
Cr^{3+}, Co^{3+}, Fe^{3+}, As^{3+}, Ce^{3+}	RS^+, RSe^+, RTe^+
Si^{4+}, Ti^{4+}, Zr^{4+}, Th^{4+}, Pu^{4+}	I^+, Br^+, HO^+, RO^+
UO_2^{2+}, $(CH_3)_2Sn^{2+}$, VO^{2+}, MoO^{3+}	I_2, Br_2, ICN, etc.
$BeMe_2$, BF_3, $B(OR)_3$	trinitrobenzene, etc.
$Al(CH_3)_3$, $AlCl_3$, AlH_3	chloranil, quinones, etc.
RPO_2^+, $ROPO_2^+$	tetracyanoethylene, etc.
RSO_2^+, $ROSO_2^+$, SO_3	O, Cl, Br, I, N
I^{7+}, I^{5+}, Cl^{7+}, Cr^{6+}	M^0 (metal atoms)
RCO^+, CO_2, NC^+	bulk metals
HX (hydrogen-bonding molecules)	CH_2, carbenes

Borderline
Fe^{2+}, Co^{2+}, Ni^{2+}, Cu^{2+}, Zn^{2+}, Pb^{2+}, Sn^{2+}, Sb^{3+}, Bi^{3+}, Rh^{3+}, Ir^{3+}, $B(CH_3)_3$, SO_2
NO^+, Ru^{2+}, Os^{2+}, R_3C^+, $C_6H_5^+$, $Ga\,H_3$

bonding in the acid-base complex, and ease of reduction, favoring strong electron transfer to the acid, are also associated with high polarizabilty.

While considerable variation can exist because of the effect of overall charge, the usual stability order overall for class (b) metal ions is[103] $S \sim C > I > Br > Cl > N > O > F$. For class (a) metal ions a strong inversion of this order occurs, so that often only oxygen and fluorine complexes can be obtained in aqueous solution.[103] It may be noted that the order given above is that of increasing electronegativity.**

** Table 3.4 lists a series of stability constants for various ligands for the typical soft acid CH_3Hg^+.

Table 1.7 Stability constants of ethylenediaminetetraacetato complexes of some metal ions at 20°C

$$M^{n+} + EDTA^{4-} \rightarrow M(EDTA)^{n-4}$$

Metal Ion	log K	Metal Ion	log K
Li^+	2.8	In^{3+}	25.0
Na^+	1.7	Sc^{3+}	23.1
H^+	10.3	V^{3+}	25.9
Mg^{2+}	8.7	Cr^{3+}	23.4[a]
Ca^{2+}	10.6	Fe^{3+}	25.1
Sr^{2+}	8.6	Y^{3+}	18.1
Ba^{2+}	7.8	La^{3+}	15.5
V^{2+}	12.7	Ce^{3+}	16.0
Cr^{2+}	13.6[b]	Pr^{3+}	16.4
Mn^{2+}	13.6	Nd^{3+}	16.6
Fe^{2+}	14.3	Sm^{3+}	17.1
Co^{2+}	16.1	Er^{3+}	17.3
Ni^{2+}	18.6	Gd^{3+}	17.4
Cu^{2+}	18.8	Tb^{3+}	17.9
Zn^{2+}	16.5	Dy^{3+}	18.3
Cd^{2+}	16.5	Er^{3+}	18.8
Hg^{2+}	21.8	Tm^{3+}	19.3
Pb^{2+}	18.0	Yb^{3+}	19.5
Pd^{2+}	18.5	Lu^{3+}	19.8
Al^{3+}	16.1	VO^{2+}	18.8
Ga^{3+}	20.3	Th^{4+}	23.2

Data from S. Chaberek and A. E. Martell, *Organic Sequestering Agents*, John Wiley and Sons, New York, 1959.

[a] R. L. Pecsok, L. D. Shields, and W. P. Schaefer, *Inorg. Chem.*, **3**, 114 (1964).

For class (a) metal ions there should be a good correlation with the basicity (towards the proton) of the ligand and the stability of its complexes. This is illustrated in Fig. 1.3 for some Cu(II) complexes. Negative deviations occur when steric factors reduce the stability of the complex. Table 1.7 shows the stabilities of a large number of complexes of different metal ions with ethylenediaminetetraacetic acid anion. It must be remembered that this is a typical hard base, and hence the complexation abilities of soft acids are underestimated. The stability constant of Co(EDTA)⁻ is not known, but Co(III) complexes are much more stable than those of Cr(III) or of Fe(III). Qualtitative data on complexes of the second and third transition series are very scanty, but there is little doubt that the stabilities

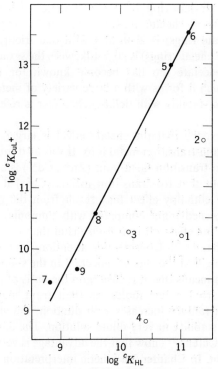

Fig. 1.3 Concentration formation constants of Cu^{2+} vs. H^+ with oxine derivatives in 50% by volume dioxane-water mixture containing $0.3\ M$ $NaClO_4$ at 20°C. Open circles refer to reagents with a substituent adjacent to the chelating nitrogen atom: (1) 2-methyloxine, (2) 1,2,3,4-tetrahydro-10-hydroxyacridine, (3) 8-hydroxy-2,4-dimethylquinazoline, (4) 8-hydroxy-4-methyl-2-phenylquinazoline. Full circles refer to other reagents: (5) oxine, (6) 5-methyloxine, (7) 8-hydroxycinnoline, (8) 8-hydroxyquinazoline, (9) 5-hydroxyquinoxaline. From reference 114.

increase within any group in passing from the first to the second to the third. Thus, complexes of Ni(II), Pd(II), and Pt(II) increase in thermodynamic stability in that order.

Among other factors which influence the stability of complexes are (1) the presence of chelate or multidentate ligands, rather than unidentate ones, (2) the size of the chelate ring, (3) steric factors, and (4) resonance effects.

Qualitative observations, such as the synthesis of $Co(en)_3^{3+}$ by the reaction of $Co(NH_3)_6^{3+}$ with an excess of ethylenediamine, suggest that the greater the number of points of attachment of each ligand to the central metal ion, the greater the stability of the complex. There is now a great deal of quantitative data in support of this observation; for example, the total formation constant ($\log \beta_n$) for the complex of Cu(II) with four ammonias (unidentate, no chelate rings) is 11.9, with two ethylenediamines (bidentate, two chelate rings) is 20.0, and with one triethylenetetramine (quadridentate, three chelate rings) is 20.5. Likewise, the sexadentate ligand ethylenediaminetetraacetate ion has become known for the unusually stable complexes which it forms with a large variety of metal ions (Table 1.7). This increase in stability with dentate character is referred to as the *chelate effect*.[104]

It has been observed[105] that the chelate effect is larger for transition metal ions than for non-transition metal ions. It was also found[106] that the chelate effect for non-transition metal ions (Zn^{2+}, Cd^{2+}) is almost entirely an entropy effect, but that for transition metals (Cu^{2+}) it is in part an enthalpy effect. The enthalpy effect may result from the greater crystal field strength of ethylenediamine compared with ammonia, which in turn has a greater stabilizing effect on transition metal than on non-transition metal complexes (Chapter 2). Considerable attention has been devoted to the theoretical treatment of the entropy effect.[107] In the simplest terms, the entropy contribution means that it is easier, on the basis of probability, to form an aggregate from a few molecules than from many molecules. Furthermore, this advantage increases with dilution, the chelates having the greatest relative stability in very dilute solution. The data cited above for $Cu(NH_3)_4^{2+}$ and $Cu(en)_2^{2+}$ show that the advantage is very large even in concentrated solution. In Chapter 3 a kinetic interpretation of the chelate effect will be given.

Although coordination compounds with five- and six-membered chelate rings are the most stable, complexes are known which have chelate ring sizes ranging from four through nine members. Carbonato, $M\!\!\begin{array}{c}O\\ \diagup\diagdown\\ \diagdown\diagup\\ O\end{array}\!\!C\!=\!O$,

and sulfato, $M\!\!\begin{array}{c}O\\ \diagup\diagdown\\ \diagdown\diagup\\ O\end{array}\!\!SO_2$, complexes are among the more common four-membered ring compounds. Another large class of such compounds consists of the bridged complexes of the type $M\!\!\begin{array}{c}X\\ \diagup\diagdown\\ \diagdown\diagup\\ X\end{array}\!\!M$, where X is OH^-, NH_2^-,

Cl^-, NO_2^-, CO, etc. Attempts to isolate chelate compounds from aqueous reaction mixtures of tetramethylenediamine, pentamethylenediamine, or hexamethylenediamine and a variety of metal ions yielded only unidentifiable oils believed to be polymeric electrolytes.[108] However, in alcoholic solution the reaction of tetramethylenediamine with Cu(II), Ni(II), Zn(II), and Cd(II) perchlorates yields seven-membered ring chelate salts. By using alcohol as a solvent, it was also possible to prepare a nine-membered ring compound.[109] That chelation occurs in alcoholic, but not aqueous, reaction mixtures must result from the greater coordinating property of water being sufficient to prevent the formation of these unstable large chelate rings. The reaction of bis(ethylenediamine)carbonatocobalt(III) ion with succinic acid yields the succinato complex,[110] a seven-membered ring, and with sulfonyldiacetic acid the sulfonyldiacetato complex,[111] an eight-membered ring.

It has been observed that, for a large variety of aliphatic chelate rings, the five- is more stable than the six-membered ring. An interesting illustration of this is afforded by 1,2,3-triaminopropanetetrachloroplatinum(IV); the triamine behaves as a bidentate, and, where both five- and six-mem-

Five-membered ring (optically active)

Six-membered ring (optically inactive)

bered rings are possible, Mann[112] was able to resolve the complex and thus demonstrate that it is the one with the five-membered ring. Thermodynamic data are now available[113] on the chelation of ethylenediamine and 1,3-propanediamine with Cu(II) and Ni(II) ions (Table 1.8). These data show that, although 1,3-propanediamine is a stronger base ($pK_{\text{tnH}^+} = 10.63$, $pK_{\text{tnH}_2^{2+}} = 8.76$) than ethylenediamine ($pK_{\text{enH}^+} = 10.00$, $pK_{\text{enH}_2^{2+}} = 7.12$), it does not form the stronger complexes. Furthermore, the data show that the greater stability of the five-membered ring complexes is chiefly due not to the entropy, but rather to the enthalpy of formation. This may result from a six-membered ring of this type being conformationally less stable than a five-membered ring, as was concluded from conformational analysis of diamine chelate rings[113c] (see discussion starting on p. 334). It is finally of interest that for aromatic ligands or chelates with conjugated linkages the six-membered chelate ring is often more stable than the five-membered ring. This is perhaps due to the wider bond angles in such

Table 1.8 Thermodynamic data (in kcal/g ion) for the formation of $Cu(AA)_2^{2+}$ and $Ni(AA)_3^{2+}$, where AA is ethylenediamine (en) and 1,3-propanediamine (tn)

	Copper (II)			Nickel (II)		
AA	$-\Delta G°$	$-\Delta H°$	$T\Delta S°$	$-\Delta G°$	$-\Delta H°$	$T\Delta S°$
en	27.3	25.4	1.9	24.9	27.9	−3.0
tn	23.4	22.8	0.6	16.4	21.3	−4.9

groups and also to the requirement of an even number of atoms for resonance in the chelate ring.

Numerous examples of steric inhibition of complex formation have been reported. Most common among these is the type where a bulky group is attached either to the donor atom or near enough to it to cause mutual repulsions between ligands, resulting in a weakening of the metal-ligand bonds. This is illustrated by the data in Fig. 1.3 for the formation constants of substituted 8-hydroxyquinolines (I) and 8-hydroxyquinazolines (II) with Cu(II).[114] Substitution in all positions except 2 shows a good correlation between the stability of the complex and the base strength of the donor ion, but, as represented by the open circles in Fig. 1.3, 2-substituted compounds form the least stable complexes. Some other examples of

this same type of steric hindrance occur with N-alkylethylenediamines[115] and 6,6'-substituted 2,2'-bipyridines (III).[116] The steric hindrance observed for 3,3'-disubstituted 2,2'-bipyridine is of a different type.[117] Since here

there can be no effect due to repulsions between ligands, it is suggested that the alkyl groups prevent the ligand from assuming a planar configuration and hence interfere with resonance stability in the ligand and introduce strain in the metal-donor bonds. Still another type of steric inhibition of chelation is shown by the lower stability of Ag(en)$^+$ compared to

$Ag(NH_3)_2^+$, which is attributed to a strained structure of the chelate ring, since it must distort the usual linear configuration of Ag(I) complexes.[118]

The significance of resonance effects in the stability or coordination compounds has been demonstrated.[119] Thus it was observed that the stability of Cu(II) chelates decreased in the order acetylacetone $>$ 2-hydroxy-1-naphthaldehyde $>$ salicylaldehyde $>$ 2-hydroxy-3-naphthaldehyde, which is also the order of the decrease in the double-bond character of the chelate rings. In the acetylacetonate ion the two double bonds are a part of the chelate ring, so that it is assigned a bond order of 2. However, in the phenolate ion of salicylaldehyde, one of the double bonds is also part of the resonating benzene ring, so that in essence it is in the chelate ring only half the time; thus, it is assigned a bond order of 1.5. Similarly, because of the resonance structures of naphthalene, one of the double bonds of the naphthalate ion is part of the chelate ring two-thirds of the time for 2-hydroxyl-1-naphthaldehyde, giving it a bond order of 1.67, and one-third of the time for 2-hydroxy-3-naphthaldehyde, so that its bond order is 1.33. This type of chelate ring resonance stabilization is perhaps also largely responsible for the extreme stability of the metal porphyrins.

Acid-base Properties of Complex Ions

Particularly important are the hydroxo complexes of metal ions. These may be considered to be derived from aquo complexes by the loss of a proton in a simple acid-base reaction. In a similar way amide complexes are related to amine complexes by the loss of a proton. Thus, complex ions containing water and ammine ligands are frequently acids of measurable strength. In Table 1.9 are given some acid ionization constants determined in water for a number of aquo complexes. These constants are also called *hydrolysis constants*. They refer to the reaction

$$M(H_2O)^{m+} \rightarrow MOH^{(m-1)+} + H^+ \tag{16}$$

The corresponding hydroxo complexes are then weak bases.

For the simple metal ions the determination of these acid constants is of fundamental importance, since their behavior in various reactions as a function of pH is governed by the pK_a values. Also, the acidic solutions produced by the dissolution of various salts of these ions in water are due to reaction 16. The older practice of estimating pK_a by measuring the pH of solutions of these salts is completely unreliable, and the values shown in Table 1.9 refer to data obtained by analyzing titration curves. Unfortunately, a wide variety of conditions has been used by different workers.

The accurate determination of pK_a values is rendered very difficult by the pronounced tendency of almost all hydroxo complexes to undergo *olation*.

Table 1.9 Acid ionization (hydrolysis) constants for some aquo ions at 25°C

Ion	pK_a	Remarks
Tl^+	13.2	
Hg_2^{2+}	5.0	
Mg^{2+}	11.4	
Ca^{2+}	12.6	
Ba^{2+}	13.2	
Mn^{2+}	10.6	
Fe^{2+}	9.5	
Co^{2+}	8.9	
Ni^{2+}	10.6	
Cu^{2+}	6.8	
Zn^{2+}	8.8	
Cd^{2+}	9.0	
Hg^{2+}	3.7	$pK_2 = 2.6$
Sn^{2+}	3.9	
Pb^{2+}	7.8	
Al^{3+}	5.1	
Sc^{3+}	5.1	
In^{3+}	4.4	$pK_2 = 3.9$
Tl^{3+}	1.1	$pK_2 = 1.5$
Bi^{3+}	1.6	
V^{3+}	2.8	
Ti^{3+}	2.2	
Cr^{3+}	3.8	
Co^{3+}	0.7	$3M$ $NaClO_4$; reference 155
Fe^{3+}	2.2	$pK_2 = 3.3$
$Co(NH_3)_5H_2O^{3+}$	6.6	1 M $NaNO_3$
cis-$Co(NH_3)_4(H_2O)_2^{3+}$	6.0	1 M $NaNO_3$
$Ru(NH_3)_5H_2O^{3+}$	4.2	reference 120
$Rh(NH_3)_5H_2O^{3+}$	5.9	
$Cr(NH_3)_5H_2O^{3+}$	5.3	1 M $NaNO_3$
cis-$Co(en)_2(H_2O)_2^{3+}$	6.1	$pK_2 = 8.2$; 1 M $NaNO_3$
$trans$-$Co(en)_2(H_2O)_2^{3+}$	4.5	$pK_2 = 7.9$; 1 M $NaNO_3$
cis-$Cr(en)_2(H_2O)_2^{3+}$	4.8	$pK_2 = 7.2$; 1 M $NaNO_3$
$trans$-$Cr(en)_2(H_2O)_2^{3+}$	4.1	$pK_2 = 7.5$; 1 M $NaNO_3$
cis-$Co(en)_2NO_2H_2O^{2+}$	6.3	
$trans$-$Co(en)_2NO_2H_2O^{2+}$	6.4	
cis-$Pt(NH_3)_2(H_2O)_2^{2+}$	5.6	at 20°C; $pK_2 = 7.3$
$trans$-$Pt(NH_3)_2(H_2O)_2^{2+}$	4.3	at 20°C; $pK_2 = 7.4$
$Pt(NH_3)_5(H_2O)^{4+}$	4	
$Pt(en)_2(H_2O)_2^{4+}$	strong acid	reference 121

Data from reference 95. Solutions dilute unless otherwise indicated.

This is the name given to the formation of polynuclear complexes by the splitting out of water between hydroxo groups:

$$2MOH \rightarrow MOM + H_2O \qquad (17)$$

The oxygen atom between the two metal atoms may be protonated, forming a hydroxo bridge. Two metal atoms may be bound by more than

Table 1.10   Acid ionization constants of some ammine complexes at 25°C

Ion	pK_a	Reference
$Co(NH_3)_6^{3+}$	>14	123a
$Co(en)_3^{3+}$	>14	123a
$Rh(NH_3)_6^{3+}$	>14	123b
$Rh(en)_3^{3+}$	>14	123b
$Pt(NH_3)_6^{4+}$	7.2	124a; $pK_2 = 10.5$
$Pt(en)(NH_3)_4^{4+}$	6.2	95
$Pt(en)_3^{4+}$	5.5	95
$Pt(NH_3)_5Cl^{3+}$	8.4	124a
$Pt(NH_3)_5Br^{3+}$	8.3	95
$Pt(NH_3)_5OH^{3+}$	9.5	95
$cis\text{-}Pt(NH_3)_4Cl_2^{2+}$	9.7	124a; $pK_2 = 12.4$
$trans\text{-}Pt(NH_3)_4Cl_2^{2+}$	11.3	124a
$trans\text{-}Pt(en)_2Cl_2^{2+}$	11.0	124a
$Os(en)_3^{4+}$	strong acid	95; $pK_2 = 5.8$
$Au(en)_2^{3+}$	~6.5	95
$Au(dien)Cl^{+\ a}$	4.0	124b; 0.5 M NaClO$_4$
$Au(Et_4dien)Cl^{+\ a}$	2.5	124c; 0.5 M NaClO$_4$

^{a} dien = $NH_2C_2H_4NHC_2H_4NH_2$; Et$_4$dien = $(C_2H_5)_2NC_2H_4NHC_2H_4N$
$(C_2H_5)_2$.

one bridge. Such polymerization eventually leads to the formation of insoluble precipitates. For a discussion of this process and the methods used to obtain pK_a data, the papers of Sillén and his co-workers are most useful.[122]

Table 1.10 gives some data on the acid strengths of a number of ammine complexes. As expected, they are generally less acidic than are aquo complexes, just as ammonium ion is a weaker acid than hydronium ion. However, the factor between H_3O^+ and NH_4^+ is 10^{11}, whereas for the highly charged complexes the factor seems to be less, being only 10^4 for Pt(IV). In the case of Co(III) complexes such as $Co(en)_3^{3+}$, an interaction between hydroxide ion and the complex occurs[123a] which is due to the formation of an ion pair rather than to acid-base neutralization.

"Outer-Sphere" Complexes or Ion Pairs

Complex ions, like other charged particles, are particularly sensistive to their environment. In addition to having thermodynamic and kinetic properties which depend heavily on the solvent, they will interact strongly with ionic species in solution.

One important aspect of this characteristic will be shown by the changes in activity coefficients of the complex ions due to the general ion atmosphere effect, as given by the Debye-Hückel theory for dilute solutions.[125] The theory gives for the activity coefficient γ_i, of a single ion

$$-\log \gamma_i = \frac{A z_i^2 \sqrt{\mu}}{1 + B\sqrt{\mu}} \qquad (18)$$

where z_i is the charge on the ion, μ is the ionic strength, and A is a constant equal to 0.509 for water at 25°C and given more generally by $A = 1.82 \times 10^6/(DT)^{3/2}$, where D is the dielectric constant of the medium and T the absolute temperature. The constant B increases with increasing size of the ion. It is of the order of magnitude of unity and may be set equal to one or treated as semiempirical. Equation 18 often gives a reasonable interpretation of activity data up to $\mu = 0.1$.

That complex ions obey 18 as well as other ions has been amply demonstrated. In fact, complex ions were often used to test various conclusions of the Debye-Hückel theory, since they can be selected to cover a wide range of charges, positive and negative, can be very stable, and can be nearly spherically symmetrical. The kinetic equivalent of the Debye-Hückel equation, the Brønsted-Bjerrum-Christiansen formulation,[126] was inspired and tested by the reactions of the Co(III) ammines. It is simply the application of equation 18 to the reactants and to the transition state, giving for a bimolecular reaction

$$\ln k = \ln k_0 + \frac{2 A z_1 z_2 \sqrt{\mu}}{1 + B\sqrt{\mu}} \qquad (19)$$

where k is the specific rate constant, k_0 is the same for infinite dilution, and z_1 and z_2 are the charges on the two reactants.

At higher concentrations 18 and 19 will no longer be valid, and unfortunately many reactions of complex ions must be carried out in concentrated solutions. It has been customary to add a term linear in μ to equation 18 to extend its range. However, there is no good theoretical method for estimating the magnitude or even the sign of the coefficient of this linear term.

Furthermore, at higher concentrations the whole concept of the ionic strength principle breaks down, that is, the principle stating that the properties of an ion depend on the ionic strength only and not on the specific ions that constitute the environment.[127] Thus, it has been customary in some studies to keep the ionic strength constant at some maximum value by the addition of an "inert" electrolyte such as $NaClO_4$, and to assume that changes due to replacing part of the $NaClO_4$ by a reagent will be negligible. This procedure has been shown to be invalid for large amounts of salt substitution, say of $NaClO_4$ by $HClO_4$, if the reaction studied involves an ion of opposite sign to that being replaced (a negative ion in this case).[128] Thus, there is no sure guide to the behavior of complex ions or any other ions at moderate to high concentrations.

In addition to the general effect on the activity coefficient discussed above, there is another kind of interaction of an ion with other ions in solution. This is a more specific effect involving only ions of opposite sign and consisting of the equilibrium formation of an ion pair between the two ions:[129]

$$A^+ + B^- \rightleftharpoons A^+, B^- \tag{20}$$

A characteristic association equilibrium constant will accompany this process:

$$K_A = \frac{[A^+, B^-]}{[A^+][B^-]} \tag{21}$$

Generally the equilibrium will be reached instantaneously on mixing A^+ and B^-. Such interaction will obviously have a considerable effect on the activities and other properties of A^+ and B^-. Although the activity of A^+ or B^- is always lowered, the effect of ion-pair formation on any measured property of the solution will depend on the contribution of A^+, B^- to that property.

The original theory for the formation of ion pairs is due to N. Bjerrum.[130] The theory is valid for certain kinds of systems only. In particular it does not apply to cases in which AB is itself a complex with a very strong bond, either covalent or ionic, directly between two atoms, e.g., $FeCl^{2+}$, $TlOH$, or $Co(NH_3)_5Cl^{2+}$, where $Co(NH_3)_5^{3+}$ is considered as A^+. The theory applies well to rather large, spherically symmetrical ions for which the only interaction is a fairly weak electrostatic one. In particular, then, it applies very well to the interaction of a substitution inert complex ion, such as $Co(NH_3)_6^{2+}$, with any anion, X^-, such that an ion pair $Co(NH_2)_6^{3+}$, X^- is formed. The descriptive name "outer-sphere complex," as opposed to an inner-sphere complex such as $Co(NH_3)_5X^{2+}$, has been given to such ion pairs.[129b,136]

The Bjerrum theory is somewhat complicated, and equally good results can be obtained from a simple model.[131] The ion pairs are assumed to be in contact with a distance a between their centers. The equation becomes, after some modification,[132]

$$K_A = \frac{4\pi N a^3}{3000} \exp\left(\frac{-z_1 z_2 e^2}{DkTa} + \frac{E_s}{kT}\right) \qquad (22)$$

where e is the charge on the electron, k is Boltzmann's constant, and D is the dielectric constant of the medium. E_s is a term for ion-dipole inter-actions, and other non-coulombic terms. The pre-exponential factor is of the order of unity, and K_A will have units of M^{-1}. For a one-to-one electrolyte in water at 25°C the factor $z_1 z_2 e^2/DkT$ is equal to unity for $a = 7.1$ A. For $Co(NH_3)_6^{3+}$, Cl^- the value of a is estimated as 4.3 A from crystallographic data.[133] This suggests that K_A will be much larger than one in water.

This is the case, as shown by Table 1.11, which gives association constants for a number of complex cations with simple anions. For values of $|z_1 z_2| > 3$, ion pairing is easily observed. For $|z_1 z_2| = 2$ ion pairing is inferred from indirect evidence, such as changes in rates of reaction. When $|z_1 z_2| = 1$, evidence for ion pairing in water is not found as a rule. In methanol, how-ever, where $D = 32$ compared to $D = 78$ for water, ion pairing is detected even for $|z_1 z_2| = 1$.

The methods by which the constants recorded in Table 1.11 are ob-tained are of interest. They have been found by conductivity studies,[140] by solubility studies,[135] by potentiometric data,[123a] and by changes in re-action rate.[133] The most general and interesting method, however, is a spectrophotometric one utilizing changes in the near-ultraviolet region.

It is observed that addition of simple anions to solutions of complex ions of high cationic charge does not materially affect the absorption bands of the complex in the visible region (d-d bands). However, the charge transfer absorption region is often markedly changed. The change consists essentially of a shift of the intense band to longer wavelengths. Figure 1.4 illustrates the effect of the halide ions on the charge transfer spectrum of $Co(NH_3)_6^{3+}$. The shift can extend out into the visible in certain cases. Thus, iodide ion causes $Ir(NH_3)_6^{3+}$ to change from colorless to yellow even though no chemical reaction occurs.[141]

Linhard[142] first proved that the spectral shifts shown in Fig. 1.4 are due to "outer-sphere complexes." He established that the equilibrium was rapid and reversible:

$$Co(NH_3)_6^{3+} + I^- \rightleftharpoons Co(NH_3)_6^{3+}, I^- \qquad (23)$$

and measured the association constant. The spectral change was shown to be due to the charge transfer absorption of the ion pair,

$$Co(NH_3)_6^{3+}, I^- \xrightarrow{hv} Co(NH_3)_6^{2+}, I \qquad (24)$$

Table 1.11 Association constants for outer-sphere complex ions at 25°C in water[a]

Ion Pair	K_A	Reference
$Co(NH_3)_6^{3+}$, Cl^-	74	134
$Co(NH_3)_6^{3+}$, Br^-	46	134
$Co(NH_3)_6^{3+}$, I^-	17	134
$Co(NH_3)_6^{3+}$, N_3^-	20	134
$Co(NH_3)_6^{3+}$, OH^-	71	133
$Co(en)_3^{3+}$, Br^-	21	134
$Co(en)_3^{3+}$, I^-	9	134
$Co(en)_3^{3+}$, N_3^-	11	134
$Co(en)_3^{3+}$, Cl^-	52	135
$Co(en)_3^{3+}$, SO_4^{2-}	2.8×10^3	135
$Co(NH_3)_6^{3+}$, SO_4^{2-}	2.2×10^3	136
$Co(NH_3)_5H_2O^{3+}$, SO_4^{2-}	1.9×10^3	136
$Co(NH_3)_6^{3+}$, $S_2O_3^{2-}$	1.8×10^3	137
$Cr(H_2O)_6^{3+}$, SCN^-	7	138
$Cr(H_2O)_6^{3+}$, Cl^-	13	139
$Co(NH_3)_5Cl^{2+}$, Cl^-	10	156
$Co(NH_3)_5Cl^{2+}$, SO_4^{2-}	2.9×10^2	156
$Co(NH_3)_5Cl^{2+}$, $CH_3CO_2^-$	5	156
$Co(NH_3)_5Cl^{2+}$, N_3^-	13	156

[a] Data at zero ionic strength.

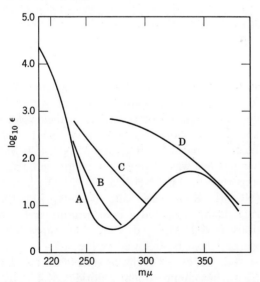

Fig. 1.4 Shifts in the ultraviolet absorption spectrum of $Co(NH_3)_6^{3+}$ produced by ion-pair formation. $A = Co(NH_3)_6^{3+}$; $B = Co(NH_3)_6^{3+}$, Cl^-; $C = Co(NH_3)_6^{3+}$, Br^-; $D = Co(NH_3)_6^{3+}$, I^-; From reference 134.

The shifts to longer and longer wavelengths shown in Fig. 1.4 for increasing size of the halide ion are in good agreement with this explanation.

It is usually easy to measure the equilibrium, as in reaction 23, by the changes in spectra in the 250–350 mμ region. The most accurate data in Table 1.11 were obtained in this way. An exception would occur if the complex ion had a ligand of low electronegativity and if the anion had a high electronegativity. In this event the new spectrum would probably be hidden by the old. It has also been shown[136b] that the molecular extinction coefficients of the free ion and the ion pair are insensitive to ionic strength. They are, however, remarkably variable with temperature. Thus, the spectrum of the solution will change with temperature, not only because the equilibrium is shifted slightly, but also because the absorption per molecule changes considerably.

For labile systems it is often quite difficult to distinguish between inner- and outer-sphere complexes, particularly if the spectral changes are not conclusive.[143] For Fe(III) aquo ion it appears that the stabilities of inner-sphere and outer-sphere complexes are very similar for anions of strong acids.[144] For basic anions such as OH^-, F^-, and N_3^-, there is an advantage in penetrating close to the central cation, and the inner-sphere complexes are more stable.[145]

Furthermore, a true complex such as $Fe(H_2O)_5Cl^{2+}$ can readily add further anions to form $Fe(H_2O)_4Cl_2^+$, etc., whereas the addition of further anions to an ion pair does not usually happen in water.†† In solvents of low dielectric constant, triple ions and higher aggregates are well known.[146]

Nomenclature

A comprehensive system of nomenclature of coordination compounds was not possible before the coordination theory of Werner.[5] As a result many of the complexes were named according to their color (Table 1.1). and then later some of the more common terms, such as *luteo*, and *purpureo*, came to be used to mean $M(NH_3)_6$ and $M(NH_3)_5Cl$, without regard to color. Another practice was to name the compound after the person who had first reported it, e.g., $NH_4[Co(NH_3)_2(NO_2)_4]$, Erdman's salt; $NH_4[Cr(NH_3)_2(NCS)_4]$, Reinecke's salt; $[Pt(NH_3)_4][PtCl_4]$, Magnus's green salt. Werner finally suggested a nomenclature system which, with some modifications, is still employed. One of his suggestions no longer used is that the metal stem be followed by the suffix -a, -o, -i, or -e to designate the $+1$, $+2$, $+3$, or $+4$ oxidation state of the metal, respectively, e.g., $[Co(NH_3)_6]Cl_3$, hexamminecobalti chloride; $K_2[PtCl_4]$, potassium

†† However, see R. Larsson, S. F. Mason, and B. J. Norman, *J. Chem. Soc.*, **1966**, 301.

tetrachloroplatinoate. The Stock[147] system of using Roman numerals in parentheses to designate oxidation state is now employed instead.

Recommendations for the nomenclature of coordination compounds, made by the Commission on the Nomenclature of Inorganic Chemistry of the International Union of Pure and Applied Chemistry (IUPAC), are available.[148] The rules listed below are taken from this source and from a review on the subject by Fernelius.[149]

1. *Order of Listing Ions.* The cation is named first, followed by the anion.

2. *Endings of Coordinated Groups.* Neutral groups are named as the molecule, positive groups end in -ium, and negative groups end in -o. Exceptions to this are aquo, H_2O, and ammine, NH_3.

$(C_2H_5)_3P$	triethylphosphine
$NH_2NH_3^+$	hydrazinium
$NH_2CH_2CH_2NH_3^+$	2-aminoethylammonium
CH_3COO^-	acetato
$HON{=}C(CH_3)C(CH_3){=}NO^-$	dimethylglyoximato

In general, if the anion name ends in -ide, -ite, or -ate, the final -e is replaced by -o, giving -ido, -ito, and -ato, respectively. Some exceptions to this are

F^-	fluoro	O^{2-}	oxo
Cl^-	chloro	OH^-	hydroxo
CN^-	cyano	O_2^{2-}	peroxo

3. *Order of Ligands.* The order of citation of ligands in complexes is (1) anionic, (2) neutral, and (3) cationic, without separation by hyphens. The anions are cited in the order H^-, O^{2-}, OH^-, simple anions, polyatomic anions, and lastly the organic anions in alphabetical order. The neutral and cationic ligands are in the order H_2O, NH_3, inorganic ligands, and then organic ligands.

$[Pt(en)(NH_3)_2NO_2Cl]SO_4$ ‡‡	chloronitrodiammineethylene-diamineplatinum(IV) sulfate
$[Co(NH_3)_4H_2OBr](NO_3)_2$	bromoaquotetraamminecobalt(III) nitrate
$[Pt(NH_2NH_3)(en)Cl]Cl_2$	chloroethylenediaminehydra-ziniumplatinum(II) chloride

‡‡ The IUPAC recommendation is that the order of listing of ligands in the formula start with the metal, which then gives $[PtClNO_2(NH_3)_2(en)]SO_4$. This system is not now in general practice and will not be used here because in substitution reactions the simplest anion is often the one that is replaced and it seems easier to focus attention on this if the anion is at the extreme right of the formula of the complex.

4. *Numerical Prefixes.* The prefixes. di-, tri-, tetra-, etc., are used before simple expressions, e.g., chloro- oxalato, glycinato, etc. The prefixes bis-, tris-, tetrakis-, etc., are used before complex expressions (chiefly expressions which contain the prefixes mono-, di-, tri-, etc., in the ligand name itself), all of which are enclosed in parentheses, e.g., ethylenediamine, trialkyl-phosphine, etc.

5. *Endings of Complexes.* The characteristic ending for anionic complexes is -ate or optionally -ic if named as an acid. There are no characteristic endings for cationic or neutral complexes.

$K_4[Fe(CN)_6]$	potassium hexacyanoferrate(II)
$H_2[PtCl_6]$	hydrogen hexachloroplatinate(IV) or hexachloroplatinic(IV) acid
$Al(H_2O)_6^{3+}$ §§	hexaaquoaluminum(III) ion
$Cu(C_5H_7O_2)_2$ §§	bis(2,4-pentanedionato)copper(II) or bis(acetylacetonato)copper(II)

6. *Oxidation State.* The oxidation state of the central elements is designated by a Roman numeral in parentheses at the end of the name of the complex, without a space between the two. The 0 is used for zero, and a minus sign before the Roman numeral indicates negative oxidation states.

$K_4[Ni(CN)_4]$	potassium tetracyanonickelate(0)
$Na[Co(CO)_4]$	sodium tetracarbonylcobaltate($-$I)

7. *Bridging groups.* Groups that bridge two centers of coordination are preceded by the Greek letter μ, which is repeated before the name of each different kind of bridging group.

$$(C_2O_4)_2Cr\underset{OH}{\overset{OH}{\diamond}}Cr(C_2O_4)_2^{4-}$$

di-μ-hydroxotetraoxalatodichromate(III) ion

$$(NH_3)_4Co\underset{NO_2}{\overset{NH_2}{\diamond}}Co(NH_3)_4^{4+}$$

μ-amido-μ-nitrooctaamminedicobalt(III) ion

$(CO)_3Fe(CO)_3Fe(CO)_3$ tri-μ-carbonylbis(tricarbonyliron)

§§ Although the complex is usually enclosed in brackets, this system is not followed here except when molecular formulas of salts are written. Brackets will not be used for individual complexions or for neutral complexes in order to avoid the confusion which arises with the expression of molar concentrations, e.g., $[[Co(NH_3)_6]^{3+}]$.

8. *Point of Attachment*. The point of attachment of a coordinated group is designated by placing the symbols (in italics) of the elements attached after the name of the group, with separation by hyphens. The following optional procedure may be used for $-NO_2^-$, nitro; $-ONO^-$, nitrito; $-SCN^-$, thiocyanato; $-NCS^-$, isothiocyanato.

K_2 [Pt (S O S O O)$_2$]   potassium dithiosulfato-*O*,*S*-platinate(II)

K_2 [Pt (O S S O O)$_2$]   potassium dithiosulfato-*O*-*O*-platinate(II)

9. *Geometrical Isomers*. Geometrical isomers are named either by using numbers or by the designation *cis* for adjacent positions and *trans* for opposite (180° apart) positions. For square complexes groups 1,3 and 2,4 are in *trans* positions.

$$(4)-M-(2)$$

with (1) above and (3) below M

$$py-Pt-NH_3$$

with Cl above and NO_2 below Pt

1-Chloro-3-nitroamminepyridineplatinum(II)
or *trans*-chloronitro-*trans* amminepyridine-
platinum(II)

The Russians have a convenient method of designating the structures of such compounds in the formula. They enclose ligands *trans* to one another in angular brackets, ⟨ ⟩. Thus, the formula of the above compound is $Pt\langle pyNH_3\rangle\langle NO_2Cl\rangle$. This same system is also readily applicable to octahedral complexes. For example, the complexes below are designated $Co\langle(NH_3)_2\rangle\langle NH_3NO_2\rangle_2{}^+$ and $Co\langle(NH_3)_2\rangle\langle NH_3NO_2\rangle\langle(NO_2)_2\rangle$, respectively. This method is especially useful for complexes containing several different types of ligands. Octahedral complexes are numbered so that the *trans* positions are 1,6; 2,4; 3,5.

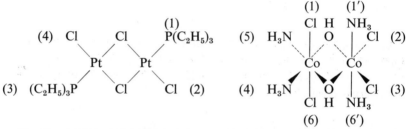

1,2-Dinitrotetraamine
cobalt(III) ion or *cis*-
dinitrotetraamine-cobalt(III) ion

1,2,6-Trinitrotriammine
cobalt(III) or *trans*-
trinitrotriamminecobalt(III)

Geometrical isomers of bridged complexes may be named by this same scheme.

Di-μ-chloro-2,4-dichlorobis(triethylphosphine)
diplatinum(II) or di-μ-chloro-*trans*-dichlorobis
(triethylphosphine)diplatinum(II)

Di-μ-hydroxo-1,2,3,6-tetrachlorotetraamminedi-
cobalt(III) or di-μ-hydroxo-*cis*-dichloro-*trans*-
dichlorotetraamminedicobalt(III) ion

10. *Optical Isomers.* There continues to be some confusion as to the choice of symbols to designate the optical rotations and the structures of optically active metal complexes. This is a subject that should receive further consideration by the IUPAC Commission on the Nomenclature of Inorganic Chemistry. The procedure given here is now largely followed by most of the authors doing research in the field. ‖ ‖

‖ ‖ Piper[150] makes the suggestion that the Greek letters Λ and Δ be used rather than D and L to designate the absolute configuration of a metal chelate. When the six-coordinated complex $M(AA)_3$ is viewed down the trigonal C_3 axis of a trigonal anti-prism, the chelate rings take on the appearance of a helix or screw. The enantiomer with a left-handed helix is then given the symbol Λ and the right-handed helix is Δ. Thus, the absolute standard becomes $\Lambda(+)$-$Co(en)_3{}^{3+}$ rather than $D(+)$-$Co(en)_3{}^{3+}$. It is apparent that the correspondence between these symbols is that D and Λ are equivalent, as are L and Δ.

The sign of rotation of an enantiomer is denoted $(+)$ or $(-)$ for the Na_D line; for another wavelength it is specified by a subscript, e.g., $(+)_{5461}$. Racemates are designated as $(\pm)$ and inactive forms as *meso*. The symbols D* and L* are used to describe absolute configurations relative to a standard absolute substance such as $D^*(+)$-Co(en)$_3^{3+}$. Small capitals, D* and L*, are used to denote the absolute configurations of optically active organic ligands. The symbols D and L, without the superscript *, are used to designate relative configurations for analogous compounds for which the absolute configuration is not known. The symbols d and l are not used.

The types of isomers are specified in the order (1) optical and (2) geometrical.

$D^*(+)$-Co(en)$_3^{3+}$ $D^*(+)$-tris(ethylenediamine)cobalt(III) ion

$L^*(+)$-Rh($-$chxn)$_3^{3+}$ $L^*(+)$-tris($-$cyclohexanediamine) rhodium(III) ion

$(+)$-*trans*-Co($-$pn)$_2$Cl$_2^+$ $(+)$-*trans*-dichloro-bis($-$propylenediamine)cobalt(III) ion

$$meso\text{-(en)}_2\text{Co} \overset{\displaystyle NH_2}{\underset{\displaystyle NO_2}{\diagup\diagdown}} \text{Co(en)}_2{}^{4+}$$

meso-μ-amido-μ-nitrotetrakis-(ethylenediamine)cobalt(III) ion

On the basis of the rules used for symbol notations, it follows that $L^*(+)$-Rh($-$chxn)$_3^{3+}$ has a $+$ rotation at the Na_D line but contains chxn, which alone has a $-$ rotation at the Na_D line, and that the absolute configuration of the complex is a "mirror image" of that of the absolute standard $D^*(+)$-Co(en)$_3^{3+}$.

11. *Metal-Metal Bonding.*[¶¶] The prefix bi- is used before the name of the metals forming a metal-metal bond.

Cl(C$_2$H$_5$NH$_2$)$_4$Pt—Pt(C$_2$H$_5$NH$_2$)$_4$Cl^{4+} *sym*-dichlorooctakis(ethylamine)biplatinum(IV) ion

---

Bailar[151] points out that, if $(+)$-Co(en)$_3^{3+}$ is viewed along one of the C_2 axes the chelate rings form a right-handed system. Because the symbols D and L have been used in different ways, he recommends the use of D* and L* to designate absolute configuration, e.g., D^*-$(+)$-Co(en)$_3^{3+}$ This system will be adopted here. It is suggested[151] that the choice of $C_2(D^*)$ over $C_3(\Lambda)$ as the axis of chirality has the following advantages: (1) historically $(+)$-Co(en)$_3^{3+}$ has been designated d or D, and this notation is still in use; (2) D* corresponds to the positive (*dextro*) specific rotation, $[\alpha]_D$, and a positive "Cotton effect" in the O.R.D. curve for the first Co(en)$_3^{3+}$ absorption band; (3) this scheme can be used for ions that do not possess a C_3 axis but do have a C_2 axis, e.g., Co(en)$_2$X$_2^+$ (see Ref. 157).

¶¶ There is currently considerable interest in metal-metal bonded compounds, and several new compounds, such as Ph$_3$PAu–Mn(CO)$_5$, have recently been discovered.[152] It is difficult to see how these compounds can be named conveniently by rule 11.

12. *Abbreviations.* A customary practice in writing formulas of co-ordination compounds is to use simple abbreviations for complicated molecules. Except in a few cases, such as en, pn, and py, there is no agreement as to the abbreviations for a particular group. Some of the abbreviations that have been used in this book are listed in Table 1.12.

Table 1.12 Symbols often used for some of the more common ligands

Ligand Name	Ligand Symbol
2,2′-Bipyridine	bipy
2,3-Butanediamine	bn
trans-1,2-Cyclopentanediamine	cptn
Diethylenetriamine	dien
Dimethylglyoximato	DMG
Ethylenediamine	en
Ethylenediaminetetraacetato	EDTA, Y
Oxalato	ox
2,4-Pentanedionato (acetylacetonato)	acac
1,10-Phenanthroline	phen
1,2-Propanediamine (propylenediamine)	pn
1,3-Propanediamine (trimethylenediamine)	tn
1,2,3-Propanetriamine	ptn
Pyridine	py
Thiourea	tu
2,2′,2″-Triaminotriethylamine	tren
Triethylenetetramine	trien
Glycinato	gly
Triphenylphosphine	PPh_3
2,2′,2″-Terpyridine	terpy
o-Phenylene-bis(dimethylarsine)	diars
Tris(*o*-diphenylarsineophenyl)arsine	QAS
1,2-Dicyanoethylene-1,2-dithiolato	MNT
1,3-Di-(2′-pyridyl)-1,2-diaza-2-propene	PAPHY

13. *Miscellaneous Terminology.* Several terms related to coordination compounds that have not yet been introduced will be defined or described. In the case of certain polyfunctional molecules and ions, it is possible for more than one atom of the group to attach itself to the same metal ion. Such a group is called a *multidentate* or *chelate* group. The adjective chelate was originally used to designate the bidentate character of a group but has been generalized to include all multidentate groups and has been

Table 1.13 Examples of different types of donor groups

Number of Points of Attachment	Name[a]	Examples
1	unidentate	H_2O, NH_3, Cl^-, CN^-, CO, PR_3, $CH_2{=}CH_2$
2	bidentate	CO_3^{2-}, $C_2O_4^{2-}$, $NH_2CH_2COO^-$, $NH_2C_2H_4NH_2$

$R_2PC_2H_4PR_2$,

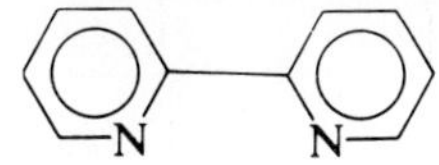

$(CH_3)_2As \qquad As(CH_3)_2$

		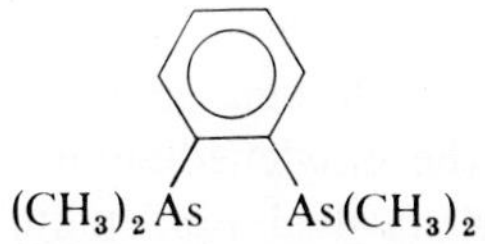
3	tridentate	$NH(CH_2COO)_2^{2-}$, $NH(C_2H_4NH_2)_2$,

$NH_2CH_2CHCH_2NH_2$,
$\qquad\qquad |$
$\qquad\quad NH_2$

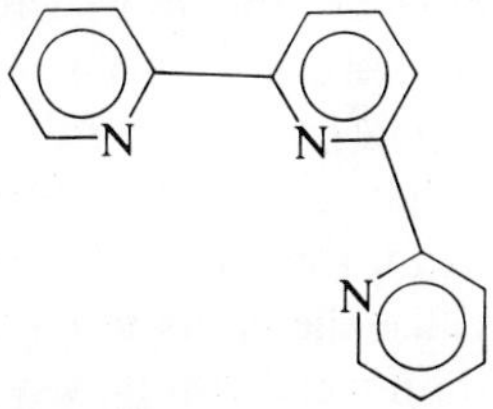

$(CH_3)_2AsC_3H_6AsC_3H_6As(CH_3)_2$
$\qquad\qquad\qquad |$
$\qquad\qquad\qquad CH_3$

4	quadridentate	$N(CH_2COO)_3^{3-}$, $N(C_2H_4NH_2)_3$,
		$NH_2C_2H_4NHC_2H_4NHC_2H_4NH_2$,

		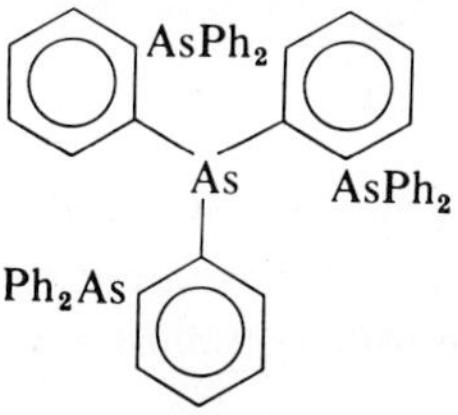
5	quinquidentate	$OOCCH_2N(R)C_2H_4N(CH_2COO)_2^{3-}$,
		$NH_2C_2H_4NHC_2H_4NHC_2H_4NHC_2H_4NH_2$,

		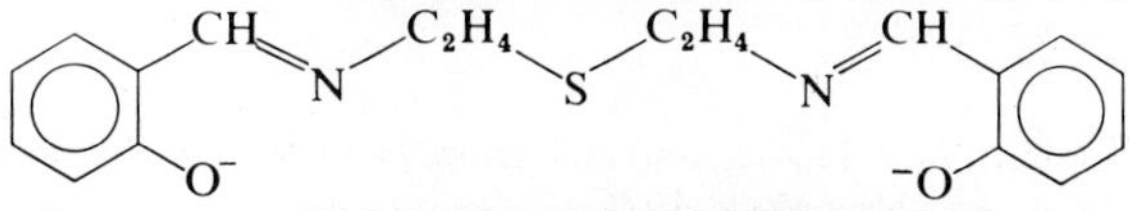
6	sexadentate	$(OOCCH_2)_2NC_2H_4N(CH_2COO)_2^{4-}$,
		$(H_2NC_2H_4)_2NC_2H_4N(C_2H_4NH_2)_2$
8	octadentate	$(OOCCH_2)_2NC_2H_4NC_2H_4N(CH_2COO)_2^{5-}$
		$\qquad\qquad\qquad\qquad |$
		$\qquad\qquad\qquad\qquad CH_2COO$

[a] It is suggested[153] that names derived solely from Greek or, alternatively, Latin roots be used. Words such as multidentate or polydontate are permissible, but bilingual hybrids such as polydentate or hexadentate are to be avoided.

used also as a noun both for the chelate group and for the complex. The preferred usage of the term may be illustrated by this figure:

$$
\begin{array}{cc}
\text{H}_2 & \text{H}_2 \\
\text{CH}_2{-}\text{N} & \text{N}{-}\text{CH}_2{}^{2+} \\
\quad\quad\diagdown\quad\diagup & \\
\quad\quad\quad\text{Cu} & \\
\quad\quad\diagup\quad\diagdown & \\
\text{CH}_2{-}\text{N} & \text{N}{-}\text{CH}_2 \\
\text{H}_2 & \text{H}_2
\end{array}
$$

for which the salt is designated as a *chelate compound*, the cation as a *chelate ion*, and the ethylenediamine as a *chelate group*. The ethylenediamine is also often called a bidentate group because it is attached to the central ion through two atoms. A few examples of different types of donor groups are shown in Table 1.13.

If the donor atom is attached to two metal ions, it is then called a *bridging group* (see rule 7). This results in the formation of a compound which is generally referred to as a "polynuclear complex"; sometimes, instead, the name *bridged complex* is applied. The latter term is preferred because the prefix poly- usually denotes a high molecular weight. Although certain metal complex systems do form high-molecular-weight species, they are often just dimeric, trimeric, etc. The dimeric complex is the simplest of these because it contains only two central ions:

$$
\begin{array}{ccc}
(\text{C}_2\text{H}_5)_3\text{P} & \text{Cl} & \text{Cl} \\
\diagdown\diagup\diagdown\diagup & & \\
\text{Pt} & \text{Pt} & \\
\diagup\diagdown\diagup\diagdown & & \\
\text{Cl} & \text{Cl} & \text{P}(\text{C}_2\text{H}_5)_3
\end{array}
$$

Generally a donor atom or ion is not coordinated to more than two metal ions, but there are exceptions: for example, the oxide ion in $Be_4O(C_2H_3O_2)_6$ is attached to each of the four beryllium ions.[154]

References

1. S. Glasstone, K. J. Laidler, and H. Eyring, *The Theory of Rate Processes*. McGraw-Hill Book Co., New York, 1941.
2. J. C. Bailar, Jr., ed., *The Chemistry of Coordination Compounds* (American Chemical Society Monograph No. 131), Reinhold Publishing Corp., New York, 1956.
3. W. L. Bragg and G. B. Brown, *Z. Krist.*, **63**, 538 (1926); H. M. Powell and A. F. Wells, *J. Chem. Soc.*, **1935**, 359.
4. B. M. Tassaert, *Ann. chim. phys.*, **28**, 92 (1798).
5. A. Werner, *Z. anorg. Chem.*, **3**, 267 (1893).
6. G. N. Lewis, *J. Am. Chem. Soc.*, **38**, 762 (1916).

7. N. V. Sidgwick, *The Electronic Theory of Valency*, Clarendon Press, Oxford, 1927.
8. J. Bjerrum, *Metal Ammine Formation in Aqueous Solution*, P. Haase and Son, Copenhagen, 1941.
9. H. Scouloudi, *Acta Cryst.*, **6**, 651 (1953); J. Bjerrum, C. J. Ballhausen, and C. K. Jørgensen, *Acta Chem. Scand.*, **8**, 1275 (1954); S. Kirschner, *J. Am. Chem. Soc.*, **78**, 2372 (1956).
10. C. Brink and H. A. S. Kroese. *Acta Cryst.*, **5**, 433 (1952); C. Brink and A. E. Van Arkel, *ibid.*, **5**, 506 (1952).
11. S. Ahrland, J. Chatt, N. R. Davies, and A. A. Williams, *Nature*, **179**, 1187 (1957); *J. Chem. Soc.*, **1958**, 264, 276.
12. A. F. Wells, *Structural Inorganic Chemistry*, Clarendon Press, Oxford, 3rd ed., 1962; L. E. Sutton, ed., *Interatomic Distances* (Spectral Publication No. 11), The Chemical Society, London, 1958.
13. D. P. Mellor, *Chem. Revs.*, **33**, 137 (1943).
14. F. W. Pinkard, E. Sharratt, W. Wardlaw, and E. G. Cox, *J. Chem. Soc.*, **1934**, 1012.
15. I. I. Chernyaev, *Ann. inst. platine USSR*, **6**, 55 (1928).
16. A. D. Hel'man and E. Gorushkina, *Compt. rend. acad. sci. USSR*, **55**, 33 (1937).
17. A. D. Hel'man, E. F. Karandashova, and L. N. Essen, *Doklady Akad. Nauk USSR*, **63**, 37 (1948).
18. W. H. Mills and T. H. H. Quibell, *J. Chem. Soc.*, **1935**, 839.
19. See, for example, L. M. Venanzi, *J. Chem. Soc.*, **1958**, 719; N. S. Gill and R. S. Nyholm, *ibid*, **1959**, 3997; D. M. L. Goodgame and F. A. Cotton, *J. Am. Chem. Soc.*, **82**, 5771, 5774 (1960); C. Furlani and A. Furlani, *J. Inorg. Nucl. Chem.*, **19**, 51 (1961); see also reference 64.
20. (a) R. G. Dickinson and L. Pauling, *J. Am. Chem. Soc.*, **45**, 1466 (1923). (b) R. Eisenberg and J. A. Ibers, *ibid.*, **87**, 3776 (1965); E. I. Steifel and H. B. Gray, *ibid.*, **87**, 4012 (1965); A. E. Smith, G. N. Schrauzer, V. P. Mayweg, and W. Heinrich, *ibid.*, **87**, 5798 (1965).
21. A. Werner, *Ber.*, **47**, 3087 (1914).
22. F. G. Mann, *J. Chem. Soc.*, **1933**, 412.
23. J. Podlaha and M. Ebert, *Nature*, **188**, 657 (1960).
24. R. C. Cass, G. E. Coates, and R. G. Hayter, *Chem. Ind.* (London), **1954**, 1485; *J. Chem. Soc.*, **1955**, 4007.
25. S. Ahrland and J. Chatt, *Chem. Ind.* (London), **1955**, 96.
26. W. S. Fyfe, *J. Chem. Soc.*, **1955**, 1032.
27. J. A. Ibers, *Ann. Rev. Phys. Chem.*, **16**, 380 (1965); E. L. Mutterties and R. A Schunn, *Quart. Rev.* (*London*), **20**, 245 (1966).
28. H. Stammreich, O. Sola, and Y. Tavares, *J. Chem. Phys.*, **30**, 856 (1959); C. W. F. T. Pistorius and P. C. Hoorhoff, *ibid.*, **31**, 1439 (1959).
29. R. D. Cramer, R. V. Lindsey, C. T. Prewitt, and U. G. Stolberg, *J. Am. Chem. Soc.*, **87**, 658 (1965).
30. W. F. Edgell, J. Huff, J. Thomas, H. Lehman, C. Angell, and G. Asato, *J. Am. Chem. Soc.*, **82**, 1254 (1960).
31. M. Angaletta, *Gazz. chim. Ital.*, **89**, 2359 (1859); **90**, 1021 (1960).
32. S. S. Bath and L. Vaska, *J. Am. Chem. Soc.*, **85**, 3500 (1963); S. J. LaPlaca and J. A. Ibers, *ibid.*, **85**, 3500 (1963).
33. D. E. C. Corbridge and E. G. Cox, *J. Chem. Soc.*, **1956**, 594.
34. (a) J. A. Brewster, C. A. Savage, and L. M. Venanzi, *J. Chem. Soc.*, **1961**, 3699; C. A. Savage and L. M. Venanzi, *ibid.*, **1962**, 1548; G. Dyer, J. G. Hartley, and L. M. Venanzi, *ibid.*, **1965**, 1293, 2771. (b) G. S. Benner, W. E. Hatfield, and D. V. Meek, *Inorg. Chem.*, **3**, 1544 (1964). (c) G. Dyer and D. W. Meek, *ibid.*, **4**, 1398

(1965). (d) J. S. Coleman, H. Petersen, Jr., and R. A. Penneman, *ibid.*, **4,** 135 (1965); K. N. Raymond and F. Basolo, *ibid.*, **5,** 949 (1966).

35. K. A. Jensen and B. Nygaard, *Acta Chem. Scand.*, **3,** 474 (1949); V. Scatturin and A. Turco, *J. Inorg. Nucl. Chem.*, **8,** 447 (1958).

36. G. A. Mair, H. M. Powell, and D. E. Henn, *Proc. Chem. Soc.*, **1960,** 415; G. A. Barclay, R. S. Nyholm, and R. V. Parish, *J. Chem. Soc.*, **1961,** 4433.

37. L. Malatesta, *Gazz. chim. Ital.*, **70,** 734 (1940); **71,** 615 (1941); L. Cambi, *Z. anorg. u. allgem. Chem.*, **247,** 22 (1941); P. R. H. Alderman and P. G. Owston, *Nature*, **178,** 1071 (1956).

38. C. H. Langford, E. Billig, S. I. Shupack, and H. B. Gray, *J. Am. Chem. Soc.*, **86,** 2958 (1964.)

39. L. Malatesta and A. Sacco, *Atti accad. nazl. Lincei Rebd.*, **15,** 93 (1953); F. A. Cotton, T. G. Dunne, and J. S. Wood, *Inorg. Chem.*, **4,** 318 (1965).

40. (a) L. Sacconi, P. Nannelli, N. Nardi, and U. Campigli, *Inorg. Chem.*, **4,** 943 (1965); P. L. Orioli, M. DiVaira, and L. Sacconi, *Chem. Comm.*, **103,** (1965). (b) M. Ciampolini, N. Nardi, and G. P. Speroni, *Inorg. Chem.*, **5,** 41, 45 (1966); M. DiVaira and P. L. Orioli, *Chem. Comm.*, 590 (1965); Z. Dori and H. B. Gray, *J. Am. Chem. Soc.*, **88,** (1966).

41. R. J. Gillespie, *Advances in the Chemistry of the Coordination Compounds* (S. Kirschner, ed.), Macmillan Co., New York, 1961, pp. 34–49.

42. G. C. Hampson and L. Pauling, *J. Am. Chem. Soc.*, **60,** 2702 (1938); W. H. Zachariasen, *Acta Cryst.*, **7,** 792 (1954).

43. M. D. Lind, M. J. Hamor, T. A. Hamor, and J. L. Hoard, *Inorg. Chem.*, **3,** 34 (1964).

44. J. L. Hoard, *J. Am. Chem. Soc.*, **61,** 1252 (1939).

45. S. Richards, B. Pedersen, J. V. Silverton, and J. L. Hoard, *Inorg. Chem.*, **3,** 27 (1964).

46. R. J. H. Clark, D. L. Kepert, R. S. Nyholm, and J. Lewis, *Nature*, **199,** 559 (1963).

47. J. L. Hoard and J. V. Silverton, *Inorg. Chem.*, **2,** 235 (1963).

48. J. L. Hoard and H. H. Nordsieck, *J. Am. Chem. Soc.*, **51,** 2853 (1939).

49. D. F. Shriver, *J. Am. Chem. Soc.*, **85,** 1405 (1963).

50. G. L. Glen, J. V. Silverton, and J. L. Hoard, *Inorg. Chem.*, **2,** 250 (1963).

51. J. L. Hoard, E. Willstadter, and J. V. Silverton, *J. Am. Chem. Soc.*, **87,** 1610 (1965).

52. J. L. Hoard, W. G. Martin, M. E. Smith, and J. E. Whitney, *J. Am. Chem. Soc.*, **76,** 3820 (1954).

53. J. V. Silverton and J. L. Hoard, *Inorg. Chem.*, **2,** 243 (1963).

54. D. Grdenic and B. Matkovic, *Nature*, **182,** 465 (1958); *Acta Cryst.*, **12,** 817 (1959).

55. L. Helmholz, *J. Am. Chem. Soc.*, **61,** 1544 (1939).

56. (a) S. C. Abrahams, A. P. Ginsberg, and K. Knox, *Inorg. Chem.*, **3,** 558 (1964). (b) M. D. Lind, B. Lee, and J. L. Hoard, *J. Am. Chem. Soc.*, **87,** 1611, 1612 (1965).

57. H. P. Klug and L. Alexander, *J. Am. Chem. Soc.*, **66,** 1056 (1944).

58. I. Lindquist, *Arkiv Kemi Mineral. Geol.* **24A,** 1 (1947).

59. J. Chatt and R. G. Wilkins, *J. Chem. Soc.*, **1951,** 2532.

60. F. Basolo and G. S. Hammaker, *Inorg. Chem.*, **1,** 1 (1962).

61. (a) F. Basolo, J. L. Burmeister, and A. J. Poe, *J. Am. Chem. Soc.*, **85,** 1700 (1963); J. L. Burmeister and F. Basolo, *Inorg. Chem.*, **3,** 1587 (1964). (b) A. Wojcicki and M. F. Farona, *ibid.*, **4,** 857 (1965). (c) A. Haim and N. Sutin, *J. Am. Chem. Soc.*, **87,** 4210 (1965); **88,** 434 (1966).

62. (a) J. Halpern and S. Nakamura, *J. Am., Chem. Soc.*, **87,** 3002 (1065). (b) J. H. Espenson and J. P. Birk, *ibid.*, **87,** 3280 (1965). (c) D. E. Peters and R. T. M. Fraser, *ibid.*, **87,** 2758 (1965). (d) H. H. Schmidtke, *ibid.*, **87,** 2522 (1965).

63. M. C. Browning, D. J. Morgan, S. A. G. Pratt, L. E. Sutton, and L. M. Venanzi, *J. Chem. Soc.*, **1962**, 693; R. G. Hayter and F. S. Humiec, *J. Am. Chem. Soc.*, **84**, 2004 (1962); *Inorg. Chem.*, **4**, 1701 (1965).

64. K. H. Holm, A. Chakravorty, and G. O. Dudek, *J. Am. Chem. Soc.*, **86**, 379 (1964); L. Sacconi, M. Ciampolini, and N. Nardi, *ibid.*, **86**, 819 (1964).

65. N. S. Kurnakow, *Z. anorg. u. allgem. Chem.* **151**, 264 (1926); F. Basolo, J. C. Bailar, Jr., and B. R. Tarr, *J. Am. Chem. Soc.*, **72**, 2433 (1950).

66. J. Chatt and B. L. Shaw, *J. Chem. Soc.*, **1959**, 4020.

67. L. Vaska, *Science*, **140**, 809 (1963).

68. J. A. Ibers and S. J. LaPlaca, *Science*, **145**, 920 (1964); *J. Am. Chem. Soc.*, **87**, 2581 (1965).

69. J. S. Griffith, *Proc. Roy. Soc. (London)*, **A235**, 23 (1956).

70. L. Vaska and J. W. Diluzio, *J. Am. Chem. Soc.*, **84**, 679 (1962); *J. Am. Chem. Soc.*, **88**, 4100 (1966).

71. G. B. Kauffman, R. P. Pinnell, and L. T. Takahashi, *Inorg. Chem.*, **1**, 544 (1962); F. Basolo, M. Lederer, L. Ossicini, and K. H. Stephen, *J. Chromatog.*, **10**, 262 (1963).

72. A. Werner, *Ann.*, **386**, 1 (1912).

73. F. P. Dwyer and F. L. Garvan, *Inorg. Syn.*, **6**, 192 (1960).

74. F. P. Dwyer and B. Halpern, *Nature*, **196**, 270 (1962).

75. R. Tsuchida, M. Kobayaski, and A. Nokamura, *J. Chem. Soc. Japan*, **56**, 1339 (1935); *Bull. Chem. Soc. Japan*, **11**, 38 (1936); J. C. Bailar, Jr., and D. F. Peppard, *J. Am. Chem. Soc.*, **62**, 105 (1940).

76. H. Krebs, J. Diewald, and J. A. Wagner, *Angew. Chem.,* **67**, 705 (1958).

77. T. Moeller and E. Gulyas, *J. Inorg. Nucl. Chem.*, **5**, 245 (1958); J. P. Collman, R. P. Blair, R. L. Marshall, and L. Slade *Inorg. Chem.*, **2**, 576 (1963).

78. E. Ferroni and R. Cini, *J. Am. Chem. Soc.*, **82**, 2427 (1960).

79. V. F. Doron and S. Kirschner, *Inorg. Chem.*, **1**, 539 (1962).

80. S. F. Mason, *Quart. Rev. (London)*, **17**, 20 (1963).

81. A. M. Sargeson, *Chelating Agents and Metal Chelates* (F. P. Dwyer and D. P. Mellor, eds.), Academic Press, New York, 1964, Chap. 5.

82. J. P. Mathieu, *Bull. soc. chim. Fr.* [5], 3, 476 (1936); T. D. O'Brien, J. P. McReynolds, and J. C. Bailar, Jr., *J. Am. Chem. Soc.*, **70**, 749 (1948); M. Martinette and J. C. Bailar, Jr., *ibid.*, **74**, 1054 (1952); T. E. MacDermott and A. M. Sargeson, *Australian J. Chem.*, **16**, No. 3, 334 (1963); R D. Gillard and G. Wilkinson, *J. Chem. Soc.*, **1964**, 1368.

83. Y. Saito, K. Nakatsu, M. Shiro and H. Kuroya, *Bull. Chem. Soc. Japan*, **30**, 795 (1957).

84. F. P. Dwyer, N. A. Gibson, and E. C. Gyarfas, *J. Proc. Roy. Soc. N.S. Wales*, **84**, 68 (1951).

85. S. M. Jørgensen, *Z. anorg. Chem.*, **5**, 169 (1893).

86. I. Lindquist and B. Strandberg, *Acta Cryst.* **10**, 176 (1957); P. C. H. Mitchell and R. J. P. Williams, *J. Chem. Soc.*, **1960**, 1912.

87. A. Turco and C. Pecile, *Nature*, **191**, 66 (1961).

88. A. Tramer, *J. chim. phys.*, **59**, 232 (1962); O. W. Howarth, R. E. Richards, and L. M. Venanzi, *J. Chem. Soc.*, **1964**, 3335; R. A. Plane, private communication.

89. K. Nakamoto, *Infrared Spectra of Inorganic and Coordination Compounds*, John Wiley and Sons, New York, 1963.

90. D. R. Eaton, W. D. Phillips, and D. J. Caldwell, *J. Am. Chem. Soc.*, **85**, 397 (1963).

91. R. S. Nyholm, *Chem. Revs.*, **53**, 263 (1953); J. R. Miller, *Advan. Inorg. Chem. Radiochem.*, **4**, 133 (1962).

92. A. Davison, W. McFarlane, L. Pratt, and G. Wilkinson, *J. Chem. Soc.*, **1962**, 3653.
93. D. F. Shriver, *J. Am. Chem. Soc.*, **85**, 3509 (1963).
94. G. W. Parshall, *J. Am. Chem. Soc.*, **86**, 361 (1964).
95. J. Bjerrum, G. Schwarzenbach, and L. G. Sillen, *Stability Constants*, The Chemical Society, London, 1957; L. G. Sillen and A. E. Martell, *ibid.*, 1964.
96. F J. C. Rossotti and H. Rossotti, *The Determination of Stability Constants*, McGraw-Hill Book Co., New York, 1961, K. B. Yatsimirskii and V. P. Vasilev, *Instability Constants of Complex Compounds*, Pergamon Press, London, 1960; H. L. Schläfer, *Komplepbildung in Lösung*, Springer-Verlag, Berlin, 1961.
97. D. P. Mellor and L. E. Maley, *Nature*, **159**, 370 (1947); **161**, 436 (1948); M. Calvin and N. C. Melchior, *J. Am. Chem. Soc.*, **70**, 3270 (1948); H. Irving and R. J. P. Williams, *Nature*, **162**, 146 (1948).
98. I. M. Kolthoff, D. L. Lenssing, and T. S. Lee, *J. Am. Chem. Soc.*, **72** 2173, 2348 (1948).
99. F. Basolo and F. P. Dwyer, *J. Am. Chem. Soc.*, **76**, 1454 (1954).
100. R. G. Pearson, *J. Am. Chem. Soc.*, **85**, 3533 (1963); *Science*, **151**, 172 (1966).
101. S. Ahrland, J. Chatt, and N. R. Davies, *Quart. Rev. (London)*, **12**, 265 (1958); see also G. Schwarzenbach, *Experentia Supp.* 5, 162 (1956); J. O. Edwards, *J. Am. Chem. Soc.*, **76**, 1540 (1954).
102. R. S. Mulliken, *J. Phys. Chem.*, **56**, 801 (1952); *J. Am. Chem. Soc.*, **74**, 811 (1952).
103. G. Schwarzenbach, *Advan. Inorg. Chem. Radiochem.*, **3**, 257 (1961).
104. G. Schwarzenbach, *Helv. Chim. Acta.* **35**, 2344 (1952).
105. J. Bjerrum and E. J. Nielsen, *Acta Chem. Scand.*, **2**, 297 (1948).
106. C. G. Spike and R. W. Parry, *J. Am. Chem. Soc.*, **75**, 2726 (1953).
107. For a review see A. E. Martell, *Essays in Coordination Chemistry*, Birkhausen Verlag, Basel, 1964, p. 52.
108. A. Werner, *Ber.*, **40**, 15 (1907); L. Tschugaeff, *J. prakt. Chem.*, [2] **75**, 159 (1907); P. Pfeiffer and E. Lubbe, *ibid.*, [2] **136**, 321 (1933).
109. P. Pfeiffer, *Naturwissenschaften*, **35**, 190 (1948).
110. J. C. Duff, *J. Chem. Soc.*, **119**, 385, 1982 (1921); **123**, 560 (1923).
111. T. S. Price and S. A. Brazier, *J. Chem. Soc.*, **107**, 1367 (1915).
112. F. G. Mann, *J. Chem. Soc.*, **1927**, 1224; **1928**, 890.
113. (a) J. Bjerrum and I. Poulsen, *Acta Chem. Scand.*, **9**, 1407 (1955). (b) F. A. Cotton and F. E. Harris, *J. Phys. Chem.*, **59**, 1203 (1955). (c) E. J. Corey and J. C. Bailar, Jr., *J. Am. Chem. Soc.*, **81**, 2620 (1959).
114. H. Irving and H. Rossotti, *Acta Chem. Scand.*, **10**, 72 (1956).
115. F. Basolo and R. K. Murmann, *J. Am. Chem. Soc.*, **74**, 5243 (1952); **76**, 211 (1954); H. Irving and J. M. M. Griffiths, *J. Chem. Soc.*, **1954**, 213.
116. F. H. Burstall, *J. Chem. Soc.*, **1938**, 1662.
117. F. W. Cagle and G. F. Smith, *J. Am. Chem. Soc.*, **69**, 1860 (1947).
118. G. Schwarzenbach, *Helv. Chim. Acta*, **36**, 23 (1953).
119. M. Calvin and K. W. Wilson, *J. Am. Chem. Soc.*, **67**, 2003 (1945).
120. J. A. Broomhead, F. Basolo, and R. G. Pearson, *Inorg. Chem.*, **3**, 826 (1964).
121. P. H. Wilks, M. S. thesis, Northwestern University, 1958.
122. L. G. Sillén, *Acta Chem. Scand.*, **8**, 299, 318 (1954); **16**, 159 (1962); N. Ingri and L. G. Sillén, *ibid.*, **16**, 173 (1962).
123. (a) R. G. Pearson and F. Basolo, *J. Am. Chem. Soc.*, **78**, 4878 (1956). (b) C. K. Jørgensen, *Acta Chem. Scand.*, **10**, 518 (1956).
124. (a) R. C. Johnson, F. Basolo, and R. G. Pearson, *J. Inorg. Nucl. Chem.*, **24**, 59 (1962). (b) W. H. Baddley, F. Basolo, H. B. Gray, C. Nölting, and A. J. Poë, *Inorg. Chem.*, **2**, 921 (1963). (c) C. F. Weick and F. Basolo, *ibid.*, **5**, 576 (1966).

125. For derivations and discussions see (a) R. A. Robinson and R. H. Stokes, *Electrolyte Solutions*, Academic Press, New York, 1955, Chaps. 4 and 9; or (b) H. S. Harned and B. B. Owen, *Physical Chemistry of Electrolytic Solutions*, Reinhold Publishing Corp., New York, 1958, Chap. 2.

126. See A. A. Frost and R. G. Pearson, *Kinetics and Mechanism*, John Wiley and Sons, New York, 1961, Chap 7, for a discussion.

127. G. N. Lewis and M. Randall, *Thermodynamics*, McGraw-Hill Book Co., New York, 1923, Chapter 28.

128. L. G. Sillén and G. Biedermann, *Arkiv Kemi*, **5**, No. 40, 425 (1953).

129. (a) See R. A. Robinson and R. H. Stokes, *Electrolyte Solution*, Academic Press, New York, 1955, Chap. 14, for a general introduction. (b) A. Werner, *Ann.*, **286**, 1 (1912). (c) A. R. Olson and T. R. Simonson, *J. Chem. Phys.*, **17**, 1167 (1949).

130. N. Bjerrum, *Kgl. Danske Videnskab. Selskab Mat. fys. Medd.*, **9**, 7 (1926).

131. J. T. Denison and J. B. Ramsay, *J. Am. Chem. Soc.*, **77**, 2615 (1955).

132. W. R. Gilkerson, *J. Chem. Phys.*, **25**, 1199 (1956); R. M. Fuoss, *J. Am. Chem. Soc.*, **79**, 3301 (1957); **80**, 5059 (1958).

133. J. A. Caton and J. E. Prue, *J. Chem. Soc.*, **1956**, 671.

134. M. G. Evans and G. H. Nancollas, *Trans. Faraday Soc.*, **49**, 363 (1953); see, however, E. L. King, J. H. Espenson, and R. E. Visco, *J. Phys. Chem.*, **63**, 755 (1959).

135. I. L. Jenkins and C. B. Monk, *J. Chem. Soc.*, **1951**, 68.

136. (a) H. Taube and F. A. Posey, *J. Am. Chem. Soc.*, **75**, 1463 (1953). (b) F. A. Posey and H. Taube, *ibid.*, **78**, 15 (1956).

137. F. G. R. Gimblett and C. B. Monk, *Trans. Faraday Soc.*, **51**, 973 (1955).

138. C. Postmus and E. L. King, *J. Phys. Chem.*, **59**, 1208 (1955).

139. R. E. Connick and M. S. Tsao, quoted in reference 138.

140. C. W. Davies, *J. Chem. Soc.*, **1930**, 2421.

141. N. V. Sidgwick, *The Chemical Elements and Their Compounds*, Oxford University Press, 1950, p. 1536.

142. M. Linhard, *Z. Elektrochem.*, **50**, 224 (1944).

143. For a general discussion see "Interactions in Ionic Solutions," *Disc. Faraday Soc.*, **24**, (1957); G. R. Choppin and W. F. Strazik, *Inorg. Chem.*, **4**, 1250 (1965).

144. (a) M. W. Lister and D. E. Rivington, *Can. J. Chem.*, **33**, 1572, 1591, 1603 (1955). (b) E. Rabinowitch and W. H. Stockmayer, *J. Am. Chem. Soc.*, **64**, 335 (1942).

145. (a) R. M. Milburn and W. C. Vosburgh, *J. Am. Chem. Soc.*, **77**, 1352 (1955). (b) H. W. Dodgen and G. K. Rollefson, *ibid.*, **71**, 2600 (1949); (c) H. H. Broene and T. DeVries *ibid.*, **69**, 1644 (1947).

146. See reference 125a, Chap 14, and 125b, Chap. 7.

147. A. Stock, *Z. angew. Chem.*, **321**, 373 (1919).

148. W. P. Jorissen, H. Bassett, A. Damiens, F. Fichter, and H. Remy, *Ber.*, **73A**, 53 (1940); *J. Am. Chem. Soc.*, **63**, 889 (1941); *ibid.*, **82**, 5523 (1960).

149. W. C. Fernelius, *Advan. Chem. Ser.*, **8**, 9 (1953).

150. T. S. Piper, *J. Am. Chem. Soc.*, **83**, 3908 (1961).

151. E. Kyuno, L. J. Boucher, and J. C. Bailar, Jr., *J. Am. Chem Soc.*, **87**, 4458 (1965).

152. C. E. Coffey, J. Lewis, and R. S. Nyholm, *J. Chem. Soc.*, **1964**, 1741.

153. F. P. Dwyer, N. S. Gill, E. C. Gyarfas, and F. Lions, *J. Am. Chem. Soc.*, **79**, 1269 (1957).

154. W. H. Bragg and G. T. Morgan, *Proc. Roy. Soc. (London)*, **A104**, 437 (1923).

155. T. J. Conocchioli, G. H. Nancollas, and N. Sutin, *Inorg. Chem.*, **5**, 1 (1966).

156. D. W. Archer, D. A. East, and C. B. Monk, *J. Chem. Soc.*, **1965**, 720.

157. However, see J. I. Legg and B. E. Douglas, *J. Am. Chem. Soc.*, **88**, 2697 (1966).

2

The Theory of the Coordinate Bond

Three theories are currently used to explain the structures, stabilities, and general properties of coordination compounds. These are (1) the electrostatic theory, including crystal field corrections, (2) the valence bond theory, and (3) the molecular orbital theory. This arrangement is in order of increasing sophistication and generality, though not necessarily of usefulness.[1]

We distinguish between two limiting kinds of chemical bond, the "purely ionic" and the "purely covalent," though recognizing that any actual bond may partake of some of the qualities of each. The ionic bond is concerned only with electrostatic attractions and repulsions due to electric charges, permanent electric dipoles, and induced dipoles. By including van der Waals repulsions between filled electron shells in a semiempirical manner, it is possible to account completely for the bonding energies of simple compounds such as NaCl both in the crystalline state and in the vapor.[2] This is done without any mention of covalent bonding or any quantum mechanical concept other than the minor one of zero point energy.

In molecular hydrogen the opposite extreme occurs in that, by definition, ionic bonding is absent although electrostatic terms are still the only ones considered in the potential energy of the system.* In this case the bonding results from the greater region in space which has an electric potential positive enough to attract the electron strongly. This greater region allows for a correspondingly smaller value of the kinetic energy for each electron than would otherwise be possible and a net reduction of total energy equal to the heat of dissociation. Thus in a purely covalent bond the emphasis is on the delocalization of the electrons in a molecule compared to their state in the free atoms. The valence bond theory brings in the delocalization by sharing electrons, usually between two atoms, but a greater number can be involved if several resonance structures can be conceived of. The

---

* The fact that, as shown in the accurate treatment of the hydrogen molecule, there is a considerable chance that both electrons will be near one nucleus at the same time is to be considered a normal attribute of the covalent bond.

52

molecular orbital theory also spreads the electrons between two or more atoms, in the limit the entire molecule being involved.

The electrostatic theory, then, essentially excludes this delocalization (or exchange or resonance) energy, though it is partly included in terms involving induced dipoles since the polarization of one atom or ion by another is equivalent to allowing the electrons of the first ion to move into the field of the second. The valence bond and molecular orbital theories, in turn, can be made to include ionic contributions to any desired extent,[3] though the result is to greatly complicate any attempt at calculations of bond energies. In fact, for anything but the simplest systems, any quantum mechanical approach can be used in only a very approximate way.

In any theory a necessary starting point is some knowledge of the unperturbed atomic orbitals on the central atom, such as would exist in the gas phase in the absence of ligands. Figure 2.1 shows the conventional boundary contours for the s, p, and d orbitals which will form the basis of further discussion.[4] These contours are only approximate; they indicate roughly the region in space which will contain almost all of the electronic charge of an electron in such an orbital. The plus and minus signs refer to the mathematical sign of the wave function, ϕ, which describes the orbital (it is ϕ^2 which is a measure of the electron density from point to point). The d orbitals are the ones most difficult to visualize and thus require brief comment. The d_{xy}, d_{xz}, and d_{yz} are mutually perpendicular with four alternating positive and negative lobes in each of the respective planes. These three sets of four lobes are situated along a 45° angle between each of the cartesian axes. There are also the $d_{x^2-y^2}$, $d_{x^2-z^2}$, and $d_{y^2-z^2}$, which are mutually perpendicular and each of which lies directly along the respective axes in one of the three different planes. Of these three equivalent orbitals only two are independent. Any pair of them can be used, or, as is usually done, the $d_{x^2-y^2}$ and a hybrid of the other two called d_{z^2} is taken. The d_{z^2} will have large positive lobes along the z axis and smaller negative lobes along both the x and y axes, forming in fact a negative sausage-like belt around the z axis symmetric about the xy plane.

Each atomic orbital can hold as many as two electrons, and in the gaseous atom electrons fill the orbitals in the order of increasing energy, $1s < 2s < 2p < 3s < 3p < 4s \simeq 3d < 4p < 5s \simeq 4d$. All the p orbitals of a given principal quantum number are equal in energy, as are all the d levels. Hund's rules are obeyed. That is, two electrons avoid being in the same orbit if possible, and their spins are parallel if they are in different singly occupied orbits of the same energy.

The three theories mentioned above now diverge in the way in which the approach of the ligands is considered to affect the central atom and its atomic orbitals.

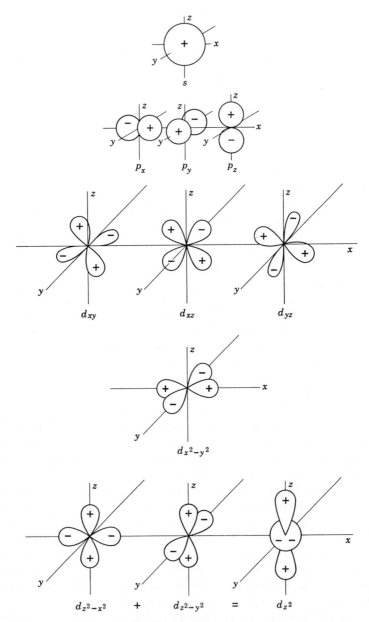

Fig. 2.1 Atomic orbitals.

The Valence Bond Theory[5]

One viewpoint is stressed by the valence bond method chiefly developed for complexes by Pauling.[6] In this theory it is considered essential that a number of orbitals on the central metal atom equal to the number of ligands be made available to form coordinate covalent bonds with orbitals on the ligands. Furthermore, by using the criterion that maximum angular overlap of two orbitals forms the strongest covalent bond, it is shown that the original atomic orbitals should be hybridized to form a new set of

Table 2.1 Hybrid orbitals and directional properties

Coordination Number	Bond Orbitals	Strength	Shape
1	s	1.00	...
1	p	1.73	...
2	sp	1.93	linear
3	sp^2	1.99	trigonal
4	sp^3, sd^3	...	tetrahedral
4	dsp^2	2.69	square planar
5	dsp^2, spd^3	...	trigonal bipyramid
5	d^2sp^2, spd^3	...	square pyramid
6	d^2sp^3	2.92	octahedral

equivalent bond orbitals with definite directional properties. In this way the familiar set of four tetrahedral orbitals is built up from one s and three p orbitals. For example, Table 2.1 shows the most important combinations of atomic orbitals for coordination compounds and their arrangement in space. This spatial arrangement fixes the shape of the resulting complexes. In addition the relative bond strengths according to angular orbital overlap are given. On this scale the non-directional bond formed by an s orbital has a strength equal to unity. In octahedral, or six-coordinated, complexes, the six hybrid orbitals are identical except that they are pointed along the six directions in space given by a set of cartesian axes. The six atomic orbitals used are the s, p_x, p_y, p_z, $d_{x^2-y^2}$, and d_{z^2}. For greatest stability, the d orbitals used are of the next lower principal quantum number than the s or p. Each hybrid orbital accepts a pair of electrons from a ligand, or rather a set of six valence bonds is formed by combining the six hybrid orbitals with six suitable orbitals, one on each of the ligands. Such bonds are called σ bonds because the electron density of the bond is symmetrical about the bond axis.

In addition there are the d_{xy}, etc., atomic orbitals on the central atom rotated 45° from the hybrid orbitals. These cannot be used for forming σ bonds. However, they are suitably placed for forming π bonds with either p or d orbitals on the ligands. A π bond is one having a nodal plane, or minimum of electron density, along the bond axis. A criterion for the formation of π bonds, as for any other bonds, is that the signs of the wave functions be the same in the regions where they overlap. The second half of a C—C double bond is also a π bond. Almost always π bonding means double bonding. Another possible kind of bond is a δ bond with two nodal planes cutting the bond axis. Such bonds might be formed from two suitably placed d orbitals on different atoms.

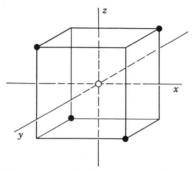

Fig. 2.2 Location of four groups (dark circles) bonded tetrahedrally to a central atom (open circle).

It has been postulated by Pauling[7] that, if a ligand has, or can have by resonance, vacant orbitals, and if the central atom has d electrons, π bonding from the metal to the ligand will occur. This will strengthen the coordinate bond (making it a double bond) and help to reduce the negative charge formed on the central atom by the addition of the ligands. Conversely, if the ligand has additional unshared pairs of electrons, and the metal atom has suitable empty orbitals, π bonding in the opposite direction can occur.

The square planar configuration is obtained by using s, p_x, p_y, and $d_{x^2-y^2}$ orbitals of the central atom to form σ bonds, thus leaving the p_z and d_{z^2} orbitals projecting above and below the plane of the complex. In addition the d_{xy}, d_{xz}, and d_{yz} orbitals can form π-type bonds with any three of the attached groups at one time. The tetrahedral arrangement is shown in Fig. 2.2 with the same axes used as for Fig. 2.1. Now none of the d orbitals is too well situated for π bonding. Actually, all five have equal possibilities for forming π bonds. Since the d_{xy}, d_{xz}, and d_{yz} orbitals can be used to form hybrid σ orbitals (Table 2.1), they are not as available as

π orbitals. The various combinations of atomic orbitals that result in hybrid orbitals appropriate for a molecule of any given symmetry are best obtained by the methods of group theory (see p. 65).

The wave function, ϕ, for a pair of electrons forming a bond between two atoms, A and B, would be given in valence bond theory by

$$\phi = h_A(1)h_B(2) + h_A(2)h_B(1)$$

where h_A is a hybrid orbital formed from a linear combination of atomic orbitals centered on atom A, and similarly for h_B. Such a bond would represent a rather equal sharing of the two electrons between the atoms and would be completely covalent. In order to impart ionic character to the bond it is necessary to add to the original wave function a term corresponding to both electrons on the same atom. For example, if B is much more electronegative than A,

$$\phi = h_A(1)h_B(2) + h_A(2)h_B(1) + \lambda h_B(1)h_B(2)$$

where λ is a constant to be evaluated by minimizing the energy.

For polyatomic molecules containing many electrons the valence bond wave function becomes very complicated, especially if the atoms can be bonded together in several ways (resonance structures) and if the bonds are polar. The calculation of the energy even by approximate methods becomes extremely difficult and has been done only for quite simple inorganic molecules.[10]

In order to account for the different magnetic properties of a given metal ion in various complexes, Pauling[6] postulated that, in the case of strong electron-donating ligands, such as CN^-, covalent bond formation would definitely occur. This would require in many cases the coupling of d electrons to provide the necessary orbitals for hybridization. For weaker or highly electronegative ligands, covalent bond formation would not occur and electrostatic forces only would be involved. Thus a subdivision into "covalent" and "ionic" complexes was made, and the observed magnetic moment was used to decide which kind of complex was at hand (the magnetic criterion of bond type). This criterion is illustrated for some complexes of Co(III):

	3d	4s	4p	
Co^{3+} (free ion)	⊙ ◯ ◯ ◯ ◯	◯	◯ ◯ ◯	
Co(NH$_3$)$_6{}^{3+}$	⊙ ⊙ ⊙ ⊙ ⊙	⊙	⊙ ⊙ ◯	covalent
CoF$_6{}^{3-}$	⊙ ◯ ◯ ◯ ◯	◯	◯ ◯ ◯	ionic

Complexes in which the number of unpaired electrons is less than in the free ion are called magnetically anomalous. The hexamminecobalt(III) ion, being diamagnetic, was considered as a covalent complex, and the hexafluoro complex, having a paramagnetism corresponding to four unpaired electrons, as ionic. It was also considered possible that four alternating covalent bonds involving the $4s$ and $4p$ orbitals were formed. Since many of the complexes which are classified as ionic by the magnetic criterion, such as tris(acetylacetonato)iron(III), have what are usually considered covalent properties, such as volatility and solubility in organic solvents,[11] the terminology "ionic" has fallen into disrepute.† The current tendency is to assume that in such cases orbital hybridization occurs between the s, p, and d orbitals of the same principal quantum number, sp^3d^2 instead of d^2sp^3. Complexes formed in this way would still be covalent but would allow for electron unpairing in the lower d levels. Furthermore, such complexes would not be as stable as the d^2sp^3 type. Taube[12] uses the terms "inner orbital" and "outer orbital" to differentiate between the kinds of complexes. These designations essentially correspond to the terms "penetration" and "normal" complexes introduced earlier by Biltz.[13]

The more electronegative atoms, such as fluorine and oxygen, favor outer orbital binding since they concentrate the bonding electrons about themselves. The higher d orbitals from the metal, having greater extension in space, can still overlap appreciably in such a case. Ligands of low electronegativity, such as phosphorus or arsenic, will utilize the lower d orbitals more efficiently. Particularly if π bonding can occur, there will be a greater tendency to use the inner d orbitals and achieve a shorter, stronger bond. Also in the case of the second and third transition groups, a greater tendency to use the lower orbitals may be assumed because the upper ones have become too diffuse to bond well.[14] Increased positive charge on the central ion will also favor covalent bond formation with the inner orbitals since the increased electronegativity of the central ion will pull the electrons from the ligands.

One unfortunate result of this historical development of the valence bond theory is that the terms "ionic" and "covalent" have come to be used as synonyms for "weak" and "strong," respectively. Thus, the incorrect concept has arisen that, in coordination chemistry, covalent bonds have a large dissociation energy and ionic bonds have a small dissociation energy. The facts are, as will be shown below, that when measured in the gas phase it is the highly polar or ionic bonds which have the largest dissociation energy, covalent bonds being weak. In solution, however, the situation is changed, at least in polar solvents. Because of strong solvation effects, dissociation into ions is greatly favored. Those

† Actually such properties give only information about intermolecular forces and none at all about intramolecular forces.

bonds which are most ionic in nature will naturally allow the formation of charged particles most easily. Hence, polar bonds in solution often have a low dissociation energy.

The Valence Shell Electron-Pair Repulsion Theory

Somewhat intermediate between the valence bond theory and the electrostatic theory to be discussed in the next section is the *valence shell electron-pair repulsion* or *V.S.E.P.R. theory*. This is a useful way of explaining or predicting the geometries of molecules or complexes of the non-transition elements and also of d^0, d^5, and d^{10} transition metals. The theory is based on ideas of Sidgewick and Powell[15] and has been elaborated by Nyholm and Gillespie.[16]

It is supposed that the stereochemistry is determined primarily by the repulsive interaction between all the electron pairs of the valence shell of the central atom. The electrons are regarded as occupying orbitals that are oriented in space so that their average distance apart is as great as possible. This is a result partly of ordinary electrostatic repulsion but, more important, of the Pauli exclusion principle. Thus, electrons of the same spin avoid each other more than electrons of opposite spin. Four electrons of the same spin would have their positions of maximum probability exactly at the corners of a regular tetrahedron, for example. Thus, for Ne or F^- there would be two sets of four electrons each with maximum probability of being found at the four corners of a tetrahedron. Bond formation would tend to bring the two tetrahedra into coincidence. The electrons may then be thought of as being in four identical, tetrahedrally disposed orbitals such as the hybrid sp^3 orbitals of valence bond theory. Four groups attached to the central atom by the four pairs of electrons would then be found at the tetrahedral corners.

From elementary considerations it can be seen (and also proved rigorously) that two pairs of electrons in the valence shell will be linear, three pairs triangular, and six pairs octahedral in arrangement. For five pairs the trigonal bipyramid and square pyramid dispositions are about equally probable. The geometries of molecules will thus be determined by the number of electron pairs in the valence shell. Table 2.2 gives the predicted shapes for a number of examples. The predictions are in agreement with experiment in every case.

By making additional postulates, for example, that bonding pairs repel adjacent electron pairs less than lone pairs, it is possible to explain small variations in bond angles from the theoretically predicted ones (H_2O is 104.5° and not 109.5°, the tetrahedral value). The theory is remarkably simple and accurate for systems in which the distribution of electron

Table 2.2   Stereochemistry and electronic repulsion

Total Number of Electron Pairs in Valence Shell	Predicted Arrangement of Electron Pairs in Space	Number of Internuclear (σ-Bonding) Pairs	Number of Lone Pairs (Non-bonding)	Example	Shape
2	linear	2	0	$HgCl_2$	linear
3	triangular plane	3	0	BCl_3	triangular plane
	plane	2	1	$SnCl_2$ (g)	V shaped
4	regular tetrahedron	4	0	CH_4	regular tetrahedron
		3	1	NH_3, $AsCl_3$	pyramidal
		2	2	H_2O	V shaped
5	trigonal bipyramid	5	0	PCl_5	trigonal bipyramid
		4	1	$TeCl_4$	irregular tetrahedron
		3	2	ClF_3	T shaped
		2	3	$[ICl_2]^-$	linear
6	regular octahedron	6	0	SF_6	regular octahedron
		5	1	IF_5, $XeOF_4$	square pyramid
		4	2	$[ICl_4]^-$, XeF_4	square planar
7	pentagonal bipyramid	7	0	IF_7	pentagonal bipyramid
8	square antiprism or dodecahedron	8	0	$[TaF_8^-]^{3-}$	square antiprism

around the central atom is spherically symmetric overall (spectroscopic S states). For the non-spherically symmetric transition metals, the theory is not so useful. Also it is concerned entirely with stereochemistry and does not deal with other properties, such as bond strengths.

The Electrostatic Theory

Van Arkel and DeBoer[17] and, particularly, Garrick,[18] following the pioneering ideas of Kossel, Magnus, and Fajans, showed that a fairly simple electrostatic picture of complexes, assuming point charges and dipoles, could account for many of their properties. The parameters needed were the charges and sizes of the central ions and the charges, dipole moments, polarizabilities, and sizes of the ligands. By using the ordinary potential energy equations of electrostatics, quantitative calculations could be made for various coordination numbers and stereochemistries.

The results, as we shall show, are remarkably good, allowing calculation not only of relative energies but also of absolute bonding energies in excellent agreement with experiment. From the relative point of view the theory explains the existence of complexes such as $CuCl_2^-$, $CuCl_4^{2-}$, and CuF_6^{3-} in terms of increasing charge on the metal ion.[19] The existence of AlF_6^{3-}, but only $AlCl_4^-$ and not $AlCl_6^{3-}$, can be explained and is a property of the relation between the size of the ligand and the size of the central ion.

From an absolute point of view Garrick[18d] was able to calculate the energies of formation in the gaseous state of such systems as BF_3, AlF_3, CrF_3, TiF_4, SnF_4, BCl_3, $AlCl_3$, $SiCl_4$, $TiCl_4$, and $SnCl_4$ with errors of less than 6% compared to experimental values. Significantly the same electrostatic calculations applied to CF_4, CCl_4, and PCl_5 gave results much smaller than the experimental energies of formation. Thus a model based on purely ionic bonds holding together C^{4+} and $4Cl^-$, for example, is insufficient in these cases, and important covalent bonding must exist.

It could also be easily demonstrated that, for coordination numbers of 2, 4, and 6, linear, tetrahedral, and octahedral complexes, respectively, should be formed since these structures minimize the electrostatic repulsions of the ligands for each other. However, the existence of square planar complexes is not explicable on the basis of the elementary theory. Also the stability of complexes involving virtually non-polar ligands such as CO was difficult to explain, as were the differences in stability between the corresponding complexes of two central ions of the same charge and size, such as Fe(III) and Co(III). And finally the greater stability of complexes of the second and third transition series metals compared to the first was puzzling since the former metals gave ions of the same charge as the latter but of greater size.

Before considering these difficulties further it will be well to show some actual calculations by the electrostatic method. These are largely based on Garrick's method with some simplification in treating repulsive terms in the potential energy function. We will calculate the binding energy *in vacuo* of a system consisting of a central cation and a number of identical ligands. The zero of energy will be the metal ion and the ligands at infinite separation from each other.

Suppose we have an Fe(II) ion surrounded octahedrally by six water molecules with the charge on the iron assumed symmetrically disposed around a sphere of radius 0.83 A and the permanent and induced dipoles of the water assumed at the center of a sphere of radius 1.38 A and pointing towards the central ion (see Fig. 2.3). The radius of the ion is the Goldschmidt crystallographic value,[20] and the radius of the water molecule is established from the closest oxygen to oxygen distance in ice.[21] Classically the potential energy of such a system is given by

$$U = -\frac{6q(\mu_0 + \mu_i)}{r^2} + \frac{6(1.19)(\mu_0 + \mu_i)^2}{r^3} + \frac{6\mu_i^2}{2\alpha} + \frac{6B}{r^9} \tag{1}$$

Here q is the charge on the central ion, μ_0 is the permanent dipole moment of water (1.85 debyes), μ_i is the induced dipole moment of water, and r is the distance $0.83 + 1.38 = 2.21$ A. The first term is the attraction between the ion and the dipoles, the second is the mutual repulsion of the dipoles, the third is the energy required to form the induced dipoles, and the last represents the van der Waals repulsions between the six ligands and the central ion. These last are the same as the filled-shell repulsions due to the operation of the Pauli exclusion principle in more modern terms. The common assumption is made that the repulsion varies as some large inverse power of the intermolecular distance. B is a constant which will be eliminated by differentiating U with respect to r and setting the differential equal to zero for $r = 2.21$ A.

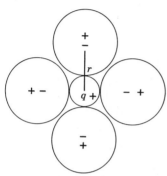

Fig. 2.3 Electrostatic diagram of symmetrical octahedral complex (two groups not shown) such as $Fe(H_2O)_6^{2+}$.

A value of μ_i is needed. This is obtained from the fundamental relation $\mu_i = \alpha E$, where α is the polarizability of water (1.48 A³) and E is the electric field at the center of the water molecule directed along the axis. This field is given by

$$E = \frac{q}{r^2} - \frac{2.37(\mu_0 + \mu_i)}{r^3} \tag{2}$$

where the first term is due to the ion and the last term is the sum of the opposing fields of the other five ligands. Solving for μ_i gives

$$\mu_i = \frac{\alpha(q/r^2 - 2.37\mu_0/r^3)}{1 + 2.37\alpha/r^3} \tag{3}$$

The resulting values of μ_i are 0.67 debye for K^+, 1.74 debyes for Fe^{2+}, and 3.08 debyes for Fe^{3+}, as illustrations of the magnitude (one full electronic charge 1 angstrom from another of opposite sign gives a dipole moment of 4.80 debyes). Simplifying, equation 1 can be written as

$$U = 6\left[\frac{-\mu_0 q/r^2 - q^2\alpha/2r^4 + 2.37\mu_0^2/2r^3}{1 + 2.37\alpha/r^3}\right] + \frac{6B}{r^9} \qquad (4)$$

and on eliminating the last term by differentiating, the final result is

$$U = 6\left[\frac{-7\mu_0 q}{9r^2} - \frac{5q^2\alpha}{18r^4} + \frac{2.37\mu_0^2}{3r^3} - \frac{10(2.37)\mu_0 q\alpha}{9r^5}\right.$$
$$\left. - \frac{4(2.37)q^2\alpha^2}{9r^7} + \frac{(2.37)^2\alpha\mu_0^2}{2r^6}\right] \div \left(1 + \frac{2.37\alpha}{r^3}\right)^2 \qquad (5)$$

An identical equation would be valid for other coordination numbers and geometries except that the factors 6 and 2.37 would be replaced by the

Table 2.3 Calculated coordinate bond energies

$$M^{m+}(g) + nL(g) \rightarrow ML_n^{m+}(g)$$

Complex	Energy per Bond, kcal	Crystal Field Corrected, kcal	Experimental, kcal[a]
$Fe(H_2O)_6^{2+}$	50	52	58
$Fe(H_2O)_6^{3+}$	109	109	116[a]
$K(H_2O)_6^+$	13	13	16[a]
$Cr(H_2O)_6^{3+}$	111	120	122[a]
$Zn(NH_3)_4^{2+}$	86[b]	86	89[a,c]
$Co(NH_3)_6^{3+}$	117	125	134[a,d]
AlF_6^{3-}	212	212	233[a,e]

[a] Calculated from heats of hydration of gaesous metal ions, plus heats of reaction in solution and Born heats of hydration of complex ion (see text).
[b] Tetrahedral structure assumed.
[c] C. G. Spike and R. W. Parry, *J. Am. Chem. Soc.*, **75**, 3770 (1953).
[d] K. B. Yatsimirskii, *Doklady Akad. Nauk SSSR*, **72**, 307 (1950).
[e] W. Latimer and W. L. Jolly, *J. Am. Chem. Soc.*, **75**, 1548 (1953).

new coordination number and by a suitably calculated geometric factor, respectively.

All the necessary terms in equation 5 are now known, and the energy can be calculated. The result is shown in the second column of Table 2.3 as kilocalories, or the energy of dissociation per bond. Table 2.3 also shows a number of similar calculations for other complex ions The mean coordinate bond energy of 50 kcal for Fe(II) is made up of 52 kcal due to ion-permanent dipole attraction, 33 kcal ion-induced dipole attraction, 20 kcal dipole-dipole repulsion, and 15 kcal van der Waals repulsion for each water molecule. The corresponding figures for Fe(III) aquo complex are 91 kcal, 107 kcal, 48 kcal, and 43 kcal. The importance of the induced dipole for highly charged cations is obvious. For potassium ion the figures are 17 kcal, 4 kcal, 5 kcal, and 3.5 kcal. The values of r used were 2.05 A for Fe(III) and 2.71 A for potassium, the sums of the ionic radii and the radius of the water molecule.

The values of r for the metal ammines were found by taking the radius of the ammonia molecule as 1.40 A. This method is chosen because it gives figures for the metal-oxygen and metal-nitrogen distances such as are found in the solid state for hydrates and ammines.[22] For the fluoro complex also the value of r used was equal to the sum of the ionic radii (as given in Table 2.10). This procedure will not work always because ionic sizes are not constants but are simply a result of balanced forces of attraction and repulsion. For strong forces of attraction, the observed interatomic distances will be less. Hence, the "size" of an ion will be a function of the compound in which it occurs. The size of a halide ion in an alkali halide crystal will not be suitable for use in a compound in which the halide is very near a small, highly charged cation. The variation in size will be most important for the more polarizable iodide and bromide ions.

The theoretical calculation of the proper value for r in different cases is not impossible but would be difficult. Garrick,[18a,b] for example, treated the van der Waals repulsion in equation 1 in a more detailed manner. The coefficient B was evaluated by considering each ion and molecule in the complex to be similar to the nearest inert gas molecule. For these gases the magnitude of the repulsion term in the intermolecular potential energy function is known from a study of the second virial coefficient. If B is known, it is possible to solve for the value of r which makes the potential energy a minimum. This method agrees very well with the one used above for hydrates and gives slightly larger values of r for ammoniates. The easiest procedure is to find the proper value of the intermolecular distance to use from published data on distances between atoms for the compound in question of some close analog.[22] This will rarely be exact since the required distances are in the gas phase and experimental data are usually for the solid state.

In any event the model used is very crude, and further refinements might be considered such as the inclusion of the London attraction forces,[2] which would add about 2 kcal to each bond energy. Or a more elaborate representation of the water or ammonia molecule than the point dipole model might be used.[23] The major need, however, is to refine the picture of the central ion since it is seen in Table 2.3 that $Fe(H_2O)_6^{3+}$ and $Cr(H_2O)_6^{3+}$ differ but little in stability according to the calculation. This is not in agreement with the observation that the iron complex exchanges its waters rapidly with the solvent, as judged by ^{18}O experiments, whereas the chromium ion does not. Also a calculation of the energy of $Fe(NH_3)_6^{3+}$ would predict the same stability as for $Co(NH_3)_6^{3+}$, again at variance with the properties of these two ions.[‡]

The Crystal Field Theory[24]

The necessary correction lies in the crystal field theory first proposed by Bethe[25] and applied to the magnetic properties of the transition metal ions by Schlapp and Penney[26] and by Van Vleck.[27] Recently, following Hartmann,[28] this theory has been widely used to explain the so-called d-d spectra of complexes in the visible region. Orgel[29] was the first to emphasize the consequences of the theory for the stability of coordination compounds of the transition elements.

The essence of the theory is that the five d orbitals, which are degenerate and equal in energy in the gaseous metal ion, become differentiated in the presence of the electrostatic field due to the ligands (the crystal field). It is the symmetry of this field, or its regular geometric properties, which gives the theory its name. Though originally applied to crystalline solids, it is equally applicable to any orderly arrangement of electrically inter-acting particles such as a single complex. In particular those orbitals lying in the direction of the ligands are raised in energy with respect to those lying away from the ligands. By preferentially filling the low-lying levels the d electrons can stabilize the system, as compared to the case of random filling of the d orbitals. The gain in bonding energy achieved in this way may be called the *crystal field stabilization energy* (C.F.S.E.). It is caused by the distribution of charge around the central atom of the complex not being symmetrical, as assumed in the earlier electrostatic calculation. If the d orbitals were occupied equally, the resulting electron density would have spherical symmetry.

For example, in an octahedral complex the $d_{x^2-y^2}$ and d_{z^2} orbitals are clearly raised in energy relative to the d_{xy}, d_{yz} and d_{xz} orbitals. At this point it is convenient to introduce some group theoretic notation useful for designating one-electron wave functions and their associated energy states.[30] The symbols are those devised by Mulliken and are assigned to the wave function according to its transformation properties during the

‡ Ammonia has a lower dipole moment than water, 1.40 debyes, but a higher polariz-ability, 2.26 A^3 Hence, with small, highly charged ions it would form somewhat more stable complexes than does water.

symmetry operations (rotation, reflection, inversion) of the various point groups. Any molecule having any symmetry whatever will belong to one of the point groups. For our purposes we need only the following information:

1. The symbols a and b are used to represent non-degenerate orbitals. The a wave functions are symmetric with respect to rotation about the principal axis (do not change sign), whereas the b functions are antisymmetric (change sign). Subscripts 1 and 2 denote other symmetry properties. An a_1 function is totally symmetric and does not change under any of the symmetry operations of the molecule.

2. Doubly degenerate levels are called e, and triply degenerate levels are called t. The subscripts g and u are used to indicate a function symmetric or antisymmetric with respect to inversion through a center of symmetry.

3. Capital letters A, B, E, T serve to designate total wave functions and total energy states for a system containing several electrons.

Using these rules, the two high-energy d orbitals of a regular octahedral complex are called e_g and three lower d orbitals are called t_{2g} orbital, since the first two are equal in energy, as are the last three. Of the first three d electrons in such a complex one would then go into each of the t_{2g} orbitals. The next few electrons would either go into the e_g orbitals or pair up and occupy the lower levels doubly. The choice would depend on the magnitude of the crystal field splitting (difference in energy between t_{2g} and e_g) and the electron pairing energy, the energy required to put two electrons originally into different orbitals, and, with parallel spin, into a single orbital with opposed spins. If the splitting is small (weak crystal field) the electrons will occupy different orbitals, their spins will be parallel and a *high-spin* complex will be formed. If the splitting is large (strong crystal field), the electrons will pair up in the t_{2g} levels and a *low-spin* compex will result.§

The separation between the two energy levels, e_g and t_{2g}, can be obtained in two ways: The visible and near-visible spectrum of an octahedral complex is usually due to transitions of one or two electrons between the t_{2g} and e_g levels. For systems with several d electrons the spectra are complicated by changes in the average interelectronic repulsions. However, thanks to crystal field theory, such spectra are quite well understood.[31] By using atomic spectra as a starting point, the theoretical spectrum of a complex can be predicted with considerable confidence as far as the number and kinds of levels are concerned. From the experimental

---

§ The alternative terms *spin-paired* and *spin-free* for low and high spin, respectively, are less desirable.

spectrum it is then possible to extract the actual energy differences between levels such as t_{2g} and e_g, and also the interelectronic repulsion parameters.

For an octahedral complex the difference between t_{2g} and e_g is usually called $10Dq$ for historical reasons though some authors call this energy difference Δ. From actual spectra the value of $10Dq$ for the aquo complexes of the divalent metal ions of the first transition series is about $10,000$ cm^{-1} (28.6 kcal). For the trivalent aquo ions of the same series the value is about $20,000$ cm^{-1}. For the second transition series $10Dq$ is about 50% larger, and for the third series about 100% larger, than for the first. The order of increasing Dq for a series of metals is given by Jørgensen[32] as Mn(II) < Co(II) $\sim$ Ni(II) < V(II) < Fe(III) < Cr(III) < Co(III) < Mn(IV) < MO(III) < Rh(III) < Ir(III) < Re(IV) < Pt(IV).

If other ligands replace water, the number of bands in the spectrum usually remains the same but the bonds are shifted. Thus, Dq is a function of the ligands as well as the metal ion. The order of increasing Dq for a series of common ligands is usually found to be[32] I$^-$ < Br$^-$ < Cl$^-$ $\sim$ $\underline{S}CN^-$ $\sim$ N$_3^-$ < (C$_2$H$_5$O)$_2$P$\underline{S}_2^-$ < F$^-$ < (NH$_2$)$_2$C$\underline{O}$ < $\underline{O}$H$^-$ < C$_2$O$_4^{2-}$ $\sim$ H$_2$$\underline{O}$ < N$\underline{C}$S$^-$ $\sim$ H$^-$ < C$\underline{N}^-$ < $\underline{N}$H$_2$CH$_2$CO$_2^-$ < $\underline{N}$H$_3$ $\sim$ C$_5$H$_5\underline{N}$ < en $\sim$ $\underline{S}$O$_3^{2-}$ < $\underline{N}$H$_2$OH < $\underline{N}$O$_2^-$ < phen < H$^-\|$ < $\underline{C}$H$_3^-$ < $\underline{C}$N$^-$. (The binding atoms are underlined.) This series is called the spectrochemical or sometimes the Fajans-Tsuchida series.

The second method of obtaining the energy differences in crystal field theory is to carry out a quantum mechanical perturbation calculation.[33] The d orbitals of the central atom are represented by a set of wave functions which are assumed to have the same angular dependence as hydrogenic wave functions but a different, unknown, radial dependence. Such orbitals are used in the theory of atomic spectra.[34] The ligands are idealized as a set of point charges or dipoles which provide the perturbation. The calculation then creates a new set of wave functions, which are linear combinations of those applying to the free atom or ion, and a new set of energy levels.

The new energy levels are just those we have discussed for a regular octahedral complex. The difference in energy in this case can be represented by the interelectron repulsion terms of the free atom and a single new parameter called $10Dq$. From the theory

$$10Dq \simeq \frac{5eq\overline{a^4}}{3r^5} \quad \text{or} \quad \frac{5e\mu\overline{a^4}}{r^6}$$

where e is the charge on the electron, q or μ is the charge or dipole moment of the six ligands, r is the metal-ligand separation, and $\overline{a^4}$ is the average

‖ Two positions have been given for the hydride ion. See J. A. Osborn, R. D. Gillard, and G. Wilkinson, *J. Chem. Soc.* **1964**, 3168.

value of the fourth power of the distance of the electron from the nucleus. This distance is unknown because the radial factor in the wave function is not known.

As an example, consider $Co(H_2O)_6^{3+}$, in which r is about 2 A and μ is about 5 debyes, counting the quite large induced dipole [see the remarks on $Fe(H_2O)_6^{3+}$ given earlier]. Since the crystallographic radius of Co^{3+} is about 0.65 A, it might be expected that $\overline{a^4}$ would be less than unity. However, to give agreement with the spectral value of $10Dq$ of 20,000 cm^{-1} a value of $\overline{a^4}$ equal to 1 A^4 is needed. As an order of magnitude calculation, the result is very satisfactory.

In spite of this agreement it soon becomes clear that the theoretical expressions for $10Dq$ cannot explain the experimental results for different metal ions and different ligands. The spectrochemical series in particular cannot be rationalized in terms of the charges and sizes of the ligand. Thus, hydroxide ion gives a smaller Dq value than water, and large, neutral ligands such as 1,10-phenanthroline give very large Dq values. The orders can be explained by involving covalent bonding, particularly π bonding. This, however, is not permitted in the purely electrostatic crystal field theory.

For structures other than that of a regular octahedron, perturbation calculations can also be made and the energies of the various d orbitals can be found. Except for the tetrahedral case more than one parameter is needed to express the results; in particular, the ratio $\overline{a^2}/r^4$ occurs in some terms instead of $\overline{a^4}/r^6$ as in the octahedral system. In what follows a reasonable factor of about three has been used to convert the first of these ratios into the second. This enables us to calculate the crystal field stabilization of systems with various numbers of d electrons and with various structures. Table 2.4 shows the appropriate theoretical single-electron energies of the several d orbitals of a central atom for a number of the important geometries found in coordination compounds. These are obtained from the papers by Ballhausen and Jørgensen[35] with the assumption mentioned above (in the terminology of Ballhausen and Jørgenson this assumption is that $B_2 = 2B_4$).

Figure 2.4 shows some of the energy levels in a schematic manner. To avoid confusion it must be recalled that, when ligands are added to a gaseous ion, the total energy of the system goes down. However, because of the negative charge of the ligands, the energy of all the d orbitals must go up. The energy of some will rise more than others. It is only the relative changes in energy (the crystal field splittings) which are correctly shown in Fig. 2.4. Thus, each structure in the figure has its own absolute energy value which cannot be related to the energies of the adjoining structures.

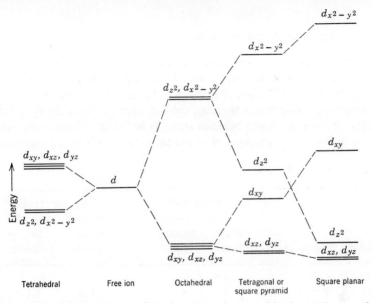

Fig. 2.4 Crystal field splittings of the d orbitals of a central ion in regular complexes of various structures.

Table 2.4 The d-orbital energy levels (in Dq) in crystal fields of different symmetries

C.N.	Structure	$d_{x^2-y^2}$	d_{z^2}	d_{xy}	d_{xz}	d_{yz}
1	...[a]	−3.14	5.14	−3.14	0.57	0.57
2	linear[a]	−6.28	10.28	−6.28	1.14	1.14
3	trigonal[b]	5.46	−3.21	5.46	−3.86	−3.86
4	tetrahedral	−2.67	−2.67	1.78	1.78	1.78
4	square planar[b]	12.28	−4.28	2.28	−5.14	−5.14
5	trigonal bipyramid[c]	−0.82	7.07	−0.82	−2.72	−2.72
5	square pyramid[c]	9.14	0.86	−0.86	−4.57	−4.57
6	octahedron	6.00	6.00	−4.00	−4.00	−4.00
7	pentagonal bipyramid[c]	2.82	4.93	2.82	−5.28	−5.28
7	octahedral wedge[c,d]	8.79	1.39[e]	−1.51[e]	−2.60[f]	−6.08[f]

See Fig. 3.2. Calculations from reference 36.

[a] Bonds lies along z axis.
[b] Bonds in the xy plane.
[c] Pyramid base in xy plane.
[d] Square pyramid with two groups above base.
[e] d_{z^2}, d_{xy} hybrids.
[f] d_{xz}, d_{yz} hybrids.

The same zero of energy is used in each case, however. This arbitrary zero is taken to be when each d orbital is randomly occupied, the spherically symmetric distribution of electronic charge. This enables us to assign an energy of $-4Dq$ to the three t_{2g} orbitals and $+6Dq$ to the e_g orbitals. In this way the difference between them is $10Dq$, and the sum $3(-4) + 2(6) = 0$. We may now proceed to calculate the stabilization energies of

Table 2.5 Crystal field stabilization energies for d^n complexes

		Octahedral		Square Planar	
System	Examples	Weak Field	Strong Field	Weak Field	Strong Field
d^0	Ca^{2+}, Sc^{3+}	$0Dq$	$0Dq$	$0Dq$	$0Dq$
d^1	Ti^{3+}, U^{4+}	4	4	5.14	5.14
d^2	Ti^{2+}, V^{3+}	8	8	10.28	10.28
d^3	V^{2+}, Cr^{3+}	12	12	14.56	14.56
d^4	Cr^{2+}, Mn^{3+}	6	16 (1)[a]	12.28	19.70 (1)[a]
d^5	Mn^{2+}, Fe^{3+}, Os^{3+}	0	20 (2)[a]	0	24.84 (2)[a]
d^6	Fe^{2+}, Co^{3+}, Ir^{3+}	4	24 (2)[a]	5.14	29.12 (2)[a]
d^7	Co^{2+}, Ni^{3+}, Rh^{2+}	8	18 (1)[a]	10.28	26.84 (1)[a]
d^8	Ni^{2+}, Pd^{2+}, Pt^{2+}, Au^{3+}	12	12	14.56	24.56 (1)[a]
d^9	Cu^{2+}, Ag^{2+}	6	6	12.28	12.28
d^{10}	Cu^+, Zn^{2+}, Cd^{2+}, Ag^+, Hg^{2+}, Ga^{3+}	0	0	0	0

[a] The figure in parentheses is the number of electrons that must be paired in going from the weak field case to the strong field case.

atoms with any number of d electrons by filling the levels in order. Actually this can only be done in a rather approximate manner since the levels shown in Table 2.4 are correct for a single d electron only (or, with inversion, nine d electrons). Systems with d^n electrons have more complicated total energies because of electron interaction.

For example, in a very weak field a d^2 (or d^7) system according to detailed calculation[33] should contain only nine-fifths of an electron in the t_{2g} orbitals, rather than the integral number two naively expected. Hence, the C.F.S.E. would be only $6Dq$ rather than $8Dq$. For very strong crystal fields the t_{2g}

electron occupancy would approach two, but at the expense of an increased interelectronic repulsion.

In view of the failure of the theory to be quantitatively exact, such complications have been ignored in constructing Table 2.5. This shows the C.F.S.E.'s for d^n systems, calculated as a simple sum of one-electron energies from Table 2.4 for regular octahedral and square planar complexes. Two sets of values are found, for the "weak field" approximation and the "strong field" approximation, that is, no electron pairing beyond that in the free ion and maximum electron pairing. In the latter case the number of extra electrons to be paired is also shown in parentheses.

It can be seen from Table 2.5 that the high-spin complex $Fe(H_2O)_6^{3+}$ has zero crystal field stabilization, whereas the low-spin (diamagnetic) complexes of Co(III) have considerable C.F.S.E. This amounts to $24Dq$ in octahedral complexes, less the energy required to pair two electrons. Since the value of $10Dq$ from the spectrum is about 56 kcal for water ligands and about 25% greater for amine ligands, the crystal field energy is considerable (about 135–170 kcal). The electron-pairing energy is less certain, but appears to be about 85–100 kcal for two electrons,[37] leaving a net gain of about 40 kcal for $Co(H_2O)_6^{3+}$. Furthermore, complexes of Cr(III) are stabilized by $12Dq$ in weak or strong fields and no electron pairing is necessary. From the spectrum $10Dq$ is 17,400 cm^{-1}, corresponding to a crystal field energy of 57 kcal for $Cr(H_2O)_6^{3+}$. The octahedral d^8 systems are also strongly stabilized without electron pairing being required. In the case of complexes of Ni(II), the stabilization is about half that of Cr(III) because of the smaller value of Dq for divalent ions.

Applications of the Crystal Field Theory

Stereochemistry. Table 2.5 may be used to illustrate one of the important applications of crystal field theory, the prediction and correlation of stereochemistry and coordination number. This is a hazardous undertaking, and indiscriminate application of the theory will lead to many disagreements with experiment. The chief reason is that, as Table 2.2 has already shown, C.F.S.E. is only a small portion of the total bonding energy of a complex. Thus, the attraction of the metal for the ligands and the mutual repulsion of the ligands bring in energies often of the order of 500–1500 kcal mole. Crystal field effects are of the order of 10–50 kcal. It is obvious that the other factors determining bond strengths will be much more important than C.F.S.E. in fixing coordination number and geometry.

Nevertheless, in many cases these other factors are so nearly balanced that crystal field effects will provide the small, extra weight needed to tip the scales in one direction or the other. The near equality of two different structures for a given metal ion and set of ligands in terms of energy is most clearly shown by the rapid substitution reactions of many complexes. Since such reactions must involve a change in coordination number and structure, the difference in energy between the structures must be small. For orientation purposes it is well to remember that, at room temperature, 1.4 kcal is one power of ten in a rate or equilibrium constant. Hence, crystal field energies, while small compared to total bonding energies, are clearly large enough to be chemically significant.

For example, Table 2.5 clearly shows that square planar complexes will be formed most easily from d^8 and d^9 systems in strong fields with d^7 systems next. This is in good agreement with properties of the Ni(II) triad and Cu(II) and Au(III) complexes. Planar complexes of the d^7 ions, Co(II) and Rh(II), have been reported.[38a] In fact, with the later transition series, where electron pairing occurs readily, systems with six or fewer d electrons form octahedral complexes most commonly and systems with more than six generally are square planar.[38b] In weak fields d^4 systems should form square planar complexes, but there is little evidence to support this conclusion. However, one other factor must be considered.

Because of the rapid falling off of the crystal field with distance r, it is possible to have the stabilization of a square planar structure and still have a coordination number of six. Thus, a system with tetragonal symmetry, with four ligands close in and with two others *trans* to each other and further away, will give essentially the crystal field of the four closer ligands only. This is undoubtedly what happens in a very large number of complexes. In fact, it can be stated that, except for linear complexes, the *Jahn-Teller distortion* in general will occur.[39] This is the result of a theorem which states that, if a system such as a complex has several total energy levels which are equal in the ground state, a distortion of the system will occur to remove the degeneracy and make one level the most stable. Essentially, it means that the best energy for a complex even with six equal ligands will not usually be that of a regular octahedron. Depending on the number of d electrons, the best arrangement will be tetragonal or even rhombic for all systems except d^3, diamagnetic d^6, paramagnetic d^8, uncoupled d^5, and, of course, d^0 and d^{10}.

Thus, x-ray and other evidence shows that for Cu(II) four groups lie in a plane close to the copper ion and two groups perpendicular to the plane lie further away.[40] If the four groups lie in the xy plane, it is the $d_{x^2-y^2}$ orbital which is half-filled, giving extra stability to the complex. The same structure is found for d^4 systems. For square planar complexes of nickel, palladium, and platinum, a simple consideration of energetics leads to the expectation that two other groups will be above and below the plane at a distance great enough not to change the crystal field.

Evidence for these two extra groups has been provided in a number of cases (see Chapter 5).

Because of the symmetrical nature of the d orbitals, a ligand on the $+x$ axis has the same effect on the energies as when on the $-x$ axis. Hence, the square pyramid structure with C.N. five gives C.F.S.E.'s intermediate between the regular octahedral and the square planar structures. This arrangement is particularly favored by Co(II), which is a d^7 system. Known examples include $Co(CN)_5^{3-}$ and $Co(triarsine)I_2$. Nickel(III) in the compound $Ni(Et_3P)_2Br_3$ [41] also has this structure. Table 4 provides some theoretical justification for these facts since good stability is obtained in a square pyramid with the $d_{x^2-y^2}$ level empty and the d_{z^2} half-filled.

Table 2.6 Weak field stabilization of d^n systems

	Tetrahedral	Octahedral
d^1, d^6	$2.67 Dq$	$4 Dq$
d^2, d^7	5.34	8
d^3, d^8	3.56	12
d^4, d^9	1.78	6
d^0, d^5, d^{10}	0	0

The d-orbital energy levels of the square pyramid may also serve as a good approximation to those of a tetragonal system in some cases.

The crystal field theory may also be used to predict the occurrence of tetrahedral complexes. It will only be necessary to compare the stabilization energies with those of octahedral complexes for the case of weak fields. For strong fields, tetrahedral structures for the transition elements are rare. The reason is that the theoretical splittings in the tetrahedral case are small, being only four-ninths of the octahedral, other factors being equal, as shown in Table 2.4.

However, in some cases it may be that four ligands are better than six (ligand repulsion large). It may then be argued that systems with no crystal field stabilization and non-transition elements, d^0, d^5, and d^{10} systems, will form tetrahedral complexes most readily. This is borne out in the case of $FeCl_4^-$, $Zn(NH_3)_4^{2+}$, $AlCl_4^-$, $Cd(NH_3)_4^{2+}$, HgI_4^{2-}, MnO_4^-, CrO_4^{2-}, SO_4^{2-}, and many others. The ready formation of tetrahedral complexes such as CoX_4^{2-}, where X is a halogen or pseudohalogen, also finds some justification from Table 2.6 since the loss of C.F.S.E. is small for d^7.

Tetrahedral complexes for Ni(II) do not seem very probable since the loss of C.F.S.E. is large. However, by using suitable ligands it has been possible to prepare many tetrahedral Ni(II) complexes.[42] The trick is to use large ligands, where sixfold coordination is not possible, of relatively weak crystal field strength so that planar, diamagnetic complexes are not formed instead. In the case of unfavorable ligands such as Cl^-, it is necessary to exclude other possible ligands by working in fused salt media or in solvents of poor coordinating ability.[43] The corresponding $PdCl_4^{2-}$ and $PtCl_4^{2-}$ are diamagnetic and square planar because of the greater ease of spin-pairing and larger C.F.S.E.

The crystal field theory only states that it is relatively difficult to form tetrahedral complexes in some cases, not impossible. The overwhelming importance of the other energy terms in the complex must be remembered. In many cases there must be a close balance in energy between different structures. For example, equilibria between square and tetrahedral structures in solution will be discussed in Chapter 5.

The theoretical predictions of Table 2.6 for the metal ions of the first transition series, M^{2+}, are borne out quite well.[44] The data used come from the heats of formation of tetrahedral MCl_4^{2-} (see p. 85).

Table 2.7 shows a summary of the simple stereochemical predictions of crystal field theory according to Nyholm. Notice that the choice between four- and sixfold coordination is not predicted on the basis of the theory, but only the structure expected if four-coordinated or six-coordinated. The coordination number is determined largely by the sizes and charges of the metal ion and the ligands.

Magnetic Properties.   The earliest use of crystal field theory, as already mentioned, was in explaining the magnetic properties of transition metal compounds. This application has been developed to a very high degree, though many refinements beyond the simple theory are necessary to explain the wealth of information available.[45]

In the simple theory it was only the value of $10Dq$ and the electron pairing energy which determined the magnetic properties. If the crystal field was strong, then electron pairing occurred to the maximum extent, as in diamagnetic $Fe(CN)_6^{4-}$. If the crystal field was weak, no electron pairing occurred, as in $Fe(H_2O)_6^{2+}$ with four unpaired spins and hence paramagnetic. In going to the second transition series and the third, it would be expected that spin pairing would be much more common because Dq is 50–100% larger in the later series and also because the spin-pairing energies become less. The latter effect results in part because the extension in space of the $4d$ and $5d$ orbitals is larger than for $3d$.

The expectation from simple theory is well borne out in that low-spin complexes are almost invariably found for the heavier transition metals in their complexes.[46] Some caution is necessary, however, in using the spectrochemical series to predict magnetic properties for the lighter transition metal complexes. Thus, the order of decreasing tendency to spin-pair predicted is $C > N > O > S > F > Cl > Br$, where only the coordinated atom is indicated. The other actually found[47] is more like $S > O$ and $Cl, Br > F$. The explanation seems to lie largely in the change of the interelectronic repulsion parameters in the complexes compared

Table 2.7 Stereochemical predictions of crystal field theory

Number of Non-bonding d Electrons	Unpaired Electrons	Four-Coordinate	Six-Coordinate
		High-Spin	
0, 10, or 5	0 or 5	regular tetrahedral	regular octahedral
9 or 4	1	square planar	tetragonal
8 or 4	2	distorted tetrahedral	regular octahedral
7 or 2	3	regular tetrahedral	almost regular octahedral
6 or 1	4	almost regular tetrahedral	almost regular octahedral
		Low-Spin	
1 or 2	...	...	...
3	1	almost regular tetrahedral	...
4	0	regular tetrahedral	almost regular octahedral
5	1	distorted tetrahedral	almost regular octahedral
6	0	distorted tetrahedral	regular octahedral
7	1	square planar	tetragonal
8	0	square planar	tetragonal

From R. S. Nyholm, *Proc. Chem. Soc.*, **1961**, 273.

to the gas phase (see below). Thus, for sulfur bearing ligands the energy required to pair two electrons is less than when no ligands are present. Another point to be remembered is that the energy required to change the spin of an electron depends upon the number of other electrons of the same spin also present (number of spin-exchange integrals). Particularly, d^5 high-spin systems are stable because all spins are parallel. A d^6 system with only four parallel spins would be easier to pair.[24] Thus, $Co(H_2O)_6^{3+}$ is diamagnetic, but $Fe(H_2O)_6^{3+}$ has all electrons unpaired even though the ligands are the same for both metals.

Redox Potentials. Crystal field theory may be used to help correlate oxidation-reduction potentials of certain complex ions.[48] For example, Table 2.8 shows the standard oxidation potentials of several Fe(II)–Fe(III) systems. Taking the aquo ions as standards, it is seen that negative ion ligands stabilize the trivalent state as might be expected since electrostatic repulsion will favor the removal of an electron from the Fe(II). However, neutral unsaturated ligands stabilize the divalent state. This inversion is partly due to the greater crystal field stabilization of a d^6 system compared to a d^5 one in strong fields (see Table 2.5). The stabilization of $24Dq$ for d^6 compared to $20Dq$ for d^5 must be weighted with the relative values of

Table 2.8 Some iron(II)-iron(III) couples

Electrode Reaction	Potential, E^0, volts
$Fe(H_2O)_6^{2+} \rightleftharpoons Fe(H_2O)_6^{3+} + e$	−0.77
$FePO_4^- + PO_4^{3-} \rightleftharpoons Fe(PO_4)_2^{3-} + e$	−0.61
$Fe(CN)_6^{4-} \rightleftharpoons Fe(CN)_6^{3-} + e$	−0.36
$Fe(bipy)_3^{2+} \rightleftharpoons Fe(bipy)_3^{3+} + e$	−1.10
$Fe(phen)_3^{2+} \rightleftharpoons Fe(phen)_3^{3+} + e$	−1.14

Dq for each ion since they will not be the same. For a ligand which owes its crystal field effect largely to π bonding, there will be a smaller difference in Dq between a divalent ion and a trivalent ion. This follows since a divalent cation can donate electrons more easily than a trivalent cation.

Other factors influence the E^0 values for the couples chosen. In the first two cases, the ferric ion is stabilized by the phenomenon of special stability of half-filled shells, being a d^5 system. This is a property of the free gaseous ion and has nothing to do with chemical bonding. It can be estimated that the required coupling energy for spin-paired Fe(III) is some 30–40 kcal greater than for Fe(II) because of this effect.[24] In strong crystal field complexes where electron pairing is complete, this is equivalent to a destabilization of the trivalent iron compared to the situation in the aquo ions. One final factor is the change in solvation energy on oxidation. For cationic species, this always favors the trivalent state and does so most when the ions involved are small, that is, the aquo iron(III) is stabilized more than the tris(2,2'-bipyridine) iron(III) ion.

The redox potentials of the couples M(II)/M(III) for the various transition series are a function of the gas-phase ionization potentials, which increase in going from lower to higher atomic numbers in any one series, and of the hydration energies of the divalent and trivalent ions, respectively. The ionization potentials show the d^5 hump and the hydration energies include C.F.S.E., as will be discussed in more detail later.[49]

Closely related to changes in E^0 for various couples are the stabilizations of valence states by complexation. The classic example is, of course, Co(III) which forms stable complexes with ligands of good crystal fields but an unstable complex with water. Other examples are the stabilization of Ag(II) and Ag(III) with unsaturated ligands that form square planar complexes.[50] Similarly we have the stabilization of Ni(IV) in octahedral complexes with C.N. six.

Stability of Complexes. Metals which can have considerable crystal field stabilization should react preferentially with ligands of large Dq values. Since ammonia and the amines have larger crystal fields than water and other oxygen bonding ligands, it is expected that the transition metals will bond preferentially to nitrogen rather than oxygen. The non-transition metals, the rare earths, Fe(III), and Mn(II), on the other hand, have a greater tendency to bond to oxygen than to nitrogen. This is in good agreement with experience. Again, other factors may enter since Cu(I), Ag(I), Au(I), Cd(II), Zn(II), and Hg(II) also prefer nitrogen to oxygen even though crystal field stabilization is not involved. This will be discussed later under the heading of "hard" and "soft" acids and bases.

Even though Cr(III) and Co(III) are both strongly stabilized by crystal field effects and form good complexes to nitrogen ligands, there is a definite tendency for cobalt to prefer nitrogen over oxygen to a greater extent than chromium does. This may be correlated with the stabilization energy of $24\,Dq$ for cobalt compared to $12\,Dq$ for chromium, the electron-pairing energy required for cobalt being roughly the same regardless of the nature of the ligands.

For example, the total stability constant, K_T, for the formation of $Cr(NH_3)_6^{3+}$ has been determined[51] to be no greater than 2×10^{13} in a medium where the stability constant for $Co(NH_3)_6^{3+}$ was found to be 10^{36} by J. Bjerrum. The difference in stabilities corresponds to 30 kcal of free energy. The theoretical difference would be $12\Delta Dq$, where ΔDq is the difference between the Dq's for NH_3 and H_2O (see below). This amounts to some 20 kcal of energy.

Table 2.9 shows some stability constants for ethylenediamine complexes of the divalent metal ions of the first transition series. The data are also represented in Fig. 2.5 in terms of the log of the product K_T, or β_3, plotted against atomic number. A value for the estimated stability constant of the unstable $Ca^{2+} - en$ complex is included.[47] Taking the d^0, d^5, and d^{10} systems as a baseline (no crystal field stabilization), it is seen that extra stability is found for the complexes of all the other metal ions. The effect is maximum at d^3 and d^4 and at d^8 and d^9. Remembering the Jahn-Teller effect, which is large for d^4 and d^9, we expect this result on the basis of

Table 2.9 Stabilities of ethylenediamine complexes of the first transition series metal ions at 25°C

	Metal							
	V^{2+}	Cr^{2+}	Mn^{2+}	Fe^{2+}	Co^{2+}	Ni^{2+}	Cu^{2+}	Zn^{2+}
pK_1	4.63	5.15	2.77	4.34	5.97	7.51	10.76	5.92
pK_2	2.95	4.04	2.10	3.31	4.91	6.35	9.31	5.14
pK_3	1.33	...	0.92	2.05	3.18	4.42	−1.0	1.86
ΔH_1, kcal	...	...	2.80	5.05	6.90	8.90	13.0	6.65
ΔH_{1+2}	...	...	6.00	10.40	13.95	18.25	25.4	13.75
ΔH_{1+2+3}	...	...	11.05	15.85	22.15	28.35	...	20.70

pK data from reference 52; ΔH data from reference 53.

crystal field theory. The C.F.S.E. of Cu^{2+} and Cr^{2+} would be $9.14Dq$ in a tetragonal complex, and for V^{2+} and Ni^{2+} the C.F.S.E. would be $12Dq$ in an octahedral complex.

Formation constants in water give only differences in free energy between water and some other ligand:

$$M(H_2O)^{m+}(aq) + L(aq) \rightarrow ML^{m+}(aq) + H_2O(aq) \qquad (6)$$

The relevant factor is the difference between Dq for water [850 cm^{-1} for Ni(II)] and ethylenediamine [1160 cm^{-1} for Ni(II)]. The excess C.F.S.E. for the amine complex over the hydrate would be $12\Delta Dq$, which works

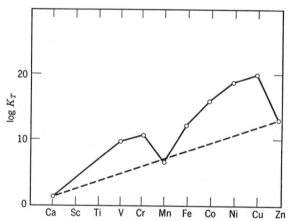

Fig. 2.5 Total stability constants for divalent metal ions of the first transition series with ethylenediamine. Adapted from reference 47.

out to be 10 kcal. This accounts well for the excess stability for Ni(en)$_3{}^{2+}$ given in Table 2.9, which amounts to about 8.5 pK units or 12.3 kcal of free energy.

Of course, C.F.S.E. is an energy term, not a free energy and it is better to look at the heats of formation of the complexes of the various metals. This is possible because of the calorimetric studies which are available.[53]

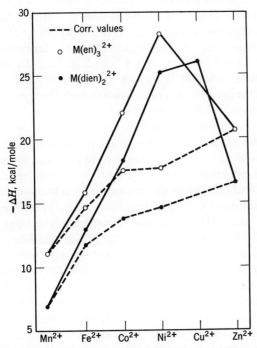

Fig. 2.6 Experimental (solid line) and corrected for crystal field stabilization (dotted line) heats of formation of M(en)$_3{}^{2+}$ and M(dien)$_2{}^{2+}$ ions in aqueous solution. From reference 53.

The heats are also shown in Table 2.9 and are plotted in Fig. 2.6 along with the heats of reaction for diethylenetriamine(dien) and the same metal ions. It can be seen that the extra stability is indeed due to an energy effect as predicted. The dotted lines in the figure show the heats of reaction after correcting for crystal field effects.

Both Cr^{2+}, which is d^4, and Cu^{2+}, which is d^9, show large stabilization only for K_1 and K_2.

$$Cr^{2+} + en \rightarrow Cr(en)^{2+} \qquad K_1 \qquad (7)$$

$$Cr(en)^{2+} + en \rightarrow Cr(en)_2{}^{2+} \qquad K_2 \qquad (8)$$

It is not possible to add a third en molecule, at least as a bidentate ligand.[54] This is in agreement with the tetragonal distortion predicted for these systems.

Figure 2.5 suggests that it is possible to explain the so-called "natural order" of stability constants for complexes,[55] which is Mn < Fe < Co < Ni < Cu > Zn. There is a constantly increasing electronegativity up to and including zinc, accounting for the greater stability of Zn(II) complexes compared to Mn(II) complexes. There is also a crystal field correction increasing to a maximum at nickel and copper and falling off abruptly to zero at zinc.[56] According to this explanation the increased stability for nickel and copper would be greatest for ligands of large Dq, as would the drop at zinc. This is generally true since amines show the large effects we have noticed, whereas oxygen atom donors display only small effects.[55]

It must be pointed out that polarizable ligands such as I^- and RS^- give very large effects also even though their crystal fields are small. Williams has emphasized that this must be due to the polarization of these ligands or to covalent bonding.[57] In this case the natural order can also be explained in terms of the apparent drops in ionization potential that occur for Mn^{2+} and Zn^{2+}. Table 2.10 lists the sums of the first two ionization potentials for the metal ions of the first transition series. Manganese and zinc appear irregular because chromium and copper have extra-large second ionization potentials due to the d^5 and d^{10}, half-filled and filled shell, extra stability. Thus, it is hard to remove the second electron from Cr^+ and Cu^+.

Conversely, it may be assumed that Cr^{2+} and Cu^{2+} attract electrons more strongly than do Mn^{2+} and Zn^{2+}. Since ligands act as electron donors towards the metal ions, the complexes of Cr(II) would be more stable than those of Mn(II), and those of Cu(II) more stable than those of Zn(II). The effect would be greater for a good electron donor such as I^- and smaller for a poor donor such as F^-. Coupled with the otherwise increasing electronegativity, this could account for the shapes of Figs. 2.5, 2.6, (and 2.7), at least in part.

The Coordinate Bond Energy. The most direct place to look for C.F.S.E.'s is data on heat of formation in the gas phase, e.g.,

$$M^{m+}(g) + nL(g) \rightarrow ML_n^{m+}(g) \qquad (9)$$

The gaseous metal ion would have no C.F.S.E., but the complex would have, and this should appear in the heat of reaction 9. We will define the coordinate bond energy as the dissociation energy of the process

$$XML^{m+}(g) \rightarrow XM^{m+}(g) + L(g) \qquad (10)$$

where X represents other ligands bound to the metal M. For an overall dissociation such as the reverse of 9, the energy required would be the

Table 2.10 Some properties of common metal ions

Ion	Radius, A	Total Ionization Potential,[a] kcal	−Heat of Hydration,[b] kcal
H^+	...	313.4	263
Li^+	0.78	124.3	125
Na^+	0.95	118.5	100
K^+	1.33	100.1	79
Rb^+	1.49	96.3	75
Cs^+	1.65	89.8	68
Cu^+	0.93[c]	178	139
Ag^+	1.13	175	116
Au^+	1.37[c]	213	154
Tl^+	1.49	141	80
Mg^{2+}	0.78	523	464
Ca^{2+}	0.99	414	382
Sr^{2+}	1.27	385	350
Ba^{2+}	1.43	351	316
Ti^{2+}	0.85[c]	471	446[d]
V^{2+}	0.82[c]	483	453
Cr^{2+}	0.80[c]	541	460
Mn^{2+}	0.91	532	445
Fe^{2+}	0.83	556	468
Co^{2+}	0.82	583	497
Ni^{2+}	0.78	596	507
Cu^{2+}	0.72[c]	646	507
Zn^{2+}	0.83	631	492
Ru^{2+}	0.81[c]	558	448
Pd^{2+}	0.80[e]	651	505
Ag^{2+}	0.93[c]	681	411
Cd^{2+}	1.03	597	437
Sn^{2+}	1.10[c]	506	374
Os^{2+}	0.88[c]	539	444
Ir^{2+}	0.92[c]	582	477
Pt^{2+}	0.80[e]	652	523
Hg^{2+}	1.12	673	441
Pb^{2+}	1.32	518	359
Al^{3+}	0.57	1228	1122
Sc^{3+}	0.76	1022	947[d]
Ti^{3+}	0.72	1105	1027[d]
V^{3+}	0.69	1094	1053[d]
Cr^{3+}	0.65	1259	1105[d]
Mn^{3+}	0.66	1328	1098[d]

Table 2.10   (*Continued*)

Ion	Radius, A	Total Ionization Potential,[a] kcal	−Heat of Hydration,[b] kcal
Fe^{3+}	0.67	1261	1072[d]
Co^{3+}	0.65	1365	1126[d]
Ga^{3+}	0.62	1319	1124
In^{3+}	0.81	1214	995
La^{3+}	1.22	835	793
Ce^{3+}	1.18	890	837
Tl^{3+}	1.05	1299	984
Ce^{4+}	1.01	1737	1542
Sn^{4+}	0.71	2152	1827
F^-	1.36	80	117
Cl^-	1.81	86	85
Br^-	1.95	81	74
I^-	2.16	72	61

Data from reference 67 except as specified in notes *d* and *e*.
[a] At 0°K.
[b] At 25°C.
[c] Largely estimated.
[d] From reference 70.
[e] From reference 22b.

average coordinate bond energy. The *n*th bond energy would not be the same as the $n - 1$ bond energy, and so on.

The coordinate bond energy is not the same as the usual bond dissociation energy. For example, in the case of $CrCl_3$ the two reactions would be

$$CrCl_3(g) \rightarrow Cr^{3+}(g) + 3Cl^-(g) \qquad (11)$$

with an average coordinate bond energy of 413 kcal, and

$$CrCl_3(g) \rightarrow Cr(g) + 3Cl(g) \qquad (12)$$

with an average bond energy of 84.5 kcal.[58] Although reaction 11 is purely hypothetical and would not occur in the gas phase whereas reaction 12 might, it is 11 which is of importance in a theoretical discussion of coordination chemistry. Also, it becomes possible to discuss neutral ligands such as water in the same terms as anionic ligands. The reaction analogous to 12 involving water would have no obvious meaning.

There are few cases in which the coordinate bond energy can be found directly in the gas phase. The heat of dissociation of $(CH_3)_3B$—$N(CH_3)_3$

is measurable and is 17.6 kcal mole. For F_3B—$N(CH_3)_3$ the corresponding value is 28.5 kcal. Also the heat of the reaction

$$L(g) + H^+(g) \rightarrow LH^+(g) \tag{13}$$

can be evaluated by straightforward thermal cycles in simple cases. This negative heat is called the proton affinity and is characteristic of the base L. When L is NH_3 the value is 209 kcal, for H_2O it is 182 kcal, for OH^- it is 375 kcal, and for Cl^- the proton affinity is 328 kcal.[59] These are the energies of the coordinate bond to hydrogen ion in each case.

From the heats of formation of the metal carbonyls and the heat of vaporization of the solid metal, it is possible to calculate the average bond energy of $Ni(CO)_4$ as 33 kcal, of $Fe(CO)_5$ as 30 kcal, and of $Cr(CO)_6$ as 29 kcal. However, these values are for the reaction

$$M(g) + nCO(g) \rightarrow M(CO)_n(g) \tag{14}$$

in which the metal atom is in the normal state $3d^84s^2$ for nickel, $3d^64s^2$ for iron, and $3d^54s^1$ for chromium. A fairer calculation would be one in which the metal atoms are first converted to $3d^{10}$, $3d^8$, and $3d^6$. This requires 42 kcal for nickel, making the average bond energy 44 kcal, and 169 kcal for chromium, making the bond energy 57 kcal. The excitation energy for iron is 152 kcal, so that the bond energy is 60 kcal.[60]

In the case of metallic ions there is no direct way of measuring or calculating the heat of reaction in the gas phase. However, the heats of hydration of a number of gaseous ions are known from various thermochemical measurements

$$M^{m+}(g) \rightarrow M^{m+}(aq) \tag{15}$$

It is possible to use these data to calculate the heat of the reaction

$$M^{m+}(g) + 6H_2O(g) \rightarrow M(H_2O)_6^{m+}(g) \tag{16}$$

with the aid of two reasonable assumptions. One is that the coordination number towards water is known. It is generally taken as six, but some other number could be used if evidence supported the choice. The second assumption is that the heat of hydration can be broken down into two parts, one due to the interaction of the central ion with the first coordination sphere and the other due to the interaction of the ion plus its first coordination sphere with the rest of the solvent. This procedure is essentially that used by Verwey[61] to calculate the hydration energies of the alkali metal ions.

The second part of the heat of hydration, that of the aquo complex, may be estimated from the familiar Born equation[62] and the variation of the dielectric constant of water with temperature. This should be valid for large, spherically symmetric ions.

$$\Delta G_{\mathrm{B}} = \frac{-q^2}{2r}\left(1 - \frac{1}{D}\right) \tag{17}$$

$$\Delta S_{\mathrm{B}} = \frac{q^2}{2Dr}\left(\frac{\partial \ln D}{\partial T}\right)_p \tag{18}$$

$$\Delta H_{\mathrm{B}} = \Delta G_{\mathrm{B}} + T\Delta S_{\mathrm{B}} \tag{19}$$

Here q is the charge on the ion and r is the radius of the central ion plus 2.76 A, the diameter of a water molecule. D is 78 for water at 25°C and $(\partial \ln D/\partial T)_p$ is -0.0046. The heat of vaporization of water, which is 10.4 kcal/mole at 25°C, is also needed.

As examples, the Born heat of hydration for $Fe(H_2O)_6^{2+}$ is calculated to be -186 kcal, and for $Fe(H_2O)_6^{3+}$ the result is -437 kcal. For a univalent ion such as $K(H_2O)_6^+$ the value is -39 kcal.

Table 2.11 gives a number of heats of hydration for ions of interest in coordination chemistry. Also listed are the total ionization potentials to form the ion, that is, the energy for the reaction

$$M(g) \rightarrow M^{m+}(g) + me(g) \tag{20}$$

The ionic radii according to Goldschmidt are also listed. Several sets of ionic radii are available which may differ by as much as 0.1 A for a given ion. None of them is completely reliable, but the Goldschmidt values are more directly related to experiment and furthermore show the irregularities in the radii of the first transition series which are predicted because of the crystal field of the neighboring anions in the solid state.[63]

From the total heat of hydration of Fe(II) ion we calculate the heat of reaction 9 as $186 - 62 - 468$ or -344 kcal. This corresponds to an average coordinate bond energy of 56 kcal. For Fe(III) the result is -697 kcal for the heat of reaction to form $Fe(H_2O)_6^{3+}$ in the vapor state. This gives a mean bond energy of 116 kcal. These values are fairly characteristic of the divalent and trivalent cations of the transition metals.

Furthermore, by using data on heats of reactions such as 6 in solution it is also possible to calculate the bonding energies for ligands other than water. Again it is necessary to estimate the Born heat of hydration of the complex ion to obtain bond energies in the gas phase. This procedure has been followed for the complexes listed in Table 2.3. Yatsimirskii has developed a somewhat different method of calculating bond dissociation energies, consisting of measuring the heat of solution of a solid complex and calculating the lattice energy of the solid by an approximate method.[64]

Table 2.11 shows the data calculated in this way for the hexammine complexes of the first transition series. Dividing the heats of reaction as given by six, we find coordinate bond energies ranging from 46 to 68 kcal bond. Similar results are found with ethylenediamine. Therefore it would appear that water and amines form bonds of similar strength. This is borne out by measurements of the heats of reaction of aquo complexes with amines. The reactions are usually exothermic by about 5 kcal per bond for divalent cations.[66] Also for most ligands the heat effect on replacing water is rarely as much as 10 kcal per bond. Even though anions are held more firmly than ligands like water or ammonia in the gas phase, this is

Table 2.11   Coordinate bond energies in hexamine complexes

$$M^{2+}(g) + 6NH_3(g) \rightarrow M(NH_3)_6^{2+}(g)$$

Cation	$-\Delta H,^a$ kcal
Ca^{2+}	273
Cr^{2+}	344
Mn^{2+}	339
Fe^{2+}	361
Co^{2+}	396
Ni^{2+}	410
Cu^{2+}	410
Zn^{2+}	394

Data from reference 65.
^{a} Divide by six to get coordinate bond energies.

not the situation in solution. The extra solvation energy of the free anion compared to a neutral ligand just compensates for the firmer bonding in the complex.

The heats of the reactions

$$M^{2+}(g) + 4Cl^-(g) \rightarrow MCl_4^{2-}(g) \tag{21}$$

were determined[68] for several metal ions. The results are -625, -642, and -638 kcal for Co^{2+}, Cu^{2+}, and Zn^{2+}, respectively. Thus, the mean coordinate bond energy is about 160 kcal in these cases. It is estimated that C.F.S.E. amounts to 5–10 kcal for tetrahedral $CoCl_4^{2-}$ and $CuCl_4^{2-}$. The crystal field effects are seen to be much larger for the octahedral ammine complexes of Table 2.11. The bonding energies of MCl_4^{2-} can be calculated by an ionic model to give agreement with experiment.

The methods discussed above for determining bond energies in the vapor state are probably reliable for symmetrical complexes. However, for unsymmetrical complexes, such as $Co(NH_3)_5Cl^{2+}$, the charge distribution is such as to create a dipole moment as well as a net charge in the molecule.

This will affect the lattice energy as well as the Born heat of hydration. It should be possible to make more reliable calculations in such cases by using the methods developed by Kirkwood[69] for solvation energies of spherical and ellipsoidal molecules with arbitrary charge distributions. For very irregularly shaped complexes, however, no reliable calculation can be made.

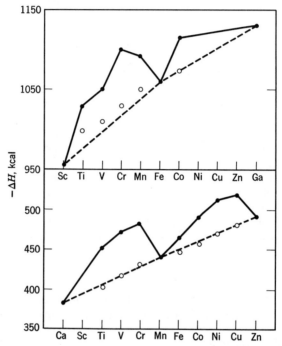

Fig. 2.7   Uncorrected (dotted line) and crystal field corrected (solid line) hydration energies of the divalent (lower) and trivalent (upper) ions of the first transition series. Data from reference 70.

The hydration energies of Table 2.10 provide indisputable evidence for the C.F.S.E., as Penney was first to show.[29b] Thus, for the divalent and trivalent ions of the first transition series, including Ca(II) to Ga(III), the heats vary in an irregular manner. However, if the estimated crystal field corrections are subtracted from the total heats, the residual values fall on a smooth curve. This is shown in Fig. 2.7.

An examination of Table 2.10 shows a very marked correlation between the total ionization potential of an ion and its hydration energy. This is reasonable since adding electrons either as such or through ligands should be influenced in a similar way by the size and effective charge of the ion.

As pointed out by Orgel,[56a] the correlation is even better if the ionization potentials are corrected to correspond to a standard configuration, i.e.,

$$M(3d)^n(4s)^2 \rightarrow M^{2+}(3d)^n + 2e \qquad (22)$$

This correction occurs for the chromium atom, which has a ground state $(3d)^5(4s)$, and for the copper atom, which is $(3d)^{10}(4s)$. It is possible to find the appropriate change in ionization potential from atomic spectroscopy, the energies 7750 cm^{-1} for chromium and 11,200 cm^{-1} for copper

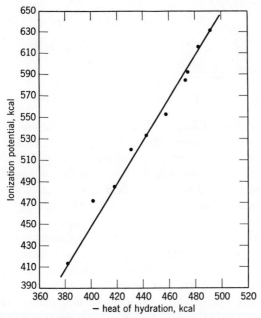

Fig. 2.8 Corrected ionization potential $[M(3d)^n(4s)^2 \rightarrow M^2 + (3d)^n + 2e]$ plotted against crystal field corrected heat of hydration, divalent cations of first transition series.

then being subtracted from the values given in Table 2.10. Figure 2.8 shows the corrected ionization potentials plotted against the heats of hydration corrected for C.F.S.E. The overall change in ionization potential from Ca(II) to Zn(II) is about 50%. The corresponding change in hydration energy is only 25%.

The lattice energies of the transition metal halides also reveal several points of interest. These are plotted in Fig. 2.9 for the first series. It is evident that there are strong crystal field effects as in the hydration energies. These amount to as much as 40 kcal mole for divalent ions and 80 kcal for trivalent ions.[71] The minima in the lattice energies at Mn(II) and Fe(III) are as predicted by theory.

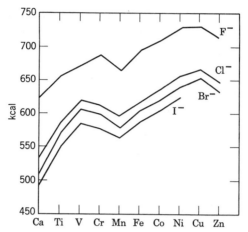

Fig. 2.9   Lattice energies of divalent halides of first transition series. From reference 45.

The Effective Ionic Charge. Theoretical calculations of the lattice energies of ionic solids, using electrostatic potential energy as we have done for complexes, work out very well for the alkali halides, as already mentioned. London dispersion energies replace the induced dipole attractions because in the solid the electric field at each ion is nearly zero as a result of symmetry. Similar calculations for the halides of copper and silver give theoretical lattice energies which are about 10% lower than the experimental.[68] Cuprous chloride has a larger experimental lattice energy than NaCl, though the interionic distances are very similar.

The variation of the heat of hydration with ionic radius is also worth noting. Within a non-transition group, the heat of hydration varies inversely with the ionic radius, as might be anticipated. The transition metals give considerable variation, as shown by the fact that Cu(I), which has virtually the same size and charge as Na(I), has a higher heat of hydration by 40%. Also, Au(I), which is larger than either of the others, has the highest heat of the three. The ionization potentials are also anomalous, being 118.5 kcal for Na, 178 for Cu(I), and 213 for Au(I). The same difficulties are encountered with the divalent and trivalent ions of the non-transition and transition metals.

All these phenomena are disturbing in view of the electrostatic theory by which we earlier calculated bond energies. Use was made of a potential function which varied from one metal to another only in the value of q, the charge on the central atom, and r, the ion size. One set of corrections has been made in that, for the d electrons, it was shown that the use of a uniform distribution of charge over the central atom was incorrect. Instead the d electrons, if possible, concentrate in the regions of less negative potential. This correction will not help for the case of Cu(I) and Au(I) mentioned above, since here we have filled d shells which must be spherically distributed.

It has become customary to attribute all of the evidence for stronger bonding in compounds of the transition metals, and for bonding which is not an obvious function of the ionic charge and size, to covalent character in these bonds. Thus, AgCl is said to be considerably more covalent than NaCl, $ZnCl_2$ much more covalent than $CaCl_2$, and the complexes of Pt(II), for example, more covalent that the corresponding complexes of Ni(II).

The basic reason for the difference between the eight-electron outer structure ions and the eighteen-electron ions can be found in simple, classical electrostatics. It is easy to show that, for a spherically symmetrical distribution of charge, all the charge exterior to a certain point (further from the center of the charge distribution than is the point) will produce a smaller electrostatic potential than if it were interior to the point. Therefore, in moving across a transition series, the increased positive potential due to increased nuclear charge is never quite balanced by the negative potential of the added electrons. This is referred to as incomplete "shielding" of the nuclear charge.

Accordingly, Zn^{2+} will show the same potential as Ca^{2+} at large distances, but at bonding distances the "effective ionic charge" of the zinc ion will be greater. The d-orbital electrons, which on the average will spend part of the time at distances from the zinc nucleus greater than the bonding distance, are responsible. We can speak of an effective charge, q', for zinc which may be 10% or so larger than the nominal charge of $+2$. This higher charge will clearly affect bonding energies even if only ionic bonding is involved. If the ligand is one of low electronegativity, it will be energetically profitable for transfer of electrons from ligand to metal to occur (covalent bonding). Such transferred electrons will feel a still greater effective charge. To summarize, inefficient shielding of the nucleus by d electrons leads to stronger ionic binding and more covalent bonding for metal ions with many outer d electrons.

The Molecular Orbital Theory

(Ligand Field Theory)

The application of molecular orbital (M.O.) theory to complex ions was first made by Van Vleck.[1] The electrons are assumed to move in molecular orbitals which extend over all the nuclei of the system. The molecular orbitals themselves are taken, for convenience, as linear combinations of atomic orbitals. In the event that a given atomic orbital (A.O.) overlaps appreciably with only one other A.O., the pair may be regarded as forming a localized M.O. holding as many as two electrons. This would correspond to the usual conception of a chemical bond.

When an A.O. overlaps several A.O.'s on different nuclei, a more extended M.O. is obtained. As many M.O.'s will exist as the number of A.O.'s considered. Half of the M.O.'s will be bonding, i.e., more stable, than the original A.O.'s, and half will be antibonding, or less stable. In the case of d orbitals on the central atom of a complex, it is clear that extended M.O.'s will be needed.

Let us consider first a simple two-center case involving a metal-ligand combination, M-L.[72] As is often done, the overlap between the A.O.'s will be ignored. The M.O. wave functions are given by

$$\phi^b = \frac{1}{\sqrt{1 + \lambda^2}} (\sigma_L + \lambda \sigma_M)$$

$$\phi^* = \frac{1}{\sqrt{1 + \lambda^2}} (\lambda \sigma_L - \sigma_M) \tag{23}$$

where λ is a mixing coefficient to be determined by minimizing the energy and σ_L and σ_M are normalized σ atomic orbitals. The superscripts b and * refer to bonding and antibonding, respectively. The two orbitals are orthogonal and normalized, i.e., $\int \phi^b \phi^* \, d\tau = 0$, $\int \phi^b \phi^b \, d\tau = 1$, etc., where $d\tau$ is the volume element and the integration is over all space. We define

$$q_L = \text{coulomb integral} = \int \sigma_L H \sigma_L \, d\tau, \text{ etc.}$$

$$\beta = \text{exchange integral} = \int \sigma_L H \sigma_M \, d\tau$$

where H is the one-electron Hamiltonian operator. If q_L, q_M, and β are assumed constant, the energy is found from the solution of the determinant

$$\begin{vmatrix} q_L - \epsilon & \beta \\ \beta & q_M - \epsilon \end{vmatrix} = 0 \tag{24}$$

This has roots (one-electron energies)

$$\frac{q_L + q_M}{2} \pm \frac{1}{2}\sqrt{(q_L - q_M)^2 + 4\beta^2} \tag{25}$$

Treating the bond energy as a dissociation into atoms, it can be seen that two valence electrons in the bonding M.O. produce an energy

$$E = q_L + q_M + \sqrt{(q_L - q_M)^2 + 4\beta^2} \tag{26}$$

which is more negative (q and β are negative quantities) than the energy of the isolated atoms ($q_L + q_M$) by just the quantity under the square root sign.

From 26 we see that a polar bond between two atoms of different electronegativity, where ($q_L - q_M$) is large, will have extra strength compared to a covalent bond where $q_L = q_M$. This was referred to by Pauling as "ionic resonance energy."[73] The parameter λ is given most simply in terms of x, the fractional ionic character of the bond or the fractional charge on M and L,[74]

$$x = \frac{1 - \lambda^2}{1 + \lambda^2} = \frac{(q_L - q_M)}{\sqrt{(q_L - q_M)^2 + 4\beta^2}} \tag{27}$$

If ($q_L - q_M$) is large compared to β, then x approaches unity, and we have an ionic compound, M^+L^-. If, however, β is large compared to the difference in coulombic energy, x goes to zero and the compound is completely covalent.

One difficulty with the above method, besides its obvious crudity, is that q_M and q_L are not constants, as was assumed. They are functions of λ or of the polarity of the molecule. It is possible to express the dependence of the coulomb integrals on x in various ways and to obtain better solutions to the wave functions and the energies (see p. 111).[74]

Let us proceed to apply M.O. theory to a regular octahedral complex of a transition element. Figure 2.10 shows the coordinate system that will be used. The description follows closely the discussion given by Gray[75]

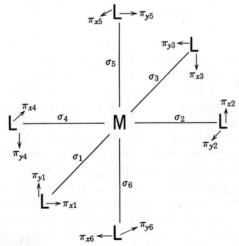

Fig. 2.10 Coordinate system for σ and π bonding in an ML_6 octahedral complex.

and the rules of Gray and Ballhausen for assigning the levels.[76] The M.O.'s will be labeled by their group theory symbols. Both σ and π bonding will be considered.

The M.O.'s will be extended over the molecule and will be of the form

Bonding

$$\phi^b = \frac{\lambda}{(1 + \lambda^2)^{\frac{1}{2}}} s + \frac{1}{(6 + 6\lambda^2)^{\frac{1}{2}}} (\sigma_1 + \sigma_2 + \sigma_3 + \sigma_4 + \sigma_5 + \sigma_6)$$

Antibonding

$$\phi^* = \frac{1}{(1 + \lambda^2)^{\frac{1}{2}}} s - \frac{\lambda}{(6 + 6\lambda^2)^{\frac{1}{2}}} (\sigma_1 + \sigma_2 + \sigma_3 + \sigma_4 + \sigma_5 + \sigma_6)$$

The symbol s is used to represent an s A.O. on the metal, and σ indicates a sigma-type A.O. on ligand atom 1, etc. Again λ is determined by minimizing the energy. It will be a function of the electronegativities of the metal and the ligand, the exchange integrals, the total number of electrons to be accommodated, and many other factors.

The metal orbitals used for σ bonds in an octahedral (O_h symmetry) complex are $3d_{x^2-y^2}$, $3d_{z^2}$, $4s$, $4p_x$, $4p_y$, and $4p_z$. These are classified by symmetry and degeneracy as follows:

$$t_{1u} \qquad (4p_x, 4p_y, 4p_z)$$

$$e_q \qquad (3d_{z^2}, 3d_{x^2-y^2})$$

$$a_{1g} \qquad (4s)$$

We now proceed to find the linear combinations of ligand σ orbitals which may bond with the $t_{1u'}$, $e_{g'}$, and a_{1g} metal orbitals. This is done by writing down (by inspection) the linear combination of σ orbitals which has the *same* symmetry properties as the metal orbital in question. For example, the linear combination of ligand σ orbitals which goes with the $4p_x$ metal orbital has a plus sign in the $+x$ direction and a minus sign in the $-x$ direction. This is the combination $\sigma_1 - \sigma_3$. Similarly, $\sigma_2 - \sigma_4$ and $\sigma_5 - \sigma_6$ are obtained to bond with $4p_y$ and $4p_z$, respectively.

The $4s$ function has the same sign in all directions. Therefore, the correct ligand combination is $\sigma_1 + \sigma_2 + \sigma_3 + \sigma_4 + \sigma_5 + \sigma_6$. The $3d_{x^2-y^2}$ function has four lobes with alternating plus and minus signs; this matches with the ligand combination $\sigma_1 - \sigma_2 + \sigma_3 - \sigma_4$.

The ligand σ-orbital combination for $3d_{z^2}$ is the only one which poses any difficulty. The analytic function for the $3d_{z^2}$ is proportional to $3z^2 - r^2$. The proper ligand σ-orbital combination is easily written down if $x^2 + y^2 + z^2$ is substituted for r^2 in $3z^2 - r^2$. This gives $2z^2 - (x^2 + y^2)$. Thus, the proper ligand combination is $2(\sigma_5 + \sigma_6) - (\sigma_1 + \sigma_2 + \sigma_3 + \sigma_4)$.

The metal orbitals which can be used for π bonding are $3d_{xy}$, $3d_{xz}$, $3d_{yz}$, $4p_x$, $4p_y$, and $4p_z$. The symmetry classification is the following:

$$t_{2g} \quad (3d_{xy}, 3d_{xz}, 3d_{yz})$$

$$t_{1u} \quad (4p_x, 4p_y, 4p_z)$$

Notice that the $4p$ orbitals (t_{1u}) are involved in both σ and π bonding The proper $t_{1u}(\pi)$ and $t_{2g}(\pi)$ ligand combinations are written in the same way as for the σ combinations.

The $t_{2g}(\pi)$ and $t_{1u}(\pi)$ ligand combinations account for only six of the twelve ligand π orbitals. The remaining six are accounted for by the $t_{1g}(\pi)$ and $t_{2u}(\pi)$ combinations, which are made up of the same π orbitals as $t_{2g}(\pi)$ and $t_{1u}(\pi)$, respectively, but with every other sign in the linear combination changed. For example, the ligand combination for the $3d_{xy}$ is $\pi_{x_1} + \pi_{y_2} + \pi_{y_3} + \pi_{x_4}$, and the corresponding $t_{1g}(\pi)$ function is $\pi_{x_1} - \pi_{y_2} + \pi_{y_3} - \pi_{x_4}$. The $t_{1g}(\pi)$ and $t_{2u}(\pi)$ ligand orbitals have no metal orbital counterparts, and therefore they are *non-bonding* with respect to the metal complex.

A summary of all the σ and π metal and ligand orbitals for an octahedral complex is given in Table 2.12.

The next step is calculate the energies, ϵ_i, of each M.O. and the values of the mixing coefficients, λ_i. For polyelectronic systems this is a formidable task, and even with modern computing techniques it can only be done in an approximate fashion. Nevertheless, some non-empirical calculations have been made, using the best available A.O.'s (Hartree-Fock self-consistent field).[77] Also a number of fairly elaborate semiempirical calculations have been carried out.[78] The chief interest in these theoretical efforts has been to obtain numbers to correlate with various kinds of spectroscopic information. As a result, binding energies have usually not been dealt with.

A common procedure has been to use a simple semiempirical method first developed by Wolfsberg and Helmholz.[79] In this method the coulomb integrals are approximated by the valence-state ionization potentials of the metal and ligand, with rough corrections for the degree of ionic character, and the exchange integrals by mean ionization potentials multiplied by the overlap integral between the metal and ligand orbitals. Thus, $q_M = -IP_M$, $q_L = -IP_L$, and $\beta = FS(q_L + q_M/2)$ or $-FS(q_L q_M)^{\frac{1}{2}}$, where F is a constant often set equal to two.

The ionization potentials are not the ordinary ones, even after correction for the effect of charge. Instead they must be further corrected to correspond to ionization of an electron from the A.O. used in M.O. formation the valence-state ionization potential. It may be noted that in the Wolfsberg-Helmholz method there is no correction for the electrostatic interaction

Table 2.12 Proper metal and ligand orbital combinations for octahedral complexes

Representation	Metal Orbital	Ligand Orbital Combination
$a_{1g}(\sigma)$	s	$\dfrac{1}{\sqrt{6}}(\sigma_1 + \sigma_2 + \sigma_3 + \sigma_4 + \sigma_5 + \sigma_6)$
$e_g(\sigma)$	d_{z^2}	$\dfrac{1}{2\sqrt{3}}(2\sigma_5 + 2\sigma_6 - \sigma_1 - \sigma_2 - \sigma_3 - \sigma_4)$
	$d_{x^2-y^2}$	$\tfrac{1}{2}(\sigma_1 - \sigma_2 + \sigma_3 - \sigma_4)$
$t_{1u}(\sigma, \pi)$	p_x	$\dfrac{1}{\sqrt{2}}(\sigma_1 - \sigma_3), \dfrac{1}{2}(\pi_{y_2} + \pi_{x_5} - \pi_{x_4} - \pi_{x_6})$
	p_y	$\dfrac{1}{\sqrt{2}}(\sigma_2 - \sigma_4), \dfrac{1}{2}(\pi_{x_1} + \pi_{y_5} - \pi_{y_3} - \pi_{x_6})$
	p_z	$\dfrac{1}{\sqrt{2}}(\sigma_5 - \sigma_6), \dfrac{1}{2}(\pi_{y_1} + \pi_{x_2} - \pi_{x_3} - \pi_{y_4})$
$t_{2g}(\pi)$	d_{xz}	$\tfrac{1}{2}(\pi_{y_1} + \pi_{x_5} + \pi_{x_3} + \pi_{y_6})$
	d_{yz}	$\tfrac{1}{2}(\pi_{x_2} + \pi_{y_5} + \pi_{y_4} + \pi_{x_6})$
	d_{xy}	$\tfrac{1}{2}(\pi_{x_1} + \pi_{y_2} + \pi_{y_3} + \pi_{x_4})$
$t_{2u}(\pi)$	$\ldots$	$\tfrac{1}{2}(\pi_{y_2} - \pi_{x_5} - \pi_{x_4} + \pi_{y_6})$
	$\ldots$	$\tfrac{1}{2}(\pi_{x_1} - \pi_{y_5} - \pi_{y_3} + \pi_{x_6})$
	$\ldots$	$\tfrac{1}{2}(\pi_{y_1} - \pi_{x_2} - \pi_{x_3} + \pi_{y_4})$
$t_{1g}(\pi)$	$\ldots$	$\tfrac{1}{2}(\pi_{y_1} - \pi_{x_5} + \pi_{x_3} - \pi_{y_6})$
	$\ldots$	$\tfrac{1}{2}(\pi_{x_2} - \pi_{y_5} + \pi_{y_4} - \pi_{x_6})$
	$\ldots$	$\tfrac{1}{2}(\pi_{x_1} - \pi_{y_2} + \pi_{y_3} - \pi_{x_4})$

energy of the central ion for the ligands, or of the ligands with each other. Since such interactions represent the whole of the binding energy for an ionic model, the error introduced in the Wolfsberg-Helmholz method must be very large for highly polar complexes.

The net charges on each atom are usually calculated in the Wolfsberg-Helmholz model to be self-consistent. That is, the values of λ_i finally adopted must yield the overall charges on the metal and ligand consistent with the values of q_M and q_L used to calculate λ_i. Since the ionic terms are ignored in minimizing the energy, the charges calculated in this way will always be too small.[4] In spite of these many shortcomings, the Wolfsberg-Helmholz method often does a remarkable job, particularly in the fitting of spectra.

An idea of the difficulty with the Wolfsberg-Helmholz method can be had by realizing that the ligand is represented as a particle with no structure or properties except for the orbitals of the bonding atom. With this limitation one would calculate about the same gas-phase bonding energies for CrF_6^{3-}, $Cr(NH_3)_6^{3+}$, and $Cr(Ar)_6^{3+}$. A method is available for correction by including the potential energies due to the charges on the metal ion and the ligands.[131] This correction may be called the *Madelung correction*.[132] With its use good estimates of bonding energy are possible.

A common procedure has been the simple device of arranging the M.O.'s in order qualitatively and then using spectroscopic data (see below) to assign the values of the energy levels. This is satisfactory for the interpretation of spectra but is of very little help in obtaining information on bond energies. In other words, the relative energies are fixed, but not the energies absolute to any known zero of energy.

Reasonable approximations for the various coulomb and exchange integrals may be summarized in three "rules":[76]

1. The order of coulomb energies is taken to be $\sigma(L)$, $\pi(L)$, $3d$, $4s$, $4p$.

2. The amount of mixing of atomic orbitals in the molecular orbitals is proportional to atomic orbital overlap and inversely proportional to their coulomb energy difference.

3. Other things being approximately equal, σ^b molecular orbitals are more stable than π^b molecular orbitals, and σ^* molecular orbitals correspondingly less stable than π^* molecular orbitals.

Using these rules, it is possible in some cases to decide the relative energies of the single-electron M.O.'s. Certainly in high-symmetry cases when the total number of levels is small, confidence may be placed in the energy level scheme arrived at. The relative M.O. energy ordering expected for a general octahedral complex is shown in Fig. 2.11.

We have yet to consider metal complexes containing ligands which have π systems of their own. A good example of such a ligand is CN^-, which has itself filled π^b and empty π^* orbitals. Interaction of metal d electrons with ligand π^* orbitals stabilizes the M.O. mainly based on the metal. Such interaction is conveniently called π *back-bonding* (or π back-donation), and such ligands are referred to as π-*acceptor* ligands. To be very effective, the π^* level of the ligand should be more stable than the $4p$ metal orbital. The relative M.O. energies for octahedral complexes containing ligands with accessible π^b and π^* levels are shown in Fig. 2.12.

In square planar complexes (D_{4h} symmetry) the metal orbitals which may be used for σ bonding are $3d_{z^2}(a_{1g})$, $4s(a_{1g})$, $3d_{x^2-y^2}(b_{1g})$, and $4p_x$, $4p_y(e_u)$. Those which may π-bond are $3d_{xz}$, $3d_{yz}(e_g)$, $3d_{xy}(b_{2g})$, $4p_z(a_{2u})$, and $4p_x$, $4p_y(e_u)$. The $4p_x$, $4p_y$ orbitals are involved in both σ and π bonding. The M.O. energy level scheme which has been estimated for square planar metal complexes is shown in Fig. 2.13. For tetrahedral complexes (symmetry T_d) the only pure metal σ orbital is $4s(a_1)$. The $3d_{xz}$, $3d_{yz}$, $3d_{xy}(t_2)$

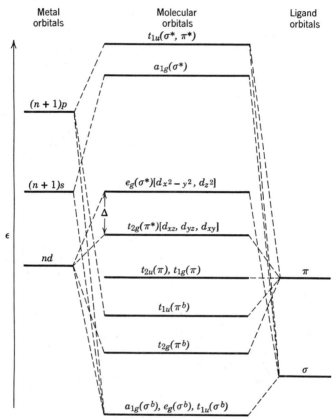

Fig. 2.11 Molecular orbital energy level diagram for octahedral metal complexes.

and $4p_x$, $4p_y$, $4p_z(t_2)$ orbitals may be used in both σ and π bonding. The $3d_{x^2-y^2}$, $3d_{z^2}(e)$ are pure π orbitals. A generally accepted energy level scheme is shown in Fig. 2.14.[80]

There may be zero to five π bonds in a tetrahedral complex, depending on the occupancy of the π^b and π^* orbitals. Maximum π bonding occurs when all the levels are filled and all the π^b levels are filled and all the π^* levels are empty. For example, the MnO_4^- complex has ten electrons in π^b orbitals [six in $t_2(\pi^b)$ and four in $e(\pi^b)$] and, therefore, five π bonds. For complexes containing π-acceptor ligands, the $e(\pi^b)$ and $t_2(\sigma^*, \pi^b)$ are not strongly antibonding, and even for d^{10} cases the number of π bonds is closer to five.

Molecular orbital energy level schemes have been worked out for most of the regular geometries encountered in coordination chemistry. These include linear,[81] trigonal bipyramidal,[82] and archimedean antiprismatic[83] structures. Complexes with one strong metal-ligand link due to π bonding, such as the metal oxycations and metal nitrosyls, require a special scheme.[84]

The orbitals are finally filled from the bottom up with the valence electrons, no more than two electrons per orbital because of the exclusion principle. When this is done for a transition metal complex, it is found that the M.O.'s derived from the metal d orbitals are only partly filled. In an octahedral complex, for example, the $t_{2g}(\pi^*)$ and $e_g(\sigma^*)$ are not filled. In Fig. 2.11 the energy difference between these two orbitals is designated by Δ. It is obvious that, if the complex absorbs light of the right frequency, an electron will be promoted from the $t_{2g}(\pi^*)$ level to the $e_g(\sigma^*)$.

This is the same kind of transition used in crystal field theory to explain the visible and near-ultraviolet absorption spectra of complexes. The

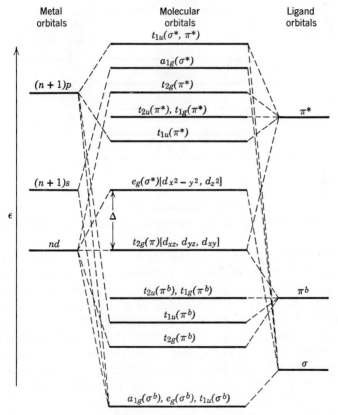

Fig. 2.12 Molecular orbital energy level diagram for octahedral metal complexes containing ligands which have π^b and relatively stable π^* orbitals.

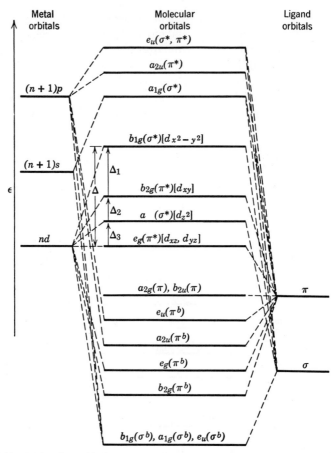

Fig 2.13   Molecular orbital energy level diagram for square planar metal complexes.

parameter Δ replaces the parameter $10Dq$. A tetrahedral complex (Fig. 2.14) also has one energy difference, Δ, between the partly filled antibonding levels derived from the atomic d orbitals. It is possible to show that this Δ has only about one-half of the value of Δ in octahedral complexes.[84] On further examination of M.O. level schemes, the same number of energy levels involving the metal d orbitals is always found, as is predicted by the crystal field theory (Fig. 2.4). Such splittings are a function only of the symmetry of the molecule and the symmetry of the d orbitals of the central atom, as far as the numbers of the levels are concerned.[85] The result is the same whether the cause is an electrostatic field or covalent bond formation. However, the spacings and the order of levels may be quite different, depending on the causes. Since the emphasis is on symmetry in both cases, M.O. theory is usually called ligand field theory when applied to metal complexes. This emphasizes the relationship to crystal field theory.

Almost all of the phenomena explained by crystal field theory can be accounted for equally well—or better—by molecular orbital theory. As a rule all of the ligand electrons can be accommodated in bonding and non-bonding orbitals which are then filled. The metal atom d electrons must be placed in the anti-bonding orbitals of the various symmetry classes derived from the d orbitals. The numbers of levels will always be the same, and the level order will usually be the same as the simple crystal field levels of Fig. 2.4. As electrons are placed in these orbitals, the same effects will be predicted for both crystal field and M.O. theory.

If the ligand is very electronegative, the bonding electrons will be heavily concentrated on the ligands and the antibonding electrons will be concentrated on the metal. That is, λ in equation 23 will be small. This will increase the resemblance of the two theories since the ionic limit ($\lambda = 0$) corresponds to crystal field theory.

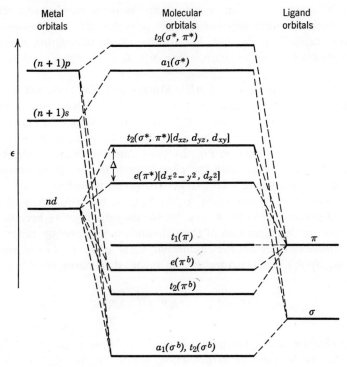

Fig. 2.14 Molecular orbital energy level diagram for tetrahedral metal complexes.

As an example, let us interpret the hydration energies of the divalent ions shown in Fig. 2.7 in terms of M.O.'s. With water as the ligand we may ignore π bonding and consider the t_{2g} orbitals of the metal to be non-bonding. Thus, electrons placed in these orbitals will have *no* effect on the hydration energies in the crude M.O. approximation. However, an electron placed in the e_g orbitals will be in a σ^* antibonding orbital and will *reduce* the hydration energy (make it more positive).

The hydration energy will include a Born hydration term, which may be considered as nearly constant, and bonding energies of the six σ^b orbitals of Fig. 2.11. In passing from Ca(II) to Zn(II), the ionization potentials and hence q_M will increase steadily as shown in Fig. 2.8. Since β will also increase as q_M increases, the bonding energies of the σ^b orbitals may be expected to increase linearly in going from calcium to zinc. We may write the expected heat of hydration, then, as

$$-\Delta H_{\text{hyd}} = a + nb - m\Delta \tag{28}$$

where a is a constant equal to the heat of hydration of Ca(II), n is the total number of d electrons, b is a constant, and m is the number of electrons in σ^* orbitals. We can see that Δ is not only the difference between the t_{2g} and e_g orbitals of Fig. 2.11, but also the net destabilization caused by having an electron in an antibonding orbital, since the t_{2g} orbitals are non-bonding.

The heats of hydration of Ca(II), Mn(II), and Zn(II) should lie on a straight line with a slope equal to $(b - 0.4\Delta)$. When Δ is taken as constant and equal to 30 kcal, the slope in Fig. 2.7 gives b a value of 23 kcal. With all constants evaluated, the theoretical heats of hydration may now be calculated and are shown in Fig. 2.15 as a function of increasing atomic number. The agreement with the experimental is very good except for Cr(II) and Cu(II), where a Jahn-Teller correction is needed.

The Jahn-Teller contribution to the heat of hydration may also be estimated. According to the theory,[24b,d] the distortion occurs because of a linear term in the expansion of the potential energy function in terms of ΔR, a displacement from the equilibrium value of R. This term must be balanced by the usual quadratic term involved in harmonic vibrations:

$$U = U_0 - d\,\Delta R + \frac{k}{2}(\Delta R)^2 \tag{29}$$

Setting $(\partial U/\partial R) = 0$ gives a net decrease in energy equal to $k(\Delta R_0)^2/2$, where ΔR_0 is the Jahn-Teller distortion. While ΔR_0 is equal to d/k, the constant d cannot easily be calculated from first principles.

Experimentally, in $Cu(H_2O)_6^{2+}$ the value of ΔR_0 is about 0.2 A, and the force constant is about 2×10^5 dynes/cm (see Chapter 6). This gives a Jahn-Teller stabilization of about 10 kcal for both Cu^{2+} and Cr^{2+}, remembering that two bonds per ion are distorted. The arrows in Fig. 2.15 show the direction of the Jahn-Teller correction. The overall agreement with experiment is now excellent.¶

The magnitude of Δ in M.O. theory is seen from Fig. 2.11 to be a function of several things. The electrostatic effects of crystal field theory

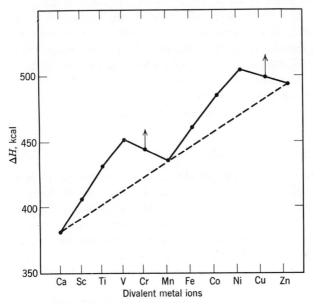

Fig. 2.15 Molecular orbital theory of heats of hydration. The arrows show direction and magnitude of Jahn-Teller stabilization.

will still be present but in a greatly modified way since the ligands are no longer considered as point charges. Metal-ligand σ bonding will increase Δ because e_g (σ^*) will be raised. Metal-ligand π bonding of the L → M type will decrease Δ because $t_{2g}(\pi^*)$ will be raised. From Fig. 2.12, however, it can be seen that π bonding of the back-bonding or M → L type will increase Δ because $t_{2g}(\pi^*)$ is lowered in energy.

The spectrochemical series on p. 67 can now be interpreted in a very satisfactory way. The ligands which are π back-bonders such as CN^-, CO, and 1,10-phenanthroline will produce large splittings (strong crystal

¶ J. P. Fackler and D. G. Holah, *Inorg. Chem.*, **4**, 954 (1965) estimate the Jahn-Teller correction as 8 kcal for Cu^{2+} and Cr^{2+}, using spectroscopic data.

fields). The ligands which are only π donors will give small splittings (weak crystal fields). This explains OH^- and Cl^-, for example. When sulfur is in a positive oxidation state, it can act as a π back-bonder (electron acceptor) and be high in the spectrochemical series, e.g., SO_3^{2-}. When sulfur is negative, as in RS^-, it is a π donor primarily and will be low in the series. Because of the greater number of possible variables, M.O. theory should usually do a better job of explaining not only spectral data, but also magnetic and chemical phenomena.

The weak point of M.O. theory is the difficulty of making *ab initio* calculations to find the magnitude of the effects, whereas such calculations are relatively easy for crystal field theory. Also, absolute bonding energies have been calculated in M.O. theory only by very empirical methods. The effects of interelectronic repulsions are taken care of by assuming that each electron moves in the average field of all other electrons. Thus, any changes in electron repulsion due to spin pairing or to spectral transitions must be considered separately from the one-electron energy levels of Figs. 2.11–2.14.

Localized Molecular Orbitals

As can be seen, the description of a molecule in terms of M.O. theory is usually rather complex, not suitable for ordinary chemical purposes. Considerable simplification can be achieved by using the concept of localized molecular orbitals (L.M.O.'s). These L.M.O.'s correspond to the usual concept of a bond between two atoms (two-center) or occasionally three atoms (three-center M.O.'s). As long as the one-electron approximation is used, any set of M.O.'s such as derived in the previous section can be converted into other M.O.'s by a simple transformation. The new M.O.'s will be, in fact, linear combinations of the old and must obey the usual conditions of normalization and mutual orthogonality. By a proper choice, the new M.O.'s can be made to be largely or entirely localized between two atoms and hence are called *localized molecular orbitals*.

If the original, delocalized M.O.'s were all equally filled, then the new L.M.O.'s when equally filled will correspond to exactly the same electron density distribution and total energy as before. The method can be illustrated by a simple example of a linear, symmetric, triatomic molecule:

$$L—M—L$$
$$1 \qquad 2$$

Imagine the s and p orbitals of the metal to be used for bonding and to be equal in energy. They are combined with σ orbitals on each of the ligand atoms. The σ orbital is set equal in energy to the s and p for convenience, and all exchange integrals are assumed equal. The usual M.O.'s would be as follows (omitting overlap):

$$\phi_s = \frac{1}{\sqrt{2}} s + \tfrac{1}{2}(\sigma_1 + \sigma_2)$$

$$\phi_s^* = \frac{1}{\sqrt{2}} s - \tfrac{1}{2}(\sigma_1 + \sigma_2)$$

$$\phi_p = \frac{1}{\sqrt{2}} p + \tfrac{1}{2}(\sigma_1 - \sigma_2)$$ (30)

$$\phi_p^* = \frac{1}{\sqrt{2}} p - \tfrac{1}{2}(\sigma_1 - \sigma_2)$$

(the p orbital has its positive lobe on the L_1 side)

There would be four bonding electrons, two in each of the ϕ_s and ϕ_p. The one-electron energies would be

$$\epsilon_s = q + \sqrt{2}\beta, \qquad \epsilon_p = q + \sqrt{2}\beta \tag{31}$$

giving a total energy of $4q + 4\sqrt{2}\beta$.

The L.M.O.'s in this case would be the sum and difference of ϕ_s and ϕ_p:

$$\phi = \frac{1}{\sqrt{2}} (\phi_s + \phi_p) = \frac{1}{\sqrt{2}} \sigma_1 + \tfrac{1}{2}(p + s)$$

$$\phi' = \frac{1}{\sqrt{2}} (\phi_s - \phi_p) = \frac{1}{\sqrt{2}} \sigma_2 + \tfrac{1}{2}(p - s)$$ (32)

But $(p + s)$ would be just a hybrid orbital pointing at ligand atom 1, and $(p - s)$ an identical hybrid pointing at ligand atom 2. Therefore, ϕ and ϕ' are L.M.O.'s corresponding to two-center bonding between M and L_1 and M and L_2, respectively. The energy of both ϕ and ϕ' is $q + \sqrt{2}\beta$, and the total energy is just what it was before.

It turns out in this idealized case that the L.M.O.'s use the same combination of A.O.'s on the central atom that we would have picked in valence bond theory (sp hybrids for a linear molecule). This results from having selected a symmetric molecule and having chosen the s and p orbitals to have equal energies and exchange integrals. Lennard-Jones has shown that, for a molecule with elements of symmetry, it is always possible to find a set of *equivalent* localized orbitals, that is, identical with each other except for orientation. If the original, delocalized M.O.'s were nearly equal in energy, then the new, equivalent orbitals will be strongly localized, corresponding to a simple, chemical bond picture.

It is not too surprising to find that in a trigonal, planar molecule the equivalent orbitals are 120° apart and contain sp^2 hybrids of the central atom. In the same way, for a regular tetrahedral molecule the equivalent orbitals contain sp^3 or sd^3 hybrids, and for a regular octahedral system, d^2sp^3 hybrids. In each case, the hybrid orbital is combined chiefly with the σ orbital on one ligand, though there may be small amounts of the σ orbitals on the other ligands if the energies of the central atom orbitals are not exactly equal.

It must be realized that these equivalent orbitals, while strongly resembling the valence bond hybrids, are not identical with them. For one thing, they are M.O.'s, not valence bond orbitals, and the methods of calculation of energies would be different. Secondly, since the energies of the $3d$, $4s$, and $4p$ orbitals of the metal are usually rather different, the L.M.O.'s that are formed will not be the same mixture of s, p, and d metal orbitals that the valence bond theory uses. For example, they will contain less of the high-energy $4p$, as a rule.

For ordinary chemical purposes it is useful to take all filled, delocalized M.O.'s of a given type, σ bonding or π bonding, and to consider them converted to localized, two-center orbitals even in the case of non-symmetric complexes.[88] For example, an octahedral system would use the a_{1g}, e_g, and t_{1u} orbitals to form six localized σ bonds to the ligands. The partly filled M.O.'s cannot be treated in this way. Also, in discussing the spectroscopic properties of a complex, it is not permissible to replace any of the delocalized orbitals involved. Electrons must be removed from, or added to, orbitals extending over the whole molecule and not L.M.O.'s. The same is true for ionization of the molecule.

Critique of the Three Theories

In the previous pages we have mentioned the three chief theories, valence bond, molecular orbital, and electrostatic, used currently to describe coordination compounds. It is desirable to give an estimate of the relative usefulness and general merit of each of the three approaches.[89] To begin with, certainly we are dealing in each case with an approximation which cannot be complete. All three approaches have their uses, and one or the other may be most convenient in any one application. All three can account for the main features of complexes, such as coordination numbers, structures, and magnetic properties, in a qualitative way.

When it comes to quantitative calculations, the electrostatic plus crystal field theory is well in the lead. In fact it is difficult to find another theory anywhere in chemistry which is so simple and still gives so many numbers which are almost correct. By using a simple model, it is possible to successfully calculate binding energies of amine, aquo, and halide complexes, as well as crystal field splittings.

For a further illustration, it is possible to calculate the vibration frequencies of metal-ligand bond stretching from the electrostatic potential energy function. This is done by setting the second derivative of U with respect to r equal to k, the force constant, $(\partial^2 U/\partial r^2) = k$. Using the relationship $v = \sqrt{k/4\pi^2 m}$, where v is the frequency and m the reduced mass of the oscillation, we can then calculate infrared and Raman frequencies as far as orders of magnitude are concerned. For typical complexes the result is in the range of 400 cm^{-1}. The calculated values agree with the magnitude of those reported in the literature for various complexes.[90]

Table 2.13 Metal-ligand stretching frequencies, v(M—Cl), as a function of oxidation state of metal ion and of coordination number

FeCl$_4^-$	378	GeCl$_4$	453	PCl$_4^+$	627
FeCl$_4^{2-}$	282	GaCl$_4^-$	386	SiCl$_4$	610
		ZnCl$_4^{2-}$	273	AlCl$_4^-$	575
CoCl$_2$		C.N. = 2		493	
CoCl$_2 \cdot 2py$		C.N. = 4		344, 304	
CoCl$_4^{2-}$		C.N. = 4		300	
CoCl$_2 \cdot 4py$ (trans)		C.N. = 6		230	

From R. J. H. Clark, *Spectrochim. Acta*, **21**, 955 (1965). Numbers are frequencies in reciprocal centimeters (cm^{-1}).

Table 2.13 shows a number of metal-ligand stretching frequencies. It can be seen that the predictions of a simple ionic model are borne out. The frequencies increase as the charge on the central atom becomes more positive. Also an increase in the number of ligands decreases the frequency, since this is equivalent to cancelling part of the positive charge on the metal. Of course similar results would be expected for models in which covalent bonding played a major role.

The strength of the electrostatic theory is also its weakness. Since complete calculations can be made, it is possible to test the theory against many experiments in a rigorous way. When this is done, the simple theory usually proves inadequate. Valence bond theory and molecular orbital theory, on the other hand, are just ambiguous enough to resist such stringent tests. Quantum mechanically, it is well known that a trial wave function may give a good value for the energy and still be a very poor wave function in every other respect, which is one reason for the success of the electrostatic theory.

There is good reason to believe that covalent bond formation does occur to some extent even for complexes with very electronegative ligands. The evidence for this will be cited shortly. The contribution to the energy would seem to be small in such cases, however. For systems in which delocalization energy is important, the electrostatic theory fails badly. This statement is particularly true for complexes in which π bonding occurs, since this is essentially a delocalization method of lowering the energy. For unsaturated ligands in general and ligands which have unfilled d orbitals, such as $P(C_2H_5)_3$, $S(C_2H_5)_2$, and the like, the electrostatic viewpoint must be replaced or supplemented with the molecular orbital or valence bond approach. As far as crystal field theory is concerned, if a simple point charge model is used for the ligands, and if hydrogenic orbitals with an effective nuclear charge are used for the metal atom, rather good agreement as to the sign and magnitude of $10Dq$ can be obtained.[91] In this model there is an unrealistic blending of classical and quantum mechanical laws. The ligands are assumed to produce only a classical electrostatic field for the d-orbital electrons to interact with.

If an improvement is made in that the electrons of the ligand are also put into suitable A.O.'s, and if better orbitals are used for both ligand and metal (Hartree self-consistent field orbitals), then the result is very disappointing in that the sign of $10Dq$ is found to be inverted.[92] That is, an electron in an orbital such as the $d_{x^2-y^2}$ which points directly at the ligands (oxide ion in chrome alum) is lower in energy than an electron in the d_{xy} orbital which is oriented away from the ligands. The reason for this anomaly is that again the role of the ligands is only to create a classical electrostatic field and the Pauli exclusion principle is ignored. Hence the $d_{x^2-y^2}$ electrons, which spend much of their time near the positive oxygen nuclei, are actually in a more favorable electrostatic environment than the d_{xy} electrons.

It is necessary to make the metal ion orbitals orthogonal to the ligand orbitals in order to obey the Pauli principle. This is the same as saying that the $d_{x^2-y^2}$ electron cannot often find itself close to the ligand nuclei because this region in space is already filled with ligand electrons. Hence, the $d_{x^2-y^2}$ electron must find a new spatial arrangement of its charge cloud, and also change to a higher average momentum value, in order to be compatible with the ligand electrons.

The most detailed calculations have been made by Sugano and Shulman for the substance $KNiF_3$.[77] Molecular orbitals have been constructed, using Hartree-Fock atomic orbitals. The energy was minimized by mixing in the proper amount of covalent binding of both the σ and the π orbitals.

The resulting M.O.'s then give a very good description of such properties as the ^{19}F magnetic resonance hyperfine interaction, the spin-orbit coupling constant, the Racah interelectronic repulsion parameters (see below), and the octahedral crystal field splitting, $10Dq$.

One must then consider these M.O.'s as very good wave functions indeed since they predict successfully so many experimental values. The disturbing feature, however, is that the correct sign and magnitude of $10Dq$ comes only from the covalent part of the wave function, that is, the exchange integrals between nickel and fluorine. Thus, the very small covalent part (a few per cent) of the wave function for these highly ionic compounds seems responsible for the crystal field splitting. This result is somewhat misleading, since it is the oversimplified L.C.A.O. type of wave function used that necessarily leads to the conclusion. If the Shulman and Sugano orbitals are improved by making them more rigorously self-consistent and orthogonal, the calculated value of $10Dq$ becomes very poor again.[93] The best statement to make at the present time is that an electron in an octahedral e_g orbital is higher in energy than an electron in a t_{2g} orbital because of a combination of electrostatic repulsions and Pauli exclusion repulsion.

The molecular orbital theory, in principle at least, is the most powerful of the three theories. It includes the electrostatic theory as a special case (no mixing of metal orbitals with ligand orbitals) and can be extended to include any degree of covalent bonding, including π bonding. Furthermore, with a reasonable selection of A.O.'s to begin with, the theory automatically includes all of the interactions which in the valence bond theory would require the inclusion of a large number of resonance forms.

Also the many successes of crystal field theory are not an exclusive property of the electrostatic method, but can be incorporated into the M.O. theory. The same qualitative model is used to explain spectra, magnetic properties, stability of complexes, bond energies, redox properties, etc. The difference is that the magnitudes are not predetermined by the theory but are left as parameters to be fit by experimental data. This gives greater flexibility to partly compensate for the loss of predictive power.

The chief defects of the M.O. theory are (1) the usual one of any quantum mechanical approach to complex systems, that quantitative calculations of the energy cannot be made, and (2) the disappearance of the nice pictures of chemically bonded atoms so useful to the chemist. The latter difficulty can be partly avoided by the use of L.M.O.'s.

The valence bond theory, in spite of its great service in the development of the theory of coordination compounds, now seems to do the poorest job of the three theories. Some of the inconsistencies and failures of the theory will be discussed in detail below, but the following generalizations can be made:

1. The theory is limited to qualitative explanations only.

2. It cannot interpret the spectra of complexes.**

3. It cannot account for magnetic properties in detail.

4. It cannot give even relative energies of different structures and different coordination numbers.

5. It cannot be extended easily to include splittings of the d energy levels (for the d orbitals not used in forming bonds).

6. The classification, by the magnetic criterion, into ionic and covalent bonds is misleading.

7. Its chief virtues are the chemically satisfying pictorial representations of the bonded atoms and the familiarity and simplicity of its basic rules and tenets.

Under point 1, the same difficulty mentioned for other quantum mechanical methods applies in that actual energies cannot be calculated. Also, there is an even greater scarcity than usual of any quantitative detail in the theory. The only numbers that the theory has to work with are those concerned with the criterion of angular overlap, and these are known to be unreliable.[94] Under points 2 and 3, both of the other theories can give considerable information and correlation since the energy levels in the two cases are very similar and of a nature suitable for discussing physical properties. The energy levels in the valence bond theory are not of the same kind and are not suitable for understanding these properties or for describing the experimental facts.

As an example of the failure of the valence bond theory from an energetic point of view, consider the hydration energies of the transition metal ions. The theory would predict very considerably larger heats of hydration for d^0, d^1, d^2, and d^3 systems since these would form inner orbital complexes even with water ligands (no electron pairing required). Except for Co(III), the other hydrates would be less stable since they would be outer orbital or ionic complexes. This is not at all what is found. The hydration energies of d^0, d^1, and d^2 systems are less than those of any of the other ions of a given series. For d^3 a considerable stabilization is found, but this exception is readily accounted for by the crystal field theory.

To reconcile the square planar, or the tetragonal, structure of Cu(II) complexes with their stability, in the valence bond theory it is necessary to promote the $3d$ electron to the empty $4p$ orbital. This is a process that would require 340 kcal in the gas phase[95] and would presumably still call

---

** An attempt by Pauling [*J. Chem. Educ.*, **39**, 461 (1962)] to rationalize spectra by the valence bond method is not very convincing.

for a goodly fraction of this energy in the complex. Where the energy comes from to balance this requirement is not easily seen. Furthermore, on this basis Cu(II) should be exceedingly easy to oxidize to Cu(III), contrary to experience.†† The similar postulation that, in complexes of Cu(II) involving electron pairing, promotion of an electron to a $5s$ orbital occurs is equally unlikely. In the gaseous state, again, this would take 485 kcal of energy.[95]

The energies are for the gaseous ions, however, and it is likely that complex formation reduces the energy separation. That is, addition of electrons from the ligands is similar to reducing the ion back to the neutral metal. For the neutral metal atoms, the $3d$-$4p$ separations are less, as are the $3d$-$5s$ separations. It is estimated that, if the intense absorption shown by all complexes at about 2000 A is partly due to a $d \rightarrow p$ transition the energy separation has been cut about in half from the free ion value.[96] The $4d$ level lies so far above the $3d$ level in energy that the benefit of using this orbital to permit covalent bond formation in the so-called outer orbital complexes (see p. 58) begins to be very doubtful.

In the event that the covalent contribution to the bonding is small, a theory which puts major emphasis on providing suitable orbitals for covalent bond formation is likely to be a poor guide. Also, from what was said about the rough equivalence of L.M.O.'s and hybrid valence orbitals, systems with incomplete subshells of electrons are apt to be difficult for valence bond theory. In summary, the valence bond theory is expected to be most useful for diamagnetic complexes with strong covalent bonding (metal carbonyls, MnO_4^-, $SnCl_6^{2-}$, SF_6, etc.), and in situations where only ground states, not excited states, are concerned.

Ionic or Covalent Bonds

A subject which is of great interest and which has been the subject of much debate is the degree of ionic (or covalent) character of the bonds in a molecule.[24a] It is worth while to examine the kinds of evidence which relate to this question. As a starting point it is well to remember that such an expression as "per cent ionic character" has no precise meaning except in terms of some imprecise model. A simple model often used is equation 27, based on M.O. theory, or a slightly more elaborate equation in which overlap is included.

Nevertheless, there are many kinds of experimental observations which

---

†† Electron spin resonance data show rather conclusively that the odd electron of Cu(II) is in a d orbital and not a p orbital [D. Kivelson and R. Neiman, *J. Chem. Phys.*, **35**, 149 (1961)].

tell us something about the distribution of charge in molecules or complexes.[75] With suitable assumptions, such experiments have often been used to calculate a "per cent ionic character." The most direct method of detecting electron density, x-ray diffraction, is not sensitive enough at present to be quantitatively useful, though the piling up of electrons around the halogen atoms of the alkali halides is quite discernible. Other methods that have been used include dipole moments,[97] e.s.r. hyperfine splittings,[98]

Table 2.14   Per cent of ionic character in metal-halide bonds estimated from various experiments

System	% Ionic	Method	Reference
NiF_6^{4-}	96	n.m.r.	99b
$CuCl_4^{2-}$	92	e.s.r.	106
CoF_6^{4-}	96	e.s.r.	107
$CoBr_6^{4-}$	95	e.s.r.	107
CoI_6^{4-}	92	e.s.r.	107
$SnBr_6^{2-}$	60	n.q.r.	108
$PdCl_6^{2-}$	43	n.q.r.	109
$PdBr_6^{2-}$	37	n.q.r.	109
$PtCl_6^{2-}$	44	n.q.r.	109
$PtBr_6^{2-}$	38	n.q.r.	109
PtI_6^{2-}	30	n.q.r.	109
$PdBr_4^{2-}$	60	n.q.r.	109
$PtBr_4^{2-}$	57	n.q.r.	109
trans-$Co(en)_2Cl_2^+$	75	n.q.r.	110

n.m.r. chemical shifts,[99] nuclear quadrupole resonance,[100] the Mossbauer effect isomer shifts,[101] x-ray absorption spectra,[102] spin-orbital coupling constants,[103] magnetic susceptibilities,[104] and changes in the interelectronic repulsion parameters of complexes compared to the gas phase.[105]

The results of all these studies may be summarized in the following way: (1) whereas strictly covalent bonds can exist, by definition, strictly ionic bonding does not; (2) many bonds are extremely polar and large charge separations do exist in molecules and complexes. Under point 1 it may be noted that the e.s.r. and n.m.r. experiments show that the unpaired electrons of the transition metal complexes, which in the ionic model are localized on the metal, are in fact partly delocalized on the ligands. This is so even when the ligands are fluoride ions which should form the most ionic bonds.

While none of the above techniques gives results free of ambiguities, Table 2.14 shows some calculated values of per cent of ionic character.

They are of interest in indicating the order of magnitude, at least, and the variation from one metal or ligand to another. The studies were made in the solid state.

A rather different kind of information is given in Table 2.15. This shows theoretical values of the per cent ionic character of metal-chlorine bonds

Table 2.15 Energies (in Electron Volts) for the reaction
$$1/n MCl_n(g) \rightarrow M^{n+}/n(g) + Cl^-(g)$$

Molecule	$E_{pol}{}^a$	$E_{cov}{}^b$	$E_{exp}{}^c$	x^d
LiCl	7.06	7.03	6.70	0.89
NaCl	5.81	5.98	5.54	0.87
KCl	5.03	4.96	4.88	0.89
RbCl	4.79	4.76	4.72	0.89
CsCl	4.57	4.53	4.51	0.89
$BeCl_2$	16.65	15.02	14.64	0.79
$MgCl_2$	11.85	12.25	11.77	0.75
$CaCl_2$	9.69	10.30	10.05	0.80
$SrCl_2$	8.98	9.76	9.58	0.80
$BaCl_2$	8.70	9.16	8.94	0.84
$ZnCl_2$	12.33	12.95	13.00	0.63
$CdCl_2$	11.42	11.84	11.99	0.64
$HgCl_2$	11.19	12.68	13.05	0.54
$AlCl_3$	18.02	19.40	18.23	0.59
$TiCl_4$	21.98	23.72	23.56	0.53
$TiCl_2$	12.25	12.29	11.59	0.83
$CrCl_2$	12.43	12.43	11.73	0.80
$MnCl_2$	11.12	11.74	11.74	0.79
$FeCl_2$	11.80	12.28	12.33	0.76
$CoCl_2$	12.59	12.95	12.33	0.73
$NiCl_2$	12.00	12.58	12.79	0.69

[a] Polarizable ion model.
[b] Molecular orbital model.
[c] These are the energies per bond. The transition metal chlorides are corrected for C.F.S.E.
[d] Fractional ionic character.

in the gaseous state.[74] The value of x, the fractional charge on each chlorine atom, is calculated from the left-hand side of equation 27. An L.M.O. calculation is used in which the coulomb integrals are expressed as a function of x, and the coulombic energy of an electron on chlorine due to the field of the metal ion and the other chlorine atoms is explicitly included. The energy of a pair of bonding electrons is given by

$$E = (1 + x)q_L + 2(1 - x^2)^{1/2}\beta + (1 - x)q_M + be^{-aR} \qquad (33)$$

For a diatomic molecule

$$q_M = -\text{I.P.}_M, \qquad q_L = -(1 - x)\text{I.P.}_L - \frac{x(\text{I.P.}_L + \text{E.A.}_L)}{2} - \frac{x}{2R} \qquad (34)$$

where I.P._M and I.P._L are the ionization potentials of the metal and the ligand, and E.A._L is the electron affinity of the ligand (chlorine). The exchange integral is roughly estimated from the geometric mean of the metal-metal and chlorine-chlorine single bond energies.[111] The last term in equation 33 is a van der Waals repulsion which can be evaluated from virial coefficient data at the equilibrium distance R.

Table 2.15 gives values of x and also the coordinate bond energies as calculated from equation 33, listed as E_{cov}, and as calculated from the polarizable ion model of equation 4, listed as E_{pol}. Comparison of the two theoretical values of the energy with the experimental results shows that both are in fair agreement, though the covalent model is better for $TiCl_4$, $ZnCl_2$, and $HgCl_2$. The smaller value of x for these molecules is in agreement with the better energies and also with what one would expect chemically. Thus, $ZnCl_2$ is less ionic (63%) than $MnCl_2$ (79%) or $CaCl_2$ (80%). Unfortunately, no experimental values of the ionic character of these molecules are available, except for the alkali chlorides, for which n.q.r. data indicate nearly 100% ionic character.[112]

One of the most interesting and easily observed effects is the lowering of interelectronic repulsions of complexes as compared to free metal ions. The d-d spectrum in each case can be interpreted in part by certain electronic repulsion terms (Racah parameters[113]). These parameters are less for a complex than for the free ion. This is simply interpreted by saying that in the complex the electron charge cloud is more diffuse than in the free ion. Hence, the average electron-electron distance is greater in the complex. The name *nephelauxetic* (cloud expanding) is suggested for this effect by Schäffer and Jørgensen.[105]

The magnitude of the nephelauxetic effect for a fixed ligand and different metal ions is[114]

Pt(IV) $\sim$ Mn(IV) > Co(III) > Rh(III) $\sim$ Ir(III) $\sim$ Fe(III) > Cr(III) > Mo(III) > Ni(II) > V(II) > Mn(II)

For a given metal ion and different ligands the nephelauxetic series is[114]

$(C_2H_5O)_2PSe_2^- > (C_2H_5O)_2PS_2^- > I^- > Br^- > CN^- \sim Cl^- > C_2O_4^{2-} \sim$ en $> NH_3 > (NH_2)_2CO > H_2O > F^-$

These orders are most easily explained by assuming that the effect is due to partial covalent bond formation.[105] Thus, the most electronegative metal ions, Pt(IV) and Mn(IV), would form the most covalent bonds with the least electronegative ligands, dsep⁻ (diethyldiselenophosphate) and dtp⁻ (diethyldithiophosphate). The bond between Mn(II) and F⁻ or H_2O would be least covalent. Cloud expansion occurs on covalent bond formation because the electrons now spend part of their time on the ligands, and because the effective nuclear charge of the metal has been reduced by electron transfer from the ligands.

The simple presence of negatively charged ligands will also cause cloud expansion by a shielding effect.[115] For this reason it is not possible to calculate the ionic character of the metal-ligand bonds directly from the effect. It is of interest that the ratio of the electron repulsion parameter in the complex to that in the gaseous ion ranges from 0.93 in $Mn(H_2O)_6^{2+}$ to 0.24 in $Ir(dtp)_3$. These values are not far off from estimates of the fractional ionic character that might be made in other ways.

Two rules have been widely used to discuss the expected charge distribution in molecules. One is the "principle of equalization of electronegativity," due to Sanderson,[116] and the other is the "postulate of essential electroneutrality," due to Pauling.[117] In the first of these it is assumed reasonably that the electronegativity of an atom is a function of its charge. On bond formation charge will flow from the least electronegative atom to the most electronegative until the two electronegativities are equal. The second rule states that in a compound or complex all the atoms will be as near to a state of electrical neutrality as is possible.

Both of these rules are essentially intuitive and lack any theoretical justification.[118] They can be safely used only to predict the direction of charge transfer, not to show the final equilibrium conditions. While electronegativity is a vaguely defined quantity, as is ionic character, the usual[119] interpretation of electronegativity suggests that the principle of electronegativity equalization would be valid only for two atoms separated by an infinite distance but connected by a hypothetical charge conductor. That is, the electrostatic interaction of the two partly charged atoms is ignored, as are the changes in kinetic energy due to delocalization of the electrons. The electroneutrality postulate seems to disagree with the large body of evidence indicating strong polarities in molecules.

Theory of Hard and Soft Acids and Bases[120]

The previous discussion of varying degrees of ionic and covalent character in chemical bonds leads to a final topic, the theory of binding in hard and soft acid-base complexes. In Chapter 1 it was pointed out that

Lewis acids of small size and high positive oxidation state [class (a) acids] prefer to bind to small, non-polarizable ligands such as F^- and H_2O. Acids of large size and low oxidation state [class (b) acids] prefer to bind to large, polarizable ligands such as I^-, R_2S, and even olefins. Calling polarizable species "soft" and non-polarizable species "hard," we have the useful rule that *soft acids bind well to soft bases and hard acids to hard bases.*

Polarizability is simply a convenient property to use as a classification. It may well be that other properties which are roughly proportional to polarizability are more responsible for the typical behavior of the two classes of acids. For example, a low ionization potential is usually linked to a large polarizability and a high ionization potential to a low polarizability. Hence, ionization potential, or the related electronegativity, may be the important property. Unsaturation, with the possibility of acceptor π bonding in the acid-base complex, and ease of reduction, favoring strong electron transfer to the acid, are also associated with high polarizability. For help in deciding which properties are of importance, it is necessary to examine the theories which have been advanced to account for the facts on which Table 1.6 is based. Different investigators, looking at different aspects, have come up with several explanations. These may be called the (1) ionic-covalent theory, (2) π-bonding theory, (3) electron correlation theory, (4) solvation theory.

The Ionic-Covalent Theory. This is the oldest and usually the most obvious explanation.[121] The hard acids are assumed to bind bases with primarily ionic forces, and the soft acids to hold bases by covalent bonds. High positive charge and small size would favor strong ionic bonding, and bases of large negative charge and small size would be held most strongly.

To see what factors influence strong covalent bonding, consider equation 25 in terms of a coordinate bond, where the energy of the separated atoms is $2q_L$ (M + L:, rather than M· + L·). Then the binding energy is

$$\Delta E = (q_M - q_L) + \sqrt{(q_M - q_L)^2 + 4\beta^2} \qquad (35)$$

If this is to be large, and if q_L is more negative than q_M, it is necessary that $(q_M - q_L)$ be close to zero. The electron affinity of the acid should be large, and the ionization potential of the base small. This is essentially the theory of acid-base interaction developed by Mulliken[122] and is suitable for soft acids and bases. In order to use the same calculation for hard acids and bases, it would be necessary to correct q_M and q_L for the charges on M and L. In particular, the stabilization due to an electron on the ligand feeling the positive charge of the metal (the Madelung correction) would be essential. In the Mulliken theory the correction may be made by adding a term to equation 35. However, it is better added as a correction to q_L and q_M.[131]

The repulsion part of the potential energy function between M and L is also important. Softness in both the acid and the base means that the repulsive part of the potential energy curve rises less sharply than for hard acids and bases. Thus, closer approach is possible and better overlap of the wave functions used in covalent bonding.

Mulliken's treatment is intended chiefly for charge transfer complexes which involve soft acids. It is not applicable to hard acids, in which, as we have seen, the base of *highest* ionization potential, e.g., F^-, is bound most strongly. In the theory of covalent bonding, it is generally considered necessary that both bonded atoms be of similar electronegativity to have strong covalent bonding.[123] That is, the coulomb integrals on both bonded atoms should be similar, and the sizes of the bonding atomic orbitals should also be similar to get good overlap. These considerations show that hard acids will prefer hard bases even when considerable covalency exists. Soft bases will mismatch with hard acids for good covalency, and ionic bonding will also be weak because of the small charge or large size of the base.

The theory is rather misleading in one respect. Many hard acids are elements of very high positive oxidation state, e.g., Cl^{7+}. Such a central atom would be expected to form strong covalent bonds to ligands, rather than ionic bonds. The final state might still be quite polar, with chlorine positive, and electrostatic effects would be important. A large residual charge on chlorine would make it match better with oxygen than with sulfur, for example. Jørgensen has suggested that, when the central atom has a high formal oxidation number, it may sometimes become a class (b) acid again.[133] For example, Mo(III) binds NCS^- through nitrogen, whereas Mo(V) seems to bind through sulfur.

The π-Bonding Theory. Chatt has emphasized another feature of the binding between acids and bases, chiefly with respect to metallic complexes.[124] The important feature of class (b) acids in his view is considered to be the presence of loosely held outer d-orbital electrons which can form π bonds by donation to suitable ligands. Such ligands would be those in which empty d orbitals are available on the basic atom, such as phosphorus, arsenic, sulfur, and iodine. Unsaturated ligands such as CO and isonitriles would also be able to accept metal electrons by the use of empty, but not too unstable, molecular orbitals. Class (a) acids would have tightly held outer electrons, but also there would be empty orbitals available, not too high in energy, on the metal ion. Basic atoms such as oxygen and fluorine particularly could form π bonds in the opposite sense, by donating electrons from the ligand to the empty orbitals of the metal.

With class (b) acids, there would be a repulsive interaction between the two sets of filled orbitals on metal and on oxygen and fluorine ligands.

With some imagination, this model can be generalized to fit most of the entries in Table 1.6. The soft acids are potential d- or p-electron donors via π bonds. The hard acids are potential π-bond acceptors. Such effects are, of course, in addition to σ-bonding interactions. The hydrogen-bonding molecules and acids such as BF_3 in class (a) do not seem to fit in with π-bonding ideas.

Electron Correlation Effects. Pitzer[125] has suggested that London or van der Waals dispersion forces between atoms or groups in the same

(a)   (b)

Fig. 2.16 Atomic orbital hybrids for (a) bonding and (b) antibonding molecular orbitals.

molecule may lead to an appreciable stabilization of the molecule. Such London forces depend on the product of the polarizabilities of the interacting groups and vary inversely with the sixth power of the distance between them. They are large when both groups are highly polarizable. Even for bonded atoms it may be argued that the electron correlations responsible for London forces will operate for the non-bonding electrons. It has been calculated that some 11 kcal of the Br-Br bond energy may be due to London forces.[126] It then seems plausible to generalize and state that additional stability due to London forces will always exist in a complex formed between a polarizable acid and a polarizable base. In this way the affinity of soft acids for soft bases can be accounted for.

Mulliken has given a rather different explanation for the extra stability of Br-Br and I-I bonds.[127] He considers the bonding, π^b, and antibonding, π^*, M.O.'s formed by the p electrons on the two atoms. It is assumed that some d orbital on each atom is hybridized with each p orbital to form two dp hybrids. One is used to form the π^b M.O. and the other the π^* M.O. Figure 2.16 shows the two dp hybrids in a somewhat exaggerated fashion. It can be seen that the bonding M.O. will be strengthened because of increased overlap and the antibonding M.O. will be weakened by decreased overlap (made less antibonding).

There is considerable similarity between the proposals of London forces and of orbital hybridization. Both represent electron correlation phenomena. The basic cause is different in the two cases, however. London correlation occurs because of the electrostatic repulsion of electrons for each other. The proposed π-orbital hybridization occurs largely because of non-bonded repulsion effects arising from the Pauli exclusion principle. It would appear that the latter would be more significant for interactions between bonded atoms and the former for more remote interactions. Thus, for the interaction of a soft acid and a soft base, orbital hybridization should usually be more important than stabilization due to van der Waals forces.

Mulliken's theory is the same as Chatt's π-bonding theory as far as the π^b-bonding orbital is concerned. The new feature is the stabilization due to the π^* molecular orbital. This effect can be of greater importance than the more usual π bonding. The reason is that the antibonding orbital is more antibonding than the bonding orbital is bonding, if overlap is included. For soft-soft systems, where there is considerable mutual penetration of charge clouds, this amelioration of repulsion due to the Pauli principle would be great. Unshared pairs of π electrons would be affected more than electrons used for bonding purposes [compare I^- and $(C_2H_5)_3P$]. An M.O. calculation, necessarily very approximate, gives some idea of the energies involved.

Consider the π interactions of a system consisting of p_π and d_π A.O.'s on an atom such as iodine and a p_π' A.O. on an atom such as oxygen. For simplicity let the p_π coulomb integrals be equal on both atoms, say q. The coulomb integral of the d_π orbital will be much nearer zero and may be set equal to zero for simplicity. The p_π-p_π' exchange integral is β, and the d_π-p_π' integral between the two atoms is β'. The d_π-p_π exchange for the same atom will be zero in the one-electron approximation.

The M.O.'s found on solving the secular equation

$$
\begin{array}{c}
\quad\quad p \quad\quad p' \quad\quad d \\
\begin{array}{c} p \\ p' \\ d \end{array}
\begin{vmatrix}
q - E & \beta & 0 \\
\beta & q - E & \beta' \\
0 & \beta' & -E
\end{vmatrix} = 0
\end{array}
\tag{36}
$$

are

$$
\phi_1 = \frac{(\psi_p + \lambda_d\psi) + (1 + \lambda)\psi_{p'}}{\sqrt{2 + 2\lambda}}
$$

$$
\phi_2 = \frac{(\psi_p - \lambda\psi_d) - (1 - \lambda)\psi_{p'}}{\sqrt{2 - 2\lambda}}
\tag{37}
$$

$$
\phi_3 = (\psi_d - \lambda\psi_{p'})
$$

The mixing parameter λ is equal to β'/q, which is small, say 0.10, and terms in λ^2 have been omitted; ϕ_1 and ϕ_2 resemble the bonding and antibonding orbitals, respectively, shown in Fig. 2.16. The corresponding energies, omitting terms in λ^2, are

$$E_1 = q + \beta + \beta'^2/q$$

$$E_2 = q - \beta + \beta'^2/q \qquad (38)$$

$$E_3 = -2\beta'^2/q$$

The net stabilization for four electrons, two in the ϕ_1 or π^b orbital and two in the ϕ_2 or π^* orbital, will be $4\beta'^2/q$. If only the usual π bonding had been considered, the net stabilization would have been equal to $2\beta'^2/q$, so in this case the two effects are equal in magnitude.

It will be noted that the effect of π bonding depends directly on the square of the exchange integral, β'^2, and inversely on the excitation energy q, between the stable p orbital and the unstable d orbital. This explains why the first-row elements cannot benefit from such π bonding, even though empty d and p orbitals exist also at an energy near zero. It also explains why the lowest empty d orbital is most suitable for π bonding even though many other states of nearly equal energy exist. It is expected that the overlap and hence β' will be best for this d orbital.

Polarizability also depends inversely on the excitation energy, q, to the excited levels.[128] This phenomenon is not restricted to the first empty d orbital but includes all excited states. It can be seen that, generally speaking, the metallic cations of class (b) are of high polarizability, not only because of large size, but also because of easily excited outer d-orbital electrons.

The Solvation Theory. A number of workers have recently stressed the effects of certain solvents in reducing the activity of small anions and hence causing large anions to be relatively more basic.[129] Water and other hydrogen-bonding solvents deactivate OH^- and F^- with respect to SH^- and I^-, for example. Aprotic solvents especially if polarizable have much less effect. For neutral bases, however, even good hydrogen-bonding solvents produce little differentiation.

What solvation can do, therefore, is to generally destroy class (a) character and enhance (b) character in the case of anionic bases and protonic solvents. The magnitude of the class (a) character in the gas phase will determine whether or not an inversion to class (b) will occur in solution for any given acid.[130] Solvation effects, while extremely important, do not explain why some acids prefer to bind to soft bases and other acids to hard bases. The explanation for this must come from interactions existing in the acid-base complex. Such interactions include ionic-covalent σ bonding, π bonding, and electron correlation effects, all of which seem to play a role in determining class (a) and (b), or hard and soft, character.

References

1. J. H. Van Vleck, *J. Chem. Phys.*, **3**, 803, 807 (1935).
2. For solids, see a discussion on lattice energies such as that by M. L. Huggins, *J. Chem. Phys.*, **5**, 143 (1937). For vapors, see E. J. W. Verwey and J. H. DeBoer, *Rec. trav. chim.*, **55**, 431 (1936); E. S. Rittner, *J. Chem. Phys.*, **19**, 1030 (1951).
3. (a) H. Eyring, J. Walter, and G. E. Kimball, *Quantum Chemistry*, John Wiley and Sons, New York, 1944, p. 207. (b) D. P. Craig, *Proc. Roy. Soc.* (*London*), **A200** 272, 401 (1950). (c) M. Simonetta, *J. Chim. Phys.*, **49**, 68 (1952).
4. For a fuller discussion see C. A. Coulson, *Valence*, Oxford University Press, London, 2nd ed., 1961, Chap. II.
5. For a review see R. S. Nyholm, *Rev. Pure Appl. Chem.*, **4**, 15 (1954).
6. L. Pauling, *The Nature of the Chemical Bond*, Cornell University Press, Ithaca, 2nd ed., 1960, Chap. IV.
7. *Ibid.*, Chap. IX.
8. F. A. Cotton, *Chemical Applications of Group Theory*, Interscience Publishers, New York, 1963, Chap. 6.
9. G. E. Kimball, *J. Chem. Phys.*, **8**, 188 (1940); J. C. Eisenstein, *ibid.*, **25**, 142 (1956)
10. Reference 3, Chaps. 12 and 13.
11. S. Sugden, *J. Chem. Soc.*, **1943**, 328.
12. H. Taube, *Chem. Revs.*, **50**, 69 (1952).
13. W. Biltz, *Z. anorg. u. allgem. Chem.*, **164**, 245 (1927).
14. D. P. Craig, A. Maccoll, R. S. Nyholm, L. E. Orgel, and L. E. Sutton, *J. Chem. Soc.*, **1954**, 332; H. H. Jaffé, *J. Chem. Phys.*, **21**, 156, 258 (1953).
15. N. V. Sidgewick and H. M. Powell, *Proc. Roy. Soc.* (*London*), **A176**, 153 (1940).
16. R. J. Gillespie and R. S. Nyholm, *Quart. Rev.* (*London*), **11**, 339 (1957); R J. Gillespie, *J. Chem. Educ.*, **40**, 295 (1963); see also C. E. Mellish and J. W. Linnett, *Trans. Faraday Soc.*, **50**, 657 665 (1954).
17. A. E. Van Arkel and J. H. DeBoer, *Rec. trav. chim.*, **47**, 593 (1928); *Die Chemische Binding als elektrostatische Erscheinung*, Leipzig, 1931.
18. F. J. Garrick *Phil. Mag.*, (a) **9**, 131 (1930); (b) **10**, 71, 76 (1930); (c) **11**, 741 (1931); (d) **14**, 914 (1932).
19. W. Klemm and E. Huss, *Z. anorg. Chem.*, **258**, 221 (1949).
20. V. M. Goldschmidt, *Skrifter Norske Videnskaps-Akad. Oslo*, **8**, 69 (1926); *Ber.*, **60**, 1263 (1927).
21. J. Morgan and B. E. Warren, *J. Chem. Phys.*, **6**, 670 (1938).
22. (a) R. W. G. Wyckoff, *Crystal Structures*, Interscience Publishers, New York, Vols. I–VI, 1948–1953. (b) L. E. Sutton, ed., *Interatomic Distances* (Special Publication No. 11), The Chemical Society, London, 1958.
23. A. Duncan and J. Pople, *Trans. Faraday Soc.*, **49**, 217 (1953).
24. Recent general reviews and treatises include (a) L. E. Orgel, *An Introduction to Transition Metal Chemistry: Ligand Field Theory*, John Wiley and Sons, New York, 1960; (b) J. S. Griffith, *The Theory of Transition Metal Ions*, Cambridge University

Press, London, 1961; (c) C. K. Jørgensen, *Absorption Spectra and Chemical Bonding in Complexes*, Pergamon Press, London, 1961; (d) C. J. Ballhausen, *Introduction to Ligand Field Theory*, McGraw-Hill Book Co., New York, 1962; (e) B. N. Figgis, *Introduction to Ligand Fields*, Interscience Publishers, New York, 1965.

25. H. Bethe, *Ann. Physik*, [5] **3**, 133 (1929).
26. R. Schlapp and W. G. Penney, *Phys. Rev.*, **42**, 666 (1932).
27. J. H. Van Vleck, *Theory of Electric and Magnetic Susceptibilities*, Oxford University Press, London, 1932.
28. F. E. Ilse and H. Hartmann, *Z. physik. Chem.*, **197**, 239 (1951).
29. (a) L. E. Orgel, *J. Chem. Soc.*, **1952**, 4756, (b) See also W. G. Penney, *Trans. Faraday Soc.*, **35**, 627 (1940).
30. For an excellent introductory treatment of group theory see reference 8.
31. Reference 24, and for a short, readable account, T. M. Dunn in *Modern Coordination Chemistry* (J. Lewis and R. G. Wilkins, eds.), Interscience Publishers, New York, 1960, Chap. 4.
32. C. K. Jørgensen, reference 24c; *Advances in Chemical Physics*, Vol. 5, Interscience Publishers, New York, 1962; D. F. Shriver, S. A. Shriver, and S. E. Anderson, *Inorg. Chem.*, **4**, 325 (1965).
33. References 24b and 24d. See also T. M. Dunn, D. S. McClure, and R. G. Pearson, *Some Aspects of Crystal Field Theory*, Harper and Row, New York, 1965, Chap. 1.
34. J. C. Slater, *Quantum Theory of Atomic Structure*, McGraw-Hill Book Co., New York, 1960; E. U. Condon and G. H. Shortley, *Theory of Atomic Spectra*, Cambridge University Press, London, 2nd ed., 1953.
35. C. J. Ballhausen and C. K. Jørgensen, *Kgl. Danske Videnskab. Selskab. Mat. fys. Medd.*, **29**, (No. 14) (1955); C. J. Ballhausen, *ibid.*, **29**, (No. 4) (1954).
36. N. S. Hush, *Australian J. Chem.*, **15**, 378 (1962).
37. J. S. Griffith, *J. Inorg. Nucl. Chem.*, **2**, 1, 229 (1956); reference 24d, p. 260.
38. (a) H. B. Gray, R. Williams, J. Bernal, and E. Billig *J. Am. Chem., Soc.*, **84**, 3596 (1962); E. Billig, S. I. Shupack, J. H. Waters, R. Williams, and H. B. Gray, *ibid.*, **86**, 926 (1964). (b) P. George, D. S. McClure, J. S. Griffith, and L. E. Orgel, *J. Chem. Phys.*, **24**, 1269 (1956).
39. H. A. Jahn and E. Teller, *Proc. Roy Soc. (London)*, **A164**, 220 (1937); J. H. Van Vleck, *J. Chem. Phys.*, **7**, 61, 72 (1939).
40. Reference 24a, Chap. 4.
41. K. A. Jensen and B. Nygaard, *Acra Chem. Scand.*, **3**, 474 (1949).
42. L. M. Venanzi, *J. Chem. Soc.*, **1958**, 719 L. Sacconi P. Paoletti, and M. Ciampolini, *J. Am. Chem. Soc.*, **85**, 411, 1750 (1963), give a number of references.
43. L. I. Katzin, *Nature*, **182**, 1013 (1958); **183**, 1672 (1959); N. S. Gill, P. Pauling, and R. S. Nyholm, *ibid.*, **182**, 168 (1958); N. S. Gill and R. S. Nyholm, *J. Chem. Soc.*, **1959**, 3997; C. R. Boston and C. P. Smith, *J. Phys. Chem.*, **62**, 409 (1958).
44. P. Paoletti and A. Vacca, *Trans. Faraday Soc.*, **60**, 50 (1964).
45. M. Kotani, *J. Phys. Soc. Japan*, **4**, 293 (1949); S. Koide and T. Oguchi, *Advances in Chemical Physics*, Vol. 5, Interscience Publishers, New York, 1962; J. B. Goodenough, *Magnetism and the Chemical Bond*, Interscience Publishers, New York, 1963; B. Figgis and J. Lewis, *Modern Coordination Chemistry*, Interscience Publishers, New York, 1960, Chap. 6.
46. R. S. Nyholm, *Quart. Rev. (London)*, **7**, 377 (1953).
47. R. J. P. Williams, *Ind. Chim. Belg*, No. 4, 389 (1963).
48. This subject is reviewed by D. D. Perrin, *Rev. Pure Appl. Chem.*, **9**, 257 (1959).
49. C. K. Jørgensen, *Acta Chem Scand.*, **10**, 1505 (1956).

50. D. Sen, P. Ray, and N. N. Ghosh, *J. Indian Chem. Soc.*, **27**, 619 (1950).
51. C. Schäffer and P. Andersen in *Theory and Structure of Complex Compounds.*, Wroclaw Symposium, 1962 (B. Jezowska-Trzebiatowska, ed.), Pergamon Press, London, 1964, p. 581.
52. R. L. Pecsok and J. Bjerrum, *Acta Chem. Scand.*, **11**, 1419 (1957); J. M. Crabtree *et. al.*, *Proc. Chem. Soc.*, **1961**, 336, for data on vanadium.
53. M. Ciampolini, P. Paoletti, and L. Sacconi, *J. Chem. Soc.*, **1960**, 4553; *Advances in the Chemistry of the Coordination Compounds* (S. Kirschner, ed.), Macmillan Co., New York, 1961, p. 303.
54. J. Bjerrum, *Acta Chem. Scand.*, **2**, 297 (1948).
55. H. Irving and R. J. P. Williams, *J. Chem. Soc.*, **1953**, 3192.
56. (a) L. E. Orgel, *Tenth Solvay Conference*, Brussels, 1956, p. 289. (b) J. Bjerrum and C. K. Jørgensen, *Rec. trav. chim.*, **75**, 658 (1956).
57. R. J. P. Williams, reference 47; *Disc. Faraday Soc.*, **26**, 123, 180 (1958).
58. T. L. Allen, *J. Am. Chem. Soc.*, **78**, 5476 (1956).
59. For a complication of proton affinity data see T. C. Waddington, *Advances in Inorganic and Radiochemistry*, Vol. 1 (H. J. Emeleus and A. G. Sharpe, eds.), Academic Press, New York, 1959.
60. F. A. Cotton, A. K. Fischer, and G. Wilkinson, *J. Am. Chem. Soc.*, **78**, 5168 (1956); H. A. Skinner and F. H. Sumner, *J. Inorg. Nucl. Chem.*, **4**, 245 (1957).
61. E. J. W. Verwey, *Rec. trav. chim.*, **61**, 127 (1942).
62. M. Born, *Z. Physik*, **1**, 45 (1920).
63. J. W. van Santen and J. S. van Wieringen, *Rec. trav. chim.*, **71**, 420 (1952).
64. K. B. Yatsimirskii and N. Astasheva, *Zhur. Obshch. Khim.*, **20**, 2139 (1950); K. B. Yatsimirskii, *Doklady Akad. Nauk SSSR*, **72**, 307 (1950); see also L. I. Katzin and J. R. Ferraro, *J. Am. Chem. Soc.*, **74**, 6040 (1954).
65. K. B. Yatsimirskii, *Advances in the Chemistry of the Coordination Compounds* (S. Kirschner, ed), Macmillan Co., New York, 1961, p. 303; see also F. A. Cotton, *Acta Chem. Scand.*, **10**, 1520 (1956).
66. (a) C. G. Spike and R. W. Parry *J. Am. Chem. Soc.*, **75**, 2726, 3770 (1953). (b) T. Davies, S. S. Singer, and L. A. K. Staveley, *J. Chem. Soc.*, **1954**, 2304. (c) I. Poulsen and J. Bjerrum, *Acta Chem. Scand.*, **9**, 1407 (1955).
67. L. Brewer, L. A. Bromley, P. W. Gilles, and N. L. Lofgren, *Chemistry and Metallurgy of Miscellaneous Materials* (L. L. Quill, ed.), McGraw-Hill Book Co., New York, 1950, pp. 165 *ff*.
68. A. B. Blake and F. A. Cotton, *Inorg. Chem.*, **2**, 906 (1963); **3**, 5 (1964).
69. J. G. Kirkwood, *J. Chem. Phys.*, **2**, 351 (1934).
70. O. G. Holmes and D. S. McClure, *J. Chem. Phys.*, **26**, 1686 (1957).
71. P. George and D. S. McClure, *Progress in Inorganic Chemistry* (F. A. Cotton, ed.), Vol. 1, Interscience Publishers, New York, 1959, p. 38, review crystal field effects on thermodynamics properties of compounds.
72. R. G. Pearson, *J. Chem. Phys.*, **17**, 969 (1949).
73. Reference 6, p. 80.
74. R. G. Pearson and H. B. Gray, *Inorg. Chem.*, **2**, 358 (1963).
75. H. B. Gray, *J. Chem. Educ.*, **41**, 2 (1964).
76. H. B. Gray and C. J. Ballhausen, *J. Am. Chem. Soc.*, **85**, 260 (1963); *Molecular Orbital Theory*, W. A. Benjamin, New York, 1964.
77. S. Sugano and R. G. Shulman, *Phys. Rev.*, **130**, 517 (1963); A. J. Freeman and R. E. Watson, *ibid.*, **120**, 1254 (1960).
78. C. J. Ballhausen and H. B. Gray, *Inorg. Chem.*, **1**, 111 (1962); L. L. Lohr, Jr., and W. N. Lipscomb, *J. Chem. Phys.*, **38**, 1607; *Inorg. Chem.*, **2**, 911 (1963).

79. M. Wolfsberg and L. Helmholz, *J. Chem. Phys.*, **20**, 837 (1952); recent applications include H. D. Bedon, S. M. Horner, and S. Y. Tyree, *Inorg. Chem.*, **3**, 647 (1964); F. A. Cotton and T. E. Haas, *ibid.*, 1004, S. Kida, J. Fujita, and R. Tsuchida, *Bull. Chem. Soc. Japan*, **31**, 79 (1958).

80. A. Carrington and M. C. R. Symons, *J. Chem. Soc.*, **1960**, 889; A. Carrington and C. K. Jørgensen, *Mol. Phys.*, **4**, 395 (1961); however, see R. F. Fenske and C. C. Sweeney, *Inorg. Chem.*, **3**, 1105 (1964), and A. Viste and H. B. Gray, *ibid.*, 1113, for other orders.

81. J. R. Perumareddi, A. D. Liehr, and A. W. Adamson, *J. Am. Chem. Soc.*, **85**, 249 (1963).

82. R. F. W. Bader and A. D. Westland, *Can. J. Chem.*, **39**, 2306 (1961).

83. G. Gliemann, *Theoret. chim. Acta*, **1**, 14 (1962); E. Konig, *ibid.*, **1**, 23 (1962).

84. C. K. Jørgensen, R. Pappalardo, and H. H. Schmidtke, *J. Chem. Phys.*, **39**, 1422 (1963); C. K. Jørgensen and H. H. Schmidtke, *Z. physik. Chem. (Neue Folge)*, **38**, 118 (1963).

85. L. E. Orgel, *J. Chem. Phys.*, **23**, 1004 (1955).

86. E. C. Lingafelter and H. Montgomery, *Proceedings of the Eighth International Conference on Coordination Chemistry* (V. Gutmann, ed.), Springer-Verlag, Vienna, 1964, p. 129.

87. J. Lennard-Jones, *Proc. Roy. Soc. (London)*, **A198**, 1, 14 (1949); J. A. Pople, *Quart. Rev. (London)*, **XI**, 273 (1957) reviews the equivalent orbital method.

88. K. Ruedenberg, *Rev. Mod. Phys.*, **34**, 326 (1962) and C. Edmiston and K. Buedenberg, *ibid.*, **35**, 457 (1963), discuss criteria for formulating the localized M.O.'s in non-symmetric molecules. They introduce the abbreviation L.M.O.

89. (a) See reference 1 for the earliest comparison. (b) C. K. Jørgensen, *Orbitals in Atoms and Molecules*, Academic Press, New York, 1962, Chap. 6. (c) F. A. Cotton, *J. Chem. Educ.*, **41**, 466 (1964).

90. R. G. Pearson, *J. Chem. Phys.*, **30**, 1537 (1959); A. Sabatini and L. Sacconi, *J. Am. Chem. Soc.*, **86**, 17 (1964); however, see A. Buchler, W. Klemperer, and A. G. Emslie, *J. Chem. Phys.*, **36**, 2499 (1962).

91. J. H. Van Vleck, *J. Chem. Phys.*, **7**, 72 (1939).

92. W. H. Kleiner, *J. Chem. Phys.*, **20**, 1784 (1952).

93. R. E. Watson and A. J. Freeman, *Quart. Progr. Rept.* No. 52, Solid State and Molecular Theory Group, M.I.T., 1964; *Phys. Rev.*, **134A**, 1526 (1964).

94. R. S. Mulliken, *J. Phys. Chem.*, **56**, 295 (1952); see also reference 14.

95. C. E. Moore, "Atomic Energy Levels," *Natl. Bur. Std. (U.S.) Circ.* 467, 1949 and 1962.

96. A. D. Liehr and C. J. Ballhausen, *Phys. Rev.*, **106**, 1161 (1957).

97. B. Lakatos, J. Bohus, and G. Medgyesi, *Acta Chim. Acad. Sci. Hung.*, **20**, 1, 115 (1959), have a compilation of data.

98. (a) J. Owen and K. W. H. Stevens, *Nature*, **171**, 836 (1953). (b) J. H. E. Griffiths and J. Owen, *Proc. Roy. Soc. (London)* A226, 96 (1954). (c) J. S. Van Wieringen, *Disc. Faraday Soc.*, **19**, 118 (1955).

99. (a) R. G. Shulman and V. Jaccarino, *Phys. Rev.*, **108**, 1219 (1957). (b) R. G. Shulman and K. Knox, *ibid.*, **119**, 94 (1960).

100. C. H. Townes and B. P. Dailey, *J. Chem. Phys.*, **17**, 782 (1949).

101. See R. H. Herber, R. B. King, and G. K. Wertheim, for example, *Inorg. Chem.*, **3**, 101 (1964).

102. R. L. Barinskii, *J. Struct. Chem.*, **1**, 183 (1960).

103. J. Owen, *Proc. Roy. Soc. (London)*, **A227**, 183 (1955); T. M. Dunn, *J. Chem. Soc.*, **1959**, 623.

104. J. Owen, *Disc. Faraday Soc.*, **19**, 127 (1955).

105. Y. Tanabe and S. Sugano, *J. Phys. Chem. Japan*, **9**, 753, 766 (1954); C. Schäffer and C. K. Jørgensen, *J. Inorg. Nucl. Chem.*, Spec. Suppl., **8**, 143 (1958); C. K. Jørgensen, reference 32.

106. J. H. M. Thornley, B. W. Mangum, J. H. E. Griffiths, and J. Owen, *Proc. Phys. Soc. (London)*, **78**, 1263 (1961).

107. C. G. Windsor, J. H. M. Thornley, J. H. E. Griffiths, and J. Owen, *Proc. Phys. Soc. (London)*, **80**, 803 (1962).

108. D. Nakamura, K. Ito, and M. Kubo, *Inorg. Chem.*, **1**, 592 (1962).

109. K. Ito, D. Nakamura, Y. Kurita, K. Ito, and M. Kubo, *J. Am. Chem. Soc.*, **83**, 4526 (1961).

110. H. Hartmann, M. Fleisner, and H. Sillescu, *Naturwissenschaften*, **50**, 591 (1963); *Theor. Chim. Acta*, **2**, 63 (1964).

111. L. Pauling and J. Sherman, *J. Am. Chem. Soc.*, **59**, 1450 (1937).

112. Reference 100; W. Gordy, *Disc. Faraday Soc.*, **19**, 14 (1955).

113. G. Racah, *Phys. Rev.*, **62**, 438 (1942); **63**, 367 (1943).

114. C. K. Jørgensen, *Progress in Inorganic Chemistry*, Vol. 4 (F. A. Cotton, ed.), Interscience Publishers, New York, 1962, Chap. 2.

115. H. B. Gray and C. J. Ballhausen, *Acta Chem. Scand.*, **15**, 1327 (1961).

116. R. T. Sanderson, Science, **114**, 670 (1951); *Chemical Periodicity*, Reinhold Publishing Corp. New York, 1960, Chap. 3.

117. L. Pauling, *J. Chem. Soc.*, **1948**, 1461 .

118. Reference 89b, Chap. 7; R. J. P. Williams, *J. Phys. Chem.*, **58**, 121 (1954).

119. A. L. Allred and E. G. Rochow, *J. Inorg. Nucl. Chem.*, **5**, 264, 279 (1958); A. L. Allred, *ibid.*, **17**, 215 (1961); G. Klopman, *J. Am. Chem. Soc.*, **86**, 1463 (1964).

120. R. G. Pearson, *J. Am. Chem. Soc.*, **85**, 3533 (1963); *Science*, **151**, 172 (1965).

121. See A. A. Grinberg, *An Introduction to the Chemistry of Complex Compounds*, translated by J. R. Leach, Pergamon Press, London, 1962, Chap. 7; G. Schwarzenbach, *Advances in Inorganic and Radiochemistry*, Vol. 3 (H. J. Emeleus and A. G. Sharpe, eds.), Academic Press, New York, 1961; reference 5.

122. R. S. Mulliken, *J. Phys. Chem.*, **56**, 801 (1952); *J. Am. Chem. Soc.*, **74**, 811 (1952).

123. C. A. Coulson, *Proc. Phil. Soc.*, **33**, 111 (1937).

124. J. Chatt, *Nature*, **165**, 859 (1950); **177**, 852 (1956); S. Ahrland, J. Chatt, and N. R. Davies, *Quart. Rev. (London)*, **12**, 265 (1958); J. Chatt, *J. Inorg. Nucl. Chem.*, **8**, 515 (1958); J. Chatt, L. A. Duncanson, and L. M. Venanzi, *J. Chem. Soc.*, **1955**, 4456.

125. K. S. Pitzer, *J. Chem. Phys.*, **23**, 1735 (1955); K. S. Pitzer and E. Catalano, *J. Am. Chem. Soc.*, **78**, 4844 (1956); see also R. S. Drago and D. A. Wenz, *ibid.*, **84**, 526 (1962).

126. G. L. Caldow and C. A. Coulson, *Trans. Faraday Soc.*, **58**, 633 (1962)

127. R. S. Mulliken, *J. Am. Chem. Soc.*, **77**, 884 (1955).

128. See reference 3, p. 121.

129. For a review see A. J. Parker, *Quart. Rev. (London)*, **14**, 163 (1962); see also R. G. Pearson and D. C. Vogelsong, *J. Am. Chem. Soc.*, **80**, 1088 (1958); D. J. Cram, *Chem. Eng. News*, **41**, 92 (1963).

130. A. J. Poë and M. S. Vaidya, *J. Chem. Soc.*, **1961**, 1023.

131. R. G. Pearson and R. J. Mawby, *International Review of Halogen Chemistry* (V. Gutmann, ed.), Academic Press, London, Vol. III, 1966.

132. C. K. Jørgensen, reference 89b, p. 88.

133. C. K. Jørgensen, *Inorg. Chem.*, **3**, 1201 (1964).

3

Substitution Reactions
of Octahedral Complexes

The Nature of Substitution Reactions

In any attempt to cover the reactions of coordination compounds in a systematic manner, classification into types of reaction is necessary. We have divided these reactions into three main categories: substitution reactions, electron transfer or oxidation-reduction reactions, and isomerization and racemization reactions. The last-named are usually only special cases of substitution reactions, but it is convenient to discuss them separately.

Substitution reactions include the replacement of one ligand by another in a complex, or one metal ion by another. Following the very convenient terminology developed by Hughes and Ingold in describing organic reactions, we can call these S_N and S_E reactions, respectively.[1] The terms refer to *nucleophilic substitution* and *electrophilic substitution*. A *nucleophilic reagent* is one which donates electrons to an atomic nucleus in a reaction. An *electrophilic reagent* is one which acquires electrons from a nucleophilic reagent. In coordination chemistry, the central atom is an electrophilic reagent and the ligands are nucleophilic reagents.

$$Y + M—X \rightarrow M—Y + X \qquad S_N \qquad (1)$$

$$M' + M—X \rightarrow M'—X + M \qquad S_E \qquad (2)$$

The strict definition makes all reducing agents also nucleophilic reagents and all oxidizing agents electrophilic. This usage, however, has not been fruitful, and the terms in practice are restricted to reagents which react by partial transfer and acceptance of a pair of electrons. With this restriction the terms become nearly synonomous with base and acid, respectively, in the broadest meaning of these latter terms: the definition given by G. N. Lewis.[2]

The newer terms have an added meaning in that they are used to describe kinetic processes and not equilibrium situations. Thus, a good nucleophilic reagent is one which reacts rapidly with electrophilic reagents.[3] It may or may not be a strong base. Certain reagents such as thiourea and iodide ion may be excellent nucleophilic reagents in that they react rapidly, even though the stability of the compounds formed by them may be less than for other, more basic, reagents.

From what has been said it is clear that substitution reactions involve the fundamental acid-base reaction

$$A + :B \rightleftharpoons A:B \tag{3}$$

The forward reaction of 3 is called *coordination*, and the reverse reaction *heterolytic* or *ionic dissociation*. The second method of breaking a chemical bond is called *homolytic* or *free radical dissociation:*

$$A:B \rightleftharpoons A \cdot + B \cdot \tag{4}$$

Such a process is characteristic of some oxidation-reduction reactions (atom or group transfer). The reverse of reaction 4 is called *colligation* or *free radical combination.*

Mechanistically a substitution reaction is more complicated than is shown in equation 3. At least two fundamentally different pathways can be conceived. These are the *displacement* and *dissociation mechanisms* called S_N2 (or S_E2) and S_N1 (or S_E1) by Hughes and Ingold. An S_N2 reaction is one involving a bimolecular rate-determining step in which one nucleophilic reagent displaces another

$$Y + M{-}X \rightarrow Y \ldots . . M \ldots . . X \rightarrow Y{-}M + X \tag{5}$$

An S_E2 reaction has one electrophilic reagent displacing another, the transition state being $M \ldots . . X \ldots . . M'$.* In these bimolecular processes the coordination number of the metal ion or of the ligand increases by one in the transition state. There is presumably a fairly definite stereochemical orientation of all of the groups concerned.

An S_N1 or S_E1 reaction goes by a two-step mechanism in which the first step is a slow unimolecular heterolytic dissociation

$$M{-}X \rightleftharpoons M + X \tag{6}$$

followed by a rapid coordination reaction of either M or X with a second reagent

$$M + Y \rightarrow M{-}Y \tag{7}$$

$$X + M' \rightarrow M'{-}X \tag{8}$$

* A reaction may be simultaneously S_N2 and S_E2 in that X is both pushed away and pulled away from M. If the influence of the solvent on stabilizing X as it is liberated is considered, all reactions are S_E2. We shall not adhere to this point of view, however, and we consider only the cases where M′ is another potential central atom of a coordination compound.

In this sequence the coordination numbers of both the ligand and the metal ion decrease by one in the rate-determining step. Furthermore there exists as an intermediate the metal ion of reduced coordination number.

Still another pathway may be visualized for substitution reactions. This is the four-center mechanism[4] in which two acid-base complexes simultaneously exchange groups:

$$M—X + M'—Y \rightarrow M \overset{X}{\underset{Y}{\diamond}} M' \rightarrow M—Y + M'—X \qquad (9)$$

This process has the virtue of not requiring the expulsion of the group X or Y into the solution as free ions or molecules. It would be expected for those cases in which X or Y is very unstable as a free particle, where the bond M—X or M'—Y is very covalent so that dissociation into ions is difficult, and where the solvent is non-polar (or absent) so that X and Y cannot be stabilized by solvation. The mechanism requires that M and X, and M' and Y, be able to expand their coordination number by one each. This may perhaps occur by the loss of weakly held solvent molecules.

Four-center mechanisms have been found or postulated for many reactions in organic chemistry, where M is carbon or another non-metallic central atom.[5] Organometallic compounds of Li, Be, Mg, B, Al, Hg, Zn, Cd, Tl, Si, and Sn are thought to substitute by a four-center mechanism.[6] It is likely that the halides of these and other metals in non-polar solvents also react in the same way. For example, the interchange reaction

$$R_2Hg + HgCl_2 \rightarrow 2RHgCl \qquad (10)$$

probably proceeds by the four-center mechanism,[7] e.g.,

$$R—Hg \overset{Cl}{\underset{R}{\diamond}} Hg—Cl$$

It is of interest that even an alkyl group, R, can expand its coordination number, presumably through the use of three-center molecular orbitals (one pair of electrons bonding over three atoms, Hg—R—Hg). Many of the four-center structures needed for the above mechanisms correspond, in fact, to quite stable bridged compounds. An example would be the dimer of trimethylaluminum, $Al_2(CH_3)_6$.[8] It has been suggested that bimolecular four-center mechanisms be called S_F2 reactions.[6b]

It is not correct to assume that a bimolecular reaction will show second-order kinetics and a unimolecular reaction first-order kinetics.[9] This may or may not be the case, depending on the relative concentrations, the experimental conditions, and the complexities of the overall mechanism. Hence the observed kinetics of a substitution reaction rarely give the mechanism unambiguously.[10] The problem of deciding from kinetics and other data what the probable mechanism is will be the subject of large sections of the pages to follow.

The detection in some manner of the intermediate of reduced coordination number is the best diagnosis of the S_N1 or S_E1 mechanism. The view may be taken that, from an operational standpoint, unless such an intermediate can be demonstrated, the reaction is automatically to be considered S_N2 or S_E2. However, this approach can be misleading because the intermediate may be of such a nature as to escape detection by even the most refined means. For example, by its very nature it may be extremely short-lived, not enduring beyond the first collision with a potential ligand.

In such a case it seems reasonable to establish other criteria for a displacement mechanism. In an S_N2 reaction, for example, the rate of substitution should be dependent on the nucleophilic character of the incoming ligand, Y, in equation 5. In an S_E2 reaction the rate should be dependent on the electrophilic character of the incoming metal ion, M'. If a dependence is found on the nature of the reagent, it must also follow that a dependence on the concentration of the reagent must exist. This may not be true for all ranges of concentration, however.

Another criterion of mechanism that has been widely used is that of stereochemistry. The S_N2 and S_N1 paths may give rise to quite different stereochemical results. However, it is not necessary that they do this, nor can the expected stereochemistry in each case be predicted beforehand without further assumptions. As a rough guide, it is common to believe that S_N2 reactions will be more stereospecific than S_N1 reactions. This follows by analogy with organic chemistry, and its validity for reactions of coordination compounds will be examined later.

Other mechanistic criteria include the effect on the rate of structural changes in M—X, including changes in M, X, and the other groups attached to M, and the effect on the rate of changes in the reaction medium. This last includes changes in solvent and added components in the solvent such as ionic species. It might also include catalytic materials present in small amount. Finally, reference will often be made to the use of isotopic labeling to determine specific pieces of information about the reaction mechanism.

No matter how much evidence can be supplied to support a particular reaction mechanism, this evidence can never be said to prove it. The reason for this is that mechanisms, particularly detailed stereochemical mechanisms, are essentially theories and as such are not capable of proof. Like other theories, mechanisms should be capable of expansion and revision to include new experimental facts. A choice between alternative mechanisms is usually made on the basis of the simplest one that accommodates all of the facts.

One of the great complicating factors in assigning mechanisms to substitution reactions is the existence of borderline or intermediate mechanisms between S_N1 and S_N2.[11] That is, an assignment made on the basis of pure S_N1 and pure S_N2 reaction is one that is possible only sometimes in practice. Frequently reactions occur by a mechanism which is

Table 3.1 Classification of nucleophilic substitution reactions

S_N1 (lim)	S_N1	S_N2	S_N2 (lim)
	Degree of Bond Breaking in Rate Step		
Large	large	appreciable	none
	Degree of Bond Making in Rate Step		
None	none to small	appreciable	large
	Evidence for Intermediate of Reduced C.N.		
Definite	indefinite	none	none
	Evidence for Intermediate of Expanded C.N.		
None	none	indefinite	definite

intermediate between the two extremes. This does not mean a reaction proceeding by a mixture of S_N1 and S_N2 steps, which might occur also, but one in which the extent of participation by the external reagent Y (or M′) is small. Thus Y, which may be the solvent, is in the transition state but at such a distance from M that its influence on the energetics of the system is small. In such a case it becomes experimentally impossible in most instances to tell the difference between an S_N2 reaction and an S_N1 reaction (Y completely absent).

A recent suggestion has been made to subdivide organic substitution reactions into three classes:[12] S_N1, in which the rate-determining step involves only bond breaking, as in the M—X bond; S_N2, in which the rate step involves about equal bond breaking in M—X and bond making in Y—M; S_N2 (lim) in which the rate step involves only bond making, as in Y—M. The last category is believed to be involved in the hydrolysis of systems such as some esters, amides, anhydrides, and acid halides. Such a classification of reaction types may prove useful in inorganic chemistry as well. A further subdivision of the unimolecular reactions into S_N1 (lim) and S_N1 may also be of value. The definition of an S_N1 (lim) mechanism to be used here will be one in which definite evidence for the existence of the intermediate of reduced coordination number can be found. An S_N1 mechanism will mean one for which such evidence cannot be presented but which otherwise satisfies the requirements of a dissociation mechanism and fails the requirements of a displacement mechanism. It is recognized that examples in which Y exists in the activated complex for the reaction, but interacts only weakly, will also be counted as S_N1 by this definition. These classifications are shown schematically in Table 3.1.

Theoretical Approach to Substitution Mechanisms

According to the transition state theory of reaction rates,[13] we can make a good estimate of the speed with which a chemical reaction occurs by knowing something about the properties of the activated complex. The *activated complex* consists of the aggregate of several reactant molecules in the configuration of highest potential energy, that is, in the act of passing over the activation energy barrier for the reaction. The region at the top of such an energy barrier is called a *transition state*, and the activated complex is in the transition state. The less the energy required to form the activated complex, the faster the reaction will proceed as a rule, though special non-energy factors can sometimes slow down a reaction. The entropy of activation, $\Delta S^{\ddagger}$, which is the difference in entropy between the activated complex and the reactants, is such a factor.

The entropy of activation is defined by the equation

$$k = \frac{RTe}{Nh} e^{-E_a/RT} e^{\Delta S^{\ddagger}/R} \tag{11}$$

from the transition state theory of reaction rates. E_a is the Arrhenius activation energy, while $\Delta H^{\ddagger}$, the enthalpy of activation in solution, is given by $\Delta H^{\ddagger} = E_a - RT$. The entropy of activation is interpreted as being the difference in entropy between the transition state and the ground state of the reactants. It is determined largely by the loss of translational and rotational freedom as several particles come together in the activated complex. Important changes in vibrational freedom may also occur if the activated complex is more or less tightly organized than the reactants.

In solution where charged particles are involved, solvation effects often dominate the entropy of activation.[14] If ions are formed from neutral molecules, for example, solvent molecules are strongly oriented or "frozen" around the ions and their entropy is lost. Hence, $\Delta S^{\ddagger}$ becomes more negative, the effect being greater the larger the charge. If ions come together in the transition state with a neutralization of charge, then solvation molecules are released and the entropy of activation becomes more positive. From both theory and experiment, these solvation effects on the entropy are larger for non-polar solvents than for water.

The activation energy is usually the dominant factor determining the rates. The implication is that, if we can estimate the total potential energy of the activated complex for several possible mechanisms, a choice may be made between them as to which is most probable. Such calculations can be made in a few cases (for symmetrical systems) by using the electrostatic method developed in Chapter 2. Consider an exchange reaction of the ligand in a symmetrical complex such as $Co(NH_3)_6^{3+}$. The transition state for an S_N2 mechanism may resemble the pentagonal bipyramid containing five ammonia molecules symmetrically placed in a plane and two other molecules above and below this plane. This is, of course, not the only possible structure for a seven-coordinated system. Another plausible arrangement would have the seventh group attached to one of the octahedral faces of a hypothetical C.N. six progenitor. If the seventh group is on one of the back faces of the octahedron, it is not easy to visualize how such an arrangement can lead to a net reaction. However, if it adds to a front face, a reasonable transition state would be formed in which the group being displaced also moves down to the front face diagonal to the entering group. This movement is required because the principle of microscopic reversibility (see p. 484) implies that the incoming group and the leaving group occupy identical positions at some point during the reaction process (*not* necessarily in the activated complex).

At any rate the energy calculated for the pentagonal bipyramid gives some idea of the stability of a possible intermediate for the S_N2 path. In a similar way the energy of a five-coordinated species such as $Co(NH_3)_5^{3+}$ gives an idea of the possibility of an S_N1 mechanism since its energy of formation from $Co(NH_3)_6^{3+}$ is the minimum activation energy for the S_N1 (lim) process in which the intermediate of C.N. five becomes completely free.

For a seven-coordinated complex, an unsymmetrical structure has been assumed. There are two axial ligands with the same value of r as for the octahedral case. The other five ligands lie in a plane and form a regular pentagon. In order to do this it is necessary to increase the metal ligand distance to r' since otherwise there is not room for five groups. The r' chosen is such that the five groups just touch, assuming a radius of 1.40 A for ammonia and 1.36 A for fluoride ion. It is about 0.3 A larger than r. The Born hydration energy is calculated by using a value for the radius of the complex which is an average, $(r + 2r')/3$. Probably there are fairly large van der Waals repulsions developed between the ligands, but these have not been included in the calculation. They are balanced in part by van der Waals-London attractions but may still be considered to make the complex of C.N. seven less stable than otherwise indicated.

In the case of the square pyramid structure for C.N. five, the hydration energy can be calculated in two ways. First, an average radius can be calculated, e.g., $(5r + r_i)/6$, where r_i is the crystallographic radius of the central ion. Second, it can be assumed that the radius for the square pyramid is the same as for the octahedron. This is equivalent to excluding solvent from the region vacated by the missing ligand. The difference in the two Born hydration energies calculated with these radii is found to be almost the same as if a water molecule had been added to the coordination sphere to form $Co(NH_3)_5H_2O^{3+}$, for example, from $Co(NH_3)_5^{3+}$.

This is, of course, very reasonable and suggests that the hydration energies of linear and square planar complexes could be found by adding water molecules to complete the octahedral configuration and calculating the Born heat of hydration in the usual way. The potential energy of the original system plus the added water molecules would then be calculated by the electrostatic theory. The distances of the added water molecules from the central ion would be larger than usual, presumably.

Table 3.2 shows the results of a number of calculations of the bonding energies of complexes presented in terms of the energy required to form certain trial configurations from the stable ones. The energies in solution are always positive, which means that the accepted configurations of these complex ions can be justified in terms of the electrostatic theory.

In the gas phase trigonal AlF_5^{2-} is more stable than octahedral AlF_6^{3-}. In solution this is changed by the greater Born heat of hydration of the triple negative ion.[15] The near stability of AlF_7^{4-} in solution is due to a very large Born heat of hydration (752 kcal) and may be greatly in error since this calculation value is not very reliable. For the cobalt ammines the data of Table 3.2 predict, then, activation energies in solution of 103 kcal for the S_N2 mechanism, 121 kcal for the S_N1 mechanism with a trigonal bipyramid structure, and 6–94 kcal for the S_N1 mechanism with a square pyramid structure. The last figure represents limits for the extreme cases where the vacated position in the coordination sphere is occupied by solvent and where it is left completely vacant (solvent excluded).

The exchange reaction of $Co(NH_3)_6^{3+}$ with aqueous NH_3 has been measured, using ^{15}N as a tracer.[16] The rate is very slow, the half-life at 25° being about 10^5 days.

$$Co(NH_3)_6^{3+} + {}^*NH_3 \rightarrow Co({}^*NH_3)_6^{3+} + NH_3 \qquad (12)$$

The activation energy was not found, but for the similar reaction,

$$Co(NH_3)_5H_2O^{3+} + H_2{}^*O \rightarrow Co(NH_3)_5H_2{}^*O^{3+} + H_2O \qquad (13)$$

Table 3.2 Theoretical energies required to change configurations and co-ordination numbers of some complexes

	ΔH, kcal
$Zn(NH_3)_4^{2+}$ (g) $+ 2NH_3$ (g) $\rightarrow Zn(NH_3)_6^{2+}$ (g)	36^a
$Zn(NH_3)_4^{2+}$ (aq) $+ 2NH_3$ (aq) $\rightarrow Zn(NH_3)_6^{2+}$ (aq)	52^a
$Fe(H_2O)_6^{2+}$ (g) $\rightarrow Fe(H_2O)_4^{2+}$ (g) $+ 2H_2O$ (g)	73^a
$Fe(H_2O)_6^{2+}$ (aq) $\rightarrow Fe(H_2O)_4^{2+}$ (aq) $+ 2H_2O$ (aq)	$53^{a,b}$
$Fe(H_2O)_6^{2+}$ (g) $\rightarrow Fe(H_2O)_5^{2+}$ (g) $+ H_2O$ (g)	$35^{b,c}$
$Fe(H_2O)_6^{2+}$ (aq) $\rightarrow Fe(H_2O_5)^{2+}$ (aq) $+ H_2O$ (aq)	$25^{b,c}$
AlF_6^{3-} (g) $+ F^-$ (g) $\rightarrow AlF_7^{4-}$ (g)	182^d
AlF_6^{3-} (aq) $+ F^-$ (aq) $\rightarrow AlF_7^{4-}$ (aq)	10^d
AlF_6^{3-} (g) $\rightarrow AlF_5^{2-}$ (g) $+ F^-$ (g)	-59^c
AlF_6^{3-} (aq) $\rightarrow AlF_5^{2-}$ (aq) $+ F^-$ (aq)	39^c
$Co(NH_3)_6^{3+}$ (g) $+ NH_3$ (g) $\rightarrow Co(NH_3)_7^{3+}$ (g)	$77^{d,e}$
$Co(NH_3)_6^{3+}$ (aq) $+ NH_3$ (aq) $\rightarrow Co(NH_3)_7^{3+}$ (aq)	$103^{d,e}$
$Co(NH_3)_6^{3+}$ (g) $\rightarrow Co(NH_3)_5^{3+}$ (g) $+ NH_3$ (g)	$131^{c,f}$
$Co(NH_3)_6^{3+}$ (aq) $\rightarrow Co(NH_3)_5^{3+}$ (aq) $+ NH_3$ (aq)	$121^{c,f}$
$Co(NH_3)_6^{3+}$ (g) $\rightarrow Co(NH_3)_5^{3+}$ (g) $+ NH_3$ (g)	105^g
$Co(NH_3)_6^{3+}$ (aq) $\rightarrow Co(NH_3)_5^{3+}$ (aq) $+ NH_3$ (aq)	$6-94^{g,h}$

[a] Tetrahedral for C.N. four.
[b] Loss of 3 kcal crystal field energy included.
[c] Trigonal bipyramid for C.N. five.
[d] Pentagonal bipyramid for C.N. seven.
[e] Loss of 47 kcal crystal field energy included.
[f] Loss of 64 kcal crystal field energy included.
[g] Square pyramid for C.N. five; loss of 22 kcal crystal field energy included.
[h] Higher value goes with assumption in note [g]. Lower value is calculated for $Co(NH_3)_5H_2O^{3+}$.

the activation energy is 27 kcal and the half-life at 25° is about 33 hr.[17] The difference in rates corresponds to a difference of 7 kcal in energy, which is in good agreement with the difference in bond energy between water and ammonia bound to $Co(NH_3)_5^{3+}$ from heats of formation. A reasonable estimate for the activation energy of reaction 12 is about 34 kcal. Only one of the theoretical values quoted above lies near this figure.

Thus it appears that the most favorable path is one involving an S_N1 mechanism with a square pyramid structure for the intermediate. It must, however, be a solvated square pyramid to reduce the activation energy to a reasonable figure, and the intermediate in this case becomes difficult to distinguish from $Co(NH_3)_5H_2O^{3+}$. The conclusion is that ligand exchange of $Co(NH_3)_6^{3+}$ would proceed by loss of an NH_3 molecule in a dissociation step, followed by instantaneous or simultaneous pickup of a water molecule. The water molecule in turn would be lost in a dissociation process to be replaced by another water, and this would also be lost, until finally an NH_3 molecule from the solution would become coordinated. At this stage exchange would have occurred.

In such a case the energy difference between $Co(NH_3)_6^{3+}$ and $Co(NH_3)_5H_2O^{3+}$ (7 kcal) is not the activation energy for exchange since the latter compound is not an activated complex but an intermediate of some stability. An activated complex is a species that exists at a maximum in a potential energy diagram. An intermediate is a species that exists at a minimum in the potential energy diagram. Figure 3.1 shows the distinction

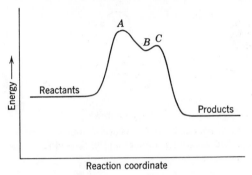

Fig. 3.1   Potential energy diagram for a chemical reaction showing location of activated complexes (at A and C) and of transient intermediate (at B).

between the two. The shallowness of the minimum determines the reactivity of the intermediate. To calculate the activation energy it is necessary to consider the stage of transition between $Co(NH_3)_6^{3+}$ and $Co(NH_3)_5H_2O^{3+}$ which is the hardest to achieve and hence highest on the energy curve.

The easiest way in which this could happen would be by an ammonia molecule beginning to dissociate by a lengthening of its coordinate bond distance, and then by a water molecule entering alongside it when the bond is sufficiently extended. For minimum repulsion from the other ligands, these two groups would take up a position twisted away from the original plane of four ligands. In this case the arrangement of groups becomes identical, except for distances, with a very good structure for an S_N2 mechanism. Figure 3.2 shows the activated complex for such a procedure as well as for the S_N2 mechanism. Five groups are close to the central atom, and two are further away. The coordination number might be called either five or seven, depending on whether the five closely attached groups or the seven groups all told are being emphasized. For the same reason the path could be said to correspond to either an S_N1 mechanism (C.N. five) or an S_N2 mechanism (C.N. seven). The reaction mechanism is borderline, and a decision as to how best describe it depends upon the extent and manner in which the water molecule coming in lowers the energy of the system. If the energetic interaction is great and if the nature of the interaction is specific and markedly dependent on the properties of the water molecule, an S_N2 label is best. If the energy interaction is small or of such a nature as to be provided by any molecule to a reasonably similar degree, an S_N1 label is most fitting.

There is undoubtedly an energy effect of substantial magnitude since the activation energy must be reduced from the 94 kcal predicted for no

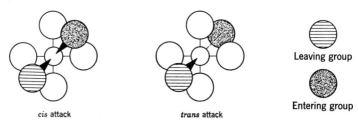

cis attack   *trans* attack   Leaving group   Entering group

Fig. 3.2 Arrangement of ligands in an octahedral complex in the transition state for approach at front octahedral face (*cis* attack) and back octahedral face (*trans* attack). One of the inert ligands is not shown.

interaction to the 34 or so kcal expected for this reaction. Because of the unsymmetrical nature of this complex, it is not too easy to calculate the potential energy in the usual way with sufficient accuracy. However, the fact that 34 kcal lies between the limits of no interaction and complete interaction of the solvent makes the energy requirement seem a reasonable one. The question still remains as to how specific the interaction is and whether it is best classified as a solvation effect or as a chemical reaction of the solvent molecule.

The detailed picture of the reaction mechanism given above has also been presented in a number of slightly different variations by various workers.[18] For example, sometimes the possibility of hydrogen bonding of a solvent molecule, either to the ammine protons of the complex or to the leaving group, or to both, has been considered as important. Figure 3.3 shows the extreme case of a water molecule hydrogen-bonded both to a leaving chloride ion and to an inert ammine group. The virtue of such hydrogen bonding is that it puts the water molecule where it will be needed. The name S_N2FS, for frontside, has been suggested for the mechanism of Fig. 3.3 by Adamson.[18b] Jones, Harris, and Wallace[18d] have proposed the very useful phrase "solvent-assisted dissociation" for the general process described above. The assistance refers to nucleophilic assistance, since solvation of the leaving group is always assumed. The name does not specify stereochemistry or the presence or absence of hydrogen bonding. Thus, a solvent-assisted dissociation† may be either a *cis* attack or a *trans* attack.

Now the reactions of Co(III) complexes have been extensively studied, and the example discussed was deliberately picked to throw light on the reactions of Co(III). This cannot be regarded as a very typical case, however, because the energy of various arrangements of ligands about Co(III) is very dependent on crystal field stabilization. Included in the activation

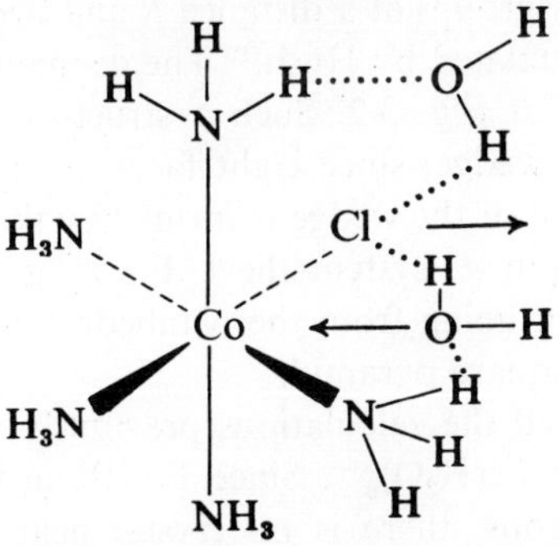

Fig. 3.3 An S_N2FS mechanism with hydrogen bonding (dotted lines) of water molecules in the second coordination sphere.

energies for the S_N2 pentagonal bipyramid path and the S_N1 trigonal bipyramid and square pyramid paths were substantial changes in C.F.S.E. It will be recalled that the stabilization amounted to $24Dq$ for a regular octahedron in a d^6 system, and was a result of the six electrons being in the t_{2g} orbitals, which are out of the way of the six ligands.

Obviously, if a seventh group is added along any edge or face of the original octahedron, it must be forced in directly towards one of those filled and previously stable d orbitals. In the same way, if a group is lost and the three remaining ligands in a plane are rearranged to a trigonal form, they can do so only by moving over and interfering seriously with the filled d orbital. The least disturbance is caused by simply removing one group and leaving five ligands in a square pyramid. Even this is accompanied by some loss of C.F.S.E. since, after all, it is the ligands which cause the original energy separation, leading to stabilization. All of these effects on the energies of the possible intermediates can be approximately calculated by using the energy levels for various structures given on p. 69. Thus, a pentagonal bipyramid with six d electrons has a C.F.S.E. of

† It has been suggested, somewhat humorously, that this be abbreviated to the SAD mechanism.

$15.5Dq$. The loss compared to the octahedral case is $8.5Dq$ or about 47 kcal. A regular trigonal bipyramid has only $12.5Dq$ stabilization energy, the loss on formation being about 64 kcal.

A square pyramid with five equal ligands has a C.F.S.E. of $20Dq$, or only 22 kcal less than the octahedral. It is this consideration which made the most plausible intermediate for the exchange reaction one with five groups left undisturbed and the entering and leaving groups both relatively far away. The dependence of the crystal field effect on distance is large enough so that this arrangement would essentially have the C.F.S.E. of a square pyramid. The crystal field energy levels for a seven-coordinated intermediate with five groups at a distance R and two groups at a distance $1.25\ R$ have been calculated by Hush.[19] The geometry is the same as that shown for *cis* attack in Fig. 3.2. Such a structure may be conveniently called an octahedral wedge, since eight faces are present as in an octahedron. The sharp end of the wedge is formed by the leaving and entering groups. For a low-spin d^6 system the C.F.S.E. is $20.37Dq$, so that the loss in stabilization in going from the octahedral ground state is slightly less even than for a square pyramid.

Suppose we repeated the calculations previously made to apply to the exchange of water in $Fe(H_2O)_6^{3+}$. Since $Fe(III)$ in this complex has five spin-uncoupled electrons, there is no crystal field stabilization, or loss thereof, to consider. We would then calculate activation energies for a pentagonal bipyramid S_N2 path of about 50 kcal and the same for a trigonal bipyramid S_N1 mechanism. A square pyramid S_N1 path would have an activation energy between 0 and 70 kcal. In fact if 22 kcal for the loss in C.F.S.E. is subtracted from the 27 kcal observed for $Co(NH_3)_5H_2O^{3+}$ we see that water exchange in $Fe(H_2O)_6^{3+}$ by the same mechanism is already down to such a low activation energy that it would be very rapid. This is in agreement with the facts (see p. 152). One of the obvious variables that we have to consider in discussing the rates of substitution reactions of complexes, then, is the loss of C.F.S.E. in systems with different numbers of d electrons and different coordination numbers.

Before taking up this topic in detail, let us use the simple coulombic picture to consider the effect of other variables on the rates of substitution reactions of coordination compounds. Imagine, for simplicity, a system with completely empty or completely filled d shells so that crystal field effects are not a factor. The variables of importance are the size and charge of the central atom and the sizes and charges of the entering and leaving groups.

Without going into numerical calculations it is easy to see that the lower the charge and the greater the size of either the central atom or the leaving group, the more rapid its reactions will be by a dissociation type of mechanism.‡ Thus, $Fe(H_2O)_6{}^{2+}$ will be expected to exchange water more rapidly than $Fe(H_2O)_6{}^{3+}$, and $Co(NH_3)_5Br^{2+}$ to react more rapidly than $Co(NH_3)_5Cl^{2+}$. Furthermore, in an S_N2 process, the smaller the size and the greater the charge of the entering group, the faster the reaction should be. Thus, the expected nucleophilic efficiency of anions in S_N2 reactions is $F^- > Cl^- > Br^- > I^-$.

The effect of increased charge on the central atom is not clearly defined for an S_N2 process. Whereas bond breaking is made more difficult, bond

Table 3.3 Effect of sizes and charges on rates of S_N1 and S_N2 reactions

	S_N1 (lim) and S_N1 Rate	S_N2 Rate	S_N2 (lim) Rate
Increased positive charge of central atom	decrease	opposing effects	increase
Increased size of central atom	increase	increase	increase
Increased negative charge of entering group	no effect	increase	increase
Increased size of entering group	no effect	decrease	decrease
Increased negative charge of leaving group	decrease	decrease	decrease
Increased size of leaving group	increase	opposing effects	decrease
Increased negative charge of other ligands	increase	opposing effects	decrease
Increased size of other ligands	increase	decrease	decrease

making is made easier. The net effect will depend on the relative contributions of the two energy effects. However, a very clear prediction can be made as to the probability of an S_N2 mechanism compared to an S_N1 mechanism. As the positive charge and size of the central atom increase, the chance of an S_N2 mechanism will increase. As the positive charge of the central atom increases, size being constant, the chance of an S_N1 mechanism diminishes.

As far as the effect of the nature of the leaving group is concerned, lower charge and greater size will lead to rapid reactions, but by either mechanism as a first approximation. In the limit of a very small, highly charged ligand, it may be argued that an S_N1 mechanism becomes impossible and, other factors not being prohibitive, an S_N2 mechanism will be required to release such a group. Similarly for very large groups to be displaced, an

‡ The assumption is made that interaction of the ligand with the central atom is greater than interaction of the ligand with the solvent.

S_N2 mechanism may become difficult for steric reasons and an S_N1 mechanism favored. This latter effect will be easier to demonstrate, however, if several of the ligands on the central atom, including those which are not labile, become very large. These other ligands can also affect the course of the reaction by their electric charge. Thus a greater negative charge on the non-reacting ligands will favor an S_N1 mechanism by repelling the reactive ligand. An S_N2 process will be discouraged because of repulsion of the incoming ligand. All of these predictions, based on electrostatic considerations and the sizes of the groups involved, are summarized in Table 3.3.

This approach is oversimplified and cannot be expected to be complete. For example, no account of π bonding has been taken. It may be anticipated that in certain cases unsaturated ligands will be effective as displacing reagents because of the chance of increased bonding in the transition state. Such double-bonded ligands will also be difficult to displace when already present in the coordination sphere. Also for complexes where covalent bonding is an especially important factor, an electrostatic picture will not be very reliable.

Nucleophilic Reactivity

A more detailed analysis of the factors determining the effectiveness of the nucleophilic reagent in S_N2 mechanisms is needed. Nucleophilic reactivity is often discussed in terms of the basicity of the nucleophile (towards the proton on water) and some other property which is a measure of the ease of distorting or removing the electrons in the nucleophile.[20] This latter property might be the polarizability, calculated from the molar refraction, the redox potential, or the electronegativity.

For example, Edwards[21] has shown that a large amount of kinetic and thermodynamic data for organic and inorganic systems can be correlated by equations such as

$$\log (k/k_0) = \alpha P + \beta H \tag{14}$$

$$\log (k/k_0) = \alpha E_n + \beta H \tag{15}$$

In these equations P is a polarizability factor, H is a proton basicity factor defined by $H = 1.74 + pK_a$, and E_n is a redox factor defined by $E_n = E^0 + 2.60$, where E^0 is the standard oxidation potential for the process

$$2Y^- \rightleftharpoons Y_2 + 2e \tag{16}$$

Also, k_0 refers to water, k to the various nucleophiles, and α and β are constants to be determined for each series of related reactions. For water

H and E_n are zero by their definitions. Table 3.4 gives pK_a values and E_n values for a number of common nucleophilic reagents. Some of the E_n values are estimated rather crudely.

Each reference acid has a different α and β value. For nucleophilic displacements of alkyl halides, α is large and β is small. For the hydrolysis of activated esters (p-nitrophenylacetate), α is small and β is large. For formation constants of complexes, it is found that class (a) metals have large β and class (b) metals have large α. An examination of a considerable number of rate data [20] discloses that hard acids are sensitive to the H value of the attacking base (β is large) and soft acids are sensitive to the E_n or P value (α is large).[22]

Since large E_n or P values belong to soft bases, and large H values usually, but not always, to hard bases, these results are perfectly reasonable. They are examples of the general principle of linear free energy relationships.[23] This principle states that there are linear relationships between the logs of the rate constants or equilibrium constants of similar series of related reactions. When β is large, the relationship expressed in 14 or 15 exists between the rate constants of equation 5 for a series of different Y molecules and the equilibrium constants for the same series of Y molecules.

$$Y + H^+ \rightleftharpoons YH^+ \tag{17}$$

The implication is really that the equilibrium constants for equation 5 will vary in the same way as those for equation 17, and that a larger equilibrium constant for 5 means a higher rate constant. It should be noted that there is no requirement that this last statement be true from any law of physical chemistry.

Since the proton is a typical hard acid, it is expected that other hard acids will be sensitive to proton basicity. Soft acids clearly need another scale of basicity, for which the E_n and P values of equations 14 and 15 are approximations. This suggests that a useful standard scale for soft acids would be a table of stability constants, under standard conditions, for a typical soft acid and a variety of bases. Table 3.4 has such a set of pK values in water for the CH_3Hg^+ ion, which acts as a unidentate acid like the proton

$$CH_3Hg^+ + Y \rightleftharpoons CH_3HgY^+ \tag{18}$$

One objection to both the $pK_{CH_3Hg}^+$ and pK_a scales is that they refer to water. Many studies, particularly of soft acids, are carried out in non-aqueous, even non-polar, solvents. Solvation effects can greatly influence the basicity of ligands or nucleophiles, particularly anionic ones (see Chapter 2).

The possible application of the data of Table 3.4 to predicting or correlating the rates and mechanism of reaction of coordination compounds will be taken up in this chapter and the following ones. One further prediction can be made.[24] An examination of the theories of acid-base interaction given in Chapter 2 shows that all acids will display more class (b) character when they form part of an activated complex in an S_N2 reaction than they do in their ground states. This is the result of the increased coordination number, which piles more negative charge on the

Table 3.4   Electron donor constants

Nucleophile	pK_a [a]	E_n [b]	$pK_{CH_3Hg^+}$ [c]
S^{2-}	12.9	3.08	21.3
CN^-	9.1	2.79	14.0
SO_3^{2-}	9.1	2.57	8.16
$S_2O_3^{2-}$	1.9	2.52	10.95
$SC(NH_2)_2$	0.4	2.18	(7)
SH^-	7.8	2.10	(16)
I^-	(-10)	2.06	8.66
SCN^-	(-0.7)	1.83	6.1
$C_6H_5NH_2$	4.5	1.78	(2.5)
NO_2^-	3.4	1.73	(2.5)
OH^-	15.7	1.65	9.42
N_3^-	4.7	1.58	6.0^d
Br^-	(-7)	1.51	6.67
$C_6H_5O^-$	10.0	1.46	6.5
HPO_4^{2-}	6.8	1.46	5.10
NH_3	9.5	1.36	7.65
Cl^-	(-4)	1.24	5.30
C_5H_5N	5.3	1.20	4.8
$CH_3CO_2^-$	4.7	0.95	3.9
SO_4^-	2.0	0.59	(1.5)
F^-	3.2	-0.27	1.55
H_2O	-1.7	0.00	-1.74
$HOC_2H_4S^-$	9.5	...	16.19
RS^-(hist)	9.0	...	15.9
RS^-(cyst)	8.6	...	15.7
p-$(C_6H_5)_2PC_6H_4SO_3^-$	(0)	...	9.2
en	10.0	...	8.3
imidazole	7.1	...	7.3
$HEDTA^{3-}$	6.2	...	6.2
HPO_3^{2-}	6.6	...	4.78
$Co(CN)_6^{3-}$	(0)	...	4.34
p-$NH_2C_6H_4SO_3^-$	3.1	...	2.64
$(C_2H_5)_3P$	8.8	...	15^e

[a] For conjugate acid of base, in H_2O at 25°C; figures in parentheses are estimates.
[b] Electrode Potential Scale, reference 21a.
[c] Dissociation constant for $CH_3HgL^+ \rightarrow CH_3Hg^+ + L$.
Data at 20–25°C from M. Schellenberg and G. Schwarzenbach, *Proceedings of the Seventh International Conference on Coordination Chemistry*, Stockholm, 1962, p. 158; R. B. Simpson, *J. Am. Chem. Soc.*, **83**, 4711 (1961). Figures in parentheses are estimates based on formation constants of Ag(I).
[d] T. R. Musgrave and R. N. Keller, *Inorg. Chem.*, **4**, 1793 (1965).
[e] G. Schwarzenbach and M. Schellenberg, *Helv. Chim. Acta*, **48**, 28 (1965).

electrophilic central atom and which also puts a premium on possible electron correlation effects. Thus, all acids will be more sensitive to polarizability as far as their rates are concerned then they are as far as equilibria are concerned. This prediction has been amply documented for organic systems.

The data of Table 3.4 may also be used to predict the effect of changing the nature of the leaving group on the rate of either an S_N2 or an S_N1 reaction. If, at equilibrium, a certain ligand is bound to a high degree, the presumption is that the coordinate bond is strong and not easily broken. Hence, the rate of substitution will be slow. This is simply another application of an expected linear free energy relationship. If a nucleophilic reagent is more (or less) reactive than expected on the basis of its equilibrium constant in the same reaction, then it necessarily follows that it will be a better (or poorer) leaving group than predicted from the equilibrium data.

The Effect of the Electronic Structure of the Central Atom

As already pointed out, it is necessary to consider not only the size and charge of the central atom but also its d electron structure in predicting the rates of substitution reactions. Before doing this in terms of the crystal field theory, it is of interest to consider the application of the valence bond theory to the same problem. Much of what follows is taken from a review by Taube.[25]

The term *labile* is applied to very reactive complexes, whereas less reactive complexes are called *inert*.§ There is, of course, no sharp division between these two classes, but rather there exists a continuous gradation. Taube has defined labile to mean systems where reactions are complete within the time of mixing (1 min, room temperature, about 0.1 M solutions). The term inert is used for reactions that are either too slow to measure or slow enough to follow at ordinary conditions by conventional techniques.

The most direct and least ambiguous test of lability is to measure the rate of exchange for a reaction of the type

$$MA_6 + {}^*A = MA_5{}^*A + A \qquad (19)$$

The equilibrium state corresponds to an almost statistical distribution of the A groups. Since the equilibrium is favorable for exchange, a labile complex will undergo immediate exchange upon mixing with tagged $^*A$. The availability of radioactive isotopes has greatly enhanced studies of this type. Data are also available on the rate of exchange of the central ion

§ The word *robust* is often used in place of *inert* by European chemists. This word seems more appropriate for thermodynamic stability.

Table 3.5 Exchange rate and stability of some cyano complexes

Complex	Dissociation Constant	Exchange Rate[a]
$Ni(CN)_4^{2-}$	10^{-30}	very fast
$Mn(CN)_6^{3-}$	10^{-27}	measurable
$Fe(CN)_6^{4-}$	10^{-37}	very slow
$Hg(CN)_4^{2-}$	10^{-42}	very fast
$Fe(CN)_6^{3-}$	10^{-44}	very slow

[a] With labeled cyanide ion. Data from reference 26.

between complexes, as in a reaction of the type

$$MA_6 + {}^*M(H_2O)_6 = {}^*MA_6 + M(H_2O)_6 \tag{20}$$

A rapid rate of exchange of the central ions is good evidence that the two complexes are labile, but a slow exchange does not necessarily mean they are inert. Reactions where there is a net chemical change as in 1 are very common but not entirely satisfactory as an estimate of lability. Failure to react cannot be taken as proof of an inert complex; it may merely be the result of an unfavorable equilibrium. Furthermore some apparently simple substitution reactions may not be "simple," and the rate-determining step may not be a measure of the lability of the metal-ligand bond. However, it does follow that the rate of substitution will be at least as rapid as the overall rate, and thus a very fast reaction is a reliable indication of a labile complex.

Additional information on the reactivity of complexes is available from studies on the isomerization of these substances. The very existence of geometric isomers and the fact that these persist in solution at non-equilibrium concentrations are good indications that the complexes involved are inert. It would appear that a similar observation for optical isomers should also be indicative of an inert complex. However, a substitution need not lead to isomerization so that the isolation of geometric isomers is not proof that the complex is inert. Furthermore, because of the possibility of intramolecular rearrangement, failure to isolate geometric isomers or to separate optical isomers cannot be accepted as absolute proof that the metal complex in question is labile.

The term inert must not be confused with the term stable. One has kinetic meaning, and the other thermodynamic. It is true that often thermodynamically stable substances are slow to react, whereas unstable compounds react rapidly. There is no absolute requirement that this be so, however. Table 3.5 illustrates the lack of correlation, in the case of some cyano complexes, between lability and stability. Although these complexes may be considered as quite stable, two are labile. By contrast $Co(NH_3)_6^{3+}$ in the presence of an acid solution is thermodynamically completely unstable [either to NH_4^+ and $Co(H_2O)_6^{3+}$, or to NH_4^+, $Co(H_2O)_6^{2+}$, and N_2] but will persist unchanged for several weeks in such a medium.

Taube[25] has suggested that many of the available data pertaining to the lability of coordination compounds can be explained on the basis of their electronic configuration as given by the valence bond theory. In general the labile complexes are either of the *outer orbital* type or of the *inner orbital* type with at least one vacant lower d orbital. Some metal ions that form labile and inert complexes and their representative electronic configurations are shown in Table 3.6. These are inner orbital or d^2sp^3 complexes.

Table 3.6   Inner orbital six-coordinate complexes

Electronic Configuration			Central Metal Ions
			Labile Complexes
d	*s*	*p*	
○ ○ ○ ◔ ⊙	⊙	⊙ ⊙ ⊙^{a}	Sc(III), Y(III), rare earths(III), Ti(IV), Zr(IV), Hf(IV), Ce(IV), Th(IV), Nb(V), Ta(V), Mo(VI), W(VI)
○ ○ ○ ⊙ ⊙	⊙	⊙ ⊙ ⊙^{a}	Ti(III), V(IV), Mo(V), W(V), Re(VI)
○ ○ ○ ⊙ ⊙	⊙	⊙ ⊙ ⊙^{a}	Ti(II), V(III), Nb(III), Ta(III), Mo(IV), W(IV), Re(V), Ru(VI)
			Inert Complexes
○ ○ ○ ⊙ ⊙	⊙	⊙ ⊙ ⊙^{a}	V(II), Cr(III), Mo(III), W(III), Mn(IV), Re(IV)
◔ ○ ○ ⊙ ⊙	⊙	⊙ ⊙ ⊙	$Cr(CN)_6^{4-}$, $Cr(bipy)_3^{2+}$, $Mn(CN)_6^{3-}$, Re(III), Ru(IV), Os(V)
⊙ ⊙ ○ ⊙ ⊙	⊙	⊙ ⊙ ⊙	$Cr(bipy)_3^{1+}$, $Mn(CN)_6^{4-}$, Re(II), $Fe(CN)_6^{3-}$, $Fe(phen)_3^{3+}$, $Fe(bipy)_3^{3+}$, Ru(III), Os(III), Ir(IV)
⊙ ⊙ ⊙ ⊙ ⊙	⊙	⊙ ⊙ ⊙	$Mn(CN)_6^{5-}$, $Fe(CN)_6^{4-}$, $Fe(phen)_3^{2+}$, $Fe(bipy)_3^{2+}$, Ru(II), Os(II), Co(III) (except CoF_6^{3-}), Rh(III), Ir(III), Ni(IV), Pd(IV), Pt(IV)

^{a} These electronic configurations are assigned on the assumption that if lower d orbitals are vacant they will be used in bond formation. Magnetic data here will not distinguish between d^2sp^3 and sp^3d^2.

It is indeed striking how the line of demarcation between labile and inert complexes falls precisely at the point where all the inner d orbitals become at least singly occupied. For example, the d^1 complexes of Mo(V) and W(V) are labile, whereas the d^3 complexes of Mo(III) and W(III) are inert. Since the first two have a higher positive charge on the central atom, it would be predicted on electrostatic grounds alone that they would react more slowly by a dissociation mechanism and not necessarily react more rapidly by a displacement mechanism. In the same way V(II) complexes appear inert (a d^3 system), whereas V(III) complexes appear labile. (Often the evidence on which lability or inertness is assigned in Table 3.6 is only qualitative.)

A reasonable assumption might be that all of these complexes are reacting by an S_N2 mechanism in which a seventh group must be added to the coordination sphere, and, in keeping with the valence bond theory, such a process is greatly aided if an empty lower d orbital is available to the incoming group. If such an orbital is not available, then the seventh group must add by using an outer d orbital of lower stability. This reaction is slower because a higher activation energy is required.

Outer orbital complexes have the electronic configuration sp^3d^2, where the order indicates that d orbitals of the same principal quantum number as the s and p orbitals are used. In general, outer orbital complexes are labile, e.g., Mn(II), Fe(II), Fe(III), Co(II), Zn(II), Cd(II), Hg(II), Al(III), Ga(III), In(III), and Tl(III). For a given isoelectronic series, the lability decreases with increasing charge on the central ion, e.g., $AlF_6^{-3} > SiF_6^{-2} > PF_6^- > SF_6$. Hence outer orbital complexes can become inert, as in SF_6, SiF_6^{2-}, PF_6^-, and $SbCl_6^-$.

Since the outer d orbitals are less stable than the inner d orbitals, it follows that bonds involving them are less stable. Hence it should be relatively easy to have a dissociation into a complex of C.N. five, since one of the unstable orbitals can now be left out of the hybridization. However, as the positive charge on the central atom increases, the bond strength increases so that eventually the compounds become inert. It may be noted at this time that the assumption, inherent in the valence bond theory, that coordinate bonds in the complexes classified as outer orbital are weaker than they would otherwise be is completely unjustified. There is experimental evidence, as discussed in Chapter 2, that the bond strengths are very much the same for inner orbital and outer orbital complexes of a given type. The variations that exist are explicable in terms of the crystal field theory but not of the valence bond theory. This seriously weakens the explanation for the lability of so-called outer-orbital-type complexes given by the valence bond theory. The other chief objection to the kinetic application of the theory is that, as always, it is purely qualitative. For example, any differences that exist, say, between a d^1 and a d^2 system, or between an inner orbital d^3 or d^4 system, cannot be predicted. Similarly all outer orbital systems are lumped together except insofar as the charge and size of the central atom are varied. No distinction based on the number of d electrons is made.

Kinetic Application of Crystal Field Theory

The importance of crystal field stabilization in determining the rates of reaction of coordination compounds was pointed out in a qualitative way by Orgel[27] and by Jørgensen.[28] Orgel noted that the reactivity of d^0, d^1, and d^2 systems compared to d^3 could be accounted for on the basis of an S_N2 mechanism whereby the entering group entered the plane in which the low-energy d orbital was empty. Thus, if the d_{xy} orbital was unoccupied, the seventh group would be added to the xy plane. In this way losses in C.F.S.E. would be minimized. This would not be possible for d^3 and higher systems. Jørgensen noted that, because of the large crystal field stabilizations of d^3, diamagnetic d^6, and d^8 systems in octahedral complexes, any reaction, whether going by C.N. five or C.N. seven, would inevitably lead to a considerable loss of energy and hence be slow.

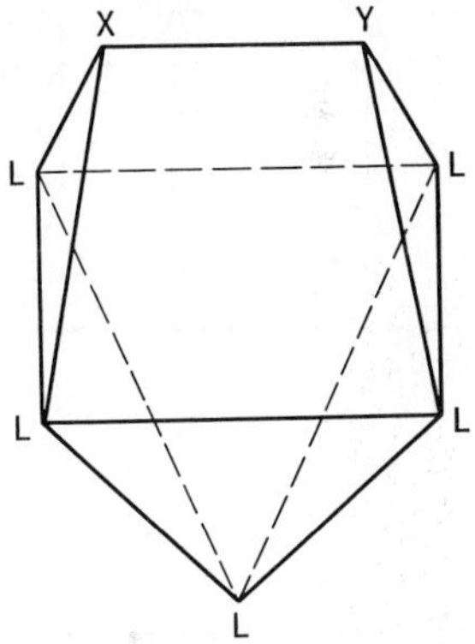

Fig. 3.4   Seven-coordinated octahedral wedge structure. X represents a leaving group, and Y an entering group.

These ideas can be put into more quantitative terms by the use of the energy values of Table 2.4. The procedure is to calculate the C.F.S.E. for various numbers of d electrons for a regular octahedral complex in weak or strong fields and also for a regular square pyramid, a pentagonal bipyramid, and the seven-coordinated octahedral wedge structure of Fig. 3.2. Another representation of this structure is shown in Fig. 3.4, with X as a leaving group and Y as an entering group. The latter two structures serve as models for an S_N2 mechanism.

The square pyramid serves as a model for an S_N1 mechanism. A trigonal bipyramid could also be considered for an S_N1 mechanism. This structure is always less favorable than the square pyramid as far as crystal field effects are concerned. On the other hand, it is better in that it reduces ligand-ligand repulsions. Also, as we shall see, it often allows better π bonding than the square pyramid arrangement.

Table 3.7 Crystal field activation energies (in Dq) for dissociation mechanism Octahedral → square pyramid

System	Strong Fields			Weak Fields		
	Octa-hedral	Square Pyramid	C.F.A.E.	Octa-hedral	Square Pyramid	C.F.A.E.
d^0	0	0	0	0	0	0
d^1	4	4.57	−0.57	4	4.57	−0.57
d^2	8	9.14	−1.14	8	9.14	−1.14
d^3	12	10.00	2.00	12	10.00	2.00
d^4	16	14.57	1.43	6	9.14	−3.14
d^5	20	19.14	0.86	0	0	0
d^6	24	20.00	4.00	4	4.57	−0.57
d^7	18	19.14	−1.14	8	9.14	−1.14
d^8	12	10.00	2.00	12	10.00	2.00
d^9	6	9.14	−3.14	6	9.14	−3.14
d^{10}	0	0	0	0	0	0

Table 3.8 Crystal field activation energies (in Dq) for displacement mechanism Octahedral → pentagonal bipyramid

System	Strong Fields			Weak Fields		
	Octa-hedral	Pentagonal Bipyramid	C.F.A.E.	Octa-hedral	Pentagonal Bipyramid	C.F.A.E.
d^0	0	0	0	0	0	0
d^1	4	5.28	−1.28	4	5.28	−1.28
d^2	8	10.56	−2.56	8	10.56	−2.56
d^3	12	7.74	4.26	12	7.74	4.26
d^4	16	13.02	2.98	6	4.93	1.07
d^5	20	18.30	1.70	0	0	0
d^6	24	15.48	8.52	4	5.28	−1.28
d^7	18	12.66	5.34	8	10.56	−2.56
d^8	12	7.74	4.26	12	7.74	4.26
d^9	6	4.93	1.07	6	4.93	1.07
d^{10}	0	0	0	0	0	0

Tables 3.7, 3.8, and 3.9 show the results of the calculations. The difference between the original octahedral and the final C.F.S.E. is considered as a contribution to E_a, the activation energy for the reaction. Following Hush,[19] it may be called C.F.A.E., crystal field activation energy. Some of the C.F.A.E. values of the tables are negative. In such cases the implication is that a distortion of the original octahedron lowers the energy. This suggests that such a distortion would, in fact, have occurred in the ground

Table 3.9 Crystal field activation energies (in Dq) for assisted dissociation mechanism

Octahedral → octahedral wedge

(five groups at distance R and two groups at 1.25 R)

	Strong Fields			Weak Fields		
System	Octa-hedral	Inter-mediate	C.F.A.E.	Octa-hedral	Inter-mediate	C.F.A.E.
d^0	0	0	0	0	0	0
d^1	4	6.08	−2.08	4	6.08	−2.08
d^2	8	8.68	−0.68	8	8.68	−0.68
d^3	12	10.20	1.80	12	10.20	1.80
d^4	16	16.26	−0.26	6	8.79	−2.79
d^5	20	18.86	1.14	0	0	0
d^6	24	20.37	3.63	4	6.08	−2.08
d^7	18	18.98	−0.98	8	8.68	−0.68
d^8	12	10.20	1.80	12	10.20	1.80
d^9	6	8.79	−2.79	6	8.79	−2.79
d^{10}	0	0	0	0	0	0

From reference 19.

state already, and hence the negative C.F.A.E.'s would be largely illusory. It can be seen in the tables that they do indeed belong to those systems where the Jahn-Teller distortion of the original structure is predicted to occur, d^1, d^2, d^4, d^7, and d^9. It is probably more realistic to take negative values of the C.F.A.E. as equal to zero.

It is also important to remember, when using Tables 3.7, 3.8, and 3.9, that *crystal field energies are only a small part of the bonding energies* in any system. There will be large contributions to the activation energy because of changes in metal-ligand attractions, ligand-ligand repulsions, etc. In any mechanism except the S_N2 (lim) the most important single factor is the strength of the bond between the central atom and the leaving group. Only a small part of this bond energy is related to crystal field effects. The use of the tables is clearly to discuss *differences* in rates for identical complexes in which only the number of d electrons of the central atom is varied.

The immediate conclusion on scanning Tables 3.7, 3.8, and 3.9 is that d^3, spin-coupled d^6, and d^8 are indeed the systems which are most affected, as far as crystal field energies are concerned, by the formation of a transition state by either an S_N1 or an S_N2 mechanism. In special circumstances a number of other systems are also predicted to react slowly because of a loss of C.F.S.E. The systems d^0, d^1, d^2, and spin-free d^5, as well as d^{10}, on the other hand, never lose any C.F.S.E. by either mechanism. It is accordingly predicted that they will react fast compared to any corresponding complexes in which the C.F.A.E. is positive.

In strong fields, which correspond to "inner orbital" complexes for systems from d^0 to d^6, it is predicted that reactions will be fast for d^0, d^1, and d^2 and slow for d^3, d^4, d^5, and d^6, with the order of rates decreasing $d^5 > d^4 > d^3 > d^6$, by either S_N1 or S_N2 mechanisms. The order is $d^4 > d^5 > d^3 > d^6$ for an assisted dissociation mechanism. In weak fields, which correspond to outer orbital complexes for systems from d^4 to d^{10}, the only systems for which reactions are predicted to be slow by either mechanism are d^3 and d^8.

Thus, there is agreement between the valence bond theory and the crystal field theory in predicting rapid reactions for complexes in which an empty lower d orbital is available. The reasons, however, are quite different in the two theories. The valence bond theory favors an S_N2 mechanism and stresses the availability of an orbital for covalent bond formation. The crystal field theory, as usual, ignores covalent bonding and orbital requirements and notes only that a transition state with either an increased or decreased coordination number can be formed without any decrease in C.F.S.E. This prediction is made regardless of mechanism. Note that it is not valid to conclude that, since complexes with an empty d orbital react rapidly, an S_N2 mechanism is required.

There is also agreement between the two theories in predicting that non-transition elements, the rare earths, and d^{10} systems will react rapidly. Again, different reasons are advanced. There is agreement that d^3 and low-spin d^4, d^5, and d^6 systems will be slow and that high-spin d^4, d^5, d^6, d^7, and d^9 systems will be fast. A major point of disagreement is high-spin d^8 octahedral complexes, for which the valence bond theory predicts the same lability as for high-spin d^4, d^5, d^6, d^7, and d^9 whereas the crystal field theory predicts inertness equal to that of a d^3 corresponding complex.

Where the theories agree, the correspondence to experiment is perfect. In fact, it is very difficult to observe a slow substitution reaction in a metal complex which is not crystal field stabilized. To do so it is necessary to go to such specialized systems as ethylenediaminetetraacetatoiron(III), which will be discussed later, or magnesium in chlorophyll which has a rigid quadridentate structure. Also the inertness of complexes of Cr(III) and spin-coupled complexes of Fe(II), Fe(III), Co(III), Rh(III), Os(III), and Ir(III), is well known.

Where the theories disagree, in the case of d^8, the evidence is definitely on the side of the crystal field theory. Virtually the only examples which can be used as a test are the paramagnetic complexes of Ni(II). The diamagnetic Ni(II), Pd(II), Pt(II), and Au(III) are planar structures which are to be discussed in Chapter 5 and whose reaction mechanisms are different. Now the high-spin complexes of Ni(II) are often considered as labile, and the rapidity of many of their reactions justifies this assignment. But what is predicted by the theories just discussed is not the absolute rate of these reactions but the relative rates for systems with different numbers of d electrons. The absolute rate is determined largely by the charge on the central atom, the nature of the ligands, etc. Certainly in comparison with the complexes of trivalent chromium or cobalt the reactions of divalent nickel will be faster.

Table 3.10 contains a collection of kinetic data on the rates of dissociation of the phenanthroline, terpyridyl, and dipyridyl complexes of the divalent metal ions of the first transition series from V(II) to Zn(II). The data, chiefly from Wilkins,[29]

$$ML_n^{2+} + H_2O \rightarrow ML_{n-1}(H_2O)^{2+} + L \qquad (21)$$

were obtained either from exchange experiments, which have rates independent of the concentration of the free ligand, or from rates of dissociation in acidic media, where the rates do not depend on the hydrogen ion concentration. The comparison to be made is between the activation energies for complexes of the same formula and the theoretical C.F.A.E.'s of the last column of Table 3.10. These are calculated for an S_N1 mechanism with a square pyramid intermediate and with allowance for a Jahn-Teller distortion in the original complex.

The agreement with crystal field theory is astonishingly good. All the rates which are too fast to measure correspond to zero C.F.A.E. For cobalt, nickel, and spin-paired iron, the C.F.A.E. is 0, 2, and $4Dq$, in the order of the experimental activation energies, e.g., 14.8, 20.8, and 28.7 kcal for the M(terpy)$_2^{2+}$ complexes. The increment corresponds to a Dq equal to 3–4 kcal whereas spectroscopic data indicate that the Dq for ligands of this kind is about 4–5 kcal (see Chapter 2). Fe(terpy)$^{2+}$ and Fe(phen)$^{2+}$ are very labile because they are high-spin complexes[31] with zero C.F.A.E. compared to the inert low-spin complexes Fe(terpy)$_2^+$, Fe(phen)$_3^{2+}$, and Fe(bipy)$_3^{2+}$.

Table 3.10 Kinetic data and C.F.A.E.'s for the dissociation of phenanthroline, dipyridyl, and terpyridyl complexes of the first transition series

System	Complex	$\Delta S^{\ddagger}$, eu	E_a, kcal	C.F.A.E., Dq
d^3	$V(phen)_3^{2+}$ [a]	-8	21.3	2
	$V(bipy)_3^{2+}$ [a]	slow	...	2
d^4	$Cr(bipy)_3^{2+}$ [b]	$+13$	22.6	1.4
d^5	$Mn(phen)_3^{2+}$	fast	...	0
	$Mnterpy^{2+}$	fast	...	0
	$Mnphen^{2+}$	-16	10.4	0
d^6	$Fephen^{2+}$ [c]	-16	12.8	0
	$Fe(phen)_3^{2+}$ [d]	$+28$	32.1	4
	$Feterpy^{2+}$ [c]	-2	18.0	0
	$Fe(terpy)_2^{2+}$ [d]	$+14$	28.7	4
	$Fe(bipy)_3^{2+}$ [d]	$+17$	28.4	4
d^7	$Cophen^{2+}$	$+5$	20.6	0
	$Co(phen)_3^{2+}$	$+5$	19.4	0
	$Coterpy^{2+}$	-3	20.2	0
	$Co(terpy)_2^{2+}$	-17	14.8	0
d^8	$Niphen^{2+}$	$+1$	25.2	2
	$Ni(phen)_3^{2+}$	$+1$	26.2	2
	$Niterpy^{2+}$	-6	24.2	2
	$Ni(terpy)_2^{2+}$	-9	20.8	2
	$Nibipy^{2+}$	$+8$	23.7	2
	$Ni(bipy)_3^{2+}$	$+2$	22.2	2
d^9	$Cu(phen)_3^{2+}$	fast	...	0
	$Cuterpy^{2+}$	fast	...	0
	$Cubipy^{2+}$	-16	14.1	0
d^{10}	$Zn(phen)_3^{2+}$	fast	...	0
	$Znterpy^{2+}$	fast	...	0
	$Znbipy^{2+}$	-14	12.1	0
	$Znphen^{2+}$	-16	12.3	0
	$Cdphen^{2+}$	-5	14.4	0
	$Hgbipy^{2+}$	-18	10.7	0
	$Ag(phen)_2^{+}$	$+12$	18.0	0

Data from references 29, 30, and 230 except as specified in notes a and b.
[a] Reference 241.
[b] Low spin, $(t_{2g})^4$. Data from B. R. Baker and B. D. Mehta, *Inorg. Chem.*, **4**, 848 (1965).
[c] High spin (paramagnetic), $(t_{2g})^4(eg)^2$.
[d] Low spin (diamagnetic), $(t_{2g})^6$.

For complexes where changes in spin do not occur, Ni(II) and Co(II), it will be noticed that the bis or tris complexes are faster than the mono. This is a common result and is to be attributed to the inductive effect of the ligands. Thus, in $Ni(bipy)_3{}^{2+}$, as compared to $Ni(bipy)(H_2O)_4{}^{2+}$, it is assumed that the stronger base bipyridine puts more negative charge on nickel than does the weaker base water. The negative charge on the metal weakens the other metal-ligand bonds and causes a higher rate of dissociation. The effect can be substantial; compare $Co(terpy)_2{}^{2+}$, $E_a = 14.8$ kcal, with $Co(terpy)(H_2O)_3{}^{2+}$, $E_a = 20.2$ kcal. Table 3.10 also shows some interesting variations in the entropies of activation. These will be discussed in Chapter 6.

$Cr(bipy)_3{}^{2+}$ dissociates quite slowly, and the activation energy is close to that for $Ni(bipy)_3{}^{2+}$. This is a rather special result for the d^4 system and is a consequence of the high field of the bipyridine ligand. Thus the complex is low spin and there is a substantial C.F.A.E. of $1.4Dq$ (Table 3.7). For the more common case of high-spin behavior, chromous complexes like those of Cu(II) are very labile (see Table 3.11). The d^3 system, V(II), is predicted to be slow in all cases. It should have the same C.F.A.E. as Ni(II). The experimental results on V^{2+} support this conclusion. Thus both $V(phen)_3{}^{2+}$ and $V(bipy)_3{}^{2+}$ dissociate slowly.[241] The smaller activation energy for $V(phen)_3{}^{2+}$ in Table 3.10 may be due to the lower effective charge on the metal ion.

The reactivity order given in Table 3.10 is Mn > Fe > Co > Ni ≪ Cu, and this order for the divalent ions has been observed repeatedly. For example, the rate of dissociation of metal complexes of the pentadentate amine penten, N,N,N′,N′-tetra-(2-aminoethyl)-ethylenediamine, has been measured at 0°C for some of the metal ions in Table 3.10.[32] The order of reactivity found is Mn > Zn ∼ Cu > Co ≫ Ni. The activation energies for dissociation of nickel diamine complexes are always about 5 kcal greater than for the dissociation of the corresponding copper diamine complexes.[33]

Table 3.11 includes the important data of Connick[34] on rates of water exchange of paramagnetic ions as found by the n.m.r line broadening method.[35] The asterisk in this case indicates a water molecule which originally is free in the body of the solution and hence in a very different

$$Ni(H_2O)_6{}^{2+} + H_2{}^*O \rightleftharpoons Ni(H_2{}^*O)_6{}^{2+} + H_2O \qquad (22)$$

magnetic environment from the water molecules which are coordinated to the paramagnetic metal ion. After a mean lifetime, τ, a coordinated water molecule becomes a free molecule. This exchange shows up experimentally as a broadening of the n.m.r. spectrum of either the proton of water or the oxygen, if ^{17}O is used. From the broadening a rate constant, k_1, or a lower

Table 3.11 Rate constants[a] for exchange of water molecules from first coordination sphere of metal ions at 25°C

Ion	k_1, sec^{-1}	E_a, kcal	Reference
Cr^{2+}	7×10^9	...	38
Mn^{2+}	3×10^7	8.7	34
Fe^{2+}	3×10^6	8.3	34
Co^{2+}	1×10^6	8.6	34
Ni^{2+}	3×10^4	12.2	34
Cu^{2+}	8×10^9	5.6	38
Be^{2+}	3×10^4	...	38
Mg^{2+}	$>10^4$	...	36
Ba^{2+}	$>10^4$	...	36
Sn^{2+}	$>10^4$	...	36
Hg^{2+}	$>10^4$	...	36
Al^{3+}	~ 1	...	38
Fe^{3+}	3×10^3	...	38
Ga^{3+}	$<10^4$	...	36
Gd^{3+}	2×10^9	...	38, 39
Bi^{3+}	$>10^4$	...	36
Cr^{3+}	3×10^{-6}	26.7	40
Rh^{3+}	4×10^{-8}	33	136

[a] The total rate of exchange would be equal to k_1 times the coordination number of the ion.

limit to this rate constant can be found. Table 3.11 gives some rate data in terms of $k_1 = 1/\tau$. Some data on first-order rate constants for water exchange on other metal ions are given in the table also. For the diamagnetic ions these were found by an indirect n.m.r method or by isotope exchange studies. The data for trivalent ions are sensitive to the absence of acid since considerable labilization can occur if a hydroxo complex is formed:

$$Fe(H_2O)_6^{3+} \rightleftharpoons Fe(H_2O)_5OH^{2+} + H^+ \qquad (23)$$

The rate constants in Table 3.11 show very clearly the effect of three variables, charge and size of the metal ion and crystal field stabilization. The effect of crystal field stabilization is evident in the very slow rate for Cr^{3+} and the relatively slow rate for Ni^{2+}. Cr^{3+} should have a C.F.A.E. of $2Dq$ for an S_N1 mechanism. This amounts to some 10 kcal from the spectrum of $Cr(H_2O)_6^{3+}$. The total activation energy for Fe^{3+} is not known but appears to be about 15 kcal. This means the total activation energy for $Cr(H_2O)_6^{3+}$ should be about 25 kcal. The increased activation energy for the nickel ion of about 3.5 kcal over Co^{2+} and Fe^{2+} (high spin) is less than for the aromatic amine complexes of Table 3.10. This difference is partly related to the lower value of Dq for aquo complexes.[41] The reactivity series is again Cu > Mn > Fe > Co > Ni.

It may be well to consider what evidence there is for a fixed number of water molecules forming the first coordination sphere of an ion in aqueous solution.[42] Classical methods such as ionic mobilities and transference numbers give variable hydration numbers for ions, sometimes as large as 20–30 molecules of water per ion. These measurements include, obviously, secondary effects ranging over several layers of solvent. Using modern techniques such as n.m.r. and isotope dilution, it has been well established that species such as $Cr(H_2O)_6^{3+}$, $Al(H_2O)_6^{3+}$, $Mg(H_2O)_6^{2+}$, and $Be(H_2O)_4^{2+}$ exist with strong binding and finite lifetimes.[37,42a,43] From interpretations of the spectra of the aquo ions of the transition metals using crystal field theory, it is fairly certain that Ni^{2+}, Co^{2+}, V^{3+}, Fe^{3+}, Mn^{2+}, and Fe^{2+} are nearly regular octahedra. Cu^{2+} and Ti^{3+} are tetragonally distorted octahedra.

The method of reasoning by analogy with coordination numbers found in the solid state is common and is fairly safe if spectral methods can be used. For many non-transition metal ions, e.g., Ag^+, Zn^{2+}, Cd^{2+}, Hg^{2+}, and Ga^{3+}, the coordination numbers in solution are really not known. There is some evidence that the rare earth ions in solution have coordination number nine, as they often have in the solid state.[42] While the x-ray evidence[43] that Li^+ in solution is tetrahedral seems reasonable, the corresponding C.N. and structure for $K(H_2O)_4^+$ are less certain. It may be, as suggested,[43] that the size of potassium ion enables it to replace one water molecule in the tetrahedral structure of hydrogen-bonded water.

It can be seen from Table 3.11 that very high rates of reaction can occur for most of the metal ions, half-lives of microseconds or milliseconds being common. This indicates the need for new techniques for studying the kinetics of very rapid chemical processes. Fortunately, a number of new experimental methods have become available.[44] The most versatile of these is the relaxation spectroscopy technique of Eigen.[45] An equilibrium system is required in which appreciable amounts of both products and reactants are present at equilibrium. A sudden perturbation such as an abrupt change in temperature, pressure, or intensity of electric field is applied, which causes a small shift in the position of equilibrium. The change of the system to the new equilibrium position occurs as a first-order process with a characteristic relaxation time:

$$ML \rightleftharpoons M + L \tag{24}$$

The relaxation time is a function of the rate constants and concentrations of the system. Complex systems with several reactions occurring can give several relaxation times.

From a study of the spectra of relaxation times, Eigen and his co-workers have assigned rate constants for a number of reactions involving labile metal ion-ligand systems.[45,46] For aquo complexes and a number of ligands, reaction 24 has been broken down into several steps. The first of these are diffusion-controlled processes with bimolecular rate constants of the order of 10^9–10^{10} M^{-1} sec^{-1}. They correspond to the aquated ions coming together to form an ion pair (Chapter 1) or other outer-sphere complex. These reaction rates are very similar for all the metal ions in the same medium. The chemically exciting reaction occurs when the outer-sphere complex is converted into an inner-sphere complex

$$M(H_2O)_6^{2+} + L \underset{k_b}{\overset{k_a}{\rightleftharpoons}} M(H_2O)_6^{2+}, L \underset{k_d}{\overset{k_c}{\rightleftharpoons}} M(H_2O)_5L^{2+} + H_2O \qquad (25)$$

In reaction 25 k_a is a diffusion rate constant, and $k_a/k_b = K_0$, an equilibrium constant for forming an ion pair. The constants k_c and k_d are sensitive functions of the metal ion, and k_d is a function of the ligand as well, whereas k_c is remarkably insensitive to the nature of the ligand. The overall stability constant of the complex, ML, is given by

$$K_1 = \frac{k_a k_c}{k_b k_d} = K_0 \frac{k_c}{k_d} \qquad (26)$$

$H_2NCH_2COO^-$, pyridine, imidazole, EDTA^{4-}, IDA^{2-} (imidodiacetic acid anion), NTA^{3-} (nitrilotriacetic acid anion), and several adenosine phosphate anions were used in these studies. For the univalent and most divalent cations k_c is the same within a factor of two or three for the different ligands. For Be^{2+}, Fe^{3+}, and Al^{3+} the value of k_c varies more, being larger the more basic the ligand. This has been attributed to proton removal in the transition state for these acidic aquo ions.

Figure 3.5 shows a survey of the results of Eigen for the rate constants k_c for a number of aquo metal ions. The figure shows the effect of charge, size, and d electron structure in the same way that Table 3.11 does. The lability of the alkali metal ions is noteworthy, as well as the relative inertness of Be^{2+} (small size) and some trivalent cations (large charge). In the first transition series the lability order is Cu $\sim$ Cr > Zn > Mn > Fe > Co > V > Ni for the divalent ions. The lability of Cr^{2+}, a d^4 system with a strong Jahn-Teller distortion, and Zn^{2+}, a d^{10} system, and the inertness of V^{2+}, a d^3 system, are predicted by crystal field theory.

There is an apparent anomaly in that the trivalent ions of the rare earths are very labile.[46] While these ions are slightly larger than the divalent transition metal ions, the effect of charge should have made the lanthanide ions less labile than Mn(II), for example. The explanation probably lies in the greater coordination number of the rare earth ions.

If this is as great as nine, the average bonding energy per water molecule would be greatly reduced.[46]

There is a remarkable correspondence between the rate data of Table 3.11 and the numbers indicated in Fig. 3.5 for the same metal ions. This strongly suggests that the rate-determining step in all of these reactions is the same—the removal of a water molecule from the inner coordination sphere and its replacement by a particle in the second coordination sphere.[45]

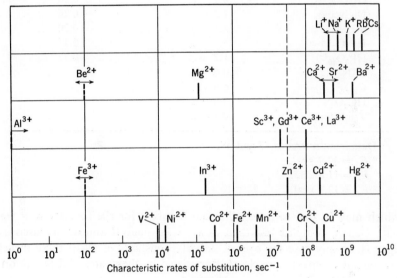

Fig. 3.5 Characteristic rate constants for H_2O substitution in the inner coordination sphere of metal ions. Patterned after reference 46.

A primarily dissociative or S_N1 mechanism is indicated by the near independence of the rate on the nature of the incoming group. The small variations may be an indication that a ligand-assisted dissociation is operating. Also, variations may result from slight differences in the rate of dissociation of water from the various outer-sphere complexes and varying probabilities for capture of a five-coordinated intermediate by ligands in the second coordination sphere. Table 3.12 shows the variation in the rate constant k_c for Ni(II) and Co(II) and a large number of ligands.[47,48] It has been necessary to estimate the value of K_0, sometimes rather crudely, in order to get a numerical value of k_c.

It has also been pointed out[49] that the experimental second-order rate constant for the formation of the mono complexes of Ni^{2+} with NH_3, N_2H_4, C_5H_5N, bipy, terpy, and phen are all about $2-3 \times 10^3$ M^{-1} sec^{-1} at 25°C. These figures are only slightly less than those listed in Table 3.12,

Table 3.12   Rates (sec^{-1}) of outer-sphere/inner sphere conversion at 25°C

$$M(H_2O)_6^{2+}, L \xrightarrow{k_c} M(H_2O)_{6-n}L^{2+} + nH_2O$$

L	$Ni(H_2O)_6^{2+}$	$Co(H_2O)_6^{2+}$
H_2O	2.7×10^4 [a]	1.1×10^6
Imidazole	1.6 ,,	0.44 ,,
Glycine	0.7 ,,	0.26 ,,
Diglycine	1.2 ,,	0.26 ,,
SO_4^{2-}	1.5 ,,	0.20 ,,
$HP_2O_7^{3-}$	1.2 ,,	0.48 ,,
$HP_3O_{10}^{4-}$	1.2 ,,	0.72 ,,
SCN^-	0.6 ,,	...
$C_2O_4^{2-}$	0.6 ,, [b]	...
$HC_2O_4^-$	0.9 ,, [c]	...
Triglycine	0.5 ,,	...

Data from reference 47 and 48.
[a] $E_a = 12.2$ kcal.
[b] $E_a = 11.8$ kcal.
[c] $E_a = 13.1$ kcal.

which may be due to an equilibrium constant for the formation of the outer-sphere complex less than unity when neutral amines are used as ligands. In any case the overall stability constants of all of these nickel and cobalt complexes are clearly dominated by their rates of dissociation, k_d, in equation 25.

It is rather surprising to find that aliphatic polyamines follow a different pattern[50] in that their formation rate constants are of the order of 2–6 × $10^5\ M^{-1}\ sec^{-1}$. This is true even for ethylenediamine. Less surprising, it is found on protonating the higher polyamines that the formation constant drops by a factor of 50 or so for each proton added. This may be attributed to electrostatic repulsion reducing K_0.

With all of the available information of Table 3.11 and Fig. 3.5 on weak field complexes, it may be asked whether a decision can be made in regard to mechanism by using the arguments of crystal field theory. The answer is that definite conclusions are rather scanty. One difficulty is that the d^3 and d^8 complexes are predicted to be slow by any mechanism and that the significance to be attached to the negative C.F.A.E.'s of Tables 3.7, 3.8, and 3.9 is doubtful. The other difficulty is that there is no reason to assume that all the metal ions will react by the same mechanism. In Chapter 5 a case will be made for considering that complexes of Cu(II) behave kinetically like planar complexes, for example.

The rapidity of reactions of copper complexes in general seems to rule out a pentagonal bipyramid structure for the activated intermediate in any case (see Table 3.8). The large C.F.A.E.'s make this structure unlikely for d^3, d^8 and low-spin d^6 also. It may be pointed out that the EDTA complex of Fe(III) in the solid state is actually seven coordinated with a distorted pentagonal bipyramid arrangement.[51a]. A water molecule is the seventh ligand. Also the EDTA complex of Mn(II) is seven coordinated with the NbF_7^{2-} structure, which rather resembles the intermediate described in Table 3.9.[51b] For these two d^5 systems, with no C.F.S.E., there seems to be no difficulty with normal size ligands in achieving the proposed structures. Some rare earth ions also are found to be nine or ten coordinated as their EDTA complexes,[51d] whereas the transition metal ions other than d^5, while not always sexadentate, seem to be six coordinated and approximately octahedral.[51]

In general, the best overall agreement between theory and experimental rate data is obtained with a simple S_N1 mechanism with a square pyramid structure for the intermediate. The difference between this and the octahedral wedge intermediate of Fig. 3.2 is usually small in terms of predictions of the crystal field theory. In some cases, e.g., $Fe(H_2O)_6^{2+}$, the distortions from octahedral symmetry in the ground state are known to be so small that one would expect to see the large negative C.F.A.E. of Table 3.9 show up experimentally. An unusually low activation energy for $Fe(H_2O)_6^{2+}$ water exchange is not found (Table 3.11).

The predictions made by crystal field theory with respect to strong field ligands will be discussed in part in the next sections, where complexes of Co(III), Rh(III), Cr(III), etc., will be taken up. In the case of cyanide complexes, the following orders of lability have been observed:[25,26]

$$V(CN)_6^{3-} > Mn(CN)_6^{3-} \gg Cr(CN)_6^{3-} > Fe(CN)_6^{3-} \sim Co(CN)_6^{3-}$$

and

$$Cr(CN)_6^{4-} > V(CN)_6^{4-} \sim Mn(CN)_6^{4-} > Fe(CN)_6^{4-}$$

$$V(CN)_6^{3-} > V(CN)_6^{4-}$$

The theoretical order for an octahedral wedge intermediate (Table 3.10) is $d^2 > d^4 > d^5 > d^3 > d^6$, which is exactly that observed. The lability order for a square pyramid intermediate is $d^2 > d^5 > d^4 > d^3 > d^6$, which inverts d^5 and d^4.

The lability of the d^4 complexes $Cr(CN)_6^{4-}$ and $Mn(CN)_6^{3-}$ has been explained in terms of an S_N2 mechanism in which the four electrons are paired in two of the t_{2g} orbitals, leaving one d orbital empty for covalent bond formation.[26a] This is certainly a possibility. However, the exchange reaction of $Mn(CN)_6^{3-}$ with $*CN^-$ is a first-order process independent of the *CN$^-$ concentration.[26a] If water is the nucleophilic reagent and not cyanide ion, it is not so important to form a covalent bond since water forms primarily ionic bonds. The exchange rates of $Cr(CN)_6{}^{3-}$, $Fe(CN)_6{}^{4-}$, and $Co(CN)_6{}^{3-}$ are also independent of the concentration of cyanide ion.[26b]

A calculation has been made of the C.F.A.E. for the reactions of the trisoxalato complexes by the dissociative path (Table 3.7) and the associative path (Table 3.9).[52] Experimental values of Dq from spectroscopic data were used. The predicted order of decreasing lability by either mechanism is Mn > V > Fe > Ru $\sim$ Cr > Co > Rh > Ir, the metal ions being trivalent. This order agrees well with experimental information such as oxalate exchange rates, racemization rates, and aquation rates. There is no real information on $Ru(ox)_3{}^{3-}$, except that it cannot be resolved into optical isomers.

Mechanism of Substitution Reactions of Complexes of Cobalt(III)

Since a survey of the reactions of labile complexes does not enable clear assignments of probable reaction mechanisms to be made, it is necessary to look at more slowly reacting systems. As might be expected, the greatest amount of kinetic study has been made on the inert complexes of Co(III), Cr(III), and a few of their related elements in the periodic table. Because of the great variety of complexes of Co(III) that can be prepared, it is anticipated that the most information on the intimate mechanism of reaction can be obtained in this case.[53] The substitution reactions have been subdivided into several categories for convenience, and each of them will be reviewed in turn.

Acid Hydrolysis. The substitution reaction most extensively investigated by kinetic methods is that commonly referred to as *aquation* and illustrated by the typical equation

$$MA_5X^n + H_2O \rightarrow MA_5H_2O^{n+1} + X^- \tag{27}$$

Likewise of common usage in the literature is the term *hydrolysis* with reference to reactions of the type

$$MA_5X^n + OH^- \rightarrow MA_5OH^n + X^- \tag{28}$$

Since both of these are essentially reactions of complex ions with water, it is suggested that both be called *hydrolysis reactions*. If the reaction product is an aquo complex (27) the reaction is termed *acid hydrolysis*, whereas, if the product is a hydroxo complex (28) the reaction is called *base hydrolysis*. Depending upon the pH of the reaction mixture and the acidity of the aquo complex, it follows that the reaction product can be an acid-base equilibrium mixture of the aquo and hydroxo complexes with both present in appreciable amounts. In such a case the reaction is simply referred to as *hydrolysis* with no specification as to acid or base hydrolysis. This terminology will be used here as it is believed to be more informative than the older terms, aquation and hydrolysis.

An appreciable amount of data is available on the rates of acid hydrolysis reactions. These studies, made in aqueous solutions, give a linear plot for first-order kinetics. This result is to be expected, since the concentration of the reactant and solvent does not change during the reaction. The rate is therefore dependent only on the concentration of the complex and is first order or pseudo first order. This observation by itself furnishes no information as to the role played by the water and does not tell anything about the molecularity of these reactions.

Nevertheless the way in which the rate constant is affected by various changes in the nature of the complex ion is expected to give us information about the mechanism. Table 3.13 contains the observed data on the acid hydrolysis of a number of Co(III) chloroammines. These data permit two conclusions to be drawn. One is that increasing chelation such as replacing two NH_3 ligands by one ethylenediamine, slows down the rate of acid hydrolysis in a progressive manner. The second is that, allowing for the first effect, the divalent monochloro complexes react about 100 times slower than the univalent dichloro complexes. This is also borne out by the fact that the acid hydrolysis of the latter complexes occurs in two steps:

$$Co(AA)_2Cl_2{}^+ + H_2O \rightarrow Co(AA)_2(H_2O)Cl^{2+} + Cl^- \qquad (29)$$

$$Co(AA)_2(H_2O)Cl^{2+} + H_2O \rightarrow Co(AA)_2(H_2O)_2{}^{3+} + Cl^- \qquad (30)$$

with the second reaction about 100 times slower than the first.[54] Table 3.13 reports only the rate constant for 29.

Table 3.13   Rates of acid hydrolysis of some chloropentaamine and dichlorotetraamine cobalt(III) complexes at pH 1

Ion	$k \times 10^4$, sec^{-1}	Ion	$k \times 10^6$, sec^{-1}
cis-$Co(NH_3)_4Cl_2{}^+$	very fast	$Co(NH_3)_5Cl^{2+}$	6.7
cis-$Co(en)_2Cl_2{}^+$	2.5	*cis*-$Co(en)_2NH_3Cl^{2+}$	1.4
cis-$Co(trien)Cl_2{}^+$	1.5	*cis*-$Co(trien)NH_3Cl^{2+}$	0.67
trans-$Co(NH_3)_4Cl_2{}^+$	18	$Co(en)(dien)Cl^{2+}$	0.52
trans-$Co(en)(NH_3)_2Cl_2{}^+$	2.3	$Co(tetraen)Cl^{2+}$	0.25
trans-$Co(en)_2Cl_2{}^+$	0.32		

Data from reference 54. Dichloro complexes at 25°C and chloro complexes at 35°C. Substitution of first chlorine only for dichloro complexes.

The interpretation of the effect of the positive charge of the complex on the rate is straightforward. Separation of negative charge in the form of the chloride ion is more difficult the greater the remaining charge on the complex. This immediately tells us that bond breaking is important and that we are not dealing with an S_N2 (lim) mechanism in any event. If the reactions are going by displacement mechanisms, then the reagent is

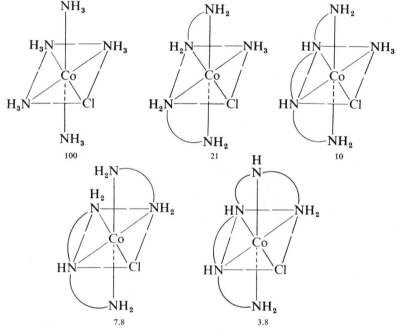

Fig. 3.6 Relative rates of acid hydrolysis for a series of chloropentammine complexes of Co(III) with different degrees of chelation. See also D. A. House and C. S. Garner, *Inorg. Chem.*, **5**, 2097 (1966).

water and the interaction of the charge of the complex with the dipole of water will be less than with the electric charge of the chloride ion. Hence an S_N2 process cannot be excluded, though the relative order "bond breaking more important than bond making" is established.

The interpretation of the effect of chelation is more ambiguous. Certainly it may be possible that a displacement mechanism acting on the opposite side of the complex from the halide ion to be displaced‖ is being hindered. Figure 3.6 illustrates how chelation ties up the back of the complex and makes an attack by a reagent more difficult. In fact in the case of Co(en) (dien)Cl²⁺ and Co(tetraen)Cl²⁺ it would appear that such a mechanism is

‖ The convenient term "backside attack" is esthetically unsatisfactory. It is therefore suggested that the terms "*cis* attack" and "*trans* attack" be used to designate the relationship of the incoming group and the leaving group in a displacement reaction (see p. 134).

virtually excluded. The fact that these complexes react only slightly more slowly than some of the others is an argument against an S_N2 *trans* attack.¶

It is possible that the inductive effect of the chelate amines compared to ammonia is responsible for the rates. Data on the acid dissociation constants of the monoprotonated onium ions are as follows: NH_4^+ 9.28, enH^+ 9.93, $dienH^+$ 9.98, $trienH^+$ 9.92.[55] Thus NH_3 is a somewhat weaker base and hence it does not give its electrons up as completely towards the Co(III) ion. But if this is true, then the chloride ion would be held more firmly by the more positive cobalt and reaction would be slow. This is opposite to what is observed.

An explanation based upon another kind of electrostatic argument can be given. As the chloride ion is lost from the original complex, an additional solvation by the water molecules making up the secondary coordination sphere is needed. That is, a trivalent cation is more intensely solvated than a divalent cation. From the Born equation it can be seen that the solvation energy is also greater the smaller the size of the ion. One effect of replacing NH_3 molecules by polyamines is certainly to increase the size of the complex. The larger the ion, the less its solvation energy will be and the less easily it can be formed. These arguments will also hold for a transition state in which the chloride ion is only partly lost. Thus the rate is slowed down by chelation because of reduced stability of the transition state due to less efficient solvation. In agreement with this view, the logs of the rate constants in Table 3.13 give a linear plot versus the number of chelate rings, or number of N—H bonds, for the chloro or *trans*-dichloro complexes. The log of the rate constant is proportional to the free energy of activation. This solvation theory, if true, does not distinguish between an S_N1 and an S_N2 mechanism. All it does is again call attention to the importance of ionic bond breaking in the transition state.

Another series of Co(III) complexes whose rates of acid hydrolysis have been measured is given in Table 3.14. Again only the rates of reaction of the first chlorine are reported. In this group of compounds, two effects are studied. For the first nine compounds, the change in structure involves carbon or nitrogen alkyl substitution on ethylenediamine. For a single methyl substituent on nitrogen, the rate is diminished by a factor of two. This is in agreement with the solvation theory previously proposed. Except for this, every increase in the number or size of the alkyl groups in place of hydrogen atoms leads to an increase in the rate of acid hydrolysis. Thus, in the case of the tetramethylethylenediamine complex, hydrolysis is instantaneous on solution in water.**

¶ However, see p. 261.

** The *trans* complex salts are all green and their solutions are also green, changing to pink or red upon hydrolysis. The half-life of the hydrolysis corresponds closely to a colorless stage, which makes possible an estimation of the rate even if very rapid.

Table 3.14   Rates of acid hydrolysis of *trans*-$Co(AA)_2Cl_2^+$ at 25°C and *pH* 1

$$Co(AA)_2Cl_2^+ + H_2O \rightarrow Co(AA)_2(H_2O)Cl^{2+} + Cl^-$$

Diamine	Symbol	$k \times 10^5$, sec^{-1}
1. NH_2—CH_2—CH_2—NH_2	en	3.2
2. NH_2—CH_2—$CH(CH_3)$—NH_2	pn	6.2
3. *dl*-NH_2—$CH(CH_3)$—$CH(CH_3)$—NH_2	*dl*-bn	15
4. *meso*-NH_2—$CH(CH_3)$—$CH(CH_3)$—NH_2	*m*-bn	42
5. NH_2—CH_2—$C(CH_3)_2$—NH_2	*i*-bn	22
6. NH_2—$C(CH_3)_2$—$C(CH_3)_2$—NH_2	tetrameen	instantaneous
7. NH_2—CH_2—CH_2—$NH(CH_3)$	meen	1.7
8. NH_2—CH_2—CH_2—$NH(C_2H_5)$	eten	6.0
9. NH_2—CH_2—CH_2—$NH(n$-$C_3H_7)$	*n*-pren	12
10. NH_2—CH_2—CH_2—CH_2—NH_2	tn	1000^a
11. NH_2—CH_2—CH_2—NH_2,		
NH_2—CH_2—CH_2—CH_2—NH_2	(en)(tn)	43
12. NH_2—CH_2—$C(CH_3)_2$—CH_2—NH_2	dan	300

Data from reference 56.

^{a} At 10°C.

Such an acceleration in rate upon increased substitution is strongly suggestive of a dissociation mechanism. Certainly increasing the crowding about the cobalt atom would not be conducive to an S_N2 mechanism in which an increase in coordination number to seven is required. On the other hand such an increase in the size of the inert ligands is expected to favor an S_N1 mechanism in which the coordination number decreases to five. The explanation would be that a sterically crowded complex is unstable because of repulsion and distortion of the ligands. Upon losing one group, a chloride ion in this case, an expansion and rearrangement of the remaining five groups could occur to relieve the steric strain. Accelerations in reaction rate due to excessive crowding of groups in the reactant have been observed in bulky organic halides.[57] Evidence that steric strain in the original complex is responsible for the rate is found in the observation that the rates of hydrolysis are correlated with the dissociation constants of the nickel complexes of the same series of diamines.[58]

For example, the 30-fold increase in the rate of acid hydrolysis of the *meso*-butylenediamine compared to the *dl*-butylenediamine complex corresponds to a 740-fold decrease in the total stability constant of $Ni(AA)_3^{2+}$. When the two methyl groups are on the same side of the five-membered chelate ring, as in the *meso* compound, there is considerable interference between them. Similarly there is a 60-fold increase in the rate of acid hydrolysis of *meso*-stilbenediamine complex, $Co(m\text{-stien})_2Cl_2^+$, compared to the corresponding *l*-stilbenediamine complex in 50% methanol. The dissociation constants of the bis nickel complexes $Ni(AA)_2^{2+}$ differ by 10^5.

The last three complexes of Table 3.14 show the effect on the rate of expanding the size of the chelate ring from five members to six by using trimethylenediamine instead of ethylenediamine. The rate is increased by 1000-fold for such a change. Again this increase in rate is connected to the observation that complexes with six-membered chelate rings are much less stable than those with five-membered rings, unless part of an aromatic system.[59] An examination of the reason for the instability shows that it lies in the 90° bond angles which are necessarily formed by the metal chelate bonds. Release of one group from the octahedron and expansion of this bond angle will relieve the strain in the complex with a six-membered ring. A peculiar result is that methyl substitution in the six-membered ring (compound 12) leads to a decrease in rate rather than an increase.

Before accepting the rate data in Table 3.14 as evidence for a dissociation mechanism, it is necessary to consider the possible influence of inductive effects further. This need arises because the base-strengthening character of the alkyl group with respect to hydrogen will lead to increased negative charge near the cobalt atom and an increased rate as observed. To test the influence of inductive effects it is desirable to prepare a series of compounds in which only inductive factors are varied and not steric or other factors.

Such series have been prepared and studied[60] in the form of compounds of the general formulas $Co(en)_2(X\text{—py})Cl^{2+}$ and $trans\text{-}Co(X\text{—py})_4Cl_2^+$. Here X is a substituent which changes the base strength of pyridine by factors as large as twenty. The rates of hydrolysis are found to vary by less than a factor of two. Since the base strengths of the substituted ethylenediamines change by only a factor of 1.5 over the entire range,[61] it may safely be concluded that inductive effects are not responsible for the increased rates shown in Table 3.14. The rates also cannot be due to solvation effects for the reasons already given.

It should further be noted that inductive effects do not always turn out as expected. As an example of what is considered normal, the rate of dissociation of NH_3 from $Ni(H_2O)_5NH_3^{2+}$ is 6.6 sec^{-1} at 25°C[49], and the rate of dissociation of $Ni(NH_3)_6^{2+}$ is at least 6.6×10^4 sec^{-1}. The latter figure is the rate of ammonia exchange as measured by n.m.r. line broadening.[62] The rate of exchange is independent of the free NH_3 concentration, which suggests a dissociation mechanism. The increased rate of 10^4 is in the direction expected for inductive effects. Table 3.15 contains most of the available rate data for acid hydrolysis of complexes of the type $M(NH_3)_5X^{2+}$, where X and M are varied. Some data where NH_3 is

Table 3.15 Rate data for acid hydrolysis of some cobalt(III) and related complexes at 25°C

Ion	k, sec^{-1}	E_a, kcal	$\Delta S^{\ddagger}$, eu	Ref.
$Co(NH_3)_5OP(OCH_3)_3^{3+}$	2.5×10^{-4}	...	...	64
$Co(NH_3)_5NO_3^{2+}$	2.7×10^{-5}	26	+6	65
$Co(NH_3)_5I^{2+}$	8.3×10^{-6}	...	...	65
$Co(NH_3)_5Br^{2+}$	6.3×10^{-6}	24	−4	65
$Co(NH_3)_5H_2O^{3+}$	5.8×10^{-6}	27	+6	17
$Co(NH_3)_5Cl^{2+}$	1.7×10^{-6}	23	−9	65
$Co(NH_3)_5SO_4^{+}$	1.2×10^{-6}	19	−24	65
$Co(NH_3)_5PO_4H_2^{2+}$	2.6×10^{-7}	...	...	64
$Co(NH_3)_5O_2CCH_3^{2+}$	1.2×10^{-7}	25	−8	66
$Co(NH_3)_6^{3+}$	$\sim 10^{-10}$	...	...	16
$Co(NH_3)_5F^{2+}$	8.6×10^{-8}	21	−26	67a
$Co(NH_3)_5NCS^{2+}$	5.0×10^{-10}	31	0	242
$Co(NH_3)_5N_3^{2+}$	2.1×10^{-9}	34	+14	67b
$Co(NH_3)_5PO_4$	very slow	...	...	64
$Co(NH_3)_5NO_2^{2+}$	very slow	...	...	68
$Co(NH_3)_5OH^{2+}$	very slow	...	...	69
$cis\text{-}Co(NH_3)_4H_2OCl^{2+}$	3.5×10^{-6}	...	...	65
$Co(CN)_5N_3^{3-}$	5.8×10^{-8}	28	−0.6	70
$Co(CN)_5SCN^{3-}$	2.7×10^{-8}	32	+12	70
$Cr(NH_3)_5I^{2+}$	1.0×10^{-3}	21	+7	71a
$Cr(NH_3)_5Br^{2+}$	6.8×10^{-5}	24	+12	71b
$Cr(NH_3)_5Cl^{2+}$	7.3×10^{-6}	24	+9	71b
$Cr(NH_3)_6^{3+}$	1.0×10^{-7}	26	−5	72
$Cr(NH_3)_5NCS^{2+}$	1.6×10^{-6}	25	−2	242
$Cr(NH_3)_2(NCS)_4^{-}$	$\sim 1 \times 10^{-6}$	27	+3	18b
$Cr(H_2O)_5F^{2+}$	6.2×10^{-10}	29	−4	73
$Cr(H_2O)_5Cl^{2+}$	2.8×10^{-7}	25	−7	73
$Cr(H_2O)_5Br^{2+}$	3.1×10^{-6}	24	−4	63
$Cr(H_2O)_5I^{2+}$	8.4×10^{-5}	23	0	73
$Cr(H_2O)_5NCS^{2+}$	1.0×10^{-7}	28	−3.5	65
$Cr(H_2O)_5N_3^{2+}$	4.6×10^{-8}	33	+16	73
$trans\text{-}Cr(H_2O)_4Cl_2^{+}$	8.3×10^{-5}	27	−9	74
$cis\text{-}Cr(H_2O)_4Cl_2^{+}$	4.3×10^{-5}	...	...	74
$Ru(NH_3)_5Cl^{2+}$	7.0×10^{-7}	23	−11	75
$RuCl_6^{3-}$	~ 1	...	...	76
$trans\text{-}Ru(H_2O)_3Cl_3$	2.1×10^{-6}	...	...	76
$Ru(H_2O)_5Cl^{2+}$	$\sim 10^{-8}$	...	...	76
$Rh(H_2O)Cl_5^{2-}$	3×10^{-4}	...	...	77
$RhCl_6^{3-}$	1.8×10^{-3}	25	+10	231
$Rh(NH_3)_5Br^{2+}$	$\sim 1 \times 10^{-8}$	26	−10	78
$Ir(NH_3)_5Br^{2+}$	$\sim 2 \times 10^{-10}$	27	−14	79b
$IrCl_6^{3-}$	9.4×10^{-6}	30	+19	80
$Ir(H_2O)Cl_5^{2-}$	$\sim 10^{-6}$	...	...	80

replaced by water are also included, and it can be seen that this does always lead to a slowing down of the rate as predicted.

The effect of the charge of the other ligands is usually, but not always, as expected. An extreme example is that of the relative rates of hydrolysis of $RuCl_6^{3-}$ and $Ru(H_2O)_5Cl^{2+}$, which differ by 10^8. Chromium(III) does show the expected effect of charge in that $Cr(H_2O)_4Cl_2^+$ is more labile than $Cr(H_2O)_5Cl^{2+}$ (see also Table 3.13). However, Reinecke's salt anion $Cr(NH_3)_2(NCS)_4^-$ does not show great reactivity compared to $Co(NH_3)_5NCS^{2+}$. Also, the cyanide anion in $Co(CN)_5N_3^{3-}$ and $Co(CN)_5SCN^{3-}$ does not produce a large increase in lability of the sixth group. An explanation for these exceptions will be given below.

For the cobalt pentaamines, the order of reactivity as far as the leaving group is concerned is $(CH_3O)_3PO > NO_3^- > I^- > Br^- > H_2O > Cl^- > SO_4^{2-} > H_2PO_4^- > CH_3CO_2^- > NH_3 > NCS^- > N_3^- > PO_4^{3-} \sim NO_2^- \sim OH^-$. This is in good agreement with the order expected on the basis of the stability constants of the complexes. Table 3.16 lists a number of equilibrium constants for the reaction

$$Co(NH_3)_5H_2O^{3+} + X \rightleftharpoons Co(NH_3)_5X^{3+} + H_2O \qquad (31)$$

Figure 3.7 gives a plot of log k for aquation versus pK_{eq}, when known, showing an approximate free energy relationship. Particularly for the case where the leaving group is a monovalent anion, the linearity is excellent. Furthermore, the slope of the straight line is 1.0. As Langford points out,[79a] this indicates that the nature of the X group in the transition state is the same as that in the product, namely a solvated anion.

Table 3.16 Equilibrium constants at 25°C for
$$Co(NH_3)_5H_2O^{3+} + X \rightleftharpoons Co(NH_3)_5X^{3+} + H_2O$$

X	K_{eq}, M^{-1}	Remarks
H_2O	0.018	$(55.5)^{-1} = K_{eq}$
NO_3^-	0.077	$\mu = 0.5$; ref. 81
Br^-	0.37	,, ,,
Cl^-	1.25	,, ,,
$H_2PO_4^-$	7.4	,, ,,
SO_4^{2-}	12.4	,, ,,
F^-	20–30	dilute; ref. 67a
NCS^-	470	$\mu = 0.5$; ref. 82
NH_3	2.5×10^4	$\mu = 2.0$; ref. 83
OH^-	2×10^8	$K_a/K_w = K_{eq}$
NO_2^-	$\sim 10^{10}$	from $\Delta H = -8.1$ kcal, ref. 84, and $\Delta S° = +18$ eu, estimated

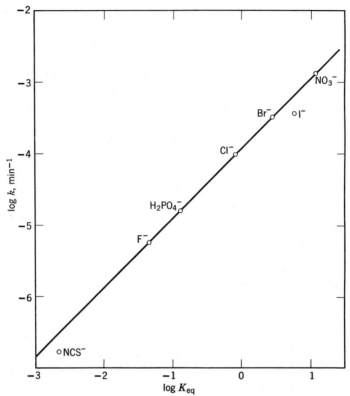

Fig. 3.7 Log k for aquation plotted against pK_{eq} for the reaction
$$Co(NH_3)_5H_2O^{3+} + X^- \rightleftharpoons Co(NH_3)_5X^{2+} + H_2O.$$
After reference 79a.

Such a conclusion agrees with our previous theoretical prediction of the reaction mechanism (p. 133), that bond breaking is much more important than bond making in the activated complex. The slope of unity does not tell us unambiguously about the role of the entering water molecule, however. Anything from no bonding to strong bonding is allowed. Following an argument by Hammond,[85] it is not likely that the entering group will be strongly bound in an activated complex resembling the products when the reaction is not strongly endothermic. The logical inference is that water is only weakly bound, if at all, in the transition state.

If there is some bonding of the incoming water, the mechanism is that of the solvent-assisted dissociation mentioned earlier (p. 134). If there is no specific bonding of water, there is still no requirement that the five-co-ordinated structure left by the loss of X be an intermediate in the phenom-enological kinetic sense. Reaction with the nearest potential ligand could occur more easily than rearrangement of the surrounding solvent shell.[79a] Thus, the interchange of groups in the first and second coordination layers could take place with or without nucleophilic assistance.

For the iridium pentaamines it is also observed[79b] that a linear free energy relationship holds for the aquation reaction

$$Ir(NH_3)_5X^{2+} + H_2O \rightleftharpoons Ir(NH_3)_5H_2O^{3+} + X^- \tag{32}$$

The slope is again near unity, about 0.9. The order of reactivity is $NO_3^- >$ $I^- > Br^- > Cl^-$.

The order of reactivity of the leaving group also correlates fairly well with the basicity of that group towards the proton. This is a consequence of Co(III) being a class (a) or hard acid, as is the proton. Some exceptions will be noted in that NCS^-, N_3^-, and NO_2^- form more stable complexes, or react more slowly, than their basicities would warrant. All these are unsaturated ligands, and it seems reasonable to attribute the extra stability of their complexes to the polarization, or π-bonding phenomenon, used to explain soft acid-soft base interactions [that is, Co(III) has some class (b) behavior].

Resonance structures such as

$$Co\!-\!N\!\equiv\!C\!-\!\overset{..}{\underset{..}{S}}: \qquad Co\!-\!N\!\equiv\!N\!-\!\overset{..}{\underset{..}{N}}: \qquad Co\!=\!N\!\overset{\textstyle :\overset{..}{O}:}{\underset{\textstyle \overset{..}{O}:}{}}$$

compared to the normal structures

$$Co\!-\!\overset{..}{N}\!=\!C\!=\!\overset{..}{S}: \qquad Co\!-\!\overset{..}{N}\!=\!N\!=\!\overset{..}{N}: \qquad Co\!-\!N\!\overset{\textstyle :\overset{..}{O}:}{\underset{\textstyle \overset{..}{O}:}{}}$$

indicate in an oversimplified way the nature of the stabilization mechanism.[86] Essentially, in each case electrons are being withdrawn, via the π systems of electrons, from the ligand atom bound to the metal. This reduces the repulsive interaction between the π electrons of the ligands and the t_{2g} electrons of the cobalt ion. From the molecular orbital point of view, we would say that empty antibonding π orbitals on the ligands are used to lower the energy of the t_{2g} electrons.

Similar structures can be drawn for CN^- and RCO_2^- ligands:

$$Co\!=\!C\!=\!\overset{..}{N}: \qquad Co\!-\!\overset{..}{O}\!=\!C\!-\!\overset{..}{\underset{..}{O}}:$$
$$\underset{\textstyle R}{|}$$

This kind of polarization by way of π bonding offers an attractive explanation for the failure of CN^- and NCS^- to produce the activation of other ligands predicted on the basis of their negative charge. The large dipoles induced by π bonding would act in the opposite sense to the net charge on the ligand and cause an electrostatic attraction of other groups. Table 3.17 has some rate data for Rh(III) complexes which show that oxalate ion does act like the cyanide ion in not causing large increases in rates of acid hydrolysis.

Table 3.17 Rates of hydrolysis in acidic solution of some rhodium(III) complexes

Complex[a]	T, °C	$k_{obs} \times 10^5$, sec^{-1} [a]	Cl_{equil}, %
$trans$-Rh(NH$_3$)$_4$Cl$_2^+$	80	12.1	39
$trans$-Rh(en)$_2$Cl$_2^+$	80	10.4[b]	26
cis-Rh(en)$_2$Cl$_2^+$	80	85	60
cis-Rh(trien)Cl$_2^+$	55	15	47
$trans$-Rh(m-bn)$_2$Cl$_2^+$	80	85	32
$trans$-Rh(dl-bn)$_2$Cl$_2^+$	80	12	30
$trans$-Rh(tetrameen)$_2$Cl$_2^+$	25	160	~50
cis-Rh(tetrameen)$_2$Cl$_2^+$	25	110	~50
$trans$-Rh(bipy)$_2$Cl$_2^+$	80	...	0
Rh(NH$_3$)$_5$Cl^{2+}	80	6.2	69
$trans$-Rh(C$_2$O$_4$)$_2$Cl$_2^{3-}$	80	1.6	100
cis-Rh(C$_2$O$_4$)$_2$Cl$_2^{3-}$	80	2.3	100

[a] Rate constant for first-order approach to equilibrium.
[b] E_a for aquation is 25.5 kcal. Data from reference 87.

The rate constants given in Table 3.17 are first order for the approach to equilibrium, which in the case of Rh(III) chloroammines does not correspond to complete aquation. The percent of ionic chloride released at equilibrium is also shown in the table. The observed constant is the sum of a rate constant for aquation and a constant for anation, the reverse process. The constants can be separated,[87] but k_{obs} in the table is a good measure of relative reactivity. It can be seen that, like Co(III), alkyl substituents on ethylenediamine ligands speed up the rate of reaction greatly. This again suggests an S_N1 dissociation mechanism, at least for the more hindered complexes. The effect of charge is less than for Co(III) since Rh(NH$_3$)$_5$Cl^{2+} and $trans$-Rh(NH$_3$)$_4$Cl$_2^+$ are about equally reactive [factor of 300 for Co(III) as shown in Table 3.13]. This, together with the results for Rh(ox)$_2$Cl$_2^{3-}$, suggests the opposite, that an S_N2 mechanism is operating, at least for unhindered complexes. At least it seems reasonable that for Rh(III), as compared to Co(III), bond making is relatively more important and bond breaking less important.

It can be seen from Table 3.15 (also see Table 3.18) that chromium complexes react faster than analogous cobalt compounds and that the activation energies run about 2 kcal lower for chromium. The activation energies plus the rates are a more reliable guide than the rates alone, since a compound with a higher activation energy than another will accelerate its rate more with increasing temperature. In fact, it may react more slowly than the other compound at low temperature and more rapidly at high temperatures. This will only be possible, however, if the frequency factor A in the expression $k = Ae^{-E_a/RT}$ is greater for the first compound. Unfortunately, activation energies are usually known less accurately than rate constants.

This greater rate and lower value of E_a for a d^3 system compared to a d^6 ion is what is predicted on the basis of the crystal field theory. The difference in energy is not as great as might have been anticipated. Removing a chloride ion ligand completely in a pentammine complex causes a change in C.F.S.E. which may be estimated in the following way. The value of Dq for Cl$^-$ is only somewhat more than half of that for NH$_3$. Hence, the C.F.S.E. of Co(NH$_3$)$_5$Cl^{2+} is estimated as $22Dq$, where Dq is the value for NH$_3$. On forming a square pyramid with C.N. five, the C.F.S.E. drops to $20Dq$. The loss in stabilization energy is thus about $2Dq$ or 12 kcal. For Cr(NH$_3$)$_5$Cl^{2+}, the loss would be half of this or 6 kcal. The expected difference in activation energies is 6 kcal. For a solvent-assisted dissociation with an octahedral wedge transition state, the difference in C.F.A.E. predicted would be slightly less than 6 kcal.

Rhodium(III) complexes react more slowly than analogous Co(III) systems, and the activation energies run about 2 kcal higher. Iridium complexes are slower still, and the scanty data indicate activation energies higher than for Rh(III). These effects are in the direction predicted by crystal field theory since from spectral data Dq for the second transition series is some 50% greater than for the first series, and that for the third series almost double that for the first.

Tables 3.8 and 3.9 predict that a low-spin d^5 system should react faster than either d^3 or d^6. The rate sequence for acid hydrolysis is found experimentally from Table 3.15 to be Cr(III) > Co(III) > Ru(III) ≫ Rh(III). Allowing for the above variation in Dq, the predicted sequence for an S_N1 mechanism is Ru(III) > Cr(III) > Co(III) > Rh(III). Thus, ruthenium complexes are not as labile as predicted with respect to cobalt and chromium, but about right with respect to rhodium.

The great difficulty with this approach to reaction rates is that only one factor out of many is being considered, i.e., the crystal field stabilization.

As already mentioned, the overall bond energy is dominated by other factors. Since Ru(III) and Rh(III) are slightly larger in size than Cr(III) or Co(III), their slower rates of reaction cannot be explained by a simple electrostatic model. A consideration of the higher effective charge for the second transition series helps somewhat but barely compensates for the increased size. Thus, the ionization potentials of the gaseous atoms are nearly the same for the first and second transition series.

Another factor which is probably important is that the bonds of the later transition metals are more covalent than those of the first series. In other words, Ir(III) and Rh(III) are softer acids than Co(III). Since chloride ion is a softer base than water, greater energy is required to replace a Rh-Cl bond with a Rh-H_2O bond than to replace Co-Cl by Co-H_2O.

It is sometimes incorrectly assumed that activation energies for a reaction of a given metal ion with a variable leaving group should vary according to the position of the leaving ligand in the spectrochemical series. That is, a ligand with a large crystal field strength should dissociate slowly. This is related to another erroneous belief, that bond energies are measured by the spectrochemical series. If the purely electrostatic crystal field theory were correct, these two assumptions would be justified since the ligand of largest crystal field would be held most firmly. As we have seen, the electrostatic theory is inadequate and the spectrochemical series is partly determined by π bonding and π antibonding effects. Such π bonds have only a minor effect on the bond energy, which is largely determined by σ bonding. There is, indeed, a rough parallelism between strength of bonding and the spectrochemical series $CN^- >$ phen $> \underline{N}O_2^- >$ en $> NH_3 > \underline{N}CS^- > H_2O > F^- > RCO_2^- > OH^- > Cl^- > Br^-$, but the exceptions can easily be seen. We are reminded by this discussion that the C.F.A.E.'s of Tables 3.7, 3.8, and 3.9 are calculated by the electrostatic model, which is admittedly inadequate.

π Bonding in Dissociation Reactions of Octahedral Complexes

The preceding section considered the influence on rates of acid hydrolysis of gross changes in the nature of the reacting complex. Hopefully, more precise information about the mechanisms of reaction might be obtained from subtle changes in the reactant. Table 3.18 contains some of the important data obtained by Tobe and his collaborators on the reaction

$$Co(en)_2LCl^+ + H_2O \rightarrow Co(en)_2LH_2O^{2+} + Cl^- \qquad (33)$$

Here L is a group which can be varied and, furthermore, can be placed either cis or trans to the leaving halide ion. The product also can exist in two isomeric forms and, if optically active cis-Co(en)$_2$LCl$^+$ is the starting material, in enantiomeric forms as well. Such stereochemical results can be particularly valuable in understanding fine details of reaction mechanisms. For reaction (33) the stereochemistry will be discussed in Chapter 4, and at this point only the rate data will be considered.

Table 3.18   Rate data for acid hydrolysis of Co(en)$_2$LCl$^+$ at 25°C

L	k, × 10^5, sec^{-1}	E_a, kcal	log A^d
$trans$-OH$^-$	160	26.2	16.4
$trans$-Br$^-$	4.5	25.2	14.1
$trans$-Cl$^-$	3.5	27.5	15.9
$trans$-N$_3^-$	22	23.1	13.3
$trans$-NCS$^-$	0.005	30.4	14.9
$trans$-NH$_3$	0.034	23.6	10.9
$trans$-H$_2$O	0.25^a	...	...
$trans$-CN$^-$	8.2^b	22.6	12.4
$trans$-NO$_2^-$	98	21.6	12.8
cis-OH$^-$	1200	23.1	15.0
cis-Br$^-$	14	23.3	15.8
cis-Cl$^-$	24	22.2	12.5
cis-N$_3^-$	20	21.7	12.3
cis-NCS$^-$	1.1	20.8	10.3
cis-NH$_3$	0.05	23.0	10.5
cis-H$_2$O	0.16^a	...	...
cis-NO$_2^-$	11	22.3	12.5
$trans$-Cl^c	2.2	23.2	12.3
$trans$-H$_2$O^c	<0.1	...	...
cis-Cl^c	33	21.1	11.9
cis-H$_2$O^c	~3	...	...

Data from reference 90 except as specified in notes a, b, and c.
^{a} Reference 88a.
^{b} Reference 88b.
^{c} Chromium(III); reference 89.
^{d} A in sec^{-1}.

The groups, L, are arranged in Table 3.18 in an order of decreasing tendency to donate electrons to cobalt and increasing tendency to accept electrons. The hydroxide ion, for example, is assumed to be a strong electron donor not only through the σ bond, but also through ligand to metal π bonding. The halide ions can behave in the same way:

$$\text{Co} = \overset{..}{\text{O}}\text{H} \qquad \text{Co} = \overset{..}{\text{C}}\text{l} :$$

The nitro and cyano groups will be π-electron acceptors, as already shown on p. 167. The positions of the isothiocyanate and azide ions is somewhat *post facto*, but in addition to the resonance forms shown on p. 167 it is possible to write

$$Co=N=C=\overset{..}{S}: \qquad Co=N=N=\overset{..}{N}:$$

since the nitrogen ligand atom can be an electron donor.

Figure 3.8 shows a schematic plot of log k for aquation plotted against the supposed order of electron donation and acceptance.[91] The *cis* and *trans* isomers behave in a similar but not identical fashion. A minimum rate is seen at L = NH_3 for the *cis* and L = NCS^- for the *trans* isomers.

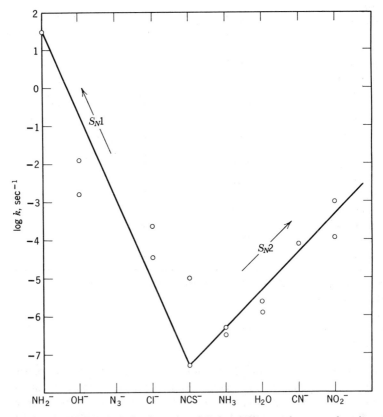

Fig. 3.8   Rates of hydrolysis of a series of $Co(en)_2LCl^+$ complexes as a function of the electron-donating or -accepting power of L. The ascending curves indicate the supposedly increasing S_N1 character (left branch) and increasing S_N2 character (right branch) in the reaction mechanism.

With these as standards, either an electron-supplying ligand or an electron-withdrawing ligand can increase the rate of hydrolysis. Furthermore, electron-donating ligands affect the rates of the *cis* isomers more, and electron-attracting substituents affect the rates of the *trans* isomers more.

To understand these stereospecific effects it is necessary to look at the geometric requirements for strong π bonding.[92] The electron-accepting groups such as nitro and cyano will withdraw t_{2g} electrons from the cobalt ion (see Chapter 2). This is shown in Fig. 3.9, and it is obvious that the electron density around the group *trans* to the nitro group is strongly reduced, whereas the *cis* position is less affected. This makes it easier for a solvent molecule (or other nucleophile) to attach itself to cobalt and to initiate an S_N2 *cis* displacement of the chloride ion if the chloro group is *trans* to the nitro group. There should be a small effect also for a nitro group at the *cis* position. The conclusion is that the electron-withdrawing groups cause rate increases by promoting an S_N2 mechanism, or at least by increasing the amount of bond making in the transition state.

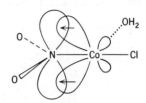

Fig. 3.9 Cobalt to nitrogen π bonding reduces electron density at *trans* ligand. The arrows show the direction of the electron drift.

The way in which an electron donor ligand can interact with the metal is more complex. The chief interaction is a repulsive one between the t_{2g} *d* electrons of the metal and the π electrons of the ligand. The metal also has the t_{1u}, or *p* orbitals, available. These are used partly for σ bonding and partly for π bonding, since they have the right symmetry for both. Now, if a ligand is removed from the metal ion, one of the *p* orbitals is partly freed from σ bonding, its energy is lowered, and it becomes more available for π bonding. If a ligand is removed from the *x* axis, it is the p_x orbital which is lowered in energy. Only a ligand *cis* to the removed ligand can form a π bond with the p_x orbital. The *trans* ligand can only π-bond with p_z and p_y. Figure 3.10 shows the nature of the π bonding in two ways: first in terms of the *p* orbitals of the metal, and second in terms of the hybrid d^2sp^3 orbital of valence bond or L.M.O. theory. In the latter case a *cis* ligand can again form a π bond to the vacated hybrid orbital, but a *trans* group cannot.††

The conclusion is that electron-donating substituents increase the rate of reaction by putting more negative charge on cobalt, thereby increasing the ease of dissociation of other groups. An S_N1 mechanism is facilitated in which bond breaking is important and bond making is minimized. This occurs much more effectively for a *cis* substituent than for a *trans*.

†† There is no real difference between the two explanations, since it is only the p_x component of the d^2sp^3 hybrid which can π-bond.

Inductive effects through the σ-bond system can also increase dissociation rates. A soft ligand which forms more covalent bonds will put negative charge on the central metal atom. This effect is also stereospecific in that covalent σ bonding to the p_x orbital can now occur (leaving group on the x axis). Electron density in this orbital will have a greater effect than electron density in the p_y and p_z orbitals, which a *cis* substituent will tend to fill. The other metal orbitals used for σ bonding, the s and e_g orbitals, will not be stereospecific since *cis* and *trans* leaving groups will be affected

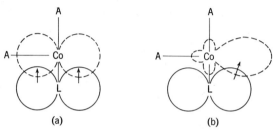

(a)   (b)

Fig. 3.10   Overlap of filled p orbital of L with vacant (a) p orbital or (b) d^2sp^3 orbital hybrid of cobalt in a five-coordinated tetragonal pyramid activated complex resulting from the dissociation of X from *cis*-CoA$_4$LX. The two A ligands not shown are above and below the plane of the paper.

equally. The high rates[89] of acid hydrolysis of *cis*-Cr(en)$_2$H$_2$OCl^{2+} and *cis*-Cr(en)$_2$H$_2$OBr^{2+} compared to their *trans* isomers may be due to this effect.

A stereochemical prediction can be made based on the π-bonding concept. If a group dissociates completely, leaving an intermediate of C.N. five, there will be a great tendency for the square pyramid structure to rearrange into a trigonal bipyramid structure. The basis for this tendency is that, by such a rearrangement, π bonding can now take place between the ligand and the empty $d_{x^2-y^2}$ orbital in the trigonal plane (Fig. 3.11). Since this orbital is lower in energy than the p_x orbital, the new π bonding will lead to a greater stabilization of the system. Such a rearrangement will have important stereochemical consequences for the products of a substitution reaction. These will be discussed in Chapter 4. It will be recalled that, on the basis of crystal field effects, rearrangement to a trigonal bipyramid is strongly forbidden for a Co(III) complex, unless other factors such as π bonding are involved.

Since *trans* groups cannot π-bond efficiently without rearranging, whereas *cis* groups can, it can also be predicted that such rearrangements will be much more common for *trans* substituents than for *cis*.

The remarkably low reactivity of *trans*-Co(en)$_2$NCSCl$^+$ and the relatively high reactivity of *cis*-Co(en)$_2$NCSCl$^+$ can be partly understood in terms of stabilization of the ground state in both cases by the π bonding shown on p. 167. For the *cis* complex an even greater stabilization of a five-coordinated intermediate can occur without stereo change. For the *trans* complex there is no compensating factor unless there is rearrangement to a trigonal bipyramid. This rearrangement costs something in crystal field stabilization energy.

A great many examples are known in octahedral coordination chemistry in which replacing some other group by a hydroxy or similar ligand produces a strong labilizing effect.[90,92] In fact, it may be said to be a universal phenomenon. Several examples will be mentioned in the following pages.

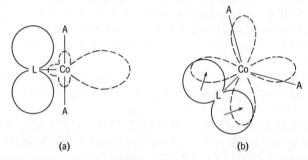

(a)   (b)

Fig. 3.11   (a) No overlap of filled p orbital of L with vacant d^2sp^3 orbital hybrid of cobalt in the tetragonal pyramid resulting from the dissociation of X from *trans*-CoA$_4$LX. (b) Efficient overlap with vacant $d_{x^2-y^2}$ if there is rearrangement to a trigonal bipyramid structure. The two A ligands not shown are above and below the plane of the paper.

In the case of halogen substituents, Table 3.15 shows strong activation. The explanation here is not clear, though the fact of greater activation in the *cis* position suggests π bonding. One might well suppose that σ covalent bonding is responsible. Thus, if an amine group forms more covalent bonds than chlorine, it would activate the group *trans* to it as described earlier. This would cause *cis*-Co(en)$_2$Cl$_2$$^+$ to be more reactive than *trans*-Co(en)$_2$Cl$_2$$^+$. The nephelauxetic series (p. 112) indicates that Cl$^-$ forms more covalent bonds than does NH$_3$, however.

Conceivably this greater *cis* reactivity might be due to electrostatic repulsions of the negative ligands, which would appear to be greater in the *cis* position than in the *trans* because of the smaller distance of separation. There are reasons why this is probably not true. For negative ligands such as nitro, the reverse is found in that *trans*-Co(en)$_2$(NO$_2$)Cl$^+$ is more reactive than *cis*-Co(en)$_2$(NO$_2$)Cl$^+$ in hydrolysis. Also indirect evidence shows that the sulfito group, like the nitro, is more activating when in the *trans* position than in the *cis* position. In the synthesis of the isomers of

$Co(en)(NH_3)_2Cl_2^+$, the key step is the replacement of two NH_3 groups *trans* to two SO_3^{2-} groups, leaving two NH_3 groups *cis* to SO_3^{2-} untouched. The acid ionization constants of *cis*- and *trans*-$Co(en)_2(H_2O)_2^{3+}$, as well as of *cis*- and *trans*-$Cr(en)_2(H_2O)_2^{3+}$, also show that electrostatic repulsion, in the case of two protons, is greater when in the *trans* position than in the *cis* position.[95] Thus in these cases the *trans* isomer is the stronger acid, and the difference in the successive ionization constants is greater for the *trans* isomer than for the *cis*. The examples in this paragraph are generally cited as instances of the *trans* effect, which states that a negative ligand *trans* to a reactive ligand will activate it. This rule, which is valid and very valuable for the square complexes of Pt(II), is discussed in detail in Chapter 5. If the π-bonding hypothesis for the reactions of octahedral complexes such as Co(III) and Cr(III) is valid, this rule will not work for such complexes in the case of ligands which form π bonds by electron donation to the central atom.

In a number of cases, activation by *trans* substituents (more than by *cis*) has been reported for octahedral complexes. Examples are $Cr(CN)_5NO^{3-}$ [96] and $Mn(CO)_5Br$,[97a] where the activating groups are NO and CO, respectively; $Ru(R_2PCH_2CH_2PR_2)_2X_2$ and $Os(R_2PCH_2CH_2PR_2)_2X_2$, where the activating group is the tertiary phosphine; *trans*-$Ru(R_2PC_2H_4PR_2)_2(H)Cl$ and *trans*-$Ru(R_2PC_2H_4PR_2)_2(CH_3)Cl$, where the activating group is H^- and CH_3^-.[97b] Connick has reported that in $Ru(H_2O)_3Cl_3$ activation by *trans* chloro groups occurs.[76] Very strong activation by iodide occurs in *trans*-$Rh(en)_2ICl^+$ and *trans*-$Rh(en)_2IBr^+$.[98] The *cis* isomers have not yet been prepared to see whether they have a greater influence. The nitro group in *trans*-$Rh(en)_2NO_2Cl^+$ also has a large activating effect.[99] In this case it is known that the *cis* isomer has a smaller rate of aquation, resembling the Co(III) system.

All of the cases of *trans* activation mentioned above are for ligands which either are unsaturated and form acceptor π bonds with the t_{2g} electrons of the metal, or are rather soft so that considerable σ covalent bonding occurs. In either case activation should affect the *trans* ligand most.

Other evidence can be cited for the type of π bonding proposed in which electrons from the ligand move into the metal atom. The binuclear complex $(NH_3)_5Cr—O—Cr(NH_3)_5^{4+}$ has a paramagnetism corresponding to two unpaired electrons instead of the six expected for two Cr(III) atoms. This and other evidence[100] suggests that two electrons from each chromium and four electrons from oxygen are paired in occupying four three-center molecular orbitals centered on Cr—O—Cr. These would be formed from the d_{xy} and d_{xz} orbitals of each chromium and from the p_y and p_z orbitals of oxygen, for example. The complex $Cl_5Ru—O—RuCl_5^{4-}$ is diamagnetic instead of having four unpaired electrons and seems to have the same kind of orbital hybridization.[101] In this case x-ray evidence shows that the Ru—O—Ru bond is linear, as is required for the proposed explanation.

The rhodochromium(III) complex is converted rapidly in basic solution to the corresponding erythro complex at a rate independent of the hydroxide ion concentration.

$$(NH_3)_5Cr—O—Cr(NH_3)_5^{4+} \xrightarrow{H_2O} (NH_3)_5Cr—O—Cr(NH_3)_4OH^{4+} \quad (34)$$
$$\overset{H}{\quad}$$

rhodo   *erythro*

Also, strong activation was found[102] for complexes of the general structure $(NH_3)_5Cr—O—Cr(NH_3)_4X^{3+}$, where X is substituted some 10^5 times faster than in $Cr(NH_3)_5X^{2+}$. These observations support the idea that π bonding, ligand to metal, produces strong activation of other ligands. In this case it is a *trans* ligand which is strongly activated because the ligand π electrons go into d_{xy} and d_{xz} orbitals of the metal rather than p_x and p_y orbitals. Some activation of the *cis* ligands would also occur.

Base Hydrolysis of Cobalt(III) Complexes

Up to now, nothing has been said about the effect of the nature of the incoming ligand on the rate of a substitution reaction. The reason for this is very simple: with the single exception of hydroxide ion, there is no good evidence for any direct reaction of a nucleophilic reagent with a Co(III) complex in water solution. Thus, in most examples that have been studied, the reaction mechanism for the substitution of X by Y has gone through the intermediate formation of an aquo complex as shown, for example,

$$Co(NH_3)_5X^{2+} + H_2O \rightleftharpoons Co(NH_3)_5H_2O^{3+} + X^- \quad (35)$$

$$Co(NH_3)_5H_2O^{3+} + Y^- \rightarrow Co(NH_3)_5Y^{2+} + H_2O \quad (36)$$

Since the order of the reaction in which X^- is liberated is always zero with respect to Y^-, there is no way to test the effect of the nature of Y^- on the rates.

The first example of the mechanism shown in 35 and 36 was provided by Ettle and Johnson,[103] who found that the rate of exchange of radioactive chloride ion with *cis*-$Co(en)_2Cl_2^+$ went through the aquo stage.

$$Co(en)_2Cl_2^+ + H_2O \rightarrow Co(en)_2(H_2O)Cl^{2+} + Cl^- \quad (37)$$

$$Co(en)_2(H_2O)Cl^{2+} + {}^*Cl^- \rightarrow Co(en)_2{}^*Cl_2^+ + H_2O \quad (38)$$

Furthermore the rate of the reaction leading to exchange was independent of the concentration of chloride ion so that no direct replacement of Cl^- by ${}^*Cl^-$ occurred.

Similar observations on the effect of added anions on the rate of hydrolysis of $Co(NH_3)_5Cl^{2+}$ were made by Garrick.[104] Except for small increases or decreases to be attributed to ion interaction effects (see p. 34), the rates were unaffected by NO_3^-, ClO_4^-, and SO_4^{2-}. Nor does the presence of more strongly basic anions have any different result. Thus the rates of chloride ion release in cis- and trans-$Co(en)_2(NO_2)Cl^+$ are independent of $[N_3^-]$ up to 0.5 M and of $[NO_2^-]$ up to 1.0 M, provided the solutions are buffered to keep $[OH^-]$ at a low value.[105] Thiocyanate ion, which is a good reagent for organic halides, is ineffective for the chloronitro complexes. Also the exchange reactions of $Cr(NH_3)_5NCS^{2+}$, $Co(NH_3)_5$-NCS^{2+}, and $Co(en)_2(NCS)_2^+$ with *NCS^- proceed by the hydrolysis mechanism of 37 and 38 with no direct reaction.[106] At high concentrations of thiocyanate ion there is a small increase in the rate of hydrolysis of $Co(NH_3)_5NCS^{2+}$, but this is ascribed to ion-pair formation.

In alkaline buffer solutions containing borate ion, acetate ion, or trimethylamine as the basic component, the increased rate of hydrolysis compared to acid conditions is due only to the hydroxide ion present.[107] If one plots the observed rate constant for the release of chloride ion from trans-$Co(en)_2Cl_2^+$ in acetic acid–acetate buffers as a function of the reciprocal of the acetic acid concentration at constant acetate ion concentration, a straight line is obtained. Upon extrapolation to infinite acetic acid concentration, the rate becomes the same as that observed in a nitric acid solution of pH 1. Hence acetate ion has no effect on the rate; cis- and trans-$Cr(en)_2Cl_2^+$ also hydrolyze at a rate independent of acetate ion concentration.

The sodium salts of polyvalent anions such as citrate, phthalate, and adipate do give an increased rate of hydrolysis[18d] for $Cr(NH_3)_5X^{2+}$. The effects are small, since only a doubling of the rate occurs even at high anion concentration. The doubling of the rate is brought about by concentrations of the anion about equal to that of the complex, and further addition changes the rate very little. Also, the product of the faster reaction continues to be $Cr(NH_3)_5H_2O^{3+}$ under conditions where the citrate, etc., complexes would be stable. There is no doubt that ion pairs are responsible for the slightly increased rate of aquation, and that the effect of the anions is an indirect one and is not related to nucleophilic attack by the anions.[18d]

Table 3.19 shows that trans-$Rh(en)_2Cl_2^+$ is insensitive to the presence of various reagents including, in this case, the basic OH^- as well as polarizable I^- and thiourea. Even five molar ammonia does not cause an increased rate of reaction. Radiobromide exchange of $Rh(NH_3)_5Br^{2+}$ and $Ir(NH_3)_5$-Br^{2+} is independent of the bromide ion concentration, and the rate is equal to that of acid hydrolysis.[108]

The same behavior, rate independence of the nature and concentration of the entering group, is found for the series of reactions[99]

$$trans\text{-}Rh(en)_2XY^+ + Z \rightarrow Rh(en)_2XZ^+ + Y \qquad (39)$$

where X, Y, and Z are the various halide ions. Even cyanide ion is ineffective as a nucleophile towards $trans\text{-}Rh(en)_2I_2^+$ [99] and $Cr(NH_3)_2$-$(SCN)_4^-$.[18b]

This reaction rate independence of the incoming group is characteristic not only of the inert complexes of Co(III), Cr(III), and Rh(III), but also of

Table 3.19 Rates of the reaction
$trans\text{-}[Rh(en)_2Cl_2]^+ + 2X \rightarrow trans\text{-}[Rh(en)_2X_2]^{n+} + 2Cl^-$
for various reagents at 80°

X	$k \times 10^5$ sec^{-1}	X	$k \times 10^5$ sec^{-1}
OH$^-$ (0.1 M)	5.1	I$^-$ (0.05 M)	5.1
NO$_2^-$ (0.1 M)	4.2	^{36}Cl$^-$ (0.01 M)	4.0
NO$_2^-$ (0.05 M)	4.2	thiourea (0.1 M)	4.9
I$^-$ (0.1 M)	5.2	NH$_3$(5.0 M)	4.0

Data from reference 87.

octahedral complexes in general, at least as far as unidentate ligands are concerned. Thus, the exchange and substitution reactions of the labile complexes of both the transition and non-transition metals are independent of the substituting reagent. Apparent exceptions occur for certain chelate ligands, but these are probably a consequence of the special mechanism for chelates. This topic will be discussed later.

Compared to all other nucleophiles, expecially for the cobalt ammines, hydroxide ion falls into a special category. It is necessary to appreciate the great influence of even low concentrations of hydroxide ion on the rate of release of halide ion and other labile ligands from ammine complexes of Co(III). Under alkaline conditions hydrolysis is very rapid, for many complexes the half-life being less than 1 sec for 0.001 M reactants at 25°C. Flow methods can be used to examine such rapid reactions,[107] or they can be studied in buffer solutions of suitable pH. In a few cases, such as for $Co(NH_3)_5Cl^{2+}$, conventional techniques for kinetic studies can be used. In all instances in which a reaction with hydroxide ion can be detected, the reactions have been found to be second order overall, first order in the complex, and first order in [OH$^-$]. Table 3.20 shows a number of the second-order rate constants for the base hydrolysis of several metal-ammine complexes.

For the pentaammines of Co(III) it is seen that the rates of base hydrolysis also decrease as the strength of the leaving group as a base increases.[109] In fact, there is a nearly constant ratio of 10^5 between the rate constants for base hydrolysis and those for acid hydrolysis. This could be an indication of a common, presumably $S_N 2$, mechanism, for both.[110] The ratio of rate

Table 3.20   Rate data for base hydrolysis of some cobalt(III) and related complexes at 25°C

Ion	k_{OH}, M^{-1} sec^{-1}	E_a, kcal	$\Delta S^{\ddagger}$, eu	Ref.
$Co(NH_3)_5I^{2+}$	23	29	+42	68
$Co(NH_3)_5Br^{2+}$	7.5	28	+40	68
$Co(NH_3)_5Cl^{2+}$	0.85	29	+36	68
$Co(NH_3)_5F^{2+}$	1.2×10^{-2}	27	+20	132
$Co(NH_3)_5O_2CCH_3^{2+}$	7.0×10^{-4}	...	...	109
$Co(NH_3)_5N_3^{2+}$	3.0×10^{-4}	33	+35	68
$Co(NH_3)_5NCS^{2+}$	8.0×10^{-4}	35	+41	242
$Co(NH_3)_5NO_2^{2+}$	4.2×10^{-6}	38	+30	68
$trans\text{-}Co(NH_3)_4Cl_2^+$	1.8×10^3	...	...	107
$Cr(NH_3)_5I^{2+}$	3.6	27	+20	71
$Cr(NH_3)_5Br^{2+}$	6.9×10^{-2}	26	+18	71
$Cr(NH_3)_5Cl^{2+}$	1.7×10^{-3}	27	+13	71
$Cr(NH_3)_5NCS^{2+}$	1.0×10^{-5}	36	+36	242
$Ru(NH_3)_5Cl^{2+}$	4.9	...	...	75
$Rh(NH_3)_5I^{2+}$	$7.3 + 10^{-5}$	33	+31	243
$Rh(NH_3)_5Br^{2+}$	3.4×10^{-4}	30.5	+26	78, 243
$Rh(NH_3)_5Cl^{2+}$	4.1×10^{-4}	28.5	+20	87, 243

constants can be rationalized by considering the equilibrium

$$Co(NH_3)_4XH_2O^{2+} + OH^- \rightleftharpoons Co(NH_3)_4XOH^+ + H_2O \qquad (40)$$

which gives the relative stabilities of an aquo complex and a hydroxo complex somewhat similar to the transition states for the two substitution reactions. The pK_a's of cis- and trans-$Co(en)_2ClH_2O^{2+}$ are reported[90a] as 6.8 and 5.8, suggesting that the equilibrium constant for 40 is $10^{-6}/10^{-14} = 10^8$. This would be an upper limit for the ratio of the rate constants since the bonding is less in a transition state than in a normal molecule.

An examination of other systems shows that such a unified mechanism is not likely to be correct, even for Co(III) complexes. The ratio of rate constants for base hydrolysis to those for acid hydrolysis is quite variable, ranging from unity to 10^9. Substituents which increase the rate of acid hydrolysis often decrease the rate of base hydrolysis and vice versa. Chromium chloroammines have a surprisingly low ratio of rates, of the order of 10^2–10^3. Rhodium(III) ammines also have a low ratio, but the ratio for $Ru(NH_3)_5Cl^{2+}$ is a high 10^7. Tables 3.21 and 3.22 present some further data on base hydrolysis of metal ammines. The extensive data on the series cis- and trans-$Co(en)_2LX^+$, where L is a variable, inert ligand again will prove very useful, since the stereochemical results of base hydrolysis are also known, thanks to Ingold, Tobe, and their colleagues.

Table 3.21 Rate constants for base hydrolysis at 0°C

$$Co(en)_2LCl^+ + OH^- \rightarrow Co(en)_2LOH^+ + Cl^-$$

Ion	k_{OH}, M^{-1} sec^{-1}	E_a	log A
trans-$Co(en)_2Cl_2^+$	85	23.2	20.5
trans-$Co(en)_2BrCl^+$	110	24.9	21.9
trans-$Co(en)_2OHCl^+$	0.017	22.8	16.4
trans-$Co(en)_2NCSCl^+$	0.35	23.2	18.7
trans-$Co(en)_2NH_3Cl^{2+}$	1.25	...	...
trans-$Co(en)_2N_3Cl^+$	0.41	...	...
trans-$Co(en)_2CNCl^+$	0.13	23.2	17.7
trans-$Co(en)_2NO_2Cl$	0.080	24.4	18.4
cis-$Co(en)_2Cl_2$	15.1	24.6	20.8
cis-$Co(en)_2BrCl^+$	23	22.7	19.5
cis-$Co(en)_2OHCl^+$	0.37	22.4	17.4
cis-$Co(en)_2NCSCl^+$	1.40	...	...
cis-$Co(en)_2NH_3Cl^{2+}$	0.50	...	...
cis-$Co(en)_2N_3Cl^+$	0.17	...	...
cis-$Co(en)_2NO_2Cl^+$	0.03	23.1	17.0

Data from S. C. Chan and M. L. Tobe, *J. Chem. Soc.*, **1962**, 4531; **1963**, 514.

At this point we will discuss only the rate data, and the stereochemistry will be covered in the next chapter.

A priori, the greatest objection to the idea of a simple S_N2 mechanism for base hydrolysis is that it seems inconceivable that only OH$^-$ can act as a nucleophilic reagent for these octahedral complexes. Cobalt(III) is only a moderately hard acid with some tendency to bind polarizable ligands more tightly, as has already been discussed. For rates, as compared to equilibria, the effect of polarizability in the ligand should be even more pronounced. It seems necessary to find a specific mechanism for the hydroxide ion, related to its unique role as the anion of the solvent (the lyate ion). In organic chemistry it is usually found that reactions whose rates depend on "specific hydroxide ion catalysis" involve acid-base equilibria before reaction.

Table 3.22   Rate constants for base hydrolysis at 25°C

Ion	k_{OH}, M^{-1} sec^{-1}	k_{OH}/k_{H_2O}	Ref.
$Co(NH_3)_5Cl^{2+}$	0.85	5×10^5	117
cis-$Co(en)_2NH_3Cl^{2+}$	54	1.1×10^8	107
cis-$Co(trien)NH_3Cl^{2+}$	160	7.3×10^8	107
cis-$Co(en)_2Cl_2^+$	1,000	4.0×10^6	107
cis-$Co(trien)Cl_2^+$	200,000	1.3×10^9	107
trans-$Co(en)_2Cl_2^+$	3,000	9.0×10^7	107
trans-$Co(pn)_2Cl_2^+$	2,300	3.7×10^7	107
trans-$Co(dl$-bn$)_2Cl_2^+$	2,100	1.4×10^7	107
trans-$Co(m$-bn$)_2Cl_2^+$	9,800	2.3×10^6	107
trans-$Co(i$-bn$)_2Cl_2^+$	9,800	4.5×10^6	107
trans-$Co(N$-meen$)_2Cl_2^+$	11,000	6.5×10^8	107
trans-$Co(N$-pren$)_2Cl_2^+$	21,000	1.8×10^8	107
trans-$Co(en)_2Br_2^+$	12,000	9.6×10^7	107
trans-$Co(en)_2F_2^+$	64	6.4×10^7	107
trans-$Co(dan)_2Cl_2^+$	17,000	5.7×10^6	107
cis-$Cr(en)_2Cl_2^+$	2.7×10^{-2}	82	118
trans-$Cr(en)_2Cl_2^+$	3.7×10^{-2}	1.7×10^3	118
cis-$Rh(en)_2Cl_2^+$	2×10^{-3}	$\sim 2 \times 10^3$	87
cis-$Rh(trien)Cl_2^+$	3×10^{-2}	$\sim 10^4$	87
trans-$Rh(NH_3)_4Cl_2^+$	$<10^{-5}$	<10	87
trans-$Rh(en)_2Cl_2^+$	$<10^{-5}$	<10	87
trans-$Rh(m$-bn$)_2Cl_2^+$	$<10^{-5}$	<10	87
trans-$Rh(dl$-bn$)_2Cl_2^+$	$<10^{-5}$	<10	87

Such a specific mechanism has been given by Garrick,[112] inspired by the earlier work of Brønsted.[113] Brønsted noted that the hydrolysis of $Co(NH_3)_5NO_3^{2+}$ is independent of pH below 3; however, that of $Co(NH_3)_4(H_2O)NO_3^{2+}$ is dependent on [H$^+$] even below pH 3. Brønsted's explanation was that the aquo complex dissociates to a hydroxo complex which reacts more rapidly:

$$Co(NH_3)_4(H_2O)NO_3^{2+} + H_2O \xrightarrow{slow} Co(NH_3)_4(H_2O)_2^{3+} + NO_3^- \quad (41)$$

$$Co(NH_3)_4(H_2O)NO_3^{2+} \underset{}{\overset{fast}{\rightleftharpoons}} Co(NH_3)_4(OH)NO_3^+ + H^+ \quad (42)$$

$$Co(NH_3)_4(OH)NO_3^+ + H_2O \xrightarrow{fast} Co(NH_3)_4(OH)H_2O^{2+} + NO_3^- \quad (43)$$

The acid-base equilibrium in 42 would be rapidly established. As already mentioned, a hydroxo group has a labilizing influence on a replaceable ligand, so that 43 would be fast. The concentration of the reactive hydroxo complex would be inversely proportional to [H$^+$], and the rate should show the same inverse proportionality. This is in agreement with the observations. A similar explanation holds for the second-order dependence on [OH$^-$] of the rate of hydrolysis[114] of $Cr(H_2O)_5Cl^{2+}$. The reactive species is chiefly $Cr(H_2O)_3(OH)_2Cl$.

Garrick's mechanism involves the formation, in a rapid acid-base equilibrium step, of the conjugate base or amido complex of the original ammine complex. This then dissociates rapidly and eventually forms the hydroxo complex, in which 45, although rapid, is the rate-determining step. Such a mechanism may be

$$Co(NH_3)_5Cl^{2+} + OH^- \overset{fast}{\rightleftharpoons} Co(NH_3)_4NH_2Cl^+ + H_2O \qquad (44)$$

$$Co(NH_3)_4(NH_2)Cl^+ \overset{slow}{\longrightarrow} Co(NH_3)_4NH_2^{2+} + Cl^- \qquad (45)$$

$$Co(NH_3)_4NH_2^{2+} + H_2O \overset{fast}{\longrightarrow} Co(NH_3)_5OH^{2+} \qquad (46)$$

conveniently called an S_N1CB *mechanism*[1] (substitution, nucleophilic, unimolecular, conjugate base).

For agreement with the observed second-order kinetics (first order in OH$^-$) it is necessary that reaction 44 occur, but only to a small extent even in 0.01 M alkali. Otherwise, all of the chloro complex would be converted to the conjugate base form at some particular value of the pH, and for further increases in [OH$^-$] no further increase in rate could occur. For $Co(NH_3)_5Cl^{2+}$ a leveling in rate does occur at high base concentration [S. C. Chan, *J. Chem. Soc.*, **A1124** (1966)]. This is due to ion-pair formation and is quite independent of conjugate base formation. Furthermore, for agreement with the observation that only hydroxide ion affects the rate and that other bases are ineffective as such, it is necessary that reaction 44 be established as an equilibrium more rapidly than the rapid overall reaction. The necessity for this arises from the certainty of a general base catalysis otherwise.[111] A proton could be removed from the original complex by any base, and the resultant amido compound could rapidly react. In such a case the rate equation for hydrolysis would be

$$\text{Rate} = k[\text{complex}] [\text{base}] \qquad (47)$$

or rather a sum of such terms for every base in solution. Only if 44 is an equilibrium will the equation for the rate be

$$\text{Rate} = k[\text{conjugate base}] = \frac{kK_a}{K_w} [\text{complex}][\text{OH}^-] \qquad (48)$$

These requirements are fulfilled apparently since cobalt ammines are acidic enough to exchange deuterium with D_2O even in acid solution,[115] but are too weak as acids to measure experimentally (see p. 33). Also it has been shown that exchange with D_2O occurs more rapidly than the net release of the chloride ion for many complexes.[116]

The S_N1CB mechanism can be used to rationalize most, but not all, of the data in Tables 3.20–3.22. From equation 48 it can be seen that the observed second-order rate constant for base hydrolysis is equal to kK_a/K_w, where k is the rate constant for the dissociation of the conjugate base as in 45 and K_a is the acid constant of the amine group. Thus, the rates for base hydrolysis are a function of two possible variables, and changes in either K_a or k can influence the relative values of the constants in the tables. The rate constant k will be dominated by the amido group since the assumption is that, by donor π bonding, this will be a very powerful promoter of an S_N1 mechanism. Figure 3.8, in fact, shows schematically how an amido ligand will cause a high rate of dissociation, more than any other known substituent.

This means that there may not be a parallelism between the rate constant, k, for the dissociation of the amido complex and the rate constant, k_{H_2O}, for acid hydrolysis, even if the latter also has a dissociation mechanism. The π-bonding acceleration of acid hydrolysis by a weak group may be completely swamped out by the stronger amido group in base hydrolysis. It may also be anticipated that the amido substituent will greatly increase the tendency of the five-coordinated intermediate of equation 45 to rearrange to a trigonal bipyramid, such as is shown in Fig. 3.11b. We shall see that there is strong evidence that this happens in the stereochemical changes found in base hydrolysis (Chapter 4).

It should be possible to say something about the way in which K_a changes from one complex to another, and hence to predict the effect on rates. Since K_a cannot be measured directly, various models must be used, such as the corresponding aquo complexes of Co(III) and the ammine complexes of Pt(IV), which are strong enough acids to measure. Some data are given in Tables 1.9 and 1.10.

Another kind of information which bears on various K_a values are the rates of the base-catalyzed deuterium exchanges of various metal ammines. Table 3.23 contains a listing of the available data, which are quite extensive. The reaction studied corresponds to equation 44. The assumption is made that the larger K_a is for the various complexes, the greater the rate of deuterium exchange will be. This seems quite reasonable, since it is simply another linear free energy relationship, often found for proton transfers.

The rates of base hydrolysis of the cobalt complexes listed in Table 3.22 can be interpreted now by noticing from Tables 1.9 and 1.10 and from Table 3.23 that increasing chelation and N-alkyl substitution have the effect of increasing K_a, and hence increasing the rate of base hydrolysis.

Table 3.23 Rates of base-catalyzed hydrogen exchange of metal ammines at 25°C in D_2O

$$M\text{---}NH + OD^- \xrightarrow{k_{ex}} M\text{---}ND + OH^-$$

Ion	k_{ex}, M^{-1} sec^{-1} $\times$ 10^{-6}	Ref.
Co(NH$_3$)$_6$$^{3+}$	1.6	119
Rh(NH$_3$)$_6$$^{3+}$	0.21	119
Ir(NH$_3$)$_6$$^{3+}$	0.015	119
Cr(NH$_3$)$_6$$^{3+}$	2.6	119
Ru(NH$_3$)$_6$$^{3+}$	600	119
Os(NH$_3$)$_6$$^{3+}$	6	119
Pt(NH$_3$)$_6$$^{4+}$	instantaneous	119
Os(en)$_3$$^{4+}$	instantaneous	119
Co(en)$_3$$^{3+}$	2.4	119
Cr(en)$_3$$^{3+}$	3.6	119
Co(pn)$_3$$^{3+}$	4.5	116a
Co(*dl*-bn)$_3$$^{3+}$	5	116a
Co(N-meen)$_3$$^{3+}$	5	116a
cis-Co(en)$_2$(NH$_3$)$_2$$^{2+}$	200 (1.3)^a	116a
Co(dien)$_2$$^{3+}$	140	116a
Co(NH$_3$)$_5$F^{2+}	0.11	116b
Co(NH$_3$)$_5$Cl^{2+}	0.15	116b
Co(NH$_3$)$_5$Br^{2+}	0.16	116b
cis-Co(en)$_2$NH$_3$Cl^{2+}	1 (0.05)^a	116b
cis-Co(trien)NH$_3$Cl^{2+}	50 (0.2)^a	116b
Co(en)$_2$C$_2$O$_4$$^+$	0.3^c	120
Co(NH$_3$)$_5$NO$_2$$^+$	0.38	120
trans-Co(NH$_3$)$_4$(NO$_2$)$_2$$^+$	0.15	120
cis-Co(NH$_3$)$_4$(NO$_2$)$_2$$^+$	0.12 (0.45)^b	120
trans-Co(en)$_2$(NO$_2$)$_2$$^+$	0.068	120
cis-Co(en)$_2$(NO$_2$)$_2$$^+$	0.072 (0.50)^b	120
trans-Co(en)$_2$F$_2$$^+$	0.001	120
Pt(en)$_2$$^{2+}$	0.16	119
Pt(dien)Cl$^+$	0.15	116b
Pt(dien)Br$^+$	0.2 (6)^b	116b
Pt(dien)NO$_2$$^+$	1.4 (100)^b	116b
Pt(dien)I$^+$	2 (200)^b	116b
Pt(dien)SCN$^+$	3 (600)^b	116b
Au(en)$_2$$^{2+}$	instantaneous	119

^{a} Rapid rate due to 25–30% of NH protons, and rate in parentheses due to remainder. Assignment uncertain.
^{b} Rate in parentheses is NH *trans* to substituent.
^{c} From rate at 35°. See reference.

This is a solvation effect and actually does not support either mechanism. Essentially, all that is implied is that charge neutralization will be easier for a cation which is not strongly solvated. C-alkyl substituents have a minor effect on pK_a. The rates of base hydrolysis are high even for highly hindered diamines, suggesting that a dissociation step is involved, rather than an S_N2 process.

The data of Table 3.21 are of particular interest because the leaving group is constant and the inert substituent L has an effect on K_a which should be predicted quite reliably. The acid strengths of $Co(en)_2LCl^{2+}$ should fall off in the order L = $H_2O > NH_3 > NO_2^- > NCS^- \sim Br^- \sim Cl^- > F^- \gg OH^-$, using all the available acidity data on octahedral model compounds. The rates decrease in the order $Br^- > Cl^- > NH_3 > N_3^- > NCS^- > CN^- > NO_2^- > OH^-$, so that the halogeno complexes are reacting faster and the cyano and nitro complexes slower than expected. The slow rate for OH^- is expected because of the very low value of K_a, which in turn is due to the inductive effect acting largely through the σ bond. The π bonding of the hydroxo group which made acid hydrolysis so rapid is now swamped by the π bonding of the amido group. The overall effect is a very low ratio‡‡ of k_{OH}/k_{H_2O} of 10–30 for *trans* and *cis* isomers.

The low reactivity of $Co(en)_2NO_2Cl^+$ to base hydrolysis, in spite of a relatively favorable K_a, can be understood in terms of a cooperative π– bonding effect

$$H_2N\!=\!\!Co\!=\!\!N\begin{matrix} \ddot{O}: \\ \\ \ddot{O}: \end{matrix}$$

Thus, the electronic charge that the amido group puts on the cobalt atom is effectively removed by the nitro group. This will have the effect of reducing the tendency of a labile group to dissociate. Futhermore, the driving force for rearrangement to a trigonal bipyramid structure will be very much less. The amido group will be easily formed (large K_a, relative to other anionic ligands, L) but will not be activating.

Other unsaturated ligands can behave similarly to NO_2^-, but to a lesser degree, e.g., CN^- and N_3^-. The halide ions cannot easily undergo such π bonding and must necessarily become activated. The ratio‡‡ of k_{OH}/k_{H_2O} is very large, 2.4×10^6 for *trans* and 6.3×10^4 for *cis*-$Co(en)_2Cl_2^+$. For $Co(en)_2NH_3Cl^{2+}$ the ratios are even larger, being 3.7×10^6 for *trans* and 1.0×10^6 for *cis*. Thus, if one allows for the inductive effect of the chloride ion on the rate of the dissociation step 45 compared to that of ammonia, the rates of base hydrolysis are in the expected order.

‡‡ k_{H_2O} is at 25°C and k_{OH} at 0°C.

Although the S_N1CB mechanism can explain rates of base hydrolysis of most cobalt complexes in a very satisfactory way, it cannot be said that such explanations confirm the mechanism. With some imagination the same data can be explained by an S_N2 mechanism.[121] The data on base hydrolysis for metals other than cobalt offer more challenge to both theories. For example, it has been shown that only Rh(III) chlorammine complexes in which there is an amine group *trans* to the chloro group have an appreciable rate of base hydrolysis. That is, $Rh(NH_3)_5Cl^{2+}$ and *cis*-$Rh(en)_2Cl_2^+$ react with base more rapidly than with acid, whereas *trans*-$Rh(en)_2Cl_2^+$ does not. An explanation in terms of the S_N1CB mechanism can be given by noting that *cis*-$Pt(en)_2Cl_2^{2+}$ is two powers of 10 stronger as an acid than *trans*-$Pt(en)_2Cl_2^{2+}$ (Chapter 1). The same effect has been noted for the $Pt(NH_3)_4Cl_2^{2+}$ complexes. Also the n.m.r. chemical shifts of NH protons of the amines in $Co(NH_3)_5X^{2+}$ show that the amine groups *trans* to a halide ion (or carboxylate) are some 100 times more acidic than ammine groups *cis*.[122] The difference in behavior of the rhodium complexes is accordingly explained by saying that K_a for *cis*-$Rh(en)_2Cl_2^+$ is larger than for *trans*-$Rh(en)_2Cl_2^+$.

The same behavior as for the dichloro complexes is found for the chloropyridine complexes.[99] That is, *cis*-$Rh(en)_2(py)Cl^{2+}$ reacts rapidly with base ($\Delta H^{\ddagger} = 23$ kcal), whereas *trans*-$Rh(en)_2(py)Cl^{2+}$ reacts very slowly ($\Delta H^{\ddagger} = 35$ kcal). In the complex $Rh(tren)Cl_2^+$

only one chloride ion is susceptible to base hydrolysis.[99] All these results agree that an amine group *trans* to chlorine is needed for a high rate of base hydrolysis.

In Chapter 4 evidence of a stereochemical nature will be cited which indicates that activation by π bonding is much less for Rh(III) than for Co(III). It is likely that inductive effects of amido groups are largely responsible for the base hydrolysis rates of $Rh(NH_3)_5Cl^{2+}$ and *cis*-$Rh(en)_2$-Cl_2^+. Such effects acting through the σ-bond system will activate a ligand in the *trans* position preferentially (p. 174). Thus, an amido group in the *trans* position would cause a high rate of dissociation, but an amido group *cis* to a leaving group would have a smaller effect. The rates of acid hydrolysis of *cis*- and *trans*-$Rh(en)_2OHCl^+$ have been found to be nearly equal.[99] This seems to say that π-bonding effects (favoring *cis*) and inductive effects (favoring *trans*) are about equally important.

Some results very similar to those for the effect of base on rhodium complexes have been found in the base hydrolysis of the chloramine complexes of Pt(IV).[123] These latter systems are complicated by the simultaneous reduction to Pt(II) of the *trans*-dichloro complexes.

Tables 3.20 and 3.22 show that, for the metals which have been studied, the order of rates of base hydrolysis is Ru(III) > Co(III) ≫ Cr(III) > Rh(III). Table 3.24 collects several properties of these four metal ions

Table 3.24   Some properties of several metal ions

Property	Cr^{3+}	Co^{3+}	Ru^{3+}	Rh^{3+}
Electron configuration	t_2g^3	t_2g^6	t_2g^5	t_2g^6
pK_a, $M(NH_3)_5H_2O^{3+}$, 25°C	5.2	5.7	4.2	5.9
k_{ex}, $M(NH_3)_6^{3+}$, 25°C, $M^{-1} sec^{-1} \times 10^{-6}$	2.6	1.6	600	0.21
Electron affinity, ev	29.5	35.5	31.0	32
C.F.A.E. for trigonal bipyramid, Dq	5.74	11.48	8.90	11.48
C.F.A.E. for octahedral wedge, Dq	1.80	3.63	1.14	3.63
k_{OH}, $M^{-1} sec^{-1}$, 25°C, $M(NH_3)_5Cl^{2+}$	1.7×10^{-3}	0.85	4.9	4.1×10^{-4}

From reference 75.

which help to explain the order of reactivity towards alkali. The acid strengths of $M(NH_3)_5H_2O^{3+}$ and the deuterium exchange rates of $M(NH_3)_6^{3+}$ are a measure of K_a. The electron affinities are a measure of the tendency of the various metal ions to accept electrons from the amido group through σ or π bonding. The C.F.A.E.'s indicate how easy it is to from the necessary transition state for an S_N1CB mechanism (trigonal bipyramid structure assumed) or for an S_N2 or S_N2CB mechanism (octahedral wedge structure assumed). The S_N2CB mechanism refers to the possibility that the amido complex may react without rearranging to a trigonal intermediate and that water may be a nucleophilic reagent. The structure of the activated complex would be $M(NH_3)_4NH_2ClH_2O^+$.

In the absence of reliable solution data for the second transition series, gas-phase ionization potentials are used for the electron affinities:

$$M^{3+}(g) + e \rightarrow M^{2+}(g) + e \qquad (49)$$

The gas-phase third ionization potential must be corrected for spin pairing in the case of the complexes. This can be done by calculating the change in the number of favorable spin exchange terms between electrons of the same spin.[124] The added electron in 49 is assumed to have zero spin and to go into an e_g orbital of the complex. The correction amounts roughly to -1.5 ev for Cr(III), 2 ev for Co(III) and Rh(III), and 2.5 ev for Ru(III). The ionization potential in the last three cases is larger in the octahedral complex than in the gaseous ion by the indicated amounts.

The order of acidities clearly favors ruthenium by a large factor, the expected order of K_a being Ru $\gg$ Cr $>$ Co $>$ Rh. The order can be explained by ligand field theory since a half-filled d orbital in Ru(III) and Cr(III) does not offer as much repulsion towards an amido group. The electron affinity gives the reactivity order Co $>$ Rh $>$ Ru $>$ Cr. The C.F.A.E. gives the order Cr $\sim$ Ru $>$ Co $>$ Rh, remembering that Dq for a metal in the second transition series is 50% greater than for a metal in the first series.

The high rate of base hydrolysis of Ru(III) seems explained best by an S_N2CB mechanism since the tendency to π-bond is not large and the C.F.A.E. for rearrangement is large. The high rate of Co(III) is due to a large electron affinity, which also suggests a strong tendency to rearrange to a trigonal bipyramid. The low rate for Rh(III) is expected on the basis of a low acidity and a large C.F.A.E., which counteracts a reasonably large electron affinity. Stereochemical evidence (Chapter 4) suggests that Rh(III) complexes do not undergo rearrangement. The low rate of Cr(III) is due to the low electron affinity, which causes the amido group to be ineffective. The comparison between cobalt and chromium electron affinities might be made equally well in terms of the ease of forming Co(II) in solution, and the difficulty of forming Cr(II).[125]

Again all the above experimental observations on rates of base hydrolysis can probably be explained equally well by an S_N2 mechanism with hydroxide ion as the nucleophile. Fortunately, several critical tests are possible for the S_N1CB mechanism. Obviously, to be operative, the co-ordination compound must contain a moderately acidic proton. It is predicted, then, that complexes without acidic protons will not react rapidly with hydroxide ion. This is true for the complexes $Co(CN)_5Br^{3-}$ and $Co(CN)_5I^{3-}$, which hydrolyze at a rate independent of pH over the alkaline range.[117] It is also true for complexes such as $Fe(CN)_5NH_3^{3-}$ and $Fe(CN)_5SO_3^{5-}$, which hydrolyze in a first-order process independent of alkali.[126] In these cases of negatively charged ions, the failure to react with hydroxide ion may be due to electrostatic repulsion and hence is not conclusive. A better example is found in the *trans*-dichlorotetrapyridine series of complexes. These compounds without acidic protons react at a rate independent of pH up to 9.18,[127] from which it may be safely concluded that the rate of reaction with hydroxide ion is very small compared to most cobalt complexes. Unfortunately, higher pH solutions cause complete decomposition of these compounds.

The dipyridyl complexes are more stable, however, and the ion cis-$Co(dipy)_2(OAc)_2^+$ hydrolyzes at essentially the same rate at pH's of 11–12 as at pH 6–8.[128] Another example[127] is $trans$-$Co(dipy)_2(NO_2)_2^+$, which hydrolyzes by a first-order process independent of alkali over the range of $[OH^-]$ equal to 10^{-4} to 10^{-3} M. The corresponding dichloro complex is very labile, and hence the more inert dinitro complex was used. Strangely enough, the cis-$Co(dipy)_2(OAc)_2^{2+}$ is less reactive than cis-$Co(en)_2(OAc)_2^+$,[128] whereas $trans$-$Co(dipy)_2Cl_2^+$ is much more reactive than $trans$-$Co(en)_2Cl_2^+$.

The complex $trans$-$Co(tep)_2Cl_2^+$ reacts at a rate independent of hydroxide ion concentration in the pH range of 9–11.[129] The symbol tep stands for the diphosphine ligand $(C_2H_5)_2PCH_2CH_2P(C_2H_5)_2$. The complex $Co(diars)_2Cl_2^+$ in methanol does not show any rate enhancement due to methoxide ion [diars $= o$-phenylene bis(dimethylarsine)].[130]

Unfortunately, these examples which seem to substantiate the S_N1CB mechanism are somewhat counterbalanced by observations in one or two cases of complexes with no acidic proton which react more rapidly in the presence of hydroxide ion than in its absence. These are rather special instances where other possible modes of action occur. The observed reaction is not a simple replacement of halide ion or other unidentate ligand. These examples will be mentioned again later.

A second test exists for the conjugate base mechanism. The ligand which appears in the final product need not always be the hydroxo group. Thus, the five-coordinated intermediate of equation 45 does not necessarily have to react with water as shown in 46. Instead, reaction with some other nucleophile can occur.

$$Co(NH_3)_4NH_2^{2+} + Y \rightarrow Co(NH_3)_4NH_2Y^{2+} \qquad (50)$$

$$Co(NH_3)_4NH_2Y^{2+} + H_2O \rightarrow Co(NH_3)_5Y^{3+} + OH^- \qquad (51)$$

In such a sequence of events OH^- would only be acting as a catalyst for the reaction with Y.

Such a result has been found[131] in the solvent dry dimethylsulfoxide. The complex $trans$-$Co(en)_2NO_2Cl^+$ [and other Co(III) complexes] reacts slowly with nitrite ion in this solvent, the half-life being 5–6 hrs, independent of the nitrite ion concentration. Addition of hydroxide ion equal to 10% of the complex ion causes a rapid reaction, complete in less than 2 min. The product is cleanly $trans$-$Co(en)_2(NO_2)_2^+$. Furthermore,

$Co(en)_2NO_2Cl^+$ reacts equally rapidly with equivalent amounts of hydroxide ion in the absence of nitrite ion to form $Co(en)_2NO_2OH^+$, which will not then react with nitrite ion except very slowly.

Other bases such as piperidine also act as catalysts, the rate increasing with the concentration of piperidine but not linearly. The rates vary approximately inversely with added piperidinium ion. For a given catalyst solution the rate of reaction is independent of the concentration of nitrite ion. Furthermore, the rate is the same for nitrite ion, thiocyanate ion, and azide ion, though different products are formed in each case.

It is clear that all these observations are accounted for by the S_N1CB mechanism, but not by the S_N2 mechanism, which can produce only hydroxo complex.

$$Co(en)_2NO_2Cl^+ + B \rightleftharpoons Co(en)(en-H)NO_2Cl + BH^+ \quad (52)$$

$$Co(en)(en-H)NO_2Cl \rightarrow Co(en)(en-H)NO_2^+ + Cl^- \quad (53)$$

$$Co(en)(en-H)NO_2^+ + NO_2^- \rightarrow Co(en)(en-H)(NO_2)_2 \quad (54)$$

$$Co(en)(en-H)(NO_2)_2 + BH^+ \rightarrow Co(en)_2(NO_2)_2^+ + B \quad (55)$$

Similar equations would be written in which N_3^- and NCS^- take the place of NO_2^-.

The same experiment cannot easily be done in water solution because water is present in overwhelming amounts, is a good coordinator, and is rapidly converted to the even better coordinating hydroxo group by a simple proton transfer.§§ However, an experiment which is exactly equivalent can be done using ^{18}O-labeled water.[132] This is possible because the isotope exchange equilibrium

$$H_2^{16}O + {}^{18}OH^- \rightleftharpoons H_2^{18}O + {}^{16}OH^- \quad (56)$$

has an equilibrium constant of 1.040. Hence, water and hydroxide ion are labeled to different degrees and can be distinguished. In an S_N2 mechanism, hydroxide ion is the reagent and also appears as the final coordinated ligand.

If we define the isotope fractionation factor, f,

$$f = \frac{(^{16}O/^{18}O) \text{ in product}}{(^{16}O/^{18}O) \text{ in solvent}} \quad (57)$$

§§ For example, base hydrolysis of $Co(NH_3)_5Cl^{2+}$ in the presence of 0.1 M oxalate ion, where strong ion pairing should favor trapping the oxalate ion, produces only $Co(NH_3)_5OH^{2+}$. However, see D. A. Buckingham, I. I. Olsen and A. M. Sargeson, J. Am. Chem. Soc., **88**, 5443 (1966).

This factor should be 1.040 if an S_N2 mechanism is operating and 1.000 if an S_N1CB mechanism is involved (some slight corrections should be made for kinetic isotope effects). Table 3.25 shows the experimental values of f found by Green and Taube[132] for the base hydrolysis of several $Co(NH_3)_5X^{2+}$. It can be seen that the factor, when corrected for the kinetic isotope effect, is very close to what is predicted for the S_N1CB mechanism and far from that of the S_N2 mechanism.

Furthermore, it is noticeable that f is independent of the group X for $X = Cl^-$, Br^-, and NO_3^-. This is predicted if the intermediate species

Table 3.25 Fractionation factor $f = \dfrac{(^{16}O/^{18}O) \text{ in product}}{(^{16}O/^{18}O) \text{ in solvent}}$ in base hydrolysis of $Co(NH_3)_5X^{2+}$

X	[OH$^-$], M		
	0.012	0.016	0.020
Cl$^-$	1.0056	1.0057	1.0056
Br$^-$	1.0056	1.0055	1.0056
NO$_3^-$	1.0056	1.0056	...
F$^-$	...	0.9975	0.9995
SO$_4^{2-}$	1.033	1.034	...

Data from reference 132.

$Co(NH_3)_4NH_2^{2+}$ has lost all memory of its original source, presuming that it is stable enough to survive a few molecular collisions. The somewhat different values of f for $X = F^-$ and SO_4^{2-} are explained as due to an S_N2CB mechanism in which water as a nucleophile attacks the conjugate base before losing the group X. This seems reasonable since F^- and SO_4^{2-} would be the groups hardest to displace of all those used.

While these experiments using ^{18}O as a label appear to be very successful, arguments based on kinetic isotope effects are much less convincing. For example, a number of studies on the deuterium isotope effect turn out to be ambiguous, at least as far as deciding between possible mechanisms for base hydrolysis.[117,133] A kinetic method, not using isotopes, has been proposed to distinguish between S_N2 and S_N1CB mechanisms in general.[134]

This is based on the observation that the anion of hydrogen peroxide, O_2H^-, has been shown to be a better nucleophilic reagent than OH^- in all reactions tested where an S_N2 mechanism seems generally accepted.‖‖ This is an example of the so-called α effect.[20a] The factor can be as large

‖‖ This is not true for proton transfers, OH^- and O_2H^- having (W. Waltz, unpublished data) similar rates.

as 10^4 for the reactivity ratio. On the other hand, H_2O_2 is a stronger acid than water, its pK_a being 11.8 in aqueous solution, so the reaction

$$OH^- + H_2O_2 \rightleftharpoons H_2O + HO_2^- \tag{58}$$

has an equilibrium constant of 150 in conventional units. Accordingly, H_2O_2 added to an aqueous solution of OH^- reacting with some substrate will cause a large increase in rate if the reaction has an S_N2 mechanism, and a large decrease if the reaction has an S_N1CB mechanism.

As an example, the addition of one molar H_2O_2 to the reaction of benzyl bromide with hydroxide ion in 50% by volume acetone-water solvent causes the rate of release of bromide ion to increase by a factor of 35 (S_N2 mechanism).[134] The same addition of H_2O_2 to a solution of ethylenechlorohydrin and alkali in water causes a reduction in rate by a factor of about 100. The base hydrolysis reaction of ethylenechlorohydrin is well known to proceed by an S_N1CB mechanism.[135]

$$C_2H_4ClOH + OH^- \rightleftharpoons C_2H_4ClO^- + H_2O \tag{59}$$

$$C_2H_4ClO^- \rightarrow C_2H_4O + Cl^- \tag{60}$$

Applying this test to the base hydrolysis of $Co(NH_3)_5Cl^{2+}$, it was found that the addition of two molar H_2O_2 caused the release of chloride ion to virtually stop.[134] This is also powerful evidence for an S_N1CB mechanism, or at least a mechanism in which hydroxide ion plays a role which cannot be usurped by one of the most powerful nucleophilic reagents known.

A recent suggestion due to Tobe[90a,130b] that the special effect of hydroxide ion is due to its mobility seems untenable. The argument is that by a Grotthus chain mechanism the hydroxide ion can appear immediately wherever needed, say when a Co-Cl bond has stretched to a critical length. Since a Grotthus chain mechanism is simply a series of proton transfers, one would assume that all bases would be able to generate hydroxide ion at the critical time and place. However, no other base is found effective.

Reactions Involving the Replacement of Coordinated Water

The replacement of water from an aquo complex is the reverse of an acid hydrolysis reaction and is sometimes called the *anation reaction.* Kinetic studies of these reactions in aqueous solutions after suitable

$$Co(NH_3)_5H_2O^{3+} + X^- \rightarrow Co(NH_3)_5X^{2+} + H_2O \tag{61}$$

corrections often find them to be second order with a rate dependent on $[X^-]$.[137] However, from this information alone it cannot be concluded that these reactions are bimolecular. The same second-order kinetics would be observed for a unimolecular process such as

$$\text{Co(NH}_3)_5\text{H}_2\text{O}^{3+} \underset{\underset{\text{fast}}{+\text{H}_2\text{O}}}{\overset{\overset{\text{slow}}{-\text{H}_2\text{O}}}{\rightleftharpoons}} \text{Co(NH}_3)_5^{3+} \xrightarrow{\overset{+\text{X}^-}{\text{fast}}} \text{Co(NH}_3)_5\text{X}^{2+} + \text{H}_2\text{O} \quad (62)$$

In such a scheme a pseudo equilibrium exists between the aquo complex and the five-coordinated intermediate. Since group X^- must compete with the solvent water for the active intermediate, it follows that the rate of formation of $\text{Co(NH}_3)_5\text{X}^{2+}$ can be dependent upon the concentration of X^-. On the other hand, there should be some high concentration of the reactant, X^-, where the rate of replacement of water would no longer be dependent upon the concentration of X^-. The rate of formation of $\text{Co(NH}_3)_5\text{X}^{2+}$ at this concentration should be equal to the rate of formation of $\text{Co(NH}_3)_5^{3+}$ and also equal to the rate of water exchange between the aquo complex and the solvent. Such a reaction scheme may be formalized by the use of the *steady-state approximation*[138] which we can apply to the set of reactions

$$A \underset{k_2}{\overset{k_1}{\rightleftharpoons}} B \quad (63)$$

$$B + C \xrightarrow{k_3} D \quad (64)$$

The rate of formation of B is given by the equation

$$\frac{d[B]}{dt} = k_1[A] - k_2[B] - k_3[C][B] \quad (65)$$

Since B is a very reactive intermediate, the steady-state approximation assumes that its concentration remains small and constant during the reaction and allows the formulation $d[B]/dt = 0$, at the steady state. Equation 65 becomes equal to zero and gives the steady-state concentration of B as

$$[B] = \frac{k_1[A]}{k_2 + k_3[C]} \quad (66)$$

Therefore the rate of formation of the final product D is given by

$$\frac{d[D]}{dt} = k_3[B][C] = \frac{k_1 k_3[A][C]}{k_2 + k_3[C]} \quad (67)$$

Two limiting cases of 67 are of interest. One is where $k_2 \gg k_3[C]$ so that

$$\frac{d[D]}{dt} = \frac{k_1 k_3}{k_2}[A][C] \quad (68)$$

Under these conditions a second-order reaction would be observed, dependent on [C]. In the example where A is $Co(NH_3)_5H_2O^{3+}$ and C is X^-, this would correspond to what is observed for the anation reaction. The other limiting case is when $k_3[C] \gg k_2$, which gives

$$\frac{d[D]}{dt} = k_1[A] \tag{69}$$

This shows that a limiting rate is reached which is first order and independent of [C], or [X^-]. Furthermore, the first-order constant k_1 will be equal to the rate constant for dissociation of the aquo complex. It should, for example, be equal to the rate of water exchange in isotopically labeled systems. Furthermore, if the symbol X^- represents a number of reagents, the same limiting rate should be reached for all at sufficiently great concentration.

Attempts have been made to discover such indications of an S_N1 mechanism for the water replacement reaction. They have usually not met with success, however, because of the complications introduced by the fact that the reactants are charged particles and very sensitive to their environment. For example, in studying the reversible reactions

$$Rh(NH_3)_5H_2O^{3+} + Br^- \rightleftharpoons Rh(NH_3)_5Br^{2+} + H_2O \tag{70}$$

Lamb[78] found that both the forward and reverse reactions followed a first-order law under conditions where the [Br^-] was of the same order as [$Rh(NH_3)_5H_2O^{3+}$]. However, adding excess bromide ion, or increasing the total concentration, increased the first-order rate constants. The explanation for the first-order constant for the forward reaction is that the activity coefficients change with changing ionic strength during the course of the reaction. Thus the reaction is actually second order overall, first order in aquo complex and first order in bromide ion. According to the Brønsted-Bjerrum-Christiansen law[139] for reactions between oppositely charged ions, decreasing ionic strength increases the rate of such a reaction. Accordingly, as bromo complex is formed, with a drop in ionic strength as charges are neutralized, the second-order rate constant increases. This compensates partly for the normal decrease in rate for a second-order process so that the net effect is close to that for a first-order process.

In going to higher concentrations of X^- other problems arise in that changes in activity coefficients cannot be controlled even by the principle of constant ionic strength. This occurs because at high concentrations particular ions have specific effects and are not interchangeable. Furthermore definite species, ion pairs, are formed which have different rates of reaction from the original reactants (see Chapter 1). Thus, in studying the rate of reaction of cis-$Co(en)_2(NO_2)H_2O^{2+}$ with azide ion and thiocyanate ion, the rate continuously increased with increasing concentration of the entering anion, being approximately first order in this concentration.[105] A limiting rate was not reached at 2 M NCS$^-$ or at 3.2 M N$_3^-$. Since evidence for ion pairs was obtained, these results cannot be used as an indication of either an S_N1 or an S_N2 reaction.

Similarly the rate of the reaction

$$Co(NH_3)_5H_2O^{3+} + SO_4^{2-} \rightarrow Co(NH_3)_5SO_4^+ + H_2O \qquad (71)$$

gradually increases with increasing sulfate ion concentration.[140] The dependence on $[SO_4^{2-}]$ is less than first order and diminishes with increasing $[SO_4^{2-}]$, but even at 2.9 M Na$_2$SO$_4$ there is no sign of reaching a limiting rate. In this case an ion pair, $Co(NH_3)_5H_2O^{3+}$, SO_4^{2-}, was definitely detected, and its equilibrium constant for formation studied (see p. 37). Even after sufficient SO$_4^{2-}$ was added so that all of the aquo complex was converted to ion pair, the rate of sulfation continued to increase with further addition of sulfate ion. Also, in a solution as concentrated as 2 M Na$_2$SO$_4$ or 3 M NaHSO$_4$, the rate of formation of the sulfato complex was less than the rate of water exchange under the same conditions. However, the rate of water exchange was less in the presence of sulfate ion than in its absence. This would suggest that there is a competition between SO$_4^{2-}$ and H$_2$O for the intermediate, whatever its nature.

A study has been made of the reaction[141]

$$Cr(H_2O)_6^{3+} + NCS^- \rightleftharpoons Cr(H_2O)_5NCS^{2+} + H_2O \qquad (72)$$

in which it is found that the forward rate law is first order in [NCS$^-$] up to the highest concentration studied, 0.1 M. There is an expected pH dependence, showing that $Cr(H_2O)_5OH^{2+}$ and $Cr(H_2O)_4(OH)_2^+$ are also reacting with thiocyanate ion. Furthermore the rate increases for the three reacting species as the positive charge diminishes. Thus the hydroxide ligand is labilizing for the replacement of water just as it is for the replacement of chloride ion. Since, in an S_N2 reaction, it would be expected that the more positive ion would react faster with the negative thiocyanate ion, these opposite results are indicative of an S_N1 mechanism. In agreement with this, the net rate of reaction 72 is only 4% of the rate of water exchange at the highest concentration studied.

The results for the anation of $Cr(H_2O)_6^{3+}$ with acetate, oxalate, malonate, citrate, and o-phthalate ions are quite different in that the rates are independent of the concentration of the anion and in fact, at a given pH, are the same for all the carboxylate ions studied.[142] Such kinetic behavior could result from an S_N1 mechanism in which the five-coordinated $Cr(H_2O)_5^{3+}$ always reacts with an anion rather than with water. The activation energies for these anations are all similar and slightly lower than that for the rate for water exchange.[142]

It seems much more likely that these results are due to ion-pair formation which is complete at the concentrations of anion used (0.1 M).[143]

Thus the rate step measured is the interconversion of an outer-sphere complex into an inner-sphere complex, the *interchange reaction*

$$Cr(H_2O)_6{}^{3+}, A^- \rightarrow Cr(H_2O)_5A^{2+} + H_2O \qquad (73)$$

The mechanism of this step cannot be assigned unambiguously from the kinetic data. The facts certainly suggest that the rate of water loss is the key process and that the loosely bound anion then slips into the vacated position.

This becomes identical to the mechanism proposed by Eigen for the anation reactions of labile aquo complexes discussed earlier (see p. 154). Such a mechanism

$$\text{free ions} \rightleftharpoons \text{ion pair}$$

$$\text{ion pair} \rightleftharpoons \text{inner-sphere complex}$$

seems applicable to all of the examples discussed. The chief difference is that in some cases ion pairing is extensive or even complete, and in other cases only trace amounts of the ion pair exist. In no case would formation of the ion pair be rate determining, except possibly for the large alkali metal ions, where binding of water would be very weak.[144] The details of the outer-sphere/inner-sphere interchange may be expected to vary when a large number of metal ions are considered of various charges, sizes, and d electron configurations.

For the more inert metal ions, such as Cr(III) and Co(III), it is likely that a true five-coordinated intermediate is never formed unless special stabilizing ligands are present. Thus $Co(NH_3)_5{}^{3+}$ and $Cr(H_2O)_5{}^{3+}$ would be too high in energy to exist. A reasonable structure for the transition state for the interchange reaction would be the octahedral wedge geometry discussed earlier for acid hydrolysis. In fact, the principle of microscopic reversibility demands this, since anation is the reverse of acid hydrolysis.

Both the leaving group (water) and the entering group would be loosely held. Thus the rate would depend little upon the nature of the entering group, in agreement with the observations. The nature and concentration of the entering group would, of course, affect the concentration of the ion pair.

As an example of the anation reactions of a moderately labile complex, the data obtained for $Fe(H_2O)_6{}^{3+}$ are of interest.[145] It is found that, when the anions of strong acids are the reactants, rates increase with decreasing $[H^+]$.[146] This suggests, as noted for similar cases, that $Fe(H_2O)_5OH^{2+}$ is more labile than $Fe(H_2O)_6^{3+}$. When anions of weak acids react, rates decrease with decreasing $[H^+]$, in the acid region.[147] This somewhat surprising result is best explained by assuming that the reaction is between $Fe(H_2O)_6^{3+}$ or $Fe(H_2O)_5OH^{2+}$ and the neutral acid, HX, at least in part. Thus, we have the possible reactions:

$$Fe(H_2O)_6^{3+} + X^- \underset{2}{\overset{k_1}{\rightleftharpoons}} Fe(H_2O)_5X^{2+} + H_2O \tag{74}$$

$$Fe(H_2O)_6^{3+} + HX \underset{k_2'}{\overset{k_1'}{\rightleftharpoons}} Fe(H_2O)_5X^{2+} + H^+ + H_2O \tag{75}$$

$$Fe(H_2O)_5OH^{2+} + X^- \underset{k_4}{\overset{k_3}{\rightleftharpoons}} Fe(H_2O)_4(OH)X^+ + H_2O \tag{76}$$

$$Fe(H_2O)_5OH^{2+} + HX \underset{k_4'}{\overset{k_3'}{\rightleftharpoons}} Fe(H_2O)_4(OH)X^+ + H^+ + H_2O \tag{77}$$

The reactions governed by k_1 and by k_3' cannot be distinguished by kinetic evidence, and both probably occur. Also the reaction governed by k_3, no doubt, is more rapid than that controlled by k_1 even for weak acid anions. It would not be observed, however, in the acid media where the anation experiments are carried out.

Table 3.26 Rate constants for the formation (and dissociation) of mono complexes of iron(III) at 25.0°C

X	$Fe^{3+} + X$, k_1 or k_1', $M^{-1} sec^{-1}$	$FeOH^{2+} + X$, k_3 or k_3', $M^{-1} sec^{-1}$	$FeX^{2+} + H_2O$, k_2, sec^{-1}
Cl^-	9.4	1.1×10^4	2.3^e
$Br^{-\,a}$	20	2.7×10^4	...
SCN^-	1.27×10^2	1.0×10^4	0.87^e
SO_4^{2-}	$(6.37 \times 10^3)^b$	3×10^5	...
HSO_4^-	...	$(1.4 \times 10^5)^d$	...
F^-	$(5.0 \times 10^3)^b$	...	...
HF	11.4	$(3.1 \times 10^3)^d$	...
N_3^-	$(1.6 \times 10^5)^b$	...	...
HN_3	4.0	$(6.8 \times 10^3)^d$	...
H_2O	$2.8 \times 10^2\ ^c$	$\sim 2 \times 10^4\ ^c$	...

^{a} At 22 ± 2°C.
^{b} Calculated from acid-independent path as k_1.
^{c} Rate of water exchange in second-order units.
^{d} Calculated from acid-independent path as k_3'.
^{e} Reference 146.
Other literature sources listed in reference 145.

Table 3.26 shows a summary of rate constants for the iron(III) system.[145] Where the interpretation is ambiguous, rate constants have been calculated in both ways. It can be seen that, if the anion is always the reactant, the rate constants, k_1, cover a wide range with the most basic reagents the most reactive. Such a result would be reasonable for an S_N2 reaction, for example. An S_N1 reaction of an ion pair is not completely ruled out because ion pairing with a basic ion may cause an increased rate of dissociation, as suggested by Eigen[148] and Wendt and Strehlow.[149] This explanation may seem unlikely since ion pairing with basic anions occurs in many other cases and the increases in rate are small, a factor of two or three.[150]

However, the latter examples involve ammine complexes rather than aquo complexes. The fact that $Fe(H_2O)_6^{3+}$ is an acid with pK_a equal to 3.0 shows that the equilibrium

$$Fe(H_2O)_6^{3+} + X^- \rightleftharpoons Fe(H_2O)_5OH^{2+} + HX \qquad (78)$$

goes nearly to completion to the right for N_3^- and F^-. The ion pair must involve a strong hydrogen-bonding effect at the very least. It would take only a simple and very rapid proton transfer to make the reactant $Fe(H_2O)_5OH^{2+}$, HX. The hydroxo group would account for the higher rate of reaction.

In no case does the measured rate of anation exceed the total rate of water exchange, so that an S_N1 mechanism with $Fe(H_2O)_5^{3+}$ as a discriminating intermediate is also possible. The objections mentioned for the existence of $Cr(H_2O)_5^{3+}$ are not valid for Fe(III) since, being a d^5 system, it can rearrange to a trigonal bipyramid without loss of C.F.S.E. Such rearrangements will stabilize $Fe(H_2O)_5^{3+}$ to a considerable degree.

On the other hand, the supposition that HX is the reactant[145] causes all the rate constants for $Fe(H_2O)_6^{3+}$ to fall between 4 and 280 M^{-1} sec^{-1} and all the constants for $Fe(H_2O)_5OH^{2+}$ to lie in the range 3×10^3 to 3×10^5 M^{-1} sec^{-1}. An S_N1 mechanism is still possible with the intermediate being less discriminatory. The charge of the nucleophilic reagent determines its reactivity towards $Fe(H_2O)_5^{3+}$ or $Fe(H_2O)_4OH^{2+}$, with $X^{2-} > X^- > HX$.

A mechanism involving the prior formation of an ion pair, followed by the interchange reaction, is also consistent with the charge effect. The greater negative charge would increase the concentration of the ion pair and hence the overall rate of anation. In the case of Fe(III) aquo ion one really cannot distinguish a simple S_N1 mechanism, with an intermediate, from the ion-pair interchange process. Indeed an S_N2 mechanism is only excluded on the inconclusive evidence that the hydroxo ligand shows an activating effect, and that such mechanisms are rare for octahedral complexes in general.

It is of considerable interest to compare k_2 from Table 3.26 with the corresponding rate constants for Cr(III).

$$M(H_2O)_5X^{2+} + H_2O \xrightarrow{k_2} M(H_2O)_6^{3+} + X^- \tag{79}$$

For Fe(III), k_2 is 0.87 sec^{-1} and E_a is 14.6 kcal, when X is NCS$^-$.[146] For Cr(III), k_2 is 9.0×10^{-9} sec^{-1} and E_a is 28 kcal for the isothiocyanate ligand at 25°C.[141] The difference in rate is almost entirely due to the difference in activation energy, chromium showing some 13 kcal of C.F.A.E. The theoretical value is $1.8\,Dq$ units for an S_N1 dissociation with an octahedral wedge structure, and $5.75\,Dq$ if a trigonal bipyramid is formed. Since Dq is about 6 kcal, the octahedral wedge is indicated, at least for Cr(III). It may also be noted that the overall free energy change for reaction 79 is the same within 0.5 kcal for both metal ions. Equilibrium favors aquation of Fe(III) by less than a factor of ten over Cr(III).

Haim and Taube[81] have proposed a limiting S_N1 mechanism for the anation of Co(NH$_3$)$_5$H$_2$O^{3+}. A discriminating Co(NH$_3$)$_5^{3+}$ ion is considered to be the intermediate both for anation and for aquation.

$$Co(NH_3)_5H_2O^{3+} \underset{k_w}{\overset{k_e}{\rightleftharpoons}} Co(NH_3)_5^{3+} + H_2O \tag{80}$$

$$Co(NH_3)_5^{3+} + X^- \underset{k_a}{\overset{k_x}{\rightleftharpoons}} Co(NH_3)_5X^{2+} \tag{81}$$

The equilibrium constant for anation would be $K = k_e k_x / k_w k_a$. The value of k_e would be given by the rate of water exchange, which is known.[17] The value of k_a, the acid hydrolysis rate constant, is also known in a number of cases (see Table 3.15). The remaining factor, k_x/k_w, depends on the relative reactivity of Co(NH$_3$)$_5^{3+}$ for X$^-$ and for H$_2$O.

The factor k_x/k_w may be calculated from measured values of K (Table 3.16), k_e, and k_a, for several different X$^-$. Also the factor k_x/k_w could be measured directly by generating the species Co(NH$_3$)$_5^{3+}$ in different ways in the presence of excess X$^-$, e.g.,

$$Co(NH_3)_5N_3^{2+} + HNO_2 + H^+ \rightarrow Co(NH_3)_5^{3+} + N_2 + N_2O \tag{82}$$

$$Co(NH_3)_5X^{2+} + Hg^{2+} \rightarrow Co(NH_3)_5^{3+} + HgX^+ \tag{83}$$

On the basis of isotope discrimination factors, it had previously been postulated[151] that the Hg(II)-catalyzed aquation of Co(III) pentaamine halides gave Co(NH$_3$)$_5^{3+}$. The reaction of the azido complex with nitrous acid, which is very fast, might also produce such an intermediate species. The ratio of subsequent products Co(NH$_3$)$_5$H$_2$O^{3+} and Co(NH$_3$)$_5$X^{2+} would give the required ratio of k_x/k_w, after allowing for the concentration of X$^-$. In a study of reactions 82 and 83 values of k_x/k_w were found[81] which agreed in some cases with those predicted from the equilibrium constant.

Whatever the mechanism of reactions 82 and 83, it can easily be shown that the basic assumptions given by equations 80 and 81 are incorrect. One needs simply to carry out the acid hydrolysis of $Co(NH_3)_5Y^{2+}$ in the presence of large amounts of X^-. According to the above mechanism a substantial amount of $Co(NH_3)_5X^{2+}$ will be formed directly by the trapping of $Co(NH_3)_5{}^{3+}$ by X^-. The remaining $Co(NH_3)_5X^{2+}$ will be formed by the slower anation reaction of $Co(NH_3)_5H_2O^{3+}$ (regardless

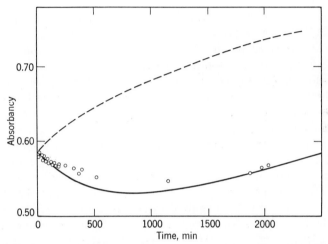

Fig. 3.12   Plot of absorbancy vs. time for aquation of $[Co(NH_3)_5NO_3](NO_3)_2$ (0.01 M) in the presence of 0.50 M NaSCN; $[H^+] = 0.02$ M. Upper curve calculated for mechanism involving a five-coordinate intermediate. Lower curve calculated for mechanism involving conversion to $Co(NH_3)_5H_2O^{3+}$, which subsequently reacts to form $Co(NH_3)_5NCS^{2+}$. Points are experimental. From reference 82.

of mechanism). When $Co(NH_3)_5NO_3{}^{2+}$ and $Co(NH_3)_5Br^{2+}$ are aquated in the presence of 0.5 M NCS^-, they are converted directly to $Co(NH_3)_5H_2O^{3+}$ to the extent of more than 98 %. No $Co(NH_3)_5NCS^{2+}$ can be detected as an immediate product.[82] Figure 3.12 shows the optical density curves as a function of time calculated for (a) the mechanism of Haim and Taube, and (b) prior formation of $Co(NH_3)_5H_2O^{3+}$ followed by anation. It is clear that the experimental points closely follow path (b).

This nearly total formation of $Co(NH_3)_5H_2O^{3+}$ in the presence of large amounts of other potential nucleophiles is the expected behavior for an S_N1 mechanism in which the intermediate is so reactive that it reacts with the first molecule or ion it encounters. It is also the expected result for the solvent-assisted dissociation path described earlier.

It has been shown[232] that the aquation of $Cr(H_2O)_5I^{2+}$ in the presence of Cl^- produces 10–20 % of $Cr(H_2O)_5Cl^{2+}$. This could be explained by the formation of $Cr(H_2O)_5^{3+}$, which then reacts in a discriminatory fashion with chloride ion and with water. A much more likely explanation can be given because of the demonstration[233] that the iodide ligand in $Cr(H_2O)_5I^{2+}$ has a strong *trans* effect. This was shown by the rapid exchange of one molecule of water (the *trans* H_2O) in $Cr(H_2O)_5I^{2+}$ with $H_2^{18}O$. In the presence of chloride ion this *trans* activation of water could lead to *trans*-$Cr(H_2O)_4ClI^+$. Rapid aquation of this species would yield the observed $Cr(H_2O)_5Cl^{2+}$.

The latter explanation is supported by the observation that the aquation of $Cr(H_2O)_5SCN^{2+}$ in the presence of Cl^- does not produce the amount of $Cr(H_2O)_5Cl^{2+}$ expected on the basis of free $Cr(H_2O)_5^{3+}$.[234] This is the unstable S-bonded linkage isomer of Cr(III). It hydrolyzes rapidly and, like the iodo complex, should show a strong *trans* effect. This would lead to some formation of $Cr(H_2O)_5Cl^{2+}$, as is indeed observed.[234] However, the amount need not be the same as when one starts with $Cr(H_2O)_5I^{2+}$ since several factors enter in.

It should be appreciated that the technique of detecting a short-lived intermediate by establishing its characteristic mode of behavior, regardless of its source, can be successful only if the lifetime is sufficiently long. Thus for the well-studied prototype, the carbonium ions of organic chemistry, the method works only for long-lived carbonium ions such as triphenyl methyl. Here discrimination factors as large as 10^5 for different nucleophiles have been found.[152] For the more reactive alkyl carbonium ions, the nature of the products formed is strongly dependent upon the environment and the nature of the leaving group.[153]

Table 3.27 shows the overall second-order rate constants for anation, either measured directly or calculated from the equilibrium constant and the rate of aquation. The constants are remarkably independent of the nature of the entering group. Such a result was already predicted by the fact that the slope of the line in Fig. 3.7 is equal to unity. This independence of rate argues against an S_N2 reaction or an S_N2IP reaction.¶¶

By microscopic reversibility, the mechanism of the anation reaction would go through the formation of the ion pair followed by the interchange reaction. The rate constant would be the product of the equilibrium constant for ion-pair formation times the rate constant for the interconversion step.

It is possible[64] to calculate the latter constant in some cases where the ion-pair equilibrium constant is known. The results are included in Table 3.27. The nature of the entering group plays some part in determining the rate, but it is a small one. Water has a statistical advantage in that one

¶¶ The unimolecular and bimolecular reactions of ion pairs are sometimes called S_N1IP and S_N2IP.

Table 3.27   Second-order rate constants for the anation reaction

$$Co(NH_3)_5H_2O^{3+} + X^- \xrightarrow{k} Co(NH_3)_5X^{2+} + H_2O$$

25°C and $\mu = 0.5$

X^-	k, M^{-1} sec^{-1}	K_0, M^{-1} [a]	k_{int}, sec^{-b} [1]
Cl^-	2.1×10^{-6}	...	...
Br^-	2.5×10^{-6}	...	...
NO_3^-	2.3×10^{-6}	...	...
NCS^-	1.3×10^{-6} [c]	4.5	2.9×10^{-7}
SO_4^{2-}	1.5×10^{-5}	11.2	1.3×10^{-6}
$H_2PO_4^-$	2.0×10^{-6}	2.75	7.3×10^{-7}
NH_3	2×10^{-6} [d]	...	...
H_2O	6.6×10^{-6} [e]	$(55)^{-1}$	6.6×10^{-6}
Cl^- [f]	1.0×10^{-7}	13	7.7×10^{-9}

Calculated from equilibrium constants and rate of reverse reaction. See reference 81.

[a] Association constant for outer-sphere complex formation.
[b] Outer-sphere inner-sphere interconversion rate constant.
[c] Determined directly, reference 82.
[d] See reference 16.
[e] Rate of water exchange.
[f] For $Cr(H_2O)_6^{3+}$, see references 40 and 196. The water exchange rate, k_e, is 3×10^{-6} sec^{-1}.

molecule, at least, is always in the right spot for reaction. The anions may be located in a position remote from the leaving water molecule.

In simple cases the ratio k_x/k_w required for a mechanism in which $Co(NH_3)_5^{3+}$ is formed as an intermediate may be calculated by dividing the anation rate constant by the first-order rate constant for water exchange ($k_e = 6 \times 10^{-6}$ sec^{-1}). Where extensive ion pairing is involved, as for sulfate ion, the calculation is more complicated.[81] Also the observation that the rate of water exchange at high sulfate concentrations is greater than at low sulfate ion concentrations cannot be unambiguously interpreted because of ion-pair formation.[140]

A very well substantiated case for a five-coordinated intermediate comes from the work of Haim, Grassie, and Wilmarth[70,154] on the reactions of $Co(CN)_5X^{3-}$ and $Co(CN)_5H_2O^{2-}$. The anation reactions of the latter were studied at constant ionic strength and with a constant cation environment, which minimize medium effects for reactions between two anions. The rate of formation of the equilibrium amount of $Co(CN)_5X^{3-}$ was studied with various excess concentrations of X^- so that pseudo first-order rate constants, k_{obs}, were obtained.

Assume the S_N1 limiting mechanism:

$$Co(CN)_5H_2O^{2-} \underset{k_w}{\overset{k_e}{\rightleftharpoons}} Co(CN)_5^{2-} + H_2O \tag{84}$$

$$Co(CN)_5^{2-} + X^- \underset{k_a}{\overset{k_x}{\rightleftharpoons}} Co(CN)_5X^{3-} \tag{85}$$

The steady state treatment for the concentration of $Co(CN)_5^{2-}$ then leads to the relationship, at constant $[X^-]$:

$$k_{obs} = \frac{k_e[X^-] + k_w k_a/k_x}{k_w/k_x + [X^-]} \tag{86}$$

This differs from the steady state treatment of equation 67 because the reverse reaction for the aquation of $Co(CN)_5X^{3-}$ is now included. If k_a is

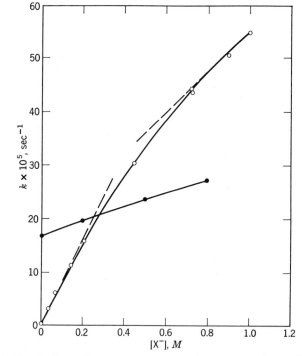

Fig. 3.13 Pseudo first-order rate constants vs. anion concentration at 40°C and ionic strength 1.0 M for the reaction

$$Co(CN)_5H_2O^{2-} + X^- \rightarrow Co(CN)_5X^{3-} + H_2O.$$

Filled circles are for $X^- = Br^-$, and empty circles are for $X^- = N_3^-$. From reference 154b.

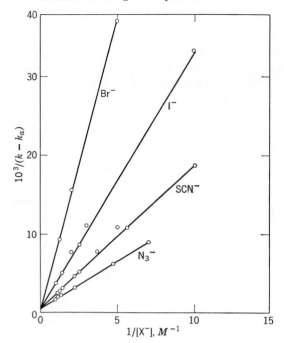

Fig. 3.14 A plot of $1/(k_{obs} - k_a)$ vs. the reciprocal of the anion concentration for several anionic nucleophiles. From reference 154b.

taken as zero, the two expressions would be the same. Equation 86 may be rewritten as:

$$\frac{1}{k_{obs} - k_a} = \frac{1}{k_e - k_a} + \frac{k_w/k_x}{(k_e - k_a)[X^-]} \qquad (87)$$

If k_{obs} is plotted against $[X^-]$, curves such as Fig. 3.13 are obtained. From equation 86 it is seen that the intercept, at $[X^-] = 0$, is equal to k_a. Also k_a may be directly measured by starting with $Co(CN)_5X^{3-}$ and omitting any excess X^- in solution. Figure 3.14 shows plots of $1/(k_{obs} - k_a)$ versus $1/[X^-]$ for several nucleophiles. The intercept is the same for all, showing that $k_e \gg k_a$, the numerical value being $1.60 \times 10^{-3} \ sec^{-1}$ at 40°C. The various slopes of Fig. 3.14 enable a calculation of the ratio k_x/k_w to be made for each X^-. Table 28 gives the kinetic parameters evaluated for several nucleophiles.

The data in the table and other, less complete[155] data show the following order of decreasing nucleophilic reactivity for the substrate $Co(CN)_5^{2-}$: $OH^- > I_3^- > HN_3 > N_3^- > SCN^- > $ thiourea $> I^- > NH_3 > Br^- > S_2O_3^{2-} > NCO^- > H_2O$. The rate factor for water has been divided by

55 to make the comparison. The sequence is a little puzzling in that $Co(CN)_5^{2-}$ is expected to be quite a soft acid substrate. The high reactivity of some of the polarizable bases is quite expected. The low reactivity of $S_2O_3^{2-}$ and, particularly, the very high reactivity of OH^- are unexpected. It is possible that the mechanism of reaction of OH^- with $Co(CN)_5^{2-}$ is special, perhaps involving a proton transfer from a water molecule in the second coordination sphere.[154]

Table 3.28   Kinetic parameters for the reaction

$$Co(CN)_5H_2O^{2-} + X^- \rightarrow Co(CN)_5X^{3-} + H_2O$$

at $T = 40°C$ and $\mu = 1.0$

X^-	k_a, sec^{-1}	E_a, kcal	$\Delta S^{\ddagger}$, eu.	k_x/k_w	K^a
N_3^-	5.5×10^{-7}	27.9	-0.6	0.53	1530
SCN^-	3.7×10^{-7}	31.7	11.5	0.34	1460
I^-	7.4×10^{-6}	30.3	12.5	0.19	42^b
Br^-	1.68×10^{-4}	...	...	0.10	1.0^b
OH^-	6.5×10^{-4}	...	...	1.58×10	6700
HN_3	3.2×10^{-3}	...	...	0.67^c	0.33^d
H_2O	1.6×10^{-3}	...	...	...	...

Data from reference 154.
^{a} Equilibrium constant for anation reaction.
^{b} Determined directly and also from $K = k_e k_x/k_a k_w$. The two methods agree very well.
^{c} From $K = k_e k_x/k_w k_a$.
^{d} From the acid ionization constants of $Co(CN)_5N_3H^{2-}$ and HN_3.

The soft acid [or class (b)] character of $Co(CN)_5^{2-}$ is shown by the higher rate of hydrolysis of $Co(CN)_5Br^{3-}$ than of $Co(CN)_5I^{3-}$. Also the hydroxo group of $Co(CN)_5OH^{3-}$ is extraordinarily labile (compare Table 3.15) for the same reason. The equilibrium constants for the anation reaction given in Table 3.28, compared to the corresponding data for $Co(NH_3)_5X^{2+}$ in Table 3.16, also show very weak binding of the hydroxo ligand.

The mechanism given by equations 84 and 85 has been confirmed in a number of ways. The aquation of $Co(CN)_5Br^{3-}$ and the acid-catalyzed aquation of $Co(CN)_5N_3^{3-}$, for example, should generate the same five-coordinated intermediate as the anation reactions. In the presence of other nucleophiles, the reactivity of $Co(CN)_5^{2-}$ should be the same regardless of its source. This has been tested with thiocyanate ion as the added nucleophilic agent. It is found that the rate of the aquation reaction is unaffected by the addition of NCS$^-$. The product, however, contains Co(CN)$_5$NCS^{3-} in amounts predicted by the ratio k_x/k_w given in Table 3.28. As expected, OH$^-$ has no effect on the rate of aquation of Co(CN)$_5$X^{3-}.

A critical test of the mechanism lies in the fact that k_e should equal the rate constant for the water exchange reaction. A direct measurement of the exchange rate, using water labeled with ^{18}O, has given k_e as being between 1.0×10^{-3} and 1.3×10^{-3} sec^{-1}, in reasonably good agreement with the value of k_e deduced indirectly from the anation studies of Co(CN)$_5$H$_2$O^{2-} (1.6×10^{-3} sec^{-1}).

The difference in the apparent stability of Co(CN)$_5^{2-}$ and Co(NH$_3$)$_5^{3+}$ lies in the special nature of the cyano ligand. (It is remarkable that a single sulfite group appears to be sufficient to allow reaction by an S_N1 (lim) mechanism. J. Halpern, R. A. Palmer, L. M. Blakly, *J. Am. Chem. Soc.*, **88**, 2877 (1966)). First, strong electon donation from the ligand to the metal in the σ bond causes an accumulation of negative charge on the metal which is only partly removed by back π-bonding. This weakens the Co-X bond and promotes an S_N1 mechanism. Second, in the higher-energy five-coordinated species, π bonding becomes more important. In particular, there is a strong depletion of the electron density in the t_{2g} orbitals. This probably allows rearrangement to a trigonal bipyramid to occur with little or no loss of ligand field stabilization energy. There is no direct evidence on the structure of Co(CN)$_5^{3-}$, however, and the examples of structures for related compounds that both trigonal bipyramidal and square pyramidal arrangements are found.[156] The one case of a five-coordinated d^6 complex whose structure has been found by X-ray diffraction is RuCl$_2$[P(C$_6$H$_5$)$_3$]$_3$.[157] This is a distorted square pyramid, but steric factors are important here.

Reactions in Non-aqueous Solvents

Mechanistic studies of complex ions have usually been made in aqueous solution. This is a natural result of the general interest in the behavior of such systems in the medium where reactions in a preparative sense are usually carried out, and also of the lack of solubility of complex ions in other solvents. It has been seen that direct replacement of one ligand by another is not common in water because of the formation of aquo compounds. In a solvent with poorer coordinating properties, it might be possible to demonstrate a direct substitution and hence find an S_N2 mechanism. A suitable solvent would be methanol, since complexes such as Co(NH$_3$)$_5$CH$_3$OH^{3+} are unstable. Thus at equilibrium a chloro complex in methanol remains almost completely the chloro complex, though racemization, isomerization, and exchange reactions may occur.

Brown and Ingold[158] have investigated the kinetics of substitution of a chloro group in cis-$Co(en)_2Cl_2^+$ by several anions in the solvent methyl alcohol, using polarimetric, spectroscopic, chemical, and radiochemical methods. Experimentally these substitutions proceed directly without any intermediate formation of a methyl alcohol complex. It was observed that some of the reagents, all weakly nucleophilic, react at the same rate, whereas other reagents react more rapidly and at different rates relative to their nucleophilic power. It was suggested that the substitutions by NO_3^-, *Cl^-, Br^-, or NCS^- proceed by an S_N1 mechanism. In agreement with this, the rates were found to be independent of the concentration of the entering anion.

The fact that all these reagents react at the same rate is in itself good evidence of a dissociation mechanism. The rate-determining step in all cases would be the rate of formation of the five-coordinated intermediate,

$$Co(en)_2Cl_2^+ \xrightarrow[-Cl^-]{slow} Co(en)_2Cl^{2+} \xrightarrow[+X^-]{fast} Co(en)_2ClX^+ \qquad (88)$$

Other observations further support this assignment of an S_N1 mechanism to these reactions. The rate of reaction is the same as the rate of racemization if optically active cis-$Co(en)_2Cl_2^+$ is used, which would be the case providing the active intermediate either is symmetrical or has sufficient time to rearrange before reaction. Finally a mass-law retardation was observed, which is usually the most diagnostic kinetic evidence for a unimolecular mechanism.

The mass-law retardation effect has been successfully applied to mechanistic studies of organic reactions.[57b] The example presented here has to do with the reaction

$$Co(en)_2Cl_2^+ + NCS^- \rightarrow Co(en)_2(NCS)Cl^+ + Cl^- \qquad (89)$$

It is found that the rate constant for the formation of $Co(en)_2(NCS)Cl^+$ decreases as the extent of the reaction progresses. Such behavior is attributed to the reaction scheme

$$Co(en)_2Cl_2^+ \underset{k_{Cl^-}}{\overset{k_{diss}}{\rightleftharpoons}} Co(en)_2Cl^{2+} + Cl^- \qquad (90)$$

$$Co(en)_2Cl^{2+} + NCS^- \xrightarrow{k_{NCS^-}} Co(en)_2(NCS)Cl^+ \qquad (91)$$

Because of the reversibility of the initial heterolysis 90, the developed chloride ion will return to the cation from which it separated to an increasing degree as reaction progresses, thereby retarding the thiocyanate substitution 91. It is also found that, as the initial excess of thiocyanate ion is increased, the progressive retardation is lessened until it becomes inappreciable at the largest excesses employed.

In spite of the excellent agreement of all of these results with the predictions of an S_N1 mechanism, it turns out on closer examination that they could be equally in agreement with an S_N2 mechanism involving the solvent methanol as the nucleophilic reagent. If it is demonstrated that the methanol complex formed in such a process is unstable, then the S_N1 and S_N2 mechanisms become kinetically indistinguishable. The reaction sequence is identical with those shown in equations 90 and 91 except that the reactive intermediate is not $Co(en)_2Cl^{2+}$ but $Co(en)_2(CH_3OH)Cl^{2+}$, formed by reversible reactions such as

$$CH_3OH + Co(en)_2Cl_2^+ \rightleftharpoons Co(en)_2(CH_3OH)Cl^{2+} + Cl^- \qquad (92)$$

There would, of course, be a mass-law retardation, and racemization could happen directly in 92, or more probably through several rapid exchange reactions such as

$$CH_3OH' + Co(en)_2(CH_3OH)Cl^{2+} \rightleftharpoons Co(en)_2(CH_3OH')Cl^{2+} + CH_3OH$$
$$(93)$$

each producing partial racemization. For this reason it is very important that the preparation of $Co(en)_2CH_3OHCl^{2+}$ has been reported[159] and that, while labile, it is not reactive enough to be the intermediate in the reactions reported above. This observation is strong evidence for the S_N1 mechanism. In a similar way the dimethylformamide solvate, $Co(en)_2(DMF)Cl^{2+}$ was prepared[160] and it was shown that it cannot be an intermediate in the isomerization of cis- and trans-$Co(en)_2Cl_2^+$ in dimethylformamide solvent.

It was originally thought that the anions NO_2^-, N_3^-, and CH_3O^- reacted at a more rapid rate and by an S_N2 mechanism, since the rates increased with rising anion concentration. However, it was shown that the high rate of reaction of these ions and of acetate ion was due to methanolysis which produced methoxide ion[161]

$$OAc^- + CH_3OH \rightleftharpoons CH_3O^- + HOAc \qquad (94)$$

Buffering the solution greatly inhibited this excess reactivity.

In the case of several ions of the type trans-$Co(en)_2Cl_2^+$ it was found that strong buffering completely destroyed the excess reactivity of basic anions. Figure 3.15 shows a plot of the observed pseudo-first-order rate constant for the replacement of chloride ion plotted against the reciprocal of the acetic acid concentration. The extrapolated value is indistinguishable from the rate of radioactive chloride exchange and the rate of reaction with thiocyanate ion for the same complex. These last two rates are independent of the concentration of radioactive chloride ion and of thiocyanate ion, as was found for the corresponding cis complex, except for small ionic strength effects. Thus, there is no direct reaction with basic anions for the *trans* complexes, and, like hydroxide ion in water, only methoxide ion shows increased reactivity.

A comparison of the rates of reaction of a number of dichloro complexes with methoxide ion in methanol and hydroxide ion in water[161] leaves little doubt that the two reactions are essentially the same. Reaction in methanol is about 100 times slower than base hydrolysis, however, even though the bringing together of opposite charges should be favored by a

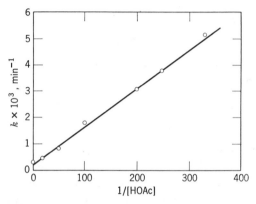

Fig. 3.15   Rate of release of chloride ion from *trans*-Co(en)$_2$Cl$_2^+$ in 0.05 M acetate ion solution in methanol at 25°C as a function of methoxide ion concentration. Value shown at zero is the rate of chloride ion exchange. From reference 161.

lower dielectric constant. The reason for this lower rate is not clear. By the same argument based on relative rates,[161] the acid hydrolysis reaction in water is the same as that first-order process which leads to radiochloride exchange and reaction with thiocyanate and other ions in methanol. Whatever the mechanism of either of these reactions in water, it is most likely that the same mechanism holds in methanol. The chief difference in the observed results is that an aquo complex is stable, whereas a methanol complex may not be. The slower rate of the acid hydrolyses in methanol by a factor of ten is reasonable in view of the lower dielectric constant compared to water, since a separation of charge in the transition state is certainly involved.

The *cis* complexes on strong buffering behave differently from the *trans*. A residual rate remains which is somewhat greater than the rate of reaction with weakly basic anions such as NO$_3^-$ and NCS$^-$ or the rate of chloride exchange. This residual rate increases with higher concentration of the basic anion up to a limiting value. Figure 3.16 shows the residual rate constant (methoxide ion reaction eliminated by buffering) as a function of concentration in the case of azide ion (the rate constant in this case is calculated for one chloride ion only being released). There is not a simple first-order dependence on the concentration of N_3^-.

The detailed shape of the curve in Fig. 3.16 can be reproduced by superimposing the effects of ion-pair formation between the reactants, and ionic strength effects on the magnitude of the ion-pair formation constant. The ionic strength effects are approximated by the Debye-Hückel theory

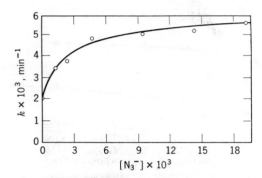

Fig. 3.16 Rate of release of chloride ion from cis-Co(en)$_2$Cl$_2^+$ in solutions of sodium azide in methanol at 25°C. Value at zero is the rate of chloride ion exchange from reference 158. Other data from reference 161.

for the activity coefficients of ions (see p. 34). The mechanism would be in outline

$$Co(en)_2Cl_2^+ + X^- \overset{fast}{\rightleftharpoons} Co(en)_2Cl_2^+, X^- \qquad (95)$$

$$Co(en)_2Cl_2^+, X^- \overset{slow}{\longrightarrow} Co(en)_2ClX^+ + Cl^- \qquad (96)$$

with reaction 96 perhaps going directly as shown (S_N2IP) or in steps such as (S_N1IP)

$$Co(en)_2Cl_2^+, X^- \overset{slow}{\longrightarrow} Co(en)_2Cl^{2+}, X^- + Cl^- \qquad (97)$$

$$Co(en)_2Cl^{2+}, X^- \overset{fast}{\longrightarrow} Co(en)_2ClX^+ \qquad (98)$$

The equation for the observed first-order rate constant would be

$$k_{obs} = \frac{k_1 + k_2 K[X^-]}{1 + K[X^-]} \qquad (99)$$

where k_1 is the rate constant for dissociation of free Co(en)$_2$Cl$_2^+$, k_2 is the rate constant for step 96, and K is the equilibrium constant for the formation of ion pairs as in 95.

The evidence for ion pairs is indirect since it can be shown in the case of cis-Co(en)$_2$Cl$_2^+$ with Cl$^-$ and Br$^-$ that ion pairs are formed.[161] The method of detection is the shift in the near-ultraviolet spectrum of the complex that results. Also $trans$-Co(en)$_2$Cl$_2^+$ does not form ion pairs with Cl$^-$ as judged by this criterion of changing spectrum. It is plausible that the ion pair is formed in the case of the cis isomer but not the $trans$ because of the net dipole moment of the former, the charges being equal. Then the negative ion must be held at the side of the complex away from the chloride ligands

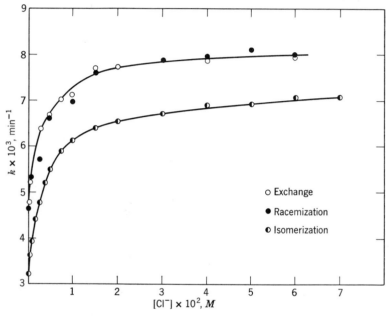

Fig. 3.17 First-order rate constants for the reactions of $(+)$-cis-Co(en)$_2$Cl$_2^+$ in methanol at 35°C plotted as a function of the chloride concentration. From B. Bosnich, C. K. Ingold, and M. L. Tobe, *J. Chem. Soc.*, **1965**, 4074.

for electrostatic reasons. The failure to show reaction with acetate ion and the failure to form ion pairs are thus related in $trans$-Co(en)$_2$Cl$_2^+$. In dimethylformamide it has been shown[162] that cis-Co(en)$_2$Cl$_2^+$ forms a strong ion pair with chloride ion and the $trans$ isomer forms only a weak ion pair.

Figure 3.17 shows the effect of chloride ion concentration down to very low concentrations for some reactions of cis-Co(en)$_2$Cl$_2^+$ in methanol at 35°C. The reactions are radiochloride exchange, racemization of optically active complex, and the $cis \rightarrow trans$ isomerization. Since almost all of the early experiments[158] were done above 0.01 M, it can be seen that the constant rates they obtained were due to complete formation of the ion pair. Presumably, the same situation exists for the nitrate and thiocyanate ion reactions.

The intercept at zero chloride ion concentration is the rate constant for the free $Co(en)_2Cl_2^+$. It reacts at about half the rate of the ion pair. Its rate of isomerization is about 70% of the rates for racemization or chloride exchange. Hence the intermediate $Coen_2Cl^+$ picks up chloride ion to form the *trans* isomer 70% of the time, and reforms *cis* isomer 30% of the time. The *cis* isomer is completely racemic, which suggests that a trigonal bi-pyramid structure is formed for the five-coordinate intermediate.

The small dependence of the rate of the reaction on whether or not an ion pair is formed seems to be best explained by an S_N1 mechanism. The ion-pair reaction leads to 86% *trans*-dichloro product and 14% racemic *cis* product. The ion pairs of active *cis*-$Co(en)_2Cl_2^+$ with azide ion and acetate ion also react with complete loss of optical activity.[161] The rate constants for the reactions of these last two ion pairs are some three times greater than the constant for the chloride ion ion pair (Fig. 3.17), which again is a rather small effect for such basic anions.

The formation of ion pairs is expected to be very common for the reactions of cationic complexes in non-aqueous solvents, especially those of lower dielectric constant than water. Ion pairs are formed with chloride ion and *trans*-$Co(en)_2NO_2Br^+$ even in the good ionizing solvent sulfolane.[163] The anation reactions of *trans*-$Co(en)_2NO_2H_2O^{2+}$ in sulfolane, acetone, and dimethylformamide are complicated by ion-pair formation.[164] If ion pairing is complete at the lowest concentrations used, then rates of anation, or replacement of one anion by another, will be found independent of the concentration of the entering anion.

It is of considerable interest that a number of substitution reactions of *cis*- and *trans*-$Co(en)_2NO_2Cl^+$ in non-aqueous solvents have been found to be independent of the nature and concentration of the entering group. Reactions include substitution by $^*Cl^-$, NCS^-, and N_3^- in methanol,[165] by NCS^- in dimethylformamide, and by NO_2^- in dimethylsulfoxide.[167] The *trans*-chloronitro complex reacts with complete retention of configuration, as it does for acid hydrolysis in water, and the *cis*-chloronitro gives some *trans* product.

While evidence is lacking, it is possible that these rates are actually those of the completely formed ion pair. If so, there is a striking rate independence of the nature of the anion present. This is somewhat surprising since Fig. 3.8 indicates that a nitro substituent should promote an S_N2 mechanism or at least require more bond making in the transition state. If the ion pair is not the reactant, the rate step is probably the formation of the solvato complex, which then reacts rapidly to form the substituted complex.

In dimethylsulfoxide *cis*- and *trans*-$Co(en)_2Cl_2^+$ isomerize by two paths.[160] One is a solvolysis in which *cis*-$Co(en)_2(DMSO)Cl^{2+}$ is formed,

Table 3.29 Rates of solvolysis of complexes in various solvents
(First-order rate constants in sec^{-1})

Solvent/Complex ($T°C$)	trans-[Co(en)$_2$Cl$_2$]$^+$ (35°C)	trans-[Co(en)$_2$NO$_2$Cl]$^+$ (35°C)	trans-[Co(en)$_2$NO$_2$Br]$^+$ (25°C)	Pt(py)$_2$Cl$_2$ (25°C)
H$_2$O[a]	1.2×10^{-4} (1)[b]	2.8×10^{-3} (1)	4.2×10^{-3} (1)	3.5×10^{-5} (1)
Dimethylsulfoxide[a]	3.7×10^{-5} (0.31)	1.4×10^{-4} (0.04)	8.0×10^{-4} (0.19)	3.8×10^{-4} (11)
DMF[a]	5.8×10^{-6} (0.05)	5.4×10^{-5} (0.02)	6.9×10^{-4} (0.16)	1×10^{-5} (0.3)
CH$_3$OH[c]	2.0×10^{-5} (0.17)	2.0×10^{-4} (0.07)	...	1.0×10^{-5} (0.28)

[a] From reference 167.
[b] Numbers in parentheses are relative rates, aquation = 1.0.
[c] From references 161 and 165 and U. Bellucco, private communication (Pt complex).

and the other is a direct isomerization. Ion pairing is extensive, and the direct path may result from the interchange reaction of coordinated chloride and ion-paired chloride ion.

In sulfolane, ion pairing of NCS^- and $trans$-$Co(en)_2NO_2Br^+$ is small, and the rate of substitution of bromide by thiocyanate ion is first order in NCS^- over the entire range studied.[163] Thus, there is a zero rate at zero thiocyanate concentration. This is consistent with the reaction having an S_N2 mechanism, the transition state being an ion pair in any case. At the very least one can say that a discriminating $Co(en)_2NO_2{}^{2+}$ species is not formed as an intermediate.

Table 3.29 shows the rates of solvolysis, or of concentration-independent anion substitutions, of several complexes in four different solvents. A platinum complex is included for comparison since the evidence is strong (see Chapter 5) that the solvent reaction is S_N2 in this case. Unfortunately, the solvent which is very reactive for Pt(II), dimethylsulfoxide, is probably bonding through sulfur in this case and through oxygen for the Co(III) complexes.[168] It can be seen that the solvent effect for all complexes is not very large. In the solvolysis of organic halides, similar changes in solvent would produce changes in rate many times greater than those shown in Table 3.29. This can mean one of two things, unfortunately.[167] The role of the solvent can be primarily that of solvating the anion,[169] and the covalent organic halides would require more solvent assistance than the ionic complex halides. Or alkyl halides may be reacting by an S_N2 mechanism, and the solvent may be demonstrating its nucleophilic properties to a greater extent than for the reactions of the complexes.

In any event an electron-donating substituent, Cl in $Co(en)_2Cl_2{}^+$, and an electron-withdrawing substituent, NO_2 in $Co(en)_2NO_2Cl^+$, produce rather similar solvent dependencies. If an S_N1 mechanism is operating for $Co(en)_2Cl_2{}^+$, as the earlier evidence suggests for some solvents at least, the solvent effect is entirely used up in solvating the anion and in other general solvation effects, and little is left over for nucleophilic variation. The best estimate of the mechanism for $Co(en)_2NO_2Cl^+$ is perhaps that of a solvent-assisted dissociation (or anion interchange) with very little dependence on the properties of the solvent (or the anion).

In summary, we find for octahedral substitution reactions in non-aqueous solvents that:

(a) A limiting rate is reached, independent of further changes in the concentration of the anion. This limiting rate may occur even at the lowest concentrations used.

(b) Ion pairs are formed extensively, and limiting rates are connected with the complete formation of ion pairs.

(c) The rate of reaction of a given complex is remarkably insensitive to its environment. The formation of ion pairs causes only small increases in rate over that of the free ion.

(d) Changes in solvent cause only modest changes in rate, probably to be attributed to differing solvation effects of the leaving group.

(e) All in all, reactions of these octahedral complexes in non-aqueous solvents are remarkably similar to the corresponding reactions in water, except that ion pairing is more noticeable and intermediate solvates tend to be unstable.

Acid Catalysis and a Special Mechanism for Chelates

The rates of most acid hydrolysis reactions are usually independent of hydrogen ion concentrations below a pH of about 4. Above this pH a very high rate of base hydrolysis may begin to make an appreciable contribution to the total observed rate of hydrolysis. It has also been observed that in some cases the acid hydrolysis reactions are acid catalyzed. The examples of much acid catalyzed reactions suggest that the determining factor to be considered is the nature of the ligand being replaced. In general, acid catalysis is observed for the replacement of two different types of ligands:

(1) Ligands that are strongly basic or have a large tendency to hydrogen-bond, e.g., $Co(NH_3)_5CO_3{}^+$, $Co(NH_3)_5ONO^{2+}$,*** $Fe(CN)_6{}^{4-}$, $Cr(CN)_5{}^{3-}$, $Co(en)_2F_2{}^+$, $Co(en)_2(N_3)_2{}^+$, $Co(NH_3)_5OOCR^{2+}$.

(2) Flexible bi- or multidentate basic ligands, e.g., $Fe(bipy)_3{}^{2+}$, $Ni(bipy)_3{}^{2+}$, $Ni(en)_3{}^{2+}$, $Fe(EDTA)^-$.

Some examples of these types of acid-catalyzed reactions will be described. The acid-catalyzed acid hydrolysis reaction[170] for the complex trans-$Co(en)_2F_2{}^+$ is shown in Fig. 3.18. There is an increase in acid hydrolysis at the lower pH due to acid catalysis, and another increase at the higher pH due to base hydrolysis. The acid-catalyzed portion of the curve is believed to result from the set of reactions

$$(en)_2FCo—F^+ + H_2O \xrightarrow[k_1]{slow} (en)_2FCo—OH_2{}^+ + F^- \qquad (100)$$

$$(en)_2FCo—F^+ + H^+ \underset{}{\overset{instantaneous}{\rightleftharpoons}} (en)_2FCo—FH^{2+} \qquad (101)$$

$$(en)_2FCo—FH^{2+} + H_2O \xrightarrow[k_2]{fast} (en)_2FCo—OH_2{}^{2+} + HF \qquad (102)$$

This means that the observed rate of reaction, k_{obs}, is a function of k_1, k_2, and the equilibrium constant for 101.

$$k_{obs} = k_1[(en)_2FCo—F^+] + k_2K_{eq}[(en)_2FCo—F^+][H^+] \qquad (103)$$

*** Acid catalysis at high acid concentrations is also found for nitro complexes [P. J. Stapler, *J. Chem. Soc.*, **1964**, 745; D. S. Lambert and J. S. Mason, *J. Am. Chem. Soc.*, **88**, 1633, 1637 (1966)].

The kinetic data are in agreement with such a mechanism. It is to be expected that the Co—F bond will be weakened as a result of hydrogen bonding to form Co—FH. Also in support of this mechanism is the observation that at a fixed acid concentration the rate of reaction is almost twice as fast in D_2O as it is in H_2O.[170] This contrasts with the acid hydrolysis of $Co(NH_3)_5Cl^{2+}$, which is about 60% slower in D_2O than in H_2O.[117,133] Similar increases in rate for other acid-catalyzed reactions in D_2O are

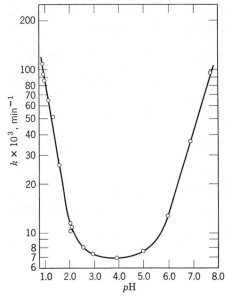

Fig. 3.18 pH dependence in the hydrolysis of *trans*-$Co(en)_2F_2^+$ at 59.3°C. From reference 170.

known and are explained in terms of differences in zero point energies for bonds involving deuterium and hydrogen.[171]

This type of acid catalysis for complexes is very closely related to the accelerating effect of Hg(II) aquo ion on the rate of release of halide ion.[172] Also silver ion and Tl(III) ion behave in a similar way. According to the classification of substitution reactions given at the beginning of this chapter, such reactions may be considered as S_E2. The possibility of help from a nucleophilic reagent in carrying the process to completion is not excluded by the observation that an electrophilic reagent is involved.

The principle of microscopic reversibility may be applied to reaction 102. If HF is the ligand lost in the dissociation step, it follows that the reverse anation reaction of $Co(en)_2FH_2O^{2+}$ must involve reaction with HF and not with F^-. Thus, the reactions of $Fe(H_2O)_5OH^{2+}$ with HF and

HN_3, rather than of $Fe(H_2O)_6^{3+}$ with F^- and N_3^-, discussed earlier,[145] become very reasonable. The aquation reaction of $Fe(H_2O)_5F^{2+}$ would occur by a proton shift to form $Fe(H_2O)_4(OH)(HF)^{2+}$, followed by loss of HF. The acid catalysis of the aquation of $Co(CN)_5N_3^{3-}$ predicts in turn that $Co(CN)_5^{2-}$ reacts with HN_3.[173]

The next kind of acceleration of rates to be discussed is specific for chelate compounds. An instance of the acid-catalyzed replacement of a basic bidentate ligand is furnished by studies on the $Fe(bipy)_3^{2+}$ complex. Baxendale and George[174] first observed this acid dependence (Fig. 3.19) and explained it on the basis of the equilibrium

$$Fe(bipy)_3^{2+} + H^+ \rightleftharpoons Fe(bipy)_3H^{3+} \tag{104}$$

with the assumption that $Fe(bipy)_3^{2+}$ reacts more slowly than does $Fe(bipy)_3H^{3+}$. A limiting rate would be reached at high acid concentrations where essentially only the latter species is present. In an aqueous solution it is unlikely that there will be much tendency to form large quantities of such a protonated species because of the weak basicity of $Fe(bipy)_3^{2+}$.

105

Furthermore, the absorption spectrum of a one molar acid solution of $Fe(bipy)_3^{2+}$ is the same as that of a neutral solution,[175] so that there cannot be any appreciable quantity of $Fe(bipy)_3H^{3+}$ present. It seems more likely[175] that instead the acid dependence is involved in the mechanism as shown in the scheme in reaction 105. Applying the steady-state approximation for the concentrations of the partly dissociated species, we obtain the observed rate constant, k_{obs}, as

$$k_{obs} = \left(\frac{k_3 + k_4[H^+]}{k_2 + k_3 + k_4[H^+]} \right) k_1 \tag{106}$$

The qualitative behavior of the acid dependence is in agreement with formula 106, but a quantitative fit is not possible without considering activity coefficients. It is apparent that a limiting rate is expected at high acidities where the values of k_2 and k_3 are negligible compared to $k_4[H^+]$, and thus $k_{obs} = k_1$. At very low acidity $[H^+]$ is negligible, and then $k_{obs} = k_1[k_3/(k_2 + k_3)]$. It was found that the ratio of the two limiting rates leads to a value of $k_3/(k_2 + k_3) = 0.16$. This means that, in solution of low

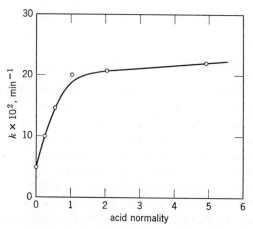

Fig. 3.19 Effect of acid on the rate of dissociation of $Fe(bipy)_3^{2+}$. From reference 173.

acidity, each time a single Fe—N bond breaks the bond will reform approximately 84% of the time, and the second bond will break, leading to complete dissociation, approximately 16% of the time.

The acid hydrolysis of the closely related $Fe(phen)_3^{2+}$ is only slightly acid dependent, as might be expected on the basis that the non-flexible 1,10-phenanthroline would not easily permit the reaction mechanism shown.[176] It is of interest that the dissociations of $Ni(en)_3^{2+}$ and $Ni(bipy)_3^{2+}$ are also acid catalyzed,[177] the interpretation given above again being applicable here. One other comment is that the Fe(II) complexes $Fe(bipy)_3^{2+}$ and $Fe(phen)_3^{2+}$ must dissociate stepwise to the hydrated Fe(II), but in both cases the first step is rate determining for this total dissociation. This is undoubtedly related to the change for low-spin tris complex to labile high-spin bis and mono complexes,[178] which would not be strongly crystal field stabilized. Nickel(II) does not show this behavior.

The mechanism in equation 105 suggests a very general kind of behavior that is possible for bi- or multidentate ligands. If such a ligand is removed by a dissociation mechanism, it is very likely that this occurs by steps. Such a step would usually be easily reversible, because the coordinating atom remains in the vicinity of the vacated spot in the metal atom co-ordination sphere. It can be prevented from reversing by either an electrophilic group's reacting with the released end of the chelate group, or by a nucleophilic reagent's reacting with the exposed metal atom. The overall dissociation would then be accelerated.

$$M\!\!\left(\begin{array}{c}A\\ \\A\end{array}\right. \rightleftharpoons M\!\!\left(\begin{array}{c}A\\ \\A\end{array}\right. \xrightarrow{+X} \underset{X}{M-\overset{\frown}{AA}} \rightarrow \underset{X}{M} + \overset{\frown}{AA} \tag{107}$$

$$\downarrow{+M'}$$

$$M-\overset{\frown}{AA}-M' \rightarrow M + \overset{\frown}{AA}-M'$$

In the examples already discussed it was H^+ which took the part of the electrophilic reagent, M'. There is no reason why another metal ion could not serve the same function. Undoubtedly many metal ion exchange reactions involving chelate groups include such a process.[179]

It is also anticipated that small, well coordinating groups like hydroxide ion can play the role of X, the nucleophilic reagent in equation 107. There is evidence of a basic catalysis, or rather a reaction with hydroxide ion, in the case of $Ni(bipy)_3^{2+}$.[180] As expected, $Ni(phen)_3^{2+}$ does not show any acceleration of its dissociation rate by base.[181] Surprisingly, $Fe(phen)_3^{2+}$ does show an acceleration by base. This will be discussed later.

Extreme examples of the effect of external reagents are afforded by the exchange reactions of multidentate ligand complexes.[182] Ligand exchange between metals, metal exchange between ligands, or double exchange between two metal complexes could be involved. A study by Margerum and Bydalek of the exchange reaction between zinc ion and nickel-EDTA (NiY^{2-}) provides some interesting effects.[183]

$$Zn^{2+} + NiY^{2-} \rightarrow ZnY^{2-} + Ni^{2+} \tag{108}$$
$$(NiYH^-) \qquad (ZnYH^-)$$

There are two chief paths between pH 3 and 5, one involving an acid-catalyzed dissociation of NiY^{2-} independent of the zinc ion, and the other a direct reaction between Zn^{2+} and NiY^{2-} or $NiYH^-$. The rate for the direct path is given by

$$\text{Rate} = k_1[Zn^{2+}][NiY^{2-}] + k_2[Zn^{2+}][NiYH^-] \tag{109}$$

The value of k_1 is $2.5 \times 10^{-6}\ M^{-1}\ \text{sec}^{-1}$ at 25°C, which is quite slow.

The mechanism presumable involves breaking several of the EDTA bonds to nickel and uncoiling the complex. At some stage, the zinc ion takes up the released chelate groups. Further release of one group by nickel and its capture by zinc insure that the exchange will go to completion. Before this rate step, the previous steps are reversible. The overall rate would then depend on the stability of the intermediate complex containing both metal ions and its further rate of dissociation.

$$NiY^2 + Zn^{2+} \overset{K}{\rightleftharpoons} ZnYNi \overset{k}{\longrightarrow} ZnY^{2-} + Ni^{2+} \qquad (110)$$

$$k_1 = kK$$

It is found that the exchange reaction of copper with Ni-EDTA is very much faster, though the form of the rate equation is similar.[184] The value of k_1 for Cu^{2+} is 1.65×10^{-2} M^{-1} sec^{-1}. If the same mechanism is assumed,

Table 3.30   Stability constants of Cu^{2+} and Zn^{2+} with segments of EDTA

	log K_1		Relative
Ligand	Cu^{2+}	Zn^{2+}	Stability
Acetate	1.65	1.03	4.2
Glycinate	8.38	5.42	910
Iminodiacetate	10.55	7.03	3300
EDTA	18.8	16.5	200

From reference 183.

it would be reasonable that k in equation 110 is not much different in the zinc case from k in the copper case. Hence, the values of K should determine the rate difference of 6500 found between the two metal ions. Table 3.30 shows some stability constants for Cu^{2+} and Zn^{2+} with various ligands. It can be seen that the relative stability of the iminodiacetate complexes agrees quite well with the relative reactivity.

This suggests that the intermediate ZnYNi or CuYNi has the structure

$$\text{Ni} \underset{O}{\overset{O}{<}} \text{N—N} \underset{O}{\overset{O}{>}} \text{Zn} \qquad (111)$$

which has the same bonding as an iminodiacetate complex. Only the bonding atoms of the chelate, $(OOCCH_2)_2NCH_2CH_2N(CH_2COO)_2$, are shown for convenience and clarity. This postulated structure would account for the variations of k_1 in terms of the stability of the intermediate. In agreement with this, Fig. 3.20 shows that log k_1 for other metal ions is a linear function of log K_1 for the iminodiacetate complex, including the H^+ case as well.

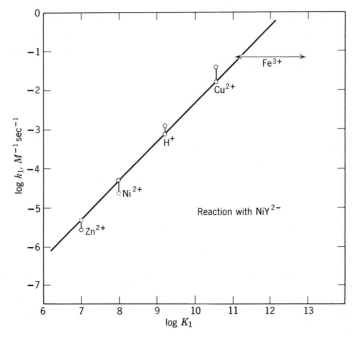

Fig. 3.20   Logarithmic plot of rate constant for the reaction

$$M^{2+} + NiY^{2-} \rightarrow MY^{2-} + Ni^{2+}$$

against equilibrium constant for iminodiacetate complexes at 25°C. Data are at two ionic strengths, 0.1 and 1.25. For Fe^{3+} the value of K_1 is uncertain, as shown by the range covered by the arrow. From reference 182.

When *trans*-1,2- diaminocyclohexanetetraacetic acid, CyDTA, is used instead of EDTA, the exchange reaction with Cu^{2+} becomes extremely slow.[185] The acid-catalyzed dissociation remains high, however. This can be understood in terms of the structure of the assumed intermediate, Cu(CyDTA)Ni, which cannot readily form for steric reasons.[185] The intermediate with hydrogen ion replacing copper can be formed without strain.

The exchange reaction between CuY^{2-} and Zn^{2+} is quite fast because of the general lability of copper complexes. This allows a novel catalysis[183] by copper ion of the slow exchange between Zn^{2+} and NiY^{2-}. The mechanism would be

$$Cu^{2+} + NiY^{2-} \xrightarrow{\text{fast}} CuY^{2-} + Ni^{2+} \qquad (112)$$

$$Zn^{2+} + CuY^{2-} \xrightarrow{\text{fast}} ZnY^{2-} + Cu^{2+} \qquad (113)$$

As little as 10^{-5} M copper ion has measurable catalytic effect.[183] Another novel catalysis occurs in the exchange reaction of triethylenetetramine-nickel(II) ion and Cu-EDTA.[186]

$$\text{Ni(trien)}^{2+} + \text{CuY}^{2-} \rightarrow \text{Cu(trien)}^{2+} + \text{NiY}^{2-} \tag{114}$$

This reaction goes essentially to completion in the direction shown but is very slow if equivalent amount of all components are used. Small excess amounts of either ligand cause a rapid exchange to occur. Since it can be shown that EDTA reacts rapidly with Ni(trien)$^{2+}$ and that trien reacts rapidly with CuY^{2-}, a chain reaction must be responsible.

$$\text{Y}^{2-}(\text{HY}^-) + \text{Ni(trien)}^{2+} \xrightarrow{\text{fast}} \text{NiY}^{2-} + \text{trien} \tag{115}$$

$$\text{trien} + \text{CuY}^{2-} \xrightarrow{\text{fast}} \text{Cu(trien)}^{2+} + \text{Y}^{2-}(\text{HY}^-) \tag{116}$$

A slight excess of either metal ion will inhibit the reaction by tying up the free ligand, which is a necessary chain carrier. The role of the free ligand in reactions 115 and 116 is to trap the metal ion in the partially unwrapped chelate (the role of X in equation 107).

The Chelate Effect

In Chapter 1 the greater stability of a complex such as Ni(en)$^{2+}$, $pK_1 = 7.2$, compared to either Ni(NH$_3$)$^{2+}$, $pK_1 = 2.8$, or Ni(NH$_3$)$_2{}^{2+}$, $\beta_2 = 4.85$, was referred to as an example of the chelate effect. It was pointed out that this was primarily an entropy-controlled phenomenon. It is of interest to examine the chelate effect in terms of kinetic and mechanistic considerations. A bidentate ligand will be compared with two molecules of a unidentate ligand, and a simple association-dissociation mechanism will be assumed.

$$\text{M} + \text{B} \underset{k_b}{\overset{k_a}{\rightleftharpoons}} \text{M—B} \tag{117}$$

unidentate

$$\text{M—B} + \text{B} \underset{k_d}{\overset{k_c}{\rightleftharpoons}} \text{MB}_2 \tag{118}$$

$$\text{M} + \text{B—B} \underset{k_b}{\overset{k_a}{\rightleftharpoons}} \text{M—B—B} \tag{119}$$

bidentate

$$\text{M—B—B} \underset{k_d}{\overset{k_c}{\rightleftharpoons}} \text{M}\!\!\left(\begin{array}{c}\text{B}\\\text{B}\end{array}\right. \tag{120}$$

In each case the total equilibrium constant is given by

$$K_{\text{eq}} = \frac{k_a k_c}{k_b k_d} \tag{121}$$

For a given metal and for two ligands, B and B—B, in which the bonding atoms are the same and the adjacent groups are similar, it is expected that k_a will not differ much because of chelation. In fact Table 3.12 shows that this is so in a number of cases.[†††] It may also be expected that k_b will not differ appreciably in the two cases, since nothing characteristic of chelation has occurred in the first step. Hence, the chelate effect has its origin in the value of k_c/k_d.

Table 3.31   Rate constants for dissociation, k_d, for some uni- and bidentate ligands in water at 25°C

Complex	k_d, sec^{-1}	log K_f	Ref.
Ni(py)$^{2+}$	38.5	1.9	49
Ni(bipy)$^{2+}$	3.3×10^{-4} [a]	7.2	49, 175
Ni(NH$_3$)$^{2+}$	5.8	2.8	49
Ni(en)$^{2+}$	0.27	7.6	49
Ni(CH$_3$CO$_2$)$^+$	$\sim 10^3$ [b]	0.7	187
Ni(C$_2$O$_4$)	3.6	4.3	48
Co(NH$_3$)$_5$(CH$_3$CO$_2$)$^{3+}$	$\begin{cases} 1.2 \times 10^{-7} \text{ acid} \\ 7.0 \times 10^{-4} \text{ base} \end{cases}$	...	66
Co(NH$_3$)$_5$(C$_2$O$_4$)$^+$	$\begin{cases} ... \quad \text{acid} \\ 6.5 \times 10^{-5} \text{ base} \end{cases}$	...	188
Co(en)$_2$(C$_2$O$_4$)$^+$	$\begin{cases} <10^{-10} \quad \text{acid} \\ <2 \times 10^{-7} \text{ [c] base} \end{cases}$	...	188, 189

[a] From rate of nickel exchange and k_2/k_3 ratio for Fe(bipy)$_3^{2+}$.
[b] From stability constant and data of Table 3.12.
[c] Less than rate of attack at carbonyl group.

Table 3.31 shows a number of rate constants for dissociation, which might be reasonably considered equal to k_d, for several cases of similar uni- and bidentate ligands. It can be seen that a chelate group such as oxalate or bipyridine dissociates considerably more slowly than a simpler ligand such as acetate or pyridine. This slower rate is accompanied by higher activation energies as well, running 6–7 kcal for the Ni(II) cases and 9 kcal for Co(III).

A reasonable interpretation of these results has been given,[33a,50] in terms of the necessity for rotation of the chelate ring after breaking the metal-ligand bond in order to (a) prevent the bond from immediately closing again or (b) allow a water molecule to move into place in the

[†††] Compared to the value for NH$_3$, k_a for ethylenediamine is anomalously large (p. 156).

coordination sphere of the metal. A barrier to rotation of several kilo-calories could certainly exist.

It would seem plausible from this to attribute the chelate effect to a small value of k_d for a polydentate ligand. A little reflection shows that this cannot be so. A potential energy barrier to rotation will slow down k_c and k_d equally, since the formation of the second metal-ligand bond by micro-scopic reversibility must necessarily mean twisting the ligand over the same barrier. Hence the ratio k_c/k_d, which determines the chelate effect, is not influenced in any way by the barrier.

What is chiefly responsible for the chelate effect is the unusually large value of k_c for the bidentate ligand. That is, in spite of the rotational barrier which reduces k_c, the important fact is that in the chelate k_c represents a unimolecular process, whereas for a simple ligand k_c is bi-molecular. This gives a large statistical advantage to k_c for the chelate which can be, of course, counterbalanced by an extremely large concentration of unidentate B.

The statistical advantage is only present providing the chelate ring to be formed is of the proper size for stability. It corresponds to a high "effective concentration" of the second ligand atom, as was first suggested by Schwarzenbach.[190] It is entirely equivalent to the neighboring group effect for nucleophilic substitution reactions of organic chemistry.[191] For example, the unimolecular reaction

$$\begin{array}{ccc} CH_2CH_2\!-\!Cl & \rightarrow & CH_2CH_2 + Cl^- \\ | & & \diagdown\!\diagup \\ O\!- & & O \end{array} \qquad (122)$$

is favored over the corresponding bimolecular reaction

$$CH_3CH_2\!-\!O^- + CH_3CH_2\!-\!Cl \rightarrow CH_3CH_2\!-\!O\!-\!CH_2CH_3 + Cl^-$$
$$(123)$$

by a factor of 10^4 because of a more positive entropy of activation.

It is usually not possible to measure k_c directly. However, the ratio k_c/k_b can sometimes be measured by methods such as were used to measure the corresponding ratio k_2/k_3 in the $Fe(bipy)_3^{2+}$ case discussed earlier. It has been found that the ratio k_c/k_b is 20–30 for $Ni(en)_3^{2+}$, $Ni(gly)_3^-$, $Ni(gly)_2$, and $Ni(gly)^+$.[192,193] In the latter cases it is undoubtedly the car-boxylate bond which breaks most easily (compare Table 3.31).‡‡‡ The breaking of the metal-amine bond would then be rate controlling for the overall dissociation in neutral media. $Co(en)_3^{2+}$ also opens one end and

‡‡‡ By n.m.r. studies it has been shown that in PbY^{2-} all metal-ligand bonds are labile, in CdY^{2-} only the Cd-O bonds are labile, and in CoY^- all bonds are inert [R. J. Day and C. N. Reilley, *Anal. Chem.*, **36**, 1073 (1964)].

recloses many times before the second end dissociates.[194] For Ni(trien)$^{2+}$ the ratio k_c/k_b is about 100.[50] When the chelate ring is very stable, as in the acetylacetonates, it can be expected that the ratio will be very large. This is found to be true for Pd(acac)$_2$ (see pp. 416–417).

An important kinetic consequence of the large value of k_c/k_b is that, for the formation of a chelate, k_a will usually be the rate-determining constant.[32,50] When one end of the chelate is attached to the metal, all subsequent ligation steps will be rapid. In the reverse process, the dissociation of a chelate, the dissociation of all bonds but the last will be reversible, and

Table 3.32 Rate limits for exchange of alcohols coordinated to metal ions

Metal Ion	Glycol, k_{ex}, sec^{-1} ^{a}	Methanol, k_{ex}, sec^{-1}
Mn(II)	>1.5 × 10^6	~2 × 10^5 ^{b}
Co(II)	>3.4 × 10^3	1.8 × 10^4 ^{c}
Ni(II)	4.4 × 10^3	1.0 × 10^3 ^{c}
Cu(II)	>1.1 × 10^5	1.0 × 10^4 ^{d}

^{a} From reference 194. Temp. 27°C.
^{b} From reference 235. Temp. 25°C.
^{c} From reference 197b. Temp. 25°C.
^{d} From reference 199. Temp. 25°C.

the last metal-ligand bond will determine the rate. These conclusions may readily be deduced from equations 119 and 120 by applying the steady state treatment to M—B—B. As we have seen, the statement is not true if other metal ions or other ligands intervene to react with the partly opened species.

An interesting deduction to be derived from the chelate effect comes from a study of the ligand exchange reaction of metal ions in ethylene glycol, studied by the n.m.r. line broadening method.[194]

$$M(glycol)_3^{2+} + {}^*glycol \rightleftharpoons M({}^*glycol)_3^{2+} + glycol \qquad (124)$$

The evidence is not extensive, but it appears that glycol acts as a bidentate chelate towards metal ions.[195] The rates of solvent exchange of glycol are given in Table 3.32 and compared with the corresponding values for exchange of methanol. While only lower limits are available in most cases, it appears certain that solvent exchange in glycol is not appreciably slower than in methanol.

This seems to be good evidence for a solvent-assisted dissociation mechanism rather than an S_N1 mechanism for the exchange process. That is, the intermediate I would be expected to reclose many times before the second end of the chelate is released to give exchange. However, the intermediate of the assisted dissociation, II, will guarantee exchange since both the entering and leaving glycol molecules have become equivalent.

$$(125)$$

It is also of interest that the rate of methanol exchange is somewhat slower than the water exchange rate for the same metal ions. This may be a steric factor in which the packing of seven CH_3OH around one metal ion becomes difficult. It is known[196] that for the case of Cr(III) the relative rates of replacement of water by water, water by methanol, and methanol by water, in water solvent at 30°C, is 1, 0.34, and 2.1. Thus, the replacement of bound methanol by water is fastest of all. At equilibrium water is bound considerably more strongly than methanol.[186b,236]

There is also some evidence that water in the coordination sphere of metal ions labilizes coordinated methanol in methanol solvent.[197] This is probably a steric factor rather than an inductive one. Anions also will usually cause an increased rate of water or methanol exchange when coordinated to the same metal ion. Thus, $Co(CH_3OH)_5Cl^+$ exchanges methanol much more rapidly than $Co(CH_3OH)_6^{2+}$. Interestingly enough, it is the methanol molecule *cis* to the chloro group which is labilized.[198] This suggests activation by π bonding.

A very large difference in the rates of exchange of coordinated water and of methanol is found for Cu(II). The rate constants are greater than 10^9 sec^{-1} for H_2O and 1.0×10^4 sec^{-1} for methanol (Tables 3.11 and 3.32). It is possible that the high rate constant found is for exchange of axial water molecules and the low rate constant for exchange of equatorial methyl alcohol molecules. The experimental methods used (^{17}O broadening for water and proton broadening for CH_3OH) are such that a very slow exchange could not be seen in the water case or a very rapid exchange in the methanol case.

One would expect that there would be an easy interconversion of axial and equatorial positions. Using the simple model previously described on p. 100 for the Jahn-Teller stabilization energy, one can easily calculate the activation energy for this process. The axial bonds shorten and one pair of equatorial bonds lengthen until they are equal. The minimum energy required for this is one-half of the Jahn-Teller stabilization. In the case of water ligands the activation energy for interconversion would be 4–5 kcal from this calculation (see p. 101). There is no obvious reason why this should be more difficult for methanol ligands.

The rates of substitution of solvent molecules by other ligands on Ni(II) in methanol solution show interesting effects when compared to the same rates measured in water solution.[237] Table 3.33 gives the observed second order rate constants. It can be seen that the charge on the ligand plays an

Table 3.33   Second-order rate constants for substitution reactions of nickel(II) in water and methanol at 25°C

$$Ni(solvent)_6^{2+} + L^q \xrightarrow{k} Ni(solvent)_nL^{q+2} + solvent$$

L	k, CH_3OH, M^{-1} sec^{-1}	k, H_2O, M^{-1} sec^{-1}
Phenanthroline	3.5×10^2	3.2×10^3
Bipyridine	1.3×10^2	1.6×10^3
$SeCN^-$	5.4×10^3 ($\mu = 0.10$)	...
SCN^-	4.3×10^3 ($\mu = 0.30$)	5.0×10^3 ($\mu = 0.5$)
$C_2O_2S_2^{2-}$ [a]	2.5×10^5 ($\mu = 0.10$)	5.8×10^4 ($\mu = 0.10$)[b]

[a] Dithiooxalate ion.
[b] Only observed product is the spin-paired $Ni(dto)_2^{2-}$. Rate $= k[Ni^{2+}][dto^{2-}]$, so first step is rate determining.

important role, neutral ligands react more slowly with Ni^{2+} in methanol than in water, univalent anions react at about the same rate in both solvents, and a bivalent anion reacts faster in methanol than in water.

These variations in rate with charge could be predicted because of the lower dielectric constant of methanol compared to water. Thus electrostatic attraction will be greater in methanol than in water and will increase with increasing charge on the anion. The fact that the rate constant for the neutral bipyridine is less in methanol than in water provides strong evidence for an interchange mechanism (pp. 154 to 156). Since $k_{obs} = K_0 k_c$ (equation 25), and since k_c is a rate constant controlled by the rate of loss of a solvent molecule, reactions in methanol can be slower than in water, providing K_0 is not too sensitive to the dielectric constant of the medium. A dissociation mechanism, in which $Ni(H_2O)_5^{2+}$ and $Ni(CH_3OH)_5^{2+}$ are formed, should always be more rapid for methanol than for water. This conclusion is based on the presumably weaker bonding of alcohol.[236]

Substitution Reactions without the Cleavage of the Metal-Ligand Bond

The substitution reactions discussed up till now require a rupture of the metal-ligand bond. However, it has been observed in some systems that reactions occur without the cleavage of this bond. Such is the case for the conversion of amminecarbonato complexes of Co(III) to the corresponding aquo complexes and for the formation of amminenitrito complexes of Co(III) from the corresponding aquo compounds.

The addition of excess acid to an aqueous solution of $Co(NH_3)_5CO_3{}^+$ results in the immediate liberation of carbon dioxide and the formation of $Co(NH_3)_5H_2O^{3+}$. Kinetic studies [200] show that the reacting species is the bicarbonato complex, $Co(NH_3)_5CO_3H^{2+}$. Since acid hydrolysis reactions of Co(III) complexes such as those mentioned earlier are generally slow, it would appear that this reaction of the bicarbonato complex may proceed by an entirely different process. This has been confirmed by studies using ^{18}O-labeled water as the solvent, which show that the Co-O bond is not severed but rather that the O-C bond is broken:

$$(NH_3)_5Co-OCO_2{}^+ + 2H_3{}^*O^+ \rightarrow$$
$$(NH_3)_5Co-OH_2{}^{3+} + 2H_2{}^*O + CO_2 \quad (126)$$

Reaction 126 takes place with little or no uptake of ^{18}O in either of the two products, $Co(NH_3)_5H_2O^{3+}$ and CO_2.[201] These results suggest a mechanism involving an attachment on the oxygen of Co—O—C by a proton followed by the rupture of the O-C bond.

(127)

Thus this is a decarboxylation reaction rather than an acid hydrolysis reaction.

Similar studies[202] have been made on the tetraammine complex, $Co(NH_3)_4CO_3{}^+$. In this system the reaction ^{18}O water yields carbon dioxide of normal abundance and a diaquo complex which derives half of its oxygen from the solvent. Such an isotopic distribution must result from the reaction scheme

$$(NH_3)_4Co\underset{O}{\overset{O}{\diagdown\diagup}}C=O \xrightarrow[\text{fast}]{H_3{}^*O^+}$$

$$(NH_3)_4Co\overset{{}^*OH_2{}^{2+}}{\underset{OCO_2H}{\diagdown\diagup}} \xrightarrow[\text{slow}]{H_3{}^*O^+} (NH_3)_4Co\overset{{}^*OH_2{}^{3+}}{\underset{OH_2}{\diagdown\diagup}} + CO_2 \quad (128)$$

The first step involves a breaking of the Co-O bond, and the second step, like that for $Co(NH_3)_5CO_3H$, requires a cleavage of the O-C bond.

Other reactions, such as the rapid liberation of sulfur dioxide from a sulfito—O metal complex or the rapid evolution of nitrogen oxide from a nitrito upon acidification, have not as yet been studied in detail. However, it would appear by analogy with the reaction of carbonatocobalt(III) ammines that reactions of this type will also occur without M-O bond cleavage. Similarly the reverse of these reactions, that of a hydroxo complex with an acid anhydride, is expected to take place by direct addition to the coordinated oxygen and without M-O bond rupture. Extensive investigations of this reverse reaction have been made in connection with the formation of a nitrito, M—ONO, complex from the corresponding aquo compound. This reaction (129) is quite rapid, which in itself suggests that the Co-O bond is not broken.

$$Co(NH_3)_5H_2O^{3+} + NO_2^- \rightarrow Co(NH_3)_5ONO^{2+} + H_2O \quad (129)$$

Kinetic studies[203] of the reaction in HNO_2—NO_2^- buffers show that the general rate expression for the formation of the nitrito complex is given by the equation

$$Rate = k[\text{aquo complex}][NO_2^-][HNO_2] \quad (130)$$

However, because of the acid-base equilibrium between the aquo and hydroxo complexes, equation 130 may also be replaced by

$$Rate = k'[\text{hydroxo complex}][NHO_2]^2 \quad (131)$$

This expression of the rate law is analogous to the rate equation frequently found[204] for the nitrosation of ammonia and amines,

$$Rate = k[\text{amine}][HNO_2]^2 \quad (132)$$

The interpretation given equation 132 is that the nitrosating agent in weakly acid solutions is N_2O_3, which attacks the unshared pair of electrons on the amine nitrogen by splitting into NO^+ and NO_2^-. Thus the observed second-order dependence on HNO_2 results from the equilibrium

$$2HNO_2 \rightleftharpoons N_2O_3 + H_2O \qquad (133)$$

Therefore it may be assumed that the formation of nitrito complexes involves an O-nitrosation type reaction which does not require Co-O bond cleavage. This reaction sequence is further supported by the

$$(NH_3)_5Co-OH_2{}^{3+} + H_2O \overset{fast}{\rightleftharpoons} (NH_3)_5Co-OH^{2+} + H_3O^+ \qquad (134)$$

$$(NH_3)_5Co-OH^{2+} + N_2O_3 \overset{slow}{\longrightarrow} (NH_3)_5Co-O\cdots\cdot H^{2+}$$

$$O{=}\overset{..}{N}\cdots\cdot O-N{=}O \qquad (135)$$
$$\downarrow fast$$
$$(NH_3)_5Co-ONO^{2+} + HNO_2$$

observation that the synthesis of a nitro complex from the corresponding chloro complex in a buffered aqueous medium (pH 4–5) takes place in a series of steps, one of which involves the formation of the nitrito complex followed by its subsequent rearrangement to the nitro product (for a discussion of nitrito-nitro isomerization see Chapter 4).

The final confirmation that the nitrito complex is formed without the cleavage of the Co-O bond was provided by studies using ^{18}O.[205] For example, the ^{18}O-enriched aquo complex reacts in ordinary water to yield the enriched nitrito product,

$$(NH_3)_5Co-*OH_2{}^{3+} + NO_2^- \rightarrow (NH_3)_5Co-*ONO^{2+} + H_2O \quad (136)$$

With a knowledge of the reaction mechanism in hand, it has been possible to plan syntheses which produce the previously unknown nitrito complexes of Rh(III), Ir(III) and Pt(IV).[206] The rate law for formation is the same as that for Co(III). The subsequent rearrangement of the nitrito complexes to nitro complexes can also be observed. Interestingly enough, the reaction of $Pt(en)(H_2O)_2{}^{2+}$ with HNO_2–NO_2^- buffer gives immediately $Pt(en)(NO_2)_2$. This probably indicates a direct nucleophilic attack on Pt(II) by nitrite ion (see Chapter 5).

In addition to the normal acid and base hydrolysis of acetatoammine complexes of Co(III), Rh(III) and Ir(III), there is an acid-catalyzed hydrolysis.[66] This is as expected because acetate ion is a weak base. Formate and propionate complexes behave in the same way.[207] The mechanism could be the same as for the acid-catalyzed hydrolysis of $Co(en)_2F_2{}^+$ discussed earlier.

The possibility also exists for basic, neutral, or acid hydrolysis that attack occurs at the carbonyl group.[20b] This would lead to C-O bond cleavage and not M-O cleavage.

$$
\begin{aligned}
&\underset{\substack{\| \\ O}}{\overset{\overset{\displaystyle R}{|}}{H_2O + C}} - O - Co(NH_3)_5{}^{2+} \rightarrow \underset{\substack{| \\ O \\ | \\ H}}{\overset{\overset{\displaystyle R}{|}}{HO - C}} - O - Co(NH_3)_5{}^{2+} \\
\end{aligned}
$$

(137)

$$
\rightarrow \underset{\substack{| \\ O \\ | \\ H}}{\overset{\overset{\displaystyle R}{|}}{HO - C}} \cdots O - Co(NH_3)_5{}^{2+} \rightarrow \underset{\substack{\| \\ O}}{\overset{\overset{\displaystyle R}{|}}{HO - C}} + HO - Co(NH_3)_5{}^{2+}
$$

Such a mechanism strongly resembles that found for the hydrolysis of organic esters.

The use of ^{18}O-labeled water can distinguish between the two possible modes of bond cleavage. In the case of base hydrolysis of $Co(en)_2(OAc)_2{}^+$ and $Co(dipy)_2(OAc)_2{}^+$, it is known to be the Co-O bond that breaks.[128] However, for the chelate, $Co(en)_2ox^+$, the first attack is at the carbonyl, opening the chelate ring, followed by normal metal-ligand cleavage.[188]

$$
(en)_2\,Co\underset{\diagdown \ O - C = O}{\overset{\diagup \ O - C = O^+}{}} + {}^*OH^- \rightarrow (en)_2\,Co\underset{\diagdown \ O - C - C\diagdown}{\overset{\diagup \ OH }{}}{}^*O \qquad (138)
$$

$$
I + {}^*OH^- \rightarrow (en)_2\,Co\underset{\diagdown \ {}^*OH}{\overset{\diagup \ OH}{}} + C_2O_3{}^*O^{2-} \qquad (139)
$$

In the base hydrolysis of $Co(NH_3)_5X^{2+}$, where X is CH_3COO, $ClCH_2COO$, Cl_2CHCOO, CCl_3COO, and CF_3COO, increasing amounts of [18]O were found in the carboxylate ion produced.[20b] It has been observed earlier that a close parallelism existed between rates of base hydrolysis and acid hydrolysis and the strength of the carboxylic acid formed.[208] That is, the trifluorocetato complex reacted most rapidly and trifluoroacetic acid was the strongest acid. This suggested metal-oxygen cleavage since the complex with the better-leaving group reacted fastest. Acyl-oxygen cleavage would be expected to show evidence of steric factors.

The discrepancy in the above results appears to be resolved by studies of Jordan and Taube.[209] The rate law for base hydrolysis is usually a simple second-order one, as for other cobalt complexes. However, for carboxylato complexes in which the carboxyl is activated by strongly negative groups, a two-term rate law is found.

$$\text{Rate} = [k_1[\text{OH}^-] + k_2[\text{OH}^-]^2] \, [\text{complex}] \tag{140}$$

Examples are $Co(NH_3)_5CF_3CO_2^{2+}$ and $Co(NH_3)_5ox^+$. By isotopic labeling it is also found[209] that the simple k_1 path leads almost completely to Co-O bond scission, whereas the k_2 path seems to be entirely one of C-O bond breaking.

The rates of hydrolysis, studied at low concentration of base, thus correspond to the normal path for base hydrolysis as postulated.[208] The incursion of the path involving attack at the carbonyl group occurs only at high base concentrations and chiefly for the more negatively substituted carboxylate groups. This path leads to incorporation of ^{18}O into the carboxylate ion produced. Some exchange also occurs in the unhydrolyzed complex.[209] The mechanism of the k_2 path probably involves the reactions

$$
\begin{array}{ccc}
& \overset{\displaystyle O^-}{\underset{\displaystyle |}{}} & & \overset{\displaystyle O^-}{\underset{\displaystyle |}{}} \\
\text{Co—O—C—R} + \text{OH}^- & \rightleftharpoons & \text{Co—O—C—R} + \text{H}_2\text{O} \\
\underset{\displaystyle |}{} & & \underset{\displaystyle |}{} \\
\overset{\displaystyle O}{\underset{\displaystyle H}{}} & & O^-
\end{array}
\tag{141}
$$

$$
\begin{array}{c}
\overset{\displaystyle O^-}{\underset{\displaystyle |}{}} \\
\text{Co—O—C—R} \;\rightarrow\; \text{Co—O}^- + \text{RCO}_2^- \\
\underset{\displaystyle |}{} \\
O^-
\end{array}
\tag{142}
$$

This sequence is entirely analogous to many other base cleavage reactions of activated carbonyl compounds.

$$
\begin{array}{c}
\overset{\displaystyle O}{\underset{\displaystyle \|}{}} \qquad\qquad \overset{\displaystyle O^-}{\underset{\displaystyle |}{}} \\
\text{R—C—X} + 2\text{OH}^- \;\rightleftharpoons\; \text{R—C—X} \;\rightarrow\; \text{RCO}_2^- + \text{X}^- \\
\underset{\displaystyle |}{} \\
O^-
\end{array}
\tag{143}
$$

Whenever X^- is a relatively unstable anion, it is found that the rate of cleavage depends on the square of the hydroxide ion concentration.[210]

Hydrolysis under neutral conditions[201b] (pH 4–5) gives normal metal-ligand bond breaking for $Co(NH_3)_5OAc^{2+}$. There is a large difference in rate between Co(III), Ru(III), and Ir(III) as is also found for the series $M(NH_3)_5Br^{2+}$ (see Table 3.15).

Hydrolysis under strongly acid conditions gives rates for cobalt and rhodium which are nearly the same, while iridium is only 50 times slower.[66] This suggests that the protonated complex undergoes attack at the acyl group to give C—O cleavage. In agreement with this hypothesis it is found that changing from acetato to pivalato complexes slows down the rate of hydrolysis in acid. There would be steric hindrance in the $(CH_3)_3$-CCOO group to attack at the carbonyl but relatively little to attack at the metal atom. Proof of acyl-oxygen cleavage during acid hydrolysis using ^{18}O failed because of extensive oxygen exchange of the products with water.[66]

Possible S_N2 Mechanisms for Octahedral Complexes

In a number of kinetic studies made on octahedral systems the results seemed to the investigators to be best explained by S_N2 mechanisms. Closer examination of all these examples leaves some room for doubt, since various complications and alternative explanations exist.

For example, a study has been made of the hydrolysis[211] of the cationic complex tris(acetylacetonato)silicon(IV), $Si(acac)_3^+$. The hope was that a d^0 system might be more open to attack by a nucleophilic reagent than the complexes of the transition metal ions. It is known that SiF_6^{2-} and GeF_6^{2-} hydrolyze at rates independent of the hydroxide ion concentration[212] and that AsF_6^- and PF_6^- are inert to alkali.[213] However, in these

Table 3.34   Rate constants for a series of nucleophiles, Y, in the reaction

$$Si(acac)_3^+ + 2H_2O \xrightarrow{Y} SiO_2 + 3Hacac + H^+$$

Nucleophile	K_a	k_Y, M^{-1} sec^{-1}
OH$^-$	1.1×10^{-16}	1.7×10^3
HOO$^-$	1.5×10^{-12}	8.0×10^4
NH$_2$NH$_2$	3.98×10^{-9}	18
HPO$_4^{2-}$	7.5×10^{-8}	3.2×10^{-2}
HOOH	...	2.4×10^{-5}
NH$_2$OH	1.58×10^{-6}	1.2
F$^-$	1.8×10^{-5}	1.7×10^{-3}
NO$_2^-$	4×10^{-4}	3.5×10^{-3}
S$_2$O$_3^{2-}$	1.38×10^{-2}	1.3×10^{-2}
(NH$_2$)$_2$CS	8.7	1.8×10^{-4} (?)[a]
H$_2$O	55.5	4.9×10^{-6}
I$^-$	(10^9)	3.0×10^{-4} (?)[a]

Data from reference 211.

[a] Rate constant less than this number.

cases, d^0 or buried d^{10}, it is possible that electrostatic repulsion is responsible for failure to react with OH^-.

It was found that the reaction

$$Si(acac)_3^+ + 2H_2O \xrightarrow{Y} SiO_2 + 3Hacac + H^+ \qquad (144)$$

was subject to general base catalysis.[211] Table 3.34 gives the second-order rate constants found for a number of nucleophilic reagents or bases. As the basicity towards the proton increases, the rate constant k_Y increases. Such a result is very reasonable for a hard acid substrate such as Si(IV). Higher reactivity is found for N_2H_4, NH_2OH, and O_2H^- than predicted from their basicities. This is a general result, however, for nucleophiles having an atom with one or more unshared pairs of electrons alpha to the nucleophilic atom. The increased reactivity is called the *alpha effect* (see p. 192).

Indeed the reactivity series shown in Table 3.34 is essentially the same as that found for nucleophilic attack at carbonyl groups, for example, the hydrolysis of p-nitrophenylacetate.

$$p\text{-}NO_2\text{-}C_6H_4O_2CCH_3 + H_2O \xrightarrow{Y} p\text{-}NO_2\text{---}C_6H_4OH + CH_3CO_2H \quad (145)$$

This raises the possibility that the initial attack on $Si(acac)_3^+$ is at the carbonyl group, even though the latter is coordinated, e.g.,

$$(146)$$

The use of ^{18}O labeling would distinguish between this mechanism and that of nucleophilic attack at Si(IV). In fact, Muetterties and Wright[214] have made such studies on the related dibenzoylmethane analog, $Si(dbm)_3^+$, and have found that exactly one-sixth of the six oxygen atoms of the ligands are enriched with ^{18}O. This agrees with the predicted value for the mechanism just given if only the first step involves carbonyl attack and all other steps do not. In a similar way, the base hydrolyses of several cationic tropolonates in ^{18}O-enriched water lead to the incorporation of 1 mole of enriched oxygen for each mole of complex.[214] Examples are $SiT_3{}^+$, $GeT_2{}^+$, and $BT_2{}^+$, where T^- refers to the tropolone anion, $C_7H_5O_2{}^-$.

The complex CoY^-, ethylenediaminetetraacetatocobaltate(III), undergoes base hydrolysis with a rate first order in hydroxide ion concentration.[214] Since there are no acidic protons, an S_N1CB mechanism does not seem possible. Furthermore, the rate of racemization of optically active CoY^- in alkali is faster than the rate of base hydrolysis.[214] Formation of a seven-coordinated Co(III) intermediate which is symmetrical could account for these facts (see Fig. 4.25). However, it is again possible that the hydroxide ion adds to the carbonyl group and causes a rapid intramolecular rearrangement as well as a C-O bond cleavage. Also, in the case of a chelate, it is always possible that the increased rate of dissociation in base is due to the trapping of a partly opened ring by OH^-.

Such an explanation is not likely for a rigid chelate, however, and the effect of basic anions on the rate of dissociation of $Fe(phen)_3{}^{2+}$, tris-(1,10-phenanthroline) iron(II), is indeed puzzling.[216] Both OH^- and CN^- at 0.1 M produce about a 10-fold increase in the rate of dissociation, which is not a large effect. However, at 1.0 M base the rate increase is up to 100 or more, so that if ion pairs are formed they are much more reactive than the free ion. Azide ion produces a much smaller effect.

On the other hand, if hydroxylamine, a powerful nucleophile (see Table 3.34), is added, there is a decrease in the rate of dissociation, rather than an increase. Also the rather similar $Ni(phen)_3{}^{2+}$ shows absolutely no effect on its rate of dissociation when OH^-, CN^-, and $N_3{}^-$ are added.[217] One is tempted to speculate that the redox properties of the central ion are in some way involved, Fe(III) being stable and Ni(III) not. It is known[238] that hydroxide ion attacks the phenanthroline ligand of $Fe(phen)_3{}^{3+}$. There is degradative oxidation of the ligand and reduction of iron to the ferrous condition. Alternatively, the difference between iron and nickel may be due to the possible excitation of low-spin $(t_{2g})^6$ to high-spin $(t_{2g})^4(e_g)^2$ for iron.[239] Such a process is not possible for nickel [see p. 314 for the racemization of $Fe(phen)_3{}^{2+}$ and $Ni(phen)_3{}^{2+}$ complexes]. The role of nucleophilic reagent, then, is to destroy the octahedral symmetry and to facilitate the spin change.

Reactions of the complex cis-$Ru(phen)_2(py)_2{}^{2+}$ with several anions have been studied in the solvents acetone and o-dichlorobenzene.[218] It was found that pyridine was replaced by Cl^-, Br^-, I^-, NCS^-, and OH^- at a common rate, independent of the concentration of the anion. Also CN^-, $N_3{}^-$, and $NO_2{}^-$ reacted at a faster rate and by a second-order process.

Ion pairing is certainly involved, and the relative rates of NO_2^-, N_3^-, and Cl^-, Br^-, or NCS^- were only $9:4:1$. Such small variations are within the limits usually found in non-aqueous solvents for different ion pairs.

Several times it has been thought that cyanide ion was a good nucleophile for certain Co(III) complexes.[219] It has been shown, however, that this appears to be so only when Co(II) is present.[220] Presumably a redox mechanism is operating in which the interesting species $Co(CN)_5^{3-}$ (see Chapter 6) is the mediator.

$$Co^{2+} + 5CN^- \rightarrow Co(CN)_5^{3-} \tag{147}$$

$$Co(CN)_5^{3-} + Co(en)_2Cl_2^+ \rightarrow Co(CN)_5Cl^{3-} + Co^{2+} + 2en + Cl^- \tag{148}$$

Perhaps the most favorable cases for finding S_N2 mechanisms for octahedral systems occur in the complexes of Pt(IV). In Fig. 3.8 it is predicted that an increased positive charge on the nucleus would favor an S_N2 reaction, since bond breaking would become difficult. Table 3.1 may also be consulted. A number of kinetic studies of substitution reaction of the haloammine complexes of Pt(IV) by Russian workers show the expected second-order rate laws.

In the first example,[221] a number of complexes such as $Pt(NH_3)_3Cl_3^+$ and $Pt(en)(NH_3)(NO_2)ClBr^+$ react with pyridine in a second-order process. It is found that, if the complexes are written as PtA_3XYZ^+, with X and Z variable groups *trans* to each other, *trans*-Br activates X more than *trans*-Cl more than *trans*-NO_2. This is a different result from the effect of *trans*-NO_2 in the case of Co(III) and also Pt(II) (see Chapter 5). Also, if X and Z are bromine and chlorine, it is chloride which is displaced more rapidly.

$$Pt(NH_3)_3ClBrCl^+ + py \rightarrow Pt(NH_3)ClBrpy^{2+} + Cl^- \tag{149}$$

trans-$Pt(NH_3)_4(NO_2)X^{2+}$ reacts with pyridine and ammonia in a second-order process to replace the nitro group. X is chlorine, bromine, or iodine.[222]

$$trans\text{-}Pt\ (NH_3)_4(NO_2)X^{2+} + py \rightarrow trans\text{-}Pt(NH_3)_4(py)X^{3+} + NO_2^- \tag{150}$$

Pyridine reacts faster than ammonia, and the rate increases in the order $X = I > Br > Cl$. *Trans*-$Pt(NH_3)_4Cl_2^{2+}$ also reacts with ammonia in a second-order process.[222]

The base hydrolysis of chlorammine complexes of Pt(IV) may be an S_N2 process, but the predominant species reacting are amido complexes.[223] The data for a number of different complexes are somewhat better accommodated by an S_N1CB mechanism, since rates can be correlated with pK_a values. The reactions of Pt(IV) are very sensitive to light and to the presence of even trace amounts of Pt(II).[224] It has been found that exchange of trans-$Pt(en)_2Cl_2^{2+}$ with radiochloride ion does not occur unless Pt(II) is present.[225] The rate of exchange in the dark is given by

$$\text{Rate} = k[Pt(II)][Pt(IV)][Cl^-] \qquad (151)$$

which suggests a bridged intermediate and an atom transfer mechanism (see Chapter 6). Considerable care must be taken to distinguish between a simple displacement mechanism and some catalyzed path. The apparently simple reaction

$$\text{trans-}Pt(en)_2Cl_2^{2+} + NO_2^- \rightarrow Pt(en)_2(NO_2)Cl^{2+} + Cl^- \qquad (152)$$

appears to occur only as a result of a Pt(II)-catalyzed process.[226] There is a slow reduction of Pt(IV) to Pt(II) by nitrite ion. If Pt(II) is added beforehand, the rate law becomes

$$\text{Rate} = k[Pt(II)][Pt(IV)][NO_2^-] \qquad (153)$$

Again a bridged intermediate may be postulated.

Extensive reduction of Pt(IV) to Pt(II) occurs in the base hydrolysis[123] of complexes such as trans-$Pt(en)_2Cl_2^{2+}$. The Pt(II) in turn can cause catalytic release of further chloride ion. It has been suggested that the substitution reaction between $PtCl_6^{2-}$ and I^- is a simple S_N2 process.[227] However, the very similar reactions of $PtCl_6^{2-}$ and Br^- and of $PtBr_6^{2-}$ with radioactive bromide ion are catalyzed by Pt(II).[228] The compounds $OsBr_6^{2-}$ and $IrBr_6^{2-}$ seem to exchange with bromide ion in a bimolecular process.[240]

In the study of the reaction of trans-$Pt(NH_3)_4Cl_2^{2+}$ with NH_3, it was definitely stated that catalysis by Pt(II) was looked for and not found.[222] Nevertheless, a more recent study[229] of the same reaction finds strong catalysis by $Pt(NH_3)_4^{2+}$. It is clear that all apparently bimolecular reactions of Pt(IV) must be scrutinized carefully to eliminate possible photochemical and catalytic phenomena.

Summary

In conclusion we can say that, with some possible exceptions mentioned above, the substitution reactions of octahedral complexes appear to occur by predominantly bond-breaking mechanisms. The S_N1 label may be attached to these processes in a generic way, but the details probably vary considerably from one case to the next. In some cases an S_N1 (lim) mechanism is operating and a true five-coordinated intermediate is formed. In other case the leaving group does not completely break its connection to the central metal atom before the entering group begins to intrude. The transition state is seven-coordinated, but with the leaving and entering groups only weakly bound. The term "(solvent) assisted dissociation" is coined to describe this process.

A characteristic feature in the case where an S_N1 (lim) mechanism is not operating is the "interchange reaction," or exchange of positions between particles in the first and second coordination spheres. If the leaving group is an anion, the entering group is almost always a solvent molecule. If the leaving group is a solvent molecule or other neutral species, the entering group may be an anion. An octahedral wedge structure for the interchange intermediate (cis attack) accounts for this specificity in terms of the desire to avoid close anion-anion repulsions. In most cases the rates are remarkably insensitive to the nature of the species in the second coordination sphere.

The same insensitivity and general pattern of behavior are found for the stable complexes of Co(III), Cr(III), etc., and the extremely labile complexes of Mg(II), Co(II), etc. Accordingly, this characteristic behavior of octahedral complexes appears to be related not to the d electron configuration but to a steric factor. That is, it is difficult to bond seven groups strongly to those metal ions which have a preferred coordination number of six.

References

1. See C. K. Ingold, *Structure and Mechanism in Organic Chemistry*, Cornell University Press, Ithaca, 1953, Chaps. 5 and 7.
2. G. N. Lewis, *Valence and the Structure of Atoms and Molecules*, Chemical Catalog Co., New York, 1923, p. 141; *J. Franklin Inst.*, **226**, 293 (1938).
3. C. G. Swain and C. B. Scott, *J. Am. Chem. Soc.*, **75**, 141 (1953).
4. See R. E. Dessy and F. Paulik, *J. Chem. Educ.*, **40**, 185 (1963).
5. J. Hine, *Physical Organic Chemistry*, McGraw-Hill Book Co., New York, 1962, Chaps. 24 and 25.
6. (a) C. R. McCoy and A. L. Allred, *J. Am. Chem. Soc.*, **84**, 912 (1962). (b) E. R. Dessy, F. Kaplan, G. R. Coe, and R. M. Salinger, *ibid.*, **85**, 1191 (1963).
7. (a) R. E. Dessy, Y. K. Lee, and J. Y. Kim, *J. Am. Chem. Soc.*, **83**, 1163 (1961); (b) M. D. Johnson *Ann. Repts. Chem. Soc.*, **IVII**, 168 (1961). (c) O. Reutov, *Record Chem. Progr.*, **22**, (1961). (d) C. K. Ingold, *Helv. chim. Acta.*, **47**, 1191 (1964).
8. P. H. Lewis and R. E. Rundle, *J. Chem. Phys.*, **21**, 986 (1953).
9. See A. A. Frost and R. G. Pearson, *Kinetics and Mechanism*, John Wiley and Sons, New York, 1961, Chaps. 1 and 12.
10. F. Basolo, *Chem. Revs.*, **52**, 459 (1953).
11. For a discussion and earlier references see V. Gold, *J. Chem. Soc.*, **1956**, 4633.
12. L. Wilputte-Steinert, P. J. C. Fierens, and H. Hannaert, *Bull. Soc. chim. Belges*, **64**, 628 (1955).
13. See reference 9, Chap. 5.
14. R. G. Pearson, *J. Chem. Phys.*, **20**, 1478 (1952).

15. F. J. Garrick, *Phil. Mag.*, **14**, 914 (1932), has calculated that AlF_6^{3-} in solution is 30 kcal more stable than AlF_5^{2-} and 150 kcal more stable than AlF_8^{5-}.

16. D. R. Llewellyn, C. J. O'Connor, and A. L. Odell, *J. Chem. Soc.*, **1964**, 196; see also A. C. Rutenberg and J. S. Drury, *Inorg. Chem.*, **2**, 219 (1963).

17. H. R. Hunt and H. Taube, *J. Am. Chem. Soc.*, **80**, 2642 (1958).

18. (a) H. R. Hunt and H. Taube, *loc. cit.* (b) A. S. Adamson, *J. Am. Chem. Soc.*, **80**, 3183, 1958. (c) M. L. Tobe, *J. Chem. Soc.*, **1959**, 3776. (d) T. P. Jones, W. E. Harris, and W. J. Wallace, *Can. J. Chem.*, **39**, 2371 (1951). (e) R. Dyke and W. C. E. Higginson, *J. Chem. Soc.*, **1963**, 2788.

19. N. S. Hush, *Australian J. Chem.*, **15**, 378 (1962).

20. General reviews of nucleophilic reactivity are given by (a) J. O. Edwards and R. G. Pearson, *J. Am. Chem. Soc.*, **84**, 16 (1962). (b) R. R. Hudson, *Chimia*, **16**, 173 (1962). (c) J. F. Bunnett, in *Annual Reviews of Physical Chemistry* (H. Eyring, ed.), Annual Reviews, Inc., Palo Alto, Vol. 14, 1963, pp. 271–290.

21. (a) J. O. Edwards, *J. Am. Chem. Soc.*, **76**, 1540 (1954). (b) *ibid.*, **78**, 1819 (1956).

22. R. E. Davis, Vol. II, Chapter 1, of *Organic Sulfur Compounds* (N. Kharasch, ed.), Pergamon Press, New York, 1964, has given a theoretical interpretation of equation 15.

23. See reference 9, Chap. 9; J. E. Leffler and E. Grunwald, *Rates and Equilibria of Organic Reactions*, John Wiley and Sons, New York, 1963, have an extended discussion of linear free energy relationships.

24. R. G. Pearson, *J. Am. Chem. Soc.*, **85**, 3533 (1963).

25. H. Taube, *Chem. Rev.*, **50**, 69 (1952).

26. (a) A. W. Adamson, J. P. Welker, and W. B. Wright, *J. Am. Chem. Soc.*, **73**, 4789 (1951). (b) A. G. MacDiarmid and N. F. Hall, *ibid.*, **76**, 4222 (1954). (c) J. J. Christensen *et al.*, *Inorg. Chem.*, **2**, 337 (1963).

27. L. E. Orgel, *J. Chem. Soc.*, **1952**, 4756.

28. C. K. Jørgensen, *Acta Chem. Scand.*, **9**, 605 (1955).

29. Peter Ellis and R. G. Wilkins, *J. Chem. Soc.*, **1959**, 299; R. Hogg and R. G. Wilkins, *ibid.*, **1962**, 341.

30. R. S. Bell and N. Sutin, *Inorg. Chem.*, **1**, 359 (1962).

31. J. A. Broomhead and F. P. Dwyer, *Australian J. Chem.*, **14**, 250 (1961).

32. G. A. Melson and R. G. Wilkins, *J. Chem. Soc.*, **1963**, 2662.

33. (a) R. G. Wilkins and A. K. Shamsuddin Ahmed, *J. Chem. Soc.*, **1959**, 3700. (b) R. G. Wilkins, *ibid.*, **1962**, 4475.

34. T. J. Swift and R. E. Connick, *J. Chem. Phys.*, **37**, 307 (1962).

35. This method is discussed by H. Strehlow in "Investigation of Rates and Mechanisms of Reactions," Part II, Vol. 8 of *Techniques of Organic Chemistry* (A. Weissberger, ed.), Interscience Publishers, New York, 1963, Chap. 17; also R. G. Pearson and M. M. Anderson, *Angew. Chem.*, Inter. Ed., **4**, 281 (1965).

36. J. A. Jackson, J. F. Lemons, and H. Taube, *J. Chem. Phys.*, **32**, 553 (1960).

37. R. E. Connick and D. Fiat, *J. Chem. Phys.*, **39**, 1349 (1963).

38. R. L. Connick, *Symposium on Relaxation Techniques*, Buffalo, N.Y. June, 1965.

39. L. O. Morgan and A. W. Nolle, *J. Chem. Phys.*, **31**, 365 (1959).

40. R. A. Plane and J. P. Hunt, *J. Am. Chem. Soc.*, **76**, 5960 (1954); *ibid.*, **79**, 3343 (1957).

41. D. S. Leussing, *Inorg. Chem.*, **2**, 77 (1963).

42. (a) H. Taube, *Progress in Stereochemistry*, Vol. 3 (P. B. D. de la Mare and W. Klyne, eds.), Butterworths, Washington, D. C. 1962, p. 95. (b) see also H. L. Schläfer in *Theory and Structure of Complex Compounds*, Wroclaw Symposium, 1962 (B. Jezowska-Trzebiatowska, ed.), Pergamon Press, London, 1964.

43. G. W. Brady, *J. Chem. Phys.*, **28**, 464 (1958); *ibid.*, **29**, 1371 (1959); G. W. Brady and J. T. Krause, *ibid.*, **27**, 304 (1957).

44. For reviews of these methods see the volume quoted in reference 35; *Z. Elektrochem.*, **64**, 1–204 (1960); reference 9, Chap. 11.

45. M. Eigen, *Z. Elektrochem.*, **64**, 115 (1960); M. Eigen and K. Tamon, *ibid.*, **66**, 93, 107 (1962); reference 35, Chap. 18 by M. Eigen and L. de Maeyer; M. Eigen, Plenary Lecture, *Proceedings of the Seventh International Conference on Coordination Chemistry*, Stockholm, 1962, Butterworths, London, 1963, p. 97; M. Eigen, *Bunsenges. physik. Chem.*, **67**, 753 (1963).

46. G. Geier, *Bunsenges. physik. Chem.*, **69**, 617 (1965).

47. G. G. Hammes and M. Lee Morrell, *J. Am. Chem. Soc.*, **86**, 1497 (1964).

48. N. Sutin and G. H. Nancollas, *Inorg. Chem.*, **3**, 360 (1964).

49. G. A. Melson and R. G. Wilkins, *J. Chem. Soc.*, **1962**, 4208.

50. D. W. Margerum, D. B. Rohrabacher, and J. F. G. Clarke, Jr., *Inorg. Chem.*, **2**, 667 (1963).

51. (a) J. L. Hoard, M. Lind, and G. S. Smith in *Advances in the Chemistry of Coordination Compounds* (S. Kirschner, ed.), Macmillan Co., New York, 1961, p. 296. (b) J. L. Hoard *et al.*, *Inorg. Chem.*, **3**, 27 (1964). (c) W. C. E. Higginson, *J. Chem. Soc.*, **1962**, 2761. (d) M. Lind, B. Lee, and J. L. Hoard, *J. Am. Chem. Soc.*, **87**, 1611, 1612 (1965).

52. R. W. Olliff and A. L. Odell, *J. Chem. Soc.*, **1964**, 2417.

53. (a) See F. Basolo, *Chem. Revs.*, **52**, 459 (1953), for a review of earlier work. (b) also D. R. Stranks in *Modern Coordination Chemistry* (J. Lewis and R. G. Wilkins, eds.), Interscience Publishers, New York, 1960, Chap. 2.

54. R. G. Pearson, C. R. Boston, and F. Basolo, *J. Phys. Chem.*, **59**, 304 (1955).

55. J. E. Prue and G. Schwarzenbach, *Helv. Chim. Acta*, **33**, 974, 985 (1950).

56. R. G. Pearson, C. R. Boston, and F. Basolo, *J. Am. Chem. Soc.*, **75**, 3089 (1953).

57. (a) H. C. Brown and R. S. Fletcher, *J. Am. Chem. Soc.*, **71**, 1845 (1949). (b) C. K. Ingold, *Structure and Mechanism in Organic Chemistry*, Cornell University Press, Ithaca, 1953, pp. 402 and 415.

58. F. Basolo and R. K. Murmann, *J. Am. Chem. Soc.*, **74**, 5243 (1952); F. Basolo, Y. T. Chen, and R. K. Murmann, *ibid.*, **76**, 956 (1954).

59. Stanley Chaberek and A. E. Martell, *Organic Sequestering Agents*, John Wiley and Sons, New York, 1959, p. 126.

60. F. Basolo, J. G. Bergmann, R. E. Meeker, and R. G. Pearson, *J. Am. Chem. Soc.*, **78**, 2676 (1956).

61. F. Basolo, Y. T. Chen, and R. K. Murman, *J. Am. Chem. Soc.*, **75**, 1478 (1953).

62. J. P. Hunt, H. W. Dodgen, and F. Klanberg, *Inorg. Chem.*, **2**, 478 (1963).

63. F. A. Guthrie and E. L. King, *Inorg. Chem.*, **3**, 916 (1964).

64. H. Taube and W. Schmidt, *Inorg. Chem.*, **2**, 698 (1963).

65. Reference 53b has a large compliation of rate data with the original references.

66. F. Monacelli, F. Basolo, and R. G. Pearson, *J. Inorg. Nucl. Chem.*, **24**, 1241 (1962).

67. (a) S. C. Chan, *J. Chem. Soc.*, **1964**, 2375. (b) G. C. Lalor and E. A. Moelwyn-Hughes, *ibid.*, **1963**, 1560.

68. G. C. Lalor and J. Long, *J. Chem. Soc.*, **1963**, 5620; S. C. Chan, K. Y. Hui, J. Miller, and W. S. Tsang, *ibid.*, **1965**, 3207.

69. M. L. Tobe and D. F. Martin, *J. Chem. Soc.*, **1962**, 1388; in $Co(en)_2NH_3OH^{2+}$, a Co-N bond breaks more readily than the Co-O bond.

70. A. Haim and W. K. Wilmarth, *Inorg. Chem.*, **1**, 573 (1962).

71. W. A. Levine, T. P. Jones, W. E. Harris, and W. J. Wallace, *J. Am. Chem. Soc.*, **83**, 2453 (1961); A. Ogard and H. Taube, *ibid.*, **80**, 1084 (1958).

72. J. Bjerrum and C. G. Lamm, *Acta Chem. Scand.*, **9**, 216 (1955).
73. (a) T. F. Swaddle and E. L. King, *Inorg. Chem.*, **3**, 234 (1964), (b) *ibid.*, **4**, 532 (1965).
74. H. B. Johnson and W. L. Reynolds, *Inorg. Chem.*, **2**, 468 (1963).
75. J. A. Broomhead, F. Basolo, and R. G. Pearson, *Inorg. Chem.*, **3**, 826 (1964).
76. R. E. Connick in *Advances in the Chemistry of Coordination Compounds* (S. Kirschner, ed.), Macmillan Co., New York, 1961, p. 15.
77. J. V. Rund, F. Basolo, and R. G. Pearson, *Inorg. Chem.*, **3**, 658 (1964).
78. A. B. Lamb, *J. Am. Chem. Soc.*, **61**, 699 (1939).
79. (a) C. H. Langford, *Inorg. Chem.*, **4**, 265 (1965). (b) A. B. Lamb and L. T. Fairhall, *J. Am. Chem. Soc.*, **45**, 378 (1923).
80. J. A. Paulsen and C. S. Garner, *J. Am. Chem. Soc.*, **84**, 2032 (1962).
81. A. Haim and G. Taube, *Inorg. Chem.*, **2**, 1199 (1963).
82. J. W. Moore and R. G. Pearson, *Inorg. Chem.*, **3**, 1334 (1964).
83. J. Bjerrum, *Metal Ammine Formation in Aqueous Solution*, P. Haase and Son, dissertation, Copenhagen, 1941.
84. K. B. Yatsimirski, *Doklady Akad. Nauk SSSR*, **72**, 307 (1950).
85. G. S. Hammond, *J. Am. Chem. Soc.*, **77**, 334 (1955).
86. See C. K. Ingold and S. Asperger, *J. Chem. Soc.*, **1956**, 2862, for a related discussion.
87. S. A. Johnson, F. Basolo, and R. G. Pearson, *J. Am. Chem. Soc.*, **85**, 1741 (1963).
88. (a) S. C. Chan, *J. Chem. Soc.*, **1963**, 5137. (b) S. C. Chan and M. L. Tobe, *ibid.*, **1963**, 514
89. D. J. MacDonald and C. S. Garner, *J. Am. Chem. Soc.*, **83**, 4152 (1961); *Inorg. Chem.*, **1**, 20 (1962); see also L. P. Quinn and C. S. Garner, *ibid.*, **3**, 1348 (1963), for similar data on bromo complexes.
90. (a) M. L. Tobe *Sci. Progr.*, **XLVIII**, 484 (1960). See also (b) P. J. Staples and M. L. Tobe, *J. Chem. Soc.*, **1960**, 4803; (c) M. E. Baldwin, S. C. Chan, and M. L. Tobe, *ibid.*, **1961**, 4637; S. C. Chan and M. L. Tobe, *ibid.*, **1963**, 5700.
91. Patterned after reference 86; C. K. Ingold, R. S. Nyholm, and M. L. Tobe, *Nature*, **187**, 477 (1960) discuss the data of Table 3-18 in terms of mechanism.
92. R. G. Pearson and F. Basolo, *J. Am. Chem. Soc.*, **78**, 4878 (1956).
93. M. E. Baldwin and M. L. Tobe, *J. Chem. Soc.*, **1960**, 4275.
94. J. C. Bailar and D. F. Peppard, *J. Am. Chem. Soc.*, **62**, 105 (1940); see also A. V. Babaeva and I. B. Baranovskii, *Russ. J. Inorg. Chem.*, **7**, 404 (1961).
95. J. Bjerrum and S. E. Rasmussen, *Acta Chem. Scand.*, **6**, 1265 (1952).
96. R. J. Myers and J. B. Spencer, *J. Am. Chem. Soc.*, **86**, 522 (1964); B. Jezowska-Trzebiatowska and J. Ziolkowski, reference 42b, p. 387.
97. (a) A. Wojcicki and F. Basolo, *J. Am. Chem. Soc.*, **83**, 525 (1961); (b) J. Chatt and R. G. Hayter, *J. Chem. Soc.*, **1961**, 896.
98. H. L. Bott, E. J. Bounsall, and A. J. Poe, *J. Chem. Soc.*, **1966A**, 1275.
99. U. Klabunde, unpublished results.
100. W. K. Wilmarth, H. Graff, and S. T. Gustin, *J. Am. Chem. Soc.*, **78**, 2683 (1956); M. Mori, S. Ueshiba, and H. Yamatera, *Bull. Chem. Soc., Japan*, **32**, 88 (1959).
101. J. D. Dunitz and L. E. Orgel, *J. Chem. Soc.*, **1953**, 2594.
102. G. Schwarzenbach and B. Magyar, *Helv. Chim. Acta*, **45**, 1425 (1962).
103. G. W. Ettle and C. H. Johnson, *J. Chem. Soc.*, **1940**, 1490.
104. F. J. Garrick, *Trans. Faraday Soc.*, **33**, 486 (1937); **34**, 1088 (1938).
105. F. Basolo, B. D. Stone, J. G. Bergmann, and R. G. Pearson, *J. Am. Chem. Soc.*, **76**, 3079 (1954).
106. A. W. Adamson and R. G. Wilkins, *J. Am. Chem. Soc.*, **76**, 3379 (1954).
107. R. G. Pearson, R. E. Meeker, and F. Basolo, *J. Am. Chem. Soc.*, **78**, 709 (1956).

108. G. B. Schmidt, *Z. physik. Chem.*, N. F. **41**, 26 (1964).
109. F. Basolo, J. G. Bergmann, and R. G. Pearson, *J. Phys. Chem.*, **56**, 22 (1952).
110. D. D. Brown, C. K. Ingold, and R. S. Nyholm, *J. Chem. Soc.*, **1953**, 2678.
111. See, for example, reference 9, Chap. 9, and reference 5, Chap. 8.
112. F. J. Garrick, *Nature*, **139**, 507 (1937).
113. J. N. Brønsted, *Z. physik. Chem.*, **122**, 383 (1926).
114. N. Bjerrum, *Z. physik. Chem.*, **59**, 336, 581 (1907; see also C. W. Merideth, W. P. Mathews, and E. F. Orlemann, *Inorg. Chem.*, **3**, 320 (1964) for the behavior of dichlorochromium(III).
115. J. S. Anderson, H. V. A. Briscoe, and N. F. Spoor, *J. Chem. Soc.*, **1943**, 361.
116. (a) F. Basolo, J. W. Palmer, and R. G. Pearson, *J. Am. Chem. Soc.*, **82**, 1073 (1960). (b) J. W. Palmer and F. Basolo, *J. Phys. Chem.*, **64**, 778 (1960).
117. A. W. Adamson and F. Basolo, *Acta Chem. Scand.*, **9**, 1261 (1955).
118. R. G. Pearson, R. A. Munson, and F. Basolo, *J. Am. Chem. Soc.*, **80**, 504 (1958).
119. J. W. Palmer and F. Basolo, *J. Inorg. Nucl. Chem.*, **15**, 279 (1960).
120. Reference 115b; see also H. Block and V. Gold, *J. Chem. Soc.*, **1959**, 966.
121. C. K. Ingold, R. S. Nyholm, and M. L. Tobe, *Nature*, **194**, 344 (1962).
122. P. Clifton and L. Pratt, *Proc. Chem. Soc.*, **1963**, 339.
123. R. C. Johnson, F. Basolo, and R. G. Pearson, *J. Inorg. Nucl. Chem.*, **24**, 59 (1962).
124. See C. K. Jørgensen, *Acta Chem. Scand.*, **10**, 1505 (1956), and L. E. Orgel, *An Introduction to Transition Metal Chemistry*, John Wiley and Sons, New York, 1960, pp. 47–50.
125. This interpretation was suggested by M. Green.
126. J. Le Gros, *Compt. rend.*, **242**, 1605 (1956).
127. R. G. Pearson, R. E. Meeker, and F. Basolo, *J. Inorg. Nucl. Chem.*, **1**, 342 (1955).
128. V. Caglioti and G. Illuminati, *Proceedings of the Eight International Conference on Coordination Chemistry*, Vienna, 1964, p.
129. M. M. Anderson, unpublished results.
130. (a) M. Tobe and A. Peloso, private communication. (b) M. Tobe, *Adv. Chem. Ser.*, **49**, 7 (1965).
131. R. G. Pearson, H. H. Schmidtke, and F. Basolo, *J. Am. Chem. Soc.*, **82**, 4434 (1960).
132. M. Green and H. Taube, *Inorg. Chem.*, **2**, 948 (1963); *J. Phys. Chem.*, **67**, 1565 (1963).
133. R. G. Pearson, N. C. Stellwagen, and F. Basolo, *J. Am. Chem. Soc.*, **82**, 1077 (1960); M. Parris and W. J. Wallace, *Inorg. Chem.*, **3**, 133 (1964).
134. R. G. Pearson and D. N. Edgington, *J. Am. Chem. Soc.*, **84**, 4607 (1962).
135. See reference 9, p. 288.
136. W. Plumb and G. M. Harris, *Inorg. Chem.*, **3**, 542 (1964).
137. B. Adell, *Z. anorg. u. allgem. Chem.*, **246**, 303 (1941).
138. Reference 9, p. 172
139. Reference 9, p. 150.
140. H. Taube and F. A. Posey, *J. Am. Chem. Soc.*, **75**, 1463 (1963); F. A. Posey and H. Taube, *ibid.*, **78**, 15 (1956).
141. C. Postmus and E. L. King, *J. Phys. Chem.*, **59**, 1208, 1217 (1955).
142. R. E. Hamm, R. L. Johnson, R. H. Perkins, and R. E. Davis, *J. Am. Chem. Soc.*, **80**, 4469 (1958).
143. See reference 18d; also D. R Lloyd, Ph.D. thesis, Cambridge University, 1962, and N. Fogel, J. M. JenTai, and J. Yarborough, *J. Am. Chem. Soc.*, **84**, 1145 (1962).
144. M. Eigen, *Pure Appl. Chem.*, **6**, 97 (1963).

145. D. Seewald and N. Sutin, *Inorg. Chem.*, **2**, 643 (1963).
146. J. F. Below, Jr., R. E. Connick, and C. P. Coppel, *J. Am. Chem. Soc.*, **80**, 2961 (1958); R. E. Connick and R. E. Coppel, *ibid.*, **81**, 6389 (1959).
147. D. Pouli and W. M. Smith, *Can. J. Chem.*, **38**, 567 (1960).
148. M. Eigen in *Advances in the Chemistry of the Coordination Compounds* (S. Kirschner, ed.), The Macmillan Co., New York, 1961, p. 371.
149. H. Wendt and H. Strehlow, *Z. Elektrochem.*, **66**, 228 (1962).
150. References 18d, 105, 140; S. H. Laurie and C. B. Monk, *J. Chem. Soc.*, **1965**, 724.
151. F. A. Posey and H. Taube, *J. Am. Chem. Soc.*, **79**, 255 (1957).
152. C. G. Swain, C. B. Scott and K. H. Lohman, *J. Am. Chem. Soc.*, **75**, 136 (1953).
153. P. S. Skell and W. L. Hall, *J. Am. Chem. Soc.*, **85**, 2852 (1963) and references cited therein.
154. (a) A. Haim and W. K. Wilmarth, *Inorg. Chem.*, **1**, 573 (1962). (b) A. Haim, R. J. Grassie, and W. K. Wilmarth, *Advan. Chem. Ser.*, **49**, (1965).
155. A. J. Haim, R. G. Grassie, and W. K. Wilmarth, *Advances in the Chemistry of Coordination Compounds* (S. Kirschner, ed.), MacMillan Co., New York, 1962, p. 276.
156. J. A. Ibers, *Ann. Revs. Phys. Chem.*, **16**, 375 (1965).
157. S. J. LaPlaca and J. A. Ibers, *Inorg. Chem.*, **4**, 778 (1965).
158. D. D. Brown and C. K. Ingold, *J. Chem. Soc.*, **1953**, 2674.
159. M. L. Tobe and B. Bosnich, *J. Chem. Soc.*, **1966A**, 1636.
160. M. L. Tobe and D. W. Watts, *J. Chem. Soc.*, **1964**, 2991; L. F. Chin, W. A. Millan and D. W. Watts, *Aust. J. Chem.*, **18**, 453 (1965).
161. R. G. Pearson, P. M. Henry, and F. Basolo, *J. Am. Chem. Soc.*, **79**, 5379, 5382 (1947).
162. M. L. Tobe and D. W. Watts, *J. Chem. Soc.*, **1962**, 4614; W. A. Millan and D. W. Watts, *Aust. J. Chem.*, **19**, 43 (1966).
163. C. H. Langford and M. L. Tobe, *J. Chem. Soc.*, **1963**, 506.
164. C. H. Langford and M. Johnson, *J. Am. Chem. Soc.*, **86**, 229 (1964); M. L. Tobe and M. Hughes, *J. Chem. Soc.*, **1965**, 1204.
165. S. Asperger, D. Pavlocic, and M. Orhanovic, *J. Chem. Soc.*, **1961**, 2142; S. Asperger, M. Orhanovic, and I. Murati, *ibid.*, **1964**, 2969 ; **1966A**, 589.
166. C. H. Langford and P. Langford, *Inorg. Chem.*, **2**, 300 (1963).
167. C. H. Langford, *Inorg. Chem.*, **3**, 228 (1964).
168. C. K. Jørgensen, *Inorganic Complexes*, Academic Press, New York, 1964, p. 103.
169. A. J. Parker, *Quart. Rev. (London)*, **16**, 163 (1962).
170. F. Basolo, W. R. Matoush, and R. G. Pearson, *J. Am. Chem. Soc.*, **78**, 4833 (1956).
171. See R. P. Bell, *The Proton in Chemistry*, Cornell University Press, Ithaca, 1960.
172. J. N. Brønsted and R. Livingston, *J. Am. Chem. Soc.*, **49**, 435 (1927).
173. Reference 154. See also P J. Staples, *J. Chem. Soc.*, **1964**, 745, for acid-catalyzed hydrolysis of $Co(en)_2(N_3)_2$.
174. J. H. Baxendale and P. George, *Trans. Faraday Soc.*, **46**, 736 (1950). See also P. Krumholz, *J. Phys. Chem.*, **60**, 87 (1956).
175. F. Basolo, J. C. Hayes, and H. M. Neumann, *J. Am. Chem. Soc.*, **75**, 5102 (1953).
176. T. S. Lee, I. M. Kolthoff, and D. L. Leussing, *J. Am. Chem. Soc.*, **70**, 3596 (1948); J. E. Dickens, F. Basolo, and H. M. Neumann, *ibid.*, **79**, 1286 (1957).
177. F. Basolo, J. C. Hayes and H. M. Neumann, *J. Am. Chem. Soc.*, **75**, 5102 (1953); J. Bjerrum, K. G. Poulsen, and I. Poulsen, *Symposium on Coordination Chemistry*, Copenhagen, August, 1963, p. 51.
178. F. Basolo and F. P. Dwyer, *J. Am. Chem. Soc.*, **76**, 1454 (1954).

179. See K. V. Krishnamurty and G. M. Harris, *J. Phys. Chem.*, **64**, 346 (1960), and D. W. Margerum, *ibid.*, **63**, 336 (1959), for example.
180. G. K. Schweitzer and J. M. Lee, *J. Phys. Chem.*, **56**, 195 (1952).
181. R. G. Wilkins and M. J. G. Williams, *J. Chem. Soc.*, **1957**, 1763.
182. For a review see D. W. Margerum, *Record Chem. Progr.*, **24**, 237 (1963).
183. D. W. Margerum and T. J. Bydalek, *Inorg. Chem.*, **1**, 852 (1962).
184. T. J. Bydalek and D. W. Margerum, *J. Am. Chem. Soc.*, **83**, 4326 (1961).
185. D. W. Margerum and T. J. Bydalek, *Inorg. Chem.*, **2**, 683 (1963).
186. D. C. Olson and D. W. Margerum, *J. Am. Chem. Soc.*, **85**, 297 (1963).
187. S. Fronaeus, *Acta Chem. Scand.*, **6**, 1200 (1952).
188. C. Andrade and H. Taube, *J. Am. Chem. Soc.*, **86**, 1328 (1964).
189. S. Sheel, D. I. Meloon, and G. M. Harris, *Inorg. Chem.*, **1**, 170 (1962).
190. G. Schwarzenbach, *Helv. Chim. Acta*, **35**, 2344 (1952).
191. Reference 9, pp. 296 ff.
192. A. K. Shamsuddin-Ahmed and R. G. Wilkins, *J. Chem. Soc.*, **1960**, 2901.
193. G. G. Hammes and J. I. Steinfeld, *J. Am. Chem. Soc.*, **84**, 4639 (1962).
194. R. G. Pearson and R. D. Lanier, *J. Am. Chem. Soc.*, **86**, 765 (1964).
195. See reference 168, p. 101.
196. (a) R. J. Baltisberger and E. L. King, *J. Am. Chem. Soc.*, **86**, 795 (1964); (b) J. C. Jayne and E. L. King, *ibid.*, **86**, 3989 (1964).
197. (a) J. H. Swinehart, T. E. Rogers, and H. Taube, *J. Chem. Phys.*, **38**, 398 (1963). (b) Z. Luz and S. Meiboom, *ibid.*, **40**, 1058, 1066 (1964).
198. Z. Luz, *J. Chem. Phys.* **41**, 1748 (1964).
199. R. G. Pearson, J. Palmer, M. M. Anderson, and A. L. Allred, *Z. Elektrochem.*, **64**, 110 (1960).
200. A. B. Lamb and K. J. Mysels, *J. Am. Chem. Soc.*, **67**, 468 (1945).
201. (a) J. P. Hunt, A. C. Rutenberg, and H. Taube, *J. Am. Chem. Soc.*, **74**, 268 (1952). (b) C. A. Bunton and D. R. Llewellyn, *J. Chem. Soc.*, **1953**, 1692.
202. F. A. Posey and H. Taube, *J. Am. Chem. Soc.*, **75**, 4099 (1953); see also H. Scheidegger and G. Schwarzenbach, *Chimia*, **19**, 166 (1965).
203. R. G. Pearson, P. M. Henry, J. G. Bergmann, and F. Basolo, *J. Am. Chem. Soc.*, **76**, 5920 (1954).
204. For a list of references see A. T. Austin, E. D. Hughes, J. H. Ridd, and C. K. Ingold, *J. Am. Chem. Soc.*, **74**, 55 (1952).
205. R. K. Murmann and H. Taube, *J. Am. Chem. Soc.*, **78**, 4886 (1956).
206. F. Basolo and G. S. Hammaker, *Inorg. Chem.*, **1**, 1 (1962).
207. K. Kuroda, *Nippon Kagaku Zasshi*, **82**, 1481 (1961).
208. F. Basolo, J. G. Bergmann, and R. G. Pearson, *J. Phys. Chem.*, **56**, 22 (1952).
209. R. B. Jordan and H. Taube, *J. Am. Chem. Soc.*, **86**, 3891 (1964).
210. R. G. Pearson, D. H. Anderson, and L. L. Alt, *J. Am. Chem. Soc.*, **77**, 527 (1955).
211. R. G. Pearson, D. N. Edgington, and F. Basolo, *J. Am. Chem. Soc.*, **84**, 3234 (1962).
212. I. G. Ryss and N. F. Kulish, *Russ. J. Inorg. Chem.* (English translation), **8**, 175 (1963).
213. H. M. Dess and R. W. Parry *J. Am. Chem. Soc.*, **79**, 1589 (1957).
214. E. L. Muetterties and C. M. Wright, *J. Am. Chem. Soc.*, **86**, 5134 (1964); **87**, 21 (1965).
215. D. W. Cooke, J. A. Im, and D. H. Busch, *Inorg. Chem.*, **1**, 13 (1962).
216. D. W. Margerum, *J. Am. Chem. Soc.*, **79**, 2728 (1957); D. W. Margerum and L. P. Morgenthaler, *ibid.*, **84**, 706 (1962).

217. L. P. Morgenthaler and D. W. Margerum, *J. Am. Chem. Soc.*, **84**, 710 (1962).
218. B. Bosnich, *Nature*, **196**, 1196 (1962).
219. H. S. Nagarajaik, A. G. Sharp, and D. B. Wakefield, *Proc. Chem. Soc.*, **1959**, 385; D. Hope and J. E. Prue, *J. Chem. Soc.*, **1960**, 2782.
220. S. C. Chan and M. L. Tobe, *J. Chem. Soc.*, **1963**, 966.
221. O. E. Zvyagintsev and E. F. Karandasheva, *Doklady Akad. Nauk SSSR*, **108**, 447 (1956).
222. O. E. Zvyagintsev and E. F. Shubochkina, *Russ. J. Inorg. Chem.* (English translation), **6**, 2029 (1961); **8**, 300 (1963).
223. A. A. Grinberg and Y. N. Kukushkin, *Doklady Akad. Nauk SSSR*, **132**, 1071 (1960); R. C. Johnson, F. Basolo, and R. G. Pearson, reference 123.
224. R. L. Rich and H. Taube, *J. Am. Chem. Soc.*, **76**, 2608 (1954); A. F. Messing, Doctoral dissertation, Northwestern University, 1957.
225. F. Basolo, P. H. Wilks, R. G. Pearson, and R. G. Wilkins, *J. Inorg. Nucl. Chem.*, **6**, 163 (1958), F. Basolo, M. L. Morris, and R. G. Pearson, *Faraday Soc., Disc.*, **29**, 1 (1960).
226. H. R. Ellison, F. Basolo, and R. G. Pearson, *J. Am. Chem. Soc.*, **83**, 3943 (1961).
227. A. J. Poë and M. S. Vaidya, *Proc. Chem. Soc.*, **1960**, 118.
228. Y. N. Kukushkin, *Russ. J. Inorg. Chem.* (English translation), **7**, 3 (1962).
229. R. C. Johnson and E. R. Berger, *Inorg. Chem.*, **4**, 1262 (1965).
230. R. Holyer, C. Hubbard, S. Kettle, and R. G. Wilkins, *Inorg. Chem.*, **4**, 935 (1965).
231. W. Robb and G. M. Harris, *J. Am. Chem. Soc.*, **87**, 4472 (1965).
232. M. Ardon, *Inorg. Chem.*, **4**, 372 (1965).
233. P. Moore, F. Basolo, and R. G. Pearson, *Inorg. Chem.*, **5**, 223 (1966).
234. A. Haim and N. Sutin, *J. Am. Chem. Soc.*, **88**, 434 (1966).
235. R. Sperling and H. Pfiefer, *Z. Naturforsch.*, **19**, 1342 (1964).
236. R. F. Pasternack and R. A. Plane, *Inorg. Chem.*, **4**, 1171 (1965); J. Bjerrum and C. K. Jørgensen, *Acta Chem. Scand.*, **7**, 951 (1953); C. K. Jørgensen, *ibid.*, **8**, 175 (1954).
237. P. Ellgen, unpublished results.
238. C. S. G. Phillips and R. J. P. Williams, *Inorganic Chemistry*, Oxford University Press, New York, 1965, p. 360.
239. R. D. Archer, *Proceedings of the Eighth International Conference on Coordination Chemistry*, Vienna, 1964, p. 111, has a similar suggestion for Co(III) complexes.
240. G. Schmidt and W. Herr, *Z. Naturforsch.*, **16**, 748 (1961).
241. O. Gansow, unpublished results.
242. D. L. Gay and G. C. Lalor, *J Chem. Soc.*, **1966A**, 1179.
243. G. W. Bushnell, G. M. Lalor, and E. A. Moelwyn-Hughes, *J. Chem. Soc.*, **1966A**, 719.

4

Stereochemical Changes in Octahedral Complexes

A discussion of the stereochemistry of substitution reactions of octahedral complexes logically follows the previous chapter on the kinetics and mechanisms of these reactions. Information on stereochemical changes accompanying such reactions can provide further insight as to the mechanisms. No reaction theory is complete unless it also adequately explains the stereochemistry of the reaction. Investigations of the steric course of reactions of geometrical and optical isomers of octahedral complexes can furnish this information. Much of the work has been done with the better-defined complexes of Co(III), and the discussion here deals mostly with the experimental results on these systems. Some information on other metal complexes is also included.

This chapter considers first the molecular rearrangement that appears *a priori* most plausible for octahedral complexes undergoing either a decrease or an increase in coordination number during reaction. These models are then used to discuss the experimentally observed steric changes, which include substitution reactions, *cis-trans* isomerizations, linkage isomerizations and racemizations. The final topic is the related phenomenon of stereospecificity in octahedral complexes.

Molecular Rearrangement Processes

Outer-Sphere Orientation. Werner[1] suggested that the stereochemical changes observed for the reactions of Co(III) complexes are due to the specific orientation of the entering group outside the complex. He assumed that, in addition to the first coordination sphere, a second sphere of molecules or ions surrounds the complex. Furthermore, he assumed that there might exist a preferred orientation of the groups in the second coordination sphere with respect to the complex. Therefore, should the incoming group Y be located in a position opposite to that of the outgoing ligand X, a *trans* isomer would yield a *cis* product (Fig. 4.1). Since the

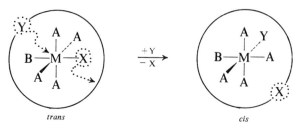

Fig. 4.1 Substitution where the entering group Y in the second coordination sphere is opposite the departing group X.

group Y is separated from X by the four ligands A, the net result is that, as X leaves, one of the A groups moves to make room for Y adjacent to B. If, on the other hand, Y groups are located near X, there would be no change in structure and a *trans* product would result (Fig. 4.2). Similarly a *cis* isomer is expected to yield a *cis* product if the entering group in the second sphere is near the departing ligand. However, if it is opposite to the group leaving, a mixture of isomers is predicted for the product (statistically three parts *cis* and one part *trans*).

This explanation was given for reactions that yielded primarily only one isomer. It was suggested that a mixture of isomers is obtained whenever there is no preferred orientation of the groups in the second sphere. Werner was forced to conclude that, as there is no way to predict the orientation of the entering group in the second sphere, it is not possible to anticipate the stereochemical change that will take place during substitution.

It should be noted that there is now considerable experimental evidence in support of the formation of a loosely held outer sphere of ligands surrounding the metal complex in solution. For ionic systems this outer sphere would include the ion pairs which are discussed in Chapter 1. Also of interest is the fact that ligand interchange between the first and second coordination spheres has been proposed as the general mechanism for octahedral substitution reactions (Chapter 3).

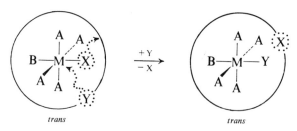

Fig. 4.2 Substitution where the entering group Y in the second coordination sphere is adjacent to the departing group X.

Dissociation (S_N1) and Displacement (S_N2) Processes. A dissociation (S_N1) process for a six-coordinated complex requires the formation of a five-coordinated intermediate. The stereochemical consequence of the formation of either a tetragonal pyramid or a trigonal bipyramid for the intermediate has been discussed.[2] These two structures appear to be the most plausible ones because (1) stable compounds of such structures

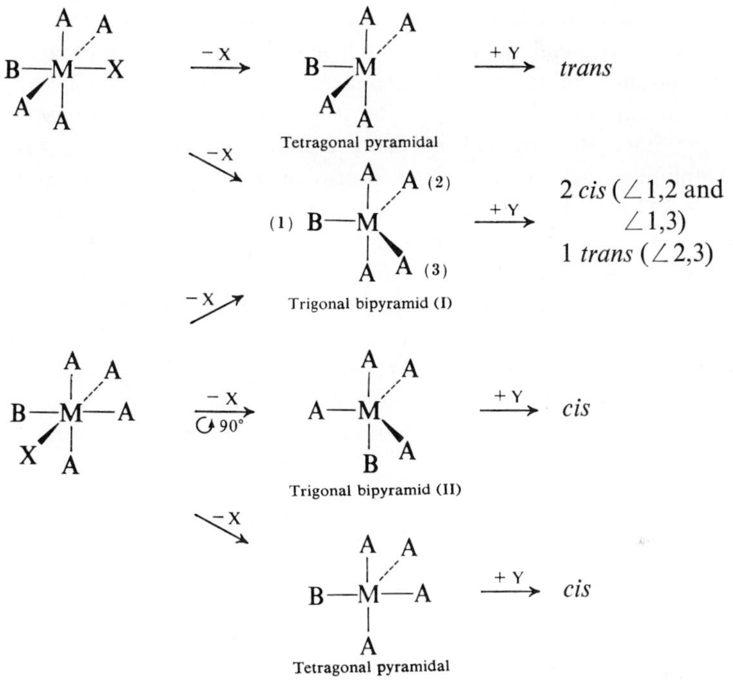

Fig. 4.3 Stereochemical changes accompanying reactions of *cis-* and *trans*-MA$_4$BX with Y by a dissociation mechanism through either a tetragonal pyramidal or a trigonal bipyramidal intermediate.

are known, (2) these structures can be derived from the octahedron with little atomic motion, and (3) such structures are in keeping with current theories of bonding in metal complexes. It is apparent that the reaction of either *cis-* or *trans*-MA$_4$BX through a tetragonal pyramid intermediate can take place without rearrangement (Fig. 4.3). The assumption is made that group Y enters the position vacated by X. This seems to be a valid assumption because the central atom is most accessible at this position and because the formation of the new octahedron requires no additional atomic motion. Furthermore, in terms of the valence bond theory, the vacant d^2sp^3 hybrid orbital is projected outward in this direction, suitable for maximum overlap with the orbital electrons of the entering group.

Alternatively, according to the crystal field theory, nucleophilic attack at this position is favored because of the low electron density.

Reactions of *cis*- and *trans*-MA$_4$BX by way of a trigonal bipyramid intermediate may lead to rearrangement (Fig. 4.3). Only trigonal bipyramid I is believed possible for the *trans* isomer, because structure II, in which B is normal to the trigonal plane, would necessitate excessive rearrangement. However, both of these are equally possible for the *cis* isomer. Subsequent addition of Y to the intermediate is assumed to take place in the trigonal plane. This is believed to be correct because the central atom is more accessible at these angles of 120° and because a minimum amount of atomic motion is required to regenerate the octahedron. Since the trigonal xy plane contains a vacant $d_{x^2-y^2}$ orbital, nucleophilic attack in this plane is also in keeping with current bond theories. Thus the addition of Y to trigonal bipyramid II yields a *cis* product, but addition to I gives a mixture of *cis* and *trans* isomers. If the group enters between either positions 1,2 or 1,3 the product will have a *cis* structure, but if it comes in between 2,3 it will give a *trans* product. In the idealized situation where the statistical factor is all that need be considered, the *trans* isomer is expected to yield a mixture of 66.6% *cis* and 33.3% *trans*, whereas the *cis* isomer gives 83.3% *cis* and 16.6% *trans*. However, both steric and electrostatic factors must play an important

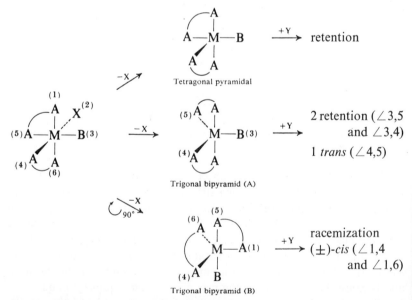

Fig. 4.4 Stereochemical changes accompanying the reaction of D*-*cis*-M(AA)$_2$BX with Y by a dissociation mechanism through either a tetragonal pyramidal or trigonal bipyramidal intermediate.

role in the position of entry of Y as well as in the formation of the trigonal bipyramid, so that the relative amount of isomers calculated on a statistical basis is probably of very little meaning. The only conclusion that can be reached is that a trigonal bipyramid intermediate permits rearrangement, whereas the tetragonal pyramid does not. Furthermore, a reaction through a trigonal bipyramid will yield more *cis* product starting with a *cis* reactant than with the corresponding *trans* isomer. It should also be mentioned that, although the five-coordinated intermediates in Fig. 4.3 represent a complete removal of the group being replaced, this need not be the case. Instead a transient intermediate with one group further removed from the central metal ion than the remaining five ligands is perhaps possible. However, such a structure would lead to the same stereochemical changes described above.

The preceding discussion was limited to stereo changes for reactions of geometrical isomers, but naturally the same treatment applies to optical isomers. Most of the studies[2] reported for substitution reactions in optically active complexes were done with Co(III) cations of the type *cis*-Co(en)$_2$AX. For an S_N1 process it is of interest to note that inversion cannot take place; there can be only retention of configuration and/or loss of optical activity (Fig. 4.4).* If the reaction goes through a tetragonal pyramid, the retention of configuration is obvious. However, if a trigonal bipyramid is involved, a mixture of isomers is expected. Any optical activity observed in the product must, however, have come from the optically active trigonal bipyramid, A, and must have the same generic configuration as that of the starting material. The loss of optical activity is due to the formation of a *trans* product via the trigonal bipyramid, A, and/or a racemic mixture of the *cis* isomer via the symmetrical trigonal bipyramid, B. The reactions of optical isomers that have been investigated and found to yield some optically active product do generally give the enantiomorph of the same generic configuration as that of the starting material. Some exceptions are discussed later.

Substitution by means of displacement (S_N2) mechanism requires the intermediate formation of a seven-coordinated complex. Stable compounds in which the central ion has a coordination number of seven are known. A few examples are given in Table 1.2. X-ray and electron diffraction data demonstrate the existence of two different structures for these compounds. Iodine heptafluoride[3] and ZrF_7^{3-} [4] both have a pentagonal bipyramidal structure. The complex NbF_7^{2-} has been assigned a trigonal prismatic

---

* It should be noted that, if the chelate ring (4,6) in the trigonal plane of trigonal bipyramid B is not symmetrical, B will be asymmetrical and capable of reacting either with inversion or retention of configuration. This may occur during the base hydrolysis of Co(en)$_2$Cl$_2^+$ if one of the amine nitrogens of en is converted to an amido group. Reference to such a possiblity is made on p. 263.

structure with a fluoride ion protruding from one of the tetragonal faces.[5] Similar structures have recently been reported for the complexes $Mn(H_2O)$-$EDTA^{2-}$ and $Fe(H_2O)EDTA^{-}$.[6] The pentagonal bipyramidal structure is readily generated from an octahedron in an S_N2 process, and stereochemical changes are discussed on the basis of this structure.†

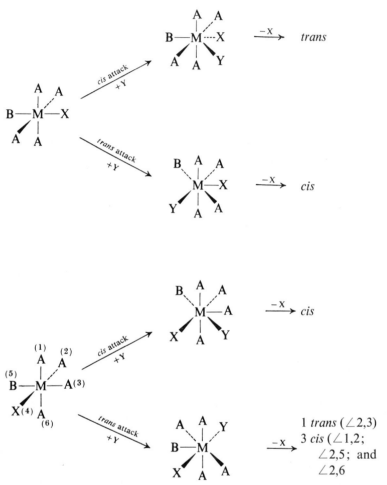

Fig. 4.5 Stereochemical changes accompanying reactions of *cis*- and *trans*-MA_4BX with Y by a displacement mechanism through a pentagonal bipyramidal intermediate.

† The pentagonal bipyramidal structure is discussed primarily because it is then easy to visualize the stereochemical changes that take place. A more probable position of attack for the entering group, as is discussed later, is at the octahedral face. However, the net stereochemical consequences are the same for the two processes. The important consideration in both cases, as shown in Figs. 4.5 and 4.6, is whether *cis* or *trans* attack occurs.

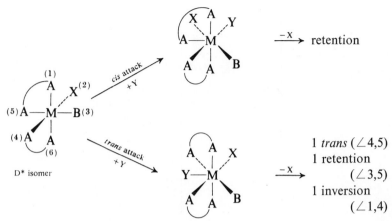

Fig. 4.6 Stereochemical changes accompanying the reaction of D*-cis-M(AA)₂BX with Y by a displacement mechanism through a pentagonal bipyramidal intermediate.

The seven-coordinated intermediate may be formed by an approach of the entering group either towards a position adjacent to that of the departing ligand (*cis* attack) or towards a position opposite to that of the departing ligand (*trans* attack). This definition of *cis* and *trans* attack is applicable to all geometric structures and is preferred to "frontside" and "backside" attack. Stereochemical changes accompanying substitution reactions of *cis*- and *trans*-MA₄BX by an S_N2 mechanism are summarized in Fig. 4.5. Replacement by means of a *cis* attack results in no net rearrangement; thus a *cis* isomer yields a *cis* product, and *trans* yields *trans*. However, for a *trans* attack, the *cis* isomer gives a mixture of *cis* and *trans* products, whereas the *trans* isomer yields only a *cis* product. This prediction that a *trans* displacement in a *trans* isomer yields exclusively a *cis* product uniquely distinguishes this process from all the other mechanisms being considered.

The same treatment can be applied to S_N2 reactions of optical isomers (Fig. 4.6). Substitution by a *cis* attack, as usual, leads to a retention of configuration. However, for a *trans* approach the S_N2 mechanism permits inversion of configuration. Furthermore, none of the seven-coordinated intermediates are symmetrical, so that loss of optical rotation is due to the formation of a trans product and/or to the same extent of reaction through the two intermediates that leads to the *cis* enantiomorphs.

If it is assumed that the stereochemical changes just described for S_N1 and S_N2 reaction processes occur with equal probability, then the data collected in Table 4.1 are expected. The assumption is that for any mechanism all possible intermediates form with equal ease and a statistical distribution of structures is obtained. It is apparent from the data in Table 4.1 that the stereochemistry of the reaction product is often not

Table 4.1 Statistical amounts (%) of isomeric products predicted for different mechanisms of substitution in octahedral complexes

Reactant	Dissociation (S_N1)				Displacement (S_N2)			
	Tetragonal Pyramid		Trigonal Bipyramid		cis Attack		trans Attack	
	cis	trans	cis	trans	cis	trans	cis	trans
trans-MA$_4$BX	0	100	66.6	33.3	0	100	100	0
cis-MA$_4$BX	100	0	83.3	16.6	100	0	75	25
D-M(AA)$_2$BX^a	D-100	0	D-33.3 DL-50	16.6	D-100	0	D-33.3 L-33.3	33.3

^{a} D and L refer to generic configuration: D → D (retention); D → L (inversion); and D → DL (racemization).

in itself diagnostic of the mechanism involved. For example, a *trans* isomer may yield exclusively a *trans* product either by an S_N1 process involving a tetragonal pyramidal intermediate or by an S_N2 reaction with a *cis* attack. A distinction can be made between these two paths only whenever the molecularity of the reaction is known.

Brown, Ingold, and Nyholm[7] have discussed the stereochemistry of octahedral substitution reactions in terms of an *edge-displacement* hypothesis. This hypothesis describes the process as involving the shift of an inert ligand along an octahedral edge to give access to the entering group and to eventually assume the position of the departed ligand. Depending on the positions occupied by the other ligands present, such a process can account for *cis-trans* isomerization and D-L conversions. In fact, the net result of the predicted stereochemical changes by an edge-displacement process is identical to that described above for a *trans* attack. Likewise, a non-edge displacement, which does not involve a ligand shift on the octahedral edge, predicts substitution without rearrangement and is analogous to a *cis* attack. This edge-displacement hypothesis, of course, deals only with bimolecular displacement reactions and says nothing about the steric course of dissociation reactions.

In an alternative *cis*- and *trans*-attack displacement process, which seems more likely than that described above, the attack is at an octahedral face and the seven-coordinated intermediate does not have a pentagonal bipyramidal structure. For such a *cis* attack the structure is shown in Fig. 4.7. It is apparent that this process readily leads to the replacement

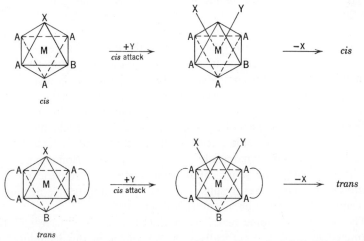

Fig. 4.7 Stereochemical changes accompanying reactions of *cis*-MA$_4$BX and *trans*-M(AA)$_2$BX with Y by a *cis* attack at an octahedral face. The seven-coordinated intermediate can be described as an octahedral wedge structure.

of X by Y with a minimum of atomic motion. As Y attacks the octahedral face, the bond M-X lengthens and X moves into the opposite octahedral face position. Thus, X and Y occupy similar geometrical positions with relation to the rest of the structure. This is in accord with the expectation that such a symmetric structure will be of lowest energy. This necessary symmetry is not readily achieved by a similar *trans*-attack displacement process. An examination of molecular models shows that the simple movement of X to the octahedral face opposite to that of Y resulting from a *trans* attack does not place X and Y in comparable positions with respect to the rest of the complex. For the two to occupy similar positions, it is necessary for other ligands to shift to intermediate positions along the octahedral edges. Because of this requirement of excessive atomic motion for a *trans*-attack displacement, it would appear that bimolecular octahedral substitutions will tend to occur by *cis* attack. This predicts that bimolecular reactions will take place with retention of configuration.

Reactions of Geometrical and Optical Isomers

Rather extensive studies have been conducted on the reactions of geometrical and optical isomers of Co(III) complexes. Werner[1] and his students made numerous qualitative observations on the relative amounts of *cis* and *trans* product obtained from various reactions. The technique they employed was to carry out the reaction and then to isolate the product and separate the geometric isomers. Their results can be given only qualitative significance because under these conditions both reactants and products may undergo rearrangement without net chemical change. Furthermore, the reactions are often complicated because of participation of the solvent water, that is, the direct replacement of one ligand by another need not take place but rather may first involve the formation of the aquo complex.[8] However, it must be concluded that, even by this procedure, whenever the *cis* and the *trans* isomers of the same compound each react under the same experimental conditions to yield different ratios of isomers of the same product, the stereochemistry of the products is at least to some extent kinetically controlled. If such reactions were entirely thermodynamically controlled, the two isomeric reactants would each yield the same equilibrium mixture of isomeric products. Therefore, in many cases, results obtained by the preparative method are indicative of the stereo change during reaction.

The products of some reactions of Co(III) complexes have also been examined spectrophotometrically.[2] The advantage of this technique over the preparative method is that it minimizes the chances of rearrangement before and after reaction. However, even this procedure is not entirely free of complications. In order to be certain that the products are a direct result of the rearrangement accompanying the substitution reaction in question, it is necessary to show that the ratio of isomeric products does not change throughout their formation. The careful work of Tobe[9] and his coworkers provides the necessary information on the steric course of the hydrolysis reactions of a number of Co(III) complexes.

Acid Hydrolysis of Cobalt(III) Complexes. Extensive investigations have been made of the kinetics and steric course in the acid hydrolysis of complexes of the type $Co(en)_2LX^{n+}$,

$$Co(en)_2LX^{n+} + H_2O \rightarrow Co(en)_2LH_2O^{1+n+} + X^- \qquad (1)$$

The results obtained and specific references are summarized in Table 4.2. The most striking characteristic of these results is that the *cis* isomers

Table 4.2   Steric course of the acid hydrolysis of some cobalt(III) complexes

$$Co(en)_2LX^{n+} + H_2O \rightarrow Co(en)_2LH_2O^{1+n+} + X^-$$

cis-L	X	% *cis* in Prod.[a]	Ref.	*trans*-L	X	% *cis* in Prod.[a]	Ref.
OH^-	Cl^-	100	10	OH^-	Cl^-	75	10
OH^-	Br^-	100	11	OH^-	Br^-	73	11
Br^-	Cl^-	100	11	Br^-	Cl^-	50	11
Cl^-	Cl^-	100	10	Br^-	Br^-	30	11
Cl^-	Br^-	100	11	Cl^-	Cl^-	35	10
N_3	Cl^-	100	12	Cl^-	Br^-	20	11
NCS^-	Cl^-	100	13	NCS^-	Cl^-	50–70	13
NCS^-	Br^-	100	13	NH_3	Cl^-	0	15
NO_2^-	Cl^-	100	14	NO_2^-	Cl^-	0	14

[a] The reaction products are a mixture of *cis* and *trans* isomers; therefore, % *trans* = 100 − % *cis*.

react with the formation of *cis* aquo products, whereas *trans* isomers generally react with some rearrangement of configuration. This can adequately be explained by making use of the hypothesis[16] that ligand to metal π bonding can enhance the rupture of the M-X bond. As was discussed in Chapter 3, the kinetic data on octahedral substitution reactions suggest that they usually proceed by a solvent-assisted dissociation process, where the dissociation of the M-X bond is of primary importance. Therefore, it is to be expected that the steric course of the reaction will be that which permits the system to make a maximum contribution to the energy needed for the rupture of the M-X bond.

Except for $L = NH_3$ and NO_2^-, all the other ligands in Table 4.2 contain p-orbital electrons, which can be donated via π bonding to vacant Co(III) orbitals of the correct symmetry. This type of π bonding can occur for a *cis* ligand without rearrangement of the complex. Thus, the filled p orbital of the ligand can overlap with the empty d^2sp^3 hybrid orbital resulting from the departure of the leaving group X^-, as shown in Fig. 3.10. The net result is essentially a dissociation process through a tetragonal pyramidal structure (Fig. 4.3) which requires that no rearrangement occur, in accord with the experimental results.

In contrast, *trans* isomers of this type react with considerable rearrangement. Continuing the above π-bonding explanation, we note that for the

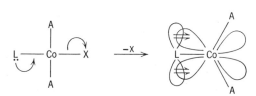

Fig. 4.8 Assisted dissociation of Co—X by π bonding of L in *trans*-$Co(AA)_2LX^{n+}$ with rearrangement to a trigonal bipyramidal structure. Only four ligands in one plane are shown; the chelate rings attached to the front and back of the plane of the paper are not included.

trans isomers the ligand p orbitals are now orthogonal to the *trans* d^2sp^3 orbital hybrid and cannot overlap with it. For the system to take advantage of the *trans* ligand and its stabilizing influence of π bonding, it must rearrange. This can occur by rearrangement to a trigonal bipyramidal structure with Co(III) having a vacant $d_{x^2-y^2}$ orbital which is of proper symmetry for efficient overlap with the filled p orbital of the ligand (Fig. 4.8). Such a structure permits entry of Y in the trigonal plane to yield a mixture of *cis* and *trans* isomeric products (Fig. 4.3). One other point of interest is that these *trans* complexes generally react slower than do the corresponding *cis* isomers. This too is in accord with the π-bonding hypothesis, because the *cis* isomers can π-bond without rearrangement whereas the *trans* isomers π-bond only at the expense of some ligand motion which can mean an expenditure of energy.

For complexes with ligands that cannot π-bond with the flow of ligand electrons to the metal ($L = NH_3$ and NO_2^-), both the *cis* and the *trans* isomers react with retention of configuration. One explanation is that in these systems there is no driving force requiring the formation of a trigonal bipyramidal structure. The reactions then proceed through a tetragonal pyramidal structure which leads to retention of configuration. Alternatively, the same steric consequence is predicted by the very closely related solvent-assisted dissociation mechanism with *cis* attack at the octahedral face (Fig. 4.7). Such a process appears most likely for a system with a *trans* ligand (NO_2^-) capable of electron withdrawal from the octahedral faces adjacent to the leaving group (Fig. 3.9). It is further of interest that in such a complex the *trans* isomer reacts more rapidly than does the *cis*, probably because the *cis* location does not permit as much removal of electron density surrounding the departing ligand as does a *trans* location.

The above discussion is an oversimplification because it does not consider the role of the leaving group in determining the steric course of

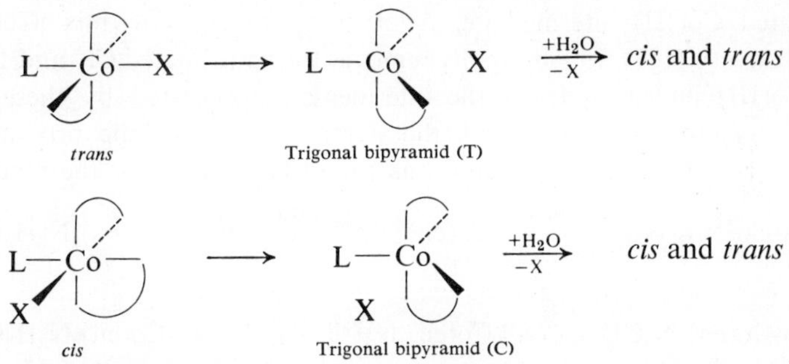

trans   Trigonal bipyramid (T)

cis   Trigonal bipyramid (C)

Fig. 4.9 Stereochemistry of the solvent-assisted dissociation of *cis*- and *trans*-$Co(en)_2LX^{n+}$. Note that structures T and C are identical except for the presence of X at some distance removed from Co(III).

the reaction. This should be included in a more complete treatment, since it is possible that the departing ligand is still weakly bonded to the metal at the time the entering group becomes attached. On this basis the results in Table 4.2 (except L = NO_2^- and NH_3) may be explained in terms of both *cis*- and *trans*-$Co(en)_2LX^+$ reacting through a trigonal bipyramidal structure containing the departing X group between two of the ligands in the trigonal plane, but at some distance removed from cobalt. Except for the presence of X, both *cis* and *trans* isomers can readily form the same trigonal bipyramidal structure (Fig. 4.9). This predicts that the two would yield the same isomeric products if it were not for X. That there is retention of configuration in the aquation of the *cis* complexes is said[11] to result from the cooperation of neighboring L and X in introducing an adjacent water molecule into the intermediate. The rearrangement found for the *trans* complexes is then believed to result from a competition between L and X in introducing a water molecule into structure T. Clearly, introduction of a water molecule adjacent to L gives a *cis* product, whereas addition next to X yields a *trans* product. On this basis, the steric courses listed in Table 4.2 permit us to write ligands L and X in a series representing their ability to introduce a water molecule, $OH^- >$ $Br^- > NCS^- > Cl^- \sim Br^- > Cl^-$, where the ions in italics are departing ligands.

Recent experimental evidence provides further light on the effect that the departing ligand can have on the steric course of a reaction of a metal complex. Loeliger and Taube[18] have investigated the stereochemistry of different types of reactions designed to generate five-coordinated Co(III) complexes as reactive intermediates. One interesting approach used is to allow a complex containing coordinated N_3^- to react with HNO_2, which rapidly generates N_2 and N_2O, while supposedly forming the five-coordinated Co(III) intermediate. Another approach is to mix a chloro complex with Hg^{2+}, which rapidly removes the coordinated Cl^- and forms the Co(III) intermediate. If the intermediates generated by these two different methods are identical, the stereochemistry of the products in both cases will be identical. This was found to be true for the reactions

$$trans\text{-}Co(en)_2(N_3)_2^+ \xrightarrow{HNO_2} \text{``}Co(en)_2N_3^{2+}\text{''} \xrightarrow{H_2O} trans\text{-}Co(en)_2N_3H_2O^{2+}$$

$$\tag{2}$$

$$trans\text{-}Co(en)_2N_3Cl^+ \xrightarrow{Hg^{2+}} \text{``}Co(en)_2N_3^{2+}\text{''} \xrightarrow{H_2O} trans\text{-}Co(en)_2N_3H_2O^{2+}$$

$$\tag{3}$$

both of which proceed with almost complete retention of configuration. Similar experiments involving the reaction of $trans\text{-}Co(en)_2H_2ON_3^{2+}$ with HNO_2 and of $trans\text{-}Co(en)_2H_2OCl^{2+}$ with Hg^{2+} to form the diaquo product $Co(en)_2(H_2O)_2^{3+}$ gave the same isomeric mixture of 60% *trans* and 40% *cis* in both cases. These results suggest that the same five-coordinated intermediate, "$Co(en)_2H_2O^{3+}$," is formed in both of these reactions. However, the reaction of $cis\text{-}Co(en)_2(N_3)_2^+$ with HNO_2 yields approximately 80% *cis*- and 20% *trans*-$Co(en)_2N_3H_2O^{2+}$. This shows that the nitrous acid reaction does not form the same intermediate starting with *cis*- and *trans*-$Co(en)_2(N_3)_2^+$.

It should be noted that the reaction of *trans*-$Co(en)_2(N_3)_2^+$ with HNO_2 yields 100% *trans*-$Co(en)_2N_3H_2O^{2+}$ compared to 80% *trans* and 20% *cis* obtained by the aquation of *trans*-$Co(en)_2N_3Cl^+$. Likewise the reaction of *cis*-$Co(en)_2(N_3)_2^+$ with HNO_2 gives 80% *cis*- and 20% *trans*-$Co(en)_2$ $N_3H_2O^{2+}$, whereas the aquation of *cis*-$Co(en)_2(N_3)Cl^+$ gives 100% *cis* aquo product (Table 4.2). It is clear that the intermediates for the two types of reaction differ. A reasonable explanation is that for the spontaneous aquation reaction the Cl^- has not completely departed and thus exerts an influence on the steric course of the reaction.

The Hg^{2+}-catalyzed aquation of D-$Co(en)_2Cl_2^+$ yields 70% D-$Co(en)_2$ H_2OCl^{2+} and 30% of the *trans* isomer.[19] This differs from the complete retention[17] observed for the uncatalyzed aquation. It is suggested that the catalyzed reaction proceeds by a trigonal bipyramidal structure and that the uncatalyzed reaction involves a *cis* displacement by water. This seems plausible because the uncatalyzed reaction would require more assistance from the entering water molecule. An alternative explanation is that the addition of a water molecule to the intermediate adjacent to the remaining Cl^- is retarded because of the presence of $HgCl^+$, which may even be bonded to the remaining coordinated Cl^-. Also, it has been suggested that the acid hydrolysis of *trans*-$Co(trien)Cl_2^+$ to yield 100% *cis*-$Co(trien)H_2OCl^{2+}$ is evidence for a *trans* attack by a water molecule.[20] Reaction through a trigonal bipyramidal structure was considered less likely because it would give a mixture of *cis* and *trans* products, unless the addition of a water molecule to the intermediate is stereospecific. However, because of the nature of the quadridentate chelate it appears that attack in the trigonal plane to give a *trans* product is more difficult than is the entry *cis* to the coordinated Cl^- in this plane. Furthermore, there is some strain in the system with all four nitrogens in the same plane so that there is a driving force towards the formation of a *cis* product.

Base Hydrolysis of Cobalt(III) Complexes. Tobe and his coworkers have made a detailed study of the kinetics and stereochemistry of base hydrolysis reactions of $Co(en)_2LX^{n+}$:

$$Co(en)_2LX^{n+} + OH^- \rightarrow Co(en)_2LX^{n+} + X^- \tag{4}$$

The stereochemical data collected, along with specific references, are summarized in Table 4.3. These results show that base hydrolysis generally proceeds with extensive rearrangement for both *cis* and *trans* isomers. This is a most significant observation because of the contrast with the fact that the acid hydrolysis of the *cis* isomers takes place with complete retention of configuration.

The mechanism of base hydrolysis of halogenoamminecobalt(III) complexes was discussed in Chapter 3. It was concluded that the experimental evidence supports an S_N1CB mechanism. Such a mechanism is used here in an attempt to explain the steric course of these reactions. The results also have been discussed in terms of an S_N2 displacement process.[9]

Since these base hydrolysis reactions proceed with extensive rearrangement and appear to involve primarily a dissociative process, it logically follows that the reactions go through a trigonal bipyramidal structure. This structure permits rearrangement and is readily generated by both the *cis* and the *trans* isomers. Furthermore, the *trans* isomer can readily form only one trigonal bipyramid, whereas two are easily formed by the *cis* isomer. One of the two is identical with that formed by the *trans* isomer

Table 4.3   Steric course of base hydrolysis of some cobalt(III) complexes

$$Co(en)_2LX^{n+} + OH^- \rightarrow Co(en)_2LOH^{n+} + Cl^-$$

| D-cis-L | X | % cis Product[a] | | | trans-L | X | % cis Product[a] | Ref. |
		D	L	Ref.				
OH⁻	Cl⁻	61	36	21	OH⁻	Cl⁻	94	21
OH⁻	Br⁻	96[b]		21	OH⁻	Br⁻	90	21
Cl⁻	Cl⁻	21	16	21	Cl⁻	Cl⁻	5	21
Cl⁻	Br⁻	30[b]		21	Cl⁻	Br⁻	5	21
Br⁻	Cl⁻	40[b]		21	Br⁻	Cl⁻	0	21
N_3^-	Cl⁻	51[b]		12	N_3^-	Cl⁻	13	12
NCS⁻	Cl⁻	56	24	12	NCS⁻	Cl⁻	76	23
NH_3	Br⁻	59	26	22	NCS⁻	Br⁻	81	23
NH_3	Cl⁻	60	24	22	NH_3	Cl⁻	76	22
NO_2^-	Cl⁻	46	20	14	NO_2^-	Cl⁻	6	14

[a] The total % cis product is the sum of D and L obtained from the D-cis starting material. The optically inactive trans isomer will of course yield racemic cis.

[b] The starting material was racemic, and the cis product must also be racemic.

(Fig. 4.3). This is a significant point in attempting a semi-quantitative interpretation of the experimental data given in Table 4.3.

Recall (Fig. 4.4) that cis-M(AA)$_2$BX can react through trigonal bipyramid A, which is an asymmetrical structure and can add an entering group in the trigonal plane with retention of configuration and with the formation of a trans product. Reaction through trigonal bipyramid B can only generate cis product by the addition of an entering group in the trigonal plane. For trans-M(AA)$_2$BX only trigonal bipyramid A can readily be formed. We can now make the definite prediction, based on an S_N1CB mechanism with rearrangement of a trigonal bipyramidal intermediate, that a cis reactant, Co(en)$_2$LX, will never give less cis product, Co(en)$_2$LOH, than the corresponding trans reactant. An examination of Table 4.3 shows that this prediction is verified.

We can also take advantage of the fact that only intermediate A is formed from trans-Co(en)$_2$LX to calculate what fraction of A and what fraction of B are formed in the base hydrolysis of cis-Co(en)$_2$LX^{n+}. Thus, trans-Co(en)$_2$Cl$_2^+$ gives 95% trans-Co(en)$_2$ClOH and 5% cis. This tells us the behavior of intermediate A. The 37% of cis-Co(en)$_2$ClOH$^+$ formed from cis-Co(en)$_2$Cl$_2^+$ must then come from the formation of 33.6% of intermediate B, which gives all cis product, and 66.4% of intermediate A, which gives $(0.05)(0.664)$ or 3.3% additional *cis* product. Table 4.4 shows the calculated fractions of trigonal bipyramids A and B formed from the other examples in Table 4.3, where sufficient data are available. Also included are the modes of reaction of intermediate B when optically active *cis* isomers are involved.

Figure 4.10 shows the stereochemistry of base hydrolysis in more detail, starting with an optically pure *cis* isomer. Now intermediate B may or

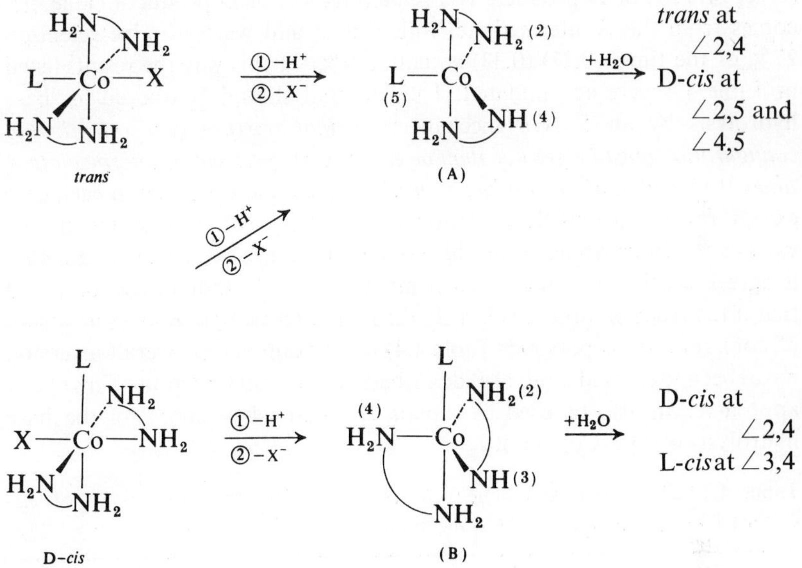

Fig. 4.10 Mechanism of reaction proposed for the base hydrolysis of $[Co(en)_2LX]^{n+}$. From reference 24a.

may not be symmetrical, depending upon the relative rate of proton transfer between amine and amido forms and the entry of water into the trigonal plane to produce sixfold coordination. As indicated earlier, it must be assumed that the amine group which has lost a proton to form amido is in the trigonal plane. This then allows strong ligand to metal π bonding. If rapid proton transfer occurs, the two ends of the ethylenediamine molecule lying in the trigonal plane become equivalent and B is a symmetrical intermediate. Only racemic *cis* product can then be formed from it.

If proton transfer is rather slow, and if conversion of B into the six-coordinated form by reaction with water is very rapid, then B is asymmetric. The two ends of the chelate ring are distinguishable, one being amide and the other amine. Reaction with water can produce two different *cis* products, the D and the L forms, and these will not be formed in equal amounts. For example, D-*cis*-Co(en)$_2$NH$_3$Cl^{2+} gives 60% D-*cis* and 24% L-*cis* product on base hydrolysis, according to Table 4.3.

To explain this we note from Table 4.4 that intermediate A is formed 67% of the time and B is formed 33% of the time. Also intermediate A forms *cis* product 76% of the time and *trans* product 24% of the time, according to the data for *trans*-Co(en)$_2$NH$_3$Cl^{2+} shown in Table 4.3. The *cis* product must have the retained, or D, configuration. This gives (0.67) (0.76) or 51% of D product. The remaining 9% of D product (Table 4.3) comes from the B intermediate, which must add water to give retention 27% of the time, (0.27) (0.33) equalling 9%. In this way the results listed in Table 4.4 were accumulated. The rule that should be obeyed for base hydrolysis by an S_N1CB mechanism *is that the per cent retention of configuration must be greater than or equal to the per cent of intermediate A times the fraction of cis product from A.*[24a] This rule is obeyed in each case except for Co(en)$_2$NCSCl$^+$. However, a change of only 2–3% in the various products would bring this system into line also, which means that it agrees within the limit of experimental error. It should also be noted that if the reaction proceeds largely through intermediate B a net inversion of configuration is possible (Table 4.4). Five examples of overall inversion have been observed and are described in the next section. This same approach can also be used to explain the stereochemistry[28d] of the base hydrolysis of D-α-Co(trien)Cl$_2$$^+$.

Table 4.4 Calculated stereochemical results in the base hydrolysis of *cis*-Co(en)$_2$LX, assuming an S_N1CB mechanism

L	X	Intermediate B,[a] %	Retention[a] for B, %
Cl$^-$	Cl$^-$	34	53
OH$^-$	Cl$^-$	50	26
OH$^-$	Br$^-$	60	...
Br$^-$	Cl$^-$	40	...
Cl$^-$	Br$^-$	26	...
N$_3$$^-$	Cl$^-$	44	...
NCS$^-$	Cl$^-$	16	0[b]
NH$_3$	Cl$^-$	33	27
NO$_2$$^-$	Cl$^-$	64	69

[a] For a discussion of estimates of per cent of B and per cent retention for B see text. For the structures of intermediates A and B see Fig. 4.10. Note also that % of A = 100-% B and that B need not be symmetrical, as discussed on p. 263.

[b] See text, p. 264.

One other very significant point is that, if the base hydrolysis of Co $(en)_2LX^{n+}$ to give $Co(en)_2LOH^{n+}$ does indeed go through the five-coordinated conjugate base $Co(en)(en-H)L^{n+}$, then for a given L the isomeric distribution of the hydroxo products must be the same for different departing groups X.[24b] This is nicely supported by the experimental results shown in Table 4.5. These results are not in accord with a bimolecular displacement process where the X group is present in the transition state and can influence the stereochemistry of the reaction.

Table 4.5   Lack of influence of X on the stereochemistry of the base hydrolysis reaction

$$Co(en)_2LX^{n+} + OH^- \rightarrow Co(en)_2LOH^{n+} + X^-$$

trans-L	X	cis, %	Ref.	cis-L	X	cis, %	Ref.
Cl	Cl	5	21	Cl	Cl	30	21
Cl	Br	5	21	Cl	Br	37	21
NCS	Cl	76	23	NH_3	Cl	84	22
NCS	Br	81	23	NH_3	Br	85	22
NCS	N_3	70	12b	NH_3	NO_3	86	22
N_3	Cl	27	12a	NCS	Cl	80	22
N_3	N_3	30	12a	NCS	N_3	70	12b
OH	Cl	94	21	N_3	Cl	59	12
OH	Br	90	21	N_3	N_3	55	12
NO_2	Cl	6	14	OH	Cl	97	21
NO_2	NCS	10	21c	OH	Br	96	21
				NO_2	Cl	67	14
				NO_2	NCS	55	12c

From reference 24b.

Optical Inversion Reactions of Some Cobalt(III) Complexes.   Substitution reactions of optically active Co(III) complexes that yield optically active products are found almost always to give products having the same generic configuration as that of the starting material. For example, the results shown in Table 4.3 for the base hydrolysis of D-cis-$Co(en)_2LX^{n+}$ are typical. The products $Co(en)_2LOH^{n+}$ are a mixture of racemic cis and trans isomers with the remaining optical activity being due to the D-cis enantiomers. Optical inversion reactions in metal complexes are rare, and at present only five different examples are known.

First, let us consider briefly some of the reactions of Co(III) complexes that take place with retention of configuration. A few examples are given in Table 4.6. Much of this work was done by Werner[1] and his students

Table 4.6 Substitution reactions in optically active complexes with retention of configuration[a]

Reactant	Reagent	Product	Ref.
$(+)$-Co(en)$_2$Cl$_2^+$	H$_2$O	$(+)$-Co(en)$_2$H$_2$OCl^{2+}	17
$(+)$-Co(en)$_2$Cl$_2^+$	K$_2$CO$_3$(H$_2$O)	$(+)$-Co(en)$_2$CO$_3^+$	1
$(+)$-Co(en)$_2$Cl$_2^+$	(NH$_4$)$_2$C$_2$O$_4$	$(+)$-Co(en)$_2$C$_2$O$_4$	1
$(+)$-Co(en)$_2$NO$_2$Cl$^+$	H$_2$O	$(+)$-Co(en)$_2$H$_2$ONO$_2^{2+}$	17
$(+)$-Co(en)$_2$NO$_2$Cl$^+$	NaNO$_2$	$(+)$-Co(en)$_2$(NO$_2$)$_2$	17
$(+)$-Co(en)$_2$NH$_3$Cl^{2+}	NaNO$_2$	$(-)$-Co(en)$_2$NH$_3$NO$_2^{2+}$	1
$(+)$-Co(en)$_2$Cl$_2^+$	KSCN	$(+)_{5461}$-Co(en)$_2$NCSCl$^+$	1

[a] Retention of configuration refers only to the optically active species. Racemization and isomerization also often occur in these reactions.

and by Mathieu.[17] The technique used by Werner was to carry out the reaction on a preparative scale and isolate the product. His assignment of relative generic configuration was then based upon the assumption that, for analogous complex ions, the antipodes which form the least soluble salts with the same resolving agent have the same configuration. Thus, the reaction

$$(+)\text{-Co(en)}_2\text{NH}_3\text{Cl}^{2+} + \text{NaNO}_2 \rightarrow (-)\text{-Co(en)}_2\text{NH}_3\text{NO}_2^{2+} + \text{Cl}^- \quad (5)$$

is said to proceed with retention of configuration because, in the resolution of these racemic complexes by fractional crystallization of their *dextro*-α-bromocamphor-π-sulfonate salts, the least soluble fractions are formed with $(+)$-Co(en)$_2$NH$_3$Cl^{2+} and $(-)$-Co(en)$_2$NH$_3$NO$_2^{2+}$, respectively. Mathieu[17] has investigated some of these reactions by determining the rotatory dispersion curves of the initial and final complexes, and these results also show that the reactions take place with retention of configuration. It must be kept in mind that this retention of configuration refers only to the optically active portion of the reaction product. Racemization and isomerization may also take place. That the optically active product has the same configuration as the starting material can be understood on the basis of either a dissociation (Fig. 4.4) or a *cis*-attack displacement (Fig. 4.6) process. Except for special circumstances, as discussed below, a much less likely *trans*-attack displacement is required for inversion of configuration to occur.

All but one of the known examples of optical inversion in substitution reactions of metal complexes have been discovered by Bailar and his students. The first of these involved the conversion of optically active *cis*-Co(en)$_2$Cl$_2^+$ into optically active Co(en)$_2$CO$_3^+$ by two different methods:[25]

$$(+)\text{-Co(en)}_2\text{Cl}_2^+ \quad \underset{\overset{\displaystyle\longrightarrow}{\text{Ag}_2\text{CO}_3}}{\overset{\text{K}_2\text{CO}_3}{\displaystyle\longrightarrow}} \quad \begin{array}{l} (+)\text{-Co(en)}_2\text{CO}_3^+ \\[1em] (-)\text{-Co(en)}_2\text{CO}_3^+ \end{array} \tag{6}$$

Rotatory dispersion studies show that *cis*-Co(en)$_2$Cl$_2^+$, *cis*-Co(en)$_2$H$_2$OCl^{2+}, and Co(en)$_2$CO$_3^+$ that are *dextrorotatory* at the Na$_D$ line, (+), have the same configuration.[17] It is then apparent that inversion takes place in the reaction with Ag$_2$CO$_3$, and reaction 6 can be written as

$$D^*\text{-Co(en)}_2\text{Cl}_2^+ \quad \underset{\overset{\displaystyle\longrightarrow}{\text{Ag}_2\text{CO}_3}}{\overset{\text{K}_2\text{CO}_3}{\displaystyle\longrightarrow}} \quad \begin{array}{l} D^*\text{-Co(en)}_2\text{CO}_3^+ \\[1em] L^*\text{-Co(en)}_2\text{CO}_3^+ \end{array} \tag{7}$$

to show the absolute configurations relative to that of the standard D*-Co(en)$_3^{3+}$. This system was initially studied[26] in some detail and has recently been the subject of further investigations.[27,28a] The early work was done by grinding the complex with the metal carbonate in a small amount of water to form a paste, followed by the extraction of the soluble products with water. Similar reactions with Hg$_2$CO$_3$ and with Ag$_2$CrO$_4$ did not give inverted products. However, when a large excess of K$_2$CO$_3$ was used, an inverted product was formed. Since the reaction of D*-Co(en)$_2$H$_2$OCl^{2+} with Ag$_2$CO$_3$ gave D*-Co(en)$_2$CO$_3^+$, it was concluded that the formation of the L* isomer necessitated direct replacement of the chloride ions without prior aquation.

A more complete study[27] of this system was made, and it was concluded that the inversion occurs as a result of base hydrolysis of D*-Co(en)$_2$Cl$_2^+$ in the presence of Ag$^+$. The inverted L*-Co(en)$_2$ClOH$^+$ then proceeds, via the dihydroxo, to the carbonato complex with retention of configuration. The following reaction sequence

$$\begin{array}{ccc}
D^*\text{-Co(en)}_2\text{Cl}_2^+ & \xrightarrow{\text{H}_2\text{O}} & D^*\text{-Co(en)}_2\text{H}_2\text{OCl}^{2+} \\
\scriptstyle\text{OH}^-\downarrow\text{Ag}^+ & \searrow_{\text{OH}^-} \quad {\scriptstyle\text{Ag}^+\downarrow\text{OH}^-} & \\
L^*\text{-Co(en)}_2\text{ClOH}^+ & \rightarrow D^*\text{-Co(en)}_2\text{ClOH}^+ & \\
\scriptstyle\text{OH}^-\downarrow\text{Ag}^+ & \scriptstyle\text{OH}^-\downarrow\text{Ag}^+ & \\
L^*\text{-Co(en)}_2(\text{OH})_2^+ & D^*\text{-Co(en)}_2(\text{OH})_2^+ & \\
\scriptstyle\downarrow\text{HCO}_3^- & \scriptstyle\downarrow\text{HCO}_3^- & \\
L^*\text{-Co(en)}_2\text{CO}_3^+ & D^*\text{-Co(en)}_2\text{CO}_3^+ &
\end{array} \tag{8}$$

summarizes the data reported on the formation of optically active Co(en)$_2$CO$_3^+$. The base hydrolysis products were also identified by reaction with NaNO$_2$ and conversion to Co(en)$_2$(NO$_2$)$_2^+$. The results were in good agreement with those obtained by the reaction with HCO_3^-. Thus, the reaction of D*-Co(en)$_2$Cl$_2^+$ with OH$^-$-Ag$^+$, followed by NO$_2^-$, gave L*-Co(en)$_2$(NO$_2$)$_2^+$. Experimental conditions for the formation of the carbonato and dinitro complexes were such that the Co-O bond in the dihydroxo complex was not broken (p. 231), thus permitting the reaction to occur without rearrangement. Silver ion is necessary for inversion, and attempts to substitute other ions such as Hg^{2+}, Pb^{2+}, and Tl$^+$ were not successful. Likewise, other anions such as NO$_2^-$ and N$_3^-$ could not be used in place of OH$^-$.

It was suggested[27] that inversion occurs as a result of a *trans*-attack displacement process involving both OH$^-$ and Ag$^+$ (Fig. 4.11a). This suggestion is at variance with the S_N1CB mechanism assigned to such base hydrolysis reactions. That Ag$^+$ is necessary for inversion makes it possible to offer alternative explanations on the basis of a dissociation mechanism. For example, in Fig. 4.11b it is assumed that the formation of the trigonal

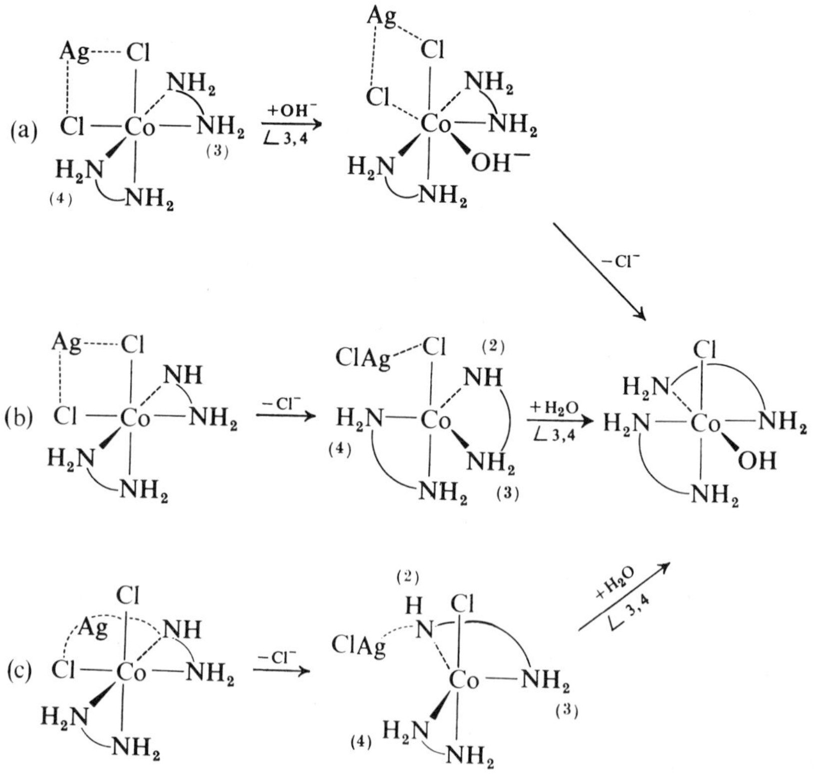

Fig. 4.11 Mechanisms proposed for the base hydrolysis inversion of Co(en)$_2$Cl$_2^+$ in the presence of Ag$^+$.

bipyramid is rapidly followed by the addition of water. If the AgCl has not had time to depart completely (being held in position by the remaining Cl⁻), it follows that attack at $\angle 2,4$ is made difficult, with the result that there is a preference for attack at $\angle 3,4$, which in turn leads to inversion. Another possibility is that the Ag^+ becomes partly bonded to the amido group adjacent to the departing chloro ligand. Again the presence of AgCl at $\angle 2,4$ may retard attack at this position and favor entry of H_2O at $\angle 3,4$ as shown by Fig. 4.11c. Unfortunately, the experimental results do not permit a choice between the several possibilities.

It was recently observed[28a] that the base hydrolysis of optically active $Co(en)_2Cl_2^+$ can occur with inversion even in the absence of Ag^+. Although in dilute solutions ($<0.01\ M$) the base hydrolysis of D^*-$Co(en)_2Cl_2^+$ yields D^*-$Co(en)_2ClOH^+$, in concentrated solutions ($>0.25\ M$) the product is L^*-$Co(en)_2ClOH^-$. This was confirmed by the experiments shown in the reaction scheme

$$D^*\text{-}Co(en)_2Cl_2^+ \quad \xrightarrow{\;H_2O\;} \quad D^*\text{-}Co(en)_2H_2OCl^{2+}$$

$$\downarrow OH^- \text{ (conc.)} \qquad\qquad \overset{OH^-}{\underset{\text{(dil.)}}{\diagdown}} \qquad \downarrow OH^-$$

$$L^*\text{-}Co(en)_2(OH)_2^+ \qquad\qquad \searrow D^*\text{-}Co(en)_2(OH)_2^+ \qquad\qquad (9)$$

$$\downarrow HAA \qquad\qquad\qquad\qquad \downarrow HAA$$

$$L^*\text{-}Co(en)_2(AA)^{n+} \qquad\qquad D^*\text{-}Co(en)_2(AA)^{n+}$$

where $HAA = HCO_3^-$, acetylacetone, and trifluoroacetylacetone. It was suggested that in dilute solution base hydrolysis proceeds by an S_N1CB mechanism with no special orientation of the hydroxide ion with respect to the complex. This cannot be true for concentrated solutions, since these reactions give inverted products. It is then possible that the formation of ion pairs in the more concentrated solutions places the OH^- in a preferred position for attack to give inversion. This is illustrated in Fig. 4.12. Still with a conjugate base mechanism, the ion pair gives an N—H proton to the OH^-, forming a trigonal bipyramidal structure with the hydrogen-bonded water molecule in position to readily attack the trigonal plane at $\angle 3,4$ and cause inversion of configuration. The same stereochemical result would, of course, also be expected for a *trans*-attack displacement process, but the conjugate base dissociation process is preferred because of the other evidence that supports it. It should be remembered that this reaction of D^*-$Co(en)_2Cl_2^+$ yields a mixture of *trans-*, *racemic cis-*, and L^*-$Co(en)_2ClOH^+$. The mechanism shown in Fig. 4.12 is only an attempt to account for the preferential formation of the L^* isomer in concentrated solutions relative to D^* in dilute solutions. Even in concentrated solution some D^* isomer is formed by the addition of water at $\angle 2,4$.

It should be noted that the mechanisms proposed (Figs. 4.11b and 11c and Fig. 4.12) for the base hydrolysis inversion of $Co(en)_2Cl_2^+$ in the

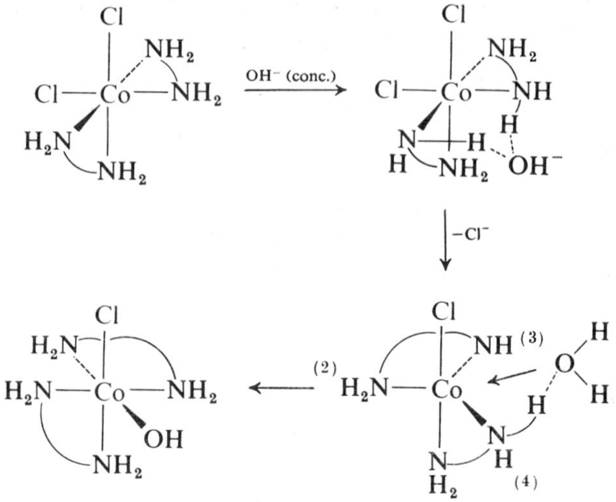

Fig. 4.12 Mechanism proposed for the inversion of configuration during the base hydrolysis of optically active Co(en)$_2$Cl$_2^+$ in concentrated solution.

presence of Ag$^+$ or high OH$^-$ concentration involve the trigonal bipyramidal structure B (Fig. 4.10). The discussion on p. 263 suggests that in base hydrolysis reactions this intermediate may be asymmetric, and the results under normal condition show that it reacts with only 53% retention. For three other analogous systems their intermediates B react with inversion largely (Table 4.4). Therefore, it seems plausible that under the special conditions described here intermediate B may well react with inversion. One other point is that for net inversion the total amount of *cis* product must come largely from B, because intermediate A gives *cis* with retention of configuration.

Another example of optical inversion in metal complexes was reported[29] for the reaction of D*-Co(en)$_2$Cl$_2^+$ with ammonia. In this case the optical rotation of the reaction product, Co(en)$_2$(NH$_3$)$_2^{3+}$, depends on the temperature. The pertinent experimental results obtained on this system are summarized by the reaction sequence

$$\text{D*-Co(en)}_2\text{Cl}_2^+ \begin{cases} \xrightarrow{\text{NH}_3\text{(l), }-50^\circ} \text{L*-Co(en)}_2\text{NH}_3\text{Cl}^{2+} \xrightarrow{\text{NH}_3} \text{L*-Co(en)}_2\text{(NH}_3)_2^{3+} \\ \xrightarrow[\text{or NH}_3-\text{CH}_3\text{OH, }30^\circ]{\text{NH}_3\text{(g), }80^\circ} \text{D*-Co(en)}_2\text{NH}_3\text{Cl}^{2+} \xrightarrow{\text{NH}_3} \text{D*-Co(en)}_2\text{(NH}_3)_2^{3+} \end{cases}$$

The suggestion was made[30a] that inversion occurs by a *trans*-attack displacement process. It was said that at a low temperature the attack takes place most readily at an octahedral face some distance removed from the chloro groups. At higher temperatures either the repulsion of ammonia by the coordinated chloro groups is sufficiently overcome to permit *cis* attack, or a dissociation mechanism is more prevalent. Recent studies[30b] also show that the reaction of optically active α-Co (trien) Cl_2^+ with liquid ammonia at low temperature leads to optical inversion, whereas reaction with gaseous ammonia at higher temperatures takes place with retention of configuration.

Further investigations[31] of the reactions of Co(III) complexes in anhydrous liquid ammonia under a variety of conditions have led to the conclusion that the inversion path appears to be insignificant in systems possessing large ligand field stabilizations. For example, under certain conditions, inversion does take place in the substitution of NH_3 in D*-$Co(en)_2Cl_2^+$, but retention of configuration is almost complete for the similar reaction of D*-$Co(en)_2NH_3Cl^{2+}$, which has a larger C.F.S.E. It is suggested that inversion may involve a high-spin intermediate, which is more readily attainable in a system of low C.F.S.E. such as $Co(en)_2Cl_2^+$. This high-spin system would not require as high an activation energy to generate a seven-coordinated transition state as would a comparable low-spin complex. The result would be a bimolecular inversion process. An alternative explanation is that a dissociation mechanism is involved and that the assumed high-spin five-coordinated intermediate has a trigonal bipyramidal structure. The tendency to form this structure, which can lead to inversion, increases with a decrease in C.F.S.E. of the system. For systems of high C.F.S.E., there is a greater tendency to form a tetragonal pyramidal structure, which then leads to reaction with retention of configuration (p. 273). Whatever the reason, it is of interest that the replacement of Cl^- in D*-$Co(en)_2Cl_2^+$ by water in aqueous solution takes place with retention of configuration, whereas replacement by ammonia in anhydrous ammonia occurs with rearrangement. Several factors may contribute to this difference, such as the fact that NH_3 is a better nucleophile than H_2O, that ion pairs are present in liquid ammonia solutions, and that the solvation energy of Cl^- is greater in water solution than in liquid ammonia.

Recently[28b] optical inversion was found to occur in the base hydrolysis of D*-α-Co(trien)ClOH$^+$, where trien is the quadridentate amine NH_2C_2 $H_4NHC_2H_4NHC_2H_4NH_2$. Starting with the optically active dichloro complex, the reactions observed are represented by

$$D^*\text{-}\alpha\text{-Co(trien)}Cl_2^+$$

$$\Big\downarrow H_2O$$

L*-β-Co(trien)(OH)$_2^+$ $\xleftarrow{\ 2OH^-\ }$ D*-α-Co(trien)H$_2$OCl^{2+} $\xrightarrow[Hg_2^+]{\ 2OH^-\ }$ D*-α-Co(trien)(OH)$_2^+$

$\Big\downarrow HCO_3^-$ OH$^-$ HCO$_3^-$ $\diagup HCO_3^-$ (11)

L*-β-Co(trien)CO$_3^+$ D*-α-Co(trien)CO$_3^+$

The α and β notations are geometric forms due to the orientations of the chelate rings. Again the detailed mechanism of inversion is not known, but is is of interest to note that the experimental results obtained on this differ from those described above for D*-Co(en)$_2$Cl$_2$$^+$. The optical inversion of D*-α-Co(trien)Cl$_2$$^+$ takes place in the absence of Ag$^+$ or Hg^{2+}, and the extent of inversion does not depend on the concentration of OH$^-$. This optical inversion of D*-α-Co(trien)OHCl$^+$ → L*-β-Co(trien)(OH)$_2$$^+$ can be explained on the basis of a conjugate-base-dissociation mechanism

Fig. 4.13 Conjugate base mechanism for the optical inversion of D*-α-[Co(trien)-OHCl]$^+$ into L*-β-[Co(trien)(OH)$_2$]$^+$ by water attack of B at $\angle$1,3. trien = NH$_2$C$_2$H$_4$NHC$_2$H$_4$NHC$_2$H$_4$NH$_2$.

as shown in Fig. 4.13. Preference for the attack of water at $\angle$1,3 of intermediate B over $\angle$1,2 may be due to the greater stability of the β form compared to the α form. In support of this is the observation[28c] that L*-β-Co(trien)Cl$_2$$^+$ reacts with OH$^-$ with almost complete optical retention to give L*-β-Co(trien)(OH)$_2$$^+$.

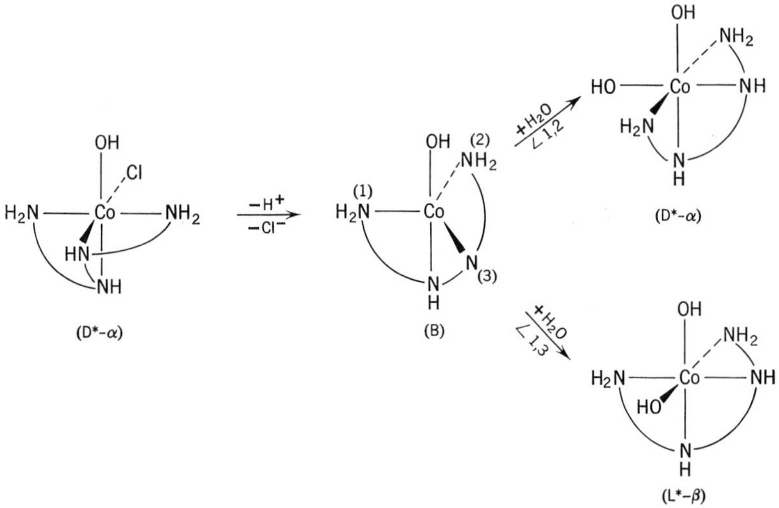

All of the optical inversion reactions reported for metal complexes in aqueous solution are base hydrolysis reactions of Co(III) complexes containing some N-H hydrogens. This suggests there may be something unusual about these reactions, and the unique behavior of OH$^-$ as a reagent in these systems was discussed in Chapter 3. Since there is considerable support for such base hydrolyses taking place by a conjugate base-dissociation mechanism, it is gratifying that this mechanism can also be used to account for the observed optical inversion reactions.[28d]

Complexes of Metals Other Than Cobalt(III). The steric course of substitution reactions of metal complexes other than Co(III) have been investigated to a limited extent. Some of the results obtained are given in Table 4.7 along with specific references. It is of interest to note that except for Cr(III) all of the complexes examined react with retention of configuration. First, let us consider the aquation of $Cr(en)_2Cl_2^+$ and of $Cr(en)_2OHCl^+$, in comparison with the analogous Co(III) systems. The *cis* isomers for both the Cr(III) and the Co(III) complexes react with almost total retention. This implies that the two systems are reacting by the same mechanism. However, such cannot be the case for the *trans* isomers, since the Cr(III) complexes give largely *trans* products, whereas the Co(III) complexes yield primarily *cis* products. This rearrangement for Co(III) systems was explained earlier on the basis of rearrangement to a

Table 4.7 Substitution reactions of some geometrical isomers of complexes of chromium(III), platinum(IV), rhodium(III), and ruthenium(III)

Reactant	Reagent	Product	cis, %	Ref.
cis-$Cr(en)_2Cl_2^+$	H_2O	$Cr(en)_2H_2OCl^{2+}$	100	32
$trans$-$Cr(en)_2Cl_2^+$	H_2O	$Cr(en)_2H_2OCl^{2+}$	some	32
cis-$Cr(en)_2OHCl^+$	H_2O	$Cr(en)_2H_2O(OH)^{2+}$	96	33a
$trans$-$Cr(en)_2OHCl^+$	H_2O	$Cr(en)_2H_2O(OH)^{2+}$	13	33a
cis-$Cr(en)_2NCSCl^+$	H_2O	$Cr(en)_2H_2ONCS^{2+}$	98	33b
$trans$-$Pt(en)_2Cl_2^{2+}$	Br^-	$Pt(en)_2Br_2^{2+}$	0	34
$trans$-$Pt(en)_2Cl_2^{2+}$	SCN^-	$Pt(en)_2(CNS)_2^{2+}$	0	34
$trans$-$Pt(NH_3)_4Cl_2^{2+}$	py	$Pt(NH_3)_4pyCl^{3+}$	0	35a
$trans$-$Pt(NH_3)_4Cl_2^{2+}$	py	$Pt(NH_3)_4pyCl^{3+}$	0	35a
$trans$-$Pt(NH_3)_4BrCl^{2+}$	py	$Pt(NH_3)_4pyBr^{3+}$	0	35a
$trans$-$Pt(NH_3)_4ICl^{2+}$	py	$Pt(NH_3)_4pyI^{3+}$	0	35a
cis-$Rh(en)_2Cl_2^+$	OH^-	$Rh(en)_2(OH)_2^+$	100	36
$trans$-$Rh(en)_2Cl_2^+$	OH^-	$Rh(en)_2(OH)_2^+$	0	36
cis-$Rh(en)_2(H_2O)_2^{3+}$	Cl^-	$Rh(en)_2Cl_2^+$	100	36
$trans$-$Rh(en)_2(H_2O)_2^{3+}$	Cl^-	$Rh(en)_2Cl_2^+$	0	36
cis-$Rh(en)_2Cl_2^+$	NH_3	$Rh(en)_2NH_3Cl^{2+}$	100	36
$trans$-$Rh(en)_2Cl_2^+$	NH_3	$Rh(en)_2NH_3Cl^{2+}$	0	36
$trans$-$Rh(en)_2Cl_2^+$	I^-	$Rh(en)_2I_2^+$	0	36
$trans$-$Rh(en)_2I_2^+$	Cl^-	$Rh(en)_2ICl^+$	0	37
$trans$-$Rh(en)_2Br_2^+$	Cl^-	$Rh(en)_2BrCl^+$	0	37
$trans$-$Rh(en)_2(NO_2)_2^+$	HCL	$Rh(en)_2NO_2Cl^+$	0	38
cis-$Rh(en)_2(NO_2)_2^+$	HCl	$Rh(en)_2NO_2Cl^+$	100	38
cis-$Ru(en)_2Cl_2^+$	OH^-	$Ru(en)_2(OH)_2^+$	100	39a
cis-$Ru(en)_2Cl_2^+$	I^-	$Ru(en)_2I_2^+$	100	39a

trigonal bipyramidal structure, permitting more efficient π bonding of ligand to metal. On this basis it appears that the driving force for the π bonding is not as large in the Cr(III) complexes, and thus there would be less rearrangement to give *cis* products. There is some support for this view in the fact that base hydrolysis, presumably involving π bonding of the amido group, is not nearly as rapid in Cr(III) systems as in Co(III) complexes.[39b] This has been discussed in Chapter 3 (p. 188).

All of the reactions of Pt(IV), of Rh(III), and of Ru(III) complexes that have been investigated proceed without steric change (Table 4.7). Most of the reactions studied for Pt(IV) are for complexes of the type *trans*-$PtA_4X_2^{2+}$. Some of these reactions are known to be Pt(II) catalyzed.[34] For such reactions the two-electron transfer mechanism through an activated bridged complex is expected to yield a *trans* product starting with a *trans* substrate (p. 237). However, the reactions with ammonia and with pyridine are reported not to be Pt(II) catalyzed and if so are perhaps a *cis*-attack displacement.[35a] Later studies[35b] show that the reaction of *trans*-$Pt(NH_3)_4Cl_2^{2+}$ with NH_3 is Pt(II) catalyzed.

The difference in the stereochemistry of analogous reactions of *cis* and *trans* complexes of Rh(III) and Co(III) is striking. That all of the reactions of Rh(III) complexes reported proceed with almost complete retention is strong evidence that they react by a different mechanism than do the analogous Co(III) complexes. The effect of base on the rate of hydrolysis of Rh(III) complexes is very much less than for Co(III) complexes. The mechanism was discussed on p. 187. The accelerating effect of base, when found, is still probably due to the formation of an amido complex. However, rearrangement to a trigonal bipyramid does not occur because the C.F.S.E. of Rh(III) is greater than that of Co(III), and the loss of C.F.S.E. is large for a reaction that goes through a trigonal bipyramidal structure. Therefore, the gain in stabilization due to π bonding is not sufficient to make up for the loss of C.F.S.E. in the Rh(III), and as a result it does not rearrange.[39b] This same explanation can be given to account for the reactions of Ru(III) complexes with retention of configuration.[39a]

Isomerization of Octahedral Complexes

That isomerization of geometrical isomers of complex compounds can occur was recognized by Jørgensen[40] as early as 1889 for the system *cis*-$Co(en)_2Cl_2^+ \rightleftharpoons trans$-$Co(en)_2Cl_2^+$. Rearrangements of this type complicate stereochemical studies of substitution reactions of the type just described. Also because of this interconversion it is generally not possible to make a structural assignment of a complex on the basis of its method of synthesis alone. Although these rearrangements are not common among square complexes, they have often been observed with octahedral complexes. For example, prolonged boiling or evaporation to dryness of the *cis* salts, $[Co(en)_2NO_2Cl]Cl$,[41] $[Co(en)_2(NO_2)_2]NO_3$,[42] $K_3[Ir(C_2O_4)_2-Cl_2]$,[43] and $K_3[Rh(C_2O_4)_2Cl_2]$,[44] is known to yield the corresponding *trans* isomers. Detailed studies of isomerization are reported for only a few systems; some of these will be discussed.

Dichlorobis(ethylenediamine)cobalt(III) Ion. The *cis-trans* isomerization most extensively studied is that between the *praseo, trans*-$Co(en)_2Cl_2^+$ and *violeo, cis*-$Co(en)_2Cl_2^+$ ions. If an aqueous solution of green *trans*-$[Co(en)_2Cl_2]Cl$ is concentrated on a steam bath, the crystals that separate from solution are violet and consist largely of *cis*-$[Co(en)_2Cl_2]Cl$. This violet salt can in turn be transformed into the green isomer by the evaporation of a hydrochloric acid solution of the *cis* salt to yield *trans*-$[Co(en)_2Cl_2]Cl·HCl·2H_2O$.

It was suggested[45] that these transformations take place by the opening up of an ethylenediamine ring and the entry of either chloride or hydroxide ion into the vacant position, followed by closing of the ring in such a way as to permit rearrangement. This suggestion was made primarily on the supposition that the green hydrochloride generally designated as *trans*-$[Co(en)_2Cl_2]Cl·HCl$ is instead $[Co(en)(enH)Cl_3]Cl$, because structures of this type are known for Pt(II) compounds.[46] However, the green color of the hydrochloride does not change with loss of hydrogen chloride to yield *trans*-$[Co(en)_2Cl_2]Cl$. This lack of change would not be expected if the trichloro structure were correct for the hydrochloride salt. That it is not correct has been shown by means of infrared and x-ray investigations.[47] The solid has the composition of a dihydrate, $[Co(en)_2Cl_2]Cl·HCl·2H_2O$, and its structure shows the presence of the bisaquohydrogen ion $H_5O_2^+$ with an O—O distance of 2.66 A.

A detailed study[48] of this system was made using radiochloride ion, and it was demonstated that the reaction mechanism need not involve the opening of a chelate ring. Isomerization in the presence of radiochloride ion is accompanied by a completely random distribution of chloride ion with coordinated chloro groups; thus, isomerization may occur as a result of an intermolecular process. It was also observed that there is no direct replacement of coordinated chloride by chloride ion. Therefore, in the absence of direct replacement of chloride, isomerization apparently is associated with the known equilibria:

$$Co(en)_2Cl_2^+ + H_2O \overset{a}{\underset{b}{\rightleftharpoons}} Co(en)_2(H_2O)Cl^{2+} + Cl^- \qquad (12)$$

$$Co(en)_2(H_2O)Cl^{2+} + H_2O \overset{c}{\underset{d}{\rightleftharpoons}} Co(en)_2(H_2O)_2^{3+} + Cl^- \qquad (13)$$

Reactions a and c take place during the initial stages of the concentration at steam bath temperatures. The reverse reactions, b and d, become important in the final stages when the chloride ion concentration reaches a maximum. The slowness of reactions b and d is responsible for failure to achieve more than partial isomerization by evaporation at room temperature. Under such conditions the product still contains appreciable quantities of the aquo complex ions.

The particular isomer that separates from solution is largely determined by the relative solubilities of the isomeric salts. The less soluble isomer, cis-[Co(en)$_2$Cl$_2$]Cl, is obtained from aqueous solution, whereas the still less soluble trans-[Co(en)$_2$Cl$_2$](H$_5$O$_2$)Cl$_2$ separates from hydrochloric acid solution. On the other hand an aqueous solution of either cis- or trans-[Co(en)$_2$Cl$_2$]NO$_3$ yields the less soluble trans isomer upon concentration. That the role played by hydrochloric acid is that of a precipitant and not that of opening up the chelate ring was shown by the use of trans-[Co(en)$_2$*Cl$_2$]Cl. This salt was dissolved in cold water and precipitated from solution by the addition of hydrochloric acid. Hydrogen chloride liberated at 110°C by this hydrochloride salt was not radioactive.

It was pointed out[48] that the following mechanism is consistent with these observations:

$$cis\text{-}Co(en)_2Cl_2^+ + H_2O \rightleftharpoons cis\text{-}Co(en)_2(H_2O)Cl^{2+} + Cl^- \qquad (14)$$

$$\Updownarrow$$

$$trans\text{-}Co(en)_2Cl_2^+ + H_2O \rightleftharpoons trans\text{-}Co(en)_2(H_2O)Cl^{2+} + Cl^- \qquad (15)$$

Studies[10] show that both cis- and trans-Co(en)$_2$(H$_2$O)Cl^{2+} isomerize to the cis-trans equilibrium mixture at rates comparable to their respective rates of formation from cis- or trans-Co(en)$_2$Cl$_2^+$. Furthermore, equation 14 is correct, but 15 is not because the aquation of trans-Co(en)$_2$Cl$_2^+$ forms directly a mixture of 35% cis- and 65% trans-Co(en)$_2$H$_2$OCl^{2+}. Likewise the isomerization at experimental conditions of steam bath temperatures (approximately 80°C) must certainly involve the diaquo complexes, so that equilibrium 13 cannot be ignored. Hence the system is sufficiently complicated to account for the observed rearrangements. On the basis of a dissociation mechanism, it is apparent (Fig. 4.14) that the cis and trans

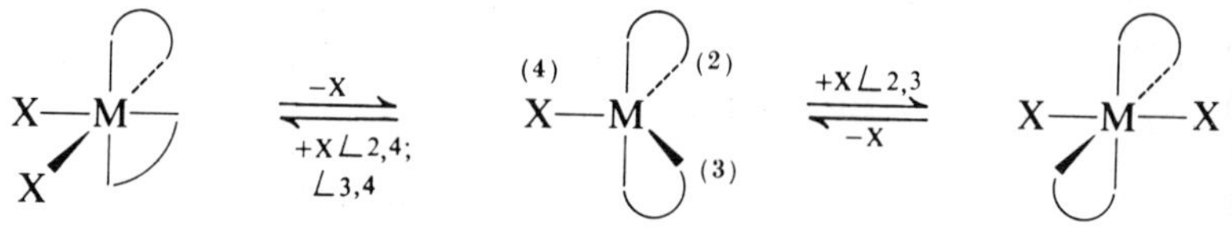

Fig. 4.14 Isomerization of cis-trans isomers of the type M(AA)$_2$X$_2$ by a dissociation mechanism.

isomers may have a common trigonal bipyramidal intermediate which readily provides a path for isomerization. Rearrangement of the system under discussion is not limited to any one set of *cis-trans* isomers, but instead X can be either chloride ion or water.

This same *cis-trans* isomerization of $Co(en)_2Cl_2^+$ has also been studied in the solvents methanol,[49,50] ethanol, propanol,[51] 2-methoxyethanol,[52] dimethylformamide, dimethylacetamide, and dimethylsulfoxide.[53] For the alcohol solvents the equilibrium mixtures are almost exclusively *trans*-$Co(en)_2Cl_2^+$, whereas for the other solvents large amounts of *cis* isomer are present at equilibrium. These systems are somewhat complicated by the formation of ion pairs. In several cases the rates of radiochloride exchange with the complex have been studied, and the results show that the steric rearrangement process involves substitution of coordinated chloride ion. This ligand interchange process is believed to proceed essentially by dissociation of the free complex ion or its ion pair, as is discussed on p. 212.

Extensive studies[49,50] have been made on the isomerization and loss in optical activity of $(+)$-$Co(en)_2Cl_2^+$ in methanol. Some of the data reported are shown in Table 4.8. The important thing to notice here is the similarity of the steric course for the substitution reactions of the free ion and the ion pair and also the complete loss of optical activity for every act of substitution. This requires that at some stage in the reaction the complex must have a symmetrical structure. The results also show that the rate of *cis* → *trans* isomerization is slower than the rate of loss of optical activity for both the free ion and the ion pair.

Diaquobis(ethylenediamine)cobalt(III) Ion.   It was observed[55] that the absorption spectra of *cis*- and *trans*-$Co(en)_2(H_2O)_2^{3+}$ change rapidly to the same spectrum in aqueous solution forming an equilibrium mixture of *cis-trans* isomers. It was later found[55] that this change is much slower in acid solution than in water, which means that the hydroxoaquo species, $Co(en)_2(H_2O)OH^{2+}$, isomerizes more readily than do the diaquo complexes. For example, *cis*- and *trans*-$[Co(en)_2(H_2O)OH]Br_2$ dissolved in water give identical spectra (30 min at room temperature), whereas if dissolved in hydrobromic acid ($pH = 1$) the spectra are different. This rather complicated system of acid-base and *cis-trans* equilibria

$$cis\text{-}Co(en)_2(H_2O)_2^{3+} \rightleftharpoons cis\text{-}Co(en)_2(H_2O)OH^{2+} \rightleftharpoons cis\text{-}Co(en)_2(OH)_2^+$$
$$\Updownarrow \qquad\qquad\qquad \Updownarrow \qquad\qquad\qquad \Updownarrow \qquad (16)$$
$$trans\text{-}Co(en)_2(H_2O)_2^{3+} \rightleftharpoons trans\text{-}Co(en)_2(H_2O)OH^{2+} \rightleftharpoons trans\text{-}Co(en)_2(OH)_2^+$$

has been investigated.[56] The equilibrium *cis/trans* ratios, the rates of isomerization, and the rates of ^{18}O exchange are summarized in Table 4.9. The rates of isomerization of the diaquo ions in acid solution and the

Table 4.8 Isomerization of $cis \rightarrow trans\text{-}Co(en)_2Cl_2^+$ and its chloride ion pair in methanol at 35°C

	$10^5 k_{cis \rightarrow trans}$, sec⁻¹	$10^5 k_{rac}$, sec⁻¹ [a]	$10^5 k_{exch}$, sec⁻¹	$trans$, %	(+), %	(−), %
(+)-Co(en)$_2$Cl$_2^+$	5.3	7.7	7.7	70	15	15
(+)-Co(en)$_2$Cl$_2^+$, Cl⁻	12	15	15	86	7	7

From reference 50.

[a] k_{rac} is the rate constant for loss of optical activity, much of it due to isomerization to the optically inactive *trans* isomer.

dihydroxo ions in basic solution are slow; equilibrium is reached in approximately 1 week at room temperature. The hydroxoaquo complexes isomerize much more rapidly, reaching equilibrium within 1 hr. Since isomerization does involve water exchange, the rapid rate for the hydroxo-aquo ions compared to the diaquo and dihydroxo is understood. In acid solution the diaquo complex undergoes water exchange by a relatively

Table 4.9[a,b]   Kinetic data for *cis-trans* isomerization of $Co(en)_2X_2^{n+}$, where $X = H_2O$, OH^- at 25°C

Reaction	$10^6 k$, sec^{-1}	$\Delta H^\ddagger$	$\Delta S^\ddagger$
cis-$Co(en)_2(H_2O)_2^{3+} \rightarrow$ *trans*	0.12^c	...	...
trans-$Co(en)_2(H_2O)_2^{3+} \rightarrow$ *cis*	6.8	25.6	4
cis-$Co(en)_2(H_2O)_2^{3+} \rightarrow H_2{}^*O$ exchange	7.5	28.8	15
trans-$Co(en)_2(H_2O)_2^{3+} \rightarrow H_2{}^*O$ exchange	11	30.6	21
cis-$Co(en)_2(OH)_2^{+} \rightarrow$ *trans*	3.7	28, 31	...
trans-$Co(en)_2(OH)_2^{+} \rightarrow$ *cis*	3.2	28, 31	...
cis-$Co(en)_2(OH)_2^{+} \rightarrow H_2{}^*O$ exchange	30	27.4	13
trans-$Co(en)_2(OH)_2^{+} \rightarrow H_2{}^*O$ exchange	2.3	30.4	20
$Co(en)_2H_2O(OH)^{2+}$	fast		

From reference 57.

[a] For $Co(NH_3)_4(H_2O)_2^{3+}$ the *cis/trans* ratio at equilibrium $= 0.17$; $t_{1/2}$ for isomerization $= 21$ min at 30°; $E_a = 25.0$ kcal/mole. From reference 58.

[b] For $Cr(en)_2(OH)_2^{+}$, *cis* $\rightarrow$ *trans* k at 25° $= 1.0 \times 10^{-6}$ sec^{-1} and $E_a = 32$ kcal/mole, and *trans* $\rightarrow$ *cis* k at 25° $= 5.2 \times 10^{-6}$ sec^{-1} and $E_a = 27$ kcal/mole. From reference 59.

[c] Estimated from the rate constant *trans* $\rightarrow$ *cis* and the *cis/trans* ratio of 58 at equilibrium. For $Co(en)_2H_2O(OH)^{2+}$ the *cis/trans* ratio is 1.4, and for $Co(en)_2(OH)_2^{+}$ it is 0.80, as reported in reference 56.

slow acid hydrolysis type of reaction, whereas the extremely rapid base hydrolysis reaction makes an appreciable contribution to the total hydrolysis rate responsible for water exchange (isomerization) of an aqueous solution (pH 7–8) of the hydroxoaquo ions. The slow rate of isomerization of the dihydroxo complex in alkali may be due to the relatively strong Co-O bond in Co—OH compared to Co—OH$_2$, which prevents rapid exchange with the solvent.

A comparison of the rate of isomerization of *trans*-$Co(en)_2(H_2O)_2^{3+}$ with its rate of water exchange shows (Table 4.9) that one molecule of water is brought into exchange with the solvent for each isomeric change.[57] This is similar to the observation that the rate of chloride ion exchange is equal to the rate of loss of optical activity of $(+)$-$Co(en)_2Cl_2^{+}$ in methanol solution. A similar type of mechanism may be involved. If this is assumed to be an interchange process between coordinated water and water in the second coordination sphere in which the main feature is the breaking of a Co-O bond, it follows that rearrangement can occur through a trigonal bipyramidal type of structure (Fig. 4.14). However, the authors[57] point out that the data cannot be explained by a single intermediate.

This situation is discussed in terms of Fig. 4.15. The reaction profile shown in Fig. 4.15a can account for the observed isomerization of *trans*

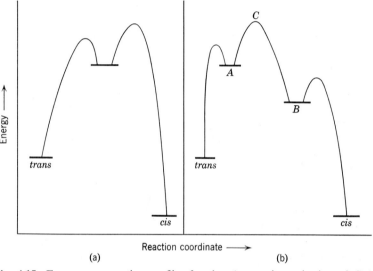

Fig. 4.15 Free energy reaction profiles for the *cis-trans* isomerization of Co(en)$_2$-(H$_2$O)$_2$$^{3+}$ through (a) one intermediate and (b) two intermediates. See text for discussion that supports reaction profile b.

to *cis* at a rate slightly less than that of water exchange of the *trans* isomer. However, it cannot account for the fact that the *cis* isomer undergoes water exchange at a rate that is approximately sixty-five times its rate of formation of the *trans* isomer. Clearly the intermediate in Fig. 4.15a would go to the *trans* isomer more readily than to the *cis*, because the difference in activation energies favors the rate formation of *trans*. This then requires that the rate of water exchange of the *cis* isomer be equal to or less than its rate of change to *trans*. Some other reaction profile such as Fig. 4.15b is required to explain also the rapid water exchange of *cis*-Co(en)$_2$(H$_2$O)$_2$$^{3+}$ compared to its rate of isomerization.

On the basis of this formulation the intermediates A and B can be regarded as being derived from the *trans* and the *cis* complexes, respectively, by the loss of a coordinated water molecule. Each of these can return to the initial substrates, suggesting that the intermediates have a tetragonal pyramidal type of structure (allows water exchange without rearrangement). The activated complex C, perhaps a trigonal bipyramidal structure, is then formed by further distortion of A and B to permit isomerization. Structure C can in fact be formulated as an intermediate, but this is not demanded by the data.

Because of the complications introduced by the presence of either the diaquo or the dihydroxo complexes, or both, in solutions of $Co(en)_2H_2$-OOH^{2+}, its reported rates of isomerization and water exchange are only approximate. However, at hydroxide ion concentrations greater than 0.01 M the only species present is $Co(en)_2(OH)_2^+$, and this has been subjected to detailed study. The results obtained show that in the isomerization of $Co(en)_2(OH)_2^+$ only a fraction of one oxygen per ion exchanges for each act of isomerization. This observation and the fact that $\Delta H^{\ddagger}$ for isomerization varies with temperature indicate that more than one mechanism operates in the isomerization of $Co(en)_2(OH)_2^+$. One of the paths may correspond to Co-O bond cleavage and the other to Co-N bond rupture, such a process being represented by this reaction scheme:

$$cis\text{-}Co(en)_2(OH)_2^+ \underset{\substack{\longleftarrow \\ Co-N}}{\overset{\substack{Co-O \\ \longrightarrow}}{\begin{array}{c} Co(en)_2OH^{2+} \\ (OH)_2(en)CoNH_2C_2H_4NH_2^+ \end{array}}} \underset{\substack{\longleftarrow \\ Co-N}}{\overset{\substack{Co-O \\ \longrightarrow}}{}} \text{---}trans\text{-}Co(en)_2(OH)_2^+ \tag{17}$$

Both paths can permit isomerization, but only that involving Co-O bond fission leads to exchange of oxygen with the solvent. It seems reasonable that the two processes should be able to compete, the lability of the Co-O bond being decreased by the loss of a proton from the water to bring it into the range of lability of the Co-N bond.

Finally, it is of interest to compare the rate of *cis* → *trans* isomerization of $Co(en)_2(H_2O)_2^{3+}$ with its rate of racemization. The specific rate of *cis* → *trans* is calculated as 1.2×10^{-7} sec^{-1} (Table 4.9). The half-life for racemization is approximately 50 days[17] at 25°, which permits an estimate of 1.6×10^{-7} sec^{-1} for the specific rate of the loss of opical activity. The agreement between these values probably is within the experimental error of the combined determinations entering into the comparisons. This suggests that the mechanism of racemization involves the formation of the optically inactive *trans* isomer. As represented here

$$(+)\text{-}cis\text{-}Co(en)_2(H_2O)_2^{3+} \rightleftharpoons trans\text{-}Co(en)_2(H_2O)_2^{3+} \rightleftharpoons$$

$$(-)\text{-}cis\text{-}Co(en)_2(H_2O)_2^{3+} \tag{18}$$

the *trans* isomer forms slowly and then rapidly returns to the (+) and (−) enantiomers with equal probability. One last point of interest is that both the rates of isomerization and of water exchange of $Co(en)_2(H_2O)_2^{3+}$ are much faster in the presence of charcoal (p. 330).

Aquoamminebis(ethylenediamine) Cobalt(III) Ions. The isomerization, racemization, and water exchange of *cis*- and *trans*-$Co(en)_2NH_3H_2O^{3+}$ and $Co(en)_2NH_3OH^{2+}$ have been studied in some detail.[60] This system differs from the one just discussed only in that it contains ammonia in place of a coordinated water molecule. Yet, as we will see, the two systems differ substantially in their behavior.

The rate of rearrangement of *trans*-$Co(en)_2NH_3H_2O^{3+}$ into the *cis* isomer at first increases with increasing pH and then becomes independent

Table 4.10 Rates of isomerization, racemization, and exchange for *cis* and *trans*-$Co(en)_2NH_3H_2O^{3+}$ and $Co(en)_2NH_3OH^{2+}$

Complex	Temp., °C	k_{isom}, sec^{-1}	k_{rac}, sec^{-1}	k_{exch}, sec^{-1}
trans-$Co(en)_2NH_3H_2O^{3+}$	30.0	5×10^{-8}	...	4.5×10^{-6}
trans-$Co(en)_2NH_3OH^{2+}$	30.0	2×10^{-5}	...	no exchange
cis-$Co(en)_2NH_3H_2O^{3+}$	25.0	...	3×10^{-8}	1.1×10^{-6}

From reference 60.

of pH. This is due to the formation of *trans*-$Co(en)_2NH_3OH^{2+}$, which isomerizes 400 times faster than the aquo complex. The rate of racemization of $(+)$-*cis*-$Co(en)_2NH_3H_2O^{3+}$ has a similar pH dependence. These observations are in accord with the following reaction scheme:

$$trans\text{-}Co(en)_2NH_3H_2O^{3+} \xrightleftharpoons{K_t} trans\text{-}Co(en)_2NH_3OH^{2+} + H^+$$

$$\downarrow slow \qquad\qquad\qquad \downarrow fast \qquad\qquad (19)$$

$$cis\text{-}Co(en)_2NH_3H_2O^{3+} \xrightleftharpoons{K_c} cis\text{-}Co(en)_2NH_3OH^{2+} + H^+$$

The acid-base equilibria, represented by constants K_t and K_c, are rapidly established. Investigations at low pH deal with only the aquo complexes, whereas at high pH only the hydroxo species are involved. Some of the kinetic data obtained are summarized in Table 4.10.

These data show that both *cis*- and *trans*-$Co(en)_2NH_3H_2O^{3+}$ exchange coordinated water with the solvent about 80 times faster than they rearrange. Even more significant is the observation that the isomerization of *trans*-$Co(en)_2NH_3OH^{2+}$ takes place with no detectable exchange of coordinated oxygen with the solvent. These results differ from those reported in the previous section for the analogous complexes

$Co(en)_2(H_2O)_2^{3+}$ and $Co(en)_2H_2O(OH)^{2+}$, where almost every exchange must result in steric change. For $trans$-$Co(en)_2NH_3H_2O^{3+}$ it is estimated that the activation energy for isomerization is approximately 5 kcal/mole greater than for water exchange. It follows that some of the water exchange takes place without rearrangement. This low-energy path can be considered to involve either dissociation through a tetragonal pyramidal structure or a cis-attack displacement. It is expected that a higher energy would be required for the reaction to go through a trigonal bipyramidal structure or for a $trans$-attack displacement. Either of these higher-energy paths permit steric change.

That the isomerization of $trans$-$Co(en)_2NH_3OH^{2+}$ into the cis isomer takes place without oxygen exchange shows that an intramolecular

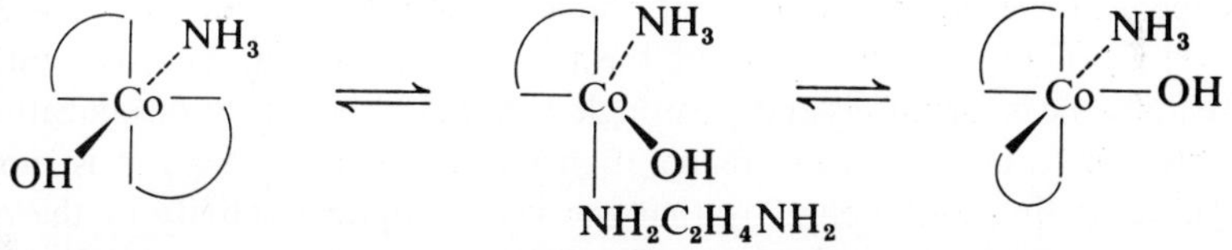

Fig. 4.16 Isomerization of cis- and $trans$-$Co(en)_2NH_3OH^{2+}$ by an intramolecular mechanism involving the opening and closing of a chelate ring.

mechanism must be involved. This can occur by some process in which none of the metal-ligand bonds is broken (p. 316) or, more likely, by the opening and reclosing of one of the ethylenediamine chelate rings (Fig. 4.16). The complete dissociation of ethylenediamine or ammonia does not occur, because under the experimental conditions used this would lead to decomposition and not isomerization. This chelate ring opening-closing mechanism is one of the reaction paths suggested for the isomerization of $Co(en)_2(OH)_2^+$.[57] Comparing complexes of the type Co $(en)_2LOH^{n+}$, we find that they undergo one of two reactions in aqueous solution, depending on the nature of the Co-L bond. When L = Cl, Br, or NCS, it is bound less strongly than ethylenediamine and aquation occurs with loss of L. When it is bound more strongly, L = NH_3 or OH, isomerization takes place by opening the chelate ring.

Dioxalatodiaquochromate(III) Ion. A solution of $K[Cr(H_2O)_2(C_2O_4)_2]$ at equilibrium consists almost entirely of the cis isomer, but if such a solution is allowed to evaporate slowly, the less soluble $trans$ isomer separates first.[61] The kinetics of isomerization[62] of the $trans$ isomer into the cis form, and of the racemization[63] of the optically active cis complex, in aqueous solution have been investigated. It was found that in the pH range 3–7 there is no dependence on pH for either the isomerization or the racemization. Furthermore, both rates are equal, having a specific rate constant of 4.3×10^{-4} sec^{-1} at 25°.

That the rates of isomerization and racemization do not depend on pH over this range indicates that the interchange of coordinated water with outer-sphere water is responsible for the steric changes. The rate of water exchange is not expected to depend on pH under conditions where the only species present is $Cr(H_2O)_2(C_2O_4)_2^-$. Unfortunately, water exchange studies have not been made, and we are left only with the plausible assumption that it does occur during rearrangement. Referring again to Fig. 4.14, it is clear that water exchange through this trigonal bipyramidal structure can provide a path for the change $trans \rightarrow cis$. The reverse process $cis \rightarrow trans$ has not been studied but must be very slow by comparison because the equilibrium is largely in the direction of the cis isomer. However, we recall that the rate of racemization of $(+)$-cis-$Cr(H_2O)_2(C_2O_4)_2^-$ is the same as the rate of $trans \rightarrow cis$. That the rates are the same is fortuitous and meaningless, but that the rate of racemization of the cis isomer is much greater than its rate of isomerization is most significant. It shows definitely that the loss of optical activity of the cis isomer cannot be due to its conversion into the $trans$, as appears to be true for $Co(en)_2(H_2O)_2^{3+}$ (18). This can be understood if cis-$Cr(H_2O)_2(C_2O_4)_2^-$ more readily generates the symmetrical trigonal bipyramidal structure, B, of Fig. 4.4 than structure A. Structure B easily permits racemization but not isomerization, in accord with the experimental results. Without reference to mechanistic details, the results require an overall process as represented by the equilibria

$$
trans\text{-}Cr(H_2O)_2(C_2O_4)_2^- \underset{\substack{\\ \text{fast}}}{\overset{}{\rule{0pt}{0pt}}}
\left[
\begin{array}{c}
\underset{slow}{\overset{fast}{\rightleftharpoons}} \;(+)\text{-}cis\text{-}Cr(H_2O)_2(C_2O_4)_2^- \\[2ex]
\Big\updownarrow {\scriptstyle fast} \\[2ex]
\underset{slow}{\overset{fast}{\rightleftharpoons}} \;(-)\text{-}cis\text{-}Cr(H_2O)_2(C_2O_4)_2^-
\end{array}
\right]
\qquad (20)
$$

In the pH range 0–2 the rates of isomerization and of racemization of the diaquo complex are both acid catalyzed. This shows that a reaction path different from that just described becomes important and contributes to the overall rate of steric change. Acid-catalyzed hydrolysis reactions of carboxalatometal complexes are common and are due to the addition of a proton to the carboxalato ligand, which in turn decreases its M-O bond strength (p. 220). For $Cr(H_2O)_2(C_2O_4)_2^-$ this permits the opening of the oxalato chelate ring to compete with water exchange as a route to rearrangement. In support of such a chelate opening-closing process is the observation that this mechanism is responsible for the racemization of $Cr(C_2O_4)_3^{3-}$ (p. 318).

1,10-*Bis(salicylideneamino)*-4,7-*dithiodecanecobalt(III) Ion.* The examples of *cis-trans* isomerization described above usually involve an intermolecular mechanism, whereas in the discussion to follow a unique example of isomerization by an intramolecular process is related. This example was found for a particular type of sexadentate complex of Co(III). Dwyer and Lions[64] have prepared many coordination compounds using sexadentate ligands of the type

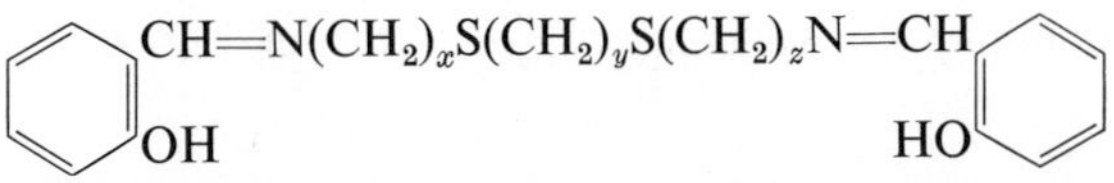

$$CH{=}N(CH_2)_xS(CH_2)_yS(CH_2)_zN{=}CH$$
$$OH \qquad\qquad HO$$

where x, y, and z may be either two or three. Whenever $x = y = z = 2$, a green Co(III) compound is isolated, whereas, if $x = y = z = 3$, a brown product is obtained. Since the C=N—C grouping must be linear, this is

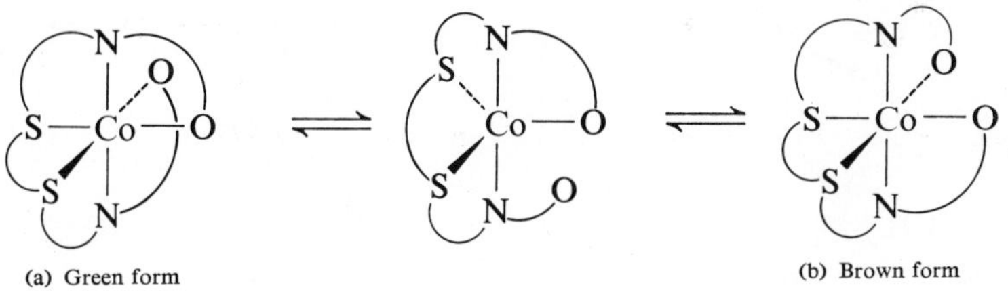

(a) Green form   (b) Brown form

Fig. 4.17 Intramolecular isomerization of 1,10-bis(salicylideneamine)-4,7-dithiodecane-cobalt(III) ion by a dissociation mechanism.

possible in the green compound, with rigid five-membered chelate rings, only if the two chelate rings formed by S—N—O lie in the same plane (Fig. 4.17). However, the greater flexibility of the six-membered chelate rings permits the existence of structure B, which is assigned to the brown form. Both the green and the brown forms were isolated for complexes in which either $x = z = 3$, $y = 2$, or $x = y = 3$, $z = 2$. The green isomer is the stable form in solution so that gentle warming of a solution of the brown cation results in its rearrangement to the green isomer. However, as the brown iodide is less soluble than the green, if a solution of the green iodide is heated it will slowly yield crystals of the brown iodide. Excellent proof that this isomerization takes place by an intramolecular process is offered by the observation that these optically active complexes isomerize without any loss of optical rotation. Thus, because of the extremely limited freedom of movement of the sexadentate ligand, the oxygen atoms must interchange position by way of a trigonal bipyramid intermediate (Fig. 4.17). The only difference between this intramolecular process and the intermolecular mechanisms described earlier is that in this complex the ligand atom that becomes unattached is not liberated into the solution but rather is held in the coordination sphere as part of the chelate molecule. It would appear that an aquo intermediate may form when the chelating group behaves as a quinquidentate. Therefore reference to this as an intramolecular process is not strictly correct.

Tris(1,1,1-*trifluoro*-2,4-*pentanediono*)*metal*(*III*) *Complexes.* Fay and Piper[65] have prepared and characterized geometrical isomers of several octahedral metal complexes of unsymmetrical β-diketones. The *cis-trans* isomers found in such systems are illustrated in Fig. 4.18. A properly

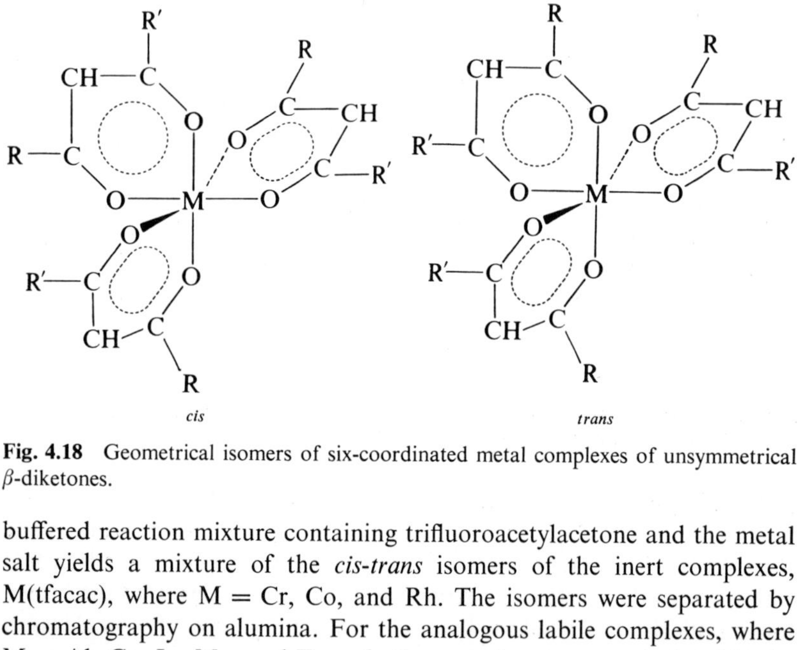

Fig. 4.18   Geometrical isomers of six-coordinated metal complexes of unsymmetrical β-diketones.

buffered reaction mixture containing trifluoroacetylacetone and the metal salt yields a mixture of the *cis-trans* isomers of the inert complexes, M(tfacac), where M = Cr, Co, and Rh. The isomers were separated by chromatography on alumina. For the analogous labile complexes, where M = Al, Ga, In, Mn, and Fe, only the *trans* isomers were isolated in the solid state.

Infrared, visible, and ultraviolet spectra are of no aid in the assignment of isomeric configurations of these complexes. The *cis* and *trans* isomers give nearly identical spectra. They have been distinguished by means of proton and fluorine magnetic resonance spectra and x-ray powder patterns. For the *cis* isomer all three methyl groups, all three CH protons, and all three trifluoromethyl groups are equivalent by a threefold rotation axis; in the *trans* isomer these are not equivalent. Therefore, the structures of the inert diamagnetic complexes of Co(III) and Rh(III) were assigned on the basis that the *cis* isomer is the one which exhibits a single n.m.r. line at each position whereas the *trans* isomer gives multiple resonances. A comparison of the crystal isomorphism of these isomers of known structures with that of the other compounds isolated allowed an assignment of structure to all of the solid metal chelates. For the inert complexes it was found that the more soluble and less easily eluted isomers from the alumina column gave single n.m.r. resonance lines and were, therefore, the *cis* isomers. The labile complexes were isomorphous with the *trans* isomers and hence had the *trans* structure.

It should not be inferred that failure to isolate both isomers for the labile complexes is due to the reaction producing only one isomer, but rather that equilibria between isomers are rapidly established and the less soluble *trans* form is the only one that separates from solution. In fact,

Table 4.11 Thermodynamic data for *trans*-M(tfacac)$_3$ ⇌ *cis*-M(tfacac)$_3$ in CHCl$_3$ at 25°

	$\Delta G°$, kcal/mole	$\Delta H°$, kcal/mole	$\Delta S°$, eu
Al(tfacac)$_3$	0.897 ± 0.016	0.24	−2.2
Ga(tfacac)$_3$	0.930 ± 0.016	0.47	−1.5
Co(tfacac)$_3$	0.887 ± 0.046	0.34	−1.8

From reference 65.

the n.m.r. spectra of these systems show that in solution both *cis* and *trans* isomers are present. Such an equilibration also occurs slowly for the inert complexes, and some thermodynamic data for this isomerization

$$trans\text{-M(tfacac)}_3 \rightleftharpoons cis\text{-M(tfacac)}_3 \qquad (21)$$

are given in Table 4.11. The enthalpy and entropy make approximately equal contributions to the small free energy difference between the two geometric structures. It is of interest to note that, for these three examples, the metal seems to play a minor role because the difference in free energy between the two isomers is about the same in each case.

Of primary interest here are the investigations of the rates of isomerization (21) and a discussion of its probable mechanism.[66] The rates of isomerization were estimated by determining the temperature at which the fluorine resonance spectra of chloroform solutions of the compounds coalesced to give single sharp resonance lines (Fig. 4.19). The coalescence of these resonance lines is attributed to all three of the trifluoromethyl groups becoming equivalent because of the rapid interchange of positions. This exchange may be viewed as a very rapid isomerization, and its rate is estimated from the temperature of coalescence.[67] The activation energies were calculated from the Arrhenius equation, using the frequency factor (10^{15} sec^{-1}) determined independently for the *cis* to *trans* isomerization of

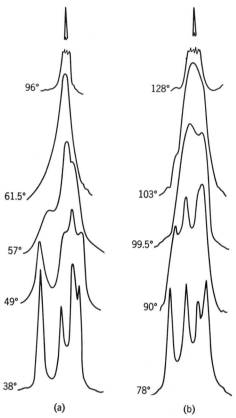

Fig. 4.19   Fluorine resonance spectra of (a) Ga(tfacac)₃ and (b) Al(tfacac)₃ at several temperatures near the coalescence region. From reference 66.

Co(tfacac)$_3$. The data obtained are given in Table 4.12. It is of interest to note that the activation energies are of reasonable magnitude, and the order, In < Ga < Al < Co < Rh, is in agreement with qualitative estimates for the relative bond energies in this series.

Turning our attention now to a consideration of the mechanism of these stereochemical rearrangements, we must first try to distinguish between an intermolecular and an intramolecular process (these processes are discussed in the section on racemization starting on p. 300). The intermolecular mechanism is one which requires the complete departure of coordinated ligand and its random mixing with any free ligand in solution:

$$M(tfacac)_3 \rightleftharpoons M(tfacac)_2{}^+ + tfacac^-$$

or $\qquad\qquad\qquad\qquad\qquad\qquad\qquad\qquad\qquad\qquad\qquad$ (22)

$$M(tfacac)_3 + tfacac^- \rightleftharpoons M(tfacac)_3 + tfacac^-$$

Table 4.12   Kinetic data for the isomerization
cis-M(tfacac)$_3$ → $trans$-M(tfacac)$_3$ in DCCl$_3$

M	Coalesence Temp., °C	k, sec^{-1} a	E_a, kcal/mole
In(III)	< −57	>36	<13.5 ± 1.1
Ga(III)	61.5	38	20.8 ± 1.6
Al(III)	103	34	23.5 ± 1.8
Co(III)	>182	1.45×10^{-3}	30.7 ± 0.6
Rh(III)	>182	$<9.2 \times 10^{-7}$	>42.4

From reference 66.
a Data for Al(III) and Ga(III) refer to the coalescence temperatures, whereas data for In(III), Co(III), and Rh(III) refer to −57, 99.2, and 163°, respectively.

Evidence for the rejection of this mechanism is provided by an investigation of the fluorine n.m.r. spectra of In(tfacac)$_3$ and Al(tfacac)$_3$ above the coalesence temperatures in the presence of excess trifluoroacetylacetone. An intermolecular process requires the coalescence of the added trifluoroacetylacetone resonance with the resonance due to the complex near 130° for Al(tfacac)$_3$ and at less than −39° for In(tfacac)$_3$. In contrast, even at temperatures above this, the spectra consist of two sharp resonance lines, one corresponding to the compounds and one to the free ligand. For the inert systems of Co(III) and Rh(III), it should be possible to check this mechanism by using isotopically labeled tfacac.

The results obtained for the Al(III) and In(III) systems suggest that these rearrangements involve an intramolecular mechanism. Several possibilities of this type exist, including twisting mechanisms and chelate ring opening-closing processes (see Fig. 4.24, p. 316). Bailar[68] and others[69] have independently suggested a trigonal twist mechanism in which racemization is achieved by twisting three of the ligands through an angle of 120° about the C_3 axis of the octahedron. Although such a process can provide a path for racemization, it is readily seen in Fig. 4.20 that this mechanism does not permit cis-$trans$ isomerization in the systems M(tfacac)$_3$.

Both the rhombic twist mechanism proposed by Ray and Dutt[70] and the bond rupture process suggested by Werner[71] can give simultaneous racemization and isomerization. The two mechanisms are pictured in Fig. 4.21. In the rhombic twist mechanism, two of the chelate rings move through an angle of 90° in opposite directions about axes which pass through the metal ion perpendicular to their own planes, while the third chelate ring remains essentially unchanged. The bond rupture mechanism

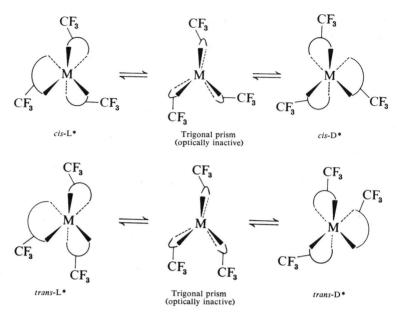

cis-L*   Trigonal prism
(optically inactive)

cis-D*

trans-L*   Trigonal prism
(optically inactive)

trans-D*

Fig. 4.20 Failure of *cis* ⇌ *trans* isomerization of M(tfacac)₃ by the trigonal (Bailar) twist mechanism. The process provides a path for racemization without isomerization.‡

cis-L*

(a)

(b)

trans-D*

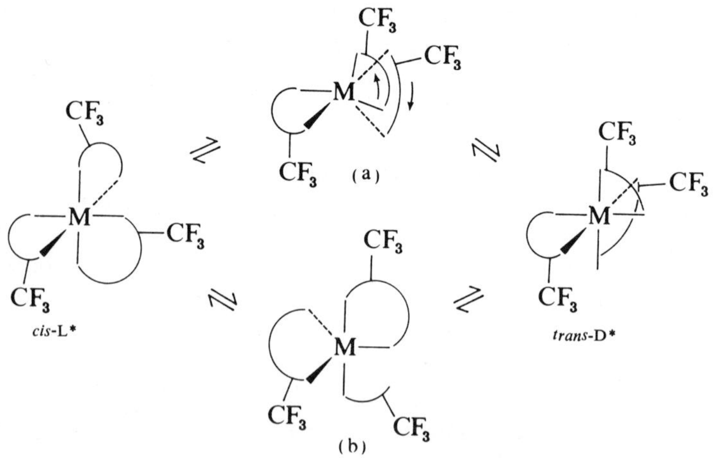

Fig. 4.21 Simultaneous *cis-trans* isomerization and inversion of M(tfacac)₃ by the rhombic (Ray and Dutt) twist (a) and the bond rupture (b) mechanisms. Similarly *trans*-L* may be converted to *cis*-D* or *trans*-D*.‡

‡ Springer and Sievers (*Inorg. Chem.*, in press) have recently pointed out that two other twisting mechanisms are possible. One of these involves a twist about a pseudo-C_3 axis of a *tris* complex, and in such a case racemization is accompanied by isomerization. Another can occur by the Bailar twist about a C_3 axis holding the chelate rings rigid. This results in racemization without isomerization.

is similar to dissociation processes considered earlier; here the intermediate is represented as a trigonal bipyramid in which the dangling ligand occupies an axial position. It should be realized that this is an arbitrary choice; other possibilities exist, including intermediates containing coordinated solvent to maintain a coordination number of six.

The mechanism of the isomerization of the M(tfacac)$_3$ compounds must at present remain somewhat equivocal. Attempts to calculate the activation energies for the rhombic twist and the bond rupture processes using a point charge model were not successful in predicting a preference for one process over the other.[66] Two pieces of experimental evidence have been cited in favor of a bond rupture process. The first is the high frequency factor of exp (15.19 $\pm$ 0.37) sec^{-1} found for the cis to trans conversion of Co(tfacac)$_3$, which is believed not to be consistent with the rhombic twist mechanism. A much lower value may be expected for a twisting process because of the low entropy of such a constrained structure. Secondly, the rate of isomerization of Al(tfacac)$_3$ increases with increasing dielectric constant of the solvent. This suggests a greater charge separation in the transition state than in the ground state and supports a bond rupture process. The expected dipole moments of the rhombic twist intermediates are less than that of the cis isomer and comparable to that of the trans isomer, predicting less charge separation in the transition state than in the ground state.

Linkage Isomerization

Nitrito-Nitro. Nitrito (M—ONO) complexes of Co(III) were first described by Jørgensen,[72] who also observed that they rearrange to the corresponding nitro (M—NO$_2$) compounds. The suggestion[73] that nitrito complexes do not exist has been proven to be incorrect,[74] and there is indeed an abundance of experimental evidence in support of nitrito-nitro isomerizations in complex ions. The ultraviolet and visible spectra of the two isomers differ, with the d-d absorption band for M—ONO being at longer wavelengths (weaker crystal field strength) than for M—NO$_2$. The two types of bonding are readily distinguished by differences in the i.r. spectra (Fig. 4.22), the best diagnostic regions being 1060 cm^{-1}, where a strong band is assigned to M—ONO stretching vibrations, and 820 cm^{-1}, assigned to M—NO$_2$ deformation vibrations.[74c] The mechanism of formation of nitrito complexes was described earlier (p. 230). The discussion that follows will summarize what is known about the process of conversion of nitrito complexes into the corresponding stable nitro form.

Adell[75] has made an extensive investigation of the nitrito-nitro isomerization. Some of his data are collected in Table 4.13 along with references.

The rates of rearrangement were determined spectrophotometrically, and in all cases the data were found to give a first-order plot. Measurements were made on the solid salts as well as their aqueous solutions, with the observed result that isomerization is ten to one hundred times faster in solution. This can be only approximate because the rate of isomerization of the solids depends on the anion portion of the salt, e.g., $[Co(NH_3)_5$ $(ONO)]X_2$, where $X = Cl^-$, I^-, and NO_3^- in Table 4.13. Likewise in

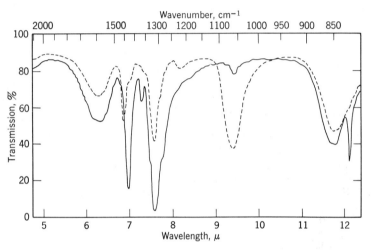

Fig. 4.22   Infrared absorption spectra of the complexes:, —nitropentamminecobalt(III) chloride, $[Co(NH_3)_5NO_2]Cl_2$; – – –, nitritopentamminecobalt(III) chloride, $[Co(NH_3)_5$-$ONO]Cl_2$. From reference 74c.

these investigations the solid state reactions were regarded as first-order processes in which nitrito is completely converted to nitro, but i.r. studies[81] show that the isomerization of $[Co(NH_3)_5(ONO)]Cl_2$ in potassium chloride disks is essentially an equilibrium process. Therefore, the data in Table 4.13a should be used with some reservations. It was concluded that, since the solid salts isomerize, this must happen by an intramolecular process. Such need not necessarily be true of rearrangements in solution. However, it was suggested[79] that an intramolecular process must also be the mechanism in solution because the rates of isomerization in solutions containing no excess nitrite ion are far too great to be compatible with an intermolecular process. That this is correct was then conclusively demonstrated by studies with ^{18}O.

It was found[82] that neither the oxygen attached to cobalt and nitrogen nor that attached only to nitrogen exchanges with the solvent or with

Table 4.13   Rates of nitrito-nitro isomerization at 20°C

Complex	k_1, sec^{-1}	k_2, sec^{-1}	E_{a_1}, kcal/mole	E_{a_2}, kcal/mole	Ref.
	(a) *Solids*				
[Co(NH$_3$)$_5$(ONO)]Cl$_2$	9.2×10^{-7}	...	22	...	75
[Co(NH$_3$)$_5$(ONO)]I$_2$	1.6×10^{-7}	...	26	...	75
[Co(NH$_3$)$_5$(ONO)](NO$_3$)$_2$	4.5×10^{-6}	...	21.9	...	75
[Rh(NH$_3$)$_5$(ONO)]Cl$_2$	5.5×10^{-5}	(22°C)	19	...	80
[Ir(NH$_3$)$_5$(ONO)]Cl$_2$	4.2×10^{-6}	(32°C)	23	...	80
[Pt(NH$_3$)$_5$(ONO)]Cl$_3$	8.7×10^{-5}	(51°C)	...	...	80
trans-[Co(en)$_2$(NCS)(ONO)]I	3.8×10^{-7}	...	25.5	...	75
trans-[Co(en)$_2$(NCS)(ONO)]ClO$_4$	2.7×10^{-7}	...	25.1	...	75
trans-[Co(py)$_2$(NH$_3$)$_2$(ONO)$_2$]NO$_3$	3.3×10^{-6}	$7 \times 10^{-7 \, a}$	19.9	24.7	76
cis-[Co(en)$_2$(ONO)$_2$]NO$_3$	5×10^{-6}	$7 \times 10^{-7 \, a}$	19.3	25.0	77
trans-[Co(en)$_2$(ONO)$_2$]NO$_3$	5×10^{-7}	$1 \times 10^{-6 \, a}$	28.0	23.8	77
	(b) *Aqueous Solutions*				
Co(NH$_3$)$_5$(ONO)$^{2+}$	1.7×10^{-5}	...	22.6	...	79
Rh(NH$_3$)$_5$(ONO)$^{2+}$	9.6×10^{-4}	(25°C)	19	...	80
Ir(NH$_3$)$_5$(ONO)$^{2+}$	4.4×10^{-5}	(25°C)	20	...	80
Co(NH$_3$)$_4$(H$_2$O)(ONO)$^{2+}$	3.8×10^{-4}	(30°C)	...	...	58
cis-Co(NH$_3$)$_4$(ONO)$_2$$^+$	1.8×10^{-4}	...	8.3	...	58
cis-Co(en)$_2$(NO$_2$)(ONO)$^+$	7.5×10^{-4}	(35°C)	...	...	79

^{a} Dinitrito complexes rearrange stepwise in the solid; thus k_1 is the value estimated for the formation of nitrito-nitro, and k_2 for its conversion to the final product dinitro.

added nitrite ion in the transformation

$$(NH_3)_5Co-*ONO^{2+}$$

$$\text{or} \qquad \xrightarrow[\text{NO}_2^-]{\text{H}_2\text{O}} (NH_3)_5Co-N*O_2^{2+} \qquad (23)$$

$$(NH_3)_5Co-ON*O^{2+}$$

The same result was obtained with *cis*-Co(en)$_2$(NO$_2$)(ONO)$^+$. Furthermore, this optically active cation mutarotates, with no racemization, at the same rate as it isomerizes to the dinitro complex.[83] These results furnish excellent proof of the fact that the nitrito ligand is not released from the immediate coordination sphere of the complex during its rearrangement to the nitro form. An $S_N i$ (*substitution, nucleophilic internal displacement*) type of mechanism has been suggested:

$$(NH_3)_5Co-ONO^{2+} \rightarrow (NH_3)_5Co \overset{O^{2+}}{\underset{N-O}{\Big|}} \rightarrow (NH_3)_5Co-NO_2^{2+} \qquad (24)$$

One other point of interest is the observation[78] that the rates of isomerization in aqueous solution are retarded by the presence of acid. Different acids show different effects, and the efficiency decreases in the order $HCl > HClO_4 > HNO_3$. Although this acid retardation of the rate of isomerization at low acid concentration does not appear to be accompanied by decomposition, it was found[82] that, if nitrogen is bubbled through a reaction mixture with ~ 0.07 N acid, small quantities of oxides of nitrogen and the aquo complex are detected. Since the rate of water exchange of $Co(NH_3)_5H_2O^{3+}$ in this acid region is essentially independent of hydrogen ion concentration,[84] the replacement of coordinated water by nitrite ion would seem not to be operative. It has been suggested[82] that the decreased rate of formation of $Co(NH_3)_5NO_2^{2+}$ in slightly acid solutions is due to an equilibrium which removes a portion of the nitrito complex,

$$(NH_3)_5Co-OH_2^{3+} + HNO_2 \underset{H_3O^+}{\overset{fast}{\rightleftharpoons}}$$

$$(NH_3)_5Co-ONO^{2+} \overset{slow}{\longrightarrow} (NH_3)_5Co-NO_2^{2+} \quad (25)$$

That different acids have different effects for the same hydrogen ion concentration is perhaps due to salt or ion-pair effects or both.

Thiocyanato-isothiocyanato. For a long time examples of linkage isomerism in metal complexes were restricted to the nitrito-nitro systems. Recently linkage isomers involving other ambidentate ligands have been reported (see Table 1.3, p. 13), but none of these has as yet been extensively investigated. Some observations of interest here have been made on the thiocyanato (M—SCN) and isothiocyanato (M—NCS) isomers. The type of bonding can be determined from the d-d spectra of the complexes,[85] since the ligand field strength of —NCS⁻ ($\sim N_3^-$) is greater than that of —SCN⁻ ($\sim Br^-$), which means that M—NCS absorbs at a higher frequency than does M—SCN. For the difference in the ultraviolet absorption spectra of two such isomers see Fig. 4.23. The i.r. spectra are also very diagnostic,[86] the most reliable feature being the C—N stretching band, which is sharp and above 2000 cm^{-1} for S-bonded complexes and broad and below 2000 cm^{-1} for N-bonded complexes. The presence of a C—S stretching frequency of $780–860 \text{ cm}^{-1}$ is indicative of M-NCS bonding, whereas a frequency of *ca.* 700 cm^{-1} indicates M-SCN bonding. However, the first overtone of the NCS deformation mode has a band at $800–880 \text{ cm}^{-1}$, which may be erroneously assigned as the C—S stretching band of a M—NCS complex. The NCS deformation mode can be used to characterize the bond type, being a single band at $460–490 \text{ cm}^{-1}$ for N-thiocyanates and a band at $410–440 \text{ cm}^{-1}$, with weaker satellites at higher frequencies, for S-thiocyanates. Recent studies[86b] show that the integrated intensity of the C—N stretching absorption band is in the range $0.8–2.3 \times 10^4$ $M^{-1} \text{ cm}^{-2}$ for the M—SCN and in the range $9–12 \times 10^4$ $M^{-1} \text{ cm}^{-2}$ for the M—NCS systems.

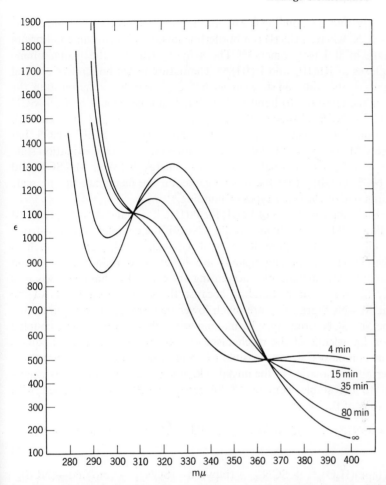

Fig. 4.23 Changes in the absorption spectrum of a solution of [(Et₄dien)Pd—SCN]PF₆ at 25°. The final spectrum, ∞, is that known for [(Et₄dien)Pd—NCS]PF₆.

The M—SCN and M—NCS linkage isomers of Pd(II) that have been isolated and characterized are at present limited to the following complexes: $Pd(As(C_6H_5)_3)_2X_2$, $Pd(bipy)X_2$, and $Pd(Et_4dien)X^+$, [88] where X is either S- or N-bonded SCN^-, bipy = 2,2′-bipyridine, and $Et_4dien = (C_2H_5)_2NC_2H_4 NHC_2H_4N(C_2H_5)_2$. The presence of linkage isomers of CdX_4^{2-} has been detected in aqueous solution[89] and of $Mn(CO)_5X$ in certain solvents.[90] The unstable isomer $(H_2O)_5Cr—SCN$ has also been obtained in water solution.[91a] Class (a) metals[92] (hard acids[93]) prefer to bond M—NCS, whereas class (b) metals (soft acids) prefer to bond M—SCN (see p. 19 and p. 23). For example, in the triad Zn(II), Cd(II), and Hg(II), Zn(II) is class (a) and the bonding is Zn—NCS, but Hg(II) is class (b) and bonds Hg—SCN, whereas Cd(II) is a borderline metal and forms an equilibrium mixture of linkage isomers.[89a] The same is true for the pentaammine complexes of Rh(III) and Ir(III).[89b] The nature of the bonding of a metal depends on its oxidation state; in general, the lower the oxidation state, the greater the tendency to bond with sulfur. Examples would be Cu^I—SCN and Cu^{II}—NCS. However, the point has been made that at some high oxidation state a metal may revert to S bonding, e.g., Mo^{III}—NCS, but possibly Mo^V—SCN.[94] Finally, for a given metal at a fixed oxidation state there may be such a small difference in energy between M—SCN and M—NCS, bonding that the other ligands on the metal can tip the scale towards one or the other types of bonding.[88, 90]

Considering complexes of Pd(II) [or Pt(II)], it is found that the preferred bonding of Pd—SCN changes to Pd—NCS if the complex contains strong π-bonding ligands such as R_3P[95] or if it contains bulky groups, such as Et_4dien.[88] The π-bonding ligands are believed to reduce the electron density on the metal, thus decreasing its class (b) character, whereas bulky ligands favor N bonding because the steric requirements of the linear M—NCS grouping are much lower than the angular requirements of the M—SCN grouping.[96] By making use of these observations, coupled with a knowledge of the mechanism of substitution reactions in square planar complexes, it was possible to design the appropriate experiments to permit the isolation of the unstable kinetic product before its rearrangement to the stable isomer.[87, 88b] Successful results were obtained with reactions of the types

$$Pd(SCN)_4{}^{2+} + Et_4dien \xrightarrow{0°} (Et_4dien)Pd—SCN^+ \xrightarrow{\Delta} (Et_4dien)Pd—NCS^+$$

$$\text{(26)}$$

$$Pd(bipy)(H_2O)_2{}^{2+} + SCN^- \xrightarrow{0°} (bipy)Pd—(SCN)_2 \xrightarrow{\Delta} (bipy)Pd—(NCS)_2$$

$$\text{(27)}$$

These methods work because substitution reactions of Pd(II) are extremely fast, and the first steps in both reactions 26 and 27 are complete within the time of mixing. There is then time to isolate the unstable S-bonded isomer in 26 because the presence of the bulky ligand decreases the rate of reaction of the Pd(II) complex by a factor of more than 10^6 (see p. 414). Reaction 27 works because sulfur is a better nucleophile towards Pd(II) than is nitrogen and because the non-ionic product separates from solution as it is formed.

It is not possible to examine the kinetics of isomerization of $Pd[As(C_6H_5)_3]_2X_2$ in solution by conventional techniques, because it is much too fast and the spectra of solutions of the two isomers are identical. In

Table 4.14   Rates of isomerization and reaction of $(Et_4dien)Pd$—SCN^+ at 25° in 0.1 M $NaClO_4$

Reaction	10^3k, sec^{-1}	$\Delta H^{\ddagger}$, kcal/mole	$\Delta S^{\ddagger}$, eu
Pd—SCN $\rightarrow$ Pd—NCS	1.1	16.2	−19.6
Pd—SCN $\rightarrow$ Pd—Br	1.1	16.2	−19.6
Pd—NCS $\rightarrow$ Pd—Br	0.51	18.4	−13.7

From reference 88*b*.

the solid state rate constants of 3.5×10^{-5} and 7.8×10^{-5} sec^{-1} at 126° and 147°, respectively, were obtained for the isomerization of this Pd—SCN isomer into the Pd—NCS form.[87] That isomerization takes place in the solid state suggests that it may proceed by an intramolecular process in the solid. However, in solution the mechanism may differ, and it appears that the isomerization of $(Et_4dien)Pd$—SCN^+, which is slow enough to measure in solution, proceeds by a dissociation process.[88b] Changes in the absorption spectrum of an aqueous solution of $(Et_4dien)Pd$—SCN^+ upon standing are shown in Fig. 4.23. The presence of two isosbestic points is a good indication of there being only two species in solution, and the final spectrum corresponds to that of the stable isomer $(Et_4dien)Pd$—NCS^+. Kinetic data on the rate of isomerization and on the rates of reaction of both isomers are given in Table 4.14. The rates of reaction with Br$^-$ are independent of its concentration for this pseudo-octahedral complex (p. 416). That the kinetic parameters are all identical for the reaction of Br$^-$ with $(Et_4dien)Pd$—SCN^+ and for its isomerization suggests that isomerization proceeds by an intermolecular process:

$$(Et_4dien)Pd\text{—}SCN^+ \xrightarrow[\text{or } k_{Br^-}]{k_{iso}} (Et_4dien)Pd^{2+} + SCN^- \qquad (28)$$

with fast pathways to $(Et_4dien)Pd$—NCS^+ and $(Et_4dien)PdBr^+$ via Br^-.

This is further supported by the fact that the N-bonded isomer reacts with Br$^-$ at a slower rate than does the S-bonded form. The solvent water is not shown in equation 28, but it must play an important role and the active intermediate is perhaps the aquo complex. It seems reasonable that an intermolecular mechanism should be involved for isomerization, because, unlike NO_2^-, the group SCN$^-$ is linear and a prohibitive amount of energy may be required to bend it in an S_Ni intramolecular process (24).

It has long been believed that the transfer of an unsymmetrical bridging group in an inner-sphere electron transfer reaction

$$(NH_3)_5Co\text{—}NCS^{2+} + Cr(H_2O)_6^{2+} \rightarrow (NH_3)_5Co\cdots NCS\cdots Cr(H_2O)_5^{4+}$$

$$\xrightarrow[H_2O]{H^+} NH_4^+ + Co(H_2O)_6^{2+} + NCS\text{—}Cr(H_2O)_5^{2+} \qquad (29)$$

would, under certain circumstances, yield the unstable linkage isomer.[91b] Early attempts to use this approach to prepare and isolate salts of $(H_2O)_5Cr\text{—}SCN^+$ were not successful.[91c,d] Recently it has been possible to utilize this type of reaction to prepare aqueous solutions containing this S-bonded isomer, and the kinetics of its aquation and isomerization have been investigated.[91a] As expected, the rates are acid dependent, and the overall rate constant, k_{obs}, is given by the equation

$$k_{obs} = (k_{H_2O} + k_{iso}) + (k'_{H_2O} + k'_{iso})K'_a/[H^+] \qquad (30)$$

where k_{H_2O}, k'_{H_2O}, k_{iso}, and k'_{iso} are the rate constants for aquation and isomerization of $(H_2O)_5Cr\text{—}SCN^{2+}$ and $OH(H_2O)_4Cr\text{—}SCN^+$, respectively and K'_a is the acid ionization constant of the pentaaquo complex. At $25°$, a plot of k_{obs} versus $1/[H^+]$ gives $(k_{H_2O} + k_{iso}) = 6.3 \times 10^{-5}$ sec^{-1} and $(k'_{H_2O} + k'_{iso})K'_a = 1.45 \times 10^{-5}$ sec^{-1}. The ratio k_{H_2O}/k_{iso} is about two, as shown by the values of the rate constants $k_{H_2O} = 4.0 \times 10^{-5}$ sec^{-1}, $k_{iso} = 2.3 \times 10^{-5}$ sec^{-1}, $k'_{H_2O}K'_a = 9.3 \times 10^{-6}$ M^{-1} sec^{-1}, and $k'_{iso}K'_a = 5.2 \times 10^{-6}$ M^{-1} sec^{-1}.

Since the rate of isomerization of $(H_2O)_5Cr\text{—}SCN^{2+}$ is comparable to its rate of aquation, for isomerization to occur it is necessary that the N-bonded isomer form before the SCN^- leaves the sphere of influence of Cr(III). If this were not the case only the stable hexaaquo complex would result, and there would be no isomerization. For the reason stated above, it seems unlikely that an S_Ni intramolecular mechanism can be operative. Much more plausible is an intermolecular process, but one in which the SCN^- remains associated with the complex, thus permitting it to rearrange and re-enter the complex to give the stable N-bonded form. The ion-pair mechanism proposed[91a] for the isomerization of $(H_2O)_5Cr\text{—}SCN^{2+}$ is shown by the reaction scheme

$$(H_2O)_5Cr\text{—}SCN^{2+}$$

$$(H_2O)_5Cr^{3+}, NCS^- \leftarrow (H_2O)_5Cr^{3+}, SCN^- \rightleftharpoons (H_2O)_5Cr^{3+} + SCN^- \qquad (31)$$

$$(H_2O)_5Cr\text{—}NCS^{2+} \qquad Cr(H_2O)_6^{3+} \qquad Cr(H_2O)_6^{3+}$$

This assumes that the dissociation of the ion pair $(H_2O)_5Cr^{3+}$, SCN^- is relatively slow compared to either its rearrangement to give the N-bonded isomer or its reaction with water. This type of mechanism has been proposed for the isomerization of benzhydryl thiocyanate in acetonitrile.[91e] The isomerization of $(H_2O)_5Cr—SCN^{2+}$ just described deals with its spontaneous isomerization. There is also a Cr(II)-catalyzed path, which presumably takes place through the bridged activated complex $(H_2O)_5$-$Cr \cdots SCN \cdots Cr(H_2O)_5{}^{4+}$.

Recent studies[97a] have made use of a reaction corresponding to 29 to prepare a solution of the unstable isomer $(H_2O)_5Cr—NC^{2+}$:

$$(NH_3)_5CoCN^{2+} + Cr(H_2O)_6{}^{2+} \rightarrow (NH_3)_5Co \cdots CN \cdots Cr(H_2O)_5{}^{4+}$$

$$\xrightarrow[H_2O]{H^+} NH_4^+ + Co(H_2O)_6{}^{2+} + CN—Cr(H_2O)_5{}^{2+} \qquad (32)$$

Since its rate of formation is faster than its rate of isomerization to $(H_2O)_5Cr—CN^{2+}$, it was possible to investigate the kinetics of isomerization. This obeys a first-order rate equation with $k_{iso} = 9 \times 10^{-3}$ sec^{-1} at 15° in 1 M HClO$_4$. The rate constant is a function of [H$^+$], increasing with rising acid concentration. This acid catalysis is perhaps due to the addition of H$^+$ to the coordinated CN$^-$, which then facilitates its rearrangement to yield the stable C-bonded isomer. Such an effect may be similar to that found for the acid-catalyzed exchange of cyanide ion with metal cyanide complexes (p. 216). It is significant that the isomerization of $(H_2O)_5Cr—NC^{2+}$ is not catalyzed by the presence of Cr(II), and that isomerization takes place without simultaneous aquation. These facts suggest that isomerization proceeds by essentially an intramolecular process. It has also been possible to detect[97b] the presence of CN—Co-(CN)$_5{}^{3-}$ in solutions resulting from the reaction of $(NH_3)_5Co—CN^{2+}$ with Co(CN)$_5{}^{3-}$. At 25° the rate of isomerization, CN—Co(CN)$_5{}^{3-} \rightarrow$ Co(CN)$_6{}^{3-}$, has a half-life of 1.6 sec, but the mechanism of isomerization is not known.

Although in simple metal cyanides M—CN bonding always seems to be preferred over M—NC, it is known that when CN$^-$ functions as a bridging group the bonding is M—C≡N—M. Shriver et al.[97c] has investigated mixed metal cyanide polymers such as K[Fe—(CN)$_6$—Mn] and estimated the site preference energies on the basis of the C.F.S.E. for the two linkage isomers. He found that the site preference energies show a good correlation with actual structures. On this basis it appeared that K[Cr^{III}—(CN)$_6$—Fe^{II}] should be less stable than K[Fe^{II}—(CN)$_6$—Cr^{III}], and it was possible to design an experiment to prepare the less stable isomer.

$$Cr(CN)_6{}^{3-} \xrightarrow{K^+, Fe^{2+}} K[Cr^{III}—(CN)_6—Fe^{II}] \xrightarrow{100°} K[Fe^{II}—(CN)_6—Cr^{III}]$$
$$\qquad\qquad\quad \text{Brick red} \qquad\qquad\qquad\qquad \text{Dark green}$$
$$(33)$$

Upon heating the red precipitate the stable green isomer is formed, and it is interesting that this isomerization can take place so readily in such a polymeric structure.

It has been possible to prepare metal complexes containing two co-ordinated thiocyanate ions one of which is N bonded and the other S bonded, e.g.,

The stability of this unique compound[97d] appears to be due to the presence of the unsymmetrical bidentate ligand. This requires that one thiocyanate anion be *trans* to phosphorus and the other *trans* to arsenic. Because of the different *trans* effects of these groups, one thiocyanate is N and one is S bonded to Pd(II), but it is not yet known which is opposite P or As. The compound Pd(4,4'-dimethyl-2,2'-bipyridine) (NCS) (SCN) has been reported.[97e] The compound reported as Cu(tren) (NCS) (SCN) has been shown to be [Cu(tren)NCS]SCN,[97f] where tren = $N(C_2H_4NH_2)_3$.

In addition to discussing the chemistry of certain linkage isomers, this section provides some convincing examples of how theories of reaction and of bonding can be used to design methods of syntheses of new metal complexes.

Racemization of Octahedral Complexes

The racemization of optically active coordination compounds often is rapid compared to that of carbon compounds. It should of course be remembered that, just as there are carbon compounds which racemize rapidly, there are also coordination compounds which racemize very slowly. Labile complexes racemize rapidly and in most cases it has not been possible to resolve ions of this type.[98] However, the resolution of certain labile complexes such as $Al(C_2O_4)_3{}^{3-}$, $Ga(C_2O_4)_3{}^{3-}$, $Fe(C_2O_4)_3{}^{3-}$, $Cd(en)_3{}^{2+}$, and $Zn(en)_3{}^{2+}$ has been reported (Table 4.15). Attempts to repeat the resolution of the Al(III), Cd(II), and Zn(II) complexes were not successful.[99,100] If these ions are indeed resolvable, this must mean that interconversions of *dextro* and *levo* forms is slow, although the coordinated groups undergo rapid substitution. In spite of these few exceptions it still is true that the bulk of the optically active complexes is found among the inert compounds. Table 4.15 provides a list of some of the optically active octahedral complexes along with specific references and comments on the optical lability of each.

The rate of loss of optical activity of aqueous solutions of these compounds varies from extremely rapid to extremely slow. In many cases the rates are such that they can be followed by conventional techniques. The question of how coordination compounds undergo this loss of optical activity has long been of interest to coordination chemists. Racemization reactions are a form of isomerization and, in most cases, also of substitution or exchange reactions. That these processes are all closely related is illustrated by the fact that it has been necessary in this chapter to make frequent reference to racemization reactions in connection with the stereochemistry of substitution reactions and isomerization. Included in this section are several further examples that have been studied of different types of mechanisms of racemization. These are conveniently classified and discussed as either intermolecular or intramolecular mechanisms.

Intermolecular Mechanism. Racemization by an intermolecular mechanism involves a ligand interchange process as represented by the equilibria

$$D—M(AA)_3 \underset{+AA}{\overset{-AA}{\rightleftharpoons}} M(AA)_2 \underset{-AA}{\overset{+AA}{\rightleftharpoons}} L—M(AA)_3 \qquad (34)$$

This is a convenient operational classification because it requires that ligand exchange be as fast as or faster than racemization. This relationship can be tested experimentally by means of isotopic exchange studies. Note that this category does not include the processes involving chelate ring opening and closing without its complete departure from the metal. It should also be noted that the early literature used the term dissociation rather than intermolecular for this classification. Since "dissociation mechanism" is generally employed with a definite meaning, it is felt that intermolecular mechanism, which is an operational definition and has no reference to mechanistic detail, is preferable.

The solvent is not included in 34, but in water solution the intermediate would surely be $M(AA)_2(H_2O)_2$. Regardless of the exact nature of the intermediate, its formation and its return to $M(AA)_3$ permit rearrangements that can result in loss of optical activity. Steric changes of the type shown in Figs. 4.4 and 4.6 and summarized in Table 4.1 provide ample opportunity for racemization.

Table 4.15 Some optically active six-coordinated complex ions

Compound	$[\alpha]_D$, deg	Ref.	Remarks[a]
Aluminum(III):			
$K_3[Al(C_2O_4)_3]3H_2O$	34	101	$t_{1/2}$ (R.T.) 1–50 hr; failure to resolve complex[98,100]
$K_3[Al(C_6H_4O_2)_3]1.5H_2O$	61.7	102	
	124.4	103	$t_{1/2}$ (R.T.) 2–3 hr in methanol
Arsenic(V):			
$K[As(C_6H_4O_2)_3]\cdot H_2O$	420	104	no rac. in alkali for hours at R.T. but rapid in acid
Cadmium(II):			
$[Cd(en)_3]Cl_2$	113.7	105	complete rac. in solution in 1.5 hr, in solid in 2 hr
Chromium(III):			
$K_3[Cr(C_2O_4)_3]\cdot 1H_2O$	$1{,}300^b$	106, 107	$t_{1/2}$ (18.2°C) = 67 min
$K[Cr(en)(C_2O_4)_2]\cdot 2H_2O$	578	107	$t_{1/2}$ (19°C) = 8.4 min
$[Cr(en)_2C_2O_4]Cl\cdot 3H_2O$	266	107	no rac., decomposition after 12 hr at 18°C
$[Cr(en)_3]I_3$	60	108	no rac., R.T.
$[Cr(en)_2Cl_2]Cl$	140^c	109	$t_{1/2}$ (R.T.) ~1 hr

The structure in the Aluminum(III) section:

$$\left[Al \left(\overset{O}{\underset{}{}} \quad CH{=}N(CH_2)_2NHCH_2{-} \right) \right]_2 NO_3$$

Cobalt(III):

Compound	Rotation	Ref.	Remarks
$K_3[Co(C_2O_4)_3] \cdot H_2O$	2,620	107, 110	$t_{1/2} (37.5°C) = 66$ min
$KBa[Co(C_2O_2S_2)_3] \cdot 5H_2O$	700	91	no rac. in 10 min at 90°C in the dark
$Na[Co(en)(C_2O_4)_2] \cdot H_2O$	500	112	$t_{1/2} = 7.5$ hr at 99°C
$Co(acac)_3{}^b$	1,250	113, 114	no rac.
$[Co(en)_3]Cl_3$	155	115, 116, 117	no rac. in 1 day at 90°C but rac. complete in 2 min in presence of charcoal
$[Co(en)_2C_2O_4]Cl \cdot 3H_2O$	646	107, 112	no rac. after 5 days at 18°C; decomp. on long boiling
$[Co(en)_2Cl_2]Cl$	630	17, 49, 118	in H_2O at 30°C $t_{1/2}$ M.R. = 23 min, $t_{1/2}$ rac. = 430 min; in CH_3OH at 35.8°C $t_{1/2}$ (rac.) = 110 min
$[Co(en)_2F_2]NO_3$	220	119	$t_{1/2}$ M.R. (25°C) = 23 hr, $t_{1/2}$ rac. = 58 hr
$[Co(en)_2(NO_2)Cl]Cl$	52	17, 120	M.R. complete in 4–5 hr, not rac. after 2 mo
$[Co(en)_2(NO_2)_2]Br$	44	121	$t_{1/2} (78°) = 27$ hr
$[Co(en)_2(NCS)Cl]ClO_4 \cdot H_2O$	560^d	17, 122	M.R. complete in 2 days, not rac. after 50 days
$[Co(en)_2(NH_3)Br]Br_2 \cdot 2H_2O$	46^e	17, 123	20% M.R. in 20 days, not rac. after 5 mo
$[Co((OH)_2Co(NH_3)_4)_3]Br_6 \cdot 2H_2O$	2,620	124	rapid rac. in water, slower in 50% acetone

Table 4.15 (*Continued*)

Compound	$[\alpha]_D$, deg	Ref.	Remarks[a]
$[Co((OH)_2Co(en)_2)_3](SbOC_4H_4O_6)_6$			
α, $0.18H_2O$	3,920	125	$t_{1/2}(40°C)\ \alpha = 2.5$ hr, $\beta = 25$ hr
β, $0.9H_2O$	3,620		
$K[Co(EDTA)] \cdot 3H_2O$	150	126, 127	$t_{1/2}(100°C) = 170$ min
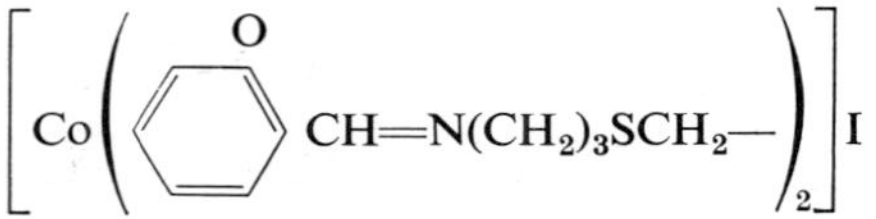 $\left[Co \left(\text{⌢}\ CH=N(CH_2)_3SCH_2— \right) \right] I_2$	11,800	64	M.R. in alcohol at 70°C, then slower rac.
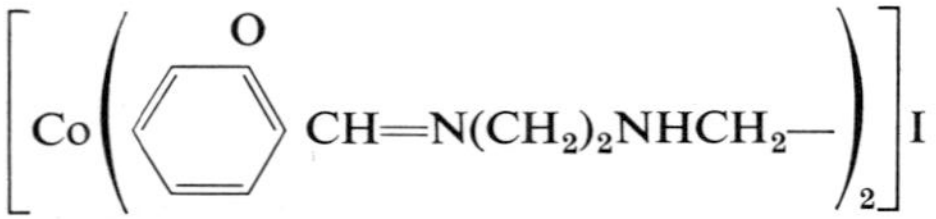 $\left[Co \left(\text{⌢}\ CH=N(CH_2)_2NHCH_2— \right) \right] I_2$	250	103	
$[Co(trien)Cl_2]Cl$	100	128	
$[Co(en)_2(dabp)]Cl_3$	α, 70; β, 60	129	no rac., dabp = 2,2′-diaminobiphenyl
Gallium(III):			
$K_3[Ga(C_2O_4)_3] \cdot 3H_2O$	16.5	130	10% rac. in 2 hr at R.T., failure to resolve complex[99].
Germanium(IV):			
$K_2[Ge(C_2O_4)_3]$	80	131	complete rac. (R.T.) in 1–2 days

304

Iridium(III):

K$_3$[Ir(C$_2$O$_4$)$_3$] · 2H$_2$O	82	132	no rac.
K$_3$[Ir(C$_2$O$_4$)$_2$Cl$_2$]	24	132	H$_2$O soln. at 130°C isomerizes to *trans*
[Ir(en)$_3$]Br$_3$ · 3H$_2$O	50	133	no rac.
[Ir(en)$_2$(NO$_2$)$_2$]Br	26	133	no rac.

Iron(II) and (III):

K$_3$[Fe(C$_2$O$_4$)$_3$] · 3H$_2$O	356	134	$t_{1/2}$ (R.T.) 15 min; failure to resolve complex[99,100]
[Fe(bipy)$_3$](ClO$_4$)$_2$ · 2H$_2$O	4,800	135, 136	$t_{1/2}$ (25°C) = 38 min
[Fe(bipy)$_3$](ClO$_4$)$_3$ · 3H$_2$O	260	136	$t_{1/2}$ (25°C) = 2.4 min
[Fe(phen)$_3$](ClO$_4$)$_2$ · 3H$_2$O	1,432	137	$t_{1/2}$ (25°C) = 35 min
[Fe(phen)$_3$]$^{3+}$	...	137, 185	$t_{1/2}$ (25°C) = 0.4 min

$$\left[\mathrm{Fe}\left(\underset{\mathrm{N}}{\bigcirc}\!\!-\!\mathrm{N=CH}\!\!-\!\bigcirc \right)_2 \right] \mathrm{I}_2 \cdot 2\mathrm{H}_2\mathrm{O}$$

2,000	138	rac. (100°C) ~2 min

$$\left[\mathrm{Fe}\left(\bigcirc\!\!-\!\mathrm{CH=N(CH_2)_2NHCH_2}\!\!-\! \right)_2 \right] \mathrm{NO_3}$$

545	103	

Nickel(II):

[Ni(bipy)$_3$]Cl$_2$ · 6H$_2$O	529[b]	139	$t_{1/2}$ (24.7°C) = 10 min
[Ni(phen)$_3$](ClO$_4$)$_2$	1,460	140	$t_{1/2}$ (25°C) = 34 hr
[Ni(bipy)$_2$(phen)]I$_2$ · 3H$_2$O	690	141, 142	$t_{1/2}$ (20°C) = 16.5 min
[Ni(phen)$_2$(bipy)]I$_2$ · 3H$_2$O	1,262	141, 142	$t_{1/2}$ (20°C) = 21 min

Table 4.15 (*Continued*)

Compound	$[\alpha]_D$, deg	Ref.	Remarks[a]
Osmium(II), (III):			
$[Os(bipy)_3]I_2 \cdot 3H_2O$	0	143	$[\alpha]_{5461} = 2200$, no rac.
$[Os(bipy)_3](ClO_4)_3 \cdot H_2O$	0	144	$[\alpha]_{5461} = 250$, no rac.
$[Os(phen)_3](ClO_4)_2 \cdot H_2O$	0	145	$[\alpha]_{5461} = 3,670$, no rac.
$[Os(phen)_3](ClO_4)_3 \cdot H_2O$	0	136	$[\alpha]_{5461} = 400$, no rac.
Platinum(IV):			
$[Pt(en)_3]Cl_4 \cdot 3H_2O$	86	146	no rac.
$[Pt(pn)_3]Cl_4 \cdot H_2O$	180	147	no rac.
$(+)\text{-}[Pt(en)_2(-pn)]Cl_4$	+133	148	no rac.
$(+)\text{-}[Pt(en)(-pn)_2]Cl_4$	+176	148	no rac.
$(+)\text{-}[Pt(-pn)_3]Cl_4$	+212	148	no rac.
$[Pt(en)_2Cl_2](d\text{-}C_{10}H_{-4}SO_4Br)_2$	+65.5	149	M.R. to $[\alpha]_D = +55.5$ at 100°C with $t_{1/2} \sim 20$
Rhodium(III):			
$K_3[Rh(C_2O_4)_3] \cdot H_2O$	0	150	$[\alpha]_{6563} = 26.4$; $[\alpha]_{5876} = 114$; no rac.
$KBa[Rh(C_2O_2S_2)_3] \cdot 6H_2O$	420	111	no rac.
$K[Rh(H_2O)(EDTA)] \cdot H_2O$	130[b]	151	$t_{1/2}$ (96°C) = 163 min
$Na[Rh(NHSO_2NH)_2(H_2O)_2]$	8.8	152	no rac. at R.T.; 30% rac. (decomp.) at 100°C in 1 hr
$[Rh(en)_3]I_3$	50	153	no rac.

Ruthenium(II), (III):			
[Ru(bipy)$_3$]I$_2$ · 3H$_2$O	819	154	no rac.
[Ru(phen)$_3$](ClO$_4$)$_2$ · 2H$_2$O	979	155	no rac.
[Ru(bipy)$_3$]$^{3+}$	465	154	rapid rac. at R.T.
Ru(phen)$_3$]$^{3+}$	311	155	rapid rac. at R.T.
Titanium(IV):			
(NH$_4$)$_2$[Ti(C$_6$H$_4$O$_2$)$_3$]	790	456	rapid rac.
Zinc(II):			
[Zn(en)$_3$]Cl$_2$	94	157	rac., soln. 2.3 hr; solid, 6 hr

[a] $t_{1/2}$ is half-life for loss of optical rotation (rac.); M.R. is mutarotation; no rac. means no change in optical rotation of a solution on standing at R.T. (room temperature) for several days.
[b] $[\alpha]_{5461}$.
[c] White light.
[d] $[\alpha]_{5270}$.
[e] Red light.

The intermolecular mechanism of racemization has been established in several cases, two of which are described here. First, let us recall the earlier discussion that the rates of water exchange of cis-Co(en)$_2$(H$_2$O)$_2$$^{3+}$ (Table 4.9) and of cis-Co(en)$_2$NH$_3$H$_2$O^{3+} (Table 4.10) are approximately sixty-five and forty times larger, respectively, than are their rates of racemization. This shows that most of the water interchange processes occur with retention, but implies that occasionally such an exchange also takes place with rearrangment.

The rate of loss of optical activity ($k = 7.7 \times 10^{-5}$ sec^{-1}) at 35° of a methanol solution of $(+)$-Co(en)$_2$Cl$_2$$^+$ is, within experimental error, equal to the rate of radiochlorine exchange of one chloro group.[49] The simplest mechanism consistent with this observation is that the complex dissociates to a symmetrical five-coordinated intermediate; thus each dissociation leads directly to a loss of optical rotation. The chloride ion then re-enters the complex, 70% of the time forming the $trans$ isomer and 30% of the time the $racemic$ cis isomer. Therefore, this is more a case of isomerization than of racemization and was described earlier (p. 277). It is further of interest that the rate of loss of optical activity of methanolic $(+)$-cis-Co(en)$_2$Cl$_2$$^+$ is essentially the same in the presence of various reagents (X = Cl$^-$, Br$^-$, NCS$^-$, and NO$_3$$^-$) which lead to the formation of Co-(en)$_2$ClX$^+$. Thus it would appear that all these reactions proceed through the same symmetrical intermediate.

The loss of optical rotation of $(+)$-cis-Co(en)$_2$Cl$_2$$^+$ in water solution was studied earlier,[17] and the behavior of this complex in aqueous solution differs markedly from that in methanol. Although the replacement of coordinated chloride ion in methanol leads directly to loss of optical rotation, its replacement by water in an aqueous solution takes place essentially with retention of configuration. Since both the acid hydrolysis reaction in water solution and the chloride exchange in methanol are believed to proceed by an interchange mechanism with the outer-sphere solvent, it is obvious that the fate of the solvato complexes must not be the same. This difference can be explained on the basis that the donor ability of water is greater than that of methanol. Therefore, a water molecule in the outer sphere of the complex will readily slip into the position vacated by the chloro group without permitting any rearrangement. A similar behavior would be expected for methanol, but, perhaps because of steric hindrance, addition of methanol would be slower and rearrangement might occur.

Mathieu[17] also found that the rate of racemization of $(+)$-cis-Co(en)$_2$ (H$_2$O)Cl^{2+}, obtained by acid hydrolysis of the dichloro complex, does not depend upon the rate of replacement of the remaining chloro group. In acid solution the racemization rate is approximately twenty-five times faster than the rate of replacement of chloride ion ($t_{1/2}$ at 30°C for racemization, 7 hr; for acid hydrolysis, 167 hr), whereas in alkaline buffers the rate of release of chloride ion may exceed the rate of loss of optical rotation. It was suggested that racemization was due to the dissociation of the aquo complex, resulting in the formation of a symmetrical five-coordinated intermediate $Co(en)_2Cl^{2+}$. This same intermediate resulting from the acid hydrolysis of $(+)$-cis-$Co(en)_2Cl_2^+$ yields the aquochloro complex primarily with retention of configuration. It therefore follows that, if the water exchange mechanism for the racemization of $(+)$-cis-$Co(en)_2(H_2O)Cl^{2+}$ is correct, the rate of water exchange must exceed the rate of racemization. Unfortunately, studies are not available on the rate of water exchange.

However, kinetic studies on this system[158] indicate that the loss of optical rotation does not result from the formation of a symmetrical five-coordinated intermediate but rather is due to *trans* isomerization (Fig. 4.14). This is based on the observation that the acid hydrolysis of cis-$Co(en)_2Cl_2^+$ yields a mixture of cis- and $trans$-$Co(en)_2(H_2O)Cl^{2+}$. Mathieu[17] reports that the rate of loss of optical activity of $(+)$-cis-$Co(en)_2Cl_2^+$ is ten times slower than its rate of acid hydrolysis. Therefore, since the loss in activity may result from the formation of either the *trans* aquochloro product or its racemic *cis* isomer, it follows that the rate of formation of $trans$-$Co(en)_2(H_2O)Cl^{2+}$ is at most one-tenth the rate of acid hydrolysis. This means that for the reaction sequence represented by

$$(+)\text{-}cis\text{-}Co(en)_2Cl_2^+ \xrightarrow{\ k\ } (+)\text{-}cis\text{-}Co(en)_2(H_2O)Cl^+ \xrightarrow{\ k'\ }$$

$$\quad\text{(A)} \qquad\qquad\qquad\qquad \text{(B)}$$

$$trans\text{-}Co(en)_2(H_2O)Cl^{2+} \qquad (35)$$

$$\text{(C)}$$

$K = k'/k = 0.1$, providing this mechanism is correct. Then the maximum concentration of B can be shown to be[159]

$$[B]_{max} = A_0 K^{K/1-K} \qquad (36)$$

and the time at which this is reached is

$$t_{max} = \frac{1}{k(K-1)} \ln K \qquad (37)$$

At 25°C t_{max} is 170 min and B_{max} is $0.77A_0$. The results obtained by this calculation [77% *cis*- and 23% *trans*-$Co(en)_2H_2OCl^{2+}$] are in good agreement with the experimentally observed mixture of 79% *cis* and 21% *trans*, and it can therefore be concluded that the original assumption that the loss of optical rotation is a result of the formation of $trans$-$Co(en)_2(H_2O)Cl^{2+}$ is essentially correct. This was recently confirmed by determining the rate of isomerization of *cis*- to *trans*-$Co(en)_2H_2OCl^{2+}$ and finding it to be the same as the rate of racemization of the optically active *cis* isomer.[160] The racemization results in methanol may also be explained by the formation of an unstable *trans*-$Co(en)_2(CH_3OH)Cl^{2+}$ and need not involve a symmetrical five-coordinated species (but see p. 212). It also appears that the racemization of $(+)$-*cis*-$Co(en)_2(H_2O)_2^{3+}$ takes place by the intermediate formation of the *trans* isomer, as represented by Fig. 4.14.

The rates of loss of optical rotation of aqueous solutions of $Co(en)_2XCL$ complexes, where $X = NH_3$, NO_2^-, or NCS^-,[17] of $(+)$-*cis*-$Co(en)_2F_2^+$ [119] and of $(+)$-$Cr(en)_2Cl_2^+$ [109] have also been investigated. In all cases the change in optical rotation takes place in two discrete steps. First, as with the dichloro complex just discussed, there is a change to the optical rotation of the aquo complexes and then a racemization of these complexes. The rates of racemization of the complexes $Co(en)_2H_2OX$ decrease in the following order of X: $Cl^- > F^- > NO_2^- \simeq NCS^- > NH_3$. Except for $Co(en)_2NH_3H_2O^{3+}$, the rates of water exchange of these aquo complexes are not known. However, the rates of acid hydrolysis of *cis*-$Co(en)_2Cl_2^+$ and of *cis*-$Co(en)_2NO_2Cl^+$ are approximately the same, suggesting that the rates of water exchange of *cis*-$Co(en)_2H_2OCl^{2+}$ and of *cis*-$Co(en)_2H_2$-ONO_2^{2+} are at least of the same order of magnitude. Hence, if the racemization is a result of water exchange, such exchange in the aquonitro complex takes place with retention of configuration a greater percentage of the time than does exchange in the aquochloro complex. That racemization does proceed by water exchange seems plausible because of the observations that the rates of water exchange for *cis*-$Co(en)_2(H_2O)_2^{3+}$ and for *cis*-$Co(en)_2NH_3H_2O^{3+}$ are faster than their rates of racemization. It also appears that water exchange is responsible for the racemization of $Cr(H_2O)_2(C_2O_4)_2^-$, and that this occurs as a result of *cis* $\rightleftharpoons$ *trans* isomerization. The kinetics of racemization and of isomerization are identical within experimental error.[63] Recent studies[28c] indicate that racemization of *cis*-β-$Co(trien)(OH)_2^+$ proceeds through the formation of the *trans* isomer as an intermediate.

Optically active metal complexes containing easily replaceable monodentate ligands appear to racemize by an intermolecular process, whereas complexes containing only polydentate ligands would be expected to racemize more often by an intramolecular process (see next section). However, the Ni(II) complexes of 1,10-phenanthroline and of 2.2'-bipyridine provide a clear-cut exception to this rule in that both $(+)$-$Ni(phen)_3^{2+}$ and $(+)$-$Ni(bipy)_3^{2+}$ racemize by an intermolecular process. An intramolecular mechanism had been suggested[161] originally because the rates of racemization were not altered by the presence of added chelating agent. It was presumed that the rate of racemization should decrease upon addition of excess chelating agent if the intermolecular mechanism

$$Ni(phen)_3^{2+} \overset{slow}{\rightleftharpoons} Ni(phen)_2^{2+} + phen \qquad (38)$$

is involved, because of the increased rate of the backward reaction. However, it is clear that, if the bis complex either were symmetrical or very rapidly lost its optical activity, the presence of chelating agent would not be expected to change the rate of racemization.

The question of the mechanism of racemization in these systems was finally settled by investigations of ^{14}C-labeled ligand exchange with the coordinated ligand.[162] These results were compared with the rates of racemization determined under the same experimental conditions. The rate constants for racemization were based on the equilibria,

$$(+)\text{-}Ni(phen)_3^{2+} \overset{k}{\rightleftharpoons} \text{optically inactive} \underset{k}{\rightleftharpoons} (-)\text{-}Ni(phen)_3^{2+} \qquad (39)$$
$$\text{product}$$

such that the rate constant, k, is obtained from the slope, m, of the usual first-order plot, by the relationship $k = -2.303m$. Alternatively, if the reaction is considered a direct inversion

$$(+)\text{-}Ni(phen)_3^{2+} \underset{k'}{\overset{k'}{\rightleftharpoons}} (-)\text{-}Ni(phen)_3^{2+} \qquad (40)$$

then k' is found from the slope of the same plot by $k = -(2.303m)/2$. The first method allows a direct comparison of rate constants, k, for exchange (dissociation) and racemization.

The results (Table 4.16) show that the rates of ligand exchange and of racemization, under the same experimental conditions, are the same for $Ni(phen)_3^{2+}$. Likewise the rates of exchange and of racemization of $Ni(bipy)_3^{2+}$ are the same in water solution. These results then provide conclusive evidence that racemization proceeds by an intermolecular process. However, nothing is known about the details of the mechanism. The actual structure of the bis complex is not known, the role of the solvent in its formation is not known, nor is anything known about the exact nature of the rearrangements which lead to a loss of optical rotation. The only limitation imposed by the results is that the bis complex either be symmetrical or lose its optical activity rapidly with respect to the rate at which recombination occurs.

Also included in Table 4.16 are the rates of dissociation of the complexes $Ni(phen)_3^{2+}$ and $Ni(bipy)_3^{2+}$ in excess acid and of the mixed complexes $Ni(bipy)(phen)^{2+}$ and $Ni(bipy)_2(phen)^{2+}$.[164] These reactions

$$Ni(AA)_3^{2+} + H^+ \rightarrow Ni(AA)_2^{2+} + HAA^+ \qquad (41)$$

Table 4.16 Rates of racemization, exchange, and dissociation of some nickel(II) complexes[a]

Complex	Solvent	Temp., °C	k_{rac}, sec^{-1}	k_{exch}, sec^{-1}	k_{diss}, sec^{-1}	Ref.
Ni(phen)$_3$$^{2+}$	H$_2$O(0.1 M NaOH)	45	1.5 × 10^{-4}	1.6 × 10^{-4}	...	162
	H$_2$O(0.1 M NaOH)	45	1.9 × 10^{-4}	1.8 × 10^{-4}	...	162
	H$_2$O(5 M HCl)	25	8.1 × 10^{-6}	...	7.8 × 10^{-6}	163
	C$_2$H$_5$OH	45	4.5 × 10^{-5}	4.8 × 10^{-5}	...	162
	C$_6$H$_5$NO$_2$	45	2.5 × 10^{-6}	2.2 × 10^{-6}	...	162
Ni(bipy)$_3$$^{2+}$	H$_2$O	25	2.3 × 10^{-3}	2.4 × 10^{-3}	...	162
	H$_2$O(5 M HCl)	13	3.7 × 10^{-3}	...	4.0 × 10^{-3}	163
Nibipy(phen)$_2$$^{2+}$	H$_2$O	25	5.5 × 10^{-4}	...	...	164
	H$_2$O(5 M HCl)	25	4.6 × 10^{-3}	...	4.5 × 10^{-3}	164
Ni(bipy)$_2$phen^{2+}	H$_2$O	25	7.0 × 10^{-4}	...	...	164
	H$_2$O(5 M HCl)	25	6.0 × 10^{-3}	...	5.8 × 10^{-3}	164

[a] For a given complex the values of E_a and $\Delta S^{\ddagger}$ are the same, within experimental error, for the racemization and either the exchange or the dissociation process:

	Ni(phen)$_3$$^{2+}$	Ni(bipy)$_3$$^{2+}$	Nibipy(phen)$_2$$^{2+}$	Ni(bipy)$_2$phen^{2+}
E_a, kcal/mole	25	22	21	20
$\Delta S^{\ddagger}$, eu	2	6	1	−1

proceed with changes in color and are conveniently studied spectro-photometrically. The rates of racemization, or more correctly the rates of loss of optical activity, have also been investigated at these same experimental conditions. In every case the kinetic parameters obtained by the spectrophotometric and the polarimetric methods are the same for the same compound at the same experimental conditions. This is in accord with an intermolecular mechanism for racemization. The rates of reaction for $Ni(phen)_3^{2+}$ are independent of acid concentration, whereas for complexes containing one or more bipyridine ligands the rates of reaction increase with increasing acid strength. This is understood on the basis of the rapid protonation of the flexible half-bonded bipy (p. 218).

That the rates of dissociation and of loss of optical activity are the same at high acid concentration is expected because each time the Nibipy chelate ring opens the free end of bipy is captured by a proton and $Hbipy^+$ rapidly leaves the complex. At lower H^+ concentrations, where chelate ring closure can compete with protonation and release of $Hbipy^+$, as shown in

$$(+)-(bipy)_2Ni \overset{N}{\underset{N}{\big\langle\quad\big\rangle}} \quad \underset{k_2}{\overset{k_1}{\rightleftharpoons}} \quad (bipy)_2NiN\frown N \tag{42}$$

$$k_4 \downarrow H^+$$

$$(bipy)_2NiN\frown NH^+ \rightarrow (bipy)_2Ni + Hbipy^+$$

it follows that the rates of dissociation and loss of optical activity may differ. However, the experimental results indicate that the rates are the same, which then requires that the chelate ring open and close with retention of configuration. This is of interest because, as is described later, the opening and closing of the oxalato chelate ring in $(+)-Cr(C_2O_4)_3^{3-}$ is responsible for its racemization.

Intramolecular Mechanism. The possibility that complex ions may racemize by an intramolecular mechanism was first suggested by Werner.[1] It has been shown that this is correct for the systems trioxalato-cobalt(III) and -chromium(III) ions, tris(acetylacetonato)cobalt(III) and -chromium(III), ethylenediaminetetraacetatocobaltiate(III) ion, and also in part for tris(1,10-phenanthroline) and tris(2,2'-bipyridine)iron(II) ions. The oxalato complexes have been the subject of extensive studies by Johnson[98] and his students. Johnson took issue with earlier statements[165] that these compounds racemize by an intermolecular process and cited as evidence against this view the facts that (1) he was unable to detect any dissociation of $Co(C_2O_4)_3^{3-}$ or $Cr(C_2O_4)_3^{3-}$ in aqueous solution, (2) salts of these complex ions undergo racemization even in the solid state,[166] and (3) the rate of racemization is not decreased by the presence of oxalate ion.[167] However, such evidence cannot be accepted as proof that an intermolecular mechanism in water solution is not possible. This question of mechanism was finally settled by studies[168] on the rate of oxalate ion exchange in the systems $Co(C_2O_4)_3{}^{3-}$—$*C_2O_4{}^{2-}$ and $Cr(C_2O_4)_3{}^{3-}$—$*C_2O_4{}^{2-}$. Since the rate of oxalate ion exchange is much slower than the rate of racemization it must be concluded that racemization of these ions takes place by an intramolecular mechanism. That the labile complexes $Al(C_2O_4)_3{}^{3-}$ and $Fe(C_2O_4)_3{}^{3-}$ undergo complete exchange with radio-oxalate ion in the time of mixing is of interest. There are some differences of opinion[98,100] as to the resolvability of these complex ions. Ligand exchange experiments have not been reported for the systems $Co(acac)_3$, $Cr(acac)_3$, and $Co(ETDA)^-$, but, as is described later, other investigations strongly suggest that these complexes racemize by an intramolecular process.

Another example of racemization of octahedral complexes by an intramolecular mechanism was observed for the complex ions $Fe(phen)_3{}^{2+}$ and $Fe(bipy)_3{}^{2+}$. The rates of racemization[169] of these ions are greater than the rates of dissociation.[170] Hence racemization must, at least in part, involve an intramolecular process. Kinetic studies on the racemization and dissociation of the Fe(II) complexes, with the same experimental conditions, suggest a dual mechanism.[171] The data obtained on the Fe(II) complexes and, for comparison, the Ni(II) complexes are summarized in Table 4.17. The intermolecular racemization rates are the spectrophoto-metrically determined rates of dissociation. Since each dissociation of the Ni(II) complexes leads to loss of optical activity, it is a reasonable assumption that the same behavior is shown by the analogous Fe(II) complexes.

Table 4.17   Rates of individual processes leading to racemization at 25°C

Complex	Intramolecular Racemization			Intermolecular Racemization		
	k, sec^{-1}	E_a, kcal	$\Delta S^{\ddagger}$, eu	k, sec^{-1}	E_a, kcal	$\Delta S^{\ddagger}$, eu
$Fe(phen)_3{}^{2+}$	6.5×10^{-4}	29	21	7.0×10^{-5}	32.1	28
$Fe(bipy)_3{}^{2+\ a}$	2.7×10^{-4}	26	12	7.8×10^{-4}	27.4	17
$Ni(phen)_3{}^{2+}$	$<1.0 \times 10^{-6}$	...	...	1.0×10^{-5}	25.0	2
$Ni(bipy)_3{}^{2+\ a}$	$<1.8 \times 10^{-3}$	...	...	1.8×10^{-2}	21.8	6

From reference 171.
^{a} These are the limiting rates in 1 M HCl.

In any event the fact that the racemization is more rapid than the dissociation shows that racemization also takes place by some intramolecular process. The observed rate of racemization will then be the sum of the two rates, and the rate of intramolecular racemization can be obtained by subtracting the rate of dissociation from the total rate. Limiting values designated (Table 4.17) for the intramolecular racemization of the Ni(II) complexes are based on the failure to observe any racemization by this process.

It is somewhat surprising that the very similar Fe(II) and Ni(II) complexes should racemize by different mechanisms. The two sets of complexes have the same charge and size but differ in stability and bond type: the Fe(II) complexes are diamagnetic low-spin d^6 systems, whereas Ni(II) complexes are paramagnetic high-spin d^8 systems. It has been suggested[172] that the intramolecular racemization of the Fe(II) complexes may result from a process of expansion which permits loss of optical activity. Thus the interatomic distances between the donor atom and the metal may increase because of excitation of the low-spin to a high-spin state which then might well rearrange before returning to the original stable state. On the basis of this interpretation, the racemization can be represented by the equilibria

$$\text{Fe(AA)}_3^{2+} \underset{k_2}{\overset{k_1}{\rightleftharpoons}} \text{Fe}\cdots(\text{AA})_3^{2+} \underset{k_4}{\overset{k_3}{\rightleftharpoons}} \text{Fe}\cdots(\text{AA})_2 + \text{AA} \qquad (43)$$

It is apparent that if $k_2 > k_3$ the racemization will occur by an intramolecular process, if $k_2 < k_3$ an intermolecular mechanism is involved, and if $k_2 \sim k_3$ both mechanisms may contribute to the observed rate of racemization.

The nature of this expanded state in terms of the crystal field theory can be understood. It would simply be the higher-energy $(t_{2g})^4(e_g)^2$ state of the complex which would have greater bond distances and hence weaker bonding as required. The energy required to attain it would not be excessive because of the lowered electron repulsion. The large entropy gain shown in Table 4.17 would be due also to the greater freedom of the ligands in this excited state. This explanation fits in neatly with the observation that Ni(II) does not show any intramolecular racemization, since such an excited state is not possible for Ni(II), which is already in the high-spin state. Hence, only the dissociation mechanism is available to it. This explanation is similar to one of the suggestions made for inversion reactions of certain Co(III) complexes (p. 271).

The exact nature of the intramolecular rearrangement leading to racemization is not known. A consideration of molecular models reveals that there are several ways in which such a process can happen, and each appears to involve approximately the same energy. Some of the methods that have been suggested are diagramed in Fig. 4.24. Although it is difficult to obtain experimental proof of the exact nature of these rearrangement processes, in a few cases evidence is available which supports one or the other of the proposed paths. Werner[1] suggested the rupture of one (a) or two (b) bidentate ligands followed by the reattachment of the

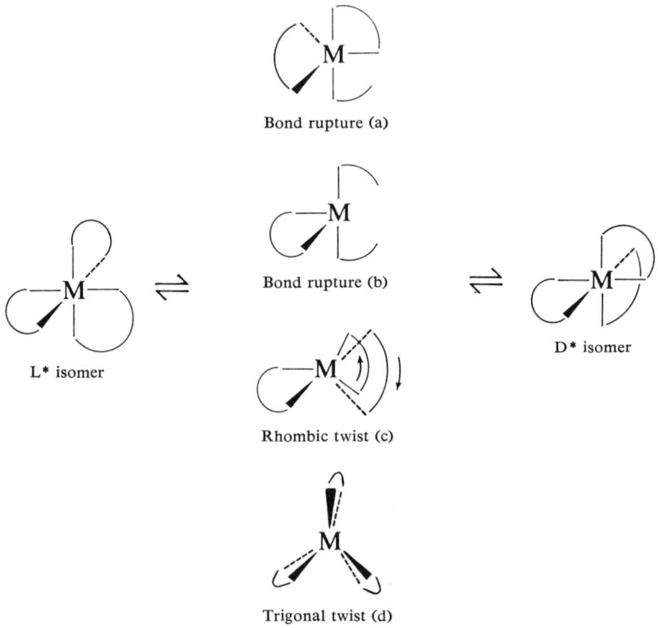

Bond rupture (a)

Bond rupture (b)

L* isomer

Rhombic twist (c)

D* isomer

Trigonal twist (d)

Fig. 4.24 Rearrangements proposed for intramolecular mechanisms of racemization of octahedral complexes. See also footnote on page 290.

open ends. Kinetic studies[171] on the dissociation and racemization of $Fe(bipy)_3^{2+}$ suggest that a bond rupture path does make some contribution to the total rate of racemization. The intramolecular racemization of this ion can take place in two ways. One method, like that of $Fe(phen)_3^{2+}$, which presumably involves shifting, but not breaking, of Fe-N bonds [rhombic twist (c)[70] or trigonal twist (d)[68,69]] is essentially independent of acid concentration. A second process would involve an intramolecular racemization of the complex with one of the chelate rings open. Since the lifetime of this species decreases with increasing acid concentration (p. 219), it follows that the rate of racemization through such a route decreases with increasing acidity and approaches zero at high acidity. Such a decrease in intramolecular racemization was observed with increasing acidity, thus supporting path (a). At high acid concentrations a constant residual intramolecular rate remained which is attributed to a twisting process such as (c) or (d). It is of interest to note that, in contrast, the analogous complex $Ni(bipy)_3^{2+}$ undergoes chelate ring opening and closing with retention of configuration.

Considering only paths (a) and (b), we find that evidence has been cited in support of (b). It was suggested that the Co(III) oxalate chelate rings can open because $Co(C_2O_4)_3^{3-}$ does racemize, whereas the Co(III) ethylenediamine ring does not open since $Co(en)_3^{3+}$ does not racemize.[1] Therefore, the racemization of $Co(en)_2C_2O_4^+$ would support the view that only one ring need be opened (a), but failure of this compound to racemize would be consistent with path (b). The loss of optical activity of this complex was found to be a result of decomposition rather than racemization. On the basis of this observation it was concluded that two chelate rings must be opened (b). However, in strongly basic aqueous solution the rate of loss of optical activity of $Co(en)_2C_2O_4^+$ is equal to its rate of oxalate ion exchange and to its rate of formation of $Co(en)_2(OH)_2^+$.[173a] This was interpreted in terms of all three processes having an identical rate-determining step, that of Co—O bond rupture to open the oxalato chelate ring.

Much of the interest in the properties of the anions $M(C_2O_4)_3^{3-}$ has centered about the discussion of the mechanism of racemization of $Cr(C_2O_4)_3^{3-}$, and considerable work has been done on these systems.[173b] The early conflict of views between Werner,[1] who suggested a chelate ring opening-closing process, and Thomas,[165] who favored an intermolecular mechanism, was resolved by Long,[168] who found that $*C_2O_4^{2-}$ did not exchange with $Cr(C_2O_4)_3^{3-}$ in the time required for complete racemization. This ruled out the intermolecular mechanism, and the question that remained was whether the intramolecular mechanism involves a bond rupture or a twisting process. This has now been settled in support of the chelate ring opening-closing process [path (a) of Fig. 4.24] by extensive investigations of ^{18}O exchange between the solvent water and the complex.[174,175]

It was observed that the rate of acid-catalyzed oxygen exchange in the system $Cr(C_2O_4)_3^{3-}$—H_2*O is slightly slower than the rate of racemization of the complex but much faster than its exchange with $*C_2O_4^{2-}$. This exchange between the solvent oxygen and the coordinated oxalato oxygen is believed to occur by attack on the carbonyl carbon. In such a case, if the chelate ring remains intact, only the carbonyl oxygens will undergo exchange, which means a total of six oxygen atoms exchanging per complex ion. What was found is that all twelve oxygen atoms in the complex exchange at the same rate, requiring that the chelate ring open and close. The mechanism proposed for ^{18}O exchange is illustrated by the following reaction scheme:

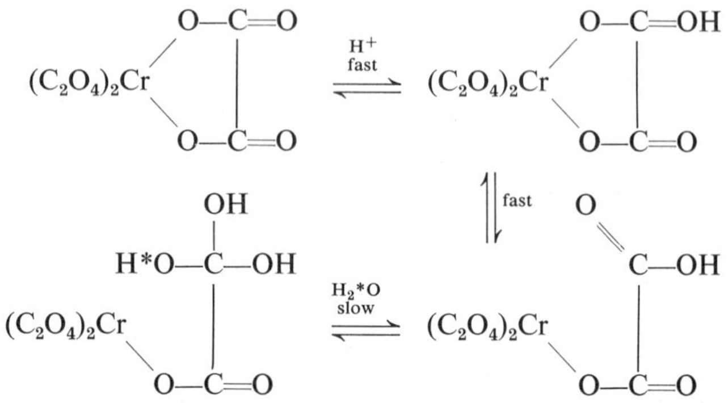

$$(C_2O_4)_2Cr\underset{O-C=O}{\overset{O-C=O}{\Big\langle}} \quad \underset{\text{fast}}{\overset{H^+}{\rightleftharpoons}} \quad (C_2O_4)_2Cr\underset{O-C=O}{\overset{O-C=OH}{\Big\langle}}$$

$$\Big\Updownarrow \text{fast}$$

$$(C_2O_4)_2Cr\underset{O-C=O}{\overset{H*O-C-OH \;(OH)}{\Big\langle}} \quad \underset{\text{slow}}{\overset{H_2*O}{\rightleftharpoons}} \quad (C_2O_4)_2Cr\underset{O-C=O}{\overset{O\backslash C-OH}{\Big\langle}}$$

(44)

There are two reasons for suggesting that the rate-determining step for the acid-catalyzed ^{18}O exchange is the addition of water to the carbon of the free carboxylic acid group. First, the rate of exchange is proportional to the stoichiometric acidity up to 2 M acid, which, according to the Hammett-Zucker[174c] hypothesis, implies a bimolecular mechanism with water in the transition state. Second, the activation energies for the exchange reactions are very similar for $Cr(C_2O_4)_3^{3-}$, $Co(C_2O_4)_3^{3-}$, and $H_2C_2O_4$, being 18.0, 18.6, and 18.4 kcal/mole, respectively, while the frequency factors are also similar: $\log A \;(\text{sec}^{-1}) = 10.35$, 10.64, and 9.96, respectively. In the aquation reaction, on the other hand, the change from Cr(III) to Co(III) is accompanied by an increase in activation energy of about 6 kcal/mole. The similarity of the activation energies for the oxygen exchanges suggests that the rate-determining step occurs at a point remote from the metal atom.

This mechanism implies that the oxalato chelate rings are rapidly opening and closing and that frequently this occurs with retention of configuration, but occasionally inversion takes place, which then is responsible for the racemization of the complex. There is also some justification for thinking that the reactive species with an open chelate ring is five-coordinated, rather than having water coordinated in the vacated position. This comes from the observation[62b] that the replacement of H_2O from $Cr(H_2O)_2(C_2O_4)_2^-$ by $C_2O_4^{2-}$ is slow and the rate does not depend on the concentration of $C_2O_4^{2-}$. These findings indicate that breaking of the Cr-OH_2 bond is slow and imply that such a bond is not formed in the reactive species $(C_2O_4)CrOOCCOOH$ of scheme 44.

It would a priori appear to be almost impossible to design an experiment which can distinguish between the rhombic (Ray and Dutt) twist (c) and the trigonal (Bailar) twist (d) mechanisms, yet it has been shown[66] how this might be accomplished by using n.m.r. techniques (p. 290). This permits the examination of a solution for the amount of cis and trans isomers of a complex of the type $M(AB)_3$, where AB is an unsymmetrical bidentate ligand. Once a twist mechanism has been shown to be involved, then, as is indicated in Figs. 4.20 and 4.21, it is possible to distinguish between the trigonal and the rhombic twists. Thus, the trigonal twist process allows the cis isomer to racemize without isomerization to the trans form, whereas the rhombic twist mechanism results in the simultaneous inversion and isomerization of cis-L* into trans-D*. If this were all that could happen, there would be not a loss in optical activity but rather a mutarotation to some different value of optical activity corresponding to the equilibrium mixture of cis-L* ⇌ trans-D*. However, the same rhombic twist mechanism, rotating a different set of chelate rings, results in the conversion of trans-D* into trans-L* and then into cis-D*. Thus, racemization and isomerization may occur as a result of the equilibria

$$cis\text{-}L^* \rightleftharpoons trans\text{-}D^* \rightleftharpoons trans\text{-}L^* \rightleftharpoons cis\text{-}D^* \qquad (45)$$

The above approach provides an elegant method of distinguishing between a trigonal twist and a rhombic twist mechanism, providing it is established that a twisting process is responsible for rearrangement. Unfortunately, an intermolecular process and a bond rupture process give the same results as does the rhombic twist mechanism (Fig. 4.21). Experiments of ligand exchange with the complex readily permit one to determine whether or not an intermolecular process is responsible for rearrangement. By making use of n.m.r., it was observed that trifluoroacetylacetone (ftacac) does not exchange with either $Al(tfacac)_3$ or $In(tfacac)_3$ during isomerization.[66] Exchange experiments utilizing ^{14}C-labeled acetylacetone on several systems of the type $M(acac)_3$-*acac show that for M = Co(III) or Cr(III) there is no exchange after 10 min.[176] This observation is of little help, because there would also be essentially no racemization during this time.

Assuming that tris(betadiketone)metal(III) complexes racemize by an intramolecular process, it may be said that this does not involve a trigonal twist mechanism (see footnote p. 290). Such a mechanism does not permit cis-trans isomerization as was found for the $M(tfacac)_3$ systems. More specifically, the racemization of tris(benzoylacetonato)chromium(III), which has a rate constant of $3.8 \times 10^{-5} sec^{-1}$ at 95.5° in 1,1,2,2-tetrachloroethane, is accompanied by cis-trans isomerization.

That a bond rupture path is favored over a rhombic twist mechanism for rearrangement in these systems was discussed earlier (p. 291) for the isomerization of the compounds $M(tfacac)_3$. Piper[177a] has also very cleverly designed an experiment that gives proof of bond rupture during racemization. The compound used for this purpose is tris(acetylacetyl-acetonato)cobalt(III), in which one of the methyl groups in the ligand is CD_3. By making use of n.m.r., it is possible to determine whether isomerization of the type shown by the equilibria

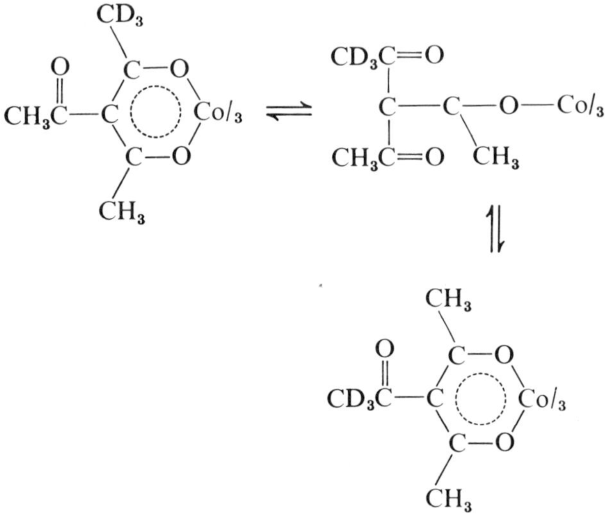

(46)

takes place in solution. This type of isomerization cannot occur by a twisting process and requires a chelate ring opening-closing mechanism. What was found is that the Co(III) compound undergoes isomerization and racemization at the same rate, providing support for a bond rupture mechanism for racemization.

However, there is also some indirect evidence that the isomerization represented in 46 may involve an intermolecular process. Investigations[177b] show that the linkage isomerization represented by the equilibrium

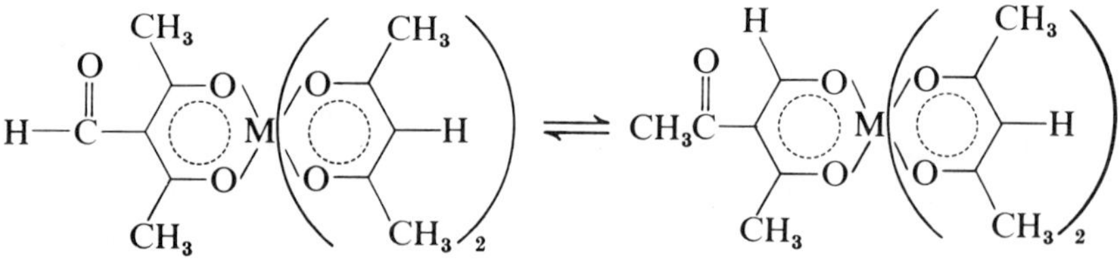

(47)

where M = Co(III) or Cr(III), accompanies ligand exchange in boiling toluene. The system is complicated because disproportionation also takes place, and equilibration results in the formation of a mixture of six different components. However, disproportionation and linkage isomerization appear to occur in a similar manner, suggesting that isomerization takes place by an intermolecular process.

It has already been mentioned that a twisting mechanism appears to be responsible for the intramolecular racemization of $Fe(phen)_3^{2+}$ and in part for $Fe(bipy)_3^{2+}$. Likewise Ray and Dutt,[70] who were the first to suggest a twisting mechanism, proposed it to account for the unusually low frequency factor of $\exp(4.16)\ \sec^{-1}$ for the inversion of the biguanidine complex $Co(bigH)_3^{3+}$. There is no information on the type of twist that might be involved.

Busch[178] and his students have investigated the racemization of $Co(EDTA)^-$ and conclude that it proceeds by a trigonal twist mechanism (Fig. 4.25). An examination of molecular models reveals that a rhombic

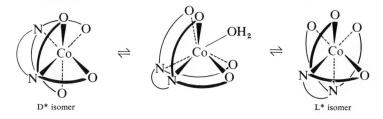

D* isomer   L* isomer

Fig. 4.25 Trigonal twist mechanism for the racemization of $Co(EDTA)^-$ with the participation of the solvent water. The base catalysis is represented in the same way except that H_2O is replaced by OH^-. From reference 178.

twist is also possible in this sexadentate system. However, bond rupture releasing only one carboxylate group results most readily in its closing again with retention of configuration. This conclusion is supported experimentally by the observation that the replacement of EDTA from the pentadentate $Co(EDTA)X^-$ results in retention of configuration.[179]

Furthermore, the rate of racemization of $Co(EDTA)^-$ is independent of pH over the range 2–4, which is sufficiently acid to protonate any free carboxylate ion (pK_a of about 3). In acid solution at $100°$ the rate constant for racemization is $4.2 \times 10^{-6}\ \sec^{-1}$ with $E_a = 40.6\ kcal/mole$ and $\Delta S^{\ddagger} = 21$ eu. In basic solution the rate of racemization is faster and shows a first-order dependence on the concentration of hydroxide ion. At $35°$ the second-order rate constant is $0.53\ M^{-1}\ \sec^{-1}$ with $E_a = 32.7\ kcal/mole$ and $\Delta S^{\ddagger} = 55$ eu. It was suggested that the base-catalyzed racemization involves a nucleophilic attack of OH^- on the Co(III) with the formation of a symmetrical trigonal prism intermediate (Fig. 4.25). In the same way a molecule of water may be coordinated to cobalt in the presumed trigonal prismatic intermediate for acid racemization; then this seven-coordinated configuration would be analogous to that found for $Mn(EDTA)H_2O^{2-}$.[180]

It should be mentioned that some complications may arise in the racemization of this system because of the presence of catalytic amounts of the labile complex $Co(EDTA)^{2-}$ (p. 329).

Salt and Solvent Effects. The rates of racemization of some complex ions are altered by changes of salt concentration or of solvent. The most extensive studies of salt effects were made on the anionic complex trioxalatochromate(III)[167] and the cationic tris(biguanidinium)cobalt(III).[70] In both cases it is reported that except for the hydroxide ion the anion has little or no effect on the rate of racemization. This acceleration of rate by the hydroxide ion is apparently a result of base hydrolysis, leading to a decomposition of the complexes. That other anions show no specific effect on the anionic complex of Cr(III) is not surprising; what is unexpected is that anions have little or no effect on the cationic Co(III) complex. However, the rate of racemization of $Co(bigH)_3^{3+}$ is essentially the same in solutions containing the same concentration of chloride, bromide, iodide, or nitrate salts of potassium. Bivalent anions could not be tested because they formed precipitates with the complex.

The rates of racemization of these two complexes are markedly altered by different cations, that of $Cr(C_2O_4)_3^{3-}$ being accelerated, whereas that of $Co(bigH)_3^{3+}$ is retarded. The enhanced rate of racemization of $Cr(C_2O_4)_3^{3-}$ may be readily explained as an electrophilic attack on the coordinated oxalato group, promoting Cr—O bond rupture. This is analogous to the acid catalysis of the aquation of $M(NH_3)_5OOCR^{2+}$ [181] and to the acid catalysis of the oxalate ion exchange of $Cr(C_2O_4)_3^{3-}$.[182] Thus the chelate ring opening

$$Cr(C_2O_4)_3^{3-} + H_2O \overset{k_1}{\rightleftharpoons} (C_2O_4)_2Cr—OCOCO_2H_2O^{3-} \qquad (48)$$

$$Cr(C_2O_4)_3^{3-} + H^+ \overset{K}{\rightleftharpoons} Cr(C_2O_4)_3H^{2-} \qquad (49)$$

is slower than that for the protonated system,

$$Cr(C_2O_4)_3H^{2-} + H_2O \overset{k_2}{\rightleftharpoons} (C_2O_4)_2Cr—OCOCOOHH_2O \qquad (50)$$

which means that the rate rises with increasing acid concentration, the rate expression being $k_{obs} = k_1 + Kk_2[H^+]$. It is also of interest to note that the effectiveness of different cations as catalysts seems to follow the order of stability of their complexes.[183] This can be understood as a process whereby the metal ion complexes with the coordinated group and assists in the opening of the chelate ring:

$$(51)$$

The cationic retardation of the rate of racemization of $Co(bigH)_3^{3+}$ is not well understood. Since the biguanidine ligand has additional nitrogens that might behave as donor atoms, it is possible that the cations may coordinate to these in a manner similar to that shown by 51. If racemization involves chelate ring opening-closing, then this would be expected to increase the rate of racemization. However, because of the unusually low frequency factor of exp (4.16) sec^{-1} for the inversion of this complex, it is believed to racemize by a twist mechanism.[70] In such a case the presence of hydrated cations on the biguanidine ligand may render its twisting motion more difficult and thus retard its rate of racemization.

A similar but smaller cationic acceleration of the rates of racemization of $Cr(en)(C_2O_4)_2^-$ and $Co(C_2O_4)_3^{3-}$ compared to $Cr(C_2O_4)_3^{3-}$ has been observed.[107] It was also found[169] that the addition of salt has only a very slight retardation effect on the rate of racemization of $Ni(phen)_3^{2+}$, but the rate is slightly increased in the presence of alkali. However, in the case of $Ni(bipy)_3^{2+}$ a specific anion effect was observed, the rates of racemization being increased by hydroxide, chloride, and fluoride ions, whereas sulfate and nitrate ions have no effect. Similar results were obtained[184] for the rates of dissociation of $Fe(bipy)_3^{2+}$ in methanol solution, indicating that perhaps the increase in rate with the smaller ions may be due to the fact that they can enter the five-coordinated intermediate (p. 220) and prevent the reclosing of the opened 2,2'-bipyridine chelate ring. Since the rate of dissociation of $Fe(phen)_3^{2+}$ in methanol solution is also accelerated by chloride ion, it would appear that a more plausible interpretation of this behavior in non-aqueous systems is the formation of ion pairs. Although the salt effect on the rate of racemization of $Fe(phen)_3^{2+}$ in water is very slight, the addition of acid or salt to a solution of $Fe(phen)_3^{3+}$ results in a very pronounced decrease in rate.[169,186] In the case of the Fe(III) complex spectroscopic studies show the formation of ion pairs. Furthermore it should be mentioned that the optical activity of $Fe(phen)_3^{2+}$, unlike that of $Ni(phen)_3^{2+}$, is rapidly lost in alkali because of decomposition. A kinetic study[186] has been made of the displacement of phen from $Fe(phen)_3^{2+}$ in the presence of OH^-, CN^-, and N_3^-. The rate of reaction depends on the concentration of these reagents, and the reagent effectiveness decreases in the order $CN^- > OH^- > N_3^-$ (p. 236).

The effects described above are those of ordinary salts. Much greater effects have been observed with large ions or compounds. This phenomenon is related to the so-called *Pfeiffer effect*,[187] which has been discussed in terms of "configurational activity."[188] In some cases the rates of racemization of diastereoisomeric salts are slower than those of ordinary salts of the labile component. This is in accord with the observation that stable optically active centers in a given molecule seem to stabilize labile centers in the same molecule. Kinetic studies reveal that diastereoisomeric pairs, (+)-A, (−)-B and (−)-A, (−)-B, may racemize at different rates. This inequality in rates, due to differences in free energies of the diastereo-isomers, was shown[189] to be the basis of the phenomenon of *first-order asymmetric transformation*. That free energy differences may exist between solid diastereoisomeric compounds and diastereoisomeric salts in non-dissociating solvents is understandable, but it is surprising that they may also occur in dissociating solvents. However, the rates of loss of optical activity of aqueous solutions of *dextro-* and *levo*-tris(biguanidium) cobalt(III) chloride *dextro*-tartrate are slightly different.[170] Similarly the rates of racemization of $Ni(phen)_3^{2+}$ in the presence of optically active ions and also in the presence of large optically inactive ions are different.[190a] Thus, the rates for the enantiomers of $Ni(phen)_3^{2+}$ differ by as much as 15% in the presence of an added optically active electrolyte. However, no difference was found in the rates of racemization of the *dextro* and *levo* forms of $As(C_6H_4O_2)_3^-$ in the presence of varying concentrations of optically active species.[104]

The effect of large ions and of polyelectrolytes on the rates of racemiza-tion and dissociation of $Fe(phen)_3^{2+}$ has been studied[191] in considerable detail, and some of the results obtained are gathered in Table 4.18. The rates of racemization and dissociation are both increased by the presence of large cations. It is believed that these are bound by van der Waals interactions with the coordinated phenanthroline molecules and that the electrostatic effect of the cation decreases the electron density on the coordinated nitrogen. Such an effect is similar to that caused by chloro-substitution on the phenanthroline ring, which is known to result in an increase in the rate of dissociation of the complex.[192]

The anion camphor sulfonate causes an increase in the rate of racemiza-tion of $Fe(phen)_3^{2+}$ but a decrease in its rate of dissociation (Table 4.18). Before presenting an explanation for this, we will consider the structure of the complex. Because of the rigid planar nature of phenanthroline, the complex is not spherical in shape; rather, the three perpendicular phen-anthroline planes have three large pockets between them. Models show that two water molecules fit compactly into each pocket, the whole aggregate now becoming roughly spherical. This is in accord with the observation that many of the phenanthroline complexes appear as hexahydrates.

It would appear likely that these water molecules will immediately occupy any coordination positions made vacant by loss of coordinated phenanthroline. Any new aggregate of the complex that tends to remove these water molecules from their close proximity to the metal should decrease the rate of dissociation of the complex. However, this would also

Table 4.18   Effect of large ions and polyelectrolytes on the rates of racemization and dissociation of $Fe(phen)_3^{2+}$ at 25°C

Solution	$10^4 k_{rac}$, sec^{-1}	$10^5 k_{diss}$, sec^{-1}
0.02 M HCl[a]	6.7	7.6
0.05 M brucine hydrochloride	8.5	8.9
0.05 M quinine hydrochloride	10	8.4
0.30 M quinine hydrochloride	23	12
0.05 M strychnine hydrochloride	...	8.2
0.05 M Na camphor sulfonate	7.7	6.7
0.50 M Na camphor sulfonate	13	3.9
0.01 % Na polystyrenesulfonate	2.7	1.8
1.00 % Na polystyrenesulfonate	2.8	1.3

From reference 191.
[a] In addition to the added salts all solutions contain 0.02 M HCl. Addition of ordinary salts has only a small effect on the rates; for example, in 2.0 M KCl solution $k_{diss} = 7.2 \times 10^{-5}$ sec^{-1}.

loosen the compact hexahydrate arrangement and give greater freedom of motion to the chelate rings, resulting in an increased rate of racemization. The results obtained with added camphor sulfonate ion are in accord with such an explanation. Furthermore, spectrochemical observations on these solutions provide evidence of ion-pair formation between $Fe(phen)_3^{2+}$ and the camphor sulfonate ion.[193]

That the rate of racemization decreases in the presence of polystyrene-sulfonate ion may be due to the sulfonate groups being linked together in the polyanion. This then gives rigidity to the system and decreases the rate of intramolecular racemization. It is of interest to note that there is an abrupt decrease in rate even at low concentrations of the polyanion, and then an almost total lack of dependence on its concentration. This suggests that the associated species is completely formed at the low concentrations, a conclusion which agrees with the large binding constant of 4×10^4 M^{-1} found by a dialysis technique.[193] Such behavior of complex ions in the presence of polyelectrolytes may be related to the biological activity of these metal complexes. For example, certain complexes injected intra-peritoneally into mice cause paralysis and death by respiratory failure, suggestive of a curare form of activity. It is believed that this activity results from the attachment of the complexes to active sites in the biological system.[194]

The rate of loss of optical rotation of complex ions is also dependent upon the nature of the solvent. Werner[1] observed that the addition of acetone to water solutions of $Cr(C_2O_4)_3{}^{3-}$ retards its rate of racemization. However, the addition of acetone to an aqueous solution of $Co(C_2O_4)_3{}^{3-}$ results in a slightly accelerated rate of racemization.[107] A more detailed study[195] of the racemization rate of $Cr(C_2O_4)_3{}^{3-}$ in binary solvents of water containing different mole fractions of methanol, ethanol, 1-propanol, 2-propanol, acetone, and 1,4-dioxane shows that in all cases there is a smooth decrease in rate with an increase in organic solvent. It was not possible to establish any definite relationships between solvents.

Racemization rates of $Ni(bipy)_3{}^{2+}$, $Ni(phen)_3{}^{2+}$, $Fe(bipy)_3{}^{2+}$, and $Fe(phen)_3{}^{2+}$ in aqueous solvent mixtures and in non-aqueous solvents have been reported.[161,184,190a] The racemization rates of the Fe(II) complexes are greater in primary alcohols and nitrobenzene than in water, whereas those of the Ni(II) complexes are smaller. Detailed kinetic data for $Ni(phen)_3{}^{2+}$ as well as the dielectric constants and viscosities of the solvents are summarized in Table 4.19. These data show clearly that there is no simple correlation between the rate of racemization and either the dielectric constant or the viscosity of a solvent. Furthermore, these solvents of extremely different coordinating properties do not greatly alter the activation energies and frequency factors for the loss of optical rotation of the complex ion. This indicates that the racemization processes in all of these systems are not too different. The fact that racemization of $Ni(phen)_3{}^{2+}$ in aqueous solution takes place by a dissociation mechanism[163] would indicate that the same process is involved in the other solvents. Furthermore, exchange studies[162] on the system $Ni(phen)_3{}^{2+}$-*phen show that the rate of ligand exchange is the same as the rate of racemization in nitrobenzene and also in absolute alcohol. Thus, racemization in these two solvents must also involve a dissociation process.

Table 4.19 Inversion rates of $Ni(phen)_3{}^{2+}$ at 25°C in different solvents

Solvent	Dielectric Constant, 25°C	Viscosity, m.p. 25°C	$k \times 10^6$, sec^{-1}	E_a, kcal	log A
Water	80.0	8.95	5.7	24.9 ± 0.3	13.0 ± 0.3
Methanol	33.7	5.5	3.7	23.7	11.9
Ethanol	25.7	11.0	2.0	24.7	12.4
n-Propanol	21.8	20.0	1.8	25.6	12.3
Acetone	21.4	3.1	5.0	24.6	12.7
Puridine	12.5	8.9	7.7	26.0	13.9
Nitrobenzene	35.0	18.0	0.57	26.1	12.9
Ethylene glycol	41.2	181.0	0.67	27.5	14.0

From reference 190a.

The inversion rates of Ni(phen)$_3$$^{2+}$ in binary solvents of water with methanol and acetone vary in a complicated manner. There is a minimum in the rate of racemization at about 0.2 mole fraction of organic component and a maximum at about 0.8, the variation amounting to approximately a twofold change in rate. Ligand exchange experiments in water-ethanol mixtures show that the dissociation mechanism does not change with changes in solvent composition.[162] Such variations in rate are not now understood but appear to be somewhat akin to the changes in rate of solvolysis of organic compounds with changes in solvent composition Studies[190b] on the partial molal heats of solution of various compounds in different solvent mixtures suggest that the peculiar variations in rates of solvolysis are due largely to the solvent effects on the ground state of the substrate. The transition state contribution seems to follow on approximate linear behavior with change in solvent.

Investigations[184] of the rates of dissociation and racemization of Fe(bipy)$_3$$^{2+}$ and Fe(phen)$_3$$^{2+}$ in water-methanol systems show that the intramolecular mechanism makes a greater contribution to the observed rate of racemization with increasing concentration of methanol. It was also observed that the rate of racemization of Fe(bipy)$_3$$^{2+}$ in methanol and methanol-rich solvents, unlike that in water, is almost independent of acid concentration. This is to be expected if the contribution made by a dissociation mechanism to the rate of loss of optical activity is negligible.

Solid State. Under ordinary conditions most optically active metal complexes do not racemize in the solid state. However, an exception is provided by the salts of Cr(C$_2$O$_4$)$_3$$^{3-}$, which were studied rather extensively in the mid-thirties.[98,166] Experiments showed that the loss of optical activity is definitely due to racemization and not decomposition, and also that the water of crystallization has an effect on the rate. For example, when (+)- or (−)-K$_3$Cr(C$_2$O$_4$)$_3$·2H$_2$O is heated at 120°C in evacuated sealed tubes, the optical activity is essentially lost in several hours, whereas this loss takes several months with the anhydrous salt. It was suggested that the water enters the coordination sphere to give an unstable "expanded" complex which may either be symmetrical or rapidly lose its optical activity. This was visualized[196] as an expansion to a symmetrical eight-coordinated system containing two molecules of coordinated water.

Investigations of the rate of racemization of K$_3$[Co(C$_2$O$_4$)$_3$]·2.6·H$_2$O in the solid state at extreme pressures of 10,000–40,000 atm show that the rate increases with a rise in pressure.[197a] The volume of activation, $\Delta V^{\ddagger}$, was found to be −1.4 and −1.8 cm^3/mole in two independent experiments. This suggests that there is a volume decrease in going from the ground state to the transition state and argues against a bond-stretching process such as is required by the chelate ring opening-closing mechanism.

It should be noted that $\Delta V^{\ddagger} = +1.2 \text{ cm}^3/\text{mole}$ for the exchange of water[197b] with $\text{Co(NH}_3)_5\text{H}_2\text{O}^{3+}$, which is believed to involve primarily a dissociation (or expansion) process. The observed negative sign for $\Delta V^{\ddagger}$ for the racemization of the oxalato complex is consistent with either a twisting mechanism or one in which there is an increase of coordination number to permit water of crystallization to enter the coordination sphere. For the twist mechanism a volume decrease of approximately 8% is estimated in going from an octahedral to a trigonal prismatic structure. For the increased coordination number process, it follows that the volume would decrease because the coordinated water occupies less volume than does lattice water. The most significant point is that racemization in the solid state does not appear to involve a bond rupture process such as is operative in solution.

Pressure is also found[197a] to exert a rate-accelerating effect on the racemization of crystalline $[\text{Fe(phen)}_3](\text{ClO}_4)_2 \cdot x\text{H}_2\text{O}$ and $[\text{Ni(phen)}_3]$ $(\text{ClO}_4)_2 \cdot x\text{H}_2\text{O}$, with values of $\Delta V^{\ddagger}$ of approximately $-1.0 \text{ cm}^3/\text{mole}$. Again the negative volume of activation supports either a twisting mechanism or one whereby the coordination number of the metal increases to permit the coordination of water molecules. It appears that both complexes racemize by the same process in the solid state, whereas we recall that in solution the Ni(II) complex racemizes by an intermolecular mechanism and the Fe(II) complex largely by an intramolecular mechanism. Neither solid racemizes over a period of 4 months at a pressure of 1 atm and room temperature. Preliminary studies have shown that the rate of racemization of $\text{K}_3\text{Cr(C}_2\text{O}_4)_3 \cdot 2\text{H}_2\text{O}$ also increases under pressure, whereas samples of $[\text{Co(en)}_3]\text{I}_3$ could not be racemized at pressures of 39,000 atm over a period of 70 hr.

Effect of Electron Transfer. The subject of electron transfer is discussed in Chapter 6. That an electron transfer reaction can greatly catalyze the racemization of complex ions has been clearly demonstrated for the systems $\text{Os(bipy)}_3^{2+ \text{ and } 3+ \text{ }198}$ and $\text{Co(en)}_3^{2+ \text{ and } 3+}$.[117] The two systems differ in that both the Os(II) and Os(III) complexes are inert and do not undergo racemization whereas the Co(II) complex is labile and does not retain any optical activity and the Co(III) complex is inert and does not readily racemize. Therefore, the enhanced rates of racemization produced by electron transfer occur by a different process for each of these two systems. In the first place complete racemization of the inert Os(II) and (III) complexes will occur only if equivalent amounts of the two with different generic configurations, D-Os(bipy)$_3^{2+}$ and L-Os(bipy)$_3^{3+}$ or *vice versa*, are mixed. Thus, the rapid electron transfer offered by the equilibrium

$$\text{D-Os(bipy)}_3^{2+} + \text{L-Os(bipy)}_3^{3+} \rightleftharpoons \text{L-Os(bipy)}_3^{2+} + \text{D-Os(bipy)}_3^{3+} \quad (52)$$

will result in a rapid loss of optical rotation. In fact, at $4°C$ rapid mixing of $1 \times 10^{-4}\ M$ D-Os(bipy)$_3^{2+}$ and L-Os(bipy)$_3^{3+}$ gives a solution that is completely racemized within the time ($\sim$15 sec) of observation by means of a polarimeter.[199] Studies[200] using an n.m.r. line broadening technique show that the second-order rate constant for electron transfer in this system is greater than $5 \times 10^4\ M^{-1}\ \text{sec}^{-1}$ at $25°$.

The racemization of Co(en)$_3^{3+}$, instead, requires only catalytic amounts of Co(en)$_3^{2+}$. Since the Co(II) complex is configuratively labile, the racemization path must involve conversion of D*-Co(en)$_3^{3+}$ into D*-Co(en)$_3^{2+}$, which racemizes instantly. This means that the simultaneously formed Co(III) complex is racemic. This behavior was used[117] in the resolution of racemic-Co(en)$_3^{3+}$ to obtain in excess of 150% of the amount of the dextro or levo isomer originally present. This was made possible by the addition of Co(en)$_3^{2+}$ to catalyze the racemization of Co(en)$_3^{3+}$. Thus, as the less soluble diastereoisomer D*-[Co(en)$_3$]-Cl(+)-C$_4$H$_4$O$_6$ separates from solution, the remaining L*-Co(en)$_3^{3+}$ is catalytically racemized, providing more of the D* form, which then crystallizes. It had previously been observed[1,137] in other systems that virtually all of a labile complex may be separated as the least soluble diastereoisomer because of the fact that the more soluble form racemizes to continually supply some of the less soluble isomer. Such a process is termed a *second-order asymmetric induction*.

A detailed kinetic study has been made[201] of the electron transfer racemization of Co(EDTA)$^-$ and of Co(PDTA)$^-$. As we shall see, the two systems differ in a most interesting fashion because of the extreme stereospecificity imposed on the cobalt complexes by the propylenediaminetetraacetate ion ligand (p. 339). There is no such effect with EDTA, so that its Co(II) complex rapidly rearranges, providing an electron transfer path for the racemization of the inert Co(III) system. Thus, racemization occurs by an uncatalyzed path

$$(+)\text{-Co(EDTA)}^- \underset{k}{\overset{k}{\rightleftharpoons}} (-)\text{-Co(EDTA)}^- \tag{53}$$

and a catalyzed path

$$(+)\text{-Co(EDTA)}^- + (\pm)\text{-Co(EDTA)}^{2-} \underset{k_e}{\overset{k_e}{\rightleftharpoons}} (+)\text{-Co(EDTA)}^{2-}$$

$$\downarrow \text{fast}$$

$$+ (\pm)\text{-Co(EDTA)}^- \qquad\qquad (\pm)\text{-Co(EDTA)}^{2-} \tag{54}$$

such that the experimentally observed rate constant, k_{obs}, is given by the contribution of the two paths:

$$k_{obs} = 2k + k_e[\text{CoEDTA}^{2-}] \tag{55}$$

At 100°C the rate constants have the values of $k = 4.2 \times 10^{-6} \sec^{-1}$ and $k_e = 7.0 \times 10^{-4} M^{-1} \sec^{-1}$. The rate constant for the catalyzed path and its kinetic parameters, $E_a = 21$ kcal/mole and $\Delta S^{\ddagger} = -15$ eu, are in good agreement with the results obtained for electron transfer by the cobalt isotope exchange method.[202] The value of k agrees with the value determined independently for a system containing no catalyst, and this path has kinetic parameters of $E_a = 41$ kcal/mole and $\Delta S^{\ddagger} = 21$ eu.

Experiments were conducted in the range of pH from 2 to 4, and in this range the rate of the uncatalyzed path was independent of pH, but that of the catalyzed path increased with decreasing pH. This suggests that the species $Co(HEDTA)H_2O^-$, where the $HEDTA^{3-}$ behaves as a quinquidentate with the free carboxylate group protonated, is a more efficient catalyst for racemization than is the sexadentate system $Co(EDTA)^{2-}$. The reason for this is not known, but experiments in D_2O give almost the same results as in H_2O, showing that there is virtually no isotope effect, which then argues against a hydrogen atom transfer process.

In much the same way the rate of racemization of L^*-$Co(-)$-$PDTA^-$ in the presence of D^*-$Co(+)$-$PDTA^{2-}$ was investigated.[201] The extreme stereospecificity of the optically active ligand fixes the configuration of the cobalt complexes so that even the labile Co(II) system maintains a preferred configuration.[203] Thus, the electron transfer-catalyzed racemization proceeds with conservation of configuration in both the Co(III) and the Co(II) chelates, and in this respect the system is similar to the racemization of D-$Os(bipy)_3^{2+}$, L-$Os(bipy)_3^{3+}$. Therefore, complete racemization occurs only when equivalent amounts of the two cobalt complexes are mixed, each containing a different enantiomer of the ligand:

$$L^*\text{-}Co(-)\text{-}PDTA^- + D^*\text{-}Co(+)\text{-}PDTA^{2-} \rightleftharpoons$$

$$L^*\text{-}Co(-)\text{-}PDTA^{2-} + D^*\text{-}Co(+)\text{-}PDTA^- \quad (56)$$

There is no uncatalyzed racemization of the Co(III) complex, and its catalyzed rate decreases slightly with increase in pH. This pH effect and the kinetic data for the PDTA system are in very close correspondence with the catalyzed racemization of $Co(EDTA)^-$ and attest to the close similarity in the electronic configuration of the two sets of reactants although their steric factors are uniquely different.

Effect of Heterogeneous Catalyst. That reactions of some metal complexes are subject to heterogeneous catalysis has been known for many years.[204] For example, when an aqueous solution of $Co(NH_3)_6^{3+}$ is shaken with decolorizing charcoal, it readily forms $Co(NH_3)_5H_2O^{3+}$ and on prolonged treatment a precipitate of cobalt hydroxide begins to separate from solution. Exactly how this catalytic effect works is not as yet understood, but the fact that it does operate for some systems has been utilized in various ways. Thus, the use of charcoal as a catalyst greatly facilitates the synthesis of $Co(NH_3)_6{}^{3+}$ and further renders this complex sufficiently labile so that its stability constant has been determined.[205] Although $Co(en)_2$ $(NH_3)_2{}^{3+}$ does not react with nitrite ion alone, in the presence of charcoal it is converted into $Co(en)_2(NO_2)_2{}^+$.[206] More recently charcoal has been used to permit the rapid equilibration of Co(III) complexes containing optically active ligands in investigations of stereospecificity in metal complexes.[207] That the rate of isomerization of some complexes may be subject to charcoal catalysis is also illustrated by the observation that the conversion of *trans*-$Co(en)_2(H_2O)_2{}^{3+}$ to the *cis* isomer is ten times faster in the presence of charcoal than in its absence.[208]

The optical rotation of a solution of (+)-$Co(en)_3{}^{3+}$ is unchanged after 24 hr at 90°C, but with added decolorizing carbon the optical activity is completely lost in 2 min.[116] Racemization studies were accompanied by *en exchange and spectrophotometric investigations, which show that the rate of ligand exchange is slower than the rate of racemization and that the extent of dissociation of the complex is small.[209] Thus, racemization occurs by primarily an intramolecular process, and there is considerable circumstantial evidence that this is due to an electron transfer process between the Co(III) complex and catalytic amounts of the labile Co(II) complex. There is, for instance, some indication that the effectiveness of the catalyst in reactions of Co(III) complexes is markedly improved by the presence of Co(II) ions.[208] Furthermore, it was found that, whenever solutions of the Co(III) complexes $Co(en)_3{}^{3+}$, $Co(acac)_3$, $Co(gly)_3$, $Co(NH_3)_6{}^{3+}$, and $Co(C_2O_4)_3{}^{3-}$ are heated for a short time with added charcoal, each of the solutions contains approximately 5% of Co(II).[210]

In one set of experiments it was observed that (+)-$Co(en)_3{}^{3+}$ is completely racemized in 3 min in boiling aqueous solution containing suspended charcoal and approximately 4% Co(II) in the resulting solution. When the experiment was repeated in 0.1 M H_2SO_4 solution, there was only *ca.* 6% racemization, but again about 4% Co(II) was found in solution. This suggests that in acid the Co(II) is present as $Co(H_2O)_6{}^{2+}$, which does not undergo electron transfer with $Co(en)_3{}^{3+}$, but that in water the Co(II) is present as $Co(en)_3{}^{2+}$, which is then an efficient electron transfer catalyst. However, the rate of racemization of $Co(en)_3{}^{3+}$ is much too fast to be due to its electron transfer with $Co(en)_3{}^{2+}$ in a homogeneous system. For example, the complete racemization of 0.055 M (+)-$Co(en)_3{}^{3+}$ in the presence of 0.02 M $Co(en)_3{}^{2+}$ and 0.24 M en at 25°C requires 8 days, whereas only 2 min is needed for 100 cc of this solution containing 2 grams of charcoal. This suggests a catalysis of the electron transfer process itself.

Kinetic studies of the charcoal catalysis of the racemization of $Co(en)_3^{3+}$ and of $Co(EDTA)^-$ show that the rates are first order in complex and first order in catalyst.[211] It was also observed that salts of SO_4^{2-} retard the racemization of $Co(en)_3^{3+}$, but salts of ClO_4^-, NO_3^-, or NO_2^- accelerate it, whereas the racemization of $Co(EDTA)^-$ is not greatly affected by added salts. The activation energy for the racemization of $Co(EDTA)^-$ on activated sugar carbon is 7.3 kcal/mole compared to values of 40.6 kcal for its uncatalyzed racemization and 21 kcal for its $Co(EDTA)^{2-}$-catalyzed rate. Wood carbon is approximately ten times more effective a catalyst than is sugar carbon. There are conflicting reports on what other solids can serve as heterogeneous catalysts for these reactions. Raney nickel decomposes $Co(en)_3^{3+}$, whereas its rate of racemization is not affected by silica gel, activated alumina, platinum asbestos, or partially reduced zinc oxide.[211] Freshly prepared platinum, palladium, or rhodium black in the presence of a reducing agent such as adsorbed H_2 or added SO_3^{2-} or C_2H_5OH is an effective catalyst.[210]

Investigation[212] of the rates of hydrolyses of several complexes adsorbed on silica gel reveals that the rates of acid hydrolyses are slightly slower and those of base hydrolyses are appreciably slower than the corresponding rates in bulk solution. This decrease in reactivity may be attributed to a decrease in the water and hydroxide ion activity at the surface of the gel. It should also be mentioned that the reactions of some metal complexes, such as $Cr(III)$[211] and $Rh(III)$,[210] are reported not to be subject to charcoal catalysis. Since the ammine complexes of these two metal ions are not readily reduced, this observation indirectly supports the view that $Co(II)$ is required in the charcoal catalysis of $Co(III)$ reactions.

Photoracemization. It has long been known that some metal complexes are sensitive to light, and the photochemistry of metal complexes is of great interest at present because the results can often be understood in terms of the current theories of bonding for these systems. Some investigations have been made of photosubstitution and photoredox reactions of Werner complexes (see pp. 654–666). Also some studies[213] have been reported on the photochemistry of metal carbonyls and π complexes (p. 547).

Investigations have been made[214] of the photochemistry of the following optically active compounds: $Cr(C_2O_4)_3^{3-}$, $Co(C_2O_4)_3^{3-}$, $Rh(C_2O_4)_3^{3-}$, $Co(EDTA)^-$, $Co(en)_2Cl_2^+$, $Co(en)_2C_2O_4^+$, $Co(en)_2(NO_2)_2^+$, and $Co(en)_3^{3+}$. The photochemistry of $Cr(C_2O_4)_3^{3-}$ was studied in some detail because for this complex there is no photochemical reaction other than photoracemization. Some of the results reported are summarized in Table 4.20, and these show that neither the solvent nor the wavelength of light used has much effect on the quantum yield. Also, although the thermal racemization is acid catalyzed, the quantum yield for photoracemization shows no detectable dependence on acidity. Experiments in D_2O indicate a reduction in the thermal racemization rate, $k_{H_2O}/k_{D_2O} = 1.26$, and a comparable reduction in the quantum yield at 420 mμ, $\phi_{H_2O}/\phi_{D_2O} = 1.24$. Similarly [18]O exchange experiments show comparable ratios of $k_{rac}/k_{exch} = 2.6$ and $\phi_{rac}/\phi_{exch} = 2.3$, respectively, for these two processes. These results suggest that the thermal and photochemical racemizations

Table 4.20 Photoracemization of $Cr(C_2O_4)_3{}^{3-}$

λ, mμ	Solvent	Temp., °C[a]	$I \times 10^6$, einsteins/sec	$R \times 10^7$, M sec^{-1}	ϕ^b
420	H_2O	1.0	1.85	1.50	0.081
420	H_2O	8.0	1.53	1.64	0.106
420	H_2O	15.0	1.98	1.85	0.093
420	30% C_2H_5OH	15.0	1.09	3.65	0.043
420	30% C_2H_5OH	4.0	0.39	0.35	0.089
570	30% C_2H_5OH	4.0	3.17	2.58	0.082
697	30% C_2H_5OH	4.0	0.27	0.18	0.068

From reference 214.

[a] The temperature dependence for thermal racemization in water is given by $k_{rac} = 1.63 \times 10^7 \exp(-15,000/RT)$ sec^{-1}, and in 30% ethanol-water by $k_{rac} = 6.23 \times 10^8 \exp(-17,600/RT)$ sec^{-1}, as compared to $\phi = 3.67 \exp(-2,100/RT)$ and $\phi = 25.8 \exp(-3,200/RT)$, respectively.

[b] The quantum yield, ϕ, is the moles of complex racemized per einstein of light absorbed.

proceed by related mechanisms, presumably of the type described earlier of chelate ring opening and closing, with the bond rupture capable of being driven photochemically.

It has been known for some time that the principal thermal and photochemical reaction of $Co(C_2O_4)_3{}^{3-}$ is one of oxidation-reduction to yield $Co(II)$ and CO_2.[215] However, for the optically active complex the rate of disappearance as deduced by following the rate of loss of optical activity is noticeably larger than that obtained from the decrease in concentration as measured directly by following the optical density decrease. It appears that about 15% of the time loss of optical activity occurs through racemization, but the precision of the results is not sufficient to allow any further conclusions.

Photochemical observations made on the decomposition and racemization of several complexes are summarized in Table 4.21. For the Co(III)

Table 4.21 Photochemical decomposition and racemization of some metal complexes

Complex	Comments[a]	
$Co(en)_3^{3+}$	no photodec.	no photorac.
$Co(en)_2C_2O_4^+$	no photodec.	no photorac.
$Co(en)(C_2O_4)_2^-$	photodec. (?)	photorac.
$Co(EDTA)^-$	sl. photodec.	no photorac.
$Co(C_2O_4)_3^{3-}$	photodec.	sl. photorac.
$cis\text{-}Co(en)_2(NO_2)_2^+$	no photodec.	no photorac.
$cis\text{-}Co(en)_2Cl_2^+$	photodec.	no photorac.[b]
$Cr(C_2O_4)_3^{3-}$	no photodec.	photorac.
$Rh(C_2O_4)_3^{3-}$	photodec.	photorac.

From reference 214 and other references cited therein.
[a] Photodec. = photodecomposition, photorac. = photoracemization, and sl. = slight.
[b] Considering only aquation to $cis\text{-}Co(en)_2H_2OCl^{2+}$, this occurs with retention as it does in the thermal aquation.

complexes of the series $Co(en)_3^{3+}$ through $Co(C_2O_4)_3^{3-}$ it is seen that the replacement of en by $C_2O_4^{2-}$ labilizes the complex toward photo (and thermal) redox decomposition and also toward photo (and thermal) racemization. This behavior supports the view of Adamson[216] that the photolability of Co(III) complexes toward racemization (and aquation) appears to be closely related to the ease of oxidation of the acido groups and thus to the ease of photoredox decomposition. Similarly, the observation that there is no photodecomposition for $Cr(C_2O_4)_3^{3-}$ and only a small amount for $Rh(C_2O_4)_3^{3-}$ is understood in terms of these metals being more difficult to reduce to the divalent state than is Co(III).

Ligand Stereospecificity

The discussion in this section is taken largely from the excellent review of Sargeson[217] on optical phenomena in metal chelates. When a dissymmetric chelate of the type $M(AA)_3$ contains an optically active ligand such as $(-)$-1,2-propylenediamine, an asymmetric bias is imparted to the system and the two possible optical isomers, $L^*\text{-}M(-)\text{-}pn_3$ and $D^*\text{-}M(-)\text{-}pn_3$, are no longer obtained in equal amounts. This preference for one optical isomer over the other is called *ligand stereospecificity*.

Most of the early experiments on this phenomenon were conducted by Jaeger[218] and coworkers, who were of the opinion that an optically active ligand favored the formation of one isomer of a metal complex to the complete exclusion of the other. For example, it was felt that only two isomers, either D*(−)(−)(−) and L*(+)(+)(+) or D*(+)(+)(+) and L*(−)(−)(−), of the eight possible isomers§

D*(+)(+)(+)   D*(+)(+)(−)   D*(+)(−)(−)   D*(−)(−)(−)

L*(+)(+)(+)   L*(+)(+)(−)   L*(+)(−)(−)   L*(−)(−)(−)

were formed by the reaction of *racemic*-AA with a metal ion to yield M(AA)₃. However, as early as 1925 Lifschitz[219] had isolated both D*(+)(+)(+) and L*(+)(+)(+) isomers of α-tris[(+)-alaninato]cobalt(III), demonstrating that the hypothesis of absolute stereospecificity is not tenable. This was also shown by the separation of both optical forms of Co(−)(pn)₂CO₃⁺.[220]

Further experimental support of the fact that ligand stereospecificity is not absolute is provided by the extensive investigations of the group working with Dwyer.[217] They have been able to isolate the D* and L* forms of the complexes [Co(−)pn₃]³⁺,[221] [Co(en)(−)pn₂]³⁺, [Co(en)₂(−)-pn]³⁺,[222] and [Pt(+)pn₂(−)pn]⁴⁺ [223] and to show that the compounds are stable. The inability of early workers to isolate such compounds containing "mixed" (+) and (−) bidentate ligands was not due to the presumed inherent instability of the complexes but to the establishment of equilibrium, among all the possible species, during the preparative procedures. Fractional crystallization does not separate all of the species and gives the spurious results that only certain stereospecific products are formed. By making use of paper chromatography it has been possible to separate and identify the complexes in such equilibrium mixtures, and for these systems the eluent results show that all of the theoretically possible complexes are present.

For example, aqueous reaction mixtures containing CoCl₂, charcoal, HCl, and varying ratios of en and (−)-pn were allowed to react and oxidize with air for a period of 3 hr at 25°. After removal of the charcoal, the solutions were chromatographed on paper with the eluent 1-butanol-H₂O-HCl, and the separation of the L* isomers is shown in Fig. 4.26. The spots were later identified by authentic samples of the isomers. The method of separation was then applied to a cellulose column, and the isomers isolated in gram quantities. For reaction mixtures containing en/(−)-pn ratios of 1/2 and 2/1, the concentrations of the complexes found at equilibrium are in agreement with the statistical distribution of the

§ See p. 42 for the meaning of symbols used for optical isomers. The representation D*(+)(+)(+) signifies a complex M(AA)₃ in which D* gives the absolute configuration of the complex and (+) designates the optical isomer of AA which is dextrorotatory at the Na_D line.

diamines among all the possible compounds. However, for a given complex such as $Co(en)_2(-)pn^{3+}$ the amounts of D* and L* isomers differ because their stabilities differ, and as a result there is a certain degree of stereospecificity in these systems.

It is now understood that the amount of stereospecificity in metal complexes is largely a property of the ligand and may vary from practically zero, as in $Co(-)pn(C_2O_4)_2^-$,[224] to almost total specificity, as in

(1)   (2)   (3)   (4)   (5)   (6)

Fig. 4.26 (1), $[Co(en)_2(—)pn]^{3+}$ equil. mixture; (2), L*-$[Co(—)pn_3]^{3+}$; (3), L*-$[Co(—)(pn)_2en]^{3+}$; (4), L*-$[Co(—)pn(en)_2]^{3+}$; (5), $[Co(en)_3]^{3+}$; (6), $[Co(—)(pn)_2en]^{3+}$ equil. mixt. From reference 222.

$Co(-)PDTA^-$.[201] Corey and Bailar[225] have successfully accounted for the stereospecificity in these systems on the basis of a conformational analysis. Coordinated ethylenediamine forms a five-membered chelate ring for which the same techniques of stereochemical analysis can be applied as were used for cyclopentane systems.[226] Thus, the bond angles and distances for the Co-en strain-free chelate ring, when calculated by vector analysis, agree well with those obtained from the x-ray structure determination of $Co(en)_3^{3+}$.[227] The puckered chelate ring contains hydrogen atoms attached to adjacent carbon and nitrogen atoms in a staggered arrangement of two possible conformations (Fig. 4.27). These conformations are mirror images and are designated k and k' with the solid lines to carbon and nitrogen representing axial, and the dashed lines equatorial, positions.

For the complex D*-$Coen_3^{3+}$ there are four possible arrangements of the three chelate rings, corresponding to kkk, $k'kk$, $k'k'k$, and $k'k'k'$. The

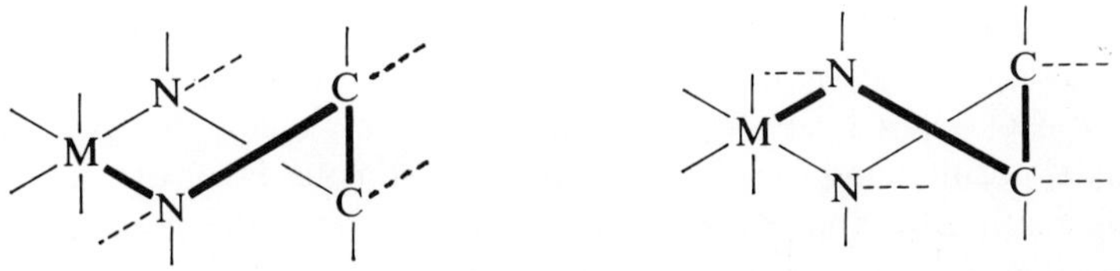

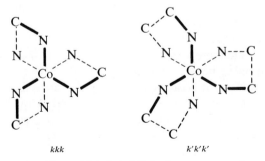

Fig. 4.27 The conformations of coordinated ethylenediamine rings where — to N and C represents axial and ---- equatorial positions. The structure for k is that found in D*-Co(en)$_3^{3+}$.

four differ in stabilities, and the relative potential energies of the two extreme forms kkk and $k'k'k'$ were estimated by considering the following atomic interactions: (1) H, H; (2) H, C between the two carbon atoms of the ring and the axial hydrogen of the NH$_2$ groups; and (3) electrostatic interactions (inverse square) between the hydrogen atoms of the NH$_2$ groups. This treatment shows that the kkk conformation for D*-Co(en)$_3^{3+}$ is more stable than the $k'k'k'$ by approximately 1.8 kcal/mole, or 0.6 kcal/mole for each chelate ring. The kkk form is more stable because of the small H, C interactions, and is present at equilibrium to the extent of 95% on the basis of these calculations. This is in accord with the crystal structure of the complex which shows that the three C—C axes of the en molecules are parallel to the threefold axis of symmetry of the complex. The two forms are represented in Fig. 4.28, which shows that the C—C axes are eclipsed in kkk but staggered in $k'k'k'$. However, in L*-Co(en)$_3^{3+}$ the $k'k'k'$ form is now the most stable because again the C—C axes are parallel to the threefold axis of symmetry of the complex.

Much of the research on stereospecificity in metal complexes has made use of ($-$)1,2-propylenediamine (pn), which, like en, forms five-membered

Fig. 4.28 The conformations of D*-Co(en)$_3^{3+}$ in the two extreme forms kkk (eclipsed C—C axes) and $k'k'k'$ (staggered C—C axes). The kkk form is the stable one. From reference 222.

chelate rings that can exist in the k and the k' conformations. The absolute configuration of $(-)$pn and its chelate ring conformations of k and k' for D^*-Co$(-)$pn$_3{}^{3+}$ are shown in Fig. 4.29. For k the methyl group is in an axial position and for k' it is equatorial; estimates favor the equatorial conformation by approximately 2 kcal/mole. Since this is larger than the value of 0.6 kcal/mole favoring the k form, it follows that for D^*-Co$(-)$pn$_3{}^{3+}$ the k' conformation predominates. This same k' conformation is even more stable in the L^*-Co$(-)$pn$_3{}^{3+}$ complex, where the

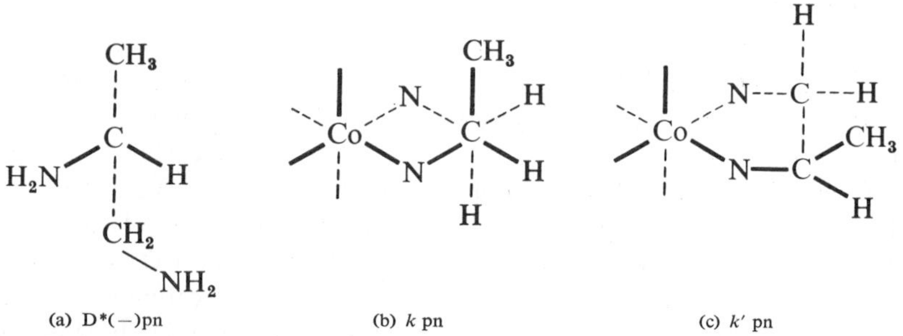

(a) D*(−)pn   (b) *k* pn   (c) *k'* pn

Fig. 4.29 The configuration of $(-)$-pn and the conformations of D^*-Co$(-)$pn$_3{}^{3+}$. Conformation b with the axial methyl group is less stable than c, where it is equatorial. From reference 222.

methyl groups are equatorial and, in addition, there is the stabilizing condition that the C—C axes are parallel to the threefold symmetry axes of the complex. Since both the D^* and L^* isomers contain equatorial methyl groups, it follows that on this basis they are of equal stability. However, in order for the methyl groups to be equatorial in the D^* isomer, it is forced to have the $k'k'k'$ conformation rather than the otherwise more stable (*ca.* 0.6 kcal for each chelate ring) kkk form. Thus, we see that for each chelate ring the L^* isomer should be more stable than the D^* form by 0.6 kcal/mole, which means that L^*-Co$(-)$pn$_3{}^{3+}$ is more stable than D^*-Co$(-)$pn$_3{}^{3+}$ by 1.8 kcal/mole.

Experimental data have been obtained[222] on the equilibrium distribution of stereoisomers in these systems, and, as is shown in Table 4.22, there is excellent agreement between the values determined by experiment and those calculated on the basis of conformational analysis. It is apparent that the free energy difference between the L^* and D^* isomers increases by approximately 0.5 kcal/mole for each $(-)$-pn in the complex. This results in a specificity favoring the L^* isomers for each $(-)$-pn equilibrium of $2:1$, $7:1$ and $15:1$.

The method of conformational analysis also predicts that the difference in stability between the L^* and D^* forms of α-tris[$(+)$-alanine]cobalt(III) should be small. The five-membered alanine rings are essentially planar,

Table 4.22 Isomer ratios for Co(III) complexes of ethylenediamine and (−)-propylenediamine

Complex	Ratio	ΔG°_{obs}, kcal/mole	ΔG°_{calc}, kcal/mole
D*-Co(en)(en)(−)pn^{3+}/L*-Co(en)(en)(−)pn^{3+} $\quad k^a \quad k \quad\quad k'^a \quad\quad k' \quad k' \quad\quad k'$	1/2.1	0.45	0.6
D*-Co(en)(−)pn(−)pn^{3+}/L*-Co(en)(−)pn(−)pn^{3+} $\quad k \quad\quad k' \quad k' \quad\quad k' \quad\quad k' \quad k'$	1/7.5	1.2	1.2
D*-Co(−)pn(−)pn(−)pn^{3+}/L*-Co(−)pn(−)pn(−)pn $\quad k' \quad\quad k' \quad\quad k' \quad\quad k' \quad\quad k' \quad\quad k'$	1/14.6	1.6	1.8

From reference 222.

[a] For definitions of k and k' see Fig. 4.27, 4.28, and 4.29.

and the distinction between axial and equatorial substituents no longer applies. This accounts for the fact that it was possible to isolate[219] both forms of the Co(III) complex. Recently, it was reported that the Cu(II) complexes of *racemic*, *dextro-*, and *levo-α*-alanine, Cu(α-alanine)$_2$, are all of equal stability.[228] Likewise appreciable quantities of both D* and L* isomers were isolated for the complexes Co(−)pn$_2$CO$_3$$^+$,[220] Co(−)pn(C$_2O_4$)$_2$$^-$, and Co(−)pn$_2C_2O_4$$^+$,[224] which show very little stereospecificity. The carbonato and oxalato rings are planar and do not contribute to the relative stabilities of the isomers; thus, the energy difference between the k' conformations of (−)-pn in the D* and L* complexes must be small.

At the other extreme, almost total stereospecificity is found in certain systems. Most notable of these is the (−)-propylenediaminetetraacetate, (−)PDTA, complex of Co(III). Whereas EDTA forms *racemic* Co-(EDTA)$^-$ the closely related ligand (−)PDTA yields only L*-Co(−)-PDTA$^-$. It has not been possible to detect even traces of the second isomer, and apparently not more than 1% of the unstable isomer is formed.[201,207] For example, the stable isomer L*-Co(−)PDTA$^-$ is compared with the unstable isomer L*-Co(+)PDTA$^-$ in Fig. 4.30. The isomers differ in the orientation of the methyl group on the N—C—C—N chelate ring. In the stable form the CH$_3$ is oriented equatorially, whereas it is axial in the unstable isomer. In the equatorial position the CH$_3$ points away from the other atoms, and this structure is stable compared with that of axial CH$_3$, which interacts strongly with one of the methylene hydrogens. Again the experimental result is in excellent agreement with the theory of conformational analysis. For a similar reason, *trans*-1,2-cyclohexane-diaminetetraacetic acid also coordinates stereospecifically.[207] Likewise the equatorial positioning of CH$_3$ in the Co(III) complex of 4-methyl-1,8-bis(salicylideneamino)-3,6-dithiaoctane is favored (85%) over the isomer where CH$_3$ is axial (15%).[229]

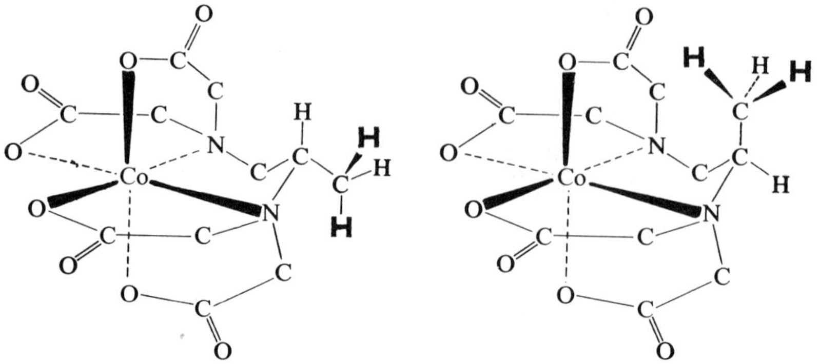

(a) L*-Co(−)PDTA⁻   (b) L*-Co(+)PDTA⁻

Fig. 4.30 Configuration of stereoisomers of propylenediaminetetraacetotocobaltate(III) anions. Structure a with the methyl group in the equatorial position is stable, and b with the group in the axial position is unstable. The methylene hydrogens are not shown.

Bailar[230] and his students have utilized this stereospecific behavior of coordination compounds both to prepare optically active complexes and to resolve diamines, carboxylic acids, and amino acids. They were able to prepare optically active Co(en)$_3$$^{3+}$, Co(en)$_2Cl_2$$^+$, and Co(en)$_2$(NO$_2$)$_2$$^+$ from the product obtained by the reaction of (±)-Co(en)$_2$CO$_3$$^+$ with (+)-tartaric acid.[231] This reaction yields a mixture of (+)-Co(en)$_2$(+)-tart$^+$ and (−)-Co(en)$_2$(+)-tart$^+$, and it was found that the two diastereomers differ in reactivity. When this mixture is shaken with ethylenediamine at room temperature, part of the material reacts within 2 hr to give (+)-Co(en)$_3$$^{3+}$; the remainder does not react even in 12 hr. As much as a 70% yield of (+)-Co(en)$_3$$^{3+}$ is obtained, so that either the two isomers of Co(en)$_2$(+)-tart$^+$ are not present in equal amount or the less reactive is converted to the more reactive as it is consumed by reaction with ethylenediamine. Similarly, reactions with hydrochloric acid and with calcium nitrite yield (+)-Co(en)$_2$Cl$_2$$^+$ and (+)-Co(en)$_2$(NO$_2$)$_2$$^+$, respectively. The same procedure, but with the formation of the (+)-antimonyltartrato instead of the (+)-tartrato complex, was used to prepare (−)-Co(en)$_2$Cl$_2$$^+$ and (−)-Co(trien)Cl$_2$$^+$.[232] The method has not been found to work for complexes with only one replaceable group, such as Co(en)$_2$(NH$_3$)Cl^{2+}, or with optically active ions such as (+)-α-bromocamphor-π-sulfonate, which would not readily enter the coordination sphere.

The treatment of Co(−)-pn$_2$CO$_3$$^+$ with (+)- and with (−)-tartaric acid gives Co(−)-pn$_2$(+)-tart$^+$ and Co(−)-pn$_2$(−)-tart$^+$, respectively, but the two isomers differ markedly in reactivity.[233] Both will react with (−)-propylenediamine to yield Co(−)-pn$_3$$^{3+}$, but, at 70°C, the latter reacts completely in 40 min, whereas the former requires 2 hr. This difference in reactivity was further demonstrated by the partial resolution of *racemic* tartaric acid. Whenever the reaction product obtained from the reaction of $Co(-)$-$pn_2CO_3^+$ with *racemic* tartaric acid is allowed to react with $(-)$-propylenediamine, the tartrate ion liberated in the initial stages of the reaction has a *levo* rotation.

A slightly different method has been used for the partial resolution of *racemic* tartaric acid[234] as well as certain other organic acids.[235] The method consists of allowing 100% excess of the racemic acid to react with $Co(-)$-$pn_2CO_3^+$. One enantiomorph of the acid enters the coordination sphere more readily than the other. This results in the resolution of the racemic acid, since the coordinated and uncoordinated acid fractions can be removed from solution separately. The same method was used to resolve a racemic mixture of propylenediamine or alanine with Cu(II), Ni(II), or Co(III) complexes of $(+)$-tartrate, $(-)$-glutamate, or $(+)$-gluconate ions.[236] The degree of resolution achieved was low, not over 5% with the Cu(II) and Ni(II) complexes or over 20% with Co(III) complexes.

Investigations have been made of the kinetics and mechanisms of of reactions of Co(III)-EDTA systems. One such study[237] of interest here is that of the reaction of en with L^*-Co(EDTA)$^-$ and with L^*-Co$(-)$-PDTA$^-$‡ to yield Co(en)$_3^{3+}$. The selectivity of substitution reactions is clearly demonstrated by the observations that L^*-Co(EDTA)$^-$ reacts to give a mixture of approximately 65% D^*-Co(en)$_3^{3+}$ and 35% L^*-Co(en)$_3^{3+}$, whereas L^*-Co$(-)$PDTA$^-$ produces $\sim$100% L^*-Co(en)$_3^{3+}$. It is remarkable that all six bonds to cobalt can be replaced without complete loss of optical activity and, even more significant, that one reaction yields a fractional inversion of configuration and the other

‡ Since the ions Co(en)$_3^{3+}$ and Co(EDTA)$^-$ have widely different symmetry properties, the relation of absolute structure is quite arbitrary. Sargeson[217] has related the structures as follows:

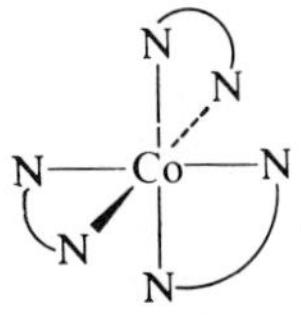

L*-Co(en)$_3^{3+}$ L*-Coen(C$_2$O$_4$)$_2^-$ L*-Co(EDTA)
(a)   (b)   (c)

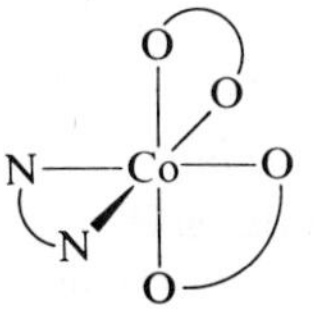

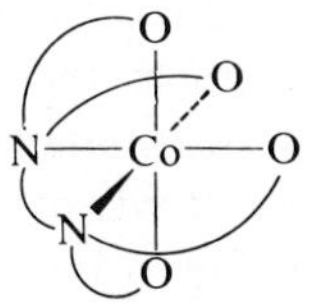

This was done because (b) and (c) have similar spectra, rotatory despersion curves, and diastereoisomer solubility and because (b) and (a) are related in structure. In reference 237, structure (c) is designated as the D* isomer. Our discussion will follow the relative designation of structures as shown by (a), (b), and (c).

involves complete retention. A satisfactory explanation of these relation-ships was offered on the basis of the proposed mechanism of reaction and the stereochemistry of the reactants.

The mechanism of the reaction is somewhat complicated, but essentially it involves the addition of the first en as the rate-determining step, followed by the rapid addition of the other two, with the formation of $Co(en)_3^{3+}$ as

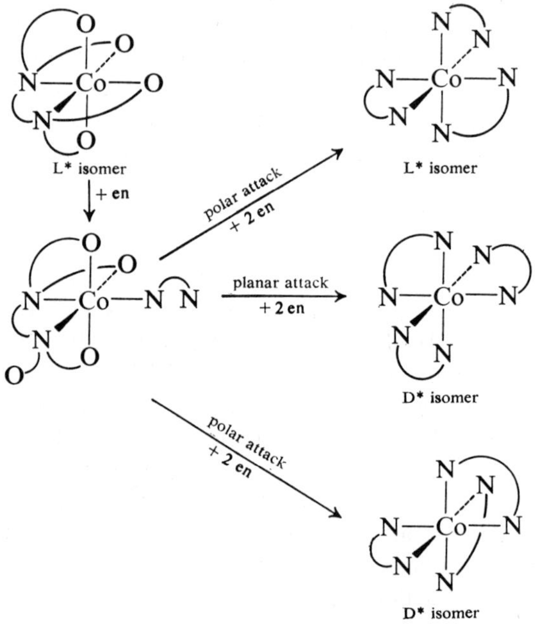

Fig. 4.31 Stereochemistry of the displacement of $EDTA^{4-}$ from L^*-$Co(EDTA)^-$ by en to yield $Co(en)_3^{3+}$.

the sole product. The inversion of configuration by some two-thirds of the cobalt atoms in the $Co(EDTA)^-$ case is understood on the basis of a statistical distribution over several virtually equivalent (energetically) paths. Two-thirds of these paths give inversion, while one-third produce retention (Fig. 4.31). The key initial step is the replacement of one of the two carbonyl groups in the unique plane (of the fused chelate rings) by one end of an ethylenediamine molecule. It is then assumed that the free end of the ethylenediamine has equal probability of replacing each of the three carboxyl groups that remain coordinated at this stage. The assump-tion of the site of initial attack is based on the fact that the bonds holding the carboxyl groups that are coplanar with the N—C—C—N chelate

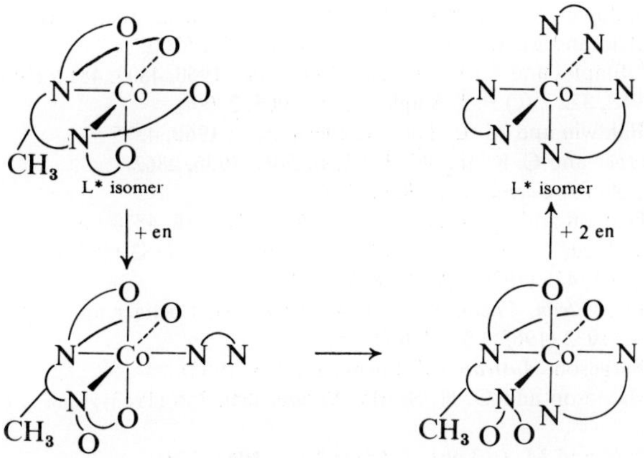

Fig. 4.32 Stereochemistry of the displacement of $(-)PDTA^{4+}$ from $L^*-Co(-)PDTA^-$ by en to yield $L^*-Co(en)_3^{3+}$.

ring are highly strained.[238] The contrasting retention for the reaction of $L^*-Co(-)-PDTA^-$ arises from an intramolecular steric effect due to the methyl group, which is so oriented that it tends to weaken two of the metal-ligand chelate rings. These are the two rings nearest the carbon atom to which the methyl group is attached, and this then determines the position of entry of en and of its ring closure. Such a process leads to the prediction of the observed complete retention of configuration in the formation of $L^*-Co(en)_3^{3+}$ (Fig. 4.32).

References

1. A. Werner, *Ann.*, **386**, 1 (1912); *Ber.*, **45**, 1228, 3061 (1912).
2. F. Basolo, B. D. Stone, and R. G. Pearson, *J. Am. Chem. Soc.*, **75**, 819 (1953).
3. K. C. Lord, M. A. Lynch, Jr., W. C. Schumb, and E. J. Slowinski, Jr., *J. Am. Chem. Soc.*, **73**, 522 (1950).
4. G. C. Hampson and L. Pauling, *J. Am. Chem. Soc.*, 2702 (1938); W. H. Zachariasen, *Acta Cryst.*, **7**, 792 (1954).
5. J. L. Hoard, *J. Am. Chem. Soc.*, **61**, 1252 (1939).
6. S. Richards, B. Pedersen, J. V. Silverton, and J. L. Hoard, *Inorg. Chem.*, **3**, 27 (1964); M. D. Lind, M. J. Hamor, T. A. Hamor, and J. L. Hoard, *ibid.*, **3**, 34 (1964).
7. D. D. Brown, C. K. Ingold, and R. S. Nyholm, *J. Chem. Soc.*, **1953**, 2673.
8. F. Basolo, *Chem. Revs.*, **52**, 459 (1953).
9. C. K. Ingold, R. S. Nyholm, and M. L. Tobe, *Nature*, **187**, 477 (1960); *ibid.*, **194**, 344 (1952); S. C. Chan and J. Miller, *Rev. Pure Appl. Chem.*, **15**, 11 (1965).

10. M. E. Baldwin, S. C. Chan, and M. L. Tobe, *J. Chem. Soc.*, **1961**, 4637.
11. S. C. Chan and M. L. Tobe, *J. Chem. Soc.*, **1963**, 5700.
12. (a) P. J. Staples and M. L. Tobe, *J. Chem. Soc.*, **1960**, 4803, 4812. (b) P. J. Staples, *ibid.*, **1963**, 3227. (c) P. J. Staples, *ibid.*, **1965**, 3300.
13. M. E. Baldwin and M. L. Tobe, *J. Chem. Soc.*, **1960**, 4275.
14. S. Asperger and C. K. Ingold, *J. Chem. Soc.*, **1956**, 2862.
15. M. L. Tobe, *J. Chem. Soc.*, **1959**, 3776.
16. R. G. Pearson and F. Basolo, *J. Am. Chem. Soc.*, **78**, 4878 (1956).
17. J. P. Mathieu, *Compt. rend.*, **199**, 278 (1934); **201**, 1183 (1935); *Bull. soc. chim. France* [5] **3**, 476 (1936); [5] **4**, 687 (1937).
18. H. Taube, *Advan. Chem. Ser.*, **49**, 49 (1965); D. Loeliger and H. Taube, *Inorg. Chem.*, **4**, 1032 (1965); **5**, 1376 (1966).
19. A. M. Sargeson, *Australian J. Chem.*, **17**, 385 (1965).
20. A. M. Sargeson and G. H. Searle, *Nature*, **200**, 356 (1963); *Inorg. Chem.*, **4**, 45 (1965).
21. S. C. Chan and M. L. Tobe, *J. Chem. Soc.*, **1962**, 4531.
22. R. S. Nyholm and M. L. Tobe, *J. Chem. Soc.*, **1956**, 1707.
23. C. K. Ingold, R. S. Nyholm, and M. L. Tobe, *J. Chem. Soc.*, **1956**, 1961.
24. (a) R. G. Pearson and F. Basolo, *Inorg. Chem.*, **4**, 1522 (1965). (b) R. B. Jordan and A. M. Sargeson, *Inorg. Chem.*, **4**, 433 (1965).
25. J. C. Bailar, Jr., and W. Auten, *J. Am. Chem. Soc.*, **56**, 774 (1934).
26. J. C. Bailar, Jr., F. G. Jonelis, and E. H. Huffman, *J. Am. Chem. Soc.*, **58**, 2224 (1936); J. C. Bailar, Jr., and J. P. McReynolds, *ibid.*, **61**, 3199 (1939); J. C. Bailar, Jr., and D. F. Peppard, *ibid.*, **62**, 820 (1940).
27. F. P. Dwyer, A. M. Sargeson, and I. K. Reid, *J. Am. Chem. Soc.*, **85**, 1215 (1963).
28. (a) L. J. Boucher, E. Kyuno, and J. C. Bailar, Jr., *J. Am. Chem. Soc.*, **86**, 3656 (1964). (b) *ibid.*, **87**, 4458 (1965). (c) E. Kyuno and J. C. Bailar, Jr. *ibid.*, **88**, 1120 (1966). (d) F. Basolo *Adv. Chem. Ser.*, **62**, 408 (1967).
29. J. C. Bailar, Jr., J. H. Hoslam, and E. M. Jones, *J. Am. Chem. Soc.*, **58**, 2226 (1936).
30. (a) R. D. Archer and J. C. Bailar, Jr., *J. Am. Chem. Soc.*, **83**, 812 (1961). (b) E. Kyuno and J. C. Bailar, Jr., *ibid.*, **88**, 1125 (1966).
31. R. D. Archer, *Proceedings of the Eight International Conference on Coordination Chemistry*, Vienna, 1964, pp. 111–113.
32. D. J. MacDonald and C. S. Garner, *J. Am. Chem Soc.*, **83**, 4152 (1961).
33. (a) D. C. Olson and C. S. Garner, *Inorg. Chem.* **2**, 558 (1963). (b) J. M. Veigel and C. S. Garner, *ibid.*, **4**, 1569 (1965)).
34. R. C. Johnson and F. Basolo, *J. Inorg. Nucl. Chem.*, **13**, 36 (1960).
35. (a) O. E. Zvyaginstev and E. F. Shubochkina, *Russ. J. Inorg. Chem.* **6**, 1038 (1961); **8**, 300 (1963). (b) R. C. Johnson and E. R. Berger, *Inorg. Chem.*, **4**, 1262 (1965).
36. S. A. Johnson and F. Basolo, *Inorg. Chem.*, **1**, 925 (1962); S. A. Johnson, F. Basolo and R. G. Pearson, *J. Am. Chem. Soc.*, **85**, 1741 (1963).
37. H. L. Bott, E. J. Bounsall, and A. J. Poë, *J. Chem. Soc.*, **1966A**, 1275.
38. U. Klabunde, private communication.
39. (a) J. A. Broomhead, private communication. (b) J. A. Broomhead, F. Basolo, and R. G. Pearson, *Inorg. Chem.*, **3**, 826 (1964).
40. S. M. Jørgensen, *J. prakt. Chem.*, **39**, 16 (1889); **41**, 449 (1890).
41. A. Werner, *Ber.*, **44**, 3278 (1911).
42. A. Werner, *Ber.*, **44**, 2452 (1911).
43. M. Delepine, *Compt. rend.*, **175**, 1409 (1922).
44. M. Delepine, *Anales real soc. espan. fis. quim.* (*Madrid*), **27**, 485 (1929).
45. H. D. K. Drew and N. H. Pratt, *J. Chem. Soc.*, **1937**, 506.

46. H. D. K. Drew and H. J. Tress, *J. Chem. Soc.*, **1932**, 2328; **1933**, 1335.

47. A. Nakahara, Y. Saito, and H. Kuroya, *Bull. Chem. Soc., Japan*, **25**, 331 (1952); S. Ooi, Y. Komiyama, Y. Saito, and H. Kuroya, *Bull. Chem. Soc. Japan.* **32**, 263 (1959); N. F. Curtis, *Proc. Chem. Soc.*, **1960**, 410; R. D. Gillard and G. Wilkinson, *J. Chem. Soc.*, **1964**, 1640.

48. G. W. Ettle and C. H. Johnson, *J. Chem. Soc.*, **1939**, 1490.

49. D. D. Brown and C. K. Ingold, *J. Chem. Soc.*, **1953**, 2680; D. D. Brown and R. S. Nyholm, *ibid.*, 2696.

50. (a) M. L. Tobe, *Advan. Chem. Ser.*, **49**, 7 (1965). (b) B. Bosnich, C. K. Ingold, and M. L. Tobe, *J. Chem. Soc.*, **1965**, 4074.

51. R. C. Brasted and C. Hirayama, *J. Am. Chem. Soc.*, **80**, 788 (1958).

52. R. F. Trimble, Jr., *J. Am. Chem. Soc.*, **76**, 6321 (1954).

53. M. L. Tobe and D. Watts, *J. Chem. Soc.*, **1962**, 4614; **1964**, 2991.

54. A. Uspensky and K. Tschibisoff, *Z. anorg. u. allgem. Chem.*, **164**, 326 (1927).

55 T. Uemura and N. Hirosawa, *Bull. Chem. Soc. Japan*, **13**, 377 (1938); F. Basolo, *J. Am. Chem. Soc.*, **72**, 4393 (1950).

56. J. Bjerrum and S. E. Rasmussen, *Acta Chem. Scand.*, **6**, 1265 (1952); J. Y. Long and P. E. Yankwich, *J. Am. Chem. Soc.*, **80**, 2664 (1958).

57. W. Kruse and H. Taube, *J. Am. Chem. Soc.*, **83**, 1280 (1961).

58. R. G. Yalman and T. Kuwana, *J. Phys. Chem.*, **59**, 298 (1955).

59. D. C. Olson and C. S. Garner, *Inorg. Chem.*, **2**, 415 (1963).

60. D. F. Martin and M. L. Tobe, *J. Chem. Soc.*, **1962**, 1388.

61. A. Werner, *Ann.*, **406**, 261 (1914).

62. (a) R. E. Hamm, *J. Am. Chem. Soc.*, **75**, 609 (1953). (b) R. E. Hamm and R. H. Perkins, *ibid.*, **77**, 2083 (1955).

63. R. E. Hamm, R. Kollrack, G. L. Welch, and R. H. Perkins, *J. Am. Chem. Soc.*, **83**, 340 (1961); G. L. Welch and R. E. Hamm, *Inorg. Chem.*, **2**, 295 (1963).

64. F. P. Dywer and F. Lions, *J. Am. Chem. Soc.*, **69**, 2917 (1947); **72**, 1546 (1950); F. P. Dwyer, N. S. Gill, E. C. Gyarfas, and F. Lions, *ibid.*, **74**, 4188 (1952).

65. R. C. Fay and T. S. Piper, *J. Am. Chem. Soc.*, **85**, 500 (1963).

66. R. C. Fay and T. S. Piper, *Inorg. Chem.*, **3**, 348 (1964).

67. H. S. Gutowsky and C. H. Holm, *J. Chem. Phys.*, **25**, 1228 (1956).

68. J. C. Bailar, Jr., *J. Inorg. Nucl. Chem.*, **8**, 165 (1958).

69. W. G. Gehman, doctorate thesis, Pennyslvania State University, State College Pennsylvania, 1954; L. Seiden, doctorate thesis, Northwestern University, Evanston, Illinois, 1957.

70. P. C. Ray and N. K. Dutt, *J. Indian Chem. Soc.*, **18**, 289 (1941); **20**, 81 (1943).

71. A. Werner, *Ber.*, **45**, 3061 (1912).

72. S. M. Jørgensen, *Z. anorg. Chem.*, **5**, 169 (1893).

73. J. Lecomte and C. Duval, *Bull soc. chim.*, [5] **12**, 678 (1945); R. Duval, C. Duval, and J. Lecomte, *ibid.*, [5] **14**, 1048 (1947).

74. (a) M. Linhard, H. Seibert, and M. Weigel, *Z, anorg. u. allgem. Chem.*, **278**, 287 (1955). (b) B. Adell, *ibid.*, **279**, 220 (1955). (c) R. B. Penland, F. J. Lane, and J. V. Quagliano, *J. Am. Chem. Soc.*, **78**, 887 (1956).

75. B. Adell, *Z. anorg. u. allgem. Chem.*, **271**, 49 (1952).

76 B. Adell, *Acta Chem. Scand.*, **4**, 1 (1950).

77. B. Adell, *Acta Chem. Scand.*, **5**, 54, 941 (1951).

78. B. Adell, *Svensk Kem. Tidskr.*, **56**, 318 (1944); **57**, 260 (1945).

79. R. G. Pearson, P. M. Henry, J. G. Bergmann, and F. Basolo, *J. Am. Chem. Soc.*, **76**, 5920 (1954).

80. F. Basolo and G. S. Hammaker, *Inorg. Chem.*, **1**, 1 (1962).

81. I. R. Beattie and D. P. N. Satchell, *Trans. Faraday Soc.*, **52**, 1590 (1956).
82. R. K. Murmann and H. Taube, *J. Am. Chem. Soc.*, **78**, 4886 (1956).
83. R. K. Murmann, *J. Am. Chem. Soc.*, **77**, 5190 (1955).
84. H. Taube and A. C. Rutenberg, *J. Chem. Phys.*, **20**, 825 (1952).
85. C. K. Jørgensen, *Absorption Spectra and Chemical Bonding in Complexes*, Pergamon Press, Oxford, 1962.
86. (a) K. Nakamoto, *Infrared Spectra of Inorganic and Coordination Compounds*, John Wiley and Sons, New York, 1963, p. 175; A. Sabatini and I. Bertini, *Inorg. Chem.*, **4**, 1665 (1965). (b) C. Pecile, *ibid.*, **5**, 210 (1966).
87. J. L. Burmeister and F. Basolo, *Inorg. Chem.*, **3**, 1587 (1964).
88. (a) F. Basolo, W. H. Baddley and J. L. Burmeister, *Inorg. Chem.*, **3**, 1202 (1964). (b) F. Basolo, W. H. Baddley, and K. J. Weidenbaum, *J. Am. Chem. Soc.*, **88**, 1576 (1966).
89. (a) A. Tramer, *J. Chim. Phys.*, **59**, 232 (1964); O. W. Howarth, R. E. Richards, and L. M. Venanzi, *J. Chem. Soc.*, **1964**, 3335. R. A. Plane, private communication. (b) H. H. Schmidtke, *J. Am. Chem. Soc.*, **87**, 2522 (1965).
90. M. F. Farona and A. Wojcicki, *Inorg. Chem.*, **4**, 857, 1402 (1965).
91. (a) A. Haim and N. Sutin, *J. Am. Chem. Soc.*, **87**, 4210 (1965); **88**, 434 (1966). (b) D. L. Ball and E. L. King, *ibid.*, **80**, 1091 (1958). (c) R. L. Carlin and J. O. Edwards, *J. Inorg. Nucl. Chem.*, **6**, 217 (1958). (d) J. L. Burmeister, doctorate thesis Northwestern University, Evanston, Illinois, 1964. (e) A. Fava, A. Iliceto, and A. Ceccon, *Tetrahedron Letters (London)*, **11**, 685 (1963).
92. S. Ahrland, J. Chatt, and N. R. Davies, *Quart. Rev. (London)*, **12**, 265 (1958).
93. R. G Pearson, *J. Am. Chem. Soc.*, **85**, 2533 (1963).
94. C. K. Jørgensen, *Inorg. Chem.*, **3**, 1201 (1964).
95. A. Turco and C. Pecile, *Nature*, **191**, 55 (1961).
96. J. Lewis, R. S. Nyholm, and P .W. Smith, *J. Chem. Soc.*, **1961**, 4590.
97. (a) J. H. Espenson and J. P. Birk, *J. Am. Chem. Soc.*, **87**, 3280 (1965). (b) J. Halpern and S. Nakamura, *ibid.*, **87**, 3002 (1965). (c) D. I. Shriver, S. A. Shriver, and S. A. Anderson, *Inorg. Chem.*, **5**, 725 (1965). (d) P. Nicpon and D. W. Meek, *ibid.* in press. (e) I. Bertini and A. Sabatini, *ibid.*, **5**, 1025 (1965). (f) K. N. Raymond and F. Basolo, *ibid.*, **5**, 1632 (1966); E. C. Lingofelter, private communication.
98. C. H. Johnson, *Trans Faraday Soc.*, **31**, 1612 (1935).
99. F. P. Dwyer and A. M. Sargeson, *J. Phys., Chem.*, **60**, 1331 (1956).
100. H. Krebs, J. Diewald, H. Arlitt, and J. A. Wagner, *Z. anorg. u. allgem. Chem.*, **287**, 98 (1956).
101. W. Wahl, *Ber.*, **60**, 399 (1927); G. J. Burrows and K. H. Lauder, *J. Am. Chem. Soc.*, **53**, 3600 (1931).
102. W. D. Treadwell, G. Szobados, and E. Haimann, *Helv. Chim. Acta*, **15**, 1049 (1932).
103. B. DasSarma and J. C. Bailar, Jr., *J. Am. Chem. Soc.*, **77**, 5476 (1955).
104. F. G. Mann and J. Watson, *J. Chem. Soc.*, **1947**, 505; J. H. Craddock and M. M. Jones, *J. Am. Chem. Soc.*, **83**, 2839 (1961); **84**, 1098 (1962).
105. P. Neogi and G. K. Mukherjee, *J. Indian Chem. Soc.*, **11**, 225 (1934).
106. A. Werner, *Ber.*, **45**, 3061 (1912); F. M. Jaeger, *Rec. trav. chem.*, **38**, 250 (1919).
107. E. Bushra and C. H. Johnson, *J. Chem. Soc.*, **1939**, 1937.
108. A. Werner, *Ber.*, **45**, 865 (1912).
109. (a) A. Werner, *Ber.*, **44**, 3138 (1911). (b) J. Selbin and J. C. Bailar, Jr., *J. Am. Chem. Soc.*, **79**, 4285 (1957).

110. F. M. Jaeger, *Rec. trav. chim.*, **38**, 247 (1919).

111. F. P. Dwyer and A. M. Sargeson, *J. Am. Chem. Soc.*, **81**, 2335 (1959).

112. F. P. Dwyer, I. K. Reid, and F. L. Garvan, *J. Am. Chem. Soc.*, **83**, 1285 (1961).

113. F. P. Dwyer and E. C. Gyarfas, *Nature*, **168**, 29 (1951); T. Moeller and E. Guylas, *J. Inorg. Nucl. Chem.*, **5**, 245 (1958).

114. J. P. Collman, R. P. Blair, R. L. Marshall, and L. Slade, *Inorg. Chem.*, **2**, 576 (1963).

115. A. Werner, *Ber.*, **45**, 121 (1912); J. A. Broomhead, F. P. Dwyer, and J. W. Hogarth, *Inorg. Syn.*, **6**, 183 (1960).

116. B. E. Douglas, *J. Am. Chem. Soc.*, **76**, 1020 (1954); see reference 211.

117. D. H. Busch, *J. Am. Chem. Soc.*, **77**, 2747 (1955).

118. A. Werner, *Ber.* **44**, 3280 (1911); J. C. Bailar, Jr., *Inorg. Syn.*, **2**, 223 (1946).

119. W. R. Matoush and F. Basolo, *J. Am. Chem. Soc.*, **78**, 3972 (1956); F. Basolo, W. R. Matoush, and R. G. Pearson, *ibid.*, **78**, 4883 (1956).

120. A. Werner, *Ber.* **44**, 3278 (1911).

121. F. P. Dwyer and F. L. Garvan, *Inorg. Syn.*, **6**, 195 (1960).

122. W. Tupizina, thesis, Zurich, 1915; *Gmelin's Handbuch der anorganischen Chemie*, Verlag Chemie, Berlin, 1930, No. 58B, p. 273.

123. A. Werner and E. Schalze, *Ber.*, **44**, 1896 (1911).

124. A. Werner, *Ber.*, **47**, 3090 (1914).

125. H. Goodwin, E. C. Gyarfas, and D. P. Mellor, *Australian J. Chem.*, **11**, 426 (1958).

126. D. H. Busch and J. C. Bailar, Jr., *J. Am. Chem. Soc.*, **75**, 4574 (1953).

127. F. P. Dwyer, E. C. Gyarfas, and D. P. Mellor, *J. Phys. Chem.*, **59**, 296 (1955); F. P. Dwyer and F. L. Garvan, *Inorg. Syn.*, **2**, 192 (1960).

128. B. Das Sarma and J. C. Bailar, Jr., *J. Am. Chem. Soc.*, **77**, 5480 (1955).

129. F. McCullough, Jr., and J. C. Bailar, Jr., *J. Am. Chem. Soc.*, **78**, 714 (1956).

130. P. Neogi and N. K. Dutt, *J. Indian Chem. Soc.*, **15**, 83 (1938).

131. T. Moeller and N. C. Nielsen, *J. Am. Chem. Soc.*, **75**, 5106 (1953).

132. M. Delepine, *Compt. rend.*, **159**, 239 (1914); **175**, 1405 (1922).

133. A. Werner and A. P. Smirnoff, *Helv. Chim. Acta*, **3**, 472 (1920).

134. W. Thomas, *J. Chem. Soc.*, **1922**, 121, 196.

135. A. Werner, *Ber.*, **45**, 433 (1912).

136. F. P. Dwyer and E. C. Gyarfas, *J. Am. Chem. Soc.*, **74**, 4699 (1952).

137. F. P. Dwyer and E. C. Gyarfas, *J. Proc. Roy. Soc. N.S. Wales*, **83**, 263 (1949).

138. F. P. Dwyer, N. S. Gill, E. C. Gyarfas, and F. Lions, *J. Am. Chem. Soc.*, **75**, 3834 (1953).

139. G. T. Morgan and F. H. Burstall, *J. Chem. Soc.*, **1931**, 2213.

140. F. P. Dwyer and E. C. Gyarfas, *J. Proc. Roy. Soc. N.S. Wales*, **83**, 232 (1949).

141. J. A. Broomhead and F. P. Dwyer, *Australian J. Chem.*, **15**, No. 3, 453 (1962).

142. J. A. Broomhead and F. P. Dwyer, *Australian J. Chem.*, **16**, No. 1, 51 (1963).

143. F. H. Burstall, F. P. Dwyer, and E. C. Gyarfas, *J. Chem. Soc.*, **1950**, 953.

144. F. P. Dwyer and E. C. Gyarfas, *J. Am. Chem. Soc.*, **73**, 2322 (1951).

145. F. P. Dwyer, N. A. Gibson, and E. C. Gyarfas, *J. Proc. Roy. Soc. N.S. Wales*, **84**, 68 (1951).

146. (a) J. P. Mathieu, *Bull. soc. chim.*, **6**, 1258 (1939). (b) *J. chim. phys.*, **33**, 78 (1936).

147. A. P. Smirnoff, *Helv. Chim. Acta*, **3**, 177 (1920).

148. F. P. Dwyer and F. L. Garvan, *J. Am. Chem. Soc.*, **81**, 1043 (1959); F. P. Dwyer and A. M. Sargeson, *ibid.*, **81**, 9272 (1959).

149. L. F. Heneghan and J. C. Bailar, Jr., *J. Am. Chem. Soc.*, **75**, 1840 (1953).

150. A. Werner, *Ber.*, **45**, 1954 (1914).

151. F. P. Dwyer and F. L. Garvan, *J. Am. Chem. Soc.*, **82**, 4823 (1960).

152. F. G. Mann, *J. Chem. Soc.*, **1933**, 412.
153. A. Werner, *Ber.*, **45**, 1229 (1912).
154. F. P. Dwyer and E. C. Gyarfas, *J. Proc. Roy. Soc. N.S. Wales*, **83**, 174 (1949).
155. F. P. Dwyer and E. C. Gyarfas, *Nature*, **163**, 918 (1949); *J. Proc. Roy. Soc. N.S. Wales*, **83**, 170 (1949).
156. A. Rosenheim B. Raibmann, and G. Schendel, *Z. anorg. u. allgem. Chem.*, **196**, 168 (1931).
157. P. Neogi and G. K. Mukherjee, *J. Indian Chem. Soc.*, **11**, 681 (1934).
158. R. G. Pearson, R. E. Meeker, and F. Basolo, *J. Am. Chem. Soc.*, **78**, 2673 (1956).
159. A. A. Frost and R. G. Pearson, *Kinetics and Mechanism*, John Wiley and Sons, New York, 1961.
160. A. M. Sargeson, *Australian J. Chem.*, **16**, 352 (1963).
161. G. K. Schweitzer and J. M. Lee, *J. Phys. Chem.*, **56**, 195 (1952); N. R. Davies and F. P. Dwyer, *Trans. Faraday Soc.*, **48**, 244 (1952); **49**, 180 (1953).
162. R. G. Wilkins and M. J. G. Williams, *J. Chem. Soc.*, **1957**, 1763.
163. F. Basolo, J. C. Hayes, and H. M. Neumann, *J. Am. Chem. Soc.*, **75**, 5102 (1953).
164. J. A. Broomhead and F. P. Dwyer, *Australian J. Chem.*, **16**, 51 (1963).
165. W. Thomas, *J. Chem. Soc.*, **1921**, 119, 1140; W. Thomas and R. Frazer, *ibid.*, **1923**, 123, 2973.
166. C. H. Johnson and A. Mead, *Trans. Faraday Soc.*, **31**, 1621 (1935).
167. N. W. D. Beese and C. H. Johnson, *Trans. Faraday Soc.*, **31**, 1632 (1935).
168. F. A. Long, *J. Am. Chem. Soc.*, **61**, 570 (1939); **63**, 1353 (1941).
169. N. R. Davies and F. P. Dwyer, *Trans. Faraday Soc.*, **48**, 244 (1952); **49**, 180 (1953); **50**, 820 (1954).
170. S. Ruben, M. D. Kamen, M. B. Allen, and P. Nahinsky, *J. Am. Chem. Soc.*, **64**, 2297 (1942); T. S. Lee, I. M. Kolthoff, and D. L. Leussing, *ibid.*, **70**, 3596 (1948); J. H. Baxendale and P. George, *Trans. Faraday Soc.*, **46**, 736 (1950).
171. F. Basolo, J. C. Hayes, and H. M. Neumann, *J. Am. Chem. Soc.*, **76**, 3807 (1954).
172. N. R. Davies, *Revs. Pure Appl. Chem.*, **4**, 66 (1954).
173. (a) S. Sheel, D. T. Meloon, and G. M. Harris, *Inorg. Chem.*, **1**, 170 (1962). (b) K. V. Krishnamurty and G. M. Harris, *Chem. Rev.*, **61**, 213 (1961).
174. (a) D. R. Llewellyn and A L. Odell, *Proc. Austral. Atomic Energy Symp.*, **5**, 623 (1958). (b) C. A. Bunton, J. H. Carter, D. R. Llewellyn, C. O'Connor, A. L. Odell, and S. Y. Yih, *J. Chem. Soc.*, **1964**, 4615, 4622, 4627. (c) L. Zucker and L. P. Hammett, *J. Am. Chem. Soc.*, **61**, 2791 (1939).
175. S. T. Spees and A. W. Adamson, *Inorg. Chem.*, **1**, 531 (1962).
176. R. W. Kluiber, *J. Am. Chem. Soc.*, **82**, 4839 (1960).
177. (a) T. S. Piper, Private communication. (b) J. P. Collman and J. Y. Sun, *Inorg. Chem.*, **4**, 1273 (1965).
178. D. W. Cooke, Y. A. Im, and D. H. Busch, *Inorg. Chem.*, **1**, 13 (1962).
179. F. P. Dwyer, E. C. Gyarfas, and D. P. Mellor, *J. Phys. Chem.*, **59**, 296 (1955); M. L. Morris and D. H. Busch, *ibid.*, **63**, 340 (1959).
180. S. Richards, B. Pedersen, J. V. Silverton, and J. L. Hoard, *Inorg. Chem.*, **3**, 27 (1964).
181. F. Monacelli, F. Basolo, and R. G. Pearson, *J. Inorg. Nucl. Chem.*, **24**, 1241 (1962).
182. F. D. Graziano and G. M. Harris, *J. Phys. Chem.*, **63**, 330 (1959); K. V. Krishnamurty and G. M. Harris, *ibid.*, **64**, 346 (1960).
183. J. H. Carter, doctorate thesis, University College of London, London, England, 1956.
184. L. Seiden, F. Basolo, and H. M. Neumann, *J. Am. Chem. Soc.*, **81**, 3809 (1959).
185. J. E. Dickens, F. Basolo, and H. M. Neumann, *J. Am. Chem. Soc.*, **79**, 1286 (1957).
186. D. W. Margerum and L. P. Morgenthaler, *J. Am. Chem. Soc.*, **84**, 710 (1962).

187. P. Pfeiffer and K. Quehl, *Ber.*, **64**, 2667 (1931); **65**, 560 (1932).

188. F. P. Dwyer, M. F. O'Dwyer, and E. C. Gyarfas, *Nature*, **167**, 1036 (1951).

189. E. E. Turner and M. M. Harris, *Quart. Rev. (London)*. **1**, 299 (1948).

190. (a) N. R. Davies and F. P. Dwyer, *Trans. Faraday Soc.*, **50**, 24, 1325 (1954). (b) E. M. Arnett, W. G. Bentrude, J. J. Burke, and P. M. Duggleby, *J. Am. Chem. Soc.*, **87**, 1541 (1965).

191. A. Jensen, F. Basolo, and H. M. Neumann, *J. Am. Chem. Soc.*, **80**, 2354 (1958).

192. W. W. Brandt and D. K. Gullstrom, *J. Am. Chem. Soc.*, **74**, 3532 (1952).

193. A. Jensen, F. Basolo, and H. M. Neumann, *J. Am. Chem. Soc.*, **81**, 509 (1959).

194. A. Shulman and F. P. Dwyer, *Chelating Agents and Metal Chelates* (F. P. Dwyer and D. P. Mellor, eds.), Academic Press, New York, 1964, Chap. 9.

195. G. K. Schweitzer and J. L. Rose, Jr., *J. Phys. Chem.*, **56**, 428 (1952).

196. R. Charonnat, *Ann. chim.*, **16**, 202 (1931).

197. (a) J. Brady, F. Dachille, and C. D. Schmulbach, *Inorg. Chem.*, **2**, 803 (1963); C. D. Schmulbach, F. Dachille, and M. E. Bunch, *ibid.*, **3**, 308 (1964). (b) H. R. Hunt and H. Taube, *J. Am. Chem. Soc.*, **80**, 2642 (1958).

198. F. P. Dwyer and E. C. Gyarfas, *Nature*, **166**, 481 (1950).

199. E. Eichler and A. C. Wahl, *J. Am. Chem. Soc.*, **80**, 4145 (1958).

200. M. W. Dietrich and A. C. Wahl, *J. Chem. Phys.*, **38**, 1591 (1963).

201. Y. A. Im and D. H. Busch, *J. Am. Chem. Soc.*, **83**, 3357, 3362 (1961).

202. A. W. Adamson and K. S. Vorres, *J. Inorg. Nucl. Chem.*, **3**, 206 (1956).

203. B. Bosnich, F. P. Dwyer, and A. M. Sargeson, *Nature*, **186**, 966 (1960).

204. R. Schwarz and W. Kronig, *Ber.*, **56**, 208 (1923).

205. J. Bjerrum, *Metal Ammine Formation in Aqueous Solution*, P. Haase and Son, Copenhagen, 1941, pp. 235–251.

206. J. C. Bailar, Jr., and J. B. Work, *J. Am. Chem. Soc.*, **67**, 176 (1945).

207. F. P. Dwyer and F. L. Garvan, *J. Am. Chem. Soc.*, **83**, 2610 (1961).

208. J. Bjerrum and S. E. Rasmussen, *Acta Chem. Scand.*, **6**, 1265 (1952).

209. D. Sen and W. C. Fernelius, *J. Inorg. Nucl. Chem.*, **10**, 269 (1959).

210. F. P. Dwyer and A. M. Sargeson, *Nature*, **187**, 1022 (1960).

211. W. C. Erdman and B. E. Douglas, *J. Inorg. Nucl. Chem.*, **24**, 1355 (1962); W. C. Erdman, H. E. Swift and B. E. Douglas, *ibid.*, **24**, 1365 (1962); H. E. Swift and B. E. Douglas, *ibid.*, **26**, 601 (1964).

212. R. L. Burwell, Jr., R. G. Pearson, G. L. Haller, P. B. Tjok, and S. P. Chock, *Inorg. Chem.*, **4**, 1123 (1965).

213. E. O. Fischer, H. P. Kögler, and P. Kuzel, *Chem. Ber.*, **93**, 3006 (1960); W. Strohmeier and K. Gerlach, *Z. Naturforsch.*, **15b**, 413 (1960).

214. S. T. Spees and A. W. Adamson, *Inorg. Chem.*, **1**, 531 (1962).

215. A. W. Adamson, H. Ogata, J. Grossman, and R. Newburg, *J. Inorg. Nucl. Chem.*, **6**, 319 (1958).

216. A. W. Adamson, *Disc. Faraday Soc.*, **29**, 163 (1960).

217. A. M. Sargeson, *Chelating Agents and Metal Chelates* (F. P. Dwyer and D. P. Mellor, eds.), Academic Press, New York, 1964, Chap. 5.

218. F. M. Jaeger, *Optical Activity and High Temperature Measurements*, McGraw-Hill Book Co., New York, 1930.

219. I. Lifschitz, *Z. physik. Chem.*, **114**, 485 (1925).

220. J. C. Bailar, Jr., and J. P. McReynolds, *J. Am. Chem. Soc.*, **61**, 3199 (1939); M. Martinette and J. C. Bailar, Jr., *ibid.*, **74**, 1054 (1952).

221. F. P. Dwyer, F. L. Garvan, and A. Shulman, *J. Am. Chem. Soc.*, **81**, 290 (1959).

222. F. P. Dwyer, T. E. MacDermott, and A. M. Sargeson, *J. Am. Chem. Soc.*, **85**, 2913 (1963).

223. F. P. Dwyer and A. M. Sargeson, *J. Am. Chem. Soc.*, **81**, 5272 (1959).
224. F. P. Dwyer, T. E. MacDermott, and A. M. Sargeson, *J. Am. Chem. Soc.*, **85**, 661 (1963).
225. E. J. Corey and J. C. Bailar, Jr., *J. Am. Chem. Soc.*, **81**, 2620 (1959).
226. E. J. Corey and R. A. Sneen, *J. Am. Chem. Soc.*, **77**, 2505 (1955).
227. Y. Saito, K. Nakatsu, M. Shiro, and H. Kuroya, *Bull. Chem. Soc. Japan*, **30**, 795 (1957).
228. R. D. Gillard, H. M. Irving, R. Parkins, N. C. Payne, and L. D. Pettit, *Chem. Comm.*, **81**, (1965); R. D. Gillard and H. M. Irving, *Chem. Revs.*, **45**, 603 (1965).
229. F. P. Dwyer and T. E. McDermott, *J. Am. Chem. Soc.*, **85**, 2916 (1963).
230. J. C. Bailar, Jr., *Record Chem. Progr.* (*Kresge-Hooker Sci. Lib.*), **10**, 17 (1949).
231. H. B. Jonassen, J. C. Bailar, Jr., and E. H. Huffman, *J. Am. Chem. Soc.*, **70**, 756 (1948).
232. B. Das Sarma and J. C. Bailar, Jr., *J. Am. Chem. Soc.*, **77**, 5480 (1955).
233. J. C. Bailar, Jr., H. B. Jonassen, and A. D. Gott, *J. Am. Chem. Soc.*, **74**, 3131 (1952).
234. H. Hamilton, thesis, University of Illinois, Urbana, Illinois, 1947.
235. A. D. Gott and J. C. Bailar, Jr., *J. Am. Chem. Soc.*, **74**, 4820 (1952).
236. B. Das Sarma and J. C. Bailar, Jr., *J. Am. Chem. Soc.*, **78**, 895 (1956).
237. D. H. Busch, K. Swaminathan, and D. W. Cooke, *Inorg. Chem.*, **1**, 260 (1962).
238. H. A. Weakleim and J. L. Hoard, *J. Am. Chem. Soc.*, **81**, 550 (1959).

5

Substitution Reactions of Square-Planar Complexes

By far the most stable square planar complexes are those of Pt(II), and as a result the syntheses and reactions of these compounds have long been the subject of extensive investigations.[1] During the past decade more quantitative studies have been made on these systems, and an appreciable effort has been devoted to investigations of the kinetics and mechanisms of their reactions.[2] Therefore, much of the discussion in this chapter deals specifically with the chemistry of Pt(II) compounds. However, other square planar, low-spin d^8 systems, such as complexes of Ni(II), Pd(II), Au(III), Rh(I), and Ir(I), have been examined to a lesser extent and will be discussed. It will be seen that square planar complexes generally undergo bimolecular nucleophilic displacement reactions in contrast to the predominantly dissociative process exhibited by octahedral complexes. A brief discussion is also included of tetrahedral substitution for a few elements other than carbon and for a five-coordinated system.

Reactions of Platinum(II) Complexes; The *trans* Effect

The concept of a square configuration, rather than a tetrahedron as is known for carbon compounds, was first introduced by Werner[3] because of the fact that the tetrahedral structure could not account for the α and β forms of $Pt(NH_3)_2Cl_2$ prepared more than a century ago by Peyrone (α)[4] and by Reiset (β).[5] The α form was obtained by the reaction of $PtCl_4^{2-}$ with ammonia, and the β form resulted from heating solid $[Pt(NH_3)_4]Cl_2$ to approximately 250°C.

Since the two forms were each found to be monomeric, Werner concluded that they must be *cis-trans* isomers. On the basis of some experimental observations made by Jørgensen,[6] which have been checked by means of paper chromatography,[7] Werner suggested that the α form had the *cis* and the β form the *trans* configuration. Reactions 1 and 2 were the two sets considered. Werner argued that, since only one complex is

isolated from reaction 1

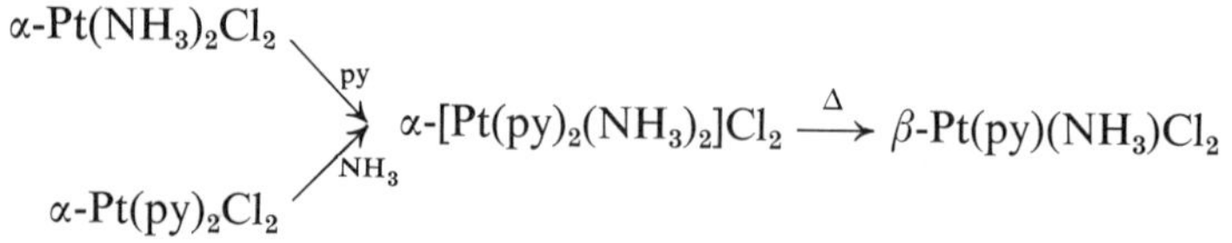
α-Pt(NH3)2Cl2
py
α-[Pt(py)2(NH3)2]Cl2
Δ
β-Pt(py)(NH3)Cl2
NH3
α-Pt(py)2Cl2

(1)

and only two complexes are obtained from reaction 2

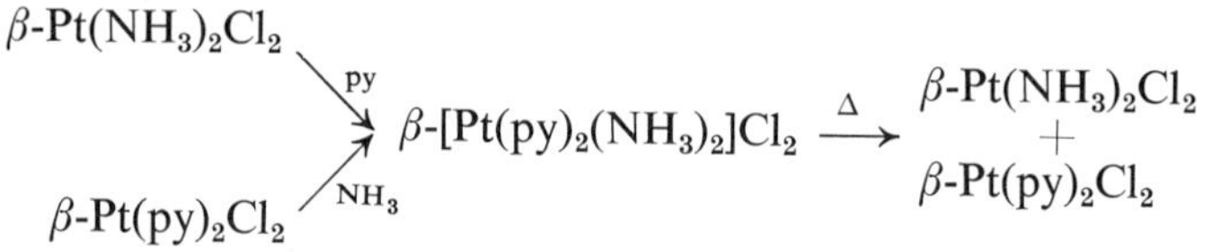
β-Pt(NH3)2Cl2
py
β-[Pt(py)2(NH3)2]Cl2
Δ
β-Pt(NH3)2Cl2
+
β-Pt(py)2Cl2
NH3
β-Pt(py)2Cl2

(2)

both the addition and elimination steps must involve stereospecific reactions. Furthermore, these results are consistent with the assignment of a *cis* structure to the α form and a *trans* structure to the β form if it is assumed that the addition of ammonia or pyridine in the first steps takes place without isomerization and that *trans* elimination occurs in the final steps. Thus, the stereochemical consequence of reactions 1 and 2 may be diagramed thus:

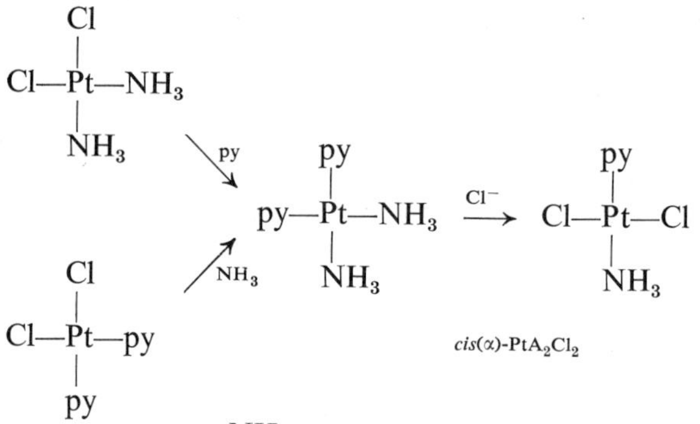
py
NH3
Cl⁻
cis(α)-PtA2Cl2

(3)

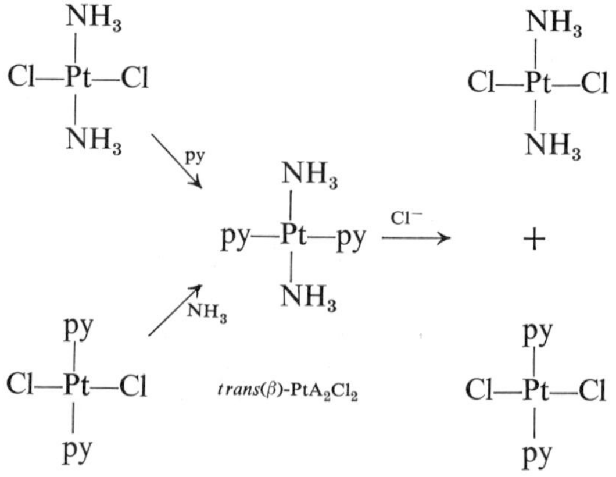
py
NH3
Cl⁻
+
trans(β)-PtA2Cl2

(4)

The assignment of structure by this method cannot be accepted as proof because of the assumptions which had to be made. However, these assumptions have since been shown to be correct, and the two representations 3 and 4 are valid.[1] It is of particular interest that the second steps in these reactions involve solely the replacement of ligands in *trans* positions. This observation was not generally utilized until after 1926, at which time Chernyaev[8] introduced the concept of the *trans effect* to correlate many of the reactions of Pt(II) complexes. Chernyaev called attention to the general phenomenon that a negative ligand, e.g., Cl⁻, has a greater labilizing effect on a group *trans* to it than it does on groups in *cis* positions. Furthermore, this labilizing effect is usually larger for a negative ligand than it is for a non-π-bonding neutral group, e.g., NH_3.

The utility of an empirical rule such as that of the *trans* effect becomes apparent if we now consider a few reactions of Pt(II) complexes. For example the *trans* elimination step of reaction 3 may be designated as a two-step process:

$$\begin{array}{ccc} py & py & py \\ | & | & | \\ py\!-\!Pt\!-\!NH_3 \xrightarrow{Cl^-} Cl\!-\!Pt\!-\!NH_3 \xrightarrow{Cl^-} Cl\!-\!Pt\!-\!Cl \\ | & | & | \\ NH_3 & NH_3 & NH_3 \end{array} \qquad (5)$$

After the first chloride ion has entered the complex, the second chloride ion will replace the group *trans* to the first since this position is labilized, the chloride ion having a larger *trans* effect than does either pyridine or ammonia. Similarly, the methods of synthesis of *cis*- and *trans*-$Pt(NH_3)_2Cl_2$ are in keeping with the concept of the *trans* effect:

$$\begin{array}{ccc} Cl & Cl & Cl \\ | & | & | \\ Cl\!-\!Pt\!-\!Cl \xrightarrow{NH_3} Cl\!-\!Pt\!-\!NH_3 \xrightarrow{NH_3} Cl\!-\!Pt\!-\!NH_3 \\ | & | & | \\ Cl & Cl & NH_3 \\ & & cis \end{array} \qquad (6)$$

$$\begin{array}{ccc} NH_3 & NH_3 & NH_3 \\ | & | & | \\ H_3N\!-\!Pt\!-\!NH_3 \xrightarrow{Cl^-} Cl\!-\!Pt\!-\!NH_3 \xrightarrow{Cl^-} Cl\!-\!Pt\!-\!Cl \\ | & | & | \\ NH_3 & NH_3 & NH_3 \end{array} \qquad (7)$$

Thus in reaction 6 the second ammonia enters a *cis* position because the *trans*-directing influence of chloride ion is greater than that of ammonia, which means that the least reactive chloro group in $PtNH_3Cl_3^-$ is the one opposite ammonia. In reaction 7 chloride ion replaces the most labile ammonia in $Pt(NH_3)_3Cl^+$, which is the one opposite the chloro group, thus resulting in the formation of *trans*-$Pt(NH_3)_2Cl_2$ (see p. 382).

This *trans*-effect rule has often been used, with considerable success, as a guide in the synthesis of desired isomeric Pt(II) complexes. Often, as with the synthesis of *cis*- and *trans*-Pt(NH$_3$)(NO$_2$)Cl$_2^-$,[9] this can be achieved just by reversing the order of introduction of groups into PtCl$_4^{2-}$:

$$
\begin{array}{ccc}
\text{Cl} & \text{Cl} & \text{NO}_2 \\
| & | & | \\
\text{Cl}-\text{Pt}-\text{Cl} \xrightarrow{\text{NH}_3} & \text{Cl}-\text{Pt}-\text{NH}_3 \xrightarrow{\text{NO}_2^-} & \text{Cl}-\text{Pt}-\text{NH}_3 \\
| & | & | \\
\text{Cl} & \text{Cl} & \text{Cl} \\
& & cis
\end{array}
\qquad (8)
$$

$$
\begin{array}{ccc}
\text{Cl} & \text{NO}_2 & \text{NO}_2 \\
| & | & | \\
\text{Cl}-\text{Pt}-\text{Cl} \xrightarrow{\text{NO}_2^-} & \text{Cl}-\text{Pt}-\text{Cl} \xrightarrow{\text{NH}_3} & \text{Cl}-\text{Pt}-\text{Cl} \\
| & | & | \\
\text{Cl} & \text{Cl} & \text{NH}_3 \\
& & trans
\end{array}
\qquad (9)
$$

Reaction 8 is analogous to 6, and reaction 9 illustrates that the *trans*-directing ability of the nitrite ion exceeds that of a chloride ion. A similar sequence of reactions can be used to prepare *cis*- and *trans*-Pt(C$_2$H$_4$)(NH$_3$)Cl$_2$; again the success depends on the *trans* effect of ethylene being greater than that of chloride ion. Chernyaev[9] demonstrated the applicability of his rule by the synthesis of the three isomers of Pt(NH$_2$OH)(py)(NH$_3$)-NO$_2^+$. The isomers of Pt(py)(NH$_3$)BrCl were prepared[10] as shown in the reactions

$$
\begin{array}{ccc}
\text{Cl} & \text{Br} & \text{Br} \\
| & | & | \\
\text{Cl}-\text{Pt}-\text{NH}_3 \xrightarrow{\text{Br}^-} & \text{Cl}-\text{Pt}-\text{NH}_3 \xrightarrow{\text{py}} & \text{Cl}-\text{Pt}-\text{NH}_3 \\
| & | & | \\
\text{Cl} & \text{Cl} & \text{py}
\end{array}
\qquad (10)
$$

$$
\begin{array}{ccc}
\text{Cl} & \text{Br} & \text{Br} \\
| & | & | \\
\text{Cl}-\text{Pt}-\text{py} \xrightarrow{\text{Br}^-} & \text{Cl}-\text{Pt}-\text{py} \xrightarrow{\text{NH}_3} & \text{Cl}-\text{Pt}-\text{py} \\
| & | & | \\
\text{Cl} & \text{Cl} & \text{NH}_3
\end{array}
\qquad (11)
$$

$$
\begin{array}{ccc}
\text{Cl} & \text{NH}_3 & \text{NH}_3 \\
| & | & | \\
\text{Cl}-\text{Pt}-\text{py} \xrightarrow{\text{NH}_3} & \text{Cl}-\text{Pt}-\text{py} \xrightarrow{\text{Br}^-} & \text{Cl}-\text{Pt}-\text{Br} \\
| & | & | \\
\text{py} & \text{py} & \text{py}
\end{array}
\qquad (12)
$$

The success of the reactions depends upon the greater *trans* effect of the ligands Br$^-$ and Cl$^-$ compared to py and NH$_3$, and the fact that the Pt-N bond strength is greater than the Pt-Cl bond strength.

In addition to its utility in the synthesis of desired Pt(II) complexes, the *trans* effect phenomenon has also been used, principally by Russian chemists, to distinguish between *cis* and *trans* isomers of the type PtA_2X_2. For example, *cis*-$Pt(NH_3)_2Cl_2$ reacts with thiourea (tu) to yield $[Pt(tu)_4]Cl_2$, whereas under the same conditions the *trans* isomer would give $Pt(tu)_2Cl_2$. This *Kurnakow test*[11] works for the dihalogenodiammineplatinum(II) complexes because the *trans*-directing influence of thiourea exceeds that of the amine and halide ion. Similar results are reported for reactions of thiosulfate ion instead of thiourea, *cis*- and *trans*-$Pt(NH_3)_2Cl_2$ reacting with excess thiosulfate ion to form $Pt(S_2O_3)_4^{6-}$ and $Pt(NH_3)_2(S_2O_3)_2^{2-}$, respectively.[12]

The chemistry of Pt(II) complexes abounds with examples of the role of the *trans* effect in the syntheses of its compounds and in their chemical reactions. These extensive observations have provided qualitative information on the *trans*-directing influence of various ligands, and, as we shall see later, there is also now a considerable amount of quantitative kinetic data. The approximate order of decreasing *trans* effect is

$$CO, CN^-, C_2H_4 > PR_3, H^- > CH_3^-, SC(NH_2)_2 > C_6H_5^-,$$
$$NO_2^-, I^-, SCN^- > Br^-, Cl^- > py, NH_3, OH^-, H_2O.$$

It is of interest to note that kinetically the effect can be large; a factor of 10^6 or more in rate is found between a complex containing a good *trans* labilizing ligand and one with a ligand that is low in the *trans* effect series. Of all the specific ligand effects on the rates of substitution reactions in metal complexes, this is surely one of the most dramatic.

The above discussion made no attempt to sharply define the *trans* effect. Several definitions have been proposed,[1,8,13] and the organizing committee of a conference on the *trans* effect held in Russia in 1952 defined it as follows:[14] "In compounds with square or octahedral structure with a central complex-forming cation, the rate of substitution of an atom or molecule linked to the central atom is determined by the nature of the substituent at the opposite end of the diagonal. Thus, the stability of the bond between this (central) atom and any substituent is little affected by the character of the neighboring atoms or molecules, but is greatly influenced by those more distant, in the *trans* position, on the diagonal of the square." When we consider that this was the work of a committee, the statement is remarkably clear and straightforward. However, this is not the definition that we will use because for octahedral complexes it does not accurately state the facts. More important, for present purposes, it requires that both the rate of reaction increase and the metal-ligand bond strength decrease for the leaving ligand opposite to a ligand of high *trans* effect. Often this may be the case, but it need not be, and therefore it seems preferable to restrict the definition of the *trans* effect to an effect on the rate of reaction, requiring the considerations of ground and transition state stabilities.

We shall define the *trans effect as the effect of a coordinated group upon the rate of substitution reactions of ligands opposite to it in a metal complex.*[2a] Complexes in which the rate influence of *trans* groups is definitely greater than the influence of adjacent *cis* groups are considered to show a *trans* effect. Thus, for the complexes

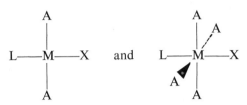

the ligand L will have a much larger influence on the rate of replacement of X than do the ligands A. Although most of the work on the *trans* effect has been done on square planar Pt(II) systems, the effect has been observed also in other systems, including octahedral complexes[2a,15] (p. 176). The discussion that follows will deal only with Pt(II) complexes, for which there is the most information.

Extrakinetic Properties of Platinum(II) Complexes

Before discussing the theories of the *trans* effect, it should be informative to review in this section some of the physical properties of Pt(II) complexes that indicate changes in Pt-X bond strengths with changes in the other ligands, particularly the group *trans* to X. In any attempt to understand the nature of the *trans* effect, it is important to have a knowledge of the Pt-X bond strength because this may influence the rate of replacement of X from the complex. Some relevant information can be obtained fairly readily, whereas it is much more difficult to find extrakinetic data on other factors that contribute to changes in the activation energy (or rate) for reaction.

Stabilities. Some thermodynamic data are available on the stabilities of Pt(II) complexes, but unfortunately this information is mostly not of the type that is of direct interest for a better understanding of the *trans* effect. Of particular interest would be a comparison of gas-phase dissociation energies for analogous *trans*-PtA_2LX compounds where A and X are kept the same but L is changed:

$$trans\text{-}PtA_2LX(g) \rightarrow PtA_2L^+(g) + X^-(g) \qquad (13)$$

Although calculations of such coordinate bond energies can be made from thermochemical cycles in certain simple cases, they are as yet not possible for square planar complexes. It is unfortunate that the available thermodynamic data, some of which are presented here, do not provide direct information on the effect of L on the Pt-X bond strength *trans* to L.

Martin and his students[16] have made a thorough study of the thermodynamics and kinetics of the acid hydrolysis of the complete series of complexes represented as $Pt(NH_3)_{4-n}Cl_n$, where n is 1 through 4. The equilibrium quotients obtained are shown in Table 5.1 and plotted in Fig.

Table 5.1 Equilibrium quotients for the acid hydrolysis of chloroammineplatinum(II) complexes

$$Pt(NH_3)_{4-n}Cl_n + H_2O \overset{20°}{\rightleftharpoons} Pt(NH_3)_{4-n}Cl_{n-1}H_2O + Cl^-$$

Complex	K, 10^5 M
$PtCl_4^{2-}$	1500
$PtNH_3Cl_3^-$	1300[a]
	130[b]
cis-$Pt(NH_3)_2Cl_2$	330
$trans$-$Pt(NH_3)_2Cl_2$	32
$Pt(NH_3)_3Cl^+$	27

From reference 16.
[a] For the Cl^- *trans* to NH_3.
[b] For a Cl^- *cis* to NH_3.

5.1. It is apparent that the extent of hydrolysis at equilibrium increases with a decrease in the charge on the complex. This amounts to *ca.* 1 kcal/mole in free energy change for each unit of charge. Furthermore, a free energy change of *ca.* 1.5 kcal/mole favors the aquation of a Cl^- group *trans* to NH_3 over that of one *trans* to Cl^- in complexes of the same charge (Fig. 5.1). Thus, the hydrolysis equilibrium quotient for *cis*-$Pt(NH_3)_2Cl_2$ is about ten times larger than that for the *trans* isomer. It was suggested[16] that this can be attributed to the reduced repulsion between two Cl^- ligands in the starting complex resulting from the larger separation in the *trans* arrangement.

That *trans*-$Pt(NH_3)_2Cl_2$ is more stable than the *cis* isomer is supported by thermochemical data which permit an estimate of the $\Delta H°$ of isomerization:[17]

$$cis\text{-}Pt(NH_3)_2Cl_2(s) \rightarrow trans\text{-}Pt(NH_3)_2Cl_2(s) + 3.0 \pm 0.2 \text{ kcal/mole} \quad (14)$$

It is tempting to try to explain the difference in stabilities of these isomers on the basis that the *trans* effect of Cl^- is greater than that of NH_3, and

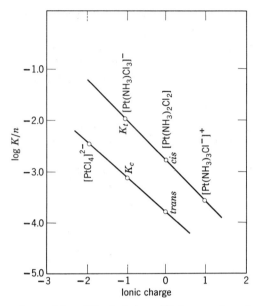

Fig. 5.1   Dependence of the acid hydrolysis equilibrium quotients for the chloroammine complexes of Pt(II) upon ionic charge. Top line K_t are constants for replacement of Cl⁻ *trans* to NH₃, whereas bottom line K_c is for the replacement of Cl⁻ *trans* to Cl⁻. From reference 16.

also that the Pt-Cl bond strength is less than that of Pt-N. Thus, in the *cis* isomer the Pt-N bond is weaker than it is in the *trans* form because of the greater bond-weakening effect of Cl⁻ compared to NH₃. For the same reason the reverse is true for the Pt-Cl bond; the bond strength is greater in the *cis* isomer, where Cl⁻ is *trans* to NH₃. However, since the Pt-Cl bond strength is less than that of Pt-N, the overall stability of the complex will be affected more by changes in Pt-N than in Pt-Cl bond strengths. This explanation then supports the view that the *trans* effect order Cl⁻ > NH₃ is a consequence of Pt-X bond weakening.

The same approach can also be used to explain the fact that for PtA₂X₂, where A = phosphines, arsines, and stibines and X = halide ions, the total bond energy of the *cis* isomer is approximately 10 kcal greater than that of the corresponding *trans* isomer[18] (p. 424). In these systems the *trans* effect order is A > Cl, and again the Pt-A bond strength is greater than Pt-Cl. Therefore, the total bond energy depends more on Pt-A than Pt-Cl, and the bond strength of Pt-A will be greater for the *cis* isomer, where A is opposite Cl⁻.

It was also found that the amount of *cis* at equilibrium for PtA₂X₂ decreases in going from X = Cl⁻ to X = I⁻. If the entropy effect is assumed to be similar for the chloro and the iodo systems, this trend towards a greater stabilization of the *trans* isomer in going from chloro to iodo is due to an enthalpy effect. This is in accord with the greater *trans* effect of I⁻ compared to Cl⁻.

Investigations[17,19] of the thermal stabilities of ammines of the type PtA_2X_2 show that the *trans* isomers are generally more stable than the corresponding *cis*. In this connection it is of interest to recall reactions of type 6, where $PtAX_3^-$ reacts to yield predominantly *cis*-PtA_2X_2 when the *trans*-directing influence of X exceeds that of A. This means that the less stable isomer is formed as the kinetic product and affords direct evidence for the stereospecific nature of these reactions. The preparative work is now supported by the observation[16] that for $PtNH_3Cl_3^-$ the chloro group *trans* to Cl⁻ is replaced by water about ten times faster than that *trans* to NH_3.

Equilibrium constants for reactions of Pt(II) complexes are not numerous, but sufficient data are available (Table 5.2) to establish that the affinities of various ligands for Pt(II) decrease in the order CN⁻ > NH_3 ∼ OH⁻ > I⁻ > SCN⁻ > Br⁻ > Cl⁻ ≫ F⁻ ∼ H_2O. Except for the position of NH_3 and OH⁻, the order parallels that of the *trans* effect. It appears somewhat anomalous that these two hard bases form very stable complexes with the soft acid, Pt(II). It is not really so since OH⁻ forms strong complexes with most positively charged acids. What is really important is that HS⁻ would form even stronger complexes with Pt(II) than OH⁻ does. In the same way the phosphine complexes would be more stable than the amine complexes. The iodo complex, as expected, is more stable than the fluoro or chloro complex.

Table 5.2 Equilibrium constants for some reactions of platinum(II) complexes in water at 25°C

$Pt^{2+} + 4X^- \rightleftharpoons PtX_4^{2-}$ [a]

X	CN⁻	NH_3	OH⁻	I⁻	Br⁻	Cl⁻
K	10^{41}	$10^{35.3}$	10^{35}	$10^{29.6}$	$10^{20.5}$	$10^{16.6}$

trans-$Pt(NH_3)_2(OH)_2 + 2X^- \rightleftharpoons$ *trans*-$Pt(NH_3)_2X_2 + 2OH^-$ [a]

X	I⁻	SCN⁻	Br⁻	Cl⁻
K	$10^{-6.3}$	$10^{-6.6}$	$10^{-8.6}$	10^{-10}

$Pt(C_2H_4)Cl_3^- + X^- \rightleftharpoons$ *trans*-$Pt(C_2H_4)Cl_2X^- + Cl^-$ [b]

X	NH_3 [c]	OH⁻	SCN⁻	I⁻	Br⁻	Cl⁻	F⁻	H_2O
K	$10^{7.8}$	10^6	$>10^2$	10^2	$10^{0.5}$	10^0	$<10^{-1.5}$	$10^{-2.5}$

[a] From reference 20.

[b] From reference 21.

[c] Corresponding values of K for X = organic amines are as follows: CH_3NH_2, $10^{8.6}$; $(CH_3)_2NH$, 10^8; $(CH_3)_3N$, $10^{5.5}$; piperidine, $10^{8.2}$; 1-methylpiperidine, $10^{6.8}$.

x-Ray Studies. One method used to evaluate bond strength is to measure bond length directly. For example, if the *trans* effect of L in *trans*-PtA$_2$LX were due to Pt-X bond weakening, an increase in bond length would be expected to parallel an increase in the *trans* effect of L. A detection of this increase would require very precise measurements of Pt-X bond lengths because the effect may be small.

x-Ray analysis can provide this information, but generally the method has been used to establish structures of Pt(II) complexes and not to systematically examine the *trans* effect on bond length. Fortunately,

Table 5.3 The effect of *trans* ligands on Pt-X bond distances

Compound	*trans* Partner	Pt—X	Bond Length, A	Ref.
K[PtNH$_3$Cl$_3$]	Cl	Pt—Cl	2.35	22
	NH$_3$	Pt—Cl	2.32	22
K[PtNH$_3$Br$_3$]	Br	Pt—Br	2.7	22
	NH$_3$	Pt—Br	2.42	22
K[PtC$_2$H$_4$Cl$_3$]·H$_2$O	Cl	Pt—Cl	2.32	23
	C$_2$H$_4$	Pt—Cl	2.42	23
K[PtC$_2$H$_4$Br$_3$]·H$_2$O	Br	Pt—Br	2.42	24
	C$_2$H$_4$	Pt—Br	2.50	24

however, some of the systems investigated do provide such information. For example, bond distances are reported for some complexes of the type PtAX$_3^-$ which show the *trans* effect of A compared to X$^-$ on the bond length of Pt-X (Table 5.3). For the complexes PtNH$_3$X$_3^-$, where the *trans* effect order is X$^- >$ NH$_3$, it is seen that the Pt-X bond *trans* to X$^-$ is longer than that *trans* to NH$_3$. Thus, an increase in bond length does parallel an increase in the *trans* effect of the ligand opposite Pt-X. For the corresponding Zeise's anion, Pt(C$_2$H$_4$)X$_3^-$, the Pt-X bond opposite C$_2$H$_4$ is longer than that adjacent to it. Here likewise the greater bond length parallels the greater *trans* effect of C$_2$H$_4$.

The H$^-$ ligand stands high in the *trans* effect series, and there is good evidence that it too causes a lengthening of the Pt-X bond opposite it. The structure of Pt[P(C$_2$H$_5$)$_3$]$_2$(H)Br has been determined by x-ray analysis,[25] and although it is not possible to locate the hydrogen ligand it must certainly be situated as a normal ligand *trans* to Br$^-$ in a square planar complex. This can be inferred from the established structure of an approximately linear P—Pt—P with Br$^-$ at nearly right angles to this axis. The H$^-$ has been located in ReH$_9^{2-}$ [26] and in Rh[P(C$_6$H$_5$)$_3$]$_3$(H)CO,[27] and in both cases it behaves as an ordinary ligand with a normal M-H bond length.* For *trans*-Pt[P(C$_2$H$_5$)$_3$]$_2$(H)Br the Pt-Br bond length is 2.56 A which is appreciably longer than the sum of the atomic radii of 2.43 A. Analogous results were reported[28] for Pt(PPh$_2$Et)$_2$(H)Cl, in which the PtCl bond distance is 2.42 A, rather than the radii sum of 2.30 A.

A comparison can also be made of the Pt-ligand bond distances in *cis*-Pt(P(CH$_3$)$_3$)$_2$Cl$_2$[29] (III) with those in *trans*-Pt(P(C$_2$H$_5$)$_3$)$_2$Cl$_2$[30] (IV).

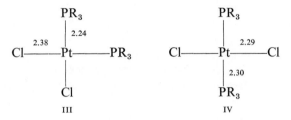

This shows that the Pt-Cl bond distance is greater if it is *trans* to PR$_3$ than if it is *trans* to Cl$^-$. Also the longer Pt-P bond is found in the *trans* isomer. Again the results are in accord with the large *trans* effect of PR$_3$ causing a weakening of the Pt-X bond *trans* to it.

Although C$_2$H$_4$, a strong *trans* labilizer, causes an increase in the Pt-halogen bond length opposite it in Zeise's salt, the same effect was not found for Pt—N. Thus for the compound *trans*-Pt(C$_2$H$_4$)NH(CH$_3$)$_2$Cl$_2$ the Pt-N bond length (2.02 A) was found[31] to be that expected from the sum of the atomic radii. In this case the olefin has little or no effect on the *trans* Pt-X bond length. The suggestion was made[31] that since the olefin is bound to Pt(II) primarily by π bonding it can have little effect on the Pt-N bond, which can have no double bond character. However, for X = Cl$^-$ or Br$^-$ the Pt-X bond may have some and the π-bonding tendency of ethylene reduces the double bond character of Pt-X and increases its bond length.

Infrared Spectra. Information on shifts in the stretching frequencies of a Pt-X bond in complexes of the type *trans*-PtA$_2$LX can be used to assess the relative effects of different *trans* L ligands on the Pt-X bond strength. Chatt and his associates[13,32] have carried out extensive and systematic studies of this type. Their initial experiments were of an indirect nature in that the N—H stretching frequencies were determined for complexes of the type *trans*-Pt(NHR$_2$)LCl$_2$. Information on the N—H frequencies leads to relative strengths of Pt-N by the following argument: as the N—H frequency increases, its bond strength increases because the nitrogen atom

* Recent studies [T. C. Farrar, S. W. Ryan, A. Davison, and J. W. Faller, *J. Am. Chem. Soc.* **88**, 184 (1966)] show a short Mn-H bond distance (1.28 ± 0.01 A) in HMn(CO)$_5$.

is more negative. This suggests that the Pt-N bond is weaker because of the nitrogen atom withholding its electrons from Pt(II). The assumption is made that higher frequencies mean higher bond strengths in general. There is no necessity that this be so, but in a series of analogous compounds varied by a remote substituent, it is probably a safe assumption.

Data collected by this method show that for the complexes *trans*-$Pt(NHR_2)LCl_2$ there is a decrease in the N—H stretching frequencies with changes of L in the order $PR_3 > SbR_3 > P(OR)_3 > AsR_3 > TeR_2 > C_2H_4 > SeR_2 > SR_2 >$ piperidine > 4-*n*-pentylpyridine. The order should be that of increasing strength of the Pt-N bonds and of decreasing tendency of L to donate electrons to Pt(II). Except for the position of C_2H_4 this order of increase in Pt-N bond strength does roughly parallel the decreasing *trans* effects of L. It should be noted that this indirect approach to the Pt-N bond strength is complicated by the intramolecular interaction between the amine hydrogen and the non-bonding d electrons of Pt(II).[32,33] Less complete data are available on the Pt—N stretching frequencies of *trans*-$PtNH_3LCl_2$. For L $= NH_3$, $S(C_2H_5)_2$, and C_2H_4, the frequencies are 507, 493, and 481 cm^{-1}, respectively, suggesting a decrease in Pt-N bond strength with an increase in the *trans* effect of L.[34]

Now that infrared spectrometers which permit measurements in the far-infrared region are commercially available, chemists are actively engaged in examining the metal-ligand stretching frequencies of metal complexes. For example, the i.r. spectra in the region 170–460 cm^{-1} of forty-three complexes of the types *cis*- and *trans*-PtL_2X_2 (X = Cl or Br; L = neutral ligand) and *trans*-$Pt(PEt_3)_2LX$ (L = H, CH_3, or C_6H_5) have been recorded.[35a] The metal-halogen stretching frequencies were assigned, and $\nu(Pt—Cl)$ falls in the range 340–270 cm^{-1}, whereas $\nu(Pt—Br)$ is in the range 250–185 cm^{-1}. The wide ranges of frequencies indicate considerable dependence of the Pt-X bond strength on L, but this is found only in systems where X is *trans* to L (Fig. 5.2). For the complexes *trans*-PtL_2X_2, $\nu(Pt—X)$ is almost insensitive to L. The most important factor determining the Pt-X bond strength is the electronegativity of L, but there are anomalies which might be attributed to π bonding in the Pt-L bond. Thus, for the Group V ligand atoms, the bond strength of Pt-X decreases with change in *trans*-L in the order L $= N \gg As > Sb > P$. Except for phosphorus, which is believed to be the best π bonder in this group of ligand atoms, the trend is for a decrease in Pt-X bond strength with a decrease in electronegativity of the *trans* L. The same is true for the Group VI ligand atoms, where it is found that the Pt-X bond strength decreases with changes in L in the order S $> Se \gg Te$. Similar studies were made on some Ir(III) complexes, and the *trans* effect observed was much the same as that found for Pt(II) systems.[35b]

With but one exception it is seen (Fig. 5.2) that there is roughly an inverse correlation between the *trans* effect of L and its influence on $\nu(Pt—X)$. Generally the ligands of highest *trans* effect, such as PR_3, H^-, CH_3^-, and $C_6H_5^-$, produce the lowest frequencies, but cyclooctadiene, which like ethylene should have a high *trans* effect, produces one of the highest Pt-Cl frequencies. This is not in accord with the observations mentioned earlier, which suggest that ethylene in the *trans* position causes

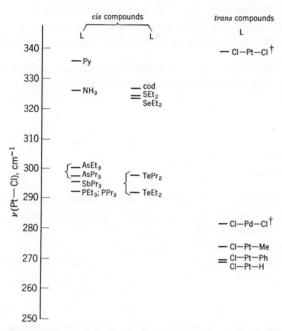

Fig. 5.2 The Pt—Cl stretching frequencies in *cis*-PtL₂Cl₂ and *trans*-Pt(PEt₃)₂LCl. For † this represents an average value for the compounds *trans*-ML₂Cl₂. From reference 35.

a decrease in the Pt-Cl bond strength. Because of this discrepancy, the influence of olefins on the Pt-X bond strength is in need of further study. One other interesting observation is that *trans*-Pd(PEt₃)₂Cl₂ has $\nu(Pd—Cl)$ at 281 cm⁻¹, much lower than its Pt(II) analog of 340 cm⁻¹, in agreement with the weaker bonding of Pd—X compared to Pt—X.

The i.r. spectra of hydride complexes[36] of metals have strong sharp bands due to the M-H stretching mode of vibration in the frequency region of 2000–2200 cm⁻¹. Shifts in $\nu(Pt—H)$ values with changes in L for compounds of the type *trans*-PtA₂LH are given in Table 5.4. It is seen that the Pt-H frequency decreases, and presumably the Pt-H bond strength decreases, with changes of L in the order $NO_3^- > Cl^- > Br^- > I^- > NO_2^- > SCN^- > SnCl_3^- > CN^-$. This is also the order of the *trans* effect of L and is therefore consistent with the view that its labilizing effect is due to a weakening of the *trans* Pt-X bond. Much smaller changes in ν(Pt—H) occur for changes in A for the same L, but it is of interest that in all cases A = AsEt$_3$ gives lower values of ν(Pt—H) than does A = PEt$_3$. Likewise, for a series of A = phosphines, the ν(Pt—H) shifts to lower frequencies in the following order: PPh$_3$ > PEtPh$_2$ > PEt$_2$Ph > PEt$_3$. It appears that the Ph-H bond strength increases slightly with increasing π-bonding tendencies of A and/or decreasing σ-bonding.

The ligand SnCl$_3^-$ is of particular current interest. It has long been known that the addition of stannous chloride to solutions of platinum metals

Table 5.4   Values (cm^{-1}) of ν(Pt—H) for the compounds *trans*-PtA$_2$LH

L =	NO$_3$	Cl	Br	I	NO$_2$	SCN	SnCl$_3$^{a}	CN
A = PEt$_3$	2242	2183	2178	2156	2150	2112	2105	2041
A = AsEt$_3$	...	2173	2167	2139	...	2108	...	...

From reference 36 except as specified in note *a*.
^{a} From reference 37.

generally results in the formation of intense colors, and colorimetric techniques may be used for the quantitative determination of certain platinum metals. Investigations[38] show that for some of these systems the species present are metal-metal bonded complexes of the type M—SnCl$_3$, where SnCl$_3^-$ behaves as a ligand. That SnCl$_3^-$ is high in the *trans* effect series is shown by the facile ligand replacement reactions in these systems and the observation that its presence in a Pt(II) complex produces an excellent homogeneous catalyst for the hydrogenation of olefins. The catalytic properties of SnCl$_3^-$ have been utilized for an improved method of synthesis of Zeise's salt.[39]

It is also of interest to consider the effect of various ligands *trans* to C$_2$H$_4$ in a Pt(II) complex on the nature of the olefin-Pt bond. Orchin and his students have made extensive investigations of such systems, and one of these[40] provides i.r. data on changes in the C=C stretching frequencies with changes in the electronic properties of the *trans* ligand. Ethylene absorbs at 1623 cm^{-1}, but when complexed with Pt(II) the value of ν(C=C) decreases by about 140 cm^{-1}, indicating a weakening of the C=C double bond. For the complexes *trans*-PtC$_2$H$_4$(o-py-Z)Cl$_2$, where o-py-Z is 4-Z-substituted pyridine N-oxide, a plot of ν(C=C) versus pK_a of the pyridine oxides is shown in Fig. 5.3. It is seen that there is a linear decrease in ν(C=C) with an increase in pK_a of the pyridine oxide. This means that the Pt-C$_2$H$_4$ bond strength increases with increasing basicity of the *trans* ligand. The greater bond strength would appear to result from an enhanced

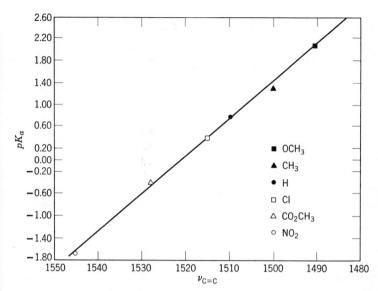

Fig. 5.3 The $\nu_{C=C}$ as a function of pK_a of 4-Z-substituted pyridine N-oxides in $Pt(C_2H_4)(o\text{-py-Z})Cl_2$. From reference 40.

population of the antibonding π^* orbitals of the olefin (metal to ligand π bonding).

Nuclear Magnetic Resonance. The n.m.r. spectra of the compounds *trans*-$Pt(PEt_3)_2LH$ listed in Table 5.4 have been measured.[36,37] The proton resonance of the hydridic hydrogen, Pt–H, is found at very high fields and shows a large chemical shift with changes in L. The chemical shift decreases from L = NO_3^- with $\tau = 33.8$ to L = CN^- with $\tau = 17.8$. Except for L = NO_2^- and SCN^-, which have anomalously high values, the gradual decrease in τ correlates the increasing *trans* effect of L.

Parshall[41] has attempted to estimate the extent of σ- and π-bond contributions to the *trans* effect of L in the series of compounds

by means of ^{19}F n.m.r. The fluorine n.m.r. shielding parameters of V and VI, given in Table 5.5, measure the ability of the fluorophenyl group to compete with the ligand L for the electron density of Pt(II). The shielding parameters for the *m*-fluorophenyl complexes (V) are sensitive to changes

Table 5.5[a] ^{19}F n.m.r. shielding parameters (S) for compounds V and VI

L	S_V[b]	S_{VI}[c]	Z'[d]
CH_3	3.93	11.7	0
C_6H_5	3.46	10.9	0.3
$P(C_2H_5)_3$	3.35	...	...
p-FC_6H_4	3.30	10.8	0.3
$C_6H_5C{\equiv}C$	3.21	10.4	0.6
m-FC_6H_4	3.07	10.6	0.3
OCN (or NCO)	2.30	10.1	0
CN	2.27	9.32	0.7
Cl	2.11	10.1	−0.2
Br	1.97	9.86	−0.1
SCN (or NCS)	1.75	9.29	0.2
I	1.56	9.54	−0.2
$SnCl_3$	−0.23	6.96	0.6

From reference 41. Acetone solution.
[a] Chemical shift in p.p.m. relative to C_6H_5F.
[b] Criterion for σ bonding.
[c] Criterion for $\sigma + \pi$ bonding.
[d] Criterion for π bonding. $Z' = (S_{VI} - S_V)_{CH_3} - (S_{VI} - S_V)_L$.

in the *trans* ligand L. The shifts presumably represent variations in electron density in the σ-bond system of the complexes induced by the σ-donor effect of L. The changes observed roughly parallel the basicities of L.

For the *p*-fluorophenyl compounds (VI), the major resonance structure which enhances the electron density in the *para* position of the benzene ring involves overlap of the filled platinum $5d_{xy}$ orbital with the adjacent carbon p_π orbital. The same *d* orbital may also take part in π bonding with the vacant orbitals on the *trans* ligand L. It follows that the greater is the tendency of the *trans* ligand to π-bond, the more it will compete for these Pt(II) electrons, which then will result in a smaller electron density at the *para* position of the benzene ring (Fig. 5.4). Hence, the ^{19}F shielding parameter of VI, after correction for inductive (σ-bonding) effects,

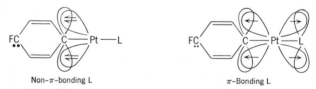

Non-π-bonding L π-Bonding L

Fig. 5.4   Resonance structure showing how a π-bonding ligand L in *trans*-$PtA_2(C_6H_4F)L$ can decrease the electron density at the *para* position of the fluorophenyl group.

provides a criterion of the ability of L to π-bond. This is represented by Z' (Table 5.5), which has values ranging from 0.7 for the strong π bonder CN^- to -0.2 for the halide ions, which show little or no π-acceptor capacity.[42] In fact the halide ions have negative Z' values relative to methyl, which should be an ideal example of a non-π-bonding ligand. This suggests that the halides may actually be weak π donors. The aryl ligands show substantial π bonding, and $SnCl_3^-$ is second only to CN^- in its π-bonding capacity. The low shielding parameter of V for L $= SnCl_3^-$ shows that it has a small tendency to σ-bond.†

These results very nicely provide extrakinetic data in support of the view that the *trans* effect is, in reality, at least two effects and that either of the two types of ligands can produce *trans* activation. Thus, strong σ-donor ligands such as H^- and CH_3^- are high in the *trans* effect series, as are strong π-acceptor ligands such as CN^-, $SnCl_3^-$, and C_2H_4.

Organic chemists have used [19]F n.m.r. shielding parameters of substituted fluorobenzenes as a sensitive probe for electronic effects in aromatic compounds.[43] It is of interest that the shielding parameter of $+11.7$ ppm for VI, where L $= CH_3$ puts the *para* Pt(II) complex substituent in the class of strong electron donors such as OH^- and OR^-. Likewise for the analogous *meta* compound V, the $+4.06$ ppm shift is much larger than that obtained when the CH_3 is attached directly to the aromatic ring ($+1.15$ ppm). The strong shielding effect of the platinum complexes can be ascribed to interaction between the filled $5d$ orbitals of Pt(II) and the benzenoid π orbitals. This interaction increases the electron density throughout the ring and in particular at the *ortho* and *para* positions.

Acid Strengths. The acid strengths of aquo complexes of the type *trans*-$PtA_2H_2OL^{n+}$ with variations in L could afford an

$$\text{trans-}PtA_2H_2OL^{n+} + H_2O \rightleftharpoons \text{trans-}PtA_2OHL^{(n-1)+} + H_3O^+ \quad (15)$$

indirect estimate of the relative Pt-O bond strengths. It is to be expected that the stronger the acid, the weaker the O-H bond and consequently the stronger the Pt-O bond. Unfortunately data of this type are rather limited and do not provide enough examples to permit generalizations on the variation of acidities with changes in L.

It must be expected that the only meaningful comparison can be made for complexes of the same charge. The limited available data largely restrict the comparison to *cis*- and *trans*-$Pt(NH_3)_2(H_2O)_2^{2+}$, which have the following pK_a values:[44] *cis*, $pK_{a_1} = 5.6$, $pK_{a_2} = 7.3$; *trans*, $pK_{a_1} = 4.3$, $pK_{a_2} = 7.4$. This has been explained in terms of the relative *trans* effect

† Recent studies show that $SnCl_3^-$ does form σ-bonded complexes with strong Lewis acids such as BF_3, M. P. Johnson, D. F. Shriver, and S. A. Shriver, *J. Am. Chem. Soc.* **88**, 1588 (1966).

$NH_3 > H_2O$ making the Pt-O bond weaker in the *cis* isomer, where it is *trans* to NH_3. Thus, the *cis* isomer is the weaker acid for the first ionization. However, the values of pK_{a_2} for both isomers are about the same because of the *trans* effects of NH_3 and OH^- being approximately similar. Consequently both forms of $Pt(NH_3)_2(H_2O)OH^+$ have about the same Pt-O bond strengths and consequently similar O-H bond strengths for $Pt—OH_2$.

This simple explanation cannot account for *trans*-$PtC_2H_4H_2OCl_2$ ($pK_a \sim$ 5) being a stronger acid than *cis*-$PtNH_3H_2OCl_2$ ($pK_a \sim 7$). For this pair of complexes the coordinated water is *trans* to C_2H_4 and Cl^-, respectively, which have a *trans* effect order of $C_2H_4 \gg Cl^-$. However, as described earlier, other results indicate that C_2H_4 does not always weaken the Pt-X bond in accord with its position in the *trans* effect series. The greater acidity of the ethylene complex suggests, in fact, that the Pt-O bond is strengthened. Other explanations can also be given, and one that seems most plausible is that the π bonding of C_2H_4 decreases the electron density in the filled d orbitals of Pt(II). This decreases the electrostatic attraction for the $Pt—OH_2$ hydrogens, which in turn become more acidic. Some information on the rate of H-D exchange[45] in Pt(dien)X$^+$ (dien = NH_2-$C_2H_4NHC_2H_4NH_2$), which is related to the acidity of the central N—H, shows a direct correlation to the rate of exchange with the *trans* effect of X.

Molar Refraction and Dipole Moments.   Grinberg[46] called attention to the direct relation between the polarizability of a ligand and its position in the *trans* effect series. Thus, I^- is more polarizable than Cl^- and is a better *trans* activator. This has led to attempts to find a quantitative correlation of the *trans* effect with measured ionic and molar refractions.[22] The problem is difficult because in a polyatomic ligand it is not clear how much of the molar refraction to use (molar refraction is related to polarizability by $R = \frac{4}{3}\pi N\alpha$).

One approach has been to measure the refractions of many solid complexes and attempt to divide the total refraction into parts characteristic of the various groups present. This procedure follows the well-known method of additive atomic refractions. Although the assignment of refractions to the various groups is ambiguous, deviations from simple additivity are readily apparent. Thus, it is clearly shown that exaltations of refraction occur if a strongly *trans* activating group is located *trans* to a weakly activating group. For example, a "coordinate refraction" can be assigned to a linear array of two ligands and the metal atom, such as $H_3N—Pt—NH_3$, by taking half of the molar refraction of $Pt(NH_3)_4^{2+}$. This gives a refraction of 11.46 cm^3, and in the same way the refractions for $O_2N—Pt—NO_2$ and $O_2N—Pt—NH_3$ are 19.76 and 16.19 cm^3, respectively. It is seen that $O_2N—Pt—NH_3$ has a refraction greater than $\frac{1}{2}(H_3N—Pt—NH_3 + O_2N—Pt—NO_2)$. This exaltation in refraction is believed to be due to the high *trans* effect of NO_2^- causing the electrons in the linear array of atoms to be displaced towards the NH_3 ligand. It is of interest to note that this lack of additivity of refractions for unsymmetrical structures offers a way of distinguishing between *cis* and *trans* isomers.

Another method that has been used to determine structures of planar complexes is the measurement of dipole moments. The net dipole of a complex will depend on the polarity and geometry of the four groups surrounding the metal atom. Data[47] of interest in this discussion are shown in Table 5.6 for the compounds *trans*-$Pt(PEt_3)_2LCl$. For changes in L, the dipole moments decrease in the order $H > CH_3 > C_6H_5 > Cl$, which is the same as the order of decreasing *trans* effect for these ligands. The results suggest that there is a larger transfer of electrons from H^-, CH_3^-, and $C_6H_5^-$ toward Pt(II) than of electrons from Cl^- toward Pt(II). Thus, the Pt-Cl bond is more polar and presumably weaker in H—Pt—Cl than in Cl—Pt—Cl. This agrees with the x-ray data on bond distances discussed earlier.

Table 5.6 Dipole moments of some *trans*-$Pt(PEt_3)_2LCl$ complexes in benzene at 25°C

L	Debye Units, μ
H	4.2
CH_3	3.4
C_6H_5	2.6
p-ClC_6H_4	1.1
Cl	0.0

From reference 47.

trans-Effect Theories

The preceding sections dealt with various experimental observations relating to the *trans* effect in Pt(II) complexes. Several theories[9,48] have been advanced in attempts to explain this phenomenon. This section will describe two theories of the *trans* effect that have been used most successfully, and then these will be unified in terms of the M.O. theory of bonding in these systems.

It should be remembered that the *trans* effect is defined as an influence on the rate of reaction. Since reaction rates are related to differences in activation energies between reactants and activated complexes, it follows that both must be considered in theories of the *trans* effect. The polarization theory stresses the importance of the ground state contribution to the rates of reaction, whereas the π-bonding theory is primarily concerned with the transition state. Some difficulty does arise because both theories deal with energies rather than free energies. Fortunately, in the Pt(II) cases where activation energies have been measured, high rates of reaction are generally found to go with low energies of activation. However, it should be borne in mind that the use of simple rate data can lead to wrong conclusions when testing theories of energetics.

The Polarization Theory. On the basis of this theory the large *trans* effect of L in *trans*-PtA$_2$LX is due to its causing a weakening of the Pt-X

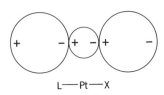

L——Pt——X

Fig. 5.5 Distribution of charge in induced dipoles in the L—Pt—X coordinate of *trans*-PtA$_2$LX.

bond. Grinberg[46] made this suggestion and explained his hypothesis in terms of the polarizability of L before any direct evidence had been obtained on the relative bond strengths of Pt-X. Now, as we saw in the previous section, there is considerable experimental support of this bond weakening hypothesis. For such systems what remains for an understanding of the *trans* effect is to be able to account for the bond weakening of Pt-X by L ligands high in the *trans* effect series.

The electrostatic-polarization theory offers an explanation on the basis of charge distribution, as is shown in Fig. 5.5. Thus, the primary charge on Pt(II) induces a dipole in L, which in turn induces a dipole in the metal. The orientation of this second dipole is such as to repel negative charge in group X. Hence, the attraction of X for platinum is reduced, and the Pt-X bond is lengthened and weakened. The virtue of this theory is that it explains the parallelism between the magnitude of the *trans* influence of L and its polarizability, e.g., H$^-$ $\sim$ I$^-$ > Cl$^-$. Also it predicts that the effect will be more important if the central metal is itself polarizable. This agrees with the experimental observation that Pt(II) is more strongly influenced and more polarizable than either Pd(II) or Pt(IV).

Since this is an electrostatic theory, it immediately arouses some objections. For example, the induced dipole on Pt(II) should depend on the net charge of L more strongly than on the induced moment. Also it will be greater if the L-Pt bond distance is small. This leads to the wrong prediction that Cl$^-$ will have a larger *trans* effect than I$^-$. This objection can be removed if the effect of covalent bonding in these systems is considered. It is probable that ligands of high polarizability will also form the most covalent bonds to Pt(II). Initially the *trans* effect due to the L-Pt covalency was explained on the basis of the V.B. theory,[48,2a] but it is now better accounted for on the basis of M.O. theory [2c](p. 372).

The π-Bonding Theory. This theory deals only with π-bonding ligands such as C_2H_4, PR_3, and CO and suggests that these are high in the *trans* effect series because they tend to stabilize the transition state for reaction. The concept of π bonding in metal complexes was first introduced by Pauling[49] in order to account for the short Ni-C bond distance in $Ni(CO)_4$ and also for the large stability of the cyanide complexes of transition metals as compared to non-transition metals. The existence and significance of

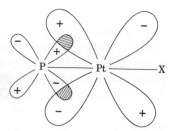

Fig. 5.6   Schematic representation of the R_3P-Pt double bond. If ligands PR_3 and X are in the xy plane, then the d orbitals shown are either d_{xz} or d_{yz}.

such double bonding are now generally recognized. A schematic representation of the double bond in Pt=PR_3 is shown in Fig. 5.6. The σ bond is formed by the donation of a pair of electrons from phosphorus to platinum, and the π bond by the overlap of a filled d orbital of platinum and a vacant d orbital of phosphorus.

It would appear that the removal of electrons from the metal by π bonding should have the effect of strengthening the bonds of the other ligands in general, and the *trans* ligand in particular. However, evidence from the various kinds of physical properties discussed earlier shows that the Pt-X bond is weakened in almost all cases where L is a good *trans* activator. Except for the case of olefins, which do not always cause bond weakening, this seems to be true even if L is a π-bonding ligand. Thus, it appears that, even for these ligands, electron donation in the σ bond is more important than electron removal in the π bond. Admittedly much of the evidence for bond strengths is quite indirect, and some uncertainty does exist. Therefore, whether or not the Pt-X bond strength parallels the *trans* effect of L, especially when L is on an unsaturated group, remains somewhat equivocal.

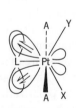

Fig. 5.7   Activated complex for the reaction *trans*-PtA_2LX $\xrightarrow{+Y}$ *trans*-PtA_2LY, where L is a π-bonding ligand.

Since it does not seem clear that bond weakening in the ground state should always be sufficient to account for the effect of good *trans* activators, the increased rate of reaction should result from a stabilization of the transition state for reaction. Chatt *et al.* and Orgel[50] independently proposed a π-bonding stabilization of the activated complex to account for the *trans* effect. The activated complex is assumed to have a trigonal bipyramidal structure as shown in Fig. 5.7. Chatt *et al.* emphasize that removal of charge from Pt(II) by π bonding of L will enhance the addition of Y and favor a more rapid reaction. Orgel stresses the increased stability of the transition state due to π bonding because the electron density on Pt(II) is reduced along the Pt-X and Pt-Y directions. Such an activated complex will lead to retention of configuration and predicts that the properties of Y and L will influence the rate of reaction in a similar way. This explanation also requires that the reactions proceed by a bimolecular displacement mechanism, which is what is found, as is discussed in a later section.

The M.O. Theory for σ- and π-trans Effects. The various theories of coordinate bonding were discussed in Chapter 2, and it is apparent that the M.O. theory affords the best explanation of the bonding in these systems. There usually is general agreement on the M.O. representation of different metal complexes, but often there is disagreement on certain specific details. For example, the energy-level ordering in square planar complexes continues to be a case where there is considerable interest and as yet no unanimity of opinion.[51] Fortunately, the area of disagreement will not affect the discussion given here.

A simplified M.O. diagram of $PtCl_4^{2-}$ is shown in Fig. 5.8. The most stable orbitals are σ bonding and are located mainly on the four chlorine groups. The same is true of the π-bonding molecular orbitals, next in order of stability. Then come the antibonding partners of these σ- and π-bonding M.O.'s. They are derived from the $5d$ atomic orbitals of Pt(II) and consist of the four relatively stable M.O.'s, with the probable order shown of π_{xz}^*, π_{yz}^*, $\sigma_{z^2}^*$ and π_{xy}^*, and the relatively unstable $\sigma_{x^2-y^2}^*$. At higher energy is the p_z valence orbital, which is not involved in σ bonding, and the antibonding orbitals σ_s^*, σ_x^*, and σ_y^*.

By making use of this type of bonding scheme, it is possible to account for the large *trans* effect for strong σ-bonding ligands L such as H^- and CH_3^-. Remembering the geometries of the atomic orbitals, we see that, of the four metal valence orbitals ($d_{x^2-y^2}$, s, p_x, and p_y) used in σ bonding in a square planar complex, only the p orbitals have *trans* directional properties. Thus, the *trans* ligand L and the leaving group X in *trans*-PtA_2LX must share the same σ_x orbital in the overall M.O. arrangements. It follows that a strong σ-bonding ligand L will take on the larger share of the bonding σ_x M.O., leaving a much smaller share for X (Fig. 5.9). This means that the Pt-X bond is weakened, as was also predicted by the polarization theory. Regardless of the mechanism of substitution, such a result is expected to lead to an increased rate of replacement of X.

It may perhaps be visualized more easily if one simply realizes that a good σ-covalent ligand, such as H^-, will put a great deal of negative charge in the p_x orbital of the metal. This in turn will repel the σ electrons of any ligand in the *trans* position which must also use the

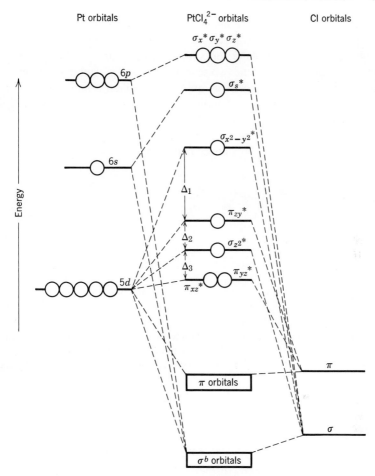

Fig. 5.8 Relative orbital energies in $PtCl_4{}^{2-}$.

same p_x orbital. Langford and Gray[2c] offer an additional explanation having to do with an increase in the stabilization of the trigonal bipyramidal intermediate, because there are more orbitals available for σ bonding in the trigonal plane than in the square planar complex. Whereas only one p orbital, p_x, is used to bond the *trans* ligands L—Pt—X

Fig. 5.9 The σ bonding of L—Pt—X, using the σ_X MO. (a) The σ-bond strengths of L and X are about equal. (b) The σ-bond strength of L is much greater than that of X.

on the x axis of the square planar complex, the addition of the entering group Y from above the xy plane causes X to move down out of the plane, resulting in a trigonal plane containing Pt, L, X, and Y (Fig. 5.10). This trigonal plane now contains two p orbitals, p_x and p_z, suitable for bonding. Thus, while originally there was only one p orbital bonding two ligands, 50% each, two orbitals now bond three ligands, 66.6% each. This suggests that good σ-bonding ligands such as H^- and CH_3^-, which can use the extra p character to firm up the σ structure in the trigonal bipyramid, will have high *trans* effects. This effect is designated as the σ *trans* effect.[2c]

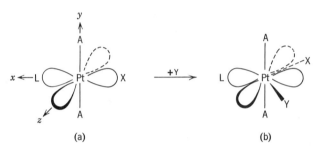

(a)   (b)

Fig. 5.10 The σ-*trans* effect due to a stabilization of the trigonal bipyramidal inter-mediate. Only on p orbital is available for σ bonding of two ligands in (a), 50% for each, whereas two p orbitals are suitable for σ bonding of three ligands in (b), 66.6% for each.

For ligands such as C_2H_4, CO, and CN^- that form strong π bonds and are good *trans* activators, the effect has been explained in terms of the π-bonding theory described earlier. It is possible to restate this in the context of the M.O. theory and to refer to it as the π-*trans effect*.[2c] Thus, in a square planar complex only three M.O.'s, the π_{xz}^*, π_{yz}^*, and π_{xy}^*, have proper symmetries for π bonding. On the addition of the entering group Y and the formation of a trigonal bipyramidal structure, four M.O.'s are of the correct symmetries for π interaction, namely, π_{xz}^*, π_{yz}^*, π_{xy}^*, and $\pi_{x^2-y^2}^*$. It is important to note that all of these orbitals are shared in π bonding with the three ligands, L, X, and Y, in the trigonal plane. Thus, the trigonal bipyramidal transition state is greatly stabilized if L is capable of bonding to the π^* orbitals. This then delocalizes electronic charge to the ligands and lowers the energy of the system. Since there are more filled π^* oribtals in the transition state than in the ground state (4 versus 3), the transition state is stabilized to the greater extent. Thus, the net effect of a good π-acceptor ligand L is to lower the activation energy for reaction.

An attempt has been made to assess the σ- and π-*trans* effects of several ligands, and the qualitative results reported[2c] are given in Table 5.7. It appears that ligands that are good *trans* activators fall in one of three categories: (1) strong σ bonding, such as H^- and CH_3^-; (2) strong π bonding such as C_2H_4 and CO; and (3) moderate σ and π bonding, such as I^- and $SC(NH_2)_2$. Ligands such as NH_3 and OH^- that are weak (covalent) σ and

Table 5.7 Estimated relative σ- and π-*trans* effects of some ligands

Ligand	σ effect[a]	π effect[a]
C_2H_4	W	VS
CO	M	VS
CN^-	M	S
$SnCl_3^-$	W[b]	S[b]
PR_3	S	M
H^-	VS	VW
$SC(NH_2)_2$	M	M
NO_2^-	W	M
I^-	M	M
CH_3^-	S	VW
$-SCN^-$	M	M
$C_6H_5^-$	M	W
Br^-	M	W
Cl^-	M	VW
Pyridine	W	W
NH_3	W	VW
OH^-	VW	VW

From reference 2c.

[a] VS, very strong; S, strong; M, medium; W, weak; VW, very weak.

[b] Assumed on the basis of n.m.r. data relative to analogous CN^- compound in Table 5.5.

π bonders are low in the *trans*-effect series. Recall the n.m.r. data recorded in Table 5.5 and note that they lend support to this explanation of the *trans* effect on the basis of the σ- and π-bonding properties of L in *trans*-PtA_2LX.

Mechanism of Substitution

In theory it would appear that square planar substitution should involve a bimolecular displacement mechanism. For both steric and electronic reasons substitution reactions in these systems would seem to proceed most readily by an expansion of coordination number to include the entering ligand. The metal is exposed for attack above and below the plane, and coordination numbers greater than four are commonplace. Furthermore these low-spin d^8 systems have a vacant p_z orbital of relatively low energy which can help accommodate the pair of electrons donated by the entering ligand.

That substitutions in square planar complexes are indeed bimolecular displacement processes is supported by at least four different kinds of experimental evidence: (1) the fact that substitution occurs with steric

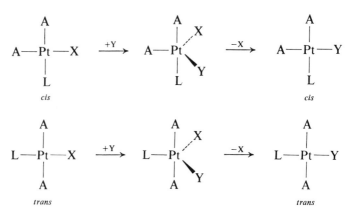

Fig. 5.11   Stereochemistry of square planar substitution through a trigonal bipyramidal structure. A *cis*-attack displacement with retention of configuration.

retention; (2) the isolation of many five- and six-coordinated d^8 systems (3) the dependence of the rate of reaction on the entering reagent; and (4) steric effects on rates.

A very large number of reactions of *cis*- and *trans*-PtA_2LX with Y to yield PtA_2LY have been studied, and without exception the *cis* substrates yield *cis* products and *trans* give *trans*.[1] That there is such complete retention of configuration requires a mechanism having a high degree of stereospecificity. This would be most unlikely for a dissociation process, because the three-coordinated species involved may at times have a nearly regular (angles of 120°) planar structure. Then, depending on whether Y enters PtA_2L adjacent to L or opposite to L, the product PtA_2LY can be either the *cis* or the *trans* isomer, respectively. Stereospecific displacement can best take place by a nucleophilic attack through a trigonal bipyramidal structure. (Fig. 5.11)

There is an abundance of evidence that low-spin d^8 four-coordinated systems have a definite tendency to add additional ligands and form five- and/or six-coordinated complexes. This has been the subject of extensive reviews,[52,53] and only a few of the more significant examples need be mentioned here. There is good evidence that $Ni(CN)_4^{2-}$ in aqueous solution containing excess CN^- forms $Ni(CN)_5^-$.[54] The $Cr(NH_3)_6^{3+}$ salt of this anion has been isolated.[55] Compounds of the type $M(diars)_2X_2$, where M = Ni(II), Pd(II), or Pt(II), are uni-univalent electrolytes in nitrobenzene,[56] and the solids where $X = I^-$ have distorted octahedral structures.[57] The compounds $Ir(PPh_3)_2(CO)_2Cl$[58] and $Rh(PPh_3)_3COH$[59] have been isolated. The Ir(I) compound is isoelectronic with Pt(II), and the Rh(I) with Pd(II). An x-ray analysis[27] of the Rh(I) compound shows

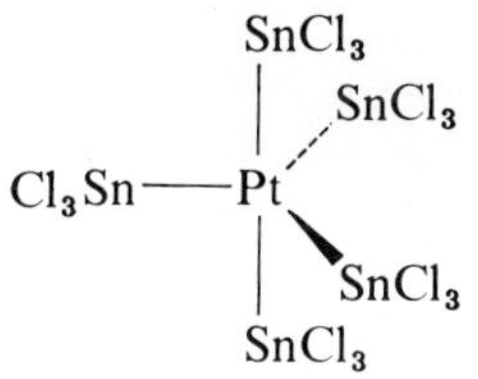

$$Cl_3Sn\!\!-\!\!-\!\!Pt\begin{matrix} SnCl_3 \\ | \quad SnCl_3 \\ \diagup \\ \diagdown \\ | \quad SnCl_3 \\ SnCl_3 \end{matrix}$$

Fig. 5.12   The structure of $Pt(SnCl_3)_5^{3-}$, a five-coordinated Pt(II) complex containing only monodentate ligands.

that it has a trigonal bipyramidal structure. This is also the structure of the complex $Pt(QAS)I^+$, where QAS is the umbrella-type quadridentate tris(o-diphenylarsinophenyl)arsine.[60]

Most significant for our discussion of substitution reactions of Pt(II) complexes is the synthesis of salts of five-coordinated Pt(II) anions, $Pt(SnCl_3)_5^{3-}$, $PtH(SnCl_3)_4^{3-}$, and $Pt(PEt_3)_2H(SnCl_3)_2^-$, which contain only monodentate ligands. The structure determination of $Pt(SnCl_3)_5^{3-}$ by x-ray diffraction[61] shows it to be a trigonal bipyramid with the Pt(II) at the center surrounded by five $SnCl_3^-$ ligands attached through Pt-Sn bonds (Fig. 5.12). It appears that strong π-bonding ligands are generally found in these five-coordinated low-spin d^8 complexes. This provides excellent support for the π-bonding hypothesis that such groups are good *trans* activators because they stabilize the five-coordinated transition state.

Lastly, there is a large amount of kinetic data on substitution reactions of square planar complexes, all of which are best explained in terms of a bimolecular displacement mechanism.[2] For reactions such as

$$MA_3X^{n+} + Y^- \xrightarrow{H_2O} MA_3Y^{n+} + X^- \qquad (16)$$

in water solution, a two-term rate law

$$\text{Rate} = k_1[MA_3X^{n+}] + k_2[MA_3X^{n+}][Y^-] \qquad (17)$$

is generally followed, where k_1 and k_2 are first-order and second-order rate constants, respectively. Under pseudo-first-order conditions containing excess Y, the experimental first-order rate constant, k_{obs}, is related to the individual rate constants as shown by the equation

$$k_{obs} = k_1 + k_2[Y] \tag{18}$$

This requires that a plot of k_{obs} versus [Y] be linear with an intercept of k_1 for the reagent-independent path and a slope of k_2 for the reagent path. Plots of this type are common for substitution reactions of square planar complexes. Such a plot is shown in Fig. 5.13 for the reaction of *trans*-$Pt(py)_2Cl_2$ with a variety of different reagents.

The two-term rate law requires a two-path reaction mechanism. In the discussion of the experiments which follow, it will be seen that the experimental evidence overwhelmingly supports the mechanism illustrated by

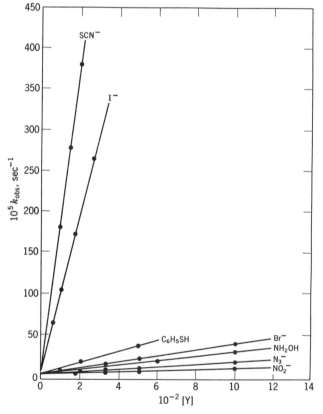

Fig. 5.13 Rates of reaction of *trans*-$Pt(py)_2Cl_2$ in methanol at 30° as a function of the concentrations of different nucleophiles. From reference 71.

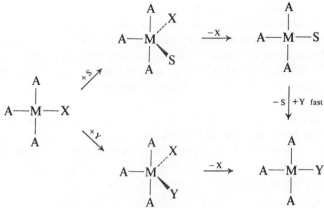

Fig. 5.14 Two-path mechanism proposed for the reaction of a square planar complex, MA_3X, with Y to yield MA_3Y. The upper path is the solvent path and the lower one is the direct path, represented by k_S and k_Y, respectively, in equation 19.

Fig. 5.14. The rate constant k_1 is due to the slow displacement of X^- by the solvent, which then is rapidly replaced by Y^-. A direct nucleophilic displacement of X^- by Y is responsible for k_2. It then becomes convenient to designate the solvent path k_1 as k_S and the reagent path k_2 as k_Y, so that equation 18 becomes

$$k_{obs} = k_S + k_Y[Y^-] \tag{19}$$

Evidence to be presented later (p. 395) suggests that the transition state for Pt(II) substitution reactions is six-coordinated. This means that the five-coordinated species is an active intermediate, and thus the energy-reaction profile may be represented by Fig. 5.15. The alternative would be

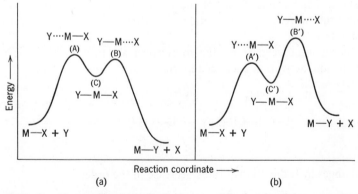

Fig. 5.15 Reaction profiles for a displacement mechanism involving a reactive intermediate, C or C'. For (a) the activation energy involves transition state A, M $\cdots$ Y bond formation, whereas for (b) it is transition state B' or M $\cdots$ X bond rupture that is important.

that the five-coordinated species is the transition state. The existence of the stable five-coordinated species mentioned earlier makes this unlikely.

In the situation represented by Fig. 5.15a, the rate-determining step is the addition of the nucleophile accompanied by structural rearrangement. However, the bond to the leaving group is still intact. The mechanism is in the $S_N2(\text{lim})$ category. For a reaction represented by Fig. 5.15b, the addition of the nucleophile is reversible and the rate step is the loss of the leaving group, accompanied by rearrangement. The mechanism is S_N2 since both bond making and bond breaking occur. In either case, the rates would show the characteristic behavior of displacement mechanisms in that the nature and concentration of the entering group would exert a major effect on the rates of reaction.

Kinetics of Substitution Reactions of Platinum(II) Complexes

In this section kinetic data are presented and discussed for substitution reactions of Pt(II) complexes. The effects on rates of reactions caused by changes in the substrate will be described first, followed by effects due to changes in the reagent. Most of the available kinetic data on square planar complexes deal with the stable and inert Pt(II) systems. However, following this discussion of Pt(II) complexes, it will be seen that sufficient data are also available to indicate that the observations made on Pt(II) are generally applicable to other square planar metal complexes.

trans Effect. The importance and the nature of the *trans* effect in Pt(II) complexes have already been dealt with at some length. All that need be done further is to provide some kinetic data to show the magnitude of this effect. This is indeed one of the more dramatic effects on the rates of substitution reactions in metal complexes, spanning many orders of magnitude.

Some quantitative data on the *trans* effect are furnished by the rate constants and activation energies reported[62] for the reaction

$$
\begin{array}{ccc}
\text{NH}_3 & & \text{NH}_3 \\
| & & | \\
\text{L--Pt--Cl} + \text{py} & \rightarrow & \text{L--Pt--py} + \text{Cl}^- \\
| & & | \\
\text{Cl} & & \text{Cl}
\end{array}
\qquad (20)
$$

For changes in L the relative rates decrease in the order:

	$C_2H_4 \gg$	NO_2^-	$> Br^-$	$> Cl^-$
Relative rates	>100	9	3	1
E_a, kcal/mole	...	11	17	19

The rate of reaction for L = C_2H_4 was too fast to measure by the experimental technique used (titrating aliquots of the reaction mixture with acid to determine the amount of unreacted pyridine). The most significant point of these results is that the increase in rate is accompanied by a decrease in activation energy. This suggests that the differences in rate are largely due to the enthalpy of activation, and therefore the previous discussion of the effect of L on the Pt-X bond strength as an explanation of the *trans* effect is justified.

Table 5.8   *trans* Effect of L on rates of reaction of some platinum(II) complexes in ethanol at 25°C

$$trans\text{-}Pt(PEt_3)_2LCl + py \rightleftharpoons trans\text{-}Pt(PEt_3)_2pyL^+ + Cl^-$$

Ligand, L	k_1, sec^{-1}	k_2, M^{-1} sec^{-1}	K_{eq}
$P(C_2H_5)_3$ [a]	1.7×10^{-2} [b]	3.8 [b]	...
H^-	1.8×10^{-2} [b]	4.2 [b]	0.03
CH_3^-	1.7×10^{-4}	6.7×10^{-2}	0.15
$C_6H_5^-$	3.3×10^{-5}	1.6×10^{-2}	0.02
$p\text{-}ClC_6H_4^-$	3.3×10^{-5}	1.6×10^{-2}	...
$p\text{-}CH_3OC_6H_4^-$	2.8×10^{-5}	1.3×10^{-2}	...
$p\text{-}C_6H_5C_6H_4^-$	1.7×10^{-5}	9.7×10^{-3}	...
Cl^-	1.0×10^{-6}	4.0×10^{-4}	...

From reference 47.
[a] For *cis*-Pt(PEt$_3$)$_2$Cl$_2$.
[b] Rate at 0°C.

The widest range of rate data on the *trans* effect of different ligands, L, is known for the reaction of *trans*-Pt(PEt$_3$)$_2$LCl with pyridine to yield *trans*-Pt(PEt$_3$)$_2$Lpy$^+$ (Table 5.8).[47] The data are reported in terms of the k_1 and k_2 of equation 18. Actually neither k_1 nor k_2 is a simple rate constant since the reactions are reversible, and both forward and reverse rates contribute to the overall observed rates. Nevertheless their magnitudes are suitable for assessing the relative activating influences of the various substituents in this series of analogous compounds.‡ The total range in reactivities covers a span of about 10^5, with L = H$^-$ and PEt$_3$ the fastest, and L = Cl$^-$ the slowest. It may be noted (Table 5.8) that only small changes in the equilibrium constant are found for large changes in rate.

cis Effect.   Although the *cis* effect of certain ligands on the rates of reaction of Co(III) complexes is fairly large (p. 171), the effect in Pt(II)

‡ C. D. Falk and J. Halpern, *J. Am. Chem. Soc.*, **87**, 3003 (1965), have extracted the true rate constants for the case of Pt(PEt$_3$)$_2$HCl.

systems is small. Thus, pyridine reacts with $PtpyCl_3^-$ only about 40% faster than it does with $PtNH_3Cl_3^-$. There is also some evidence that Cl^- is replaced from a Pt(II) complex when *cis* to NH_3 about 20% faster than when *cis* to NO_2^-. This gives a *cis* effect order of py $>$ NH_3 $>$ NO_2^- and has prompted the suggestion that a good *trans*-activating ligand will be a poor *cis* activator.[63]

This is surely not a good generalization because data are available which do not support an inverse correlation between the *cis* and *trans* effects. Thus, the rates of reaction of *cis*-$Pt(PEt_3)_2LCl$ with pyridine increase by a factor of three with changes in L in the order CH_3^- $>$ $C_6H_5^-$ $>$ Cl^-.[47] The same order is found for the *trans* effect of L in the corresponding reactions of *trans*-$Pt(PEt_3)_2LCl$, but the spread in rates is much larger (Table 5.8). A comparison of the *cis* effects of pyridine and triethylphosphine is possible from the rates of reaction of *trans*-$Pt(py)_2Cl_2$ and *trans*-$Pt(PEt_3)_2Cl_2$ (see Table 5.16). Sometimes one complex reacts faster and at other times it reacts slower, depending on the reagent. An exhaustive investigation[16] has been made of the rates of hydrolyses of the series of complexes from $PtCl_4^{2-}$ through $Pt(NH_3)_3Cl^+$. The results suggest that in these systems, for which the ligands are weakly *trans* directive, the *cis* neighbor has a somewhat greater influence on the kinetics than the *trans* neighbor to the leaving group. Hence the classical experiments typified by reaction 6 and 7 may give the results observed mainly because of a *cis* effect. However, the important point to keep in mind is that the *cis* effect is generally small, whereas the *trans* effect can be very large.

Effect of Leaving Group. Studies of substitution reactions should logically include the assessment of the ease of replacement of different groups from closely analogous substrates. If the rate of replacement of X from a metal complex inversely parallels the M-X bond strength, this tells us that there is some M-X bond rupture in the transition state.

The earliest kinetic studies[64] of Pt(II) complexes were radioligand exchange studies with PtX_4^{2-}. The half-lives for exchange at 25°C decreased in the order:

$X =$	CN^-	I^-	Br^-	Cl^-
$t_{1/2}$ min $=$	1	5	8	280

The stability data presented earlier in Table 5.3 show that the formation constants decrease in going from $Pt(CN)_4^{2-}$ to $PtCl_4^{2-}$. Likewise, exchange of thiourea with $Pt[SC(NH_2)_2]_4^{2+}$ is fast, whereas the less stable $Pt(NH_2C_2H_5)_4^{2+}$ undergoes exchange with ethylamine very slowly.[65] Grinberg attributed this direct correlation of the more stable system being also the more labile to the *trans* effect order $CN^- \gg Cl^-$, such that the complex $Pt(CN)_4^{2-}$ is much more reactive than is the less stable $PtCl_4^{2-}$.

Clearly, what is needed in an investigation solely of the effect of the leaving group in a system in which this is the only thing that changes. Such a system

$$Pt(dien)X^+ + py \rightarrow Pt(dien)py^{2+} + X^- \qquad (21)$$

has been studied,[66] and the kinetic data obtained are given in Table 5.9. In this complex the three other coordination positions are kept constant by using the inert dien ligand, and the entering ligand is always pyridine. The

Table 5.9 Effect of leaving group on rates of reaction of some Platinum(II) complexes in water at 25°C

$$Pt(dien)X^+ + py^a \rightarrow Pt(dien)py^{2+} + X^-$$

Ligand, X	$10^6 k_{obs}$, sec^{-1}
NO_3^-	very fast
H_2O	1900[b]
Cl^-	35
Br^-	23
I^-	10
N_3^-	0.83
SCN^-	0.30
NO_2^-	0.050
CN^-	0.017

From reference 66 except as specified in note b.
[a] For [py] = 0.0059 M.
[b] From reference 69.

only variable is X^-, and therefore its effect on the rate of reaction is investigated. The data show a decreasing rate for changes in X^- in the order:

$$NO_3^- > H_2O > Cl^- > Br^- > I^- > N_3^- > \underline{SCN}^- > \underline{NO_2}^- > CN^-.$$

The spread in rates of approximately 10^6 in this series of reactions shows that the leaving group has a substantial effect on the rates of reaction, indicating that considerable Pt-X bond breaking is involved in forming the transition state (T.S.). This does not demand a dissociation process, but merely requires that Pt-X bond breaking make a contribution comparable to that of Pt-py bond forming. In terms of Fig. 5.15 either the T.S. for the formation of the five-coordinated intermediate, A, or the T.S. for its decomposition, B', may determine the rate of reaction. Whichever of the two is higher will be rate limiting. In either case there will be some weakening of the M-X bond, either because five bonds are being formed instead of four or because X is being dissociated. The T.S. B′ should involve a higher degree of bond breaking. The intermediate will, of course, have the 100 % of new bond formation, but the transition states will also correspond to a certain amound of bond formation, $< 50\%$ for path a and $> 50\%$ for path b.

It is significant that, with only X changing in these systems, the order of labilities of the complexes does parallel their order of instabilities. Thus, the complex Pt(dien)Cl$^+$ reacts with pyridine 2000 times faster than does the more stable complex Pt(dien)CN$^+$. Furthermore the leaving groups high in the *trans* effect series are slowly replaced. This is in accord with the combined σ- and π-*trans* effect theory, which suggests that good *trans* activators are strongly bonded to the metal. The reverse, that a poor *trans* activator is readily replaced, need not be true. Both NH$_3$ and OH$^-$ are low in the *trans* effect series, but they are very difficult to replace in a Pt(II) complex. Thus, no exchange of ^{15}NH$_3$ with Pt(NH$_3$)$_4$$^{2+}$ at 25°C was observed after 217 days.[68]

This lack of correlation of the bond strength with *trans* effect is not surprising since the amount of covalent bonding into the σ_x orbital must be small for electronegative ligands such as OH$^-$ and NH$_3$, because of the high energy of the $6p$ orbital of platinum. Thus, the bond strength is determined largely by the non-stereospecific σ_s and σ_d bonds and by ionic interactions.

Recent investigations provide more information relative to the nature of the leaving group and its ease of replacement from these systems. Temperature dependence studies[67] have been made on the reaction of Pt(dien)X$^+$ with thiourea to give Pt(dien)(tu)$^{2+}$. The results show (refer to Table 5.20) that the activation energies for reaction increase with changes in X in this order: Cl$^- \sim$ Br$^- \sim$ I $\ll$ N$_3$$^- \sim$ NO$_2$$^- <$ SCN$^- <$ CN$^-$. Thus, there appear to be two types of leaving groups: (1) ligands which are readily replaced and for which the rate of replacement is almost independent of the leaving group, and (2) ligands which are more difficult to displace and for which the rate of displacement depends on the leaving group. This behavior may be surprising if one considers that the halide ions are all replaced with about equal ease, although the Pt-X bond strength increases for changes in X in the order Cl$^- <$ Br$^- <$ I$^-$.

These observations are readily understood, assuming that the mechanism of reaction involves the formation of an active intermediate as is represented by Fig. 5.15. In such a case, reaction profile a corresponds to leaving groups in category 1, which are replaced at a rate almost independent of the leaving group. This follows because the higher activation energy between the ground state and the transition state is that with T.S. A, which involves chiefly bond formation with the nucleophile Y and little rupture of the Pt-X bond. Thus, the nature of X can have only a secondary effect on the formation of A.

In contrast to this, reaction profile b of Fig. 5.15 corresponds to leaving groups in category 2, which are replaced at a rate that depends on the nature of the leaving group. This follows because now the activation energy is determined by T.S. B'. Since B' involves primarily a breaking of the Pt-X bond, the rate of its displacement will depend on the nature of X. It is also clear that for some combination of leaving group X and entering group Y the T.S.'s A and B will be of about equal energy, which means that for such reactions bond making and bond breaking will be of comparable importance.

Effect of Charge. Information on the mechanism of substitution can sometimes be provided by the effect of the charge on the complex on its rate of reaction. Thus, if the reaction involves primarily a separation of charges, as in a dissociation process, then for an analogous series of complexes the rate will decrease with a decrease of the charge on the complex. However, if the reaction is largely associative in type, the charge neutralization process requires that an increase in positive charge on the complex be accompanied by an increase in rate of reaction. For a bimolecular displacement process, where dissociation and neutralization are of comparable importance, there would be opposing effects and the rates of reaction would not change very much with changes of the charge on the complex.

Martin[16] and his students have made extensive investigations of the hydrolysis of the series of complex $PtCl_4^{2-}$ through $Pt(NH_3)_3Cl^+$. Their results (Table 5.10) show that for this series of complexes, where there is a three-unit change in charge on the complex, the rates of hydrolyses are all approximately the same. This suggests that in the transition state both bond making and bond breaking are important, and T.S.'s A and B in Fig. 5.15 are of about the same energy. Thus, the solvent path, k_S, like the direct displacement path, k_Y, seems to be a bimolecular displacement process.

Similarly, the rates of direct radiochloride ion exchange, k_{Cl}, with these Pt(II) complexes are only slightly affected by changes in the charge on the complex. However, there are small but significant effects on the k_Y term for certain reagents. For example, it was found[69] (Table 5.11) that NO_2^- is a better reagent towards $Pt(dien)Br^+$, but a worse one towards $Pt(dien)H_2O^{2+}$, than is Cl^-. That NO_2^- appears to be a relatively better reagent towards substrates of lower positive charge suggests that the electrophilic character of NO_2^- makes a contribution to its reactivity. Complexes with a low positive charge have their filled d orbitals in a more expanded state and can thus interact more effectively with the vacant p

Table 5.10 Effect of charge on the complex on its rate of hydrolysis for a series of platinum(II) chloroammines at 20°C

$$Pt(NH_3)_nCl_{4-n} + H_2O \xrightarrow{k_{H_2O}} Pt(NH_3)_nH_2OCl_{3-n} + Cl^-$$

$$Pt(NH_3)_nH_2OCl_{3-n} + H_2O \xrightarrow{k'_{H_2O}} Pt(NH_3)_n(H_2O)_2Cl_{2-n} + Cl^-$$

Complex	$10^5 k_{H_2O}$, sec^{-1}	$10^5 k'_{H_2O}$, sec^{-1}
$PtCl_4^{2-}$	3.9	3.3
$PtNH_3Cl_3^-$ *trans*[a]	0.62	12.5
cis[b]	5.6	8[c]
cis-$Pt(NH_3)_2Cl_2$	2.5	3.3
trans-$Pt(NH_3)_2Cl_2$	9.8	5
$Pt(NH_3)_3Cl^+$	2.6	...

From reference 16.
[a] For replacement of Cl^- *trans* to NH_3.
[b] For replacement of Cl^- *cis* to NH_3.
[c] For replacement of Cl^- *trans* to NH_3.

orbital on nitrogen of the entering NO_2^-. This is also in accord with the relative reactivities of NO_2^- and Cl^- towards the substrates *trans*-Pt (pip)$_2$Cl$_2$ and *trans*-Pt(PEt$_3$)$_2$Cl$_2$[71] (Table 5.11). That NO_2^- is relatively a less efficient reagent towards the latter compound is explained by metal to ligand π bonding in the transition state, which makes less available the d_π electrons for bonding with the entering NO_2^-. Since NO_2^- appears

Table 5.11 Effect of the nature of the platinum(II) complex on the relative reactivities of Cl^- and NO_2^-

Complex	$10^4 k_Y$, M^{-1} sec^{-1}, for reaction with	
	Cl^-	NO_2^-
$Pt(dien)H_2O^{2+}$ [a]	1.0×10^4	0.56×10^4
$Pt(dien)Br^+$ [b]	8.8	37
trans-$Pt(pip)_2Cl_2$ [c]	9.3	20
trans-$Pt(py)_2Cl_2$ [c]	4.5	6.8
trans-$Pt(PEt_3)_2Cl_2$ [c]	0.29	0.27

[a] From reference 69. Water solution, 25°C.
[b] From reference 70. Water solution, 25°C.
[c] From reference 71. Methanol solution, 30°C.

to behave both as a nucleophile and an electrophile in these reactions, it is called a *biphilic* reagent.[72] Reagent reactivities are further discussed starting on p. 396.

Steric Effects.   An almost classical approach for obtaining information on the molecularity of a substitution reaction is to investigate the steric effect on its rate of reaction. If a bimolecular displacement is involved the

Table 5.12   Steric effects on the rates of substitution reactions of some platinum(II) complexes

Complex	Conditions	k_{obs}, sec^{-1}
Pt(PEt$_3$)$_2$LCl^a		
$\quad$ cis-L = phenyl	[py] = 0.0062 M, 0°C	8.0 × 10^{-2}
$\quad\quad$ o-tolyl	,, ,, ,,	2.0 × 10^{-4}
$\quad\quad$ mesityl	,, ,, 25°C	1.0 × 10^{-6}
$\quad$ trans-L = phenyl	,, ,, ,,	1.2 × 10^{-4}
$\quad\quad$ o-tolyl	,, ,, ,,	1.7 × 10^{-5}
$\quad\quad$ mesityl	,, ,, ,,	3.4 × 10^{-6}
cis-Pt(4-ampy)$_2$Cl$_2$^{a}	[Cl$^-$] = 0.005 M, 25°C	6.5 × 10^{-4}
cis-Pt(α-pic)Cl$_2$^{a}	,, ,, ,,	2.9 × 10^{-5}
Pt(dien)Cl$^+$ ^{b}	[Br$^-$] = 0.020 M, 25°C	1.9 × 10^{-4}
Pt(Et$_4$dien)Cl$^+$ ^{c}	[Br$^-$] = 0.10 M, 80°C	8.5 × 10^{-6}

^{a} From reference 47. 4-ampy = 4-amylpyridine; α-pic = α-picoline.
^{b} From reference 70.
^{c} From reference 73. For this complex k_{obs} does not depend on the concentration of Br$^-$.

increased steric hindrance causes a decrease in rate, whereas steric acceleration is generally observed for a dissociation process.

Therefore the data[47] in Table 5.12 afford compelling experimental evidence that the reaction of Pt(PEt$_3$)$_2$LCl with pyridine involves a nucleophilic attack on Pt(II). The effect of increasing steric hindrance is to decrease the rate of reaction. Molecular models show that the o-methyl groups on the phenyl ligand are above and below the square plane and thus tend to shield the central platinum. Furthermore, models show that for the formation of a trigonal bipyramidal geometry the *cis* isomer offers more efficient shielding than does the *trans* form. Both isomers appear to offer approximately the same amount of hindrance towards the formation of a tetragonal pyramidal structure. The experimental results show that *cis* blocking causes the relative rate to drop by 1/80,000 from L = phenyl to L = mesityl, whereas *trans* blocking results in a drop of only 1/36. The experimental results support an approximate trigonal bipyramidal structure for the active intermediate in these reactions.

Other examples of steric retardation of the rates of planar substitution are also included in Table 5.12. That the k_S path of $^{36}Cl^-$ exchange for cis-Pt(α-pic)$_2$Cl$_2$ is only 1/20 as fast as it is for cis-Pt(4-ampy)$_2$Cl$_2$ in ethanol is strong evidence in support of a displacement mechanism for the solvent path.

It is to be expected that if the central metal of a square planar complex were completely shielded, a displacement process would be impossible and any substitution would have to involve a dissociation mechanism. Such steric blocking has almost been achieved with the complexes M(Et$_4$dien)X^{n+}, where M = Pd(II), Pt(II), and Au(III) and Et$_4$dien = (C$_2$H$_5$)$_2$NC$_2$H$_4$NHC$_2$H$_4$N(C$_2$H$_5$)$_2$. The four terminal ethyl groups are above and below the plane and render virtually impossible any access to the central metal (see also p. 415 and Fig. 5.21). A comparison of the rate of reaction of Pt(Et$_4$dien)Cl$^+$ with that of the analogous unhindered Pt(dien)Cl$^+$ shows (Table 5.12) that the hindered systems reacts more slowly by several orders of magnitude. Furthermore, the rate of reaction of the hindered system does not depend on the reagent. This is an unique behavior for a planar substitution, because the two-term rate law generally observed for these systems no longer applies. The results resemble the behavior of six-coordinated complexes and strongly suggest that the reaction is largely dissociative in type.

Steric effects have also been observed[74] for the reactions of the five-coordinated complex Pt(QAS)X$^+$, with an umbrella-type structure, compared to the analogous planar complex Pt(TAS)X$^+$ (Fig. 5.16). Several such complexes of this tetraarsine, QAS, have been prepared by Venanzi and his students and found to have an approximate trigonal bipyramidal structure.[60] The reactions of the planar complexes Pt(TAS)X$^+$ are approximately 10^4 times faster than are the reactions of the more sterically crowded complexes Pt(QAS)X$^+$. A significant observation is that

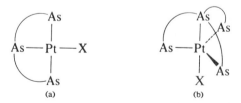

Fig. 5.16 Structures of (a) Pt(TAS)X$^+$ and (b) Pt(QAS)X$^+$, where TAS = bis(o-diphenylarsinophenyl)phenylarsine and QAS = tris(o-diphenylarsinophenyl)arsine. The phenyl groups are not shown.

the rates of reaction of Pt(QAS)X$^+$ depend on the nature and the concentration of reagent Y$^-$:

$$Pt(QAS)X^+ + Y^- \rightarrow Pt(QAS)Y^+ + X^- \qquad (22)$$

The reactivities of different reagents decrease in the order: CN$^-$ > S=C(NH$_2$)$_2$ > SCN$^-$ $\sim$ I$^-$ $\sim$ P(C$_6$H$_5$)$_3$ > N$_3^-$ > NO$_2^-$ $\gg$ C$_5$H$_{11}$N. The nucleophiles are in the same order generally observed for reactions with square planar Pt(II) complexes, except that the importance of steric factors makes some reagents react slower than expected. Thus, P(C$_6$H$_5$)$_3$ and to a lesser extent NO$_2^-$, C$_5$H$_{11}$N, and CH$_3$OH are less reactive towards Pt(QAS)X$^+$ than towards a typical square planar complex such as trans-Pt(py)$_2$Cl$_2$ (see Table 5.16, p. 399).

This investigation of the reactions of Pt(QAS)X$^+$ is of interest because it represents one of the detailed kinetic studies of substitution in a trigonal bipyramidal metal complex.§ Since this is the structure postulated for the active intermediates in reactions of square planar Pt(II) complexes, it would not have been surprising had the reaction been dissociative in type. However, the results show that the complex is intermediate, in its steric properties and kinetic behavior, between planar complexes, which are open to nucleophilic attack, and octahedral complexes, which are closed to nucleophilic attack.

Kinetic data for reaction 22 show that these reactions follow a two-term rate law resembling that for reactions of planar complexes. However, for Pt(QAS)X$^+$ the two-term rate law differs from other cases in that k_1 is not constant but varies with the reagent. The explanation[74] for this behavior is that in methanol there is extensive ion-pair formation between the reactants. Reaction can occur either between the free complex, RX$^+$, and the reagent, Y$^-$, or between the ion pair and the reagent:

$$RX^+ + Y^- \overset{K}{\rightleftharpoons} RX^+, Y^- \qquad (23)$$

$$RX^+ + Y^- \overset{k_c}{\longrightarrow} RY^+ + X^- \qquad (24)$$

$$RX^+, Y^-, Y^- \overset{k_{I.P.}}{\longrightarrow} RY^+, Y^- + X^- \qquad (25)$$

This mechanism leads to the rate law, for excess of Y$^-$,

$$k_{obs} = \frac{k_c[Y^-] + k_{I.P.}\, K[Y^-]^2}{1 + K[Y^-]} \qquad (26)$$

§ Kinetic studies have recently been made on substitution reactions of Fe(CO)$_4$-P(C$_6$H$_5$)$_3$ (E. E. Siefert and R. J. Angelici, *J. Organometal. Chem.*, in press) and of MnNO(CO)$_4$ (H. Wawersik and F. Basolo, *J. Am. Chem. Soc.*, in press). The Fe compound reacts by an S$_N$1 and the Mn by an S$_N$2 mechanism.

Independent determination of K from conductance measurements shows that $K[Y^-] \gg 1$ for the values of $[Y^-]$ used in the kinetic studies. Hence 26 reduces to 17 in form, but whereas k_2 is equal to $k_{1\text{I.P.}}$, k_1 is equal to k_c/K and is therefor not a constant. Apparently k_S for the solvent is too small to detect.

The extensive ion pairing even in dilute solution, is ascribed to the high polarizability of $PtQASX^+$. The binding results largely from van der Waals interactions of Y with the apical arsenic, because non-ionic reagents such as thiourea and triphenylphosphine behave the same as anionic

Table 5.13 Effect of solvent on the rate of $^{36}Cl^-$ exchange with *trans*-$Pt(py)_2Cl_2$ at 25°C

Solvents in Which Rate Is Independent of $[Cl^-]$	$10^5 k$, sec^{-1}	Solvents in Which Rate is Dependent on $[Cl^-]$	k_{Cl^-}, $M^{-1}\,\text{sec}^{-1}$
DMSO	380	CCl_4	10^4
H_2O	3.5	C_6H_6	10^2
CH_3NO_2	3.2	$t\text{-}C_4H_9OH$	10^{-1}
C_2H_5OH	1.4	EtOAc	10^{-2}
$n\text{-}C_3H_7OH$	0.42	$(CH_3)_2CO$	10^{-2}
		DMF	10^{-3}

From reference 72[a].

reagents. This is also in accord with the term $[Y^-]^2$ in the kinetic expression 26. A first-order term in Y would be expected if Y were adjacent to the leaving group X, but with Y in a remote position, a second Y is required to enter the complex. Although there must be considerable steric crowding in the six-coordinated transition state, that this is possible is strongly supported by the fact that stable octahedral complexes of the type $M(QAS)X_2^{n+}$ have been isolated.[60]

Solvent Effect. Since there is considerable evidence that the solvent path for planar substitution involves a direct displacement by the solvent, it is to be expected that the contribution made by this path to the overall rate of reaction would increase with an increase in the coordinating ability of the solvent. This is in accord with the experimental results[72a] of the solvent effect on the rate of $^{36}Cl^-$ exchange with *trans*-$Pt(py)_2Cl_2$ (Table 5.13). Under the conditions of the experiments, moderately low concentrations of Cl^-, the solvents were roughly divided into two different groups. One group, the good coordinating solvents, provide almost entirely a solvent path for exchange ($k_S \gg k_{Cl}[Cl^-]$). The poor coordinating solvents, such as benzene, carbon tetrachloride, and sterically hindered alcohols, contribute little to the overall rate of reaction. The exchange occurs by Cl⁻ acting as a nucleophile ($k_{Cl}[Cl^-] > k_S$). For the "good" solvents it is of interest to note that the values of k_S increase in the order ROH $< H_2O \sim CH_3NO_2 <$ DMSO. It is significant that the rate of exchange is faster in dimethylsulfoxide than in water. This strongly suggests that Pt-solvent bond making is important in the transition state. Since the ligand atom sulfur is a better nucleophile than oxygen towards Pt(II) (see the section starting on p. 23), it follows that DMSO is a better reagent than is H_2O. It is known that Pt(II) forms stable complexes with DMSO and that the bonding is Pt-S.[75] If the role of the solvent were primarily that of solvating the departing Cl⁻, then H_2O rather than DMSO would be the more efficient solvent for reaction. Such would be the case if bond breaking were of primary importance, and therefore the experimental results argue against this.

It should be noted that CH_3NO_2, which does not form stable compounds with Pt(II), is nevertheless an efficient solvent for reaction. The suggestion was made[72a] that this is due to its biphilic properties. Closely related is the discussion in the next section of the effect of electrophilic substances on the rates of reaction of certain Pt(II) complexes.

In Table 5.13 it can be seen that the rate constant for chloride ion acting as a nucleophile is very large in non-polar solvents such as CCl_4 and C_6H_6, and quite small in polar solvents such as dimethylformamide (DMF). This is understandable in terms of the poor solvating powers towards anions of the former class of solvents. Thus chloride ion has a high activity in CCl_4 and is reactive. It may be noted that in such a poor solvent one would not expect to find a large value of k_S for two reasons. First, the solvent could not coordinate to the metal ion and act as a nucleophile; second, solvation of the leaving anion would be very ineffective. A further discussion of solvent effects appears on p. 207.

Gray[69] has designed some clever competition experiments providing direct proof that the role of the solvent is that of a nucleophile in its contribution to the rate of substitution in Pt(II) complexes. He examined the reactions of Pt(dien)X⁺ and started by determining the rates of replacement of water by different reagents Y in the reaction

$$Pt(dien)H_2O^{2+} + Y^- \rightarrow Pt(dien)Y^+ + H_2O \qquad (27)$$

For reactions in water solution, the aquo complex is the presumed active intermediate of the solvent path in the two-path replacement of X by Y:

$$Pt(dien)X^+ + Y^- \rightarrow Pt(dien)Y^+ + X^- \qquad (28)$$

To be consistent with the observed first-order term, the rate of reaction 27 must be much faster than the rate of replacement of X by H_2O, k_{H_2O}.

This requirement is met for every ligand studied, and it was further observed that the rates of reaction 27 decrease for different Y ligands in the order $OH^- \gg I^- > SCN^- > Br^- > Cl^- > NO_2^- > py$.

The very striking high reactivity of OH^- towards this substrate is due to its not being a usual ligand replacement but rather a rapid proton transfer reaction:

$$Pt(dien)H_2O^{2+} + OH^- \rightleftharpoons Pt(dien)OH^+ + H_2O \qquad (29)$$

Normally OH^- is a very poor reagent, as will be discussed in the section on reagent reactivity. The fact that OH^-, relative to other reagents Y, is 100% efficient in capturing $Pt(dien)H_2O^{2+}$ and at the same time relatively inert towards $Pt(dien)X^+$ allows competition experiments to determine whether or not $Pt(dien)H_2O^{2+}$ is generated directly in the solvent path.

Two types of experiments were performed. The first was that of determining the rate of reaction of $Pt(dien)X^+$ with OH^- in the presence of varying amounts of X^-:

$$Pt(dien)X^+ + OH^- \xrightarrow{X^-} Pt(dien)OH^+ + X^- \qquad (30)$$

The results showed that the presence of X^- has no effect on the rate of reaction and that the rate constant has the same value as k_{H_2O} determined independently. If the solvent were only assisting the removal of X^- by a dissociative process

$$
\begin{array}{c}
\overset{H_2O}{Pt(dien)X^+ \rightleftharpoons Pt(dien)^{2+} + X^-} \\
\big\uparrow\big\downarrow {\scriptstyle H_2O} \\
Pt(dien)H_2O^{2+} \xrightarrow{OH^-} Pt(dien)OH^+
\end{array}
\qquad (31)
$$

the presence of added X^- should result in a slower rate because of a mass-action retardation effect. However, the experimental results support a solvent path which involves a nucleophilic displacement of X^- by the solvent

$$
\begin{array}{c}
\overset{\displaystyle X}{Pt(dien)X^+ + H_2O \rightleftharpoons (dien)Pt} \\
\big\uparrow\big\downarrow \qquad {}^{\cdot\cdot}OH_2 \\
(dien)PtOH_2^{2+} \xrightarrow{OH^-} Pt(dien)OH^+
\end{array}
\qquad (32)
$$

The second type of experiment performed involves a competition of different reagents Y^- with OH^- for the replacement of X^- in the reaction

$$Pt(dien)X^+ + Y^- + OH^- \rightarrow Pt(dien)Y^+ \text{ or } Pt(dien)OH^+ + X^- \qquad (33)$$

The results of such experiments provide information on whether or not $Pt(dien)H_2O^{2+}$ is generated in the reagent path. In such a case for reaction mixtures containing both Y^- and OH^-, the aquo intermediate would rapidly and completely convert to $Pt(dien)OH^+$. However, if the reagent path is indeed a direct displacement by Y (Fig. 5.14), then the initial product of reaction 33 would be $Pt(dien)Y^+$. This follows because Y^- is a much better nucleophile than H_2O and therefore $k_Y[Y^-] \gg k_{H_2O}$. The initially formed $Pt(dien)Y^+$ would then react more slowly to generate the stable

Table 5.14 Competition experiments of reagents Y^- with OH^- for the reaction of $Pt(dien)X^+$ in water solution at 25°C;

$$[OH^-] = 0.001\text{–}0.005 \ M$$

$$Pt(dien)X^+ + Y^-, OH^- \xrightarrow{k_Y} Pt(dien)Y^+ \xrightarrow{k_{H_2O}} Pt(dien)OH^+$$

Complex	Y	$10^4 k_Y, \ M^{-1} \ \text{sec}^{-1 \ a}$	$10^4 k_{H_2O}, \ \text{sec}^{-1 \ a}$
$Pt(dien)Cl^+$	Br^-	50 (53)	1.32 (1.32)
	I^-	2000 (2000)	0.42 (0.42)
$Pt(dien)Br^+$	Cl^-	9 (8.8)	1.0 (1.0)
	I^-	2300 (2300)	0.42 (0.42)

From reference 2c.
^{a} Values in parentheses were measured independently in the absence of OH^-.

final product $Pt(dien)OH^+$. The rate of its formation should correspond to the k_{H_2O} for $Pt(dien)Y^+$. Likewise the rate of the initial formation of $Pt(dien)Y^+$ in the presence of OH^- should be the same as that of k_Y determined independently in the absence of OH^-. The data in Table 5.14 show that this is what is found, affording excellent proof of a direct reagent displacement mechanism.

The significance of this kind of experiment is that it rules out another possible mechanism[76] for planar complexes in which a square pyramidal structure is possessed by the five-coordinated intermediate. Such a structure is common for C.N. 5, though no examples of Pt(II) with such a structure are definitely established. Figure 5.17 shows a plausible reaction sequence with a square pyramid intermediate. Both a solvent reaction (path I) and a nucleophile reaction (path II) are shown. It can be seen that there is a necessary formation of the aquo complex in the nucleophile path before the nucleophile can enter the final product.

There is a theoretical reason for postulating the square pyramid structure. Use of the energy levels of Table 2.4 leads to the prediction that

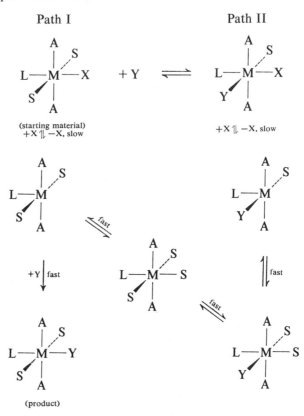

Fig. 5.17 Reaction mechanism of a square planar complex through a square pyramidal intermediate, where S = solvent.

the C.F.A.E. for a d^8 system going from a square planar structure to a trigonal bipyramid is $10.42\,Dq$ units. The C.F.A.E. in going to a square pyramid structure is only $6.28\,Dq$ units. Crystal field stabilization thus favors a square pyramid intermediate. Since Dq for Pt(II) is of the order of 4–5 kcal from spectral data, the C.F.A.E.'s are large.

This forbiddingly large energy barrier is compensated for by the formation of a fifth strong bond in both cases. The mutual repulsion of the five ligands for each other is less for the trigonal bipyramid structure than for the square pyramid. In fact, in the hypothetical case of $PtCl_5^{3-}$, using a simple electrostatic model, the difference in repulsion energies just balances the difference in crystal field effects.[77] Also strong π-bonding ligands in the trigonal plane will greatly reduce the losses in C.F.S.E. for a trigonal bipyramid.

Electrophilic Catalysis. During the investigation of the solvent effect on the rate of $^{36}Cl^-$ exchange with *trans*-Pt(py)$_2$Cl$_2$, it was also observed that the rate of exchange markedly increases with the addition of certain acids, such as CH$_3$COOH, CF$_3$COOH, and H$_3$BO$_3$.[72a] This accelerating effect was attributed to the ability of these compounds to interact with the electrons in the filled d orbitals on Pt(II) by making use of empty π orbitals on the acids.

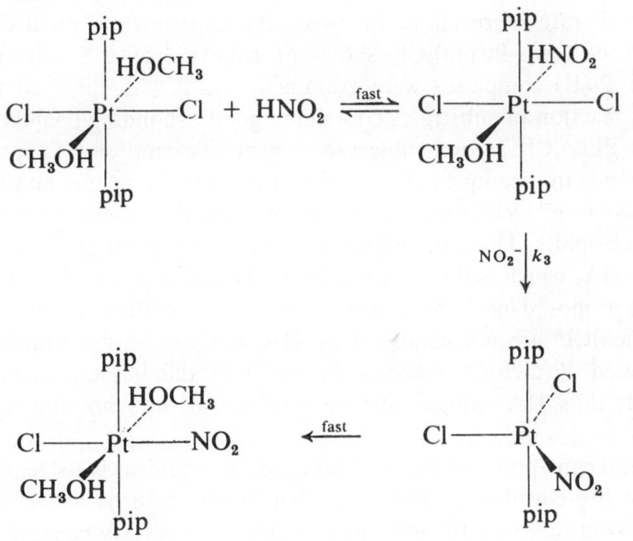

Fig. 5.18 Mechanism proposed for the acid (HNO$_2$)-catalyzed path for the reaction of *trans*-Pt(pip)$_2$Cl$_2$ with NO$_2^-$ in methanol solution. From reference 78.

A similar observation with HNO$_2$ as the catalyst was made[78] for the $^{36}Cl^-$ exchange of *trans*-Pt(piperdine)$_2$Cl$_2$ and its reaction with NO$_2^-$:

$$trans\text{-}Pt(pip)_2Cl_2 + Y^- \xrightarrow{HA} trans\text{-}Pt(pip)_2ClY + Cl^- \qquad (34)$$

A kinetic study of this system with added acid (HA = HNO$_2$ or H$_3$BO$_3$) shows that the three-term rate law

$$Rate = (k_1 + k_2[Y^-] + k_3[Y^-][HA])[Complex] \qquad (35)$$

is followed. In addition to the usual solvent path, k_1, and the reagent path, k_2, there is an acid-catalyzed reagent path, k_3. The mechanism proposed for this catalyzed path is shown in Fig. 5.18. It is similar to that for the uncatalyzed path except that HA has replaced a molecule of solvent on the elongated z axis. The catalysis occurs because HA removes d valence orbital electrons from Pt(II), and it can then more readily accept σ-bonding electrons from the nucleophile Y.

There is evidence to support this idea that increasing the positive charge on the central atom accelerates the rate of reaction of planar complexes. For example, Au(III) complexes react about 10^4 times faster[79] than the analogous isoelectronic Pt(II) complexes. It is also noteworthy that the reactions of cationic Au(III) complexes proceed almost exclusively by the reagent path, with the solvent making only a negligible contribution to the overall rate of reaction. Likewise, the experimental results for the reaction of trans-Pt(pip)$_2$Cl$_2$ show no catalysis of the solvent path.

Other Pt(II) complexes were examined, and it was observed that the rates of reaction of substrates containing good π-bonding ligands such as trans-Pt(PEt$_3$)$_2$Cl$_2$, are not subject to electrophilic catalysis. It appears that such ligands in a complex can π-bond in the transition state and alleviate the stress caused by excess electrons brought into the system by the addition of a nucleophile. Thus, these ligands serve the function attributed to the catalyst HA, which is then not required. One other point, also in keeping with the proposed mechanism, is that the reactions of the sterically hindered Pt(Et$_4$dien)Cl$^+$ are not catalyzed by HA, but catalysis is found for the unhindered Pt(dien)Cl$^+$. Access to Pt(II) in the hindered complex is blocked; thus HA cannot interact with it and does not function as a catalyst.

A significant point of the acid-catalyzed mechanism is its requirement that the five-coordinated species shown in Fig. 5.18 be an active intermediate and not an activated complex. This is necessary because the rate data show that the acid is present in the transition state. Since the five-coordinated species does not contain acid, it therefore cannot be the activated complex. Thus evidence is provided in support of the reaction profile shown earlier in Fig. 5.15, an S_N2(lim) process.

Effect of Nucleophile. One of the most fascinating problems involved in nucleophilic displacement reactions is that of trying to understand what properties of a reagent make it a good nucleophile. There have been several attempts to correlate the extrakinetic properties of the reagent with its reactivity, and some of these have been moderately successful. All of them are based on the principle of linear free-energy relationships (L.F.E.R.).[80] One point that has become abundantly clear is that, just as there is no one scale of acid-base strengths, also there is no one scale of nucleophilic reactivities.[81] The substrate is most important and must be considered in any discussion of relative order of nucleophilic strengths of various reagents. Fortunately, a qualitative but useful generalization is possible.[82] The existing kinetic data on many different substrates show that soft ("polarizable") nucleophiles are most effective towards soft substrates.

Similarly *hard nucleophiles, such as* OH^-, *are most effective towards hard substrates.* A further rule is that *polarizability in the nucleophile is always more important for rates than for equilibria.*

Brønsted[83] successfully applied the L.F.E.R. principle to displacement reactions at hydrogen in various compounds. He found a linear relationship between the log of the rate constant for proton transfer and the log of the ordinary base strength of the reagent. It should be noted that the base strengths are towards the acid H^+, and the displacements also involve an attack on hydrogen. Swain and Scott[84] found that the rates of displacement at carbon do not adequately parallel the base strength of the reagent and used the rates of reaction of methyl bromide to prepare a nucleophilicity scale towards carbon. Edwards[85a] made the significant suggestion that in order to account for the nucleophilic properties of different reagents a two-parameter equation would be necessary. His equations are given in Chapter 3 (p. 138).

Earlier work on complexes of Pt(II) had established[70,76] the nucleophilic reactivity order $R_3P > tu > I^- \sim SCN^- \sim N_3^- > NO_2^- > Br^- >$ py $>$ aniline $\sim$ olefin $\sim NH_3 \sim Cl^- > H_2O > OH^-$. The most detailed study of relative reactivity is that made by Bellucco[71] for a series of reactions in methanol solution:

$$trans\text{-}PtA_2Cl_2 + Y^- \rightarrow trans\text{-}PtA_2ClY + Cl^- \qquad (36)$$

Some of the results obtained are given in Table 5.15. One very striking feature is that the nucleophilic character of the reagents does not correlate their base strength. In fact the strongest bases, OCH_3^- and OH^-, are about the only reagents that do not compete with the solvent in displacements at Pt(II). Since basicity is of little importance, it appears that polarizability must play a major role in determining the reactivity of the nucleophile. This is roughly borne out, as can be seen, by a comparison of the kinetic data in Table 5.15, with several different properties given in Table 3.4 (p. 140) for the various nucleophiles.

One of these is the E^0 value for the reagent acting as a reducing agent. This is one of the parameters used by Edwards[85a] to correlate a considerable body of rate and equilibrium data. The equation

$$\log (k/k_0) = \alpha E^0 + \beta H \qquad (37)$$

has been called[85c] the *oxibase scale*. It is most useful if unknown or uncertain E^0 values are adjusted to fit certain rate data. A plot of the $\log k_Y$ values of Table 5.15 versus E^0 values does show a strong correlation, but some points consistently deviate.

That the reactivity of Y does not correlate with its base strength is to be expected if one considers that the pK_a values are for the hard acid H^+,

Table 5.15 Rates of reaction for some platinum(II) complexes with different nucleophiles in methanol at 30°C and $\mu = 0.1$

Y	trans-Pt(py)$_2$Cl$_2$	trans-Pt(pip)$_2$Cl$_2$	trans-Pt(AsEt$_3$)$_2$Cl$_2$	trans-Pt(PEt$_3$)$_2$Cl$_2$	trans-Pt(SeEt$_2$)$_2$Cl$_2$
CH$_3$OH	1 × 10^{-5}	1.2 × 10^{-5}	...	...	2 × 10^{-5}
CH$_3$O$^-$	≤0.1	≤0.1	...	...	≤0.1
^{36}Cl$^-$	0.45	0.925	0.69	0.029	...
NH$_3$	0.47	0.6	...	...	...
C$_5$H$_5$N	0.55	...	...	...	...
NO$_2^-$	0.68	2.04	0.1	0.027	1.11
N$_3^-$	1.55	5.30	0.8	0.2	7.5
NH$_2$OH	2.9	...	...	...	...
H$_2$NNH$_2$	2.93	...	...	...	...
Br$^-$	3.7	6.16	1.63	0.93	6.35
C$_6$H$_5$SH	5.7	...	...	...	...
SO$_3^{2-}$	250	400	...	...	...
I$^-$	107	...	650	236	1,100
SCN$^-$	180	399	565	371	675
SeCN$^-$	5,150	3,310	12,300	6,950	13,500
C$_6$H$_5$S$^-$	6,000	...	...	...	...
S=C(NH$_2$)$_2$	6,000	3,500	...	...	22,900
S$_2$O$_3^{2-}$	9,000	...	...	...	...

From reference 71. Values of $10^3 k_Y$ in M^{-1} sec^{-1} and k_S in sec^{-1}.

whereas values of k_Y are for displacements at the soft acid Pt(II). A much better correlation would be expected if the reagent basicities (formation constants) were measured towards a soft acid preferably Pt(II). Since data on the stability constants of Pt(II) are not extensive, it was decided to use the soft reference acid CH$_3$Hg$^+$, for which there are more data. Again the values of log k_Y roughly correlate the values of $pK_{CH_3Hg^+}$ for the different nucleophiles Y. However, there are many deviations, the worst being for OH$^-$, which is bound strongly at equilibrium but is a poor reagent for Pt(II).‖

An approach which is successful is to devise a new nucleophilic scale for Pt(II) substrates, using trans-Pt(py)$_2$Cl$_2$ as the standard. Thus the *nucleophilic reactivity constants*, n^0_{Pt}, are defined by the equation

$$\log (k_Y/k_S)_0 = n^0_{Pt} \qquad (38)$$

where the rate constants are for the reaction of trans-Pt(py)$_2$Cl$_2$ in methanol at 30°. The solvent rate constant, k_S, has been divided by 26 M, the concentration of methanol. In this way the parameter n^0_{Pt} is dimensionless. The values of n^0_{Pt} are given in Table 5.16. Also included are values of $n^0_{CH_3I}$ for the same nucleophiles. These are defined by equation 38 also, but the rate constants refer to nucleophilic displacement of iodide ion

‖ The poor reactivity of OH$^-$ may be attributed to large π-antibonding effects in the trigonal bipyramid structure. This may also be described as a loss of C.F.S.E.

Table 5.16 Some properties of different nucleophiles

Nucleophile	n^0_{Pt}	pK_a	$n^0_{CH_3I}$
$CH_3CO_2^-$	<2.4	4.75	4.3
CH_3O^-	<2.4	15.8	6.29
$C_6H_5NH_2$	3.02	4.62	5.60
$^{36}Cl^-$	3.04	(−5.74)	4.37
NH_3	3.06	9.25	5.50
C_5H_5N	3.13	5.23	5.23
NO_2^-	3.22	3.33	5.37
$(C_6H_5CH_2)_2S$	3.29	...	4.84
N_3^-	3.58	4.74	5.78
NH_2OH	3.85	5.82	6.5
H_2N-NH_2	3.85	7.93	6.6
C_6H_5SH	4.15	...	5.7
Br^-	4.18	(−7.7)	5.79
$(C_2H_5)_2S$	4.38	...	5.34
$(CH_3)_2S$	4.73	−5.3	5.54
$(CH_2)_5S$	4.88	...	5.42
$(CH_2)_4S$	5.00	−4.8	5.66
$(C_6H_5CH_2)_2Se$	5.39	...	5.23
I^-	5.42	(−10.7)	7.42
$(CH_3)_2Se$	5.56	...	6.23
SCN^-	6.65	−1.8	6.62
SO_3^{2-}	5.79	7.26	...
$C_6H_{11}NC$	6.20	...	1
$(C_6H_5)_3Sb$	6.65	...	<1
$(C_6H_5)_3As$	6.75	...	4.77
CN^-	7.0	9.1	6.70
$(CH_3O)_3P$	7.08	...	~5.7
$SeCN^-$	7.10	...	7.85
$C_6H_5S^-$	7.17	6.52	9.92
$S=C(NH_2)_2$	7.17	−0.96	7.27
$S_2O_3^{2-}$	7.34	1.9	~8.5
$(C_2H_5)_3As$	7.54	<2	6.9
$(C_6H_5)_3P$	8.79	2.61	7.00
$(C_4H_9)_3P$	8.82	8.8	8.69
$(C_2H_5)_3P$	8.85	8.86	8.72

Data for Pt from reference 71 and from H. Sobel, unpublished results.
Data for CH_3I from J. Songstad, unpublished results.

from methyl iodide. There is a rough correlation of the n^0_{Pt} and the $n^0_{CH_3I}$ values, but many exceptions are noticeable.

Plots of log k_Y for other Pt(II) complexes against n^0_{Pt} are linear (Fig. 5.19), suggesting the L.F.E.R. given by the equation

$$\log k_Y = sn^0_{Pt} + \log k_S \qquad (39)$$

The constant s depends on the complex and is called the *nucleophilic discrimination factor* (N.D.F.). A large value of s means that the rates of

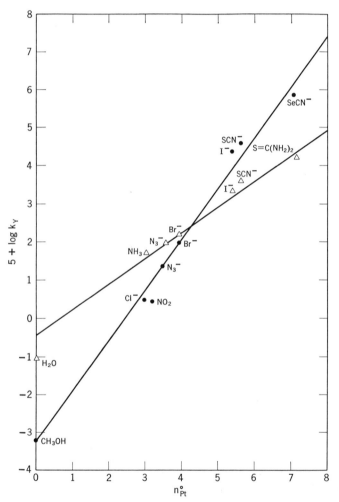

Fig. 5.19 Correlation of the rates of reaction of Pt(II) complexes with the standard *trans*-Pt(py)$_2$Cl$_2$ for different nucleophiles: ●, *trans*-Pt(PEt$_3$)$_2$Cl$_2$ in methanol at 30°; △, Pt(en)Cl$_2$ in water at 35°. From reference 71.

reaction are very sensitive to changes in the nucleophilic character, n^0_{Pt}, of Y. The intercept of a plot of log k_Y against n^0_{Pt} turns out to be very nearly equal to the log rate constant for the solvent reaction, log k_S, when the latter is known. In other cases where the solvent rate constant is too small to detect, a very large negative intercept is found. This is presumably the log of the extremely small k_S value.

The discrimination factors s for some complexes are given in Table 5.17 along with values of log k_S. It appears that there is an inverse correlation between s and k_S. This seems reasonable if we interpret k_S as a

Table 5.17 Nucleophilic discrimination factor (N.D.F.), s, and intercepts, log k_S, for several platinum(II) complexes

Complex	s	log k_S
trans-Pt(PEt$_3$)$_2$Cl$_2$ [a]	1.43	−8.82
trans-Pt(AsEt$_3$)$_2$Cl$_2$ [a]	1.25	−7.49
trans-Pt(SeEt$_2$)$_2$Cl$_2$ [a]	1.05	−6.13
trans-Pt(pip)$_2$Cl$_2$ [a]	0.91	−5.82
Pt(en)Cl$_2$ [b]	0.64	−5.26
Pt(dien)Br$^+$ [b]	0.75	−5.16
Pt(dien)Cl$^+$ [b]	0.65	−4.56
Pt(dien)H$_2$O^{2+} [b]	0.44	−1.08

From reference 189; k_S is in M^{-1} sec^{-1}.
[a] Methanol.   [b] Water.

measure of the "intrinsic" reactivity of the complex; that is, it is the rate constant for the poorest nucleophile whose effect can be measured in a solvent S. With such a poor nucleophile, the greatest burden is put on the complex to reach the activated complex for reaction. If k_S is small, this implies that the tendency for the complex to react is small and that it will rely more on the nucleophile and therefore be more sensitive to changes in it.

The arsine and phosphine complexes have the largest values of s and the smallest k_S of the complexes listed in Table 5.17. It may be significant that these ligands are capable of dative π bonding with Pt(II) in the transition state. This may facilitate the addition of the electrons of the nucleophile to Pt(II), thus making possible a greater contribution of the entering group to the formation of the transition state. It then follows that the rate of reaction of such a system would exhibit a greater sensitivity to changes in the nucleophile.

In the initial investigation[76] on the reactivities of different reagents with Pt(II) complexes, the point was made that in general the good reagents stand high in the *trans* effect series and poor reagents stand low. This generalization is amply borne out by the large amount of data now available. Such a parallelism is a natural result on the basis of the proposed mechanism of reaction. While the activated complex is probably not a trigonal bipyramid, its energy is close to that of the presumed intermediate of such a structure. The intermediate would have the leaving group, the entering group, and the ligand initially *trans* to the leaving group all in the trigonal plane (Fig. 5.11). Therefore, the entering group Y and *trans* ligand L occupy equivalent positions and can play equivalent roles in the stabilization of the intermediate. Since the *trans* effect is qualitatively explained in terms of the σ- and π-*trans* hypothesis, it would appear too that the nucleophilic strength of a reagent towards Pt(II) must depend on at least two parameters which measure σ and π bonding. Unfortunately, the necessary quantitative data on σ- and π-bond strengths are not available to permit a detailed test of this concept.

It is further of interest to note the effect of solvent on the nucleophilic strengths of various reagents towards Pt(II) substrates. Many studies of this type have been made for substitution reactions on carbon substrates.[86] What is found is that the order of nucleophilic strength ($Cl^- < Br^- < I^-$) in protic solvents such as water and alcohol is often completely reversed ($Cl^- > Br^- > I^-$) for the same reaction in aprotic solvents such as acetone and dimethylformamide. This is attributed to the solvation of the reagent ions. Thus, in protic solvents the retarding effect in the rate of reaction of small anions is their greater energy of solvation relative to the large anions.

In aprotic solvents there may be only weak solvation of all ions, or it even may be that large anions (soft bases) are solvated more than small anions (hard bases). The intrinsic reactivity than shows up. That is, just as in the gas phase, fluoride ion would form a stronger bond to most elements than does iodide ions.

This reversal in order of reagent reactivity with changes in solvent has not been observed for reactions of Pt(II) complexes.[87] Kinetic data on the effect of solvent on the reaction of *trans*-Pt(pip)$_2$Cl$_2$ with various nucleophiles are shown in Table 5.18. These data show that the same order of nucleophilic strength is maintained in each solvent but the spread of reactivity is greater in the protic solvent than in the aprotic solvents This is indicated by the lower values of the N.D.F. in aprotic solvents compared with methanol (Table 5.19). Therefore, it appears that, although solvation effects are also important in reactions of Pt(II) substrates, they are less significant than for carbon substrates. This suggests that the polarizability of the nucleophile makes a large contribution to its reactivity towards the class (b) metal of Pt(II) complexes.

Table 5.18   Effect of solvent on nucleophilic strengths of Y in the reaction

$$trans\text{-Pt(pip)}_2Cl_2 + Y^- \rightarrow trans\text{-Pt(pip)}_2ClY + Cl^-$$

Values of k_Y in $10^{-3}\ M^{-1}\ sec^{-1}$.

Y	CH_3OH	$(CH_3)_2CO$	$(CH_3)_3SO$	$HCON(CH_3)_2$	CH_3CN	CH_3NO_2
S^a	1.2	8	70	4	3	2.5
Cl^-	0.9	3.5	1.0	0.56	1.1	1.5
N_3^-	5.3	...	...	...	...	...
Br^-	6.2	80	5.2	6.7	13	15
I^-	300^b	165	18	27	86	78
SCN^-	400	375	15	...	...	...
$SeCN^-$	...	...	...	...	910	710
Tu	3,500	10,600	480	780	...	...

From reference 87. Temp. 25°C. pip = piperidine.
^{a} S = solvent. Values for $10^5 k_S$, sec^{-1}.
^{b} Estimated from equation 39.

Effect of Temperature. Investigations of the effect of temperature on the rates of reaction permit an estimate of the kinetic parameters, enthalpy ($\Delta H^{\ddagger}$) and entropy ($\Delta S^{\ddagger}$) of activation. These parameters must be considered in any complete discussion of the mechanism of reaction. Such data have been collected,[67] and some of the results reported are given in Table 5.20.

Since several factors contribute to the enthalpy and entropy of reaction,[80] it is rarely possible to assess in detail the specific effects responsible for changes in $\Delta H^{\ddagger}$ and $\Delta S^{\ddagger}$. Furthermore, these values must vary appreciably in order for differences to be meaningful because they usually are not determined with high precision. Thus, it is easy to establish that one reaction goes twice as fast as another, but difficult to prove that one activation energy exceeds another by 0.40 kcal.

Table 5.19   Effect of solvent on the nucleophilic discrimination factors (N.D.F.) for the reactions of $trans\text{-PtL}_2Cl_2$ at 25°C

Solvent	L = pip	L = $P(C_2H_5)_3$
CH_3OH	0.91	1.43
CH_3COCH_3	0.78	1.25
$(CH_3)_2SO$	0.61	1.06
CH_3CN	0.70	...
CH_3NO_2	0.64	...

From reference 87. pip = piperidine.

Table 5.20 Activation parameters for the reactions of some platinum(II) complexes

Complex	Nucleophile Y^-	$\Delta H^{\ddagger}_Y$, kcal/mole	$\Delta S^{\ddagger}_Y$, eu/mole
[Pt(dien)Cl]Cl [a]	H_2O	20	−18 [c]
	Br^-	13	−25
	N_3^-	16	−17
	I^-	11	−25
	SCN^-	10	−28
	$SeCN^-$	...	...
	thiourea	8.5	−31
[Pt(dien)Br]Br [a]	H_2O	19.5	−17 [c]
	N_3^-	15.5	−17
	I^-	11	−25
	SCN	9.5	−27
	$SeCN^-$	...	...
	thiourea	8.5	−29
[Pt(dien)I]I [a]	N_3^-	15.5	−16
	SCN^-	10.5	−25
	$SeCN^-$	...	...
	thiourea	9	−27
[Pt(dien)N$_3$]N$_3$ [a]	I^-	14.5	−19
	SCN^-	14	−22
	$SeCN^-$	13	−21
	thiourea	13	−24
	$S_2O_3^-$	9.5	−29
[Pt(dien)SCN]NO$_3$ [a]	thiourea	15.5	−14
[Pt(dien)NO$_2$]NO$_3$ [a]	thiourea	13.5	−30
trans-Pt(PEt$_3$)$_2$Cl$_2$ [b]	NO_2^-	15.1	−31
	N_3^-	15.5	−24
	SCN^-	10.0	−28
	$SeCN^-$	8.5	−27
	Cl^-	23.0	
trans-Pt(PEt$_3$)$_2$Br$_2$ [b]	NO_2^-	12.4	−34
	N_3^-	13.0	−24
trans-Pt(PEt$_3$)$_2$I$_2$ [b]	NO_2^-	11.0	−30
	N_3^-	12.5	−16
trans-Pt(piperidine)Cl$_2$	Cl^-	14.7	−21
	Br^-	13.8	−23
	NO_2^-	13.7	−25
	N_3^-	10.8	−33
	SCN^-	9.1	−30
	$SeCN^-$	8.4	−28

Table 5.20   (*Continued*)

Complex	Nucleophile Y^-	$\Delta H^{\ddagger}_Y$, kcal/mole	$\Delta S^{\ddagger}_Y$, eu/mole
trans-Pt(AsEt$_3$)$_2$Cl$_2$ [b]	SCN$^-$	11.2	-23
	SeCN$^-$	7.9	-28
Pt(NH$_3$)$_3$Cl$^+$ [a]	H$_2$O	18	-26^c
	Br$^-$	77	-16
cis-Pt(NH$_3$)$_2$Cl$_2$ [a]	H$_2$O	20	-22^c
trans-Pt(NH$_3$)$_2$Cl$_2$ [a]	H$_2$O	20	-19^c
Pt(NH$_3$)Cl$_3^-$ [a]	H$_2$O	19	-23^c
PtCl$_4^{2-}$ [a]	H$_2$O	21	-16^c

From reference 67.
[a] Water solution.
[b] Methanol solution.
[c] Rate constants corrected to second-order units.

In spite of these limitations the data in Table 5.20 reveal two important features for reactions of Pt(II) complexes. The first is that generally an increase in rate of reaction is largely due to a decrease in $\Delta H^{\ddagger}$. This is important because the discussion of the rates of reaction is made primarily on the basis of the energetics of the system. This assumes that for closely related systems the entropies of activation remain about the same and that changes in the enthalpies of activation are responsible for changes in the rates of reaction The second significant point is that all of these reactions have a negative entropy of activation, varying from -15 to -30 eu/mole.

One predominating effect, often responsible for the entropy of activation of reactions in solution, is that of changes in solvation.[80] If the transition state is more polar and more highly solvated than the ground state reactants, there results an enhancement in the ordering of the solvent and a decrease in the entropy of the system. Since the entropies of activation appear to always be negative for reactions of Pt(II) complexes, regardless of the charge on the substrate, the entering group, or the leaving group, it follows that solvation effects do not play a major role in these reactions.

The large negative entropies and the rather small enthalpies of activation suggest that formation of the transition state is accompanied by a net increase in bonding. Because of this the entire structure is tightened and made more rigid, and a decrease in entropy results. Whatever the reason for these negative entropies of activation, such a result is in accord with thermodynamic data on the formation of octahedral complexes by the addition of two ligands to square planar compounds (see Table 5.26). In both cases the reactions involve an expansion in coordination number.

Other Effects. A few isolated observations have been made on other factors that influence the rates of reaction of certain Pt(II) complexes. For example, it has been suggested[88] that chelate ring aromaticity in Pt(II) complexes may enhance their reactivity. Thus, for the reaction

$$
\begin{array}{c}
\text{A} \\
| \\
\text{A—Pt—Cl}
\\
| \\
\text{Cl}
\end{array}
+
\begin{array}{c}
\text{S}{=}\text{C—NH}_2 \\
| \\
\text{S}{=}\text{C—NH}_2
\end{array}
\xrightarrow{\text{CH}_3\text{OH}}
\begin{array}{c}
\text{A} \\
| \\
\text{A—Pt—S} \\
| \quad\ \diagdown \\
\text{S} \quad \text{CNH}_2 \\
\diagdown \ \diagup \\
\text{CNH}_2
\end{array}
+ 2\text{Cl}^- \qquad (40)
$$

the relative rates for three Pt(II) complexes are as follows:

| 1.4 | 1 | 90 |

The rates of reaction of Pt(en)Cl$_2$ and cis-Pt(py)$_2$Cl$_2$ are approximately the same, but that of Pt(bipy)Cl$_2$ is much faster. Similarly, the rate of reaction of the saturated system Pt(dien)Cl$^+$ with pyridine is slower than that of the unsaturated system Pt(tripy)Cl$^+$ by a factor of 10^3.[66] The explanation given[88] is that for the bipy and tripy substrates the aromaticity in the platinum-α-diimine chelate ring enhances the reactivity of the complexes. Since there is presumed to be considerable π bonding in such systems, their reactivity can be attributed to a π-trans effect (p. 374).

It is well known that both electronic and steric factors of the ligands in a metal complex alter its rate of reaction. In addition, some substituents may influence a reaction by becoming bonded or partially bonded to the reaction center. This behavior is called *neighboring group participation* and is said to provide *anchimeric assistance* to the rate of reaction. Such a behavior is well known for organic reactions[89a] but has received little attention for reactions of metal complexes.

There is some evidence of anchimeric assistance in reactions of certain Pt(II) complexes. Although the rates of hydrolysis of Pt(II) compounds do not depend on the concentration of hydroxide ion, it was observed[89b] that the rate of release of Cl^- from $trans$-$Pt(NH_2C_2H_4OH)_2Cl_2$ increases with an increase in OH^- concentration. A two-term rate law is involved, and at 25°C $k_S = 9 \times 10^{-4} sec^{-1}$ and $k_{OH^-} = 1 \times 10^{-2} M^{-1} sec^{-1}$. It is believed that the function of the OH^- is to rapidly convert the ethanolamine into ethoxideamine:

$$Pt(NH_2C_2H_4OH)_2Cl_2 + OH^- \xrightleftharpoons{\text{fast}}$$

$$Pt(NH_2C_2H_4OH)(NH_2C_2H_4O)Cl_2^- + H_2O \quad (41)$$

which can in turn displace the chloro group:

$$Pt(NH_2C_2H_4OH)(NH_2C_2H_4O)Cl_2^- \xrightarrow{k'_{OH^-}}$$

$$Pt(NH_2C_2H_4OH)(NH_2C_2H_4O)Cl + Cl^- \quad (42)$$

In support of such a process is the observation that the analogous ethoxyamine $trans$-$Pt(NH_2C_2H_4OC_2H_5)_2Cl_2$ reacts at a rate independent of OH^- concentration.

It is abundantly clear that in metal complexes chelating ligands are more difficult to displace than are unidentate ligands. Of course, the same is true for reactions of Pt(II) complexes. An example[90] is provided by the study of $^{14}C_2O_4^{2-}$ exchange with $Pt(C_2O_4)_2^{2-}$. At 25°C the $C_2O_4^{2-}$-independent path has $k_1 = 10^{-9} sec^{-1}$ and the $C_2O_4^{2-}$-dependent path has $k_2 = 10^{-7} M^{-1} sec^{-1}$, both of which are smaller by approximately four orders of magnitude than the values for comparable unidentate systems. The rate of ^{18}O exchange with $Pt(C_2O_4)_2^{2-}$ was also studied and found to be faster than oxalate ion exchange. In addition, all eight of the oxygens exchange at the same rate, suggesting a chelate ring opening-closing process similar to that described earlier for $Cr(C_2O_4)_3^{3-}$ (p. 317).

Although five- and six-membered chelate rings are stable and such ligands are not easily displaced from a complex, four-membered chelate rings are somewhat strained and presumably require much less energy to open. Most of the four-ring systems are found in bridged complexes of the type $A_nM\diagup^{X}_{\diagdown X}\diagdown^{\diagup}MA_n$, and as yet there are very few quantitative kinetic data on their reactions. Several Pt(II) complexes of this type are known, and the symmetrical bridge-cleavage reaction represented by

$$\underset{X}{\overset{X}{\diagdown}}\underset{}{\overset{X}{\diagup}}Pt\underset{X}{\overset{X}{\diagdown}}\underset{}{\overset{X}{\diagup}}Pt\underset{X}{\overset{X}{\diagdown}} + 2Y \rightarrow 2PtX_3Y \quad (43)$$

has been used to prepare certain Pt(II) complexes.[91] Kinetic studies[92] of this reaction have been reported, and some of the data are given in Table 5.21. The most significant point about these results is that the rates of reaction of the bridged complexes are about two to three orders of magnitude faster than those for the corresponding monomeric complex. This supports the view that there is considerable strain in the four-ring bridge system, resulting in a weaker Pt-X bond for the bridging groups than for the terminal groups.

Table 5.21   Rates of reaction of some platinum(II) bridged complexes with pyridine in dimethylformamide at 25°

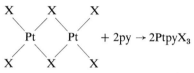

Complex	k_S, sec^{-1}	k_{py}, M^{-1} sec^{-1}
$Pt_2Br_6^{2-}$	8×10^{-4}	8×10^{-2}
$Pt_2I_6^{2-}$	1×10^{-4}	2×10^{-2}
$Pt_2(pip)_2Cl_4$	7×10^{-4}	2×10^{-2}
$PtBr_4^{2-}$	2×10^{-6}	3×10^{-5}
$Pt(pip)Cl_3^-$	2×10^{-6}	2×10^{-5}

From reference 92.

Nevertheless, the chelate bridge appears to require the aid of a nucleophile to open, and the usual two-term rate law is observed. The mechanism proposed is shown in Fig. 5.20. This is essentially the same in its rate-determining step as that for ordinary planar substitution. Thus, one of the bridging ligands is displaced by either the solvent or the reagent to give as the initial product a monobridged complex. This is not expected to be very stable, because compounds of this type are generally not known, and the final reaction is assumed to be fast.

In this connection it is of interest to note that a bridged intermediate has been postulated[93a] as one of the predominate paths in the exchange of ^{36}Cl$^-$ with the chloro groups *cis* to ethylene in an equilibrium solution of $PtC_2H_4Cl_3^-$ and *trans*-$PtC_2H_4H_2OCl_2$. The rate law for exchange is given by the equation

$$\text{Rate} = k_1[PtC_2H_4Cl_3^-] + k_2[PtC_2H_4H_2OCl_2] +$$

$$k_3[PtC_2H_4H_2OCl_2]^2[Cl^-] \quad (44)$$

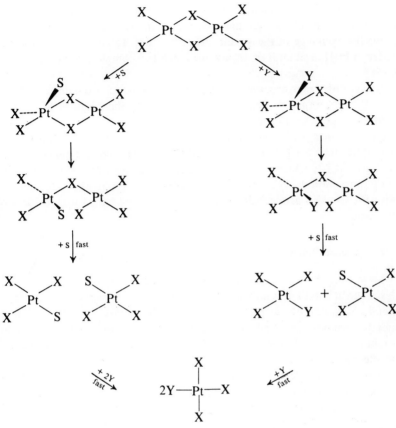

Fig. 5.20 Mechanism proposed for the symmetrical cleavage of halogen-bridged Pt(II) complexes. From reference 92.

where at 25°C $k_1 = 2.9 \times 10^{-6}$ sec^{-1}, $\Delta H^{\ddagger} = 21$ kcal/mole, $k_2 = 2.8 \times 10^{-5}$ sec^{-1}, $\Delta H^{\ddagger} = 22$ kcal, $k_3 = 8.6 \times 10^{-3}$ sec^{-1} M^{-1}, $\Delta H^{\ddagger} = 19$ kcal. The exchange path represented by k_3 is believed to involve a rapid dimerization of $PtC_2H_4H_2OCl_2$

$$2C_2H_4\text{---}\underset{\underset{Cl}{|}}{\overset{\overset{Cl}{|}}{Pt}}\text{---}OH_2 \rightleftharpoons \underset{C_2H_4}{\overset{Cl}{\diagdown}}Pt\underset{Cl}{\overset{Cl}{\diagup}}Pt\underset{Cl}{\overset{C_2H_4}{\diagup}} + 2H_2O \qquad (45)$$

followed by its exchange with ^{36}Cl$^-$. Thus, the ethylene, in addition to providing rapid substitution of the initial *trans* chloro group, also permits the rapid formation of dimers with bridge groups *trans* to ethylene. The bridged complex can then participate in exchange. This process is not observed for the chloroaquouammineplatinum(II) complexes. One of the paths for exchange in the system $PtBr_4^{2-}$—*Br^- was found to be second order in Pt(II) and appears to involve a bridged complex in the transition state.[93b]

It has also been observed[94a] that the spontaneous exchange of $^{36}Cl^-$ with $PtCl_4^{2-}$, although slow, can be catalyzed by the addition of the $1e^-$ oxidizing agent Ce(IV) in amounts sufficient to oxidize only 3% of the Pt(II). No effect is observed if the $2e^-$ oxidizing agent Cl_2 is added, or with the addition of $PtCl_6^{2-}$. It is suggested that the $1e^-$ oxidant generates the catalyst $PtCl_5^-$, which is labile and rapidly reaches isotopic equilibrium with the solution. The catalyst also undergoes rapid electron transfer with $PtCl_4^{2-}$ and as a result provides a low-energy path for chloride ion exchange.

Other Square-Planar Metal Complexes

Now that the substitution reactions of Pt(II) complexes have been described at length, it is important that this discussion be extended to other metals of square planar complexes. Although exhaustive studies of these metals have not been made, it is gratifying that the limited data available are in harmony with the deductions drawn for square planar substitution on the basis of the Pt(II) systems.

Gold(III).   Isoelectronic with Pt(II) is Au(III), and it too forms very stable low-spin, square planar complexes. The kinetic data on substitution reactions of Au(III) complexes show significant differences from and similarities with the data for corresponding Pt(II) systems. In fact, the two-term rate law, now known to be common for square planar substitution reactions, was first recognized[94b] for the exchange of $^{36}Cl^-$ with $AuCl_4^-$.

The complexes $Au(dien)X^{2+}$ and $Au(dien—H)X^+$ have been prepared, and the rates of reaction of the chloro species with a variety of different reagents have been investigated.[79] The data obtained permit a comparison with those for the analogous Pt(II) reactions and can be summarized as follows: (1) complexes of Au(III) react approximately 10^4 times faster than those of Pt(II); (2) the solvent path is much less important for reactions of Au(III) than for Pt(II); (3) the nucleophilic properties of different reagents towards the Au(III) substrate parallel those for Pt(II).

Some of the kinetic data reported for reactions of Au(III) complexes are shown in Table 5.22 and compared with those for the corresponding Pt(II) reactions. Perhaps the most striking contrast is that Au(III) complexes react much faster than do those of Pt(II). Such a result is in accord with a displacement process in which bond making is more important than bond breaking in the transition state. Thus, the larger positive charge on the central metal favors the addition of the entering group, resulting in an increased rate of reaction. Were this the only factor responsible for the difference in rate, one would expect an appreciable difference in the enthalpies of activation. However, the results show that the differences in rate are sometimes due to a difference in entropies of activation. That $\Delta S^{\ddagger}$ for the reaction of Au(dien)Cl^{2+} is less negative than for Pt(dien)Cl^{+} can be understood in that solvation effects are more important in the complex

Table 5.22 Comparison of kinetic data for reactions of some gold(III) and platinum(II) complexes[a]

Reaction	k_{H_2O}, sec^{-1}	k_Y, M^{-1} sec^{-1}	$\Delta H^{\ddagger}_{H_2O}$, kcal	$\Delta H^{\ddagger}_Y$, kcal	$\Delta S^{\ddagger}_{H_2O}$, eu	$\Delta S^{\ddagger}_Y$, eu
AuCl$_4^-$ + ^{36}Cl$^-$ [b]	0.006	1.47	15	16.5	-16	-2
Au(dien)Cl^{2+} + Br$^-$ [c]	0.5	154	...	13	...	-4
PtCl$_4^{2-}$ + ^{36}Cl$^-$ [d]	3.8×10^{-5}	0	21	...	-8	...
Pt(dien)Cl$^+$ + Br$^-$ [c]	8.0×10^{-5}	5.3×10^{-3}	18	14	-16	-23

[a] Temp. 20°C for Au(III) and 25°C for Pt(II).
[b] From reference 94d.
[c] From reference 79.
[d] From reference 95.

of higher charge. Thus, there is a greater release of solvent in the neutralization reaction to form the transition state and, as a result, a more positive entropy of activation.

Other data support the view that bond making (charge neutralization) is more important than bond breaking (charge separation) in the transition state for reactions of Au(III) complexes. For example, the cation Au(dien)Cl^{2+} reacts approximately 100 times faster than does the anion AuCl$_4^-$ (Table 5.20). Likewise, the complex Au(dien)Cl^{2+} reacts twice as fast as its conjugate base Au(dien—H)Cl$^+$. A related observation is that the solvent path makes only a very minor contribution to the overall rate of reaction of Au(III) complexes. This points to the greater significance of charge neutralization in the Au(III) systems relative to the Pt(II) complexes.

Recent investigations suggest that bond forming need not always predominate in reactions of Au(III) complexes, and that these reactions also seem to involve the mechanisms represented in Fig. 5.15. For example, the reaction of AuACl$_3$ with Y$^-$ to yield AuCl$_3$Y$^-$ has been investigated[96a] as a function of changes in the amine A and in the nucleophile Y$^-$. Some of the results of this investigation are given in Table 5.23. A surprising result is that the amine is replaced more readily than Cl$^-$ from this complex, although one expects the bond strength of Au-N to exceed that of Au-Cl. Of interest is the observation that for $Y^- = Cl^-$ the rates of reaction decrease with increasing base strengths of the amine (presumably increasing Au-N bond strengths), whereas for $Y^- = NO_2^-$ or N_3^- there is an increase in rate followed by a decrease for the same series of complexes. These results are readily explained. It appears that the reactions with Cl^- involve T.S. B′ of Fig. 5.15, which means that Au-N bond rupture is important, and this becomes more difficult as the bond strength increases

Table 5.23 Rate constants (k_Y, M^{-1} sec^{-1}, 25°C, CH_3OH) for the reactions

$$AuACl_3 + Y^- \rightarrow AuCl_3Y^- + A$$

A	$pK_a{}^a$	CH_3OH^b	Cl^-	NO_2^-	N_3^-
Quinoline	4.95	3.0	0.25	1.5	29
Isoquinoline	5.14	5.8	0.25	6.8	72
Pyridine	5.17	7.5	0.42	6.8	108
3-Methylpyridine	5.68	7.0	0.20	41	78
4-Methylpyridine	6.02	6.1	0.10	43	68
3,5-Dimethylpyridine	6.34	7.0	0.09	35	51
3,5-Dimethylpyridine	6.75	6.2	0.04	26	25

From reference 96a.
[a] pK_a of conjugate acid.
[b] First order 10^4k, sec^{-1}.

with rising basicity of the amine. Since Cl^- forms a weaker Au-X bond than does either NO_2^- or N_3^-, it seems that these two anions react with the complexes containing amines of lower basicity by T.S. A of Fig. 5.15 and of higher basicity by T.S. B′. The latter case is explained as was done for the Cl^- reactions. The initial increase in rate with increasing basicity of the amine suggests easier bond formation of the entering group in T.S. A. This may be due in part to a greater electron density on Au(III), which in turn can more effectively π-bond with the appropriate vacant orbitals on NO_2^- and N_3^-.

The point of closest similarity between the reactions of Au(III) and Pt(II) complexes is the nucleophilic properties of different reagents. Substitution reactions of Au(dien-H)Cl$^+$ with different reagents Y^- decreases in rate at 25°C in the order:

Y^-	$I^- > SCN^- > Br^- > N_3^- \gg OH^-$
k_Y, M^{-1} sec^{-1}	6100 1300 190 80 small

The rates of the reaction do not correlate the basicity of the reagent but rather parallel its polarizability. A qualitative correlation is obtained with the nucleophilic constants n^0_{Pt} (Table 5.16). The relative order $I^- > SCN^-$ for Au(III) is the reverse of that for Pt(II), but both are good reagents for the two substrates.

Studies[96b] have been made on the rates of reaction of $Au(Et_4dien)Cl^{2+}$ and of $Au(Et_4dien—H)Cl^+$. The results show that these sterically hindered systems behave as pseudo-octahedral complexes in that their rates of reaction do not depend on the entering reagent [see the following section on Pd(II)]. It is significant that the rate of reaction at 25°C of $Au(Et_4dien—H)Cl^+$ ($k = 1.3 \times 10^{-4}$ sec^{-1}) is $ca.$ seventy times faster than that of $Au(Et_4dien)Cl^{2+}$ ($k = 1.9 \times 10^{-6}$ sec^{-1}). This provides direct proof that the amido complex reacts more rapidly than the corresponding ammine and supports the conjugate base mechanism for the effect of OH^- on the rate of reaction of $Pd(Et_4dien)Cl^+$ (see equations 51–53). This is also good evidence for the same mechanism being responsible for the base hydrolysis of octahedral ammine complexes containing N—H hydrogens (p. 183).

A kinetic study[97] by means of a polarographic method has been made of the reaction of $AuCl_4^-$ with ethylenediamine to form $Au(en)_2^{3+}$. The results show a typical two-term rate law with one of the terms zero order and the other first order in ethylenediamine concentration. The rate of reaction also increases with rising pH, as is expected in a pH region which would generate more of the free diamine at the higher alkalinity.

During the investigations of chloride ion exchange in the system $AuCl_4^-$—*Cl^- it was observed[94b] that an exchange was induced by some impurity in ordinary distilled water. This led to a study of the exchange induced by various reducing agents, and it was found that the system is paticularly sensitive to one-electron reducing agents, e.g., Fe^{2+}. Thus, the storage of solutions in green glass containers will generate enough Fe(II) ion to cause a significant amount of induced exchange. For every Fe^{2+} oxidized by $AuCl_4^-$, it is estimated that approximately 10^4 chloride ion substitutions are effected. Similarly V(IV) ion is a good catalyst, but its efficiency is diminished by the accumulation of V(V). However, two-electron reducing agents such as Sn(II) and Sb(III) ions have little or no catalytic effect on the rate of chloride ion exchange. Similarly Au(I) induces, at most, only a slow exchange.

Therefore the exchange induced by one-electron reducing agents is believed to be due to the formation of a labile Au(II) species which is not generated by the two-electron reagents. The kinetics of the reaction catalyzed by Fe^{2+} are consistent with a mechanism whereby Au(II) is produced by a second-order reaction (46) between $AuCl_4^-$ and Fe^{2+}; the Au(II) chloro complex then undergoes rapid exchange (47); it may also undergo a rate-determining exchange (48) with $AuCl_4^-$, and is finally disproportion- ated (49) to terminate the sequence of reactions

$$AuCl_4^- + Fe^{2+} \xrightarrow{k_1} Fe^{3+} + AuCl_4^{2-} \qquad \text{Rate} \qquad k_1[AuCl_4^-][Fe^{2+}] \qquad (46)$$

$$AuCl_4^{2-} + {}^*Cl^- \longrightarrow Au^*Cl_4^{2-} + Cl^- \qquad \text{very rapid} \qquad (47)$$

$$Au^*Cl_4^{2-} + AuCl_4^- \xrightarrow{k_2} AuCl_4^{2-} + Au^*Cl_4^- \qquad k_2[AuCl_4^-][Au^*Cl_4^{2-}] \qquad (48)$$

$$2Au(II) \xrightarrow{k_3} Au(I) + Au(III) \qquad k_3[Au(II)]^2 \qquad (49)$$

The exact nature of the Au(II) chloro species (written as $AuCl_4^{2-}$) is not known, but its lability may be attributed to its being a d^9 system like Cu(II). The latter system is very labile in all of its simple unidentate complexes.

Palladium(II). Investigations of the kinetics of substitution reactions of Pd(II) complexes are rather limited but sufficient data are available to show that these reactions are typical of square planar substitutions. Some of the data reported are collected in Table 5.24. Corresponding values for Pt(II)

Table 5.24 Comparison of some rates of reaction of palladium(II) and platinum(II) complexes with pyridine in water solution at 25°

Complex	k_{obs}, sec^{-1}	
	Pd(II)^a	Pt(II)^b
M(dien)Cl$^+$	fast	3.5×10^{-5}
M(dien)Br$^+$	fast	2.3×10^{-5}
M(dien)I$^+$	3.2×10^{-2} ^{c}	1.0×10^{-5}
M(dien)SCN$^+$	4.3×10^{-2} ^{d}	3.0×10^{-7}
M(dien)NO$_2^+$	3.3×10^{-2}	2.5×10^{-7}
trans-M(PEt$_3$)$_2$(o-tolyl)Cl ^{e}	5.8×10^{-1}	6.7×10^{-6}
M(Et$_4$dien)Cl$^+$	2.1×10^{-3} ^{f}	8.5×10^{-6} ^{g}

From reference 66 except as specified in notes e, f, g.

^{a} For [py] = 0.00124 M.

^{b} For [py] = 0.00592 M.

^{c} At 0°C.

^{d} At 0°C $k_{obs} = 6.6 \times 10^{-3}$, 8.2×10^{-3}, 2.5×10^{-2} for [py] = 0.00124, 0.00248, 0.0124 M, respectively.

^{e} From reference 47. Values are for the solvent reaction $k_{C_2H_5OH}$.

^{f} From reference 98. Rate is zero order in reagent concentration.

^{g} From reference 73. Rate at 80° is zero order in reagent concentration.

are also included, which show that the Pd(II) systems are approximately 10^5 times more reactive. This is in accord with a much weaker Pd-X bond strength; also the rate of replacement of X^- inversely parallels the stabilities of Pd(dien)X^+. The data further indicate that the rate of the reaction

$$Pd(dien)X^+ + py \rightarrow Pd(dien)py^{2+} + X^- \qquad (50)$$

increases with rising pyridine concentration, but that the solvent path makes an appreciable contribution to the overall rate of reaction. Thus, the solvent path contribution seems to decrease in the order Pd(II) > Pt(II) >

Fig. 5.21   Molecular models of (a) the unhindered M(dien)Cl$^+$ and (b) the sterically hindered M(Et$_4$dien)Cl$^+$, where dien = NH$_2$C$_2$H$_4$NHC$_2$H$_4$NH$_2$ and Et$_4$dien = (C$_2$H$_5$)$_2$NC$_2$H$_4$NHC$_2$H$_4$N(C$_2$H$_5$)$_2$.

Au(III), which perhaps indicates a decrease in the ratio of bond breaking to bond making in the transision state.

However, that bond making is also important for reactions of Pd(II) is clearly demonstrated by the extreme steric retardation observed[98] for the reaction of Pd(Et$_4$dien)Cl$^+$ (Table 5.24). Molecular models show (Fig. 5.21) that in this compound the Pd(II) is almost completely shielded, whereas it is readily accessible in the much more reactive complex Pd(dien)Cl$^+$. Not only does the hindered complex react about 10^5 times slower, but it also shows a unique behavior for a square planar complex. Its rate of reaction does not depend on the reagent concentration, except for OH$^-$, which is normally a poor reagent and for which there is an alternative explanation (Fig. 5.22). This result is very similar to that observed for reactions of octahedral complexes (see Chapter 3), and for this reason the square planar complex may be called a *pseudo-octahedral* complex.

The reactivity of OH$^-$ towards Pd(Et$_4$dien)Cl$^+$ is believed to be due to a conjugate base dissociation of the type discussed for the base hydrolysis of Co(III) ammines (p. 177). Thus, the reaction sequence involves a

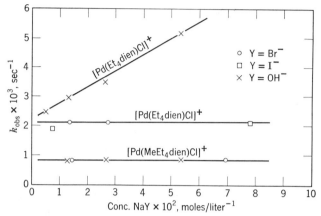

Fig. 5.22   Rates of reaction of pseudo-octahedral Pd(II) substrates with various reagents at 25° in water. From reference 98.

rapid acid-base equilibrium

$$Pd(Et_4dien)Cl^+ + OH^- \overset{K}{\rightleftharpoons} Pd(Et_4dien-H)Cl + H_2O \qquad (51)$$

followed by the rate-determining dissociation of the conjugate base

$$Pd(Et_4dien-H)Cl \overset{k}{\longrightarrow} Pd(Et_4dien-H)^+ + Cl^- \qquad (52)$$

and then the rapid addition of water

$$Pd(Et_4dien-H)^+ + H_2O \overset{fast}{\longrightarrow} Pd(Et_4dien)OH^+ \qquad (53)$$

Since the conjugate base dissociates more rapidly than does the parent acid, the experimental rate constant will increase with increasing concentration of the conjugate base (or OH^-) as is shown by Fig. 5.22. Excellent evidence in support of this mechanism is provided by the observation that OH^- has no effect on the rate of reaction of Pd(MeEt$_4$-dien)Cl$^+$. This complex cannot undergo the conjugate base mechanism because it contains no acidic N—H hydrogen, that in the ligand Et$_4$dien having been replaced by a methyl group.

The kinetic investigations described above give no information on reagent reactivity for a Pd(II) substrate. This is known from studies on substitution reactions of Pd(acac)$_2$.[99] The reactions studied include acid hydrolysis, base hydrolysis, and halide substitution in acidic media. The mechanism of reaction is rather complex. However, the rate step

$$\text{O—Pd—O} + Y \longrightarrow \text{O—Pd—Y} \qquad (54)$$

involves an opening of the chelate ring, and the order of nucleophilic reactivity for Y is this step is $SCN^- > I^- > Br^- > Cl^- > H_2O \sim OH^-$. This order parallels the nucleophilic constants n^0_{Pt}.

The rate of substitution rises not only with increasing $[Y^-]$ but also with increasing $[H^+]$. However, a limiting rate is reached at high $[H^+]$ concentration. This apparently complicated rate behavior is perfectly explained by a combination of the two-term rate law for planar complexes, and the pH dependence for chelate complexes (p. 218). The role of H^+ is to trap the half-opened chelate of 54 and to prevent its reclosing. The limiting rate is reached when the value of $[H^+]$ is great enough so that trapping occurs in every case, before reaction 54 can be reversed.

Nickel(II). High spin octahedral complexes of Ni(II) have been the subject of extensive kinetic investigations.[100] Low-spin square planar complexes, of interest here, have been studied to a much lesser extent. The best-known square-planar Ni(II) complex containing unidentate ligands is $Ni(CN)_4^{2-}$. Its exchange with $^{14}CN^-$ was found to be complete in 30 sec at room temperature.[101] The assumption was made that the rapid exchange was due to a low-energy bimolecular displacement process. No kinetic data are available to confirm this assumption, but it is strongly supported by the fact that $Ni(CN)_5^{3-}$ does form in solutions[54,55] of $Ni(CN)_4^{2-}$ with high concentrations of CN^-. The exchange of $Ni(CN)_4^{2-}$ with radionickel has also been investigated.[102] If the radionickel is in the form of a cation such as $Ni(H_2O)_6^{2+}$ exchange is very fast, but with an anionic species such as $Ni(C_2O_4)_2^{2-}$ exchange is slow. Probably the latter complex must dissociate before exchange can occur.

Evidence for the mechanism of substitution reactions of square planar Ni(II) complexes containing unidentate ligands was obtained by an investigation of the reaction[47]

$$\textit{trans-}Ni(PEt_3)_2(o\text{-tolyl})Cl + py \rightarrow$$

$$\textit{trans-}Ni(PEt_3)_2(o\text{-tolyl})py^+ + Cl^- \quad (55)$$

The rate of reaction increases with increasing pyridine concentration and follows the typical two-term rate law. Rate constants for the solvent path are given in Table 5.25. Compared with values for the corresponding Pd(II) and Pt(II) systems, the results show that the rates of reaction decrease in the order:

	Ni(II)	>	Pd(II)	>	Pt(II)
Relative rates	5×10^6		10^5		1

Thus, the rates of reaction decrease with an increase in the stability of the complex. Also in keeping with a bimolecular displacement process is the marked steric retardation found in going from L = o-tolyl to L = mesityl for $\textit{trans-}Ni(PEt_3)_2LCl$.

The most complete study[103] of substitution in planar Ni(II) chelates is that of the exchange of ^{14}C-labeled α-amineoximes with their Ni(II) complexes, as well as the reaction of the complexes with EDTA:

$$(56)$$

$$\text{+ EDTA}^{4-} \longrightarrow$$

$$\text{NiEDTA}^{2+} + \text{RAO}-\text{H}^- + \text{RAO}$$

AO stands for the amineoxime where $R = H$, MeAO for $R = CH_3$, and En(AO)$_2$ for $RR = C_2H_4$. The results obtained (Table 5.25) are very similar to those described for the reaction of Pd(acac)$_2$. At constant pH and ionic strength the familiar two-term rate law is observed. That the rate of reaction of Ni(AO)$_2$—H$^+$ is approximately 100 times faster than that of Ni(MeAO)$_2$—H$^+$ is believed to be due to the steric shielding by the methyl group. The slower reactivity of Ni(En(AO)$_2$)—H$^+$ is attributed to its greater stability. It has been further found that the addition of chelating agents such as ethylenediamine, glycinate, oxalate, malonate,

Table 5.25 Rates of reaction of some square planar nickel(II) complexes

Complex	Conditions	k_{obs}, sec^{-1}
trans-Ni(PEt$_3$)$_2$(o-tolyl)Cl^a	py, 25°C	3.3×10^1
trans-Ni(PEt$_3$)$_2$(mesityl)Cl^a	,, ,,	2.0×10^{-2}
Ni(AO)$_2$—H$^{+\,b}$	EDTA, pH = 9.48, 25.3°C	1.6×10^{-3}
Ni(MeAO)$_2$—H$^{+\,b}$	,, ,, ,,	1.9×10^{-5}
Ni(En(AO)$_2$)—H^b	,, ,, ,,	1.3×10^{-5}
Ni(NH$_2$CRR′CR″R‴NH$_2$)$_2^+$		
R = R′ = R″ = R‴ = CH$_3$	0.10 M HCl, 0°C	4.7^c
R = R′ = R″ = CH$_3$, R‴ = C$_2$H$_5$	,, ,,	15^c
R = R″ = CH$_3$, R′ = R‴ = C$_2$H$_5$	,, ,,	50^c

^{a} From reference 47. Values are for the solvent reaction $k_{C_2H_5OH}$.
^{b} From reference 103. For reaction 52.
^{c} From reference 104. Values given are of $t_{1/2}$ in minutes for the dissociation reaction Ni(AA)$_2^{2+} \rightarrow$ Ni(AA)$^{2+}$.

and adipate ions catalyze the rate of reaction. The effectiveness of the catalysts roughly parallels their stability constants with Ni(II). It appears that the catalyst, like the solvent, provides a path which contributes to the overall rate of reaction.

Table 5.25 also contains the rates of dissociatiion of C-substituted ethylenediamine complexes of Ni(II), all of which have a planar structure. Again these results show that the rates of reaction decrease with an increase in steric hindrance.

That low-spin Ni(II) complexes react by a bimolecular displacement process typical of square planar complexes causes no surprise. For the triad Ni(II), Pd(II), and Pt(II), the largest tendency to exhibit six co-ordination is shown by Ni(II). It has long been recognized that low-spin, four-coordinated Ni(II) complexes can add two additional ligands to form stable high-spin, six-coordinated systems.[105] Sacconi and his students have made extensive studies of the solution chemistry of Ni(II) chelates of Schiff bases and in one series of papers[106] report thermodynamic data for the equilibria

Some of the data reported are shown in Table 5.26. Both inductive effects and steric factors were considered in attempts to explain the results obtained. In general, for the nitrogen bases, where steric factors are not important, the base strengths towards this Ni(II) reference acid parallel the base strengths towards H^+. Worthy of note is that trialkylphosphines form adducts that are considerably more stable than the corresponding trialkylamine adducts. Thus, Ni(II) in this chelate shows class (b) character. It is unfortunate that no kinetic data are available on the rates of formation of such adducts. These rates are expected to be fast. More recent studies[107] provide additional data on such equilibria.

Table 5.26   Thermodynamic data for Ni(DBH) adducts in benzene solution at 25°C

$$Ni(DBH) + 2\ Base \rightleftharpoons Ni(DBH) \cdot 2\ Base$$

Base	pK_a ^{a}	log K	$-\Delta H^0$, kcal/mole	$-\Delta S^0$, eu
NH_3	9.27	2.11	15	39
CH_3NH_2	10.64	3.75	16	36
$(CH_3)_2NH$	10.71	6.47	14	19
$(CH_3)_3N$	9.80	3.40	14	31
$(C_2H_5)_3N$	10.74	1.32	13	38
Pyridine	5.23	3.78	15	33
2-Methylpyridine	5.97	0.48	13	41
3-Methylpyridine	5.68	3.90	15	33
4-Methylpyridine	6.02	4.45	16	32
Piperidine	11.13	5.70	14	20
$(C_2H_5)_3P$	...	6.18	14	18
$(C_3H_7)_3P$	...	5.74	14	20

From reference 106. See equation 57 for formula of Ni(DBH).
^{a} Values of pK_a are for acid dissociation of BaseH.$^+$

Rhodium(I) and Iridium(I).   Low-spin d^8 complexes of Rh(I) and Ir(I) are square planar and isoelectronic with the corresponding systems of Pd(II) and Pt(II), respectively. The low oxidation states of Rh(I) and Ir(I) are stabilized by π-bonding ligands such as CO and PR_3, and the stable compounds of these systems generally contain one or more such ligands.[108] Of particular current interest are the reversible addition reactions of *trans*-Ir(P(C_6H_5)$_3$)$_2$COCl with hydrogen and with oxygen (p. 14). Also of interest at this point are the investigations of substitution reactions of these complexes. Investigations of ^{14}CO exchange with Rh[P(C_6H_5)$_3$]$_2$COCl show that this exchange is much too rapid to measure by conventional techniques.[109] It was also observed that ^{36}Cl$^-$ exchange and phosphine replacement are extremely rapid.[110] Since the compound is very stable, these observations provide evidence that is is an excellent example of a very labile, but thermodynamically stable, system.

The compounds Rh(p-anisidine)(CO)$_2$Cl and Ir(p-toluidine)(CO)$_2$Cl are somewhat more amenable to study, and at $-80°C$ both undergo exchange with ^{14}CO at about the same rate. The rates of exchange depend on the CO concentration, and second-order rate constants of about $2\ M^{-1}\ sec^{-1}$ were obtained.[110] These results are in keeping with the usual bimolecular displacement processes for square substitutions. Strong support that an active trigonal bipyramid intermediate is involved comes from the isolation of the five-coordinated compounds Ir(PPh$_3$)$_2$(CO)$_2$Cl [58] and HM(PPh$_3$)$_3$CO,[59] where M = Rh(I) and Ir(I).

By making use of n.m.r. it was found[111] that the exchange of C$_2$D$_4$ with Rh(C$_2$H$_4$)$_2$(acac) has a half-life of less than 10^{-4} sec at 25°C. Furthermore the rate of exchange depends on the concentration of ethylene. The second-order process is that expected for square substitution.

Copper(II). It may be argued that Cu(II) complexes should not be included in this discussion of square planar substitution reactions of low-spin d^8 systems. However, there is justification for this inclusion in that the reactions of d^9 tetragonal Cu(II) complexes resemble those of square planar systems more closely than octahedral systems. Evidence for this is supplied by the unusual lability of Cu(II) complexes and by the steric retardation observed for their reactions. That complexes of Cu(II) are much more labile than corresponding high-spin six-coordinated complexes of Fe(II), Co(II), and Zn(II) is now well documented (p. 152).

This lability is usually explained on the basis of the distorted octahedral structure of Cu(II), which renders two of the ligands on the elongated z axis weakly held and thus readily replaceable. If the six ligands coordinated to Cu(II) are the same, such as Cu(H$_2$O)$_6{}^{2+}$, then a rapid intra-molecular transformation of the tetragonal structure makes all of the positions equivalent and accounts for a rapid ligand exchange.[112] However, with a complex of the type CuA$_4$(H$_2$O)$_2{}^{n+}$, where the H$_2$O molecules are on the z axis, and one considers the exchange or replacement of A, the system resembles more closely a square planar system and is expected to undergo bimolecular displacement reactions. Evidence in support of this is the observation of steric retardation for these reactions. Thus, the rates of the reaction

$$Cu(AA)_2(H_2O)_2{}^{2+} + 2H_3O^+ \rightarrow Cu(AA)(H_2O)_4{}^{2+} + AAH_2{}^{2+} \qquad (58)$$

where AA = H$_2$NCRR'CR''R'''NH$_2$, decrease in the order:[104]

R	R'	R''	R'''	Relative Orders
H	H	H	H	200
CH$_3$	CH$_3$	CH$_3$	CH$_3$	13
C$_2$H$_5$	CH$_3$	CH$_3$	CH$_3$	4
CH$_3$	C$_2$H$_5$	CH$_3$	C$_2$H$_5$	1

The exchange of free amino acid anion with coordinated amino acid

$$M(gly)_{2-3} + {}^*gly^- \rightleftharpoons M({}^*gly)_{2-3} + gly^- \qquad (59)$$

has been studied by n.m.r. line broadening methods.[113] For the metal chelates of Mn(II), Fe(II), Co(II), Ni(II), and Cu(II), the usual order of lability was found, Mn > Fe > Co > Ni ≪ Cu. Only the exchange of the copper system was totally second order, the rate depending directly on the concentration of free glycinate ion. The octahedral cobalt and nickel

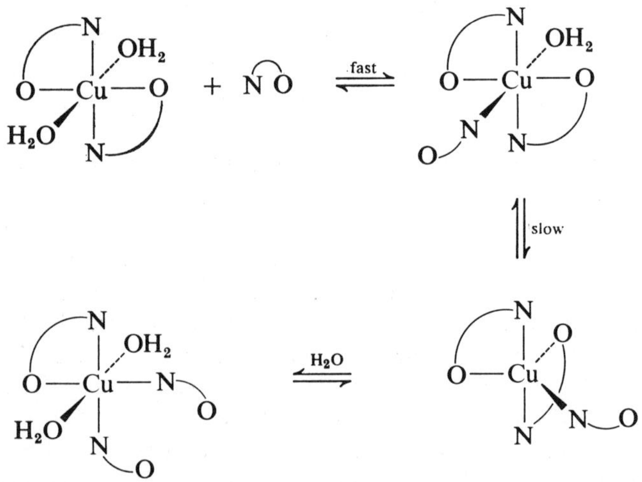

Fig. 5.23 Mechanism proposed for the exchange of amino acid (N—O) with its Cu(II) chelate.

systems showed mixed first and second-order kinetics, most of the exchange occurring by a path independent of the glycinate concentration. This supports a bimolecular displacement mechanism for the tetragonal, almost square planar Cu(II) complexes. A possible mechanism of exchange is shown in Fig. 5.23; it is very similar to that proposed for substitution reactions of Pt(II) complexes. The first step is the facile replacement of a loosely bound axial water by the entering ligand. This is then followed, probably, by rearrangement to a trigonal bipyramidal structure, opening of one of the chelate rings, and return to a "planar" structure. At this point exchange by a second-order process is assured, since two of the ligands are identical.

Also significant is the fact that the rate of exchange of Cu(II) complexes decreased with increasing steric hindrance by the amino acid, in the order glycine > sarcosine > dimethylglycine. Exactly the reverse order was found for Co(II) and Ni(II), suggesting the usual steric acceleration of a dissociation mechanism for these octahedral complexes.

Isomerization of Square Planar Complexes

Square planar complexes containing unidentate, MA_2B_2, and bidentate, $M(AB)_2$, ligands form geometrical isomers but generally cannot form optical isomers. One classical exception is the complex $Pt(i\text{-}bn)(m\text{-}stien)^{2+}$, where i-bn $= NH_2C(CH_3)_2CH_2NH_2$ and m-stien $= meso\text{-}NH_2CH(C_6H_5)\text{-}CH(C_6H_5)NH_2$, which was prepared and resolved by Mills and Quibell.[114] That this complex is optically active was cited as proof that the four nitrogen ligand atoms cannot be at the corners of a tetrahedron surrounding the central Pt(II). Such a structure has a plane of symmetry and does not form mirror image isomers, whereas a square planar structure does permit the existence of such isomers. The complex is optically stable, and its oxidation to $Pt(i\text{-}bn)(m\text{-}stien)X_2^{2+}$, followed by reduction to the original complex, takes place without cleavage of the Pt-N bond.[115]

In addition to the formation of geometrical isomers, some four-coordinated complexes of Ni(II) also form conformational isomers. In most cases the square-tetrahedral isomers are not isolated, but are shown to exist in rapid equilibrium in solution. Investigations on the mechanism of isomerization in these systems have as yet not been reported. An appreciable amount of thermodynamic data has been collected, and some of this is presented here and discussed briefly.

Geometrical Isomerization. Most of the *cis-trans* isomers of square-planar complexes that have been isolated are compounds of Pt(II). This is understandable because these systems are relatively inert and it is possible to isolate the less stable isomer before its rearrangement to the more stable form. Very few such isomers have been isolated for the more reactive square planar complexes of Ni(II), Pd(II), and Au(III).[1a] Systems of this type are generally sufficiently labile so that any given reaction may yield only one isomer, that which is the more stable or the least soluble under the conditions of the experiment. Nevertheless, in a few cases it has been possible to isolate both isomers,[116] and some of these were observed to undergo isomerization. For example, two interconvertible forms of the complex bis(benzylmethylglyoximato)nickel(II) have been observed.[117] Essentially the same observation was made[118] on the corresponding Pd(II) compound. In neither case are the structures of the two forms known, and although it appears logical that they are *cis-trans* isomers, there is as yet no definite proof that this is so.¶

Substitution reactions of Pt(II) complexes appear always to proceed with retention of configuration (Fig. 5.11). However, *cis-trans* isomerization

¶ Recent studies [K. A. Jensen, B. Nygaard, and R. B. Jensen, *Acta Chem. Scand.* **19,** 770 (1965)] suggest that the two forms of the Ni(II) compound are not *cis-trans* isomers but are different crystalline forms.

has been observed for some systems under rather special experimental conditions (see also p. 358). An appreciable amount of thermodynamic data has been collected[18] on *cis-trans* equilibria in benzene solutions of $Pt(MR_3)_2X_2$, where M = P, As, and Sb; R = methyl to *n*-pentyl; X = Cl^- and I^-. Both *cis*- and *trans*-$Pt(PEt_3)_2Cl_2$ are stable in benzene solution at room temperature, but if a trace of PEt_3 is added isomerization to an equilibrium mixture is complete within a half hour. This equilibration can be quenched by the addition of the bridged complex $[Pt(PEt_3)_2Cl_2]_2$, which

Table 5.27   Thermodynamic data for the isomerizations

$$cis\text{-}PtA_2X_2 \rightleftharpoons trans\text{-}PtA_2X_2$$

in benzene at 25°C

Complex	*cis* Isomer at Equi- librium, %	K	$-\Delta G^0$, cal	ΔH^0, cal	ΔS^0, eu
$Pt(PEt_3)_2Cl_2$	7.5	12.2	1480	2470	13.3
$Pt(PPr_3)_2Cl_2$	3.3	29.5	2000	1980	13.3
$Pt(PPr_3)_2I_2$	0.55	180	...	...	...
$Pt(PBr_3)_2Cl_2$	3.77	25.5	...	...	...
$Pt(AsEt_3)_2Cl_2$	0.57	176	3070	1180	14.2
$Pt(SbEt_3)_2Cl_2$	34.4	1.90	380	2410	9.4
$Pt(SbEt_3)_2I_2$	21	290	...	...	...
$Pd(SbEt_3)_2Cl_2$	6.0	15.7	...	...	...

From reference 18.

removes the catalyst PEt_3 by reacting with it to form the monomeric compound $Pt(PEt_3)_2Cl_2$.

Since the *cis* isomer has a dipole moment of 10.7 debyes, whereas the *trans* isomer has a zero moment, it is possible to determine the amounts of these two isomers at equilibrium by measuring the dielectric constant of their benzene solutions. Measurements were made at different tempera- tures, and the thermodynamic data summarized in Table 5.27 were calculated. These data are of interest on several accounts. In the first place it has generally been assumed that the *trans* isomer of square complexes is the more stable and that heat is evolved in the transformation of a *cis* isomer into the *trans* form. The data clearly show that this is not correct, that heat is in fact absorbed in this process, and that the greater stability of the *trans* isomer is a result of an increase in entropy. This increase in entropy is attributable to the greater solvation of the highly dipolar *cis* isomer so that isomerization to the *trans* form is accompanied by the release of benzene. Something of the order of 2 moles of benzene liberated per mole of *cis* complex converted would be sufficient to account for the observed entropy increase. It was estimated that the total bond energy of the *cis* isomer is approximately 10 kcal greater than that of the corresponding *trans* complex. This was explained in terms of the contribution made by π bonding to the total bond energy.

This explanation assumed that for a typical set of isomers, *cis*- and *trans*-Pt(PR$_3$)$_2$Cl$_2$, the one with the more efficient π bonding would have the greater total bond strength. Since phosphine ligands have a larger tendency to form metal to ligand π bonds than do chloro groups, it follows that the isomer which permits the greater amount of Pt-P double bond character would have the larger overall bond strength. This would be the *cis* isomer, in which the phosphines are *trans* to the chloro groups, R$_3$P—Pt—Cl, and compete with them for the same d orbital electrons. Such a competition greatly favors delocalization of electron density towards the stronger π-bonding phosphine ligands. This contribution to the overall bond strength would be less in the *trans* isomer, where the phosphine ligands would compete with one another for the d orbital electrons of Pt(II).

An alternative explanation was given on p. 358, based on the *trans* effect order PR$_3$ $\gg$ Cl$^-$ and the relative bond strengths Pt-P > Pt-Cl. Since the total bond strength depends more on the Pt-P than on the Pt-Cl bonds, it is more important that the Pt-P bonds be as strong as possible. This is achieved better in the *cis* isomer because of the smaller *trans* effect of the chloro group. There is x-ray evidence showing that the Pt-P bond length is greater in *trans*-Pt(PR$_3$)$_2$Cl$_2$ than in the *cis* isomer (p. 361).

Data in Table 5.27 also show the effect of various systematic changes in PtA$_2$X$_2$ on the *cis-trans* equilibrium. The percentage of *cis* isomer at equilibrium increases in the order As < P < Sb. The difference between the arsenic and phosphorus series of compounds is largely due to a change in the heat of isomerization, but that between the phosphorus and antimony series is caused by a change in entropy. For a series in which only the alkyl groups change, the equilibrium lies increasingly towards the *trans* isomer as R goes from methyl to *n*-propyl and then levels off to *n*-pentyl. This stabilization of the *trans* form is probably mainly steric in origin because differences between the inductive effects of the alkyl groups are small for these complexes.[13] Replacement of Cl$^-$ by I$^-$ in a given complex results in a large shift of the equilibrium towards the *trans* isomer. This is perhaps due to the greater bond strength of Pt—I compared to Pt—Cl, which means that the Pt-X bond makes a larger contribution to the overall bond strengths of the iodo compounds than to those of the chloro compounds. In terms of the previous discussion, the σ- and π-bonding properties of I$^-$ exceed those of Cl$^-$ in these systems. Therefore, there is a smaller difference in bond energy between the two iodo isomers than between the two corresponding chloro isomers. Finally, a comparison of $Pt(SbEt_3)_2Cl_2$ with $Pd(SbEt_3)_2Cl_2$ reveals that the Pd(II) complex contains far less *cis* isomer at equilibrium than does the Pt(II) compound. In fact, the amount of *cis* isomers in benzene solutions of phosphine and arsine complexes of Pd(II) is too small to detect by the method of dielectric constant measurements.

Thus, although *cis-trans* isomerizations of Pt(II) complexes are not common, they do occur. Unfortunately, neither kinetic nor exchange studies have been made in an attempt to obtain information on the mechanism of isomerizations. However, some observations have been made which suggest that isomerization proceeds by an intermolecular process. The most compelling evidence in support of this is the fact that these isomerizations appear to require a trace of some catalyst. However, since substitution reactions of Pt(II) complexes are generally stereospecific, at least two steps are required to permit isomerization (Fig. 5.24). The first step is the replacement of the chloro group by the catalyst PR_3 to

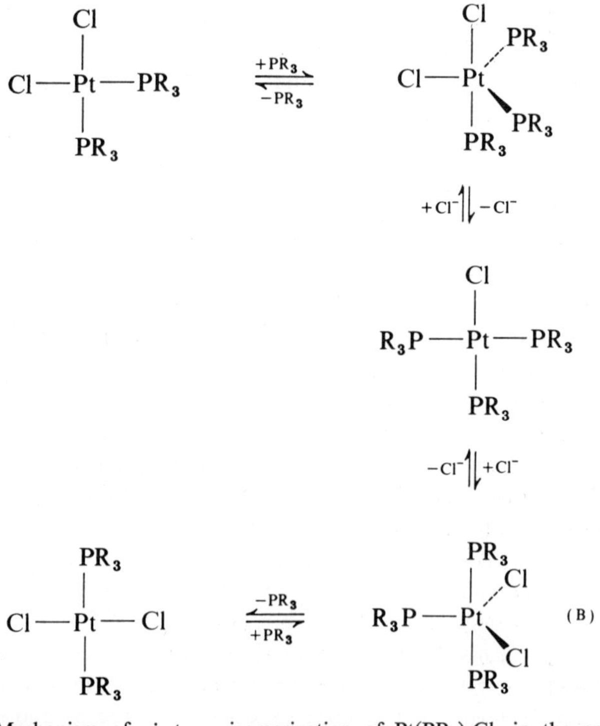

Fig. 5.24 Mechanism of *cis-trans* isomerization of $Pt(PR_3)_2Cl_2$ in the presence of catalytic amounts of PR_3.

form $[Pt(PR_3)_3Cl]Cl$. In the second step the reverse happens, and the complex $Pt(PR_3)_2Cl_2$ is formed along with the catalyst. If this second step goes through trigonal bipyramid A the original *cis* isomer is regenerated, but if it goes through B the *trans* isomer is formed. This type of mechanism was suggested for the isomerization of $Pt(SEt_2)_2Cl_2$ in solutions containing excess SEt_2.[1b,119]

This tentative mechanism is consistent with the information now available that (1) *cis-trans* isomerization of the more labile Ni(II) and Pd(II) square complexes is rapid, presumably as a result of displacements involving the solvent; (2) the more inert Pt(II) complexes isomerize only in the presence of a catalyst which is known to be a good nucleophilic reagent; and (3) square planar substitution reactions appear to involve a trigonal bipyramidal intermediate. Other mechanisms that can lead to isomerization of square complexes without excessive atomic motion are a dissociation process with a symmetrical planar trigonal intermediate and an intramolecular rearrangement with a tetrahedral intermediate. The dissociation process seems most unlikely because substitution reactions of square complexes always seem to proceed by a displacement mechanism. However, the intramolecular rearrangment represented by the equilibria

$$
\begin{array}{ccc}
X & X & X \\
| & | & | \\
X-Ni-A \rightleftharpoons & Ni & \rightleftharpoons A-Ni-A \\
| & X \quad A & | \\
A & A & X
\end{array}
$$

is certainly a possible route for isomerization, particularly for Ni(II) complexes, as will be shown in the next section.

Conformational Isomerism.   Coordination chemists are always intrigued by the fascinating chemistry of Ni(II) complexes.[120] This metal ion readily forms a variety of complexes, having different coordination numbers and structures. Six-coordinated high-spin d^8 systems of the type $Ni(H_2O)_6^{2+}$ have an octahedral structure and are common. Less common are the five-coordinated Ni(II) complexes, which have a trigonal bipyramidal structure and are either low-spin, such as $[Ni(QAS)Br]Br^{121b}$ or high-spin, such as $[NiN(C_2H_4N(CH_3)_2)_3Cl]Cl.^{122a}$ Least common are the five-coordinated Ni(II) complexes, which have a distorted tetragonal pyramidal structure and are either low-spin, such as $NiCH_3As(C_3H_6As(CH_3)_2Br_2,^{121b}$ or high-spin like the Schiff base complexes[122b] of Ni(II).** Four-coordinated complexes of the type $Ni(CN)_4^{2-}$ are square planar and diamagnetic,

** Recent x-ray studies show that the compound $[Cr(en)_3][Ni(CN)_5]1.5H_2O$ has two $Ni(CN)_5^{3-}$ per unit cell. One has a tetragonal pyramidal structure and the other is a distorted trigonal bipyramidal (K. N. Raymond, private communication). The complex $Ni(P(OCH_2)_3CCH_3)_5^{2+}$ has a trigonal bipyramidal structure (J. G. Verkade, private communication).

whereas $NiBr_4^{2-}$ [123] is tetrahedral and paramagnetic. The coordination numbers and structures of Ni(II) complexes are exceptionally sensitive to the steric and inductive properties of the ligands.

Four-coordinated Ni(II) complexes containing ligands of high field strength and low ligand-ligand repulsion interaction have a square planar structure, whereas ligands of low field and high repulsion interaction tend to generate tetrahedral Ni(II) complexes. This is primarily due to the larger crystal field stabilization energy of the square planar low-spin d^8 system compared to the corresponding tetrahedral, high-spin system (p. 69). Several complexes are known in which these factors are in close balance, and the difference in energy between the two structures is small. Systems of this type provide the remarkable examples of *conformational isomers* in which one form has a square planar structure and the other a tetrahedral structure.

Generally, only one form is isolated in the solid state, but experiments clearly show that both forms may be present in rapid equilibrium in solution. This can be conveniently demonstrated by methods which depend upon the ground electronic states of the two isomers being different. The square planar form is in the singlet state and is diamagnetic, whereas the tetrahedral form is in the triplet state and is paramagnetic. Therefore, the d–d spectra differ, and an examination of the absorption spectra permits an estimate of the two isomers in solution. Also, a measurement of the magnetic susceptibility of the solution gives a direct measure of the amount of paramagnetic species present.

N.m.r. studies[124] show that certain Ni(II) complexes in solution exhibit isotropic proton hyperfine contact shifts which can be used to estimate the amount of tetrahedral complex in solution. These shifts were first observed with the bis(N,N-disubstituted aminotroponeimine)Ni(II) chelates and are attributed to the delocalization of the unpaired electrons of Ni(II) to the ligand by the overlap of appropriate Ni(II) d orbitals with nitrogen p_π orbitals of the ligand. In the valence bond formulation, this delocalization can be described by structures such as the following:

$$(61)$$

The arrow represents an unpaired electron. The presence of unpaired π-electron spin density on the carbon atoms of the seven-membered ring is manifested in the proton magnetic resonance spectrum by large high field (positive spin density) shifts. Thus, the contact shift for a given proton of the chelate depends on its average susceptibility and hence on the fraction of paramagnetic molecules present. This will be true only if the equilibrium between the two forms is established in a time which is shorter than the reciprocal of the contact shifts (in cycles per second) and if the electron relaxation and/or exchange time is small compared to the reciprocal of this shift. Both of these conditions appear to be fulfilled for the Ni(II) complexes that have been examined by this technique.

It has long been known that certain diamagnetic Ni(II) complexes dissolve to give paramagnetic solutions.[125] For good coordinating solvents, such as pyridine, magnetic moments of about 3.3 B.M. are obtained. Such values correspond to the magnetic susceptibilities found for six-coordinated Ni(II) complexes containing two unpaired electrons. In these systems it has been definitely established[105] that two molecules of the solvent add on the z axis to form an octahedral complex (see Table 5.26). For essentially non-coordinating solvents, such as benzene, the solutions of certain Ni(II) complexes exhibit magnetic moments intermediate between zero and about 3 B.M. Earlier explanations, based on the valence bond model, suggested that the paramagnetism arose from the presence of tetrahedal species.[105,123] Later it was suggested that the paramagnetism might be due to some form of axial interaction sufficient to produce a triplet ground state.[126] This possibility stimulated a vigorous reinvestigation of these systems by Sacconi[127] and by Holm.[128] Careful and extensive studies show that, depending on the system, the presence of either tetrahedral species or axial interaction, or both, can be responsible for the observed paramagnetism.

In summary it is now recognized that four-coordinated Ni(II) complexes can achieve partial or complete occupancy of a triplet spin state by one or any combination of the following effects: (1) the presence of an in-plane ligand field whose intrinsic strength, in the absence of any axial interactions, is insufficient to pair electron spins; (2) the imposition, through the agency of solvent or solute, of an axial component on a given in-plane field so as to reduce the tetragonality of the field and produce a triplet ground state; (3) the presence of tetrahedral species. As yet, no examples of effect 1 are known. Paramagnetic behavior arising from effect 2 is well established. For good coordinating solvents this effect is due to a solvent-solute interaction to form six-coordinated species. For essentially non-coordinating solvents it is the result of solute-solute interaction. Examples of this effect are reported for Ni(II) complexes of certain N-substituted salicylaldimines[127,128] and certain β-diketones.[129] Measurements of molecular weights and of absorption spectra show that molecular association is responsible for the paramagnetism of these solutions. This is supported by the x-ray evidence that Ni(acac)$_2$ is in fact a trimer in the solid state.[130]

Of interest to this section on conformational isomerism is the paramagnetism of solutions of Ni(II) complexes arising from effect 3, that due to tetrahedral species. Three different types of Ni(II) complexes have been investigated which exhibit this kind of behavior. One of these consists of the chelates of the Schiff bases of the type shown in the equilibrium.

$$\tag{62}$$

However when R = CH$_3$ or n-alkyl the paramagnetism of the solutions is due not to tetrahedral species but to polymeric species.[127,128] However, polymerization becomes more difficult as the size of R increases, and for R = sec- or t-alkyl the paramagnetism is almost entirely due to the presence of tetrahedral species.[131,132] For R = isopropyl, the solid Ni(II) chelate is paramagnetic and x-ray evidence shows that it has a distorted tetrahedral structure.[133]

The effect of the size of the alkyl group is also shown by compounds of the type[134]

The qualitative dependence of the magnetic properties of CDCl$_3$ solutions of the compounds at 23°C on the sizes of R is as follows:

R = R′ = H	Diamagnetic
R = H; R′ = alkyl	Diamagnetic
R = R′ = CH$_3$	Slightly paramagnetic (1%)
R = R′ = aryl	25–75% paramagnetic
R = R′ = C$_2$H$_5$ or higher alkyl	Almost completely paramagnetic (99%)

The planar forms, in those systems where equilibria have been measured, are usually more stable than the tetrahedral by 1–5 kcal of enthalpy. The entropy factor favors the tetrahedral forms by 1–10 eu.

Monodentate complexes of the type $Ni(PR_3)_2X_2$ also form conformational isomers, and again this seems to be largely controlled by the steric requirements of the ligands. Thus, the halogeno compounds $Ni(PEt_3)_2X_2$ are planar in the solid state and in solution, whereas the $Ni(PPh_3)_2X_2$ compounds have pseudo-tetrahedral structures both in the solid state and in solution.[135] Intermediate compounds of the type $Ni(PRPh_2)_2X_2$ show intermediate behaviors, and it is with these systems that conformational isomers were found to exist in solution. In fact, it has even been possible to isolate both forms of the compound $Ni(PEtPh_2)_2Br_2$.[136] Other conformational isomers that have been isolated include compounds of the type $Ni(PRPh_2)_2X_2$, where X = Br (R = n-Pr, i-Pr, n-Bu) and X = Cl (R = n-Bu). These afford excellent support to the physicochemical evidence of the equilibrium

$$R_3P-\underset{\underset{X}{\overset{\displaystyle |}{\displaystyle |}}}{\overset{\overset{\displaystyle X}{\overset{\displaystyle |}{\displaystyle |}}}{Ni}}-PR_3 \quad \rightleftharpoons \quad \underset{R_3P}{\overset{X}{\diagdown}}Ni\underset{X}{\overset{PR_3}{\diagup\!\!\!\blacktriangleright}} \tag{63}$$

in solution.

There can no longer be any doubt that conformational isomers of Ni(II) complexes exist and that they are in rapid equilibrium in solution. The mechanism of this isomerization process is not known but would appear to involve an intramolecular twisting process. It is unlikely that an intermolecular process involving the solvent would provide a path for isomerization, since the solvents are of such low polarity and poor coordinating ability. Kinetic data are not available on the rates of isomerization, except the n.m.r. observations, which show only a single resonance averaged over the two isomeric forms. This requires a lifetime for isomerization of less than 10^{-4} sec.[134] But light absorption by both species is observed in the electronic spectra of the solutions.

That a ligand interchange process is not responsible for isomerization is supported by the observation[137] that the rate of PPh_3 exchange with $Ni(PPh_3)_2I_2$ at room temperature is slow by the n.m.r. criterion. The resonances found for a solution containing both the complex and the ligand are at the exact positions corresponding to each of the two observed separately. The corresponding dichloro complex with added ligand exchanges rapidly and shows resonances at intermediate positions between those of the ligand and of the complex. The dibromo compound exchanges with ligand at a rate that results in line broadening of the n.m.r. spectrum and allows an estimate of the lifetime for exchange of the order of 10^{-3} sec. The same exchange rate is reached for the diiodo compound at a temperature of $+60°C$ and for the dichloro compound at $-20°C$.*

The exchange of multidentate ligands with Ni(II) chelates is much slower, and several of these have been studied by conventional isotopic labeling and exchange methods.[138] The interchange of ligands in Schiff base complexes of Ni(II) has been observed[139] and is attributed to the equilibria

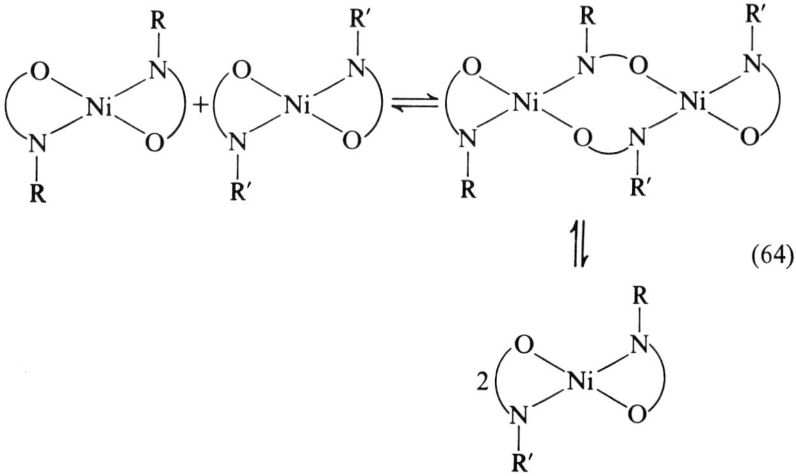

(64)

The rate is faster if at least one of the complexes is tetrahedral but is still very slow compared to the lifetime for conformational isomerization.

That isomerization takes place rapidly by presumably an intramolecular process appears to be closely related to the rapid ligand interchange observed for several five-coordinated systems having a trigonal bipyramidal structure. Gutowsky[140] and his students examined the ^{19}F-resonance spectrum of PF_5 and found only a single fluorine resonance peak, split into a doublet due to P—F coupling. This means that either the five fluorines become equivalent to a measurement as slow as n.m.r., or the chemical shifts and P—F couplings are accidentally identical for fluorines at the equatorial and axial positions of the trigonal bipyramid. The latter possibility is rather unlikely, since several oposite examples are known.

The compound PF_5 is found to have an apparently normal i.r. spectrum for a trigonal bipyramidal structure.[140] This suggests that the fluorine atoms may become equivalent at a rate slow compared with the time necessary to establish sharp vibrational levels, and fast compared with the inverse line widths associated with n.m.r. measurements. Hence, any

---

* It is of interest that $Ni(PPh_3)_2 X_2$ exchanges more rapidly than $Co(PPh_3)_2 X_2$, as predicted by crystal field theory, W. D. Horrocks, Jr., and Z. H. Pignolet, *J. Am. Chem. Soc.* 1 **88**, 5930 (1966).

exchange process which the fluorines undergo should occur at a frequency between about 10^{-8} and 10^{-2} sec. This phenomenon has been discussed[141] in terms of an intramolecular tunneling process viewed somewhat as shown in Fig. 5.25. Since some five-coordinated systems are known to have a stable tetragonal pyramidal structure, the energy difference between such a structure and its trigonal bipyramid isomer in certain systems may be small.

Rapid intramolecular conformational isomerism in five-coordinated systems is quite common, and spectroscopic equivalence of ligands is

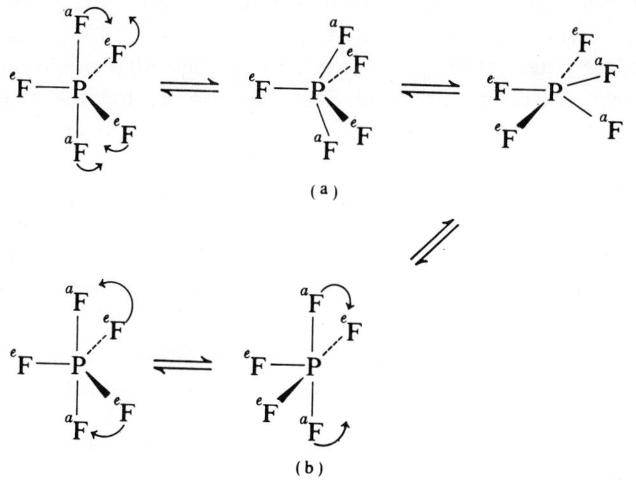

(a)

(b)

Fig. 5.25 Intramolecular rearrangement of PF_5 with the synchronous motion of axial ^aF and equatorial ^eF through (a) or the stepwise motion through tetragonal pyramid (b).

found for $Fe(CO)_5$[142] with ^{13}C n.m.r. and for PF_3Cl_2, PF_3Br_2, RPF_4, R_2NPF_4, $RNSF_4$, AsF_5,[143] and SOF_4[144] with ^{19}F n.m.r. In a few systems it has been possible to estimate the activation energy for this intramolecular exchange process by analysis of the exchange broadening of the n.m.r. lines over a suitable temperature range. For PF_3Cl_2 the value is 6 ± 2 kcal/mole, and qualitative observations suggest that the value is smaller for PF_3Br_2. An estimate of 6–12 kcal/mole is reported for $(C_2H_5)_2NPF_4$.[143]

Muetterties[145] has emphasized the important point that certain compounds have stereochemically non-rigid structures, particularly inorganic compounds. The classical example of NH_3 is well recognized. It now becomes clear that five-coordinated systems may often have non-rigid structures. We saw previously that the energy differences between square planar and tetrahedral structures are small for certain complexes of Ni(II). Also, eight-coordinated species may not have rigid structures. For example, x-ray analysis shows that $Mo(CN)_8^{4-}$, as the potassium salt, has near D_{2d}

(dodecahedral) symmetry with two equally populated cyanide environments.[146] The most plausible structural alternative is the D_{4d} square antiprism with all cyanide groups equivalent. There are conflicting reports supporting each of these structures in solution.[147] Recent ^{13}C n.m.r. absorption studies[145] show a single sharp resonance. This may indicate a rapid intramolecular interchange of cyanide groups. The process could also involve the two structures of D_{2d} and D_{4d} symmetry, because the energy difference between the two is small and the distortion required to interconvert these structures is also small.[148]

Liehr[149] has presented theoretical arguments against the assignment of rigid structures and suggests that stereochemistry should be considered in terms of the potential energy surface encompassing all possible geometries for a given molecular aggregate. Such an approach focuses attention on structural interrelations, potential intramolecular rearrangements, and the feasibility of separation of optical or geometrical isomers. Experimentally, there is some justification for this approach to dynamic, rather than static, molecular structures. At the very least one must be cognizant of the fact that the lifetime of some structures of certain molecules is small and cannot, therefore, be determined by experimental techniques that are slow by comparison.

Some examples of non-rigid molecules and the time scale for various structural techniques are given in Table 5.28. It is important to note that

Table 5.28 Ground state lifetimes for non-rigid molecules and time scale for structural techniques

Species	Lifetime, sec	Techniques	Time Scale, sec
NH_3	2.5×10^{-11}	elect. diff.	10^{-20}
PH_3	10^{-3}	neutron diff.	10^{-18}
AsH_3	10	x-ray diff.	10^{-18}
CH_4	10^{15}	ultraviolet	10^{-15}
PF_5	10^{-5}	visible	10^{-14}
PCl_5	10^4	i.r.	10^{-13}
PF_3Cl_2	10^{-3} ($-50°$)	Raman	10^{-13}
IF_7	between 10^{-3} and 10^{-12}	e.s.r.	10^{-4}–10^{-8} [a]
ReH_9^{2-}	,, ,, ,, ,,	n.m.r.	10^{-1}–10^{-9} [a]
$Mo(CN)_8^{4-}$	,, ,, ,, ,,	quadrupole r.	10^{-1}–10^{-9} [a]
B_2Cl_4	,, ,, ,, ,,	Mossbauer (iron)	10^{-7}
		molecular beam	10^{-6}
		exptl. sepn. of isomers	$>10^2$

From reference 145.

[a] Time scale sensitivity defined by chemical systems under investigation.

all the new resonance techniques have time scale ranges comparable to those of ground state geometries in non-rigid molecules. In fact, as we have discussed, one of these resonance techniques, n.m.r., has detected a large number of low-energy intramolecular rearrangements. Thus, any comparison or application of structural data for a non-rigid molecule must take into account its physical state and the time scales of the techniques employed.

Substitution Reactions of Tetrahedral Complexes

The mechanism of substitution reactions of tetrahedral metal complexes has been little studied. One reason is that such structures are usually found only for systems which are not stabilized by crystal field effects. This means in turn that their reactions are generally quite rapid and not easy to study kinetically or stereochemically. However, the application of techniques for studying fast reactions now makes it possible to investigate the kinetics of substitution reactions in these systems. For example, the n.m.r. line broadening technique has been used to obtain semiquantitative data on the rate of $P(C_6H_5)_3$ exchange with $Ni[P(C_6H_5)_3]_2X_2$.[137] By means of the T-jump method the rate of water replacement in $Be(H_2O)_4^{2+}$ was reported to have a specific rate constant of $10^2 \sec^{-1}$ at 25°C.[150] Optically active tetrahedral chelate compounds such as bis(benzoylacetonato)-beryllium(II)[151] and bis(8-quinolinato-5-sulfonic acid)zinate(II)[152] have been resolved, suggesting that these systems may be slow to undergo ligand exchange or replacement. It would be of interest to investigate the rates of ligand exchange in these systems and to correlate them with the rates of racemization of the complexes. Finally, tetrahedral compounds of transition metals are rather common among the metal carbonyls, and the kinetics and mechanism of substitution reactions of the isoelectronic and isostructural compounds. $Ni(CO)_4$, $CoNO(CO)_3$, and $Fe(NO)_2(CO)_2$ have been investigated (p. 572).

The well-studied prototype of tetrahedral systems would be the organic compounds containing four groups bound to carbon. It is well established that both S_N1- and S_N2-type reactions occur for such carbon compounds, but not S_N2 (lim), which is restricted to unsaturated carbon compounds. The bond strengths of ligands attached to C(IV) are usually much greater than for other central elements of interest in coordination chemistry. This may be considered as a factor which would promote dissociation-type mechanisms in tetrahedral complexes compared to organic compounds.

As opposed to this, the larger size of other central elements than carbon will greatly favor a displacement-type mechanism in that a fifth group can be held without steric crowding. Such an intermediate may often be one of some stability so that, in effect, an S_N2 (lim) mechanism is operating. The presence of either empty or filled d orbitals on the central atom may help stabilize such a five-coordinated species. By analogy with the case of carbon, where the fact of inversion on bimolecular substitution has been often demonstrated, one would expect this intermediate to be a trigonal bipyramid, with the entering group and the leaving group lying on the diagonal axis.

There is no stereochemical proof for this reasonable assumption in the case of tetrahedral transition metal compounds, but evidence is available for compounds other than carbon, such as P(V) and Si(IV) systems. What has been demonstrated for certain transition metal systems is that a bimolecular displacement on the metal does occur. For example, the neutral methanolysis of an ester of chromic acid with optically active tertiary alkoxy radicals attached to Cr(VI) gives an optically active alcohol:[153]

$$
\begin{array}{c}
\text{O} \\
\| \\
\text{R*—O—Cr—OR*} \xrightarrow{\text{CH}_3\text{OH}} \text{R*OH} + \text{CH}_3\text{O—Cr—OR*} \\
\| \\
\text{O}
\end{array} \qquad (65)
$$

(Oxidation-reduction of the methyl chromate than follows.) This can only mean an attack of methanol on chromium, displacing the optically active alcohol without breaking the C-O bond, a conclusion substantiated by hydrolysis experiments of chromate esters in water labeled with ^{18}O.[154] Furthermore, since a much more rapid methanolysis occurs when methoxide ion is present, we have all the earmarks of an S_N2 attack on the metal atom,

$$
\left[\begin{array}{c}
\text{O} \quad\;\; \text{O} \\
\diagdown\; \diagup \\
\text{CH}_3\text{O} \cdots \text{Cr} \cdots \text{OR*} \\
| \\
\text{OR*}
\end{array} \right]^-
$$

This is similar to the results found in a kinetic study of the reaction

$$ \text{Cr}_2\text{O}_7{}^{2-} + 2\text{OH}^- \rightarrow 2\text{CrO}_4{}^{2-} + \text{H}_2\text{O} \qquad (66) $$

of hydroxide ion and dichromate ion, a binuclear complex of Cr(VI).[155] The reaction is first order in hydroxide ion and first order in dichromate ion, which is only reasonable in terms of a bimolecular displacement of $\text{CrO}_4{}^{2-}$ by OH^- acting on chromium

$$
\left[\begin{array}{c}
\text{O} \quad\;\; \text{O} \quad\;\; \text{O} \\
\diagdown\; \diagup \qquad\; | \\
\text{HO} \cdots \text{Cr} \cdots \text{O—Cr—O} \\
| \qquad\qquad | \\
\text{O} \qquad\;\; \text{O}
\end{array} \right]^{3-}
$$

followed by rapid neutralization of $\text{HCrO}_4{}^-$ with OH^-.

The rate of reaction of $Cr_2O_7^{2-}$ with different bases has been further investigated by a variety of methods.[156,157] The results obtained show the reactions to be first order in $Cr_2O_7^{2-}$ and first order in reagent. The mechanism of reaction appears to be analogous to that proposed for the reagent OH^-. Thus, the slow step in all of these reactions is the attack on chromium by the base

$$O_3Cr\text{—}O\text{—}CrO_3^{2-} + B \xrightarrow{k_B} BCrO_3 + CrO_4^{2-} \qquad (67)$$

followed by the rapid reactions

$$BCrO_3 + H_2O \rightarrow BH^+ + HCrO_4^- \qquad (68)$$

$$HCrO_4^- + B \rightarrow BH^+ + CrO_4^{2-} \qquad (69)$$

For different bases the rates of reaction at 25°C vary in the order shown in Table 5.29. The base constants are also given in terms of the Edwards H

Table 5.29 Rate constants for the reaction

$$B + Cr_2O_7^{2-} \xrightarrow{k_B} BCrO_3 + CrO_4^{2-}$$

in water at 25°C

Base	k_B, $M^{-1}\,sec^{-1}$	H^a
OH^-	460	17.5
CO_3^{2-}	10	12.1
$C_6H_5O^-$	27	11.7
NH_3	740	11.2
2,6-Lutidine	0.5	8.4
CrO_4^{2-}	2300	7.6
$C_2H_3O_2^-$	2.0	6.5
H_2O	9.3×10^{-5} [b]	0.0

[a] Data from references 156, 157, and 158. Base constants in terms of the Edwards H values, where $H = pK_a + 1.7$ (see p. 138).
[b] First-order constant divided by 55.5.

values. The anionic bases are expected to react slower than neutral bases for electrostatic reasons, and a comparison of reagent reactivity is best made for reagents of the same charge. Such a comparison shows that the strongest base is usually also the best reagent. The slow rate of reaction of 2,6-lutidine is attributed to the steric effect of the two methyl groups *ortho* to the pyridine nitrogen.

The very rapid rate for the CrO_4^{2-} itself acting as a base is remarkable. This reaction was studied by n.m.r. line broadening methods using the ^{17}O resonance.[158] It corresponds to an exchange reaction, since no net chemical reaction occurs. The large rate constant is quite out of line with the basicity of CrO_4^{2-}, especially if the electrostatic effect is considered. Since Cr(VI) is expected to be a hard acid, it is not likely that polarizability is an important factor. A more reasonable explanation is that π bonding in the Cr—O—Cr link favors the formation of the transition state (see p. 176).

Although information on substitution reactions of tetrahedral transition metal complexes is conspicuous largely because of its absence, the same is not true of tetrahedral compounds for non-transition elements. The kinetic data and stereochemical observations on these systems provide overwhelming evidence that the reactions are usually of the bimolecular displacement type. This is not too surprising, since the central atoms involved are known to readily exhibit coordination numbers greater than four. For example, stable six-coordination systems are known, such as SiF_6^{2-}, PF_6^-, SF_6, and $SnCl_6^{2-}$, and there are five-coordinated systems such as $[(C_6H_5)_3Si(bipy)]I$[159] and the pentaoxyphosphoranes,[160] e.g., $C_{14}H_6O_2P(OC_3H_7)_3$.

Most of the studies on substitution reactions for compounds of Group IV elements, except for carbon, have been done with silicon compounds. With the synthesis of optically active α-NpPhMeSiX,[161] where α-Np $=$ α-naphthyl and X $=$ H, OR, RCOO, or the halogens, it has become possible to investigate the stereochemistry of substitution reactions on Si(IV). Sommer and his students are responsible for this significant contribution, and Sommer has written an excellent book on silicon substitution.[162] By making use of optically active silicon compounds, it is found that ligand replacement on silicon takes place either with inversion or with retention of configuration, depending largely on the nature of the leaving group. Examples of racemization have also been observed and investigated.

All of the kinetic data on substitution reactions of tetrahedral Si(IV) compounds indicate that an S_N2 mechanism is involved. Even systems such as triphenylsilyl chloride, which would presumably be prone to react by an S_N1 process, as in the case of the carbon analog, seem to react bimolecularly.[163] Steric retardation in rate of reaction is observed, as is expected for a displacement mechanism. For example, the base-catalyzed solvolysis of trialkylphenoxysilanes

$$R_3SiOC_6H_5 + C_2H_5O^- \rightarrow R_3SiOC_2H_5 + C_6H_5O^- \qquad (70)$$

in ethanol-water solution at 25°C has a specific rate constant $k = 3.3 \times 10^2\ M^{-1}\ sec^{-1}$ for $R_3Si = (CH_3)_3Si$ and a value of $1.7 \times 10^{-2}\ M^{-1}\ sec^{-1}$ for $R_3Si = (t\text{-}C_4H_9)(CH_3)_2Si$.[164] The steric effect of the entering reagent is shown by the rate of reaction of a given substrate with different alcohols, increasing in the order of relative rates:

$$(CH_3)_2CHOH(1) < C_2H_5OH(10^3) < CH_3OH(10^4).^{[165]}$$

In general it is also found that an increased ability of the leaving group to accept a negative charge results in an increase in the rate of reaction. This is consistent with an enhancement of a nucleophilic attack on the more positive silicon and is exemplified by the observation[166] that the base-catalyzed solvolysis of p-$NO_2C_6H_4CH_2Si(CH_3)_3$ is 2×10^6 faster than that of $C_6H_5CH_2Si(CH_3)_3$.

The stereochemistry of ligand displacement reactions on silicon can be roughly summarized as follows. (1) Inversion of configuration occurs for

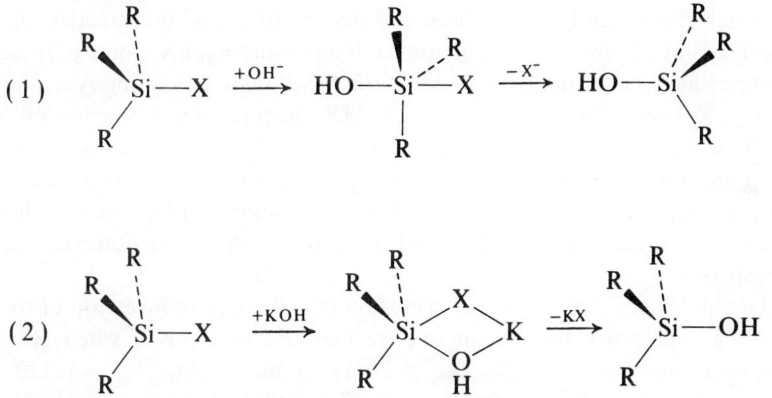

Fig. 5.26 Stereochemistry of nucleophilic displacement reactions on silicon. (1) Inversion of configuration by *trans* attack involving a trigonal bipyramidal structure. (2) Retention of configuration by *cis* attack through a four-centered system.

the replacement of X in R_3SiX, where $X = Cl^-$, Br^-, $RCOO^-$, or p-toluenesulfonate ion. The displacement is believed to involve a *trans* attack and proceed through a trigonal bipyramidal structure as shown in Fig. 5.26. (2) Retention of configuration is found for the replacement of X in R_3SiX, where $X = H^-$ or OR^-. This would appear to involve a *cis* attack, and perhaps a four-centered mechanism of the type illustrated in Fig. 5.26.

Reactions in category 1 are generally faster than those in 2, and the suggestion is made[162] that, if the leaving group X has a strong tendency to exist in the form of an anion, its displacement takes place with inversion. For $X = F^-$ both inversion and retention reactions are known. It should also be mentioned that some studies have been made of the racemization of certain optically active silicon compounds. For example, the rate of racemization of $(+)$-α-NpPhMeSiCl is the same as its rate of chloride ion exchange in chloroform solution.[162] This suggests the formation of a siliconium ion pair which is symmetrical or rearranges rapidly to permit racemization; the ion-pair chloride ion is in rapid equilibrium with radio-chloride ion in solution:

$$(+)\text{-}R_3SiCl \rightleftharpoons R_3Si^+,Cl^- \rightleftharpoons (-) - R_3SiCl \tag{71}$$

However, it must not be assumed that chloride ion exchange at asymmetric silicon will always give a ratio of 1 for k_{rac}/k_{ex}. The situation is probably much more complicated. For example, the addition of cyclohexylammonium chloride would provide a much higher concentration of free chloride ion in a more polar solvent. This then should give faster rates by an S_N2 mechanism and result in the observation that $k_{rac}/k_{ex} = 2.0$.

Much less extensive have been the investigations of the kinetics and mechanisms of substitution reactions of R_3GeX and R_3SnX. Some of these systems have been studied[167] in comparison with corresponding reactions of R_3SiX. For analogous compounds R_3MX, the rates of reaction generally increase in the order $Si < Ge < Sn$, and the solvolysis reactions of germanium and tin halides often do not go to completion as do those of silicon. Again both steric and inductive effects support a bimolecular displacement mechanism where bond making in the transition state is dominant.

One point of interest is the observation that there is an inversion of the relative rate order for silicon and germanium in R_3MCl, when R is changed from isopropyl ($k_{Ge}/k_{Si} > 20:1$) to phenyl ($k_{Ge}/k_{Si} = 1:120$). One explanation offered[167] for this inversion is that silicon is considerably more effective in π bonding to an aromatic ring than is germanium,[168] and a trigonal bipyramidal structure is particularly well suited for π bonding. This driving force towards more π bonding in the transition state may then be responsible for the greater rate of reaction of the silicon compound compared to the germanium.

Investigations of nucleophilic displacement reactions of tetrahedral compounds of Group V elements are largely limited to reactions of P(V). These compounds are important, since many of them show biological effects.[169] Reviews[170] have been written on the subject of substitution reactions of P(V) compounds.

The experimental evidence, both kinetic and stereochemical, is in accord with bimolecular displacements on tetrahedral phosphorus substrates. Second-order rate laws are observed for such reactions, and the rates of reaction roughly parallel the basicity of the reagent. For example, the solvolysis of methylisopropoxyphosphoryl fluoride

$$Me(i\text{-}Pro)POF + H_2O \xrightarrow{Y} Me(i\text{-}Pro)PO(OH) + HF \tag{72}$$

is very sensitive to the nature and concentration of the reagent Y, which displaces F^- in a rate-determining step

$$Me(i\text{-}Pro)POF + Y^- \xrightarrow{slow} Me(i\text{-}Pro)POY + F^- \tag{73}$$

followed by the rapid solvolysis of the intermediate to give the final acid product

$$Me(i\text{-}PrO)POY + H_2O \xrightarrow{\text{fast}} Me(i\text{-}PrO)PO(OH) + HY \qquad (74)$$

The reactivity for different reagents[171] Y decreases in the order $OOH^- > OH^- \sim OCl^- > NH_2OH > NO_2^- > N_3^- > H_2O$. In ethanol, the order $F^- > C_2H_5O^- > C_6H_5O^-$ was found. Sulfur nucleophiles such as $S_2O_3^{2-}$ and $C_6H_5S^-$ do not seem to be particularly reactive, and the ions Cl^-, Br^-, and I^- are non-reactive.

The conclusion that P(V) is a hard acid with preference for a hard base seems certain. There appears to be an unusually high reactivity of fluoride ion and of oxygen nucleophiles with unshared electrons on the α atom. This suggests that π bonding between the non-bonding electron pairs on fluorine or oxygen and the empty d orbitals on phosphorus may result in a lowering of the activation energy for reaction.[81] In regard to the leaving group, it is reported[172] that the rates of reaction decrease in the orders $Cl^- \gg F^-$ and $RS^- > RO^-$. That the leaving group departs less readily as it becomes more basic is evidence that some bond breaking occurs in the transition state.

Stereochemical studies of substitution reactions using optically active P(V) compounds provide excellent evidence that the reactions involve a direct displacement mechanism. The reactions take place with inversion of configuration,[170] suggesting *trans* displacement through a trigonal bipyramidal structure [Fig. 5.26 (1)]. For example, (−)-methyisopropoxy-phosphoryl chloride was found to undergo substitution reactions such as

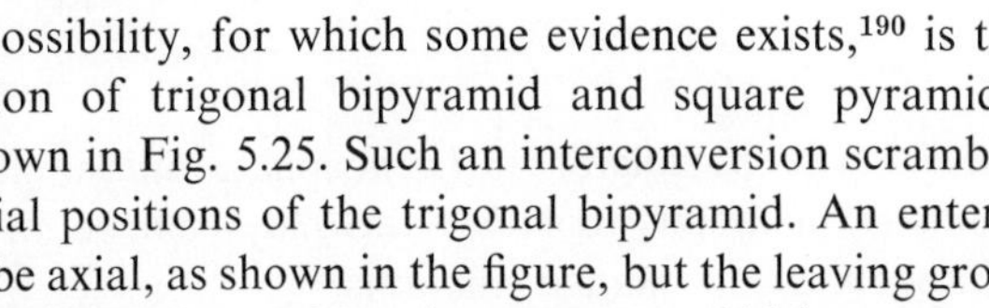

$$\underset{\text{O}i\text{-Pr}}{\overset{\overset{\displaystyle\text{O}}{\|}}{\underset{Me}{P}}}-Cl + EtO^- \rightarrow EtO-\underset{\text{O}i\text{-Pr}}{\overset{\overset{\displaystyle\text{O}}{\|}}{\underset{Me}{P}}} + Cl^- \qquad (75)$$

without racemization but with inversion.[173]

Another possibility, for which some evidence exists,[190] is that a rapid interconversion of trigonal bipyramid and square pyramid structures occurs as shown in Fig. 5.25. Such an interconversion scrambles the axial and equatorial positions of the trigonal bipyramid. An entering nucleophile would be axial, as shown in the figure, but the leaving group could be equatorial. The entering and leaving groups would become equivalent in the square pyramid form. The net stereochemical result could be inversion of configuration.

Investigations of substitution reactions of tetrahedral S(VI) compounds are not numerous, but do suggest that these also take place by a displacement mechanism. No data are available from which a quantitative scale of nucleophilic character for different reagents towards a S(VI) substrate can be derived. However, some information can be obtained from available data on competitive reactions. Thus, the ratio of products obtained from the reaction between a mixture of p-nitrophenyl and p-toluenesulfonate with various reagents was determined.[174] The most striking result was that very basic nucleophiles preferred to attack sulfur, whereas more polarizable reagents attacked the aromatic carbon atom. From observations of this type, it has been concluded[81] that the order of nucleophilic strength towards S(VI) is $OH^- > CH_3O^- > C_6H_5O^- > RNH_2 > C_6H_5NH_2 > C_6H_5S^-$. Thus, basicity appears to be of prime importance since S(VI) is a hard center.

Other experiments on acid hydrolysis of sulfate esters[175] similarly suggest nucleophilic attack on S(VI). Nucleophilic attack on sulfur atoms in lower valence states is also well known.[176] These centers are soft, and polarizable nucleophiles are most reactive.

Although the exact mechanism of acid-catalyzed oxygen exchange in oxyanions has not been determined, it is abundantly clear that the addition of protons to XO_m^{n-} greatly increases its rate of oxygen exchange with the solvent water. This is to be expected because regardless of mechanism the X-O bond should be stronger in X—O than it is in X—OH. However, it is of interest that the rate of oxygen exchange with phosphate over the pH range 1–9 shows a maximum at about pH 5.[177] At this pH there is a maximum concentration of $H_2PO_4^-$, and it appears that this species exchanges more rapidly than does either HPO_4^{2-} or H_3PO_4. Much the same behavior is observed for the hydrolyses of monoalkyl esters of phosphoric acids, where $ROPO_3H^-$ is the most reactive species. It is suggested that since two protons (or one proton and one alkyl group) give the most reactive species, a dissociation process represented by

$$H_2PO_4^- \rightleftharpoons \underset{O\quad O}{\overset{\overset{\displaystyle H}{\overset{\displaystyle O \;|}{\underset{|}{\nearrow}} \; O}}{P}} \diagdown H \rightleftharpoons \underset{O\quad O}{\overset{O}{\overset{\|}{P}}} {}^- + H_2O \qquad (76)$$

is responsible.[179] The postulated metaphosphate anion intermediate is not known but is analogous to NO_3^- and may well be an active intermediate in these oxygen exchange reactions.

The sulfate ion does not undergo exchange at 100°C, the bisulfate ion exchanges slowly, and sulfuric acid exchanges rapidly.[178] This suggests, but does not prove, a unimolecular dissociation into H_2O and SO_3 as the slow step.

$$H_2SO_4 \rightarrow H_2O + SO_3 \qquad (77)$$

Although bimolecular displacements are by far the more common for tetrahedral systems, unimolecular dissociations must also occur in special cases.

Boron trihalides and bases readily form 1:1 molecular addition compounds:

$$\text{Base} + BX_3 \rightleftharpoons \text{Base}:BX_3 \tag{78}$$

Systems containing an excess either of base or of BX_3 rapidly undergo acid-base exchange, as do also systems initially containing two different addition compounds. Although this exchange is too rapid to be observed by conventional techniques, it may often be measured conveniently with n.m.r. methods. Several such studies have been made, and the results are contained in a review on the subject.[180] We shall describe only a few examples which are fairly typical and serve to illustrate the kind of information obtained and the problems involved.

By means of n.m.r. using ^{19}F resonance, the kinetics of the exchange of BF_3 between $(C_2H_5)_2OBF_3$ and $(CH_3)_2OBF_3$ was investigated.[181] The spectra of the mixed addition compounds are very simple, consisting at low temperatures of a pair of peaks which, as the temperature is raised, broaden, merge, and fuse to a single peak. This almost ideal behavior permits very rapid exchanges to be observed; under the most favorable conditions mean lifetimes, τ, as short as 1.5×10^{-5} sec were measured. In the temperature range of this study, the rate of exchange decreased as a larger portion of the ether was complexed.

The activation energy for exchange of BF_3 varied from 11 kcal/mole ($\tau = 3 \times 10^{-5}$ sec at $0°$) in those mixtures containing a significant excess of uncomplexed ether to 16 kcal/mole ($\tau = 7 \times 10^{-3}$ sec at $0°$) for mixtures in which the ether was completely complexed. The data thus indicate two modes of exchange. In the presence of excess ether the exchange process takes place by the replacement of one ether by another:

$$(CH_3)_2O \cdot BF_3 + (C_2H_5)_2O \rightleftharpoons (C_2H_5)_2O \cdot BF_3 + (CH_3)_2O \tag{79}$$

The exchange is presumed to proceed by a nucleophilic displacement on boron, since the activation energy of exchange is somewhat less than the heats of formation of the ether—BF_3 compounds.[182]

The higher activation energy exchange, for systems containing no excess ether, appears to involve a direct interchange of ether (or BF_3) between the two addition compounds:

$$(C_2H_5)_2O \cdot {}^*BF_3 + (CH_3)_2O \cdot BF_3 \rightleftharpoons (CH_3)_2O \cdot {}^*BF_3 + (C_2H_5)_2O \cdot BF_3$$

$$\tag{80}$$

The mechanism of this exchange is not known but could be a four-centered process through a diether bridged system, such as

$$
\begin{array}{c}
(C_2H_5)_2 \\
| \\
O \\
F_3\overset{*}{B} \diagup \quad \diagdown BF_3 \\
\diagdown \quad \diagup \\
O \\
| \\
(CH_3)_2
\end{array}
$$

There is no experimental evidence that requires this mechanism, but it appears plausible because it is analogous to displacements in other systems in solvents of low dielectric strength [Fig. 5.26 (2)]. Other alternatives can be suggested, including the dissociation of the addition compound to provide free ether, which can in turn react by the direct displacement process (79).

An interesting comparison of the exchanges between ether—BF_3 adducts can be made with those between alcohol—BF_3 adducts.[183] Values of τ at $0°$ were 9×10^{-4} sec at $BF_3/ROH = 0.8$ and 1×10^{-2} sec at $BF_3/ROH = 0.4$ for the system BF_3—CH_3OH—C_2H_5OH. The rate of exchange in the alcohol system increases rapidly with BF_3 content for mixtures of $BF_3/ROH > 0.5$. The effect of changing the BF_3 content thus is opposite in direction to that observed for the analogous ether adducts. This difference is explained in terms of hydrogen bonding in the alcohol systems. Thus, for $BF_3/ROH < 0.5$, dialcohol complexes of BF_3 are formed in which two alcohol molecules are associated through hydrogen bonding. With increasing BF_3/ROH ratios, progressively smaller mole fractions of the more stable BF_3-dialcohol adduct are present, qualitatively accounting for the increase in exchange rate.

Beryllium acetylacetonate, $Be(acac)_2$, can be cleaved by the addition of either acid or base:

$$
Be(acac)_2 + 2H^+ \rightarrow Be^{2+} + 2Hacac \tag{81}
$$

$$
Be(acac)_2 + 4OH^- \rightarrow Be(OH)_4^{2-} + 2acac^- \tag{82}
$$

The cleavage reactions are vey rapid, the half-lives being in the millisecond range, so that flow methods can be used to study the kinetics.[188] The acid cleavage (81) has a rate law

$$
Rate = k[Be(acac)_2][H^+] \tag{83}
$$

The role of the hydrogen ion again seems to be that of trapping a half-open chelate ring (see p. 218).

The surprising result is that adding various nucleophiles, such as F^-, Br^-, OAc^-, SCN^-, and hydroxylamine, scarcely affects the rate of the acid cleavage reaction.[188] Thus the expected S_N2 mechanism is not found. The explanation seems to be that the small size of the beryllium ion prevents the easy attainment of coordination number five, at least with the acetylacetonates as the other ligands. The complex behaves like an octahedral system, probably reacting by a solvent-assisted dissociation mechanism. Substitution reactions of $Be(H_2O)_4{}^{2+}$ with basic anions are complicated by the formation of $Be(H_2O)_3OH^+$.[150]

Redistribution or Scrambling Reactions

The exchange reactions described for these boron systems, although somewhat complicated, are relatively simple compared to some other ligand redistribution reactions that have been investigated. It is now abundantly clear that ligand scrambling between mixtures of different compounds is very common. Extensive investigations of these types of reactions have been made by Van Wazer and co-workers,[184] and a review of the subject has appeared.[180] Although a considerable amount of kinetic data has been collected on many different systems, these redistribution reactions are generally sufficiently complicated that it is difficult to reach definite conclusions as to their mechanisms. Only a few examples will be mentioned to illustrate the kind of information that is available.

Three types of intermolecular redistribution reactions are possible:

1. Ligand interchange

$$MX_n + MY_n \rightleftharpoons MX_{n-1}Y + MX_{n-1}X \rightleftharpoons \text{etc.} \tag{84}$$

2. Central atom interchange

$$MX_n + M'X_n \rightleftharpoons M'X_n + MX_n \tag{85}$$

3. Interchange of both

$$MX_n + M'Y_n \rightleftharpoons MX_{n-1}Y + M'Y_{n-1}X \rightleftharpoons \text{etc.} \tag{86}$$

A considerable amount of thermodynamic data is available for the various equilibria in such systems. For example hydrogen n.m.r. was used to determine the species at equilibrium in a mixture initially of $Si(OCH_3)_4$ and $SiCl_4$, and estimates of the equilibria constants were made. The results indicate that the mixed species $Si(OCH_3)_nCl_{4-n}$ are largely favored. However, ester interchange in $Si(OCH_3)_4$ and $Si(OC_2H_5)_4$ shows almost the expected equilibria for ideal random interchange. Deviation from random behavior is larger for the system $Si[N(CH_3)_2]_4$ *versus* $SiCl_4$ than for the corresponding methoxychloride system. This is similar to the situation found with the analogous phosphorus compounds. It is concluded that the central atom is of little importance and the ligands are of major importance in determining the equilibrium distribution of products.

There is also a considerable amount of kinetic data on these scrambling reactions. Some of the reactions are sufficiently slow to study by conventional techniques and even to permit the isolation of the various species at equilibrium.[185] However, in most cases the systems are labile, and rapid reaction techniques must be used to follow the rates of equilibration. In general the rates of scrambling for analogous compounds vary as follows: $Sn(IV) > Ge(IV) > Si(IV) \gg C(IV)$; $Tl(III) > Al(III)$; $As(III) > P(III)$, and for these central ions with different ligands the rates vary thus: halogens > esters > alkoxides > alkyls and $Br^- > Cl^- > F^-$. The variations in rate are the same as those found for ordinary substitution reactions in these systems. This is to be expected because the redistribution reactions are nothing more than a large number of substitution steps.

Many of the available kinetic data show that these scrambling reactions are second order, being first order in each of the two species involved. Studies[186] have been made on the kinetics of the first-step reactions in the systems $Sb(CH_3)_3$ *versus* $SbCl_3$, $Ti[N(CH_3)_2]_4$ *versus* $Ti[OC(CH_3)_3]_4$, and $Si(OCH_3)_4$ *versus* $SiCl_4$. The reaction

$$Sb(CH_3)_3 + SbCl_3 \rightleftharpoons (CH_3)_2SbCl + CH_3SbCl_2 \qquad (87)$$

in dimethylformamide has a second-order rate constant of 6.7×10^{-5} $M^{-1} sec^{-1}$ at 72°C, $E_a = 18$ kcal/mole, and $\Delta S^{\ddagger} = -25$ eu. The corresponding first step for the Ti(IV) system has the following kinetic parameters: k at 72°C $= 2.3 \times 10^{-4}$ $M^{-1} sec^{-1}$, $E_a = 10$ kcal/mole, and $\Delta S^{\ddagger} = -47$ eu. The suggestion is made that both systems react by a four-centered mechanism. That the Ti(IV) system has a much more negative entropy of activation than the Sb(III) system is attributed to the greater steric hindrance in the Ti(IV) compounds because of their larger coordination number and because of the larger size of their ligands. In support of this steric argument is the fact that if the less bulky isopropoxyl group is used in place of the *tert*-butoxyl, the reaction rate increases by more than five orders of magnitude. This is also good evidence in support of a mechanism that involves a nucleophilic attack on Ti(IV).

Summary

Since several different topics were discussed in this chapter, it is desirable to summarize by focusing attention on a main theme, which is the mechanism of substitution reactions of metal complexes having coordination numbers less than six. For transition metals most of the available information deals with square planar complexes of the low-spin d^8 type. However, for non-transition elements, there have been extensive studies of tetrahedral systems and some investigations of three- and five-coordinated systems. Except under certain special circumstances, all of these "low"-coordinated complexes react by means of a bimolecular displacement mechanism. This result is in direct contrast to that for octahedral substitution, discussed in Chapter 3, where it appears that dissociation processes play a primary role.

Such a result seems perfectly plausible, since "low"-coordinated systems can often very readily expand their coordination numbers. This would suggest that in addition to the three-, four-, and five-coordinated complexes described in this chapter one- and two-coordinated systems should also undergo bimolecular displacement reactions. Such is certainly the case for one- coordinated hydrogen compounds, as was shown by the early experiments of Bronsted.[83] An example of a two-coordinated compound is provided by reactions of the type

$$CH_3HgOH + Y^- \rightarrow CH_3HgY + OH^- \tag{88}$$

Kinetic studies[187] show that this reaction in water solution is second order, and the rate constant, k, M^{-1} sec^{-1}, at 25° has values of 1.1×10^4, 2.2×10^5, and 7.0×10^6 for $Y^- = Cl^-$, Br^-, I^-, respectively. The best nucleophile is I^-, which is also optimum for displacement reactions on a Pt(II) substrate. This is to be expected in view of the class (b) nature of CH_3Hg^+.

References

1. (a) D. P. Mellor, *Chem. Revs.*, **33**, 137 (1943). (b) J. V. Quagliano and L. Schubert, *ibid.*, **50**, 201 (1952). (c) A. A. Grinberg, *An Introduction to the Chemistry of Complex Compounds* (D. H. Busch and R. F. Trimble, Jr., eds.), Addison-Wesley, Reading, Mass., 1962, Chap. 5.
2. (a) F. Basolo and R. G. Pearson, *Progr. Inorg. Chem.* **4**, 318 (1962). (b) F. Basolo, *Advan. Chem. Ser.*, **49**, 81 (1965). (c) C. Langford and H. B. Gray, *Ligand Substitution Processes*, W. A. Benjamin, New York, 1966.
3. A. Werner, *Z. anorg. Chem.*, **3**, 267 (1893).
4. M. Peyrone, *Ann.*, **51**, 15 (1845).
5. J. Reiset, *Compt. rend.*, **18**, 1103 (1844).
6. S. M. Jørgensen, *J. prakt. Chem.*, **33**, 489 (1886).
7. F. Basolo, M. Lederer, L. Ossicini, and K. H. Stephen, *Ric. Sci.* (II-A), **32**, 485 (1962).
8. I. I. Chernyaev, *Ann. inst. platine USSR.*, **4**, 261 (1926).

9. I. I. Chernyaev, *Ann. inst. platine USSR.*, **4,** 243 (1926); **5,** 102, 118 (1927); **6,** 55 (1928).
10. A. D. Hel'man, E. F. Karandashova, and L. N. Essen, *Dokl. Akad. Nauk SSSR.*, **63,** 37 (1948).
11. N. S. Kurnakow, *J. prakt. Chem.*, **50,** 483 (1894).
12. D. I. Ryabchikov, *Compt. rend. acad. sci. URSS.*, **32,** 344 (1941).
13. J. Chatt, L. A. Duncanson, and L. M. Venanzi, *J. Chem. Soc.*, **1955,** 4456.
14. Report of Conference Organizing Committee, *Izv. Sektora Platiny i Drug. Blagorodn. Metal. Inst. Obshch. Neorgan. Khim. Akad. Nauk SSSR.*, **28,** 12 (1954); I. I. Chernyaev, *Zh. Neorgan. Khim.*, **2,** 475 (1957).
15. F. Basolo, E. J. Bounsall, and A. J. Poë, *Proc. Chem. Soc.*, **1963,** 366.
16. M. A. Tucker, C. B. Colvin, and D. S. Martin, Jr., *Inorg. Chem.* **3,** 1373 (1964), and references cited therein.
17. I. I. Chernyaev, V. A. Palkin, R. A. Baranova, and N. N. Kuzmina, *Zh. Neorgan. Khim.*, **5,** 1428 (1960).
18. J. Chatt and R. G. Wilkins, *J. Chem. Soc.*, **1952,** 273 4300; **1953,** 70; **1956,** 525.
19. A. V. Nikolaev and A. M. Rubinstein, *Bull. Sect. Platinum*, **21,** 125 (1948).
20. A. E. Martell and L. G. Sillen, *Stability Constants of Metal-Ion Complexes*, The Chemical Society, London (Special Publication No. 17), 1964.
21. J. Chatt and I. Leden, *J. Chem. Soc.*, **1955,** 2936; J. Chatt and G. A. Gamlen, *ibid.*, **1956,** 2371.
22. S. S. Batsanov, *Zh. Neorgan. Khim.*, **2,** 2553 (1957); *J. Inorg. Chem. (USSR)*, **4,** 773 (1959).
23. J. A. Wunderlich and D. P. Mellor, *Acta Cryst.*, **7,** 130 (1954); **8,** 57 (1955).
24. G. B. Bakii and G. A. Kukina, *Akad. Nauk SSSR Krist.*, **2,** 400 (1957).
25. P. G. Owston, J. M. Partridge, and J. M. Rowe *Acta Cryst.*, **13,** 246 (1960).
26. S. C. Abrahams, A. P. Ginsberg, and K. Knox, *Inorg. Chem.*, **3,** 558 (1964).
27. S. J. LaPlaca and J. A. Ibers, *Acta Cryst.*, **18,** 511 (1965).
28. R. Eisenberg and J. A. Ibers, *Inorg. Chem.*, **4,** 773 (1965).
29. G. G. Messmer, E. L. Amma, and J. A. Ibers, *Inorg. Chem.*, in press.
30. G. G. Messmer and E. L. Amma, *Inorg. Chem.*, **5,** 1775 (1966).
31. P. R. H. Alderman, P. G. Owston, and J. M. Rowe, *Acta Cryst.*, **13,** 149 (1960). See also G. H. W. Milburn and M. R. Truter, *J. Chem. Soc.* **1966A,** 1609.
32. J. Chatt, L. Duncanson, B. Shaw, and L. Venanzi, *Disc. Faraday Soc.*, **26,** 131 (1958); D. M. Adams, J. Chatt, and B. Shaw, *J. Chem. Soc.*, **1960,** 2047.
33. K. Nakamoto, P. J. McCarthy, J. Fujita, R. A. Condrate, and G. T. Behnke, *Inorg. Chem.*, **4,** 36 (1965).
34. D. B. Powell, *J. Chem. Soc.*, **1956,** 4495.
35. (a) D. M. Adams, J. Chatt, J. Gerratt, and A. D. Nestland, *J. Chem. Soc.*, **1964,** 734. (b) J. M. Jenkins and B. L. Shaw, *ibid.*, **1965,** 6789.
36. J. Chatt and B. L. Shaw, *J. Chem. Soc.*, **1962,** 5075.
37. R. V. Lindsey, Jr., G. W. Parshall, and U. G. Stolberg, *J. Am. Chem. Soc.*, **87,** 568 (1965).
38. R. D. Cramer, E. L. Jenner, R. V. Lindsey, Jr., and U. G. Stolberg, *J. Am. Chem. Soc.*, **85,** 1691 (1963); A. G. Davies, G. Wilkinson, and J. F. Young, *ibid.*, **85,** 1692 (1963).
39. R. Cramer, *Inorg. Chem.*, **4,** 445 (1965).
40. S. I. Shupack and M. Orchin, *J. Am. Chem. Soc.*, **85,** 902 (1963).
41. G. W. Parshall, *J. Am. Chem. Soc.*, **86,** 5367 (1964); **88,** 704 (1966).
42. F. A. Cotton, *Inorg. Chem.*, **3,** 702 (1964).

43. R. W. Taft, E. Price, I. R. Fox, I. C. Lewis, K. K. Anderson, and G. T. Davis, *J. Am. Chem. Soc.*, **85**, 709, 3146 (1963).

44. A. A. Grinberg and D. I. Ryabshikov, *Acta Physicochim. USSR*, **3**, 55 (1935); K. A. Jensen, *Z. anorg. Chem.*, **242**, 87 (1939).

45. J. W. Palmer and F. Basolo, *J. Phys. Chem.*, **64**, 778 (1960).

46. A. A. Grinberg, *Acta Physicochim. USSR*, **3**, 573 (1935).

47. F. Basolo, J. Chatt, H. B. Gray, R. G. Pearson, and B. L. Shaw, *J. Chem. Soc.*, **1961**, 2207.

48. Y. K. Syrkin, *Bull. acad. sci. USSR Classe sci. chim.*, 69 (1948); *C.A.*, **42**, 5368 (1948); H. M. E. Cardwell, *Chem. & Ind.*, **1955**, 422.

49. L. Pauling, *The Nature of the Chemical Bond*, Cornell University Press, Ithaca, N.Y., 3rd ed., 1960, p. 332.

50. J. Chatt, L. A. Duncanson, and L. M. Venanzi, *J. Chem. Soc.*, **1955**, (1955); L. E. Orgel, *J. Inorg. Nucl. Chem.*, **2**, 137 (1956).

51. J. Chatt, G. A. Gamlen, and L. E. Orgel, *J. Chem. Soc.*, **1958**, 486; R. F. Fenske, D. S. Martin, Jr., and K. Ruedenberg, *Inorg. Chem.*, **1**, 441 (1962); J. R. Perumareddi, A. D. Liehr, and A. W. Adamson, *J. Am. Chem. Soc.*, **85**, 249 (1963); H. B. Gray and C. J. Ballhausen, *ibid.*, **85**, 260 (1963).

52. C. M. Harris and S. E. Livingstone, *Rev. Pure Appl. Chem.*, **12**, 16 (1962); L. M. Venanzi, *Angew. Chem. Intern. Ed. Engl.*, **3**, 453 (1964).

53. J. A. Ibers, *Ann. Rev. Phys. Chem.*, **16**, 380 (1965); E. L. Muetterties and R. A. Schunn, *Quart. Rev. (London)*, **20**, 245 (1966).

54. J. S. Coleman, H. Petersen, Jr., and R. A. Penneman, *Inorg. Chem.*, **4**, 135 (1965).

55. K. N. Raymond and F. Basolo, *Inorg. Chem.*, **5**, 949 (1966).

56. C. M. Harris, R. S. Nyholm, and D. J. Phillips, *J. Chem. Soc.*, **1960**, 4379.

57. N. C. Stephenson, *J. Inorg. Nucl. Chem.*, **24**, 791 (1963); *Acta Cryst.*, **17**, 1517 (1964).

58. M. Angaletta, *Gazz. Chim. Ital.*, **89**, 2359 (1959); **90**, 1021 (1960).

59. S. S. Bath and L. Vaska, *J. Am. Chem. Soc.*, **85**, 3500 (1963).

60. J. A. Brewster, C. A. Savage, and L. M. Venanzi, *J. Chem. Soc.*, **1961**, 3699; G. A. Mair, H. M. Powell, and L. M. Venanzi, *Proc. Chem. Soc.*, **1961**, 170; J. G. Hartley, L. M. Venanzi, and D. C. Goodale, *J. Chem. Soc.*, **1963**, 3930.

61. R. D. Cramer, R. V. Lindsey, Jr., C. T. Prewitt, and U. G. Stollberg, *J. Am. Chem. Soc.*, **87**, 658 (1965).

62. O. E. Zvyagintsev and E. F. Karandasheva, *Dokl. Akad. Nauk SSSR*, **101**, 93 (1955).

63. A. A. Grinberg, *J. Inorg. Chem. (USSR)*, **4**, 683 (1959); I. B. Bersuker, *J. Struct. Chem.*, **4**, 419 (1963).

64. A. A. Grinberg and L. E. Nikol'skoya, *Zh. Prikl. Khim.*, **22**, 542 (1949); **24**, 893 (1951).

65. A. A. Grinberg and S. S. Borzokova, *J. Inorg. Chem. (USSR)*, **2**, 2368 (1957); A. K. Grinberg and E. N. Inkova, *ibid.*, **3**, 135 (1958).

66. F. Basolo, H. B. Gray, and R. G. Pearson, *J. Am. Chem. Soc.*, **82**, 4200 (1960).

67. U. Belluco, R. Ettore, F. Basolo, R. G. Pearson, and A. Turco, *Inorg. Chem.*, **5**, 591 (1966).

68. D. R. Llewellyn, C. J. O'Connor, and A. L. Odell, *J. Chem. Soc.*, **1964**, 196.

69. H. B. Gray and R. J. Olcott, *Inorg. Chem.*, **1**, 481 (1962).

70. H. B. Gray, *J. Am. Chem. Soc.*, **84**, 1548 (1962).

71. U. Belluco, L. Cattalini, F. Basolo, R. G. Pearson, and A. Turco, *J. Am. Chem. Soc.*, **87**, 241 (1965).

72. (a) R. G. Pearson, H. B. Gray, and F. Basolo, *J. Am. Chem. Soc.*, **82**, 787 (1960). (b) B. Bosnich, *Nature*, **196**, 1196 (1962), suggested amphililic. See also L. Cattalini, A. Orio and M. Nicolini, *J. Am. Chem. Soc.* **88**, 5734 (1966).

73. R. Wanguo, Master's thesis, Northwestern University, Evanston, Ill., 1965.

74. R. G. Pearson, M. M. Muir, and L. M. Venanzi, *J. Chem. Soc.* **1965**, 5521.

75. F. A. Cotton and R. Francis, *J. Am. Chem. Soc.*, **82**, 2986 (1960); D. W. Meek, D. K. Straub, and R. S. Drago, *ibid.*, **82**, 6013 (1960).

76. D. Banerjea, F. Basolo, and R. G. Pearson, *J. Am. Chem. Soc.*, **79**, 4055 (1957).

77. H. B. Gray, Ph.D. dissertation, Northwestern University, Evanston, Ill., 1960.

78. U. Belluco, L. Cattalini, F. Basolo, R. G. Pearson, and A. Turco, *Inorg. Chem.*, **4**, 925 (1965).

79. W. H. Baddley, F. Basolo, H. B. Gray, C. Nolting, and A. J. Poë, *Inorg. Chem.*, **2**, 921 (1963); W. H. Baddley and F. Basolo, *ibid.*, **3**, 1087 (1964).

80. J. E. Leffler and E. Grunwald, *Rates and Equilibria of Organic Reactions*, John Wiley and Sons, New York, 1963; A. A. Frost and R. G. Pearson, *Kinetics and Mechanism*, John Wiley and Sons, New York, 2nd ed., 1961.

81. J. O. Edwards and R. G. Pearson, *J. Am. Chem. Soc.*, **84**, 16 (1962).

82. R. G. Pearson, *J. Am. Chem. Soc.*, **85**, 3533 (1963).

83. J. N. Brønsted, *J. Am. Chem. Soc.*, **51**, 428 (1929).

84. C. G. Swain and C. B. Scott, *J. Am. Chem. Soc.*, **85**, 141 (1953).

85. (a) J. O. Edwards, *J. Am. Chem. Soc.*, **76**, 1540 (1954); **78**, 1819 (1956). (b) D. H. McDaniel and A. Yingst, *ibid.*, **86**, 1334 (1964). (c) R. E. Davis, *ibid.*, **87**, 3010 (1965).

86. A. J. Parker, *Quart. Rev.* (*London*), **16**, 163 (1962); J. F. Bunnett, *Ann. Rev. Phys. Chem.*, 271 (1963). B. W. Clare, D. Cook, E. C. F. Ko, Y. C. Mac and A. J. Parker, *J. Am. Chem. Soc.*, **88**, 1911 (1966).

87. U. Belluco, M. Martelli, and A. Orio, *Inorg. Chem.*, **5**, 582, 1125, 1370 (1966).

88. P. Haake and P. A. Cronin, *Inorg. Chem.*, **2**, 879 (1963).

89. (a) B. Capon, *Quart. Rev.* (*London*), **18**, 45 (1964). (b) F. Basolo and K. H. Stephen, *Inorg. Nucl. Chem. Letts.*, **2**, 23 (1966).

90. J. E. Teggins and R. M. Milburn, *Inorg. Chem.*, **3**, 364 (1964); **4**, 793 (1965).

91. J. Chatt and L. M. Venanzi, *J. Chem. Soc.*, **1955**, 2787, 3858; C. M. Harris, S. E. Livingstone, and N. C. Stephenson, *ibid.*, **1958**, 3697; S. E. Livingstone and A. Whitley, *Aust. J. Chem.*, **15**, 175 (1962).

92. R. G. Pearson and M. M. Muir, *J. Am. Chem. Soc.*, **88**, 2163 (1966).

93. (a) S. J. Lokken and D. S. Martin, Jr., *Inorg. Chem.*, **3**, 562 (1963); (b) D. S. Martin, Jr., private communication.

94. (a) R. L. Rich and H. Taube, *J. Am. Chem. Soc.*, **76**, 2608 (1954). (b) *J. Phys. Chem.*, **58**, 1, 6 (1954). (c) V. P. Kazakov, *Zh. Neorgan. Khim.*, **10(5)**, 1276 (1965). (d) F. H. Fry, G. A. Hamilton, and J. Turkevich, *ibid.*, **5**, 1943 (1966).

95. L. F. Grantham, T. S. Elleman, and D. S. Martin, Jr., *J. Am. Chem. Soc.*, **77**, 2965 (1955).

96. (a) L. Cattalini and M. L. Tobe, *Inorg. Chem.*, **5**, 1145, 1674 (1966). (b) C. F. Weick and F. Basolo, *ibid.*, **5**, 576 (1966).

97. P. Beran and A. A. Vlcek, *Collection Czech. Chem. Commun.*, **24**, 3572 (1959).

98. W. H. Baddley and F. Basolo, *J. Am. Chem. Soc.*, **86**, 2075 (1964); **88**, 2944 (1966).

99. R. G. Pearson and D. A. Johnson, *J. Am. Chem. Soc.*, **86**, 3983 (1964). 2944

100. R. G. Wilkins and M. Eigen, *Advan. Chem. Ser.*, **49**, 55 (1965).

101. A. W. Adamson, J. P. Welker, and M. Volpe, *J. Am. Chem. Soc.*, **72**, 4030 (1950).

102. F. A. Long, *J. Am. Chem. Soc.*, **73**, 537 (1951).

103. R. K. Murmann, *Inorg. Chem.*, **2**, 116 (1963); D. L. Lewis and R. K. Murmann, *J. Inorg. Nucl. Chem.*, **25**, 1431 (1963).

104. R. G. Wilkins, *J. Chem. Soc.*, **1957**, 4521.

105. J. B. Willis and D. P. Mellor, *J. Am. Chem. Soc.*, **69**, 1237 (1947); F. Basolo and W. R. Matoush, *ibid.*, **75**, 5663 (1953).

106. L. Sacconi, G. Lombardo, and P. Paoletti, *J. Chem. Soc.*, **1958**, 848; L. Sacconi, G. Lombardo, and R. Ciofalo, *J. Am. Chem. Soc.*, **82**, 4182, 4185, 6266 (1960).

107. R. L. Carlin, J. S. Dubnoff, and W. T. Huntress, *Proc. Chem. Soc.*, **1964**, 228.

108. L. Vallerino, *J. Chem. Soc.*, **1957**, 2287.

109. A. Wojcicki and F. Basolo, *J. Am. Chem. Soc.*, **83**, 525 (1961).

110. A. Wojcicki and H. B. Gray, *Proc. Chem. Soc.*, **1960**, 358; *Abstracts 141st National Meeting of the American Chemical Society*, Washington, D.C., 1962, p. 32M.

111. R. Cramer, *J. Am. Chem. Soc.*, **86**, 217 (1964).

112. T. J. Swift and R. E. Connick, *J. Chem. Phys.*, **37**, 307 (1962).

113. R. G. Pearson and R. D. Lanier, *J. Am. Chem. Soc.*, **86**, 765 (1964); R. G. Pearson and M. M. Anderson, *Angew. Chem.*, **4**, 281 (1965).

114. W. H. Mills and T. H. H. Quibell, *J. Chem. Soc.*, **1935**, 839.

115. A. F. Messing and F. Basolo, *J. Am. Chem. Soc.*, **78**, 4511 (1956).

116. K. A. Jensen, *Z. anorg. allgem. Chem.*, **229**, 265 (1936); W. Klemm and K. H. Raddatz, *ibid.*, **250**, 207 (1942); F. G. Mann, D. Crowfoot, D. Gottiker, and N. Wooster, *J. Chem. Soc.*, **1935**, 1642.

117. S. Sugden, *J. Chem. Soc.*, **1932**, 246; H. J. Cavell and S. Sugden, *ibid.*, **1935**, 621.

118. F. P. Dwyer and D. P. Mellor, *J. Am. Chem. Soc.*, **57**, 605 (1935).

119. H. D. K. Drew and G. H. Wyatt, *J. Chem. Soc.*, **1934**, 56.

120. R. S. Nyholm, *Chem. Revs.*, **53**, 263 (1953).

121. (a) G. Dyer, J. G. Hartley, and L. M. Venanzi, *J. Chem. Soc.*, **1965**, 1293; G. S Benner, W. E. Hatfield, and D. W. Meek, *Inorg. Chem.*, **3**, 1544 (1964). (b) G. A. Mair, H. M. Powell, and D. E. Henn, *Proc. Chem. Soc.*, **1960**, 415.

122. (a) M. Ciampoline and N. Nardi, *Inorg. Chem.*, **5**, 41 (1966). (b) L. Sacconi, P. Nannelli, N. Nardi, and U. Campigli, *Inorg. Chem.*, **4**, 943 (1965).

123. N. S. Gill and R. S. Nyholm, *J. Chem. Soc.*, **1959**, 3997.

124. D. R. Eaton, A. D. Josey, R. E. Benson, W. D. Phillips, and T. L. Cairns, *J. Am Chem. Soc.*, **84**, 4100 (1962), and references therein.

125. D. P. Mellor and D. P. Craig, *J. Proc. Roy. Soc. N.S. Wales*, **74**, 475 (1941); H. S. French, M. Z. Magee, and E. Sheffield, *J. Am. Chem. Soc.*, **64**, 1924 (1942); H. C. Clark and A. L. Odell, *J. Chem. Soc.*, **1956**, 520.

126. H. Hartmann and H. Fischer-Wasels, *Z. physik. Chem.*, **4**, 5 (1955); G. Maki, *J. Chem. Phys.*, **28**, 651 (1958); **29**, 162, 1129 (1958); C. J. Ballhausen and A. D. Liehr, *J. Am. Chem. Soc.*, **81**, 538 (1959).

127. L. Sacconi, P. Paoletti and G. Del Re, *J. Am. Chem. Soc.*, **79**, 4062 (1957); L. Sacconi, P. Paoletti, and R. Cini, *J. Inorg. Nucl. Chem.*, **8**, 492 (1958); *J. Am. Chem. Soc.*, **80**, 3583 (1958); L. Sacconi, R. Cini, M. Ciampolini, and F. Maggio, *ibid.*, **82**, 3487 (1960).

128. R. H. Holm and T. M. McKinney, *J. Am. Chem. Soc.*, **82**, 5506 (1960); R. H. Holm, *ibid.*, **83**, 4683 (1961); R. H. Holm and K. Swaminathan, *Inorg. Chem.*, **1**, 599 (1962).

129. F. A. Cotton and J. P. Fackler, Jr., *J. Am. Chem. Soc.*, **83**, 2818, 3775 (1961).

130. D. P. Graddon and E. C. Watton, *Nature*, **190**, 906 (1961).

131. L. Sacconi, P. L. Orioli, P. Paoletti, and M. Ciampolini, *Proc. Chem. Soc.*, **1962**, 255; L. Sacconi, P. Paoletti, and M. Ciampolini, *J. Am. Chem. Soc.*, **85**, 411 (1963); L. Sacconi, *J. Chem. Soc.*, **1963**, 4608; L. Sacconi and M. Ciampolini, *J. Am. Chem.*

Soc., **85**, 1750 (1963); L. Sacconi, M. Ciampolini, *ibid.*, **86**, 819 (1964); J. D. Thwaites and L. Sacconi, *Inorg. Chem.*, **5**, 1029, 1036 (1966).

132. R. H. Holm and K. Swaminathan, *Inorg. Chem.*, **2**, 181 (1963); A. Chakravorty and R. H. Holm, *ibid.*, **3**, 1010 (1964); R. H. Holm, A. Chakravorty, and G. O. Dudek, *J. Am. Chem. Soc.*, **86**, 379 (1964); A. Chakrovorty, J. P. Fennessey and R. H. Holm, *Inorg. Chem.*, **4**, 26 (1965); G. W. Everett, Jr. and R. H. Holm, *J. Am. Chem. Soc.*, **88**, 2442 (1966).

133. M. R. Fox, E. C. Lingafelter, P. L. Orioli, and L. Sacconi, *Nature*, **197**, 1104 (1963).

134. D. R. Eaton, W. D. Phillips, and D. J. Caldwell, *J. Am. Chem. Soc.*, **85**, 397 (1963).

135. L. M. Venanzi, *J. Chem. Soc.*, **1958**, 719; *ibid.*, **1961**, 2705; M. C. Browning, R. F. B. Davies, D. J. Morgan, L. E. Sutton, and L. M. Venanzi, *ibid.*, **1961**, 4816; F. A. Cotton, O. D. Faut, and D. M. L. Goodgame, *J. Am. Chem. Soc.*, **83**, 344 (1961).

136. R. G. Hayter and F. S. Humiec, *Inorg. Chem.*, **4**, 1701 (1965).

137. E. A. LeLancette and D. R. Eaton, *J. Am. Chem. Soc.*, **86**, 5145 (1964).

138. R. G. Duffield and M. Calvin, *J. Am. Chem. Soc.*, **68**, 557 (1946); B. O. West, *J. Chem. Soc.*, **1952**, 3115 and **1954**, 395, 573; N. F. Hall and B. R. Willeford, *J. Am. Chem. Soc.*, **73**, 5419 (1951); H. C. Clark and A. L. Odell, *J. Chem. Soc.*, **1955**, 3435.

139. A. Chakravorty and R. H. Holm, *J. Am. Chem. Soc.*, **86**, 3999 (1964).

140. H. W. Gutowsky, D. W. McCall, and C. P. Slichter, *J. Chem. Phys.*, **21**, 279 (1953); H. S. Gutowsky and A. D. Liehr, *ibid.*, **20**, 1652 (1953).

141. R. S. Berry, *J. Chem. Phys.*, **32**, 933 (1960).

142. F. A. Cotton, A. Danti, J. S. Waugh, and R. W. Fessenden, *J. Chem. Phys.*, **29**, 1427 (1958); R. Bramley, B. N. Figgis, and R. S. Nyholm, *Trans, Faraday Soc.*, **58**, 1893 (1962).

143. E. L. Muetterties, W. Mahler, and R. Schmutzler, *Inorg. Chem.*, **2**, 613 (1963); E. L. Muetterties, W. Mahler, K. J. Packer and R. Schmutzler, *ibid.*, **3**, 1298 (1964).

144. F. B. Dudley, J. N. Shoolery, and G. H. Cady, *J. Am. Chem. Soc.*, **78**, 568 (1956).

145. E. L. Muetterties, *Inorg. Chem.*, **4**, 769 (1965).

146. J. L. Hoard and H. H. Nordsieck, *J. Am. Chem. Soc.*, **61**, 2853 (1939).

147. H. S. Stammreich and O. Sala, *Z. Elektrochem.*, **65**, 149 (1961).

148. J. L. Hoard and J. V. Silverton, *Inorg. Chem.*, **2**, 235 (1963).

149. A. D. Liehr, *J. Phys. Chem.*, **67**, 471 (1963).

150. M. Eigen, "Seventh International Conference on Coordination Chemistry, Stockholm, 1962," *Pure Appl. Chem.*, **6**, No. 1, 97 (1963); see also reference 38, Chap. 3.

151. D. H. Busch and J. C. Bailar, Jr., *J. Am. Chem. Soc.*, **76**, 5352 (1954).

152. J. C. I. Lin and J. C. Bailar, Jr., *J. Am. Chem. Soc.*, **73**, 5432 (1951).

153. H. H. Zeiss and C. N. Matthews, *J. Am. Chem. Soc.*, **78**, 1694 (1956).

154. M. Anbar, I. Dostrovsky, D. Samuel, and A. D. Yoffe, *J. Chem. Soc.*, **1954**, 3603.

155. B. Chance, *J. Franklin Inst.*, **229**, 758 (1940).

156. A. Lifshitz and B. Perlmutter-Hayman, *J. Phys. Chem.*, **65**, 2098 (1961); *ibid.*, **69**, 1736 (1965).

157. (a) P. Moore, S. F. A. Kettle, and R. G. Wilkins, *Inorg. Chem.*, **5**, 220 (1966). (b) J. H Swinehart and G. W. Castellan, *Inorg. Chem.*, **3**, 278 (1964).

158. B. Figgis, R. G. Kidd, and R. S. Nyholm, *Can. J. Chem.*, **43**, 145 (1965).

159. J. Y. Corey and R. West, *J. Am. Chem. Soc.*, **85**, 4034 (1963).

160. W. C. Hamilton, S. J. LaPlaca, and F. Ramirez, *J. Am. Chem. Soc.*, **87**, 127 (1965).

161. L. H. Sommer and C. L. Frye, *J. Am. Chem. Soc.*, **81**, 1013 (1959).

162. L. H. Sommer, *Stereochemistry, Mechanism and Silicon*, McGraw-Hill, Book Co., New York, 1965.

163. C. G. Swain, R. M. Esteve, Jr., and R. H. Jones, *J. Am. Chem. Soc.*, **71**, 965 (1949).

164. E. Akerman, *Acta Chem. Scand.*, **10**, 298 (1956).

165. A. D. Allen, J. C. Charlton, C. Eaborn, and G. Modena, *J. Chem. Soc.*, **1957**, 3668; A. D. Allen and G. Modena, *ibid.*, **1957**, 3671.

166. C. Eaborn and S. H. Parker, *J. Chem. Soc.*, **1955**, 126.

167. R. H. Prince, *J. Chem. Soc.*, **1959**, 1783; J. R. Chipperfield and R. H. Prince, *ibid.*, **1963**, 3567.

168. J. A. Bedford, J. R. Bolton, A. Carrington, and R. H. Prince, *Trans. Faraday Soc.*, **59**, 53 (1963).

169. R. D. O'Brien, *Toxic Phosphorus Esters*, Academic Press, New York, 1960.

170. E. M. Kosower, *Molecular Biochemistry*, McGraw-Hill Book Co., New York. 1962; R. F. Hudson, *Angew. Chem.*, **75**, 47 (1963); R. F. Hudson, *Structure and Mechanism in Organo-Phosphorus Chemistry*, Academic Press, London, 1965.

171. A. L. Green, G. L. Sainsbury, B. Saville, and M. Stansfield, *J. Chem. Soc.*, **1958**, 1583; I. Dostrovsky and M. Halmann, *ibid.*, **1953**, 502, 508, 511, 516; G. Aksnes, *Acta Chem. Scand.*, **14**, 1515 (1960).

172. L. Larsson, *Svensk Kem. Tidskr.*, **70**, 405 (1959).

173. H. S. Aaron, R. T. Uyeda, H. F. Frock, and J. I. Miller, *J. Am. Chem. Soc.*, **84**, 617 (1962).

174. J. F. Bunnett and J. Y. Bossett, *J. Am. Chem. Soc.*, **81**, 2104 (1959).

175. R. L. Burwell, Jr., *J. Am. Chem. Soc.*, **74**, 1462 (1952).

176. A. J. Parker and N. Kharasch, *Chem. Revs.*, **59**, 583 (1959); W. A. Pryor, *Mechanisms of Sulfur Reactions*, McGraw-Hill Book Co., New York, 1962.

177. C. A. Bunton, D. R. Llewellyn, C. A. Vernon, and V. A. Welch, *J. Chem. Soc.*, **1961**, 1636.

178. S. C. Data, J. N. E. Day, and C. K. Ingold, *J. Chem. Soc.*, **1937**, 1968; G. A. Mills, *J. Am. Chem. Soc.*, **62**, 2837 (1940); T. C. Hoering and J. W. Kennedy, *ibid.*, **79**, 56 (1957).

179. J. O. Edwards, *Inorganic Reaction Mechanisms*, W. A. Benjamin, New York, 1964, p. 146.

180. J. C. Lockhart, *Chem. Revs.*, **65**, 131 (1965).

181. A. C. Rutenberg, A. A. Palko, and J. S. Drury, *J. Am. Chem. Soc.*, **85**, 2702 (1963).

182. D. E. McLaughlin and M. Tamres, *J. Am. Chem. Soc.*, **82**, 5618 (1906).

183. P. Diehl, *Helv. Phys. Acta*, **31**, 685 (1958).

184. K. Moedritzer and J. Van Wazer, *J. Am. Chem. Soc.*, **86**, 802 (1964); *J. Chem. Phys.*, **41**, 3122 (1964); *Inorg. Chem.*, **4**, 893, 1753 (1965).

185. K. Moedritzer and J. Van Wazer, *Inorg. Chem.*, **3**, 268 (1964).

186. H. Weingarten and J. R. Van Wazer, *J. Am. Chem. Soc.*, **87**, 724 (1965); **88**, 2700 (1966).

187. M. Eigen, G. Geier, and W. Kruse, *Essays in Coordination Chemistry* (W. Schneider, G. Anderegg, and R. Gut, eds.), Birkhauser Verlag, Basel, 1964.

188. J. W. Moore and R. G. Pearson, *Inorg. Chem.* **5**, 1528 (1966).

189. U. Bellucco, *Coordination Chemistry Reviews*, Elsevier Publishing Co., New York, 1966, p. 111.

190. E. A. Dennis and F. H. Westheimer, *J. Am. Chem. Soc.*, **88**, 3431, 3432 (1966).

6

Oxidation-Reduction Reactions

The classical definition of oxidation and reduction in terms of gain or loss of oxygen has in modern times been abandoned in favor of the concept of electron loss (oxidation) and electron gain (reduction). It is now customary to discuss an oxidative process in terms of an ion-electron or half-cell equation, e.g.,

$$Fe^{2+} \rightarrow Fe^{3+} + e \tag{1}$$

The implication that redox reactions occur by coupled electron-loss and electron-gain steps may be quite incorrect as far as mechanism is concerned. Operationally we define oxidation-reduction reactions in terms of changes in oxidation states or oxidation numbers. The alleged transfer of electrons is a book keeping device for effecting the changes in oxidation states and for balancing the equations. Since the oxidation states are themselves calculated according to an arbitrary and sometimes unrealistic set of rules, there may be little relation between what is shown in the two half-cell equations representing a redox reaction and what actually occurs when the reagents are mixed.

For example, the reaction of a halogen with alkali such as

$$I_2 + OH^- \rightarrow I^- + IOH \tag{2}$$

is clearly an oxidation-reduction reaction by the usual rules (the oxidation number of iodine changing from zero to $+1$ and -1. Mechanistically, however, this reaction can be classified as a typical S_N2 reaction with the nucleophile hydroxide ion displacing iodide ion from the electrophile iodonium ion, I^+. Or it can be considered a typical acid-base reaction involving the Lewis acid I^+. Edwards[1] has a discussion of many redox reactions considered as displacement processes.

Particularly in aqueous solution it is usually possible to imagine atom or group transfer, rather than electron transfer, as occurring in a redox reaction. For example, Fe(II) ion may act as a reducing agent by transferring a hydrogen atom from its hydration shell to a substrate:

$$Fe(H_2O)_6^{2+} + R\cdot \rightarrow Fe(H_2O)_5OH^{2+} + RH \tag{3}$$

Iron(III) ion may act as oxidizing agent by transferring hydroxyl radical to a substrate:

$$Fe(H_2O)_6{}^{3+} + R\cdot \rightarrow Fe(H_2O)_5{}^{2+} + H^+ + ROH \qquad (4)$$

In general, transfer of a positive group or atom is equivalent to the transfer of electrons, and transfer of a negative group or atom is equivalent to the taking up of electrons.

The problem, then, in studying the mechanism of an oxidation-reduction reaction, is to find out whether atom transfer or electron transfer occurs, which atoms are transferred or how many electrons are transferred, and what intermediates, stable or unstable, are formed. A complete study would include a detailed picture of the transition state for all steps involved. Not only the composition but also the geometry of the transition state is desired.

As we shall see, two general classes of transition states emerge for redox reactions involving metal complexes, the so-called *"outer-sphere"* and *"inner-sphere"* types.[2] In the first of these, the inner coordination shells of both metal ions are intact in the transition state. In the second case, the two metal ions are connected through a bridging ligand common to both coordination shells. In both cases either atom or electron transfer can occur. It is also possible that outer-sphere reactions can have weak bridging groups connecting the two coordination shells.

Electron Transfer Reactions

In view of the preceding discussion it is fair to raise the question as to whether or not simple electron transfer reactions exist. For gaseous systems the evidence is clear that direct electron transfer between molecules does occur.[3] In a number of cases the probability of transfer, expressed as a collision diameter, is known. Even monatomic molecules can have large effective diameters for accepting an electron in certain cases. The values found can be several times the diameters determined by viscosity measurements.[4]

In particular electron transfer is very efficient when occurring between a rare gas molecule and its ion,

$$A + A^+ \rightarrow A^+ + A \qquad (5)$$

This efficiency is due to the operation of a quantum mechanical resonance effect. The modern picture of an electron in an atomic orbit as an electron cloud with charge density falling off with distance from the nucleus enables us to understand how it may occasionally be found far from the nucleus. However, even if an electron comes much closer to another nucleus than to its original parent, it will only transfer if the law of conservation of energy can be maintained. This condition exists if the two atoms, except for the transferring electron, are identical, as in reaction 5.

The transition probability is calculated from time-dependent perturbation theory:[5]

$$P(t) = \sin^2(2\pi H_{12}t/h) \tag{6}$$

H_{12} is the exchange integral between the initial state with wave function ϕ_1 and the final state with wave function ϕ_2.

$$H_{12} = \int \phi_1 \hat{H} \phi_2 \, d\tau \tag{7}$$

$\hat{H}$ is the Hamiltonian of the transferring electron. Hence an electron initially in the orbital described by ϕ_1 will oscillate back and forth between it and the orbital described by ϕ_2 with a frequency $\nu = 2H_{12}/h$, or the interaction energy divided by Planck's constant. Since the interaction energy depends on the extent to which the orbitals centered on the two nuclei overlap each other, we see that the rate of electron transfer is large for two orbitals which occupy much the same region in space. There are also symmetry restrictions depending on the sign of the wave function associated with the orbital and the energy restriction mentioned earlier. The simultaneous transfer of two electrons is less probable, but not by a large factor.[6]

The situation in a solution in the liquid state is more complicated. The same restrictions operate as before, but now not even approximate quantum mechanical calculations can be made because of the large number of particles that must be considered. From a qualitative view it seems reasonable that an electron transfer which would go readily in the gas phase between two particles will be hindered by the presence of solvent molecules because such molecules prevent the extension into space of the orbitals on the exchanging particles. In particular the ligands of a complex ion (unless of special character) will act as good insulating groups for electrons and orbitals of the central metal ion.

The energy requirement will not be as stringent in the liquid phase, however, because the large number of energy levels possible for a system of interacting particles will make it easier to find configurations which allow energy to be conserved. Interestingly enough, the transition which was easiest in the gas phase, between an atom and its ion, now becomes more difficult. For any two central particles which differ only by one unit of charge, interaction with the environment will be different enough so that unequal energies will result if an electron transfers.[7]

It might be thought that rearrangement of the coordinated groups could occur simultaneously with the movement of the electron. This is forbidden, however, according to the Franck-Condon principle,[8] which states that the motion of nuclei is so slow compared to that of electrons that an electron transfer occurs without any appreciable movement of the nuclei.

The situation can be made clearer by considering a specific case involving the aquo Fe(III) and Fe(II) ions:

$$Fe(H_2O)_6^{3+} + Fe(H_2O)_6^{2+} \rightarrow Fe^*(H_2O)_6^{2+} + Fe^*(H_2O)_6^{3+} \quad (8)$$

The star indicates an ion in an energy-rich state. The unstarred ions have the average energies characteristic of their species. If electron transfer occurred between two such average-energy ions, energy-rich products would be formed because the average ions of each charge type would have the ligand water molecules, in particular, held by them at a distance which leads to a minimum potential energy. This distance would be different for the two charge types, being smaller for the more highly charged ion. If electron transfer occurred, the water molecules would be at the wrong distance from the central ion, either too close or too far, and the potential energy would be increased. These energy-rich ions would then lose energy to the medium by collision, liberating heat.

$$\overset{*}{Fe}(H_2O)_6^{3+} + \overset{*}{Fe}(H_2O)_6^{2+} \rightarrow Fe(H_2O)_6^{3+} + Fe(H_2O)_6^{2+} + heat \quad (9)$$

The whole process of equation 8 plus equation 9 is a violation of the law of conservation of energy in that heat energy is created.

A way in which the proposed reaction can occur is to rearrange the hydration shells of the ions to some intermediate position before electron transfer occurs. This requires energy from the solution, but an equivalent amount of energy will be released when the products revert to the average state.

For conservation of energy both ions can rearrange to various intermediate configurations. The most favorable intermediate will be the one requiring the least amount of energy to form, since this rearrangement energy constitutes a barrier which must be surmounted before electron transfer can occur. The least energy will be required to form two identical configurations so that electron transfer involves a symmetrical transition state intermediate between Fe^{2+} and Fe^{3+} arrangements. It is of interest to try to evaluate the magnitude of the energy involved.

The hydration energies of divalent cations of the transition metals are of the order of 450–500 kcal, and for trivalent cations about 1100 kcal as discussed in Chapter 2. These values suggest that some alarmingly large energies may be needed to put the hydration shells of both kinds of ions in some intermediate configuration. However, this is not the case, as can be shown by using the simple electrostatic model employed for calculating coordinate bond energies in Chapter 2.

This model gave the potential energy of an ion and its first hydration layer in terms of the charge on the ion, the dipole moment and polarizability of water, and the distance, r, of the ligands from the central ion. The energy of all other layers of water was given by the Born charging equation. For ions such as $Fe(H_2O)_6{}^{2+}$ and $Fe(H_2O)_6{}^{3+}$, the total energy is given explicitly as a function of the distance r, the equilibrium value of which was taken as 2.21 A for Fe(II) and 2.05 A for Fe(III).

The energy increase on changing r for both ions to some common value can easily be calculated. This can be done by direct substitution into equation 4 of Chapter 2, or by solving for the force constant as indicated on p. 105. The change in energy for six bonds in both ions will then be given by

$$\Delta U = 3k_2 (\Delta r_2)^2 + 3k_3 (\Delta r_3)^2 \tag{10}$$

where k_2 and k_3 are the force constants for divalent and trivalent iron, respectively, and Δr_2 and Δr_3 are the changes from the corresponding equilibrium values of r. The calculated values of k_2 and k_3 are 1.49×10^5 and 4.16×10^5 dynes/cm, corresponding to vibrational frequencies $\nu_2 = 430$ cm^{-1} and $\nu_3 = 718$ cm^{-1}.[9] For comparison the experimental ν_2 of Zn $(H_2O)_6{}^{2+}$ (symmetrical breathing frequency) is 394 cm^{-1},[10] but it is not clear how much larger the frequency should be for a trivalent ion.[11]

From equation 10 it is easy to calculate the best compromise values of Δr_2 and Δr_3 to make both values of r equal with minimum energy expenditure.[12] The best value, r_e, is given by

$$r_e = \frac{k_3 r_3 + k_2 r_2}{k_2 + k_3} \tag{11}$$

which is 2.09 A. The energy required is 9.2 kcal for $Fe(H_2O)_6{}^{3+}$ and 2.9 kcal for $Fe(H_2O)_6{}^{3+}$. Actually less energy is needed because of zero point and thermal vibrational energies already present at room temperature. These amount to some 0.6 kcal/bond for $Fe(H_2O)_6{}^{2+}$ and 1.0 kcal for $Fe(H_2O)_6{}^{3+}$ (for bond-stretching vibrations). Thus the metal-ligand bond distance in $Fe(H_2O)_6{}^{3+}$ can become stretched by 0.04 A without supplying any additional energy. Correcting $Fe(H_2O)_6{}^{2+}$ in the same way reduces the required energy for reorganization to only 5.6 kcal. Electron transfer would have to occur during the out-of-phase combination of the "breathing" modes of the two ions.

In addition to the above, there will also be a change in the Born hydration energy. This must be calculated in a special way as described below. At any rate it can be seen that the Franck-Condon barrier is not too large. If two electrons are transferred simultaneously, the rearrangement energies required will be very much larger, since the charge on the complexes will change by two units.

In the more common event that reaction takes place between two metal ions that are not the same, an examination of equations 8 and 9 shows that exothermic reactions are greatly favored. That is, since heat is to be evolved anyway, the lack of energy conservation shown in 8 and 9 is no longer necessarily a factor. It is essential only that the products be formed in some suitably activated state to release the correct amount of heat on thermal equilibration.[7] On the other hand, endothermic reactions will be strongly hindered, both the heat of reaction and the rearrangement energy being required.

Another important restriction on the transfer of an electron from one molecule to another is that no overall change in electron spin should occur. That is, the spins of the other electrons in the system must be undisturbed by the electron that transfers. This can be important for a metal ion in a complexing environment such that one oxidation state of the metal is spin paired and the other oxidation state is spin free. It will be recalled that this is frequently the case for complexes in which the ligands have fairly strong crystal fields but not strong enough to couple the electrons in the lower valence state of the metal, e.g., $Co(NH_3)_6^{3+}$ and $Co(NH_3)_6^{2+}$. In such a case it is required that electron transfer occur between the ions when at least one ion is in an excited state.* The best path would have the ligand distances equal and the magnetic properties the same except for the exchanging electron.

The Electron Tunneling Hypothesis. Considerable insight into the electron transfer process in solution is given by the electron tunneling theory developed by Weiss[13] and by Marcus, Zwolinski, and Eyring.[14] The possibility of an electron leaking through a potential energy barrier that would be classically impenetrable is a well-known quantum mechanical phenomenon. The result is that the electron can transfer at distances considerably greater than would correspond to actual collision of the reactants. The tunneling effect is thus related to the extension in space of the electronic orbitals mentioned in connection with gas-phase transfer processes.

Figure 6.1 shows schematically a potential energy diagram for illustrating barrier leakage. The energy is plotted as a function of the distance of the electron from the centers of the two ions involved in the transfer. Only the potential energy of the transferring electron is shown. If the barrier is approximated as a triangular one, the probability of transfer, κ, is given by the Gamow equation[15]

$$\kappa = e^{-(8\pi d/3h)[2m(U-W)]^{1/2}} \tag{12}$$

---

* There will be a reaction between the unexcited ions accompanied by the rearrangement of spins of other electrons. This process, being forbidden, will go very slowly and usually contribute little to the actual reaction.

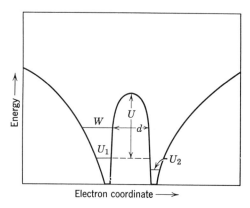

Electron coordinate ⟶

Fig. 6.1   Electron transfer by penetration of a potential energy barrier. U_1 and U_2 refer to the ground states of the electron in cations 1 and 2, respectively. From reference 14.

where U = height of the barrier, W = kinetic energy of the electron, m = electron mass, d = width of the barrier at the height of penetration, and h = Planck's constant.

W can be equated to the ionization potential of the electron in the initial state, but U is more difficult to evaluate. The shape of the curve is a function of the distance between the two ions and the nature of the medium between the ions as well as of the ions themselves. The energy barrier is not the same, nor is it directly related to the energy used to rearrange the hydration shells mentioned earlier. It is assumed that any such rearrangement has already occurred in constructing Fig. 6.1.

As an approximation one may consider an electron moving in the coulomb field of two cations and calculate the potential energy by the simple coulomb equation

$$U' = \frac{q_1 q_2}{Dd} - \frac{eq_1}{Dx} - \frac{eq_2}{D(d-x)} \tag{13}$$

where q_1 and q_2 are the charges on each of the ions not counting the electron, D is the dielectric constant of the solvent, x is the distance of the electron from the cation of charge q_1. From 13 and from U_1 it is possible to calculate the barrier U as a function of d. This distance is picked to give the best balance between repulsion of the two cations as given by 13 and the probability of transfer as given by 12. U_1 is the ground state potential energy of the electron on cation 1 and may be set equal to $-2W$ by the virial theorem.[16] U is calculated from the maximum value of the last two terms of equation 13, which give the electronic potential energy.

More specifically the rate constant for electron transfer is written according to the transition state theory[17] as

$$k = \kappa \frac{RT}{Nh} e^{-\Delta G^{\ddagger}/RT} \tag{14}$$

where κ is the transmission coefficient given by equation 12, and $\Delta G^{\ddagger}$ includes the free energy of rearrangement, if any, and the electrostatic repulsion term. The value of d is now picked to maximize k. By using reasonable values of W and U, it is possible to get reasonable values for k for a number of reactions if the energy of rearrangement is chosen as 8 kcal. The values of d range from 3.4 to 9.3 A for ions of varying charge. The energy barriers are of the order of several electron volts. However, this particular kind of calculation must be regarded as merely informative rather than as essentially correct. The use of the coulomb law for the potential is very crude, especially since the critical distance d is based on it as well.

One further feature of the electron tunneling theory is that the transmission factor κ is not markedly temperature dependent (in which barrier leakage phenomena differ from thermal barrier-crossing processes). Hence from equation 14 there will be a contribution to the apparent entropy of activation

$$\Delta S_t = R \ln \kappa \tag{15}$$

Since the probability of transmission is always less than unity this will be a negative entropy term. Its magnitude from the calculations of Marcus, Zwolinski, and Eyring is of the order of -15 eu. The theory is a nonadiabatic one in that the electron jumps from one potential energy surface to another. Laidler and Sacher have an improved electron tunneling theory.[18] The reorganization energy of the ions is estimated as outlined above, and saturation of the dielectric constant in the neighborhood of the ions is considered.

The Marcus-Hush Theory. R. A. Marcus[19] and N. S. Hush[20] have developed adiabatic theories of electron transfer reactions which are based on the idea of a single potential energy surface.† All electrons are assumed able to adjust themselves at all times to the changing nuclear positions as in any chemical reaction. A single wave function describes the state of the transferring electron, e.g.,

$$\psi = (1 - m)^{1/2}\phi_1 + m^{1/2}\phi_2 \tag{16}$$

where ϕ_1 and ϕ_2 are the wave functions for the initial and final states at such a distance that there is no interaction. The mixing parameter, m varies smoothly from 0 to 1 during the course of the reaction.

† A somewhat similar theory has been given by V. G. Levich and R. R. Dogonadze, *Collection Czech. Chem. Commun.*, **26**, 193 (1961)

The fundamental assumption is that there is only a small overlap of the orbitals ϕ_1 and ϕ_2 so that the interaction energy $2H_{12}$ is small, less than 0.03 eV, and can be neglected. Nevertheless the interaction must be sufficient so that the barrier of Fig. 6.1 is low enough that the electron can move freely through it ($\kappa = 1$). The square of the wave function, which is the electron probability distribution, can be written as

$$\psi^2 = (1 - m)\phi_1{}^2 + m\phi_2{}^2 \tag{17}$$

Accordingly m has the simple meaning of the average fraction of the electron which has transferred.[20]‡

The rate constant for the electron transfer reaction is still given by equation 14 with κ set equal to 1. The problem is to calculate $\Delta G^{\ddagger}$. The transition state is at the top of an energy barrier reckoned as due to the positions of all the particles of the system and not just the electronic coordinates shown in Fig. 6.1. It corresponds to an electron distribution given by $m^{\ddagger}$, which in turn is that value of m which minimizes the energy when the internuclear coordinates are fixed. $\Delta G^{\ddagger}$ includes the coulomb energy of repulsion of the reactants, the changes of the inner hydration shell, and the changes in the Born hydration energy on going from the reactants to the transition state. It also includes any other changes in free energy that occur in forming a transition state in a bimolecular reaction.

Figure 6.2 shows the kind of potential energy surface which is being considered. A transition between reactants and products can only occur by reaching the set of coordinates corresponding to the transition state. The electronic distribution of the activated complex corresponds to

$$O^{(Z_1 - m^{\ddagger})} \cdots R^{(Z_2 + m^{\ddagger})}$$

where O is the oxidizing ion of charge Z_1, and R is the reducing ion of charge Z_2. For simplicity O and R are both represented as spheres of radii a_1 and a_2, respectively. Typically they would be complex ions including, of course, their inner coordination shells.

Transition state theory for the case of two structureless spheres (atoms) reacting gives the result,[21] in place of 14,

$$k = \left(\frac{8\pi RT}{N\mu}\right)^{1/2} d^2 e^{-\Delta G^{\ddagger}/RT} \tag{18}$$

The pre-exponential factor is simply the usual collision frequency in solution. Experimentally its value is about 10^{11} M^{-1} sec^{-1} at 25°C, though theory[22] suggests a value of about 10^{13} M^{-1} sec^{-1}. The quantity d is the collision diameter, which is set equal to $a_1 + a_2$, and μ is the reduced mass.

‡ In the formulation of Marcus, m has a somewhat different meaning.

The term $\Delta G^{\ddagger}$ now includes only those changes due to the transfer of the electron itself. Its value is given by[19,20]

$$\Delta G^{\ddagger} = \frac{Z_1 Z_2 e^2}{dD} + \frac{me^2}{dD}(Z_1 - Z_2 - 1) + m\,\Delta G^0 - m(1-m)(\lambda_0 + \lambda_i)$$

(19)

The first two terms are related to the work needed to bring the two spheres together and to adjust their charges to the critical value. The third term depends upon the free energy difference of an electron in the product and

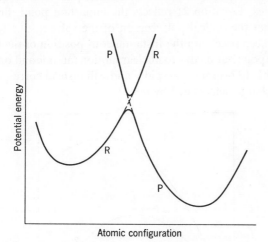

Atomic configuration

Fig. 6.2 Profile on N-dimensional potential energy surfaces plotted against an atomic configurational coordinate of the entire system. Curve R denotes reactants ($ox_1 + red_2$); curve P, products ($red_1 + ox_2$). Dotted lines show intersection of surfaces (zero electronic interaction case), and solid lines indicate the splitting for the case of weak interaction. From reference 19b.

reactants at the temperature and in the medium involved. It is simply the difference between the depths of the two potential energy wells shown in Fig. 6.2. The last two terms are the reorganizational energy of the inner coordination sphere, λ_i, and of the solvent, λ_0, needed before the electron can have the same energy in both ions.

A value of λ_i can be calculated from an assumed potential function, or from known force constants for metal-ligand stretching. This would be similar to equations 10 and 11. However, allowance must be made for the new average charges on each ion in the transition state. Assuming that the force constant is a linear function of the charge, Marcus[19b] derives the following expression:

$$\lambda_i = \sum_j \frac{k_j k_j'}{k_j + k_j'}(q_j - q_j')^2$$

(20)

Here k_j is the force constant of the jth vibrational coordinate for reactant, and k_j' is the corresponding force constant for the product: $(q_j - q_j')$ is the change in the equilibrium value of the coordinate in going from reactant to product.

The change in the Born hydration energy is given by

$$\lambda_0 = \left(\frac{1}{2a_1} + \frac{1}{2a_2} - \frac{1}{d} \right) \left(\frac{1}{D_0} - \frac{1}{D} \right) e^2 \tag{21}$$

where D_0 is the optical dielectric constant equal to the square of the refractive index. Equation 21 reflects the important point, first made by Marcus,[19a] that the optical polarization of the solvent, due to electronic motion, will keep pace with the instantaneous position of the transferring electron. The polarization due to nuclear motion (atomic and orientational) will not be able to respond as rapidly and will instead correspond only to the average charge determined by $m^{\ddagger}$.

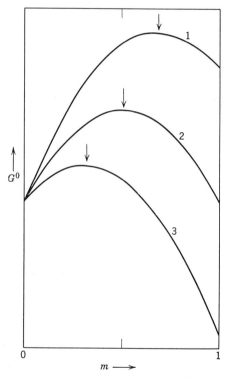

Fig. 6.3   Standard free energy of redox system as a function of the mixing parameter, m. The arrows indicate the value of $m^{\ddagger}$ for (1) an overall positive free energy change; (2) an overall zero free energy change; and (3) an overall negative free energy change. From reference 20c.

Equation 19 can now be minimized with respect to m to find the value of $m^{\ddagger}$. The result is

$$m^{\ddagger} = \frac{1}{2} + \frac{\Delta G^0 + (Z_1 - Z_2 - 1)e^2/dD}{2(\lambda_0 + \lambda_i)} \tag{22}$$

which leads to

$$\Delta G^{\ddagger} = \frac{Z_1 Z_2 e^2}{dD} + m^{\ddagger 2}(\lambda_0 + \lambda_i) \tag{23}$$

For the important case of isotope exchange reactions, such as the Fe^{2+}–Fe^{3+} exchange, ΔG^0 is equal to zero, as is $(Z_1 - Z_2 - 1)$. Hence $m^{\ddagger}$ is equal to $\frac{1}{2}$, as expected, since the transition state should be symmetrical with respect to both ions. Figure 6.3 shows the variation of $m^{\ddagger}$ expected for reactions with overall free energy changes.

Equations 20–23, together with 18, represent a complete prediction of the rate of outer-sphere electron transfer processes, providing the necessary distances and force constants can be estimated. The entropy of activation can also be predicted by differentiating 23 with respect to temperature and changing the sign. To this must be added -9 eu to allow for the loss in translational entropy in forming the activated complex

$$\Delta S^{\ddagger} = \frac{e^2}{Dd}\left(\frac{\partial D}{\partial T}\right)[Z_1 Z_2 + m^{\ddagger}(Z_1 - Z_2 - 1)]$$
$$+ m^{\ddagger} \Delta S_0 + \text{small terms} - 9 \quad (24)$$

Table 6.1 shows some calculated values of $\Delta H^{\ddagger} = \Delta G^{\ddagger} + T\Delta S^{\ddagger}$ and of $\Delta S^{\ddagger}$ for several reactions which may go by an electron transfer mechanism. No correction has been made for the fact that the theoretical calculations refer to infinite dilution, whereas the experiments with which they are compared were done at rather high ionic strengths.

It may be seen that there is considerable variation in the theoretical value of $\Delta H^{\ddagger}$ for the exchange reactions of the divalent-trivalent ions of the first transition series. These variations arise from crystal field effects.[23] The energy required to equalize the metal-ligand distances for the two ions depends on the amount of C.F.S.E. in the two valence states. For V(II) a d^3 ion, and V(III), a d^2 ion, the metal-ligand distances are nearly the same naturally, because of strong stabilization of the divalent state. For Cr(II), a d^4 ion, on the other hand, the difference in bond distance between it and Cr(III) is probably large and the reorganization energy is large. In general it should be easier to transfer an electron from a stable t_{2g} orbital than from an unstable e_g orbital.[23] This paradoxical result comes about because of the effect of the t_{2g} electron in reducing the amount of inner-shell reorganization energy.

Table 6.1 Calculated and experimental heats and entropies of activation in water at 25°C

$$M^{m+} + M^{(m-1)+} \rightarrow M^{(m-1)+} + M^{m+}$$

System	$\Delta H^{\ddagger}$ (calc.), kcal	$\Delta S^{\ddagger}$ (calc.), eu	E_a (exp.), kcal	$\Delta S^{\ddagger}$ (exp.), eu
Ce^{4+}/Ce^{3+}	6.8	−40	7.7	−40 [a]
NpO_2^{2+}/NpO_2^{+}	9.6	−15	11.6	−12 [b]
Pu^{4+}/Pu^{3+}	8.1	−41	7.1	−31 [c]
V^{3+}/V^{2+}	7.5	−25	13.2	−25 [d]
Cr^{3+}/Cr^{2+}	18	−26	$k \leq 2 \times 10^{-5}$	[e]
Mn^{3+}/Mn^{2+}	11.9	−25	$k \sim 10^{-4}$	[f]
Fe^{3+}/Fe^{2+}	10.8	−26	10.5	−21 [g]
Co^{3+}/Co^{2+}	10.0	−26	11.0	−21 [h]

$\Delta H^{\ddagger}$ calculated in reference 20c. $\Delta S^{\ddagger}$ calculated as in text for a standard state of 1 mole/liter. Experimental data at ionic strengths ranging from $\mu = 0.5$ to 2.0.

[a] J. W. Gryder and R. W. Dodson, *J. Am. Chem. Soc.*, **73**, 2890 (1951); however, see F. R. Duke and F. R. Parchen, *ibid.*, **78**, 1540 (1956).

[b] Reference 85.

[c] Reference 90.

[d] Reference 52; $k = 1 \times 10^{-2}\,M^{-1}\,\sec^{-1}$.

[e] Reference 55.

[f] Reference 72.

[g] Reference 65; $k = 4.0\,M^{-1}\,\sec^{-1}$.

[h] H. S. Habib and J. P. Hunt, *J. Am. Chem. Soc.*, **88**, 1668 (1966); $k = 3\,M^{-1}\,\sec^{-1}$. $\Delta H^{\ddagger}$ is calculated for high-spin Co^{3+}.

The $\Delta H^{\ddagger}$ calculations in Table 6.1 include corrections which are again crystal field activation energies (C.F.A.E., compare p. 147) estimated by Hush[20c] from known C.F.S.E.'s. They are part of λ_i and, like the other contributions to λ_i, are difficult to evaluate *a priori*.

Atom Transfer Reactions

Turning now to the other possibility for oxidation-reduction reactions involving atom or group transfer, we are in a more familiar field as far as kinetic theory is concerned. If the transfer of an atom is rate determining then the usual adiabatic assumption can be made that the electrons can easily follow the motions of the nuclei. Thus the peculiar restrictions on electron transfer no longer apply (except for the spin restriction). We are dealing, in short, with ordinary chemical reactions. They will not, however, be without some unusual features.

Evidence for atom transfer comes from several sources. In oxidation-reduction reactions of oxy anions it is possible to show oxygen atom transfer by using ^{18}O labeling, provided that rapid exchange with the solvent oxygen does not occur.[24] In this way atom transfer has been demonstrated for the oxidation of SO_3^{2-} with ClO^-, ClO_2^-, ClO_3^-, and BrO_3^- and for the oxidation of NO_2^- with $HClO$.[24] Such reactions can be regarded as nucleophilic attacks on an oxygen atom acting as a Lewis acid or electrophile, an anion being displaced.

$$\begin{bmatrix} O \\ \backslash\backslash \\ N \cdots \cdots {}^{18}O-Cl \\ / \quad\quad | \\ O \quad\quad H \end{bmatrix}^- \xrightarrow{H_2O} \begin{bmatrix} O \\ \backslash\backslash \\ N-{}^{18}O \cdots\cdots Cl \\ / \quad\quad | \\ O \quad\quad H \end{bmatrix}^- \rightarrow$$

$$\begin{array}{c} O \\ \backslash\backslash \\ \quad N-{}^{18}O^- + HCl \quad (25) \\ / \\ O \end{array}$$

By the ingenious selection of Cr^{2+} as a reducing agent, Taube and his co-workers have been able to demonstrate the transfer of a large number of univalent atoms and groups.[25] The essential feature is that Cr(II) complex ions are labile but the complexes of Cr(III) are inert. Hence, if atom transfer occurs during the oxidation of Cr(II), the atom will remain as part of the coordination sphere of the Cr(III) long enough to be detected. With $CrCl^{2+}$, $FeCl^{2+}$, $AuCl_4^-$, and $Co(NH_3)_5Cl^{2+}$ as oxidizing agents, the transfer of chlorine atoms has been shown.[25] By using $Co(NH_3)_5X$ as an oxidant, the transfer of X has been demonstrated for $X = NCS^-$, N_3^-, PO_4^{3-} acetate, oxalate, $P_2O_7^{4-}$, Br^-, and SO_4^{2-}.[26]

In the cases of $X = H_2O$ and OH^-, oxygen transfer has been shown by ^{18}O labeling.[27]

$$Cr^{2+} + (NH_3)_5Co(H_2{}^{18}O)^{3+} + 5H^+ \rightarrow$$
$$(H_2O)_5Cr(H_2{}^{18}O)^{3+} + 5NH_4^+ + Co^{2+} \quad (26)$$

Similar results have been obtained[28] for reactions between Cr(II) and complexes of the types $Cr(H_2O)_5X^{2+}$ and $Cr(NH_3)_5X^{2+}$.

Regardless of the charge of the transferred group, it acts as a univalent radical since the change in oxidation number of the chromium is always from plus two to plus three. Thus these reactions can be classified as free radical displacements. Note the similarity of the reactions

$$H + Br_2 \rightarrow HBr + Br \quad\quad\quad (27a)$$
$$Cr^{2+} + Br_2 \rightarrow CrBr^{2+} + Br \quad\quad\quad (27b)$$

27a being a step in the free radical chain reaction between H_2 and Br_2 and 27b being a reaction demonstrated by Taube.

An interesting point in Cr(II) reductions occurs in the reaction with the complex ion $IrCl_6^{2-}$. Here the products are $Cr(H_2O)_6^{3+}$ and $IrCl_6^{3-}$. Although the possibility for chlorine atom transfer exists as in previous cases, it does not occur. Taube explains this by the greater stability of $IrCl_6^{3-}$ compared to $Cr(H_2O)_5Cl^{2+}$, whereas in the other examples the Cr(III) complex is more stable than the Fe(II) or Co(II) complexes. Thus the atom transfer is not a necessary part of these reactions, which may in fact go by electron transfer in every case. Transfer of a group immediately following will then depend on the relative stabilities of the possible products.

That transfer does happen in many cases demonstrates, however, that bridging of the Cr(II) ion to the oxidizing agent is a necessary part of the reaction.

$$(NH_3)_5Co^{(III)}Cl \cdots Cr^{(II)}(H_2O)_5 \tag{28}$$

The close approach of the metal ions allowed by bridging accounts for the increase in the rate of the redox reaction when a good bridging group is present. Thus the reaction between $Cr(H_2O)_6^{2+}$ and $Cr(H_2O)_6^{3+}$, using radioactive isotope labeling, is extremely slow, whereas the exchange between $Cr(H_2O)_6^{2+}$ and $Cr(H_2O)_5Cl^{2+}$ is very rapid.[29] Atom transfer occurs in the latter case.

The mechanism for such inner-sphere reactions can be broken up into at least two steps, formation of the bridged complex and its dissociation into products.

$$M—X + M' \underset{k_2}{\overset{k_1}{\rightleftharpoons}} M—X—M' \underset{k_4}{\overset{k_3}{\rightleftharpoons}} M + X—M' \tag{29}$$

It is very likely that the species M—X—M' is an intermediate rather than an activated complex. Since binuclear complexes held together by a single bridge are rare at least in solution, it is a transient intermediate of high energy.

The steady state treatment may be applied in such a case to the rate of formation of M'—X from M—X.

$$\text{Rate} = \frac{k_1 k_3}{k_2 + k_3} [M—X][M'] \tag{30}$$

In the case of an isotope exchange where M and M' are the same element in two different oxidation states, $k_2 = k_3$ and, except for a factor of one-half, the rate constant for the redox reaction is given by k_1. Also, if the overall reaction 29 goes well to completion, it is likely that $k_3 \gg k_2$. In both cases the overall rate is governed by a reaction which is a simple substitution reaction of one ligand for another and not strongly related to redox properties.§ The presumption is that some labile group on M′, usually H_2O, is lost before or during the coordination of M—X to M′.

It is also possible to have an atom transfer mechanism for an outer-sphere mechanism, at least for the case of hydrogen atom transfer. This was first suggested by Dodson and Davidson[30] for the Fe^{2+}-Fe^{3+} and Fe^{2+}-$FeOH^{2+}$ exchanges. A picture of the transition state in the latter case would look as follows:

$$(H_2O)_5Fe^{(II)}\!\!-\!\!\overset{\displaystyle \overset{H}{|}}{O}\cdots\!\!H\!\!-\!\!\underset{\displaystyle \underset{H}{|}}{O}\!\!-\!\!Fe^{(III)}(H_2O)_5 \tag{31}$$

in which the dotted line indicates the atom transfer from Fe(II) to Fe(III). For the case of the aquo ions, the principle of microscopic reversibility also strongly implies, but does not demand, that a symmetrical transition state exists as in 32.

$$(H_2O)_5Fe^{(II)}\!\!-\!\!O \overset{\textstyle \overset{H}{\diagup}\ \ \overset{H}{\diagup}}{\underset{\textstyle \underset{H}{\diagup}\ \ \underset{H}{\diagup}}{}} O\!\!-\!\!Fe^{(III)}(H_2O)_5 \tag{32}$$

The dotted lines in this case indicate a hydrogen atom transferring from Fe(II) to Fe(III), while simultaneously a H^+ ion transfers from Fe(III) to Fe(II).

The evidence for hydrogen atom transfer is of three kinds:

1. The activation energies of a large number of redox reactions of aquo ions are close to 10 kcal, and their activation entropies are close to −25 eu. This suggests a common mechanism for which the water ligand is required.[31]

2. At least one ligand must be water in certain redox reactions of metal complexes. One CN^- of $Fe(CN)_6{}^{4-}$ must be replaced by H_2O before reaction with H_2O_2 occurs, for example, and electron exchange reactions appear to be very slow in solvents such as nitromethane and alcohols.[32]

3. The rates of the Fe^{3+}-Fe^{2+} and $FeOH^{2+}$-Fe^{2+} exchange reactions are slowed by a factor of two in going from H_2O to D_2O solvent.[33] This is consistent with the isotope effect expected for breaking an O-D bond compared to an O-H bond.

None of the above lines of evidence is actually very compelling. Under point 2, it may well be that a labile group such as water is needed so that an inner-sphere complex can easily be formed. In less polar solvents

§ However, see p. 501.

reactions between ions of the same charge type would be expected to be slow. Furthermore, exchange between Fe^{3+} and Fe^{2+} is very fast in the high dielectric, good coordinating solvent dimethylsulfoxide.[32c] The species are probably $Fe(DMSO)_6^{2+}$ and $Fe(DMSO)_6^{3+}$ in this medium.

Under point 3, it may be noted that even larger isotope effects are found for the oxidations of Cr(II) by $Co(NH_3)_5H_2O^{3+}$ and $Co(NH_3)_5OH^{2+}$, which are known to involve oxygen transfer.[34] Similar isotope effects are known for a number of reaction rates and equilibria of complex ions in H_2O and D_2O solvents. They may be explained in terms of solvation effects by means of a simple electrostatic theory.[35]

A modified view of the role of water in these reactions is given by Stranks,[36] who suggests that coupling of the hydration shells of the two ions by hydrogen bonding lowers the energy of the activated complex and also provides a favorable path for electron transfer. Transfer of a hydrogen ion following the electron movement may or may not occur, depending on the proton affinities of the two hydration shells after the electron transfer.

Hydrogen bonding would be most effective, not as in 32, but with another water molecule from the solvent interposed.

$$(H_2O)_5Fe^{(II)}\!-\!O\!-\!H\cdots O\cdots H\!-\!O\!-\!Fe^{(III)}(H_2O)_5 \tag{33}$$

It has also been suggested[31,32b] that a number of hydrogen bridged water molecules can intervene between the two reactant ions. Reaction would occur by either hydrogen atom transfer or electron transfer over a long, but highly organized path. Such a process might be possible in the hydration layer of a protein, for example.[37]

A number of atom transfer mechanisms have been proposed in the oxidation of organic substrates by inorganic oxidants.[38] For example, with permanganate ion hydrogen atom transfers have been suggested,

$$RH + MnO_4^- \rightarrow R\cdot + HMnO_4^- \tag{34}$$

hydride ion transfers,

$$R_2CHO^- + MnO_4^- \rightarrow R_2CO + HMnO_4^{2-} \tag{35}$$

and finally oxygen atom donation,

In addition some oxidants such as ferricyanide ion seem to react by electron transfer[39]

$$RS^- + Fe(CN)_6^{3-} \rightarrow RS\cdot + Fe(CN)_6^{4-} \qquad (37)$$

$$2RS\cdot \rightarrow RSSR \qquad (38)$$

The subject of the oxidation and reduction of organic substances is a complex one and will not be dealt with further here. The reader is referred to several excellent reviews.[38]

A number of reactions of metal ion complexes occur with free radicals and atoms, both organic and inorganic. The following kinds of reaction are well documented:[40]

$$R\cdot + Cu^{2+} \xrightarrow{HX} RX + Cu^+ + H^+ \qquad (39)$$

where HX = H_2O, HCl, HOAc, etc., and

$$R\cdot + Cu^{2+} \rightarrow olefin + Cu^+ + H^+ \qquad (40)$$

Other oxidizing metal ions may replace Cu(II). The mechanism is not certain, atom and electron transfer both being possible, e.g.,

$$R\cdot + CuX^+ \rightarrow RX + Cu^+ \qquad (41)$$

$$R\cdot + CuX^+ \rightarrow R^+ + CuX \qquad (42)$$

The carbonium ion, R^+, could either capture X^- to form RX or lose a proton to form an olefin.

Dainton and his coworkers[41] have measured the combined rates of reaction 39 plus 40 for the special case where R· is the growing radical chain in the polymerization of acrylamide and the metal ion is varied. Table 6.2 gives a survey of the available results. It can be seen that the reactions are characterized by very low activation energies (indeed sometimes they are negative) and also by very low frequency factors, A. These correspond to large negative entropies of activation.

These kinetic parameters are in better agreement with an electron transfer by the tunneling mechanism (κ very small) than with an atom transfer process.[41a] The negative activation energies may indicate that a complex is formed first which reversibly dissociates many times before reacting. The value of E_a will include the ΔH of the complexation step. The large rate constants for the substitution inert complexes, such as $Fe(dipy)_3^{3+}$ and $Fe(CN)_6^{3-}$, also strongly suggest an electron transfer mechanism. There is no correlation of the rate constants with the overall free energy changes in the reactions of Table 6.2.

Table 6.2   Kinetic factors for the reactions

$$R\cdot + M^{m+} \rightarrow \text{molecule} + M^{(m-1)+}$$

at 25°C in acidic aqueous solution

Ion	k, $M^{-1}\,sec^{-1}$	A, $M^{-1}\,sec^{-1}$	E_a, kcal
$Fe(H_2O)_6{}^{3+}$	2.8×10^3	1.5×10^5	2.3
$Cu(H_2O)_4{}^{2+}$	1.2×10^3	1.1×10^7	5.4
$Ag(H_2O)_2{}^{+}$	0.0	...	...
$Hg(H_2O)_2{}^{2+}$	1.0	4.2×10^4	6.2
$Tl(H_2O)_6{}^{3+}$	0.34	2.1×10	2.5
$VO_2{}^{+}$	1.1×10^3	...	...
$FeOH^{2+}$	2.1×10^4	$4\ \times 10^4$	0.3
$FeCl^{2+}$	8.1×10^4	2.7×10^5	0.7
$FeCl_2{}^{+}$	1.7×10^4	...	...
$FeCl_3$	1.0×10^6	...	...
$FeBr^{2+}$	1.7×10^6	2.3×10^5	−1.2
$FeN_3{}^{2+}$	1.6×10^6	3.6×10^6	0.5
$FeNCS^{2+}$	1.4×10^7	2.4×10^5	−2.4
$Fe(dipy)_3{}^{3+}$	8.1×10^4	...	...
$Fe(o\text{-phen})_3{}^{3+}$	3.1×10^5	2.2×10^2	−4.3
$Fe(CN)_6{}^{3-}$	8.5×10^5	1.6×10^7	1.2

Data from reference 41a. $R\cdot$ is the growing polymer radical of polyacrylamide,

$$-(CH_2-CH)_n-CH_2-CH\cdot$$
$$\quad\ \ |\qquad\qquad\ \ |$$
$$\quad CONH_2\qquad CONH_2$$

The rate constants for the reaction of Cu(II) with simple alkyl radicals such as ethyl and propyl have also been determined.[42] In aqueous acetic acid at 57°C the second-order constants are of the order of $10^8\ M^{-1}\ sec^{-1}$. These are much higher than the $10^3\ M^{-1}\ sec^{-1}$ shown in Table 6.2. This difference occurs because the amide group in $-CH_2\text{-}CHCONH_2$ is electron withdrawing. The electron density at the tricoordinated carbon atom is diminished, and the radical is a poorer reducing agent.

The similar radical oxidation mechanisms

$$Co(NH_3)_5I^{2+} + CH_3\cdot + 5H^+ \rightarrow CH_3I + Co^{2+} + 5NH_4{}^{+} \qquad (43)$$

$$CuCl^+ + CH_3\cdot \rightarrow CH_3Cl + Cu^+ \qquad (44)$$

almost certainly proceed by an atom transfer mechanism.[40,43] Also the reactions of organic free radicals, and of the hydroxyl radical, with reducing metal ions are better described as hydrogen atom abstraction reactions or atom transfer.[41]

$$R\cdot + V(H_2O)_6{}^{2+} \rightarrow RH + V(H_2O)_5OH^{2+} \qquad (45)$$

The activation energies are larger (6–11 kcal), and the entropies of activation are normal. A good correlation exists between the rate of the reaction and the ionization potential of the metal ion corrected for solvation effects.

Organic free radicals may also be produced by the reaction of some substances, notably peroxides,[44] with transition metal ions. A typical reaction would be with a reducing metal ion, and it is extremely likely that coordination occurs first.

$$(H_2O)_5Ti(HOOR)^{3+} \rightarrow (H_2O)_5TiOH^{3+} + RO. \qquad (46)$$

This corresponds to a group transfer reaction. Oxidizing metal ions are usually ineffective at decomposing peroxides.

The reactions of hydroperoxides with most other reducing agents are usually classified as nucleophilic displacement reactions on oxygen,[45] equivalent to the transfer of the group OH^+. For example, in the reaction

$$ROOH + Br^- \rightarrow RO^- + HOBr \qquad (47)$$

the rates are related to the stability of the anion RO^-. Thus, if ROH is acidic, the displacement reaction goes rapidly.

One-Electron and Two-Electron Transfers

It was mentioned earlier that quantum mechanical calculations indicate somewhat lower probability for simultaneous transfer of two or more electrons. The term simultaneous is ambiguous. Experimentally we can only tell whether a reaction involving a change in oxidation number greater than unity proceeds by steps by detecting the intermediates in some fashion. On the basis of several such intermediates (such as the semi-quinones) Haber and Weiss[46] and Michaelis[47] promoted the general doctrine of compulsory one-electron steps in oxidation-reduction reactions.

Several comments may be made on this doctrine. First, if atom or group transfer occurs, then it is clear that changes in oxidation number greater than one may occur. Second, at the present time there is no compelling evidence that simultaneous, or nearly simultaneous, transfer of more than one electron in a true electron transfer reaction has occurred. The Franck-Condon barrier is also greater for a two-electron transfer, as mentioned. Nevertheless, particularly for an adiabatic process, the energy and probability factors are not excessive. Two-electron transfers have been suggested[48] for the oxidation of Hg_2^{2+} by Tl^{3+} and for the Tl^{3+}-Tl^+ exchange reaction. In the latter case, the formation of Tl^{2+} is also a possibility (see p. 490), but the rate law for the former reaction, $k[Hg_2^{2+}][Tl^{3+}]/[Hg^{2+}]$, suggests the mechanism

$$Hg_2^{2+} \rightleftharpoons Hg^{2+} + Hg^0$$

$$Hg^0 + Tl^{3+} \rightarrow Hg^{2+} + Tl^+ \qquad (48)$$

It will be noted that the several kinds of atom transfer reactions that have been mentioned can be classified as either acid-base or free radical reactions depending on whether a change in oxidation state of two units or one unit occurs in the individual step. Since chemical reactions in general are usually acid-base, free radical, or electron transfer, it would appear that changes of oxidation number greater than two will not occur in a single step of any redox reaction. This seems to be the case.[49]

Higginson[50] suggests the following semiempirical rules:

(a) Species derived from the transition elements will react with each other by a series of univalent changes.

(b) Species derived from the non-transition elements will react with each other in a series of bivalent changes *unless* at least one of the reactants is a free radical, in which case univalent change occurs.

(c) Species derived from a transition element and a non-transition element will react with each other by either univalent or bivalent changes, univalent changes being more common.

These rules are not to be construed as assuming anything about the mechanism, whether atom or electron transfer. One consequence of these rules concerning valence changes is that unusual valences are to be expected for intermediates in redox reactions.

A related consequence is expressed by Shaffer's principle of equivalence change.[51] This refers to the observation that non-complementary reactions between one-equivalent reductants and two-equivalent oxidants (or vice versa) are often slow compared to complementary reactions in which both oxidant and reductant change valence by the same amount. This principle, which is not always obeyed, is based on the low probability of termolecular mechanisms, as one possibility,

$$2Fe^{2+} + Tl^{3+} \rightarrow 2Fe^{3+} + Tl^+ \qquad (49)$$

or the formation of unstable valence states as the other possibility, in non-complementary reactions.

Experimental Results

We turn now to a consideration of experimental data. Table 6.3 gives the results of a number of kinetic studies on redox reactions of complex ions. The data are presented in terms of the assumed reactants, the second-order rate constant at 25°C, the heat of activation, and the entropy of activation.

Table 6.3 Rates of redox reactions in water at 25°C

Reaction	k, M^{-1} sec^{-1}	$\Delta H^{\ddagger}$, kcal/mole	$\Delta S^{\ddagger}$, eu	Reference
$V^{2+} + VOH^{2+}$	~1.8	...	...	52
$VOH^{2+} + VO^{2+}$	~1	10.1	-24	53
$V^{3+} + VO_2^{+}$	~1.7×10^{-2}	16.1	~5	54
$VOH^{2+} + VO_2^{+}$	~10^5	...	...	54
$Cr^{2+} + CrOH^{2+}$	0.7	...	...	55
$Cr^{2+} + CrF^{2+}$	22×10^{-3}	13.7	-20	56
$Cr^{2+} + cis\text{-}CrF_2^{+}$	8.7×10^{-3}	13.0	-24	57
$Cr^{2+} + CrNCS^{2+}$	1.8×10^{-4}	...	...	
$Cr^{2+} + Cr(NH_3)_5F^{2+}$	2.7×10^{-4}	13.4	-30	28
$Cr^{2+} + Cr(NH_3)_5Cl^{2+}$	5.1×10^{-2}	11.1	-23	28
$Cr^{2+} + Cr(NH_3)_5Br^{2+}$	0.32	8.5	-33	28
$Cr^{2+} + Cr(NH_3)_5I^{2+}$	5.5	...	...	28
$MnO_4^{-} + MnO_4^{2-}$	3.6×10^3	10.0	-9	8, 9, 26, 27
$Fe^{2+} + FeOH^{2+}$	3.2×10^3	6.9	-18	58
$Fe^{2+} + FeF^{2+}$	40	8.6	-21	59
$Fe^{2+} + FeF_2^{+}$	11	9.0	-22	59
$Fe^{2+} + FeCl^{2+}$	38	11.0	-15	60
$Fe^{2+} + FeBr^{2+}$	17	8.0	-25	61
$Fe^{2+} + FeSCN^{2+}$	$\begin{cases}18 \\ 31\end{cases}$	9.2 7.4	-21 -27	61 62
$Fe^{2+} + FeN_3^{2+}$	1×10^4	13.3	7	63
$Fe^{2+} + Fe(C_2O_4)^{+}$	2,140	8.6	-14	64^a
$Fe^{2+} + Fe(C_2O_4)_2^{-}$	4,520	...	...	64^a
$Fe^{2+} + FeSO_4^{+}$	677	...	...	65
$Fe^{2+} + Fe(SO_4)_2^{-}$	2.0×10^4	...	...	65
$FeSO_4 + FeOH^{2+}$	2×10^6	...	...	65
$Fe^{2+} + Fe(EDTA)^{-}$	4.0×10^{-4}	...	...	66
$Fe^{2+} + Fe(dipy)_3^{3+}$	2.7×10^4	...	...	67
$Fe^{2+} + Fe(tripy)_2^{3+}$	8.5×10^4	...	...	67
$Fe^{2+} + Fe(phen)_3^{3+}$	3.7×10^4	~0.2	-37	68
$Fe(CN)_6^{4-} + Fe(CN)_6^{3-}$	740	4.1	-32	69^b
$Fe(CN)_6^{4-} + Fe(phen)_3^{3+}$	10^8	...	...	70
$Fe(phen)_3^{2+} + Fe(phen)_3^{3+}$	10^5	...	...	71
$Fe(d\text{-}dipy)_3^{2+} + Fe(phen)_3^{3+}$	10^8	...	...	70
$Fe^{2+} + Mn^{3+}$	1.7×10^4	...	...	72
$Fe(phen)_3^{2+} + Mn^{3+}$	1.8×10^3	...	...	72
$Fe^{2+} + H_2O_2$	54	9.4	-15	73
$Fe^{2+} + S_2O_8^{2-}$	70	11.4	-8	73
$Fe^{2+} + (CH_3)_3COOH$	13	8.6	-22	73
$Fe^{2+} + C_6H_5(CH_3)_2COOH$	18	9.4	-18	73
$Fe(EDTA)^{2-} + C_6H_5(CH_3)_2COOH$	2×10^3	9.4	-10	73
$Fe^{2+} + Tl^{3+}$	1.6×10^{-2}	17.8	-7	74
$Tl^{+} + Tl^{3+}$	7.0×10^{-5}	17.4	-21	75
$Tl^{+} + TlOH^{2+}$	2.5×10^{-5}	...	...	75
$HO_2^{-} + Fe^{3+}$	• 5×10^3	27	$+50$	76
$HO^{-} + Fe^{3+}$	3.3×10^{10}	19	$+53$	77
$HO_2^{-} + Fe(dipy)_3^{3+}$	3×10^7	6.4	-5	78
$HO_2^{-} + Co^{3+}$	4×10^{12}	18	$+55$	78
$Co(phen)_3^{2+} + Co(phen)_3^{3+}$	15	16.4	$+4$	79^c
$Co(NH_3)_n^{2+} + Co(NH_3)_6^{3+}$	10^{-9}	...	...	80^d
$Co(NH_3)_n^{2+} + Co(NH_3)_6^{3+}, OH^{-}$	5.5×10^{-3}	12.2	-35	80^d

475

Table 6.3 (*Continued*)

Reaction	k, M^{-1} sec^{-1}	$\Delta H^{\ddagger}$, kcal/mole	$\Delta S^{\ddagger}$, eu	Reference
$Co(NH_3)_n{}^{2+} + Co(NH_3)_6{}^{3+}$, Cl^-	7.3×10^{-4}	12.9	-37.5	80[d]
$Co(NH_3)_n{}^{2+} + Co(NH_3)_5OH^{2+}$	9×10^{-4}	12.7	-33.1	80[d]
$Co(NH_3)_n{}^{2+} + trans\text{-}Co(NH_3)_4(OH)_2{}^+$	4×10^{-3}	13.1	-29.0	80[d]
$Co(NH_3)_n{}^{2+} + cis\text{-}Co(NH_3)_4(OH)_2{}^+$	2.5×10^{-2}	13.2	-28.3	80[d]
$Co(en)_n{}^{2+} + Co(en)_3{}^{3+}$	5×10^{-5}	13.2	-31.0	81, 82
$Co(en)_n{}^{2+} + Co(en)_3{}^{3+}$, OH^-	1×10^{-3}	13.3	-27.1	82[e]
$Co(en)_n{}^{2+} + Co(en)_3{}^{3+}$, Cl^-	5×10^{-4}	13.0	-28.9	82[e]
$Co(en)_n{}^{2+} + Co(en)_3{}^{3+}$, Br^-	3×10^{-4}	13.2	-29.5	82[e]
$Co(en)_n{}^{2+} + Co(en)_3{}^{3+}$, I^-	2×10^{-4}	13.3	-30.0	82[e]
$Co(en)_n{}^{2+} + Co(en)_3{}^{3+}$, $SO_4{}^{2-}$	1.3×10^{-4}	13.1	-31.5	82[e]
$Co(en)_n{}^{2+} + Co(en)_2(H_2O)_2{}^{3+}$	2.7×10^{-4}	13.3	-29.6	82[e]
$Co(en)_n{}^{2+} + Co(en)_2(H_2O)OH^{2+}$	$\sim 1 \times 10^{-3}$	13.0	-27.8	82[e]
$Co(en)_n{}^{2+} + Co(en)_2(OH)_2{}^+$	2×10^{-3}	13.1	-26.1	82[e]
$CuCl_2{}^- + CuCl_4{}^{2-}$	5×10^7	...	...	83
$IrCl_6{}^{3-} + IrCl_6{}^{2-}$	10^3	...	...	89
$Fe(DMphen)_3{}^{2+} + IrBr_6{}^{2-}$	1.7×10^8	...	...	86
$Fe(DMphen)_3{}^{2+} + IrCl_6{}^{2-}$	1.1×10^9	0	-18	85
$Os(dipy)_3{}^{2+} + Mo(CN)_8{}^{3-}$	2×10^9	...	...	87
$Os(dipy)_3{}^{2+} + Os(dipy)_3{}^{3+}$	5×10^4	...	...	71
$Ru(phen)_3{}^{2+} + RhCl_6{}^{2-}$	2.5×10^9	...	...	86
$Fe(phen)_3{}^{2+} + Co^{3+}$	1.4×10^4	...	...	88
$Fe(CN)_6{}^{4-} + IrCl_6{}^{2-}$	3.8×10^5	...	...	88
$Mo(CN)_8{}^{4-} + IrCl_6{}^{2-}$	1.9×10^6	...	...	88
$W(CN)_8{}^{4-} + IrCl_6{}^{2-}$	6.1×10^7	...	...	88
$W(CN)_8{}^{4-} + Mo(CN)_8{}^{3-}$	5.0×10^6	...	...	88
$Fe(CN)_6{}^{4-} + Mo(CN)_8{}^{3-}$	3.0×10^4	...	...	88
$W(CN)_8{}^{4-} + Fe(CN)_6{}^{3-}$	4.3×10^4	...	...	88
$NpO_2H^{2+} + NpO_2{}^{2+}$	15[f]	14	...	89
$Pu^{3+} + PuOH^{3+}$	2.0×10^4	2.2	-32	90
$Pu^{3+} + PuO_2{}^{2+}$	2.7	4.8	-40	91
$Pu^{4+} + PuO_2{}^+$	37	13.6	-6	91

[a] Temp. = 20°C.
[b] Temp. = 0.1°C.
[c] Temp. = 0°C.
[d] Temp. = 64.5°C.
[e] Temp. = 50°C.
[f] Third-order rate constant, M^{-2} sec^{-1}.

The reactants that have been selected are those best fitting the rate data as a function of the various concentrations. However, there is often a choice of reactants. For example, the pair of reactants Fe^{2+}-$FeCl^{2+}$ cannot easily be distinguished kinetically from the three reactants Fe^{2+}-Fe^{3+}-Cl^-. Similarly the dependence of rate on pH has been interpreted in terms of reasonable oxy and hydroxo complexes believed to exist over the pH range studied. Several choices are usually possible in such cases, and chemical intuition has been freely used to pick the most reasonable combination, but there is no assurance that it is the correct one. The reason for this difficulty lies in the various mobile equilibria that exist, such as

$$Fe^{3+} + Cl^- \rightleftharpoons FeCl^{2+} \tag{50}$$

$$H_2O_2 \rightleftharpoons H^+ + O_2H^- \tag{51}$$

Rate data will not tell us whether the left-hand or right-hand components of such equilibria are involved in the activated complex.

The rate constants given also depend on the particular assignment of reactants made and would be incorrect if the reactants were chosen wrongly. If equilibria such as 50 and 51 are involved, the corresponding equilibrium constants must usually be known to get the rate constants from the experimental data. The exception would occur if, under the conditions of the experiments, almost all of the added reagent existed in the form assumed to be the reactant.

The heat and entropy of activation are derived from the theory of absolute reaction rates, the equation being

$$k = \frac{RT}{Nh} e^{-\Delta H^{\ddagger}/RT} e^{\Delta S^{\ddagger}/R} \tag{52}$$

The heat of activation, $\Delta H^{\ddagger}$, is less than the activation energy, E_a, by RT or 0.6 kcal for reactions in solution.

In addition to the data shown in Table 6.3, it is known that a great many redox reactions with positive ΔE^0 values are too rapid to measure by conventional techniques.[92] Many of the reactions in Table 6.3 are for electron exchange processes between an element in two different valence states. Such reactions are usually studied by the use of a radioactive or other isotope as a tracer. It may be considered that $\Delta E^0 = 0$ for reactions of this type. Strictly speaking ΔE^0 would not be identically zero for such a reaction

$$A^n + {}^*A^m \rightleftharpoons {}^*A^n + A^m \tag{53}$$

because of small isotope effects favoring the heavier isotope in one state or another. However, except for the lightest elements, these effects can be neglected.

If radioisotopes are used, the reaction is followed by separating the two oxidation states and measuring the radioactivity in each form. The McKay[93] equation should be followed

$$\ln(1 - x/x_{\infty}) = -Rt(a + b)/ab \tag{54}$$

where x is the activity at time t of the form originally inactive, x_{∞} is the equilibrium value of the activity, and a and b are the analytical concentrations of the two forms of the element which remain constant during the run. R is the rate of the exchange reaction and is equal to some function of the various concentrations involved and one or more rate and equilibrium constants. For a simple bimolecular reaction

$$R = kab \tag{55}$$

In such studies care must be taken that the separation techniques used does not induce the exchange reaction and give erroneous rates.

It has been shown that, if separation-induced exchange is incomplete but constant and reproducible, the rate of exchange can still be found.[94] However, the time required for separation, either physical or chemical, greatly limits the range of velocities that can be studied. Dwyer and Gyarfas[95] have suggested an ingenious method to eliminate the necessity for separation. If the exchanging species can be obtained with at least one form optically active, exchange can be followed by studying changes in optical rotation.

If no change in the configurations occurs on transfer of an electron, the following reactions can occur, as examples,

$$(+)A^n + (-)A^m \rightarrow (+)A^m + (-)A^n \tag{56}$$

$$(+)A^n \rightarrow (-)A^n \tag{57}$$

$$(-)A^m \rightarrow (+)A^m \tag{58}$$

The relative rates of the several steps determine the changes in rotation that are observed. If 57 and 58 are both slow, then the rate of 56 will determine the initial changes in optical activity. This seems to be the case for $Os(dipy)_3^{2+}$-$Os(dipy)_3^{3+}$, though the rates obtained by Dwyer and Gyarfas[95] appear to be wrong (see p. 328[71]).

If either 57 or 58 is fast, as when one of the complexes is labile, 56 again determines the overall loss of activity. In this case, total racemization will be found, whereas in the osmium dipyridyl case only a mutarotation occurred. The $Co(EDTA)^2$-$Co(EDTA)^-$ system corresponds to the case of complete racemization, since $Co(II)$ is labile (see p. 322[96]).

Another method that may be useful for very rapid electron transfers in systems where the equilibrium constant is close to unity involves n.m.r. spectroscopy.[97] If one of the atoms in a reactant has a nuclear moment, the frequency of resonance absorption will vary somewhat with the oxidation state, causing a broadening of the absorption line from which the rate constant can be calculated.[71,83] The rate must be large to have an effect, half-lives of the order of microseconds being most convenient.

Electron spin resonance can also be used. Exchange reactions with half-lives in the millimicrosecond range can be measured by this technique. The width of an e.p.r. line depends on the lifetime of a magnetic state. Chemical exchange can shorten the lifetime and broaden the line.[98] Also useful for very rapid redox reactions are flow methods[70,72] and relaxation methods.[85,86]

It is fortunate that such methods are available because it can be seen in Table 6.3 that some of the rate constants approach 10^9–10^{10} M^{-1} sec^{-1}, which is the limit for a diffusion-controlled bimolecular process. That is, reaction occurs on the first encounter, or collision, of the reactants.[99]

An equation due to Debye[100] may be used to calculate the maximum rate constant for such a diffusion-controlled process involving ions of charges q_A and q_B.

$$k = \frac{4\pi q_A q_B D N^2}{1000\epsilon RT \left[e^{(q_A q_B N/\epsilon RT\sigma)} - 1\right]} \tag{59}$$

Here ϵ is the dielectric constant, and σ is the collision diameter. D is the sum of the diffusion coefficients of the two particles. When the electrostatic energy is very large and negative, 59 becomes

$$k = \frac{4\pi\Lambda N}{1000\epsilon(9 \times 10^{11})} \; M^{-1} \sec^{-1} \tag{60}$$

the Langevin equation. Λ is the molar conductance of the hypothetical salt of the two opositely charged ions. If the electrostatic energy is small or zero, equation 59 becomes

$$k = \frac{4\pi\sigma D N}{1000} \tag{61}$$

which is the Smoluchowski equation.

Inner-Sphere and Outer-Sphere Mechanisms

Even after the reactants have been identified and something about the rates and energetics of the reaction is known, it still remains a major problem to decide between inner-sphere and outer-sphere mechanisms and between electron and atom transfer. In a number of instances it seems reasonably clear that an outer-sphere mechanism with electron transfer must be involved. These are the cases of two substitution inert complexes such as $Fe(CN)_6^{4-}$-$Fe(CN)_6^{3-}$, MnO_4^{2-}-MnO_4^{-}, $IrCl_6^{3-}$-$IrCl_6^{2-}$, and the like. Here the overall rate of reaction is much greater than any possible mechanism based on dissociation and atom transfer.

In some cases where only one reactant is inert, outer-sphere transition states are again extremely likely. These are complexes where possible bridging ligands are missing, as in $Co(NH_3)_6^{3+}$ or $Ru(NH_3)_6^{2+}$. All aquo or hydroxo complexes, however, offer the possibility of bridging. This is also true for halogeno complexes of either inert or labile systems, e.g., Fe^{2+}-$FeCl^{2+}$ and Cr^{2+}-$CrCl^{2+}$.

For the examples where electron transfer is indicated, excellent agreement with the theoretical arguments presented earlier is found. For the isotope exchange reactions, the rate is relatively great for two ions of very similar goemetry so that little rearrangement is needed to symmetrize the transition state, for example, $Mn(CN)_6^{4-}$-$Mn(CN)_6^{3-}$ and $Fe(phen)_3^{2+}$-$Fe(phen)_3^{3+}$. This will generally be the case for complexes differing by one electron in the low-energy t_{2g} orbitals not used in ligand bonding. The rates will be the greatest if the ligands are unsaturated and π bonding, metal to ligand, occurs. This will stabilize the lower valence state more than the higher, and hence the geometries will be more nearly equal. Thus the exchange in $Fe(CN)_6^{4-}$-$Fe(CN)_6^{3-}$ will be faster than in $Fe(H_2O)_6^{2+}$-$Fe(H_2O)_6^{3+}$, even though an electron from a low-energy orbital is transferred in each case.

If the geometry of the two ions is very different, however, the reaction is slow, as predicted. This is the case for ions where the electron to be transferred occupies one of the e_g orbitals used to hold a ligand. The prime examples are Co(II)-Co(III) in their various complexes and Cr(II)-Cr(III) Contrary to earlier reports,[101a] it is now known that the Co—N distances in $Co(NH_3)_6^{2+}$ and $Co(NH_3)_6^{3+}$ are not extremely dissimilar. In the former case, the bond distance is 2.11 A, and in the latter case, 1.9 A.[101b] However, another restriction on exchanges between Co(II) and Co(III) is the differing electron multiplicities, as mentioned earlier.

Many reductions by Cr^{2+} unequivocally are bridging or inner-sphere mechanism, because atom transfer can be demonstrated. This suggests that a comparison of the rates of a large number of reactions in which Cr^{2+} and other reductants are used might enable one to decide whether the other reductants behave like Cr^{2+} and hence also form inner-sphere transition states. $Ru(NH_3)_6^{2+}$, which is an inert reductant, must react by outer-sphere mechanisms[102] and may be used as a standard for such a path.

Table 6.4 shows the rate constants for reduction of a series of Co(III) complexes of the type $Co(NH_3)_5X^{3-n}$, where X^{-n} is variable, with the reducing agents Cr^{2+}, V^{2+}, Eu^{2+}, $Cr(bipy)_3^{2+}$, $Ru(NH_3)_6^{2+}$, and $Co(CN)_5^{3-}$. If we accept the premise that Cr^{2+} reacts by a bridging mechanism [except for $Co(NH_3)_6^{3+}$] and $Ru(NH_3)_6^{2+}$ by an outer-sphere mechanism, a criterion of mechanism is that much larger variations in rate occur for an inner-sphere reaction than for an outer-sphere one. This is particularly true for small, good bridging ligands.

By this analogy, an assignment of an outer-sphere mechanism can be made for $Cr(bipy)_3^{2+}$, as had been previously concluded on the basis of more limited evidence.[103] Reduction of the two electron oxidant Pt(IV) by

Table 6.4 Second-order rate constants (k, M^{-1} sec^{-1}) for the reduction of various cobalt(III) complexes at 25°C

$$R = Co(NH_3)_5$$

Oxidant	Reductant						
	Cr^{2+} [a]	V^{2+} [a]	Eu^{2+} [a]	$Cr(bipy)_3^{2+}$ [b]	$Ru(NH_3)_6^{2+}$ [c]	$Co(CN)_5^{3-}$ [c]	$Fe(H_2O)_6^{2+}$ [a]
RNH_3^{3+}	8.9×10^{-5} [d]	3.7×10^{-3} [d]	2×10^{-2} [b]	6.9×10^2	0.011	8×10^4 [e]	...
ROH_2^{3+}	0.5	~ 0.5	0.15	5×10^4	3.0	...	...
ROH^{2+}	1.5×10^6	...	...	3×10^4	0.04	9.3×10^4 [f]	...
RF^{2+}	2.5×10^5	2.6	2.6×10^4	1.8×10^3	...	1.9×10^4 [g]	6.6×10^{-3}
RCl^{2+}	6×10^5	~ 5	3.9×10^2	8×10^5	2.6×10^2	5×10^7 [f]	1.35×10^{-3}
RBr^{2+}	1.4×10^6	25	2.5×10^2	5×10^6	1.6×10^3	2×10^9 [f]	7.26×10^{-4}
RI^{2+}	3×10^6	1.2×10^2	1.2×10^2	...	6.7×10^3	...	...
RN_3^{2+}	$\sim 3 \times 10^5$	13	1.9×10^2	4.1×10^4	1.2	1.6×10^6 [f]	8.8×10^{-3}
$RNCS^{2+}$	19	0.3	~ 0.7	1.0×10^4	...	1.1×10^6 [f]	0.003
RSO_4^+	18	7.8	1.4×10^2	4.5×10^4	...	4×10^4 [e]	...
$ROAc^{2+}$	0.18	0.43	0.18	1.2×10^3	0.35 [h]	1.1×10^4 [e]	0.05
RNO_3^{2+}	~ 90	...	$\sim 1 \times 10^2$	...	34	2.4×10^5 [e]	...
RCN^{2+}	61 [i]	...	...	...	...	2.9×10^2 [f,j]	...
R(maleate)$^+$	...	...	...	1.0×10^3	...	7.5×10^3 [e]	...
R(maleateH)$^{2+}$	180	12	...	...	200	...	...
R(OxH)$^{2+}$	400	17	...	...	0.6	5.2×10^2 [c]	3.8×10^{-3} [k]
RPO_4	4.8×10^9	1.4×10^7	...	...	...	...	...
RPO_4H^+	8.3×10^3	1.6×10^2	5×10^2	...	...	...	...
$RPO_4H_2^{2+}$	0.3	2.3	6	...	...	...	...

[a] $\mu = 1.0$. [b] $\mu = 0.1$. [c] $\mu \simeq 0.2$. [d] $\mu = 0.4$. [e] Outer-sphere mechanism from products. [f] Inner-sphere mechanism from products. [g] 90% outer, 10% inner-sphere mechanism from products. [h] Butyrato complex. [i] Reference 220. [j] Reference 221. [k] k' in sec^{-1}. Rate equation is $k[ROXH^{2+}][Fe^{2+}]/[H^+]$.
Data from references 102, 104, 107, and 111 except as specified in notes i and j.

$Cr(bipy)_3^{2+}$ also seems to occur by an outer-sphere mechanism (J. K. Beattie, doctorate thesis, Northwestern University, Evanston, Illinois, 1967). The reactions of V^{2+} also seem to be outer sphere on this basis.[104] It may be noted that V(II), a d^3 ion, would be considerably slower than Cr(II), a d^4 ion, in its substitution reactions. Referring to equations 29 and 30, it would be the rate of formation of the bridged species which would be the slow step in an inner-sphere reaction with a large negative free energy change. Both Cr(II) and V(II) would have favorable free energy changes in their reactions with $Co(NH_3)_5X^{3-n}$. For an inner-sphere mechanism, a simple substitution reaction would be rate determining.

Furthermore, from the discussion in Chapter 3 of substitution reactions of octahedral complexes, the rate of loss of coordinated water would put a limit on the rate of formation of a bridge to either V^{2+} or Cr^{2+}. Some of the rate constants of Table 6.4 for Cr^{2+} do approach the limit of about 10^9 sec^{-1} estimated for the rate of water exchange in $Cr(H_2O)_6^{2+}$ (see p. 152).

The evidence is that the rate of water exchange for $V(H_2O)_6^{2+}$ is somewhat less than that for $Ni(H_2O)_6^{2+}$, which is about 10^4 sec^{-1}; thus the high rate of reaction with $Co(NH_3)_5PO_4$ can hardly be accounted for except by an outer-sphere mechanism.

The order of reactivity for the halides is $I^- > Br^- > Cl^- > F^-$ for known examples of both inner-sphere and outer-sphere mechanisms in Table 6.4. The strength of the bridge formed would usually increase in the opposite order with F^- giving the strongest bridge. The ability to transmit an electron and to undergo homolytic bond breaking would be greatest for I^- and least for F^-. Except for $Co(CN)_5^{3-}$, the stability of the product would be greatest for F^- and least for I^-, if atom transfer occurred. Probably the rate of formation of a bridge, considered as a nucleophilic attack on the reducing agent, would be greatest for I^- and least for F^-. For different systems one factor or another of all of these may be more important.

It can be seen in Tables 6.3 and 6.4 that the reactions of Eu^{2+} and Fe^{2+} with $Co(NH_3)_5X^{3-n}$, and of Fe^{2+} with FeX^{3-n}. follow the halide reactivity sequence $F^- > Cl^- > Br^- > I^-$. Otherwise the pattern of reactivity for Eu^{2+} appears to be that of an inner-sphere mechanism. The fact that the Fe(II)-Fe(III) exchange rate shows so little effect in going from water ligands to halide ions suggests that bridging is not important, at least for the halide ions. For OH^- and N_3^-, the effect on the rate is large and bridging is indicated.

It has been pointed out[106,107] that the relative rates of reduction of azido and thiocyanato complexes can be used to distinguish between inner-sphere and outer-sphere mechanisms. This method would be valid only where the reducing metal ion and the oxidizing metal ion prefer the same end of the thiocyanate ligand. The argument is based on the stability of the symmetrical transition state,

$$M—N≡N≡N—M'$$

compared to the unstable, unsymmetrical transition state,

$$M—N≡C—S—M'$$

which would lead to the formation of the unstable product $M'—S—C≡N$. Table 6.5 gives some rate constant ratios for various oxidizing and reducing agents. A small value shows an outer-sphere mechanism, and a large

Table 6.5   Relative rates of reduction of azido and thiocyanato complexes at 25°C

Oxidizing Agent	Reducing Agent	$k_{N_3^-}/k_{NCS^-}$
$Co(NH_3)_5X^{2+}$	Cr^{2+}	10^4
,,	V^{2+}	27
,,	Eu^{2+}	300
,,	Fe^{2+}	$>3 \times 10^3$
,,	$Cr(dipy)_3^{2+}$	4
,,	$Co(CN)_5^{3-}$	1.6
$Cr(H_2O)_5X^{2+}$	Cr^{2+}	4×10^4
$Fe(H_2O)_5X^{2+}$	Fe^{2+}	260

Reference 107.

value an inner-sphere mechanism, at least for the azido complex. On this basis all the systems shown except V^{2+}-$Co(NH_3)_5X^{2+}$ and $Cr(bipy)_3^{2+}$-$Co(NH_3)_5X^{2+}$ are inner sphere. The low ratio for $Co(CN)_5^{3-}$ has a special interpretation which will be discussed below.

That a bridged inner-sphere complex with atom transfer does occur for the Cr^{2+}-$FeCl^{2+}$ system has been shown by Dulz and Sutin.[108] Even though $FeCl^{2+}$ is labile, its rate of formation is slow enough to study in a flow apparatus. By mixing a solution containing chromous ions and chloride ions with one containing ferric ions, it was possible to show that the rate law for the oxidation of Cr^{2+} is given by

$$Rate = k_1[Cr^{2+}][Fe^{3+}] + k_2[Cr^{2+}][FeOH^{2+}]$$
$$+ k_3[Cr^{2+}][FeCl^{2+}] + k_4[Cr^{2+}][Fe^{3+}][Cl^-] \qquad (62)$$

The last two terms in the rate law both correspond to reactions in which $Cr(H_2O)_5Cl^{2+}$ was the product. It is only reasonable that k_3 corresponds to the bridged atom transfer reaction

$$FeCl^{2+} + Cr^{2+} \xrightarrow{k_3} Fe^{2+} + CrCl^{2+} \qquad (63)$$

The reaction given by k_4 is less certain, but most probably is the outer-sphere electron transfer reaction

$$Fe(H_2O)_6^{3+} + Cr(H_2O)_5Cl^+ \xrightarrow{k_4} Fe(H_2O)_6^{2+} + Cr(H_2O)_5Cl^{2+} \quad (64)$$

A somewhat different kind of information has been obtained in a study of the Fe^{2+}-Fe^{3+} exchange reaction in the presence of chloride ions.[109a] Again using flow methods, it was found that ferrous ion catalyzes the rate of dissociation of $FeCl^{2+}$. The dependence on Fe^{2+} concentration was first order. This catalysis is reasonably explained by the reaction

$$Fe(H_2O)_5Cl^{2+} + Fe(H_2O)_6^{2+} \rightarrow Fe(H_2O)_5Cl^+ + Fe(H_2O)_6^{3+} \quad (65)$$

followed by a rapid dissociation of very labile $FeCl^+$. Reaction 65 is an electron transfer reaction. Its rate constant is such that the exchange reaction involving Fe^{2+}-Fe^{3+}-Cl^- occurs about 40% by electron transfer as in 65. The remaining 60% logically occurs by the atom transfer path

$$FeCl^{2+} + Fe^{2+} \rightarrow Fe^{2+} + FeCl^{2+} \quad (66)$$

It should be noted that, by the principle of microscopic reversibility, both the forward and the reverse of reaction 65 contribute equally to the exchange process.‖

The reaction of Fe^{3+} with F^- to form FeF^{2+} is also rather slow, particularly at 0°C. By working under conditions where this formation rate is comparable to the isotope exchange rate, it has been shown that Fe^{2+} and FeF^{2+} are indeed the reactants in the exchange reaction.[109b]

The case of $Co(CN)_5^{3-}$ as a reducing agent is particularly interesting. This species is a diamagnetic dimer in the solid state but was shown to be a paramagnetic monomer with one unpaired electron in solution.[110] The assumption is that it is five coordinated or can easily become five coordinated. It is very easily oxidized by an atom transfer process with bromine and iodine.

$$Co(CN)_5^{3-} + X_2 \rightarrow Co(CN)_5X^{3-} + X\cdot \quad (67)$$

The species $Co(CN)_5X^{3-}$ is inert. For oxidation by a number of $Co(III)$ complexes, atom transfer also occurs.[111]

$$Co(NH_3)_5X^{2+} + Co(CN)_5^{3-} \rightarrow Co(CN)_5X^{3-} + 5NH_3 + Co(II) \quad (68)$$

For other $Co(III)$ complexes a different course is followed:[112]

$$Co(NH_3)_5X^{2+} + Co(CN)_5^{3-} + CN^- \rightarrow Co(CN)_6^{3-} + 5NH_3 + Co(II) + X^- \quad (69)$$

‖ This is an example of a multipath isotope exchange process. There is no symmetrical intermediate. See reference 135.

Furthermore the rate laws are different. For reaction 68 the rate law is

$$\text{Rate} = k[\text{Co(NH}_3)_5\text{X}^{2+}][\text{Co(CN)}_5^{3-}] \tag{70}$$

and for reaction 69 the rate law is

$$\text{Rate} = k[\text{Co(NH}_3)_5\text{X}^{2+}][\text{Co(CN)}_5^{3-}][\text{CN}^-] \tag{71}$$

It seems reasonable that 68 occurs by a bridged mechanism with atom transfer, and that 69 occurs by an electron transfer with Co(CN)_6^{4-} as the electron donor, and an outer-sphere transition state being formed.[112] Thus the products of reaction can be used as a diagnosis of mechanism. Table 6.4 shows the assignment of inner-sphere or outer-sphere mechanisms for Co(CN)_5^{3-} on the basis of the products formed.

Both thiocyanate and azide are listed as being transferred by an inner-sphere mechanism in this table. Yet Table 6.5 shows a ratio of reactivities near unity which is characteristic of an outer-sphere mechanism. The discrepancy is explained easily by thiocyanate being a good bridging group in the case of Co(CN)_5^{3-} as the reducing agent. Since $\text{Co(NH}_3)_5^{3+}$ is a hard acid unit whereas Co(CN)_5^{2-} is a soft acid unit,[112] the stable N-bonded $\text{Co(NH}_3)_5\text{NCS}^{2+}$ is converted to the stable[113a] S-bonded $\text{Co(CN)}_5\text{SCN}^{3-}$.

The cyanide ion can also act as a bridging group and is transferred[113b] in the reaction between $\text{Co(NH}_3)_5\text{CN}^{2+}$ and Co(CN)_5^{3-}. The product is normal C-bonded Co(CN)_6^{3-}. If the abnormal $\text{Co(CN)}_5\text{NC}^{3-}$ is formed first, it is probably rapidly converted to the normal form by a second group transfer to excess Co(CN)_5^{3-}. The spectrum of a transient attributed to $\text{Co(CN)}_5\text{NC}^{3-}$ has been observed.[221] It decays to the spectrum of Co(CN)_6^{3-} with a half-life of 1.6 sec at 25°C.

Figure 6.4 shows a plot of the log of the rate constants for reduction by V^{2+} and Cr(bipy)_3^{2+} of various $\text{Co(NH}_3)_5\text{X}^{3-n}$, related to $\text{Co(NH}_3)_5\text{H}_2\text{O}^{3+}$ as unity. The parallelism between the two sets of rates is obvious, though the occasional high values for V^{2+} may indicate a bridging mechanism for those oxidants. Also included in Figure 6.4 are the rate constants for reduction of $\text{Co(NH}_3)_5\text{X}^{3-n}$ at the dropping mercury electrode. As previously pointed out by Vlček,[114] the parallelism here indicates a common electron transfer mechanism for all three reductants. Thus the electrode reaction corresponds to an outer-sphere transition state. The linear relationship between the logs of the chemical and electrochemical rates of reduction implied in Fig. 6.5 is predicted by the Marcus-Hush theory.[20a,b,115]

Occasionally a bridged mechanism can be verified by the detection of the product as a stable bridged species. Thus the redox reaction between V^{2+} and VO^{2+} forms a bridged product 65% of the time:[116]

$$\text{V}^{2+} + \text{VO}^{2+} \rightarrow \text{VOV}^{4+} \tag{72}$$

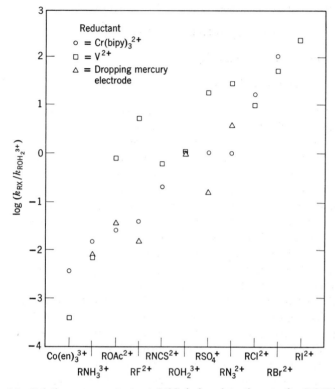

Fig. 6.4 Relative rate constants at 25°C (referred to the rate for ROH_2^{3+}) for the reduction of various Co(III) complexes. Ionic strengths: $Cr(bipy)_3^{2+}$, 0.1; V^{2+}, 1.0; dropping mercury electrode, 0.4. From reference 104a.

The species VOV^{4+} is moderately stable but is cleaved by acid.

$$VOV^{4+} + 2H^+ \rightarrow 2V^{3+} + H_2O \qquad (73)$$

The remaining 35% of the reaction goes to form V^{3+} directly and probably has an electron transfer mechanism.

The binuclear ions,

$$(NC)_5Co\!-\!O_2\!-\!Co(CN)_5^{6-} \quad \text{and} \quad (NC)_5Co\!-\!NC\!-\!Fe(CN)_5^{6-},$$

are formed[117] in the oxidation of $Co(CN)_5^{3-}$ by O_2 and $Fe(CN)_6^{3-}$. Binuclear species are often formed in the oxidation of Co(II) and Cr(II) by O_2 and two-equivalent oxidizing agents.[118] Such products seem compatible only with bridging mechanisms.

In Table 6.3 it is seen that $\Delta S^{\ddagger}$ is usually a large negative number. This is explained by the electron tunneling theory as due to a low value of κ.

In the Marcus-Hush theory, it is predicted for two reactants of the same charge sign. Occasionally a large positive $\Delta S^{\ddagger}$ is observed, e.g., HO_2^--Fe^{3+}. This is reasonably explained by the formation of a complex between the reactants.

$$Fe^{3+} + HO_2^- \rightleftharpoons FeO_2H^{2+} \tag{74}$$

$$FeO_2H^{2+} \rightarrow Fe^{2+} + HO_2\cdot \tag{75}$$

Reaction 75 is followed by

$$Fe^{3+} + HO_2\cdot \rightarrow Fe^{2+} + O_2 + H^+ \tag{76}$$

or, depending on the pH, O_2^- may be the reactant. The positive entropy is due to the loss of water of hydration when the charge neutralization step of 74 occurs.

Since $Fe(dipy)_3^{3+}$ oxidizes HO_2^- even faster and is inert, an outer-sphere electron transfer reaction seems possible in place of 74 and 75. It is generally found that dipyridyl ligands cause rapid electron transfer, either because a more favorable electron path is presented through unsaturated ligands, or because the lower valence state is stabilized.

Reactions 74–76 are part of the classical Haber-Weiss mechanism[46] for the decomposition of hydrogen peroxide in the presence of ferrous salts (Fenton's reagent). In spite of a very large number of studies, there is still no agreement as to the detailed mechanism of this reaction, except for the initial step,

$$Fe^{2+} + H_2O_2 \rightarrow FeOH^{2+} + HO\cdot \tag{77}$$

In place of 75–76, formation of Fe(V) has been suggested.[119]

$$Fe^{3+} + O_2H^- \rightarrow FeO^{3+} + OH^- \tag{78}$$

Effect of Ions on the Rate

As has already been indicated, the rates of exchange and redox reactions of complex ions are very sensitive to the presence of other ions in the solution. Usually added anions have the greatest influence on the rate of reaction of two cations with each other, and added cations influence the rate for two anions with each other. Large effects of anions on the rate are usually attributed to the formation of bridged species if labile complexes are involved.

In addition, other ways in which an anion can increase the rate of reaction between two cations can easily be imagined. In equation 65, or rather its reverse, and in 64 we have examples of the reducing agent being complexed first. This will stabilize it in the oxidized form and presumably speed up its rate of oxidation. Also the mere presence of a negative ion should enable two positive ions to approach each other more easily. This will be most effective if the negative ion is between the two cations in the transition state.

In this way small anions might act as pseudo bridges even for reactions which go by electron transfer. The large catalytic effects of OH^- and Cl^- on the exchange between $Co(NH_3)_6^{3+}$ and $Co(NH_3)_6^{2+}$ may be explained in this way:[80]

$$\left[\begin{array}{c} Co(NH_3)_6 \cdots O \cdots (NH_3)_6Co \\ H \end{array} \right]^{4+}$$

Alternatively OH^- may be directly coordinated to Co(II):

$$\left[\begin{array}{c} Co(NH_3)_6 \cdots O{-}Co(NH_3)_5 \\ H \end{array} \right]^{4+}$$

Since the newly formed Co(III) species appears as $Co(NH_3)_5OH^{2+}$, the latter formulation seems more reasonable.

If the oxidizing agent is complexed first, this may stabilize it and slow down its rate of reaction. For example, the rate of the reaction between $Ru(bipy)_3^{2+}$ and Ce^{4+} is reduced strongly by forming $Ce(SO_4)_3^{2-}$ first.[120] This shows, in agreement with theory, that coulombic repulsion between the reactants do not play a dominant role. The conclusion to be drawn is not that the electrostatic factors do not exist, but that other factors (reorganization energies) are of greater importance.

Some remarkable effects of cations are noted in the exchange reactions of MnO_4^{2-}-MnO_4^- [121] and $Fe(CN)_6^{4-}$-$Fe(CN)_6^{3-}$.[122] In spite of coulombic repulsions, these exchanges are extremely fast because the bond distances are similar in the two oxidation states. Thus little energy is needed to symmetrize the transition state. Since the complexes are all substitution inert, electron transfer mechanisms are indicated. Nevertheless the rates vary markedly with the cation which must necessarily be present. For the MnO_4^{2-}-MnO_4^- system the order of efficiency is $Cs^+ > K^+, Na^+ > Li^+$, so large cations are more effective. The rate constant is a linear function of the Cs^+ concentration.[123]

For $Fe(CN)_6^{4-}$-$Fe(CN)_6^{3-}$ the order is found to be[124] $Cs^+ > Rb^+ > K^+, NH_4^+ > Na^+ > Li^+ > H^+$ and $Sr^{2+} > Ca^{2+} > Mg^{2+}$. The very large cation, $(C_6H_5)_4As^+$, gives only a low rate of exchange, however. All these results indicate that the transition state contains a partly desolvated cation between the two exchanging anions[122]

$$[MnO_4 \cdots K \cdots MnO_4]^{2-}$$

An ion which is too large will not be effective, nor will one that is hard to desolvate, since it is effectively too large. For the ferrocyanide exchange, measurements have been extended into very concentrated solutions (saturated KCl).[124] Under these conditions a limiting rate is reached, no longer increasing with K^+ concentration. The transition state is probably

$$[KFe(CN)_6 \cdots K \cdots Fe(CN)_6 K]^{4-}$$

Some further insight into the role of the bridging cation is given by studies of the electron transfer between organic molecules and their anions.[125] These rapid reactions (k is $10^7-10^9 \ M^{-1} \ sec^{-1}$ at 25°C) are studied by e.p.r. line broadening methods. Solvents such as tetrahydrofuran and dimethoxyethane must be used. The rates vary not only with the solvent but also with the cations present. An example would be naphthalene and its negative ion, which is generated by the addition of an alkali metal:

$$C_{10}H_8 + Na \rightleftharpoons C_{10}H_8^-, Na^+ \tag{79}$$

In these cases it is known that the anion and the cation are strongly associated. Hence the electron transfer reaction is probably of the following nature:

$$C_{10}H_8 + C_{10}H_8^-, Na^+ \rightleftharpoons C_{10}H_8^-, Na^+ + C_{10}H_8 \tag{80}$$

Thus the cation would transfer with the electron to form a new ion pair.[126] In this case it is indistinguishable from a sodium atom transfer. Direct evidence that the sodium transfers together with the electron comes from the change in the e.p.r. spectrum of sodium benzophenone ketyl when benzophenone is added.[127] The fine structure due to the sodium nucleus (spin $\frac{3}{2}$) is not destroyed by electron transfer, though the proton fine structure is. Hence the unpaired electron does not change its sodium ion environment upon transfer.

The above conclusion drawn from experiments in slightly polar solvents may not necessarily be valid in water, where the isotope exchange reactions are studied. There are always effects on kinetic and thermodynamic properties when ionic reactants are subjected to changes in ionic environment. Even the non-specific influence of the ionic strength can be important. For example, the rate of the redox reaction between $Co(NH_3)_5Br^{2+}$ and $Ru(NH_3)_6^{2+}$ is decreased by a factor of twenty in going from an ionic strength of 0.2 to infinite dilution. Usually at higher concentrations the ionic strength principle is not valid, and the effects of various ions become more specific. At this point it becomes reasonable to assume that inner-sphere or outer-sphere complexes (ion pairs) have been formed, even when such species as ClO_4^- are involved.[128]

Complementary Two-Equivalent Exchanges

The previous discussion dealt with complementary one-equivalent changes in oxidation state. Studies of two-equivalent changes should show

some interesting features. The new questions that are raised concern
the possibilities of two-electron transfer mechanisms, the possibility of
doubled bridged mechanisms, and the possible formation of unstable
valence states.

A typical example is the exchange reaction of Tl^+-Tl^{3+}, which has been
extensively studied.[129] Nevertheless, there is still not agreement as to
whether the reaction occurs in a single two-electron transfer step or in a
series of steps with unstable Tl^{2+} as an intermediate. The extreme sensitivity which Tl^{2+} shows to traces of oxidizing or reducing metal ions
(p. 498 and reference 222) makes it rather unlikely that the exchange goes
by this intermediate.

The hydrolysis reaction

$$Tl(H_2O)_n^{3+} \rightleftharpoons Tl(H_2O)_{n-1}OH^{2+} + H^+ \tag{81}$$

introduces a pH dependence for the rate. The mechanisms would be

$$Tl^{3+} + Tl^+ \rightleftharpoons Tl^+ + Tl^{3+} \tag{82}$$

and

$$TlOH^{2+} + Tl^+ \rightleftharpoons Tl^+ + TlOH^{2+} \tag{83}$$

or

$$Tl^{3+} + Tl^+ \rightleftharpoons 2Tl^{2+} \tag{84}$$

$$TlOH^{2+} + Tl^+ \rightleftharpoons TlOH^+ + Tl^{2+} \tag{85}$$

$$Tl^{2+} + Tl^{3+} \rightleftharpoons Tl^{3+} + Tl^{2+} \tag{86}$$

$$Tl^{2+} + Tl^+ \rightleftharpoons Tl^+ + Tl^{2+}, \text{etc.} \tag{87}$$

The two mechanisms are kinetically indistinguishable. They lead to the
theoretical rate equation

$$k_{obs} = \frac{k_1[H^+] + k_2 K_a}{K_a + [H^+]} \tag{88}$$

where k_1 is the rate constant for the reaction of Tl^{3+}, and k_2 for $TlOH^{2+}$.
K_a is the equilibrium constant for 81. The experimental results fit equation
88 with K_a equal[140] to 7.3×10^{-2}. The values of k_1 and k_2 are 7.4×10^{-5}
$M^{-1} \sec^{-1}$ and 8.3×10^{-5} $M^{-1} \sec^{-1}$ respectively, in 3 M perchlorate solution at 25°C.[129c] Unlike previous examples, the hydroxo group does not
produce an accelerating effect in this exchange.

Even more remarkable is the effect of added anions.[129,130] Nitrate ion
has a simple accelerating effect, but Cl^-, Br^-, and CN^- show a complicated behavior. Small amounts of these ions inhibit the rate of the reaction.
A reduction to 1/200 of the original rate in the absence of cyanide ion is

found at a ratio of $[CN^-]/[Tl(III)] = 3.5$. This is a minimum value, and addition of more cyanide ion increases the rate approximately as the cube of the cyanide ion concentration. At $0.5\ M$ cyanide ion, the rate is 60 times as great as in the absence of cyanide. The only reasonable interpretation seems to be that complexes such as $TlCN^{2+}$ and $Tl(CN)_2^+$ are inert, whereas complexes such as $Tl(CN)_4^-$ and possible $Tl(CN)_2^-$ are reactive. Figure 6.5 shows the variation of the observed rate constant for $Tl(I)$-$Tl(III)$ exchange as a function of chloride concentration. The initial inhibition and subsequent speeding up are apparent. The minimum value of the rate occurs at about 2 moles of Cl^- bound per mole of $Tl(III)$.

Also shown on Fig. 6.5 are the fractions of $Tl(III)$ existing as species containing no chloride coordinated, α_0, one chloride coordinated, α_1, and so on. These were calculated by Nord-Waind[132] from equilibrium data in the literature obtained at the same (3.0) ionic strength. Rate constants can now be extracted from the exchange data to give the following results for the various paths:[132]

Reactants	Rate Constant
$[Tl^{3+}][Tl^+]$	$6.7 \times 10^{-5}\ M^{-1}\sec^{-1}$
$[TlCl^{2+}][Tl^+]$	2.8×10^{-6}
$[TlCl_4^-][Tl^+]$	4.6×10^{-5}
$[TlCl_4^-][TlCl_2^-]$	1.3×10^0
$[TlCl_4^-][TlCl_3^{2-}]$	1.9×10^1

Although these figures will reproduce the rate data, they cannot be taken as firmly established. Small changes in the equilibrium constants will influence them. There is considerable evidence[133] for species containing more chloride ion than $TlCl_4^-$, but such species were not considered in the calculations. However, the fact that the minimum in the rate constant occurs when the species $TlCl_2^+$ is maximal is good evidence for its relative inertness.

The similar system with Br^- added has also been studied in detail.[134] At $30°C$ and $\mu = 0.5$ the rate law for exchange is

$$\text{Rate} = k_0[Tl^{3+}][Tl^+] + k_2[TlBr_2^+]$$

$$+ k_3[TlBr_3] + k_4[Tl^+][TlBr_4^-] \tag{89}$$

$$+ k_6[TlBr_4^-][TlBr_2^-]$$

where $k_0 = 1.9 \times 10^{-4}\ M^{-1}\sec^{-1}$, $k_2 = 2.2 \times 10^{-6}\sec^{-1}$, $k_3 = 1.3 \times 10^{-6}$ $\sec^{-1}$, $k_4 = 1.3 \times 10^{-3}\ M^{-1}\sec^{-1}$, and $k_6 = 6.6 \times 10^{-1}\ M^{-1}\sec^{-1}$. The first term includes the rate due to both hydrolyzed and unhydrolyzed Tl^{3+}. The second and third terms, which are independent of the $Tl(I)$

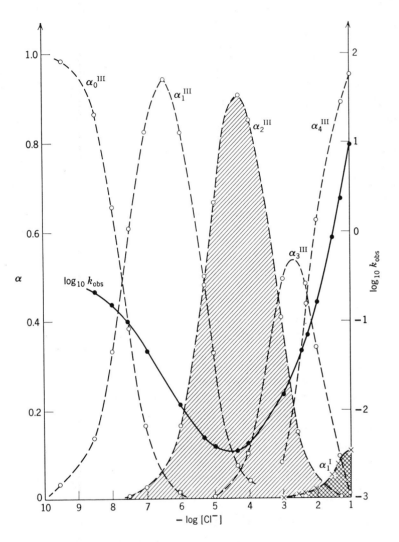

Fig. 6.5 Variation (logarithmic scale) of the observed rate constant for Tl(I)-Tl(III) exchange with chloride ion concentration. Also shown are the fractions of $Tl^{3+}(\alpha_0^{III})$, $TlCl^{2+}(\alpha_1^{III})$, $TlCl_2^+(\alpha_2^{III})$, $TlCl_3(\alpha_3^{III})$, $TlCl_4^-(\alpha_4^{III})$, and $TlCl(\alpha_1^{I})$, as a function of chloride ion concentration. From reference 132.

concentration, are probably governed by the rates of the dissociation reactions,

$$TlBr_2^+ \xrightarrow{k_2} Tl^+ + Br_2 \tag{90}$$

$$TlBr_3 \xrightarrow{k_3} Tl^+ + Br_2 + Br^- \tag{91}$$

followed by their rapid reversals.

For reaction 90 this conclusion was checked by measuring the rate of the reverse reaction directly and comparing the ratio of forward and reverse rate constants with the directly measured equilibrium constant. However, the reverse reaction of 91 could not be detected. That is, the rate of oxidation of Tl^+ by Br_2 was not dependent on the bromide ion concentration. Scavenging of Br_2 by organic reducing agents, such as phenol, greatly reduced the exchange rate. At the same time Tl(I) was formed at a rate equal to that predicted from 90 and 91.

The fact that the rate law 89 corresponds to activated complexes containing only even numbers of bromide ions suggests that a doubled-bridged species is formed for the exchange process, e.g.,

The activated complex containing seven chloride ions in the previous example, however, suggests a single chloro bridge:[132]

There is no absolute reason why a symmetrical structure must be formed in these exchanges, but it is usually found that symmetric structures are of lower energy.[135]

Exchanges between Sn(II)-Sn(IV)[136] and Sb(III)-Sb(V)[137] have also been studied in strong HCl. The exchange certainly occurs between species containing large numbers of chloride ions. For the tin case the composition is not known,¶ but for antimony the rate seems to be greatest for $SbCl_3$-$SbCl_6^{3-}$. Symmetry would be achieved by two octahedra sharing one face, or three chloride bridges.

¶ It is known that the most reactive reducing species of Sn(II) is $SnCl_3^-$, not $SnCl_2$ or $SnCl_4^{2-}$ [G. P. Haight, Jr., and C. v. Frankenberg, *Acta Chem. Scand.*, **15**, 2026 (1961)].

Experiments in non-aqueous solvents in which ions are superseded by neutral species are of some further help. In alcohols[138] the exchange reaction of $SnCl_2$-$SnCl_4$ follows the simple rate law

$$\text{Rate} = k[SnCl_2][SnCl_4] \tag{92}$$

The rate laws for exchange of $SbCl_3$ with $SbCl_5$[139] and of PCl_3 with PCl_5[140] in carbon tetrachloride solvent show that the dissociation paths are important,

$$SbCl_5 \rightleftharpoons SbCl_3 + Cl_2$$
$$\tag{93}$$
$$PCl_5 \rightleftharpoons PCl_3 + Cl_2$$

There is no simple relationship between the change in oxidation state and the number of bridges which is most favorable. For example, the reduction of cis-$Cr(H_2O)_4F_2^+$ or of cis-$Co(en)_2(H_2O)_2^{2+}$ with Cr^{2+} results in the transfer of only one group[151]

$$CrF_2^+ + Cr^{2+} \rightarrow CrF^+ + CrF^{2+} \tag{94}$$

Presumably only one bridge is formed. On the other hand cis-$Cr(H_2O)_4$-$(N_3)_2^+$ reacts with Cr^{2+} to give exchange, but with no change in the structure of the complex.[142]

$$Cr(N_3)_2^+ + Cr^{2+} \rightarrow Cr^{2+} + Cr(N_3)_2^+ \tag{95}$$

This can only be explained by a double bridge, even though just one electron is transferred.

$$\left[\begin{array}{c} N{=}N{=}N \\ Cr \diagup \hspace{2em} \diagdown Cr \\ N{=}N{=}N \end{array} \right]^{3+}$$

There is at least one case of two-equivalent exchange in which a single halide bridge seems to be clearly indicated. This is the Pt(II)-Pt(IV) system. Studies[143] of the exchange of radiochloride with $trans$-$Pt(en)_2Cl_2^{2+}$ show that the rate of exchange is extremely slow unless catalyzed by $[Pt(en)_2]^{2+}$. The rate law expression for the catalyzed exchange was found to be

$$\text{Rate} = k[Pt(IV)][Pt(II)][Cl^-] \tag{96}$$

The mechanism proposed for chloride exchange is given by equations 97 and 98. Equilibrium 97

$$Pt(en)_2^{2+} + Cl^- \underset{\text{fast}}{\overset{\text{fast}}{\rightleftharpoons}} Pt(en)_2Cl^+ \tag{97}$$

is established rapidly because it involves the very labile fifth and sixth positions along the z axis above and below the xy plane of the Pt(II) complex. Equilibrium 98

$$Pt(en)_2Cl^+ + \textit{trans-}Pt(en)_2Cl_2{}^{2+} \overset{slow}{\underset{fast}{\rightleftharpoons}} \begin{matrix} en & & en \\ Cl-Pt-Cl-Pt-Cl^{3+} \\ en & & en \end{matrix} \qquad (98)$$

is rate determining and amounts to a two-electron transfer via a bridged activated complex. This mechanism is also a path for Pt(II)-Pt(IV) exchange. In fact it has been shown that platinum exchange occurs at the same rate and with the same rate law as chloride exchange.[144]

The exchange of radiochloride with other chlorammine Pt(IV) cations has been investigated.[145] It was found that $\textit{trans-}Pt(NH_3)_4Cl_2{}^{2+}$ and $\textit{trans-}Pt(en)_2Cl_2{}^{2+}$ exchange approximately 10^3–10^4 times faster than do $Pt(NH_3)_5$-Cl^{3+} and $\textit{cis-}Pt(NH_3)_4Cl_2{}^{2+}$. Furthermore two of the chloride ions in

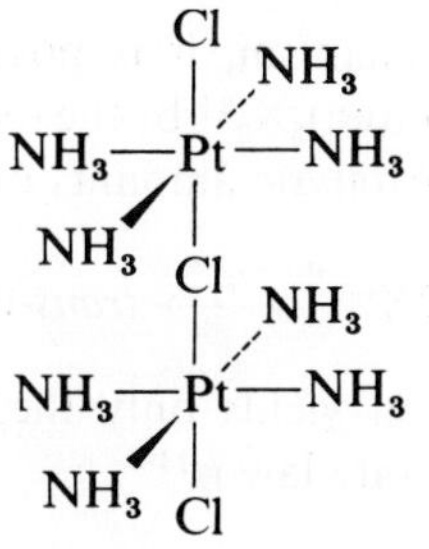

Fig. 6.6 Bridged intermediate proposed for the $Pt(NH_3)_4{}^{2+}$-catalyzed chloride exchange of $\textit{trans-}Pt(NH_3)_4Cl_2{}^{2+}$.

$\textit{trans-}Pt(NH_3)_3Cl_3{}^+$ exchange much more rapidly than does the third. These results are readily explained in terms of the bridged intermediate mechanism proposed in equations 97 and 98. Exchange of $\textit{trans-}$dichloro groups, Cl—Pt—Cl, in a complex occurs easily as a result of the formation of a linear bridged system of the type Cl—Pt—Cl—Pt—Cl. Cleavage of a terminal Pt-Cl bond must accompany exchange (Fig. 6.6). Instead, for complexes where Cl^- is $\textit{trans}$ to NH_3, Cl—Pt—NH$_3$, exchange by this mechanism involves the bridged system Cl—Pt—Cl—Pt—NH$_3$ and cleavage of the Pt-N bond (Fig. 6.7). Since the Pt-N bond is stronger than the Pt-Cl, it follows that chloride exchange in complexes containing only Cl—Pt—NH$_3$ will be slower than in analogous systems having the $\textit{trans}$ grouping Cl—Pt—Cl. The formation of $\textit{trans-}Pt(NH_3)_4Cl_2{}^{2+}$ from the reaction of $Pt(NH_3)_5Cl^{3+}$ with HCl in the presence of $Pt(NH_3)_4{}^{2+}$ was first reported by Rubinstein.[146] No explanation was given for the catalytic role of $Pt(NH_3)_4{}^{2+}$, but it now has been shown that the rates of chloride exchange and of $\textit{trans-}Pt(NH_3)_4Cl_2{}^{2+}$ formation are the same.[145] This is in agreement with the bridged redox mechanism.

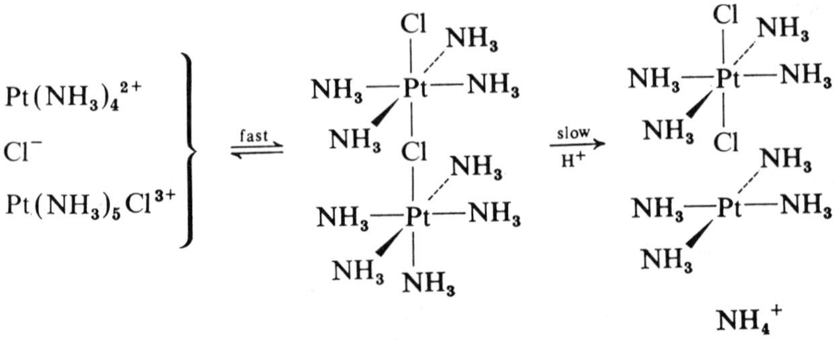

Fig. 6.7 Mechanism proposed for chloride exchange and reaction of acid solution containing $Pt(NH_3)_4^{2+}$ and $Pt(NH_3)_5Cl^{3+}$.

As suggested by this mechanism, it is possible to prepare[147] several complexes of the type *trans*-$Pt(en)_2X_2^{2+}$ by the reaction of *trans*-$Pt(en)_2Cl_2^{2+}$ with X^- in the presence of catalytic amounts of $Pt(en)_2^{2+}$:

$$trans\text{-}Pt(en)_2Cl_2^{2+} + 2X^- \xrightarrow{Pt(en)_2^{2+}} trans\text{-}Pt(en)_2X_2^{2+} + 2Cl^- \qquad (99)$$

The reaction with nitrite ion yields only the monosubstituted product *trans*-$Pt(en)_2NO_2Cl]^{2+}$. The rate law is[148]

$$\text{Rate} = k[Pt(II)][Pt(IV)][NO_2^-] \qquad (100)$$

similar to that for chloride exchange. Failure to form the dinitro compound is attributed to the failure of the nitro group to form a suitable bridge for the redox reaction. Bridged complexes in which NO_2 is the bridging group are known. These necessarily involve metal-oxygen bonding in one part of the bridge. It can be seen that the redox mechanism would lead to the formation of an unstable Pt-ONO bond, and hence this reaction is unlikely.

$$O_2N\text{—}Pt\text{—}O\overset{O}{\diagdown}N\text{—}Pt\text{—}Cl \rightarrow O_2N\text{—}Pt\text{—}ONO + Pt\text{—}Cl \qquad (101)$$

Since in the reactions of Pt(IV) it is almost impossible to avoid all traces of Pt(II), there is a strong likelihood that most substitution reactions of Pt(IV) complexes occur by the catalytic paths shown (see Chapter 3).

It is possible that substitution reactions of other metal ions having valence states differing by two units are catalyzed in a similar way. The reaction of $Rh(H_2O)Cl_5^{2-}$ with pyridine to form *trans*-$Rhpy_4Cl_2^+$ is catalyzed by reducing agents.[149] It has been suggested that a planar Rh(I) complex is the catalyst by way of a bridged mechanism.[150] Instead, a hydrido complex of Rh(III) may be the active catalyst.[151]

Table 6.6 Rate data at 25°C for the reaction

$$Pt(NH_3)_5X^{3+} + Y^- \xrightarrow{Pt(NH_3)_4^{2+}} trans\text{-}Pt(NH_3)_4XY^{2+} + NH_3$$

X	Y	$k, M^{-2} \sec^{-1}$	$\Delta H^{\ddagger}$, kcal	$\Delta S^{\ddagger}$, eu
I	I⁻	3.9×10^2	6	−29
I	Br⁻	1.2×10^4	8	−15
I	Cl⁻	5.6×10^2	11	−10
Br	Br⁻	1.2×10^1	10	−19
Cl	Cl⁻	1.2×10^{-3}	18	−13

Data from reference 152.

Table 6.6 gives the third-order rate constants for the reaction

$$Pt(NH_3)_5X^{3+} + Y^- \xrightarrow{Pt(NH_3)_4^{2+}} Pt(NH_3)_4XY^{2+} + NH_3 \qquad (102)$$

for several combinations of X and Y.[152] By taking similar pairs in which the nucleophile is constant and the bridging atom varies, it may be concluded that the order of bridging efficiency is I⁻ > Br⁻ > Cl⁻ in the ratios of 400,000:400:1. Since these are all cases in which the bridge is probably broken and formed many times before an ammonia molecule is released, the ratios reflect principally the thermodynamic stability of the bridged intermediates and not kinetic properties. That is, they are a measure of k_1/k_2 in equations 29 and 30, with $k_2 \gg k_3$. Since both Pt(II) and Pt(IV) are soft metal ions, the greater stability of an iodide bridge is not surprising.

Not all Pt(II)-Pt(IV) exchanges occur by the bridged mechanism. Exchange between $PtCl_4^{2-}$ and $PtCl_6^{2-}$ is accelerated by light and inhibited by one-electron reducing agents such as $IrCl_6^{3-}$. It is suggested[153] that the primary exchange path is disproportionation to Pt(III),

$$Pt(II) + Pt(IV) \rightleftharpoons 2Pt(III) \qquad (103)$$

It is found[153] that radiochloride exchange of $PtCl_6^{2-}$ is catalyzed by $PtCl_4^{2-}$. This is explained by assuming that Pt(III) is labile.

Exchange between $PtBr_6^{2-}$ and Br⁻ is also catalyzed by $PtBr_4^{2-}$ and other reducing agents and inhibited by oxidizing agents.[154] The rate laws are not simple, though in one case, reaction of $PtBr_6^{2-}$ with Cl⁻, a rate law similar to 96 has been observed.[155]

Unstable Oxidation States

For non-complementary redox reactions it may be expected that mechanisms in which species in unusual oxidation states are formed will be common. These species will be short-lived transients. The alternatives to these unstable species will be improbable termolecular and polymolecular mechanisms. Another expected feature of these reactions will be the frequent occurrence of catalysis, since the normal paths will be slow.

The reductions of Tl(III) are somewhat slower than corresponding reactions of other metal ions in which one-equivalent valence changes are possible. There is evidence that this slowness is due to the formation of unstable Tl(II) in some of these reactions.[156]

The reaction of Tl^{3+} with Fe^{2+} is first order in each reactant during most of the reaction, indicating a rate-determining step as either

$$Fe^{2+} + Tl^{3+} \rightleftharpoons Fe^{3+} + Tl^{2+} \tag{104}$$

or

$$Fe^{2+} + Tl^{3+} \rightleftharpoons Fe^{4+} + Tl^{+} \tag{105}$$

The second-order rate constant declines after the first 60% of reaction. This indicates that the reversal of 104 or 105 begins to compete with the follow-up step,

$$Fe^{2+} + Tl^{2+} \rightarrow Fe^{3+} + Tl^{+} \tag{106}$$

or

$$Fe^{2+} + Fe^{4+} \rightarrow 2Fe^{3+} \tag{107}$$

It was found that the addition of Fe^{3+} slowed down the reaction markedly, whereas Tl^{+} has no effect on the rate. This shows that 104 and 106 form a possible mechanism, whereas 105 and 107 do not. Furthermore an integrated rate equation including the reverse of reaction 104, and using the steady state approximation for $[Tl^{2+}]$, fits the concentration-time data out to more than 90% of the reaction. The reductions of Tl^{3+} with V(III) and V(IV) also seem to go through the formation of Tl(II).[157]

Interconversions between Cr(III) and Cr(VI) always appear to involve the unstable states Cr(IV) and Cr(V). In a classic study King and Tong[158] have worked out the details of the complex redox reaction

$$3Ce^{4+} + Cr^{3+} + 4H_2O \rightarrow 3Ce^{3+} + HCrO_4^{-} + 7H^{+} \tag{108}$$

In a constant concentration of H_2SO_4 the rate law as found to be

$$\text{Rate} = \frac{k[Ce(IV)]^2[Cr(III)]}{[Ce(III)]} \tag{109}$$

This rate law is very reasonably explained by the mechanism

$$Ce(IV) + Cr(III) \rightleftharpoons Ce(III) + Cr(IV) \qquad \text{fast} \tag{110}$$

$$Ce(IV) + Cr(IV) \rightarrow Ce(III) + Cr(V) \qquad \text{slow} \tag{111}$$

$$Ce(IV) + Cr(V) \rightarrow Ce(III) + Cr(VI) \qquad \text{fast} \tag{112}$$

The first step is a rapid equilibrium, and the second step, the interconversion of Cr(IV) and Cr(V), is rate determining. The rate also depends inversely on the square of the bisulfate ion concentration, but this merely reflects differences in the degree of complexing of Ce(IV) and Ce(III) and is relatively unimportant.

Excellent support for this mechanism comes from a study of a related one, the oxidation of vanadyl ion by chromate ion in acid[159]

$$3VO^+ + HCrO_4^- + H^+ \rightarrow 3VO_2^+ + Cr^{3+} + H_2O \qquad (113)$$

The rate law is

$$Rate = \frac{[VO^{2+}]^2(k[HCrO_4^-] + k'[HCr_2O_7^-])}{[VO_2^+]} \qquad (114)$$

The mechanism for the first term is

$$V(IV) + Cr(VI) \rightleftharpoons V(V) + Cr(V) \qquad \text{fast} \qquad (115)$$

$$V(IV) + Cr(V) \rightarrow V(V) + Cr(IV) \qquad \text{slow} \qquad (116)$$

$$V(IV) + Cr(IV) \rightarrow V(V) + Cr(III) \qquad \text{fast} \qquad (117)$$

The second term of 114 would be due to a similar sequence in which $HCr_2O_7^-$ rather than $HCrO_4^-$ was the Cr(VI) starting species. A rate law quite analogous to 114 is found for the analytically important oxidation of ferrous ion by chromate.[160]

It is significant that in all of these examples the changeover from Cr(V) to Cr(IV), or vice versa, is rate determining. This may be related to the likelihood that at this stage a change in coordination number from 4 to 6 occurs.[158] The unstable ions CrO_4^{3-} and CrF_6^{2-} are known to have a tetrahedral[161] and an octahedral[162] structure, respectively.

Further proof for the existence of reactive intermediates in the reduction of Cr(VI) comes from the observation of induced oxidation of iodide ion during the course of these reactions.[160] The direct reaction of chromate and iodide ions is slow, but adding Fe^{2+} or VO^{2+} will cause rapid oxidation of I^- by reaction with Cr(V) and Cr(IV). A related phenomenon is seen in the oxidation of As(III) by persulfate ion. This slow reaction is accelerated, or oxidation is induced, by adding Fe(II).[163] The reaction is postulated to go by the formation of As(IV) from the reaction,

$$As(V) + SO_4^- \rightarrow As(IV) + SO_4^{2-} \qquad (118)$$

The formula SO_4^- refers to the radical anion from the reaction of Fe^{2+} with $S_2O_8^{2-}$,

$$Fe^{2+} + S_2O_8^{2-} \rightarrow Fe(III) + SO_4^{2-} + SO_4^- \qquad (119)$$

This reaction is analogous to 46.

Silver(III) is probably an intermediate in the reduction of Ag(II).[164] For the reaction,

$$2Ag^{2+} + H_2O \rightarrow 2Ag^+ + 2H^+ + \tfrac{1}{2}O_2 \tag{120}$$

the rate law is, in perchlorate medium,

$$\text{Rate} = k\,\frac{[Ag^{2+}]^2[ClO_4^-]^2}{[Ag^+][H^+]^2} \tag{121}$$

This suggests the equilibrium

$$2Ag^{2+} \rightleftharpoons Ag^+ + Ag(III) \tag{122}$$

as a fast, first step followed by a slow reaction of Ag(III). It is of interest that the exchange reaction[165] between Ag^+ and Ag^{2+} also appears to proceed via reaction 122. The direct electron transfer is apparently quite slow.

Other examples of unusual oxidation states are Pb(III) in the reduction of Pb(IV)[166] and Sn(III) in the reduction of Sn(IV).[167] Evidence for Fe(IV) has been obtained in the reaction of Fe^{2+} with the two-electron oxidants, Cl_2, HOCl, and O_3.[168] Surprisingly H_2O_2 does not seem to give Fe(IV), though this oxidation state has often been postulated in the Fe^{2+}-H_2O_2 reaction.[119]

The slow reaction between Tl^+ and Ce(IV) can be catalyzed by Ag^+. The sequence seems to be[157]

$$Ce(IV) + Ag^+ \rightarrow Ce(III) + Ag^{2+} \qquad \text{fast} \tag{123}$$

$$Tl^+ + Ag^{2+} \rightarrow Tl^{2+} + Ag^+ \qquad \text{slow} \tag{124}$$

$$Tl^{2+} + Ce(IV) \rightarrow Tl^{3+} + Ce(III) \qquad \text{fast} \tag{125}$$

A similar catalysis by Ag^+ of the oxidation of Hg_2^{2+} by Ce(IV) is observed.[157]

Copper(II) is famous as a catalyst for redox reactions, particularly when O_2 is the oxidant. An example is the oxidation of U(IV), which is believed to go by a chain mechanism.[169] The initiation step is

$$U(IV) + Cu^{2+} \rightarrow U(V) + Cu(I) \tag{126}$$

The catalyst is regenerated by the rapid reoxidation of cuprous copper with molecular oxygen,

$$Cu(I) + O_2 \rightarrow Cu(II) + O_2^- \tag{127}$$

This facile oxidation may be related to the formation of a π complex of O_2 with Cu(I).

Electron Transfer Through Extended Bridges

In this section we discuss the situation where an inner-sphere bridge is formed between two metal or other atoms and the transfer of electrons through the bridge from one atom to the other becomes rate determining. This would be a case where $k_2 \gg k_3$ in equation 29 and 30. If the bridge consists only of a single atom, such as a halogen, then the molecular orbital theory of valence would show the transferring electron already distributed over all three atoms. This is probably true even for the highly conjugated azide ion, which would form a three-atom bridge. The requirement is that there be a large overlap between the orbitals on each neighboring pair of atoms, including the two metal atoms.

In such cases electron transfer would not be a slow step and, as already discussed, formation of the bridge would be rate determining, provided the bridge cleaved at least half the time to form the product. This would be the case for an isotope exchange reaction. In these and similar cases there would be extensive electron transfer in the bridged intermediate, and probably considerable transfer in the transition state leading to it. Thus the redox properties would play a role in influencing the rate of the overall reaction.

An interesting comparison may be made[170] between the two reactions, exchange between $CrCl^{2+}$ and Cr^{2+} and aquation of $CrCl^{2+}$ catalyzed by Hg^{2+}. In each case a bridge is postulated:

$$CrCl^{2+} + Cr^{2+} \rightleftharpoons Cr-Cl-Cr^{4+} \rightleftharpoons Cr^{2+} + ClCr^{2+} \qquad (128)$$

$$CrCl^{2+} + Hg^{2+} \rightleftharpoons Cr-Cl-Hg^{4+} \rightleftharpoons Cr^{3+} + ClHg^{+} \qquad (129)$$

The probability of decomposition of the bridged complex is symmetric in the first case. The overall free energy change is $\Delta G^0 = 0$. The Hg^{2+} aquation reaction is much slower than the exchange reaction by a factor of 10^3, even though the overall reaction has $\Delta G^0 = -7.6$ kcal at $25°C$.

The variation between the rates and the total free energy changes seems to throw some doubt on the postulated similarity of mechanism. However, the slower rate is explained quite easily. Reaction 128 forms Cr(II) with a reduced coordination number of five, whereas 129 forms Cr(III) with a reduced coordination number. The latter would surely be more difficult. In each case a water molecule would enter the coordination sphere when the metal-chlorine bond is long enough. This would make the overall process in 129 energetically favorable, but a large barrier for the bridge breaking would exist.

For the problem of slow electron transfer, the question becomes one of electronic conduction, or permeability to electrons of various ligands.

Studies of outer-sphere electron transfer mechanisms are relevant, and it is true in general that large unsaturated or polarizable ligands such as o-phenathroline, dipyridyl, and cyanide ions speed up such reactions. Also electron transfer is slower to $Coen_3{}^{3+}$ than to $Co(NH_3)_6{}^{3+}$, which might be blamed on the ethylene backbone of en being an insulating group. In all these cases the effect of the ligands in changing the reorganization energy is probably more important than electron permeability. Also it has been shown[171] that solvation effects accompanying the reduction may be quite different for NH_3 and en and will affect the rates.

The best evidence that electron transfer can occur through an extended bridge of atoms, and detailed information as to how the nature of the bridge influences the rate, come from the studies by Taube and his students on the reaction

$$
\begin{array}{c}
\qquad\qquad O \\
\qquad\qquad \| \\
Co(NH_3)_5O\!-\!C\!-\!R^{q+} + Cr^{2+} \rightarrow
\end{array}
$$

$$
\begin{array}{c}
\qquad\qquad O \\
\qquad\qquad \| \\
Co^{2+} + 5NH_3 + Cr(H_2O)_5O\!-\!C\!-\!R^{q+}
\end{array}
\qquad (130)
$$

The group R is varied to include a range of saturated and unsaturated systems and substituents containing donor atoms which are capable of coordinating Cr(II). Table 6.7 contains a number of rate constants and related data for examples of reaction 130.

The results for acetato, butyrato, and acid succinato all suggest a similar mechanism in which the chromous ion coordinates to the carbonyl group which is already attached to cobalt. The rate for the methyl succinate ester is also similar. The succinate ion accelerates the rate somewhat, which is normal since the other reactant is a cation. The increased rates for oxalate, fumarate, and maleate are striking. They are attributed[172] to easy co-ordination of the Cr(II) to the free carboxylate group of these acids. The unsaturated nature of the ligands can then allow easy electron flow to the cobalt. Close approach of Cr^{2+} to the cobalt atom is avoided together with electrostatic and steric repulsions. The intermediate would be, for fumaric acid,

$$
\begin{array}{ccc}
(NH_3)_5Co\!-\!O & & O\!-\!Cr(H_2O)_5{}^{3+} \\
\diagdown & & \diagup\!\!\diagup \\
& C\!-\!CH\!=\!CH\!-\!C & \\
\diagup\!\!\diagup & & \diagdown \\
O & & OH
\end{array}
$$

It will be noted that the unsaturated system is conjugated. Also the rate law for these accelerated systems contains a term proportional to $[H^+]$.

Table 6.7   Rates of reduction of $Co(NH_3)_5OCOR^{q+}$ by chromous ion at 25°C

Ligand	$k, M^{-1} sec^{-1}$	$\Delta H^{\ddagger}$, kcal	$\Delta S^{\ddagger}$, eu	Reference
CH_3CO_2	0.18	3.0	−52	173
$n\text{-}C_3H_7CO_2$	0.08	...	...	174
Succinic acid	0.17	...	...	173
Succinate ion	1.0	...	...	173
Me-succinate ester	0.22	...	...	173
CF_3CO_2	0.05	...	...	175a
$C_6H_5CO_2$	0.14	4.9	−46	176
HCO_2	7.0	...	...	177
Oxalic acid	450	...	...	
Maleic acid	200	...	...	
Fumaric acid	1.3	6.7	−36	173
o-Phthalic acid	0.055	4.5	−47	173
o-Phthalate ion	~10	...	...	173
m-Phthalic acid	0.10	2.1	−56	173
p-Phthalic acid	0.20	...	...	175b
Glycolate	3.1	9.0	−26	177a
Malonate ion	2.5×10^3	...	...	177a
Pyridine-2-carboxylate	2×10^5	...	...	175a
Salicylic acid	0.15	...	...	175a
Salicylate ion	2×10^8	...	...	175a
p-Formylbenzoate	29^b	...	...	175a
o-Carbamic acid	9.1	...	...	181
N-urethane	400	...	...	181
Imidazole	10^{-4}	...	...	175b
Pyridine	6×10^{-3}	...	...	175b

Ionic strength = 1.0.

This is explained by assuming that protonation of the carbonyl adjacent to Co(III) improves the conjugation because of greater symmetry.

$$(NH_3)_5Co—O \diagdown \qquad\qquad O—Cr(H_2O)_5{}^{4+}$$
$$C—CH{=}CH—C$$
$$HO \diagup \qquad\qquad\qquad OH$$

The entire process whereby the electron flows through the conjugated system is called *resonance transfer*.

Oxalic acid, maleic acid, and formic acid also have high rates even though they are not capable of full conjugation (maleic for steric reasons). It has been suggested[172] that in these cases a different mechanism for electron transfer by the bridging group is possible. The electron is transferred from Cr(II) to the ligand, and a lag occurs before it is finally transferred to the oxidizing metal ion. The ligand remains coordinated to the Co(III) in the form of a radical ion. It is significant that oxalate, formate, and maleate as free acids or ions are easily reduced, whereas the phthalic acids are not.

p-Phthalic acid, in spite of being capable of a fully conjugated path for resonance transfer, does not react by remote attack.[175b] It is possible that resonance transfer is an uncommon phenomenon, but that radical ions are common. The usual behavior is that the radical ion transfers the electron to the Co(III) ion and reverts back to the normal ligand. Cases are known, however, where the ligand is itself reduced.[175b]

Kinetic evidence for the radical ion theory exists in a study of the oxidation of formatopentamminecobalt(III) ion by permanganate ion.[178] The stoichiometry follows one of two paths:

$$3Co(NH_3)_5OCHO^{2+} + MnO_4^- \rightarrow 3CO_2 + 3Co^{2+} + MnO_2 \quad (131)$$

$$3Co(NH_3)_5OCHO^{2+} + 2MnO_4^- \rightarrow 3CO_2 + 3Co(NH_3)_5H_2O^{3+} + 2MnO_2 \quad (132)$$

The ratio of unreduced to reduced cobalt is found to depend on the MnO_4^- concentration,

$$[Co(NH_3)_5H_2O^{3+}]/[Co^{2+}] = 3 \times 10^2[MnO_4^-] \quad (133)$$

A large deuterium isotope effect of 10.5 is found on substituting $Co(NH_3)OCDO^{2+}$ for the faster-reacting protium complex.

These observations support the mechanism

$$Co(NH_3)_5OCHO^{2+} + MnO_4^- \rightarrow Co(NH_3)_5(CO_2^-)^{2+} + HMnO_4^-$$
$$Co(NH_3)_5(CO_2^-)^{2+} \rightarrow Co^{2+} + CO_2 \quad (134)$$

or

$$Co(NH_3)_5(CO_2^-)^{2+} \xrightarrow{MnO_4^-} Co(NH_3)_5H_2O^{3+} + CO_2 \quad (135)$$

The radical ion intermediate, $Co(NH_3)_5(CO_2^-)^{2+}$, can have one of two fates, depending on the permanganate concentration.

Other observations which support the idea of a radical ion mechanism include the partial isomerization of maleate and methyl maleate (but not the fumarates) when used as bridging ligands.[179b] Hydrogen isotope exchange occurs when these same reactions are run in D_2O. It may be noted that in all of these cases involving Co(III) as the oxidizing metal the electron to be accepted must go into an e_g orbital of the metal. These orbitals in octahedral complexes do not overlap (form π bonds) with ligand orbitals of the π type. Hence resonance transfer can only occur by random destruction of octahedral symmetry such as vibrational distortion. The electron from Cr(II) also comes from an e_g orbital.

Possible evidence that Cr^{2+} does attack a remote position from the carboxyl group coordinated to Co(III) comes from studies of the reduction of half-esters of fumaric and p-phthalic acid used as ligands.[180a,b] Reduction of $Co(NH_3)_5OCOCH{=}CHOCOMe^{2+}$ reportedly leads to the hydrolysis of the ester and the association of the methyl group, as methyl alcohol, to Cr(III) after the redox reaction. This result implies that Cr^{2+} coordinates to the ester function before being oxidized. V^{2+} and Eu^{2+} also cause ester hydrolysis, but Fe^{2+}, $Cr(dipy)_3^{2+}$, and $V(dipy)_3^{2+}$ do not.[179a,180]

The very rapid reduction of p-formylbenzoate coordinated to $Co(NH_3)_5^{3+}$ also offers proof for remote attack (Table 6.7). The products of oxidation are $Cr(H_2O)_6^{3+}$ and free p-$HCOC_6H_4COOH$. In this case complexing of Cr^{3+} to the formyl group does not lead to a stable complex, and the free ligand is obtained.** A number of other cases are known with similar behavior.[175]

The entries in Table 6.6 also show that possible chelation of Cr(II) has an accelerating effect. The influence can be rather small, as for glycolic acid, $CH_2OHCOOH$, or very large, as for the anion of salicylic acid, o-$HOOCC_6H_4O^-$. In the latter case, there is the possibility of not only chelation but also of the transmission of the electron through the conjugated system. A study has been made [177b] of the products of reduction of malonatopentamminecobalt(III) with Cr^{2+}. The product is the chelated $Cr(H_2O)_4(mal)^+$ in amounts greater than 85%. Since the ring closure of the monodentate $Cr(H_2O)_5(mal)^+$ is quite slow, the chelation must have occurred with Cr(II) before oxidation to Cr(III), e.g.,

$$\begin{array}{c} CH_2 \\ \diagup \ \diagdown \\ (NH_3)_5Co{-}O{-}C \qquad C{-}OH^{4+} \\ \colon \qquad \colon \\ O \qquad O \\ \diagdown \ \diagup \\ Cr \end{array}$$

(I)

When the half-ester of malonic acid is used as the carboxylato function, the chelated $Cr(H_2O)_4(mal)^+$ is also formed as a major product.[180c] This is obviously accompanied by ester hydrolysis. The implication is that an intermediate such as I, but with an alkyl group in place of the proton, was formed before electron transfer. The hydrolysis would follow the oxidation of Cr(II) to inert Cr(III). The reducing ions V(II) and Eu(II) do not cause ester hydrolysis with malonate half-esters. In these cases the oxidized

---

** Complexes resulting from remote attack are formed in the reduction of nicotinamide complexes of cobalt(III) by Cr^{2+} [F. R. Nordmeyer and H. Taube, *J. Am. Chem. Soc.*, **88**, 4295 (1966)].

forms would be labile. We can conclude that the mere observation of ester hydrolysis does not necessarily mean remote attack.

When a ligand such as ethyl carbamate (urethane) is bonded to $Co(NH_3)_5{}^{3+}$ through a nitrogen atom, a very high rate of reduction is found.[181] A comparison of acetato, carbamato, and urethano complexes in Table 6.7 shows that the relative rates of electron transfer along the series

$$O{=}C{\cdots}\overset{\leftarrow}{O}, \qquad O{\cdots}C{\cdots}\overset{\leftarrow}{N}, \qquad \text{and} \qquad N{-}C{=}\overset{\leftarrow}{O}$$

varies as $1:50:2500$. In the last case only remote attachment is possible since the Cr(II) cannot be attached to nitrogen in

$$Co(NH_3)_5NH_2COOC_2H_5{}^{3+}$$

The greater rate of reduction may be related to the greater covalency of the metal-nitrogen bonds compared to metal-oxygen bonds. Electron donation, through the σ bonds, would put electron density into the e_g orbital of the cobalt ion. Surprisingly, the bond system N=C—N leads to a very low rate of reduction. This is shown by the imidazole and pyridine entries of Table 6.7.

The theory of resonance transfer in conjugated systems has been developed by Halpern and Orgel.[182] Approximate quantum mechanical solutions to equation 6 are found. For the states

$$M_1X^-M_2{}^+ \qquad \text{and} \qquad M_1{}^+X^-M_2$$

where M_1 and M_2 are metal atoms and X is some bridging group, the processes of direct and double exchange can be identified. Direct exchange means a term in the exchange integral H_{12} corresponding to an electron exchanging between atoms M_1 and M_2. Double exchange refers to an electron from M_1 transferring to X simultaneously with an electron from X transferring to M_2. A third, or superexchange, mechanism seems less important.[183]

The result is found[182] that the exchange frequency, ν, is proportional to the mobile bond order[184] between the two exchanging atoms,

$$\nu = \text{const.} \sum_{i=1}^{N} C_{ir}C_{is} \tag{136}$$

The mobile bond order, $\sum C_{ir}C_{is}$, is summed over all N filled orbitals. C_{ir} and C_{is} are the coefficients for atoms r and s in the ith molecular orbital

$$\phi_i = \sum_k C_{ik}\psi_k \tag{137}$$

where the ψ_k are atomic orbitals, as usual. The bond order may be considered as a measure of the degree to which atoms r and s are bonded together by the conjugated system.

The theory of Halpern and Orgel has been modified somewhat[185] by considering the effect of electrostatic forces between the two reacting ions. These forces will lengthen or shorten the time, t, during which the ions are bridged and electron transfer can occur. This is the same t as in equation 6. The modified theory roughly correlates the available rate data, but many other factors such as the influence of heteroatoms and steric hindrance must come into the picture as well.

Tests of the Marcus-Hush Theory

The calculation *a priori* of rate constants for redox reactions of the inner-sphere type is about as difficult as for any chemical reaction where bonds are broken and formed. In the Marcus-Hush theory for outer-sphere electron transfer reactions, we have a fairly reliable method of estimating rate constants. This possibility results from the inherent simplicity of the reaction itself. However, a great problem here is to be sure that the reaction in question not only is outer sphere in mechanism, but also does not have other peculiarities which make it unsuitable for the theory.

For example, reactions in which Co(III) or Co(II) is part of the redox system are ordinarily to be excluded because of the change in multiplicity that must accompany the interconversion of low-spin Co(III) to high-spin Co(II). Indeed rate constants for complexes in which Co(III) is the oxidizing ion are much lower than the theory would predict.[185]

In an interesting study of electron transfer between the heteropoly tungstate complexes of Co(II) and (III), $CoO_4W_{12}O_{36}^{6-}$, $CoO_4W_{12}O_{36}^{5-}$, a rate constant at $O°C$ and zero ionic strength of about 10^{-3} M^{-1} sec^{-1} was found.[186] The Marcus-Hush theory predicts a rate constant of 3×10^3 M^{-1} sec^{-1}. In both ions the cobalt atom is at the center of a tetrahedron of oxygen atoms, and both oxidation states are high spin.[187] The slow rate must be attributed to the difficulty of an electron penetrating the WO_4 groups which surround the cobalt atoms. Thus overlap is too small, even when the two ions are in contact, for the theory to be applicable.

As mentioned earlier, the greatest uncertainty in the numerical calculation, even for cases where the theory is valid, lies in the use of equation 20. Attempts to estimate this term may be seriously in error. Apparent agreement with experiment may be due to fortuitous cancellation of errors. For example, a value of $\Delta G^{\ddagger}$ of 10.1 kcal/mole was calculated for the $Fe(CN)_6^{4-}$-$Fe(CN)_6^{3-}$ exchange.[19] This agrees very well with a measured value (from the rate of exchange) of 10.9 kcal.[124] However, the conditions of the experiment were such that $KFe(CN)_6^{2-}$ and $K_2Fe(CN)_6^{2-}$ were the dominant species, and a bridging by cations seems involved (see p. 489). The theoretical calculation considered only the simple ions.

A somewhat safer way to test the theory is shown in Table 6.8. Here a number of rate data for redox reactions of systems that are surely outer sphere are listed as $\Delta G^{\ddagger}$ (obs.) values. At the same time values of $\Delta G^{\ddagger}$ (calc.) obtained from equations 22 and 23 are given. However, the unknown

Table 6.8 Observed and calculated free energies of activation of oxidation-reduction reactions at 25.0°C

Reaction	d, A^a	ΔG^0, kcal	$\Delta G^{\ddagger}$ (obs.), kcal	$\Delta G^{\ddagger}$ (calc.), kcal
$Fe(CN)_6^{4-} + IrCl_6^{2-}$	8.8	-15.2	9.2	4.2
$Fe(CN)_6^{4-} + OsCl_6^{2-}$	8.7	-1.6	18.5	8.5
$Os(dipy)_3^{2+} + IrCl_6^{2-}$	11.3	-5.3	6.5	2.0
$Os(dipy)_3^{2+} + Fe(phen)_3^{3+}$	14	-5.3	6.5	1.2
$Os(dipy)_3^{2+} + Ru(dipy)_3^{3+}$	14	-10.1	6.5	0.2
$Fe(CN)_6^{4-} + Fe(CN)_6^{3-}$	4.0	0.0	12.8^b	8.8

Reference 188.
^{a} Distance of separation, equation 19.
^{b} At 0°C.

λ_i is set equal to zero. The difference between $\Delta G^{\ddagger}$ (obs.) and $\Delta G^{\ddagger}$ (calc.) should always be greater than zero and should be essentially equal to λ_i. The differences are indeed positive and seem to indicate reorganization energies ranging from 8 kcal for $OsCl_6^{2-}$ to about 2 kcal for $Fe(phen)_3^{2+}$ or $Os(dipy)_3^{2+}$.

In these calculations[188] an attempt was made to correct for the ionic strength of each solution by using an equation due to Debye.[100] The work required to bring the reactants together is written as

$$w = \frac{Z_1 Z_2 e^2}{dD} e^{-\kappa d}$$

where

$$\kappa = \left(\frac{4\pi \sum n_i e^2 Z_i^2}{DkT} \right)^{1/2}$$

(138)

and n_i is the concentration in molecules per cubic centimeter of ionic species i. The κ is the usual Debye value for the reciprocal thickness of the ionic atmosphere.

Another test of the Marcus-Hush theory comes from an extension due to Marcus.[115] Equations 22 and 23 are assumed to be valid for calculating three different rate constants, k_{11}, k_{22}, and k_{12}, where k_{11} and k_{22} are the isotopic exchange rate constants [say Fe^{2+}-Fe^{3+} and Ce^{3+}-$Ce(IV)$] and k_{12} is the rate constant for the cross reaction

$$Ox_1 + Red_2 = Red_1 + Ox_2 \tag{139}$$

or

$$Ce(IV) + Fe^{2+} = Ce^{3+} + Fe^{3+} \tag{140}$$

The result is that

$$k_{12} = \left(k_{11} k_{22} K_{12} f e \, \frac{-\Delta w}{RT} \right)^{\frac{1}{2}} \tag{141}$$

where K_{12} is the equilibrium constant for reaction 139, Δw is a small difference in work term which usually may be ignored, and

$$\ln f = \frac{(\ln K_{12})^2}{4} \ln \frac{k_{11} k_{22}}{Z^2} \tag{142}$$

The Z in 142 is the frequency factor of 10^{11}.

Equation 142 may also be written as

$$\Delta G_{12}^{\ddagger} = 0.50 \Delta G_1^{\ddagger} + 0.50 \Delta G_2^{\ddagger} + 0.50 \Delta G_{12}^0 - 1.15 RT \log f \tag{143}$$

Figure 6.8 shows a test of this equation in which $\Delta G_{12}^{\ddagger} - 0.50 \Delta G_2^{\ddagger} - 1.15 RT \log f$ is plotted against ΔG_{12}^0, the overall free energy change.[185] The data refer to the oxidation of a series of substituted phenanthroline complexes of Fe(II) by Ce(IV), and a series of reductions of the same phenanthroline complexes of Fe(III) by Fe^{2+}. The slope of the straight line is 0.50 as predicted by the theory. The intercept gives 13.0 kcal for the unknown value of $\Delta G_2^{\ddagger}$. This corresponds to an average value of $2 \times 10^3 \, M^{-1} \, sec^{-1}$ for the exchange reaction, $Fe(phen-X)_3^{2+}$-$Fe(phen-X)_3^{3+}$ between the various substituted iron phenanthroline complexes. An approximate value of this k_{22} was needed to estimate f. Fortunately f is close to unity, and 143 is not sensitive to it.

Although Fig. 6.8 is a nice confirmation of the theory, there are still pitfalls in the use of equation 141 to calculate unknown k_{12} values from known k_{11}, k_{22}, and ΔG^0 values. For example, a theoretical value of $6 \times 10^5 \, M^{-1} \, sec^{-1}$ at 25°C may be calculated for the k_{12} of reaction 140. This seems to agree well with a directly measured value of $1.3 \times 10^6 \, M^{-1} \, sec^{-1}$ for Ce(IV) and Fe(II) in H_2SO_4.[185] However, the reactants in the latter case are $CeSO_4^{2+}$ and Fe^{2+}. When the reactants Ce(IV) and Fe^{2+} are measured in $HClO_4$ solution,[189] the rate constant k_{12} is found to be only $7 \times 10^2 \, M^{-1} \, sec^{-1}$. Similarly a rate constant of $10^{-2} \, M^{-1} \, sec^{-1}$ at 25° has been calculated[185] for the reaction

$$V^{3+} + Cr^{2+} \rightarrow V^{2+} + Cr^{3+} \tag{144}$$

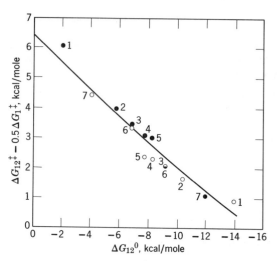

Fig. 6.8 Relation between $(\Delta G_{12}^{\ddagger} - 0.5\Delta G_1^{\ddagger})$ and the standard free energy change of the oxidation–reduction reactions at 25.0°: open circles, $Fe(phen)_3^{2+}$–Ce(IV) reactions in 0.50 M H_2SO_4; closed circles, Fe^{2+}–$Fe(phen)_3^{3+}$ reactions in 0.50 M $HClO_4$; (1) tris-(3,4,7,8-tetramethyl-1,10-phenanthroline); (2) tris-(5,6-dimethyl-1,10-phenanthroline); (3) tris-(5-methyl-1,10-phenanthroline); (4) tris-(1,10-phenanthroline); (5), tris-(5-phenyl-1,10-phenanthroline); (6) tris-(5-chloro-1,10-phenanthroline); (7), tris-(5-nitro-1,10-phenanthroline). From reference 185.

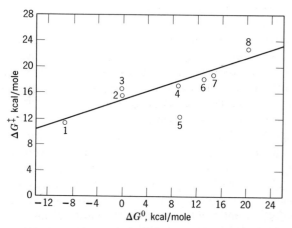

Fig. 6.9 Free energy of activation plotted against the standard free energy change for the oxidation of ferrous ion by various oxidizing agents: (1) $Fe(phen)_3^{+3}$; (2) $FeCl^{+2}$; (3) Fe^{+3}; (4) 2,6-dichlorosemiquinone; (5), $FeOH^{+2}$; (6) benzosemiquinone; (7) tolusemiquinone; (8) durosemiquinone. From reference 191.

510

The observed rate constant is some 60 times higher and probably proceeds by an inner-sphere mechanism. While an observed value higher than the predicted one for such a reaction can be explained by an inner-sphere mechanism taking precedence over the outer-sphere one, the reverse case is more involved. Thus the indication is that either the Ce^{3+}-Ce(IV) exchange or the Fe^{2+}-Fe^{3+} exchange, or both, occur by an inner-sphere mechanism.

Another useful application or test of the Marcus-Hush theory is the correlation with electrochemical rate constants.[115] It is possible to predict the rates of heterogeneous electron transfers between ions and electrodes. The needed information is the rate of the isotope exchange reaction for the ion, assuming always an outer-sphere mechanism.

A linear free energy relationship between rates and ΔG^0 cannot be taken as evidence for a common outer-sphere mechanism for a series of related reactions. Figure 6.9 shows a plot of the free energy of activation, $\Delta G^{\ddagger}$ against the standard free energy change, ΔG^0, for the oxidation of ferrous ion by various oxidizing agents.[191] There is a fair linearity, though the slope is only 0.33 and not 0.50. Oxidation by the semiquinones (rates calculated from the reverse reaction and from ΔG^0) almost certainly occurs by an inner-sphere mechanism (see p. 487). It is not, of course, unreasonable that rates would increase as ΔG^0 becomes more positive regardless of mechanism.

Crystal Field Effects

Upon examination of the data in Table 6.3, and other available rate data on redox reactions, it will be noticed that one general rule is obeyed: a one-equivalent change in which the added electron appears in a t_{2g} orbital of the reduced product is always very fast. This statement applies to transition metal octahedral complexes or distorted octahedral complexes. It is equally true in the polarographic reduction of metal ions.[192] It was first explained by Vlček in terms of the valence bond theory, an electron added to a t_{2g} orbital not requiring any disruption of the presumed d^2sp^3 hybridization of the complex.

The rule can also be explained in terms of crystal field theory. Adding an electron to a t_{2g} orbital or removing an electron from this orbital is easy compared to the same operations for an e_g orbital. An electron in an e_g orbital, being antibonding, causes an increase in the metal-ligand bond distance. This exaggerates the difference between the geometries of the reduced and the oxidized forms. The reorganization energy required as an essential part of either electron or atom transfer will then be large. Thus oxidation of Mn^{2+} by Ce(IV) is slow, $k = 0.2\ M^{-1}\,sec^{-1}$ at 20°C (e_g electron being transferred),[193] whereas oxidation of Fe^{2+} by Ce(IV) is fast, $k = 3 \times 10^5\ M^{-1}\,sec^{-1}$ at 0°C (t_{2g} electron being transferred).[189]

In the reactions of Table 6.1 it can also be seen that Fe^{2+}-Fe^{3+}, Co^{2+}-Co^{3+}, and V^{2+}-V^{3+} exchange relatively fast (t_{2g} electron transferred) and Cr^{2+}-Cr^{3+} and Mn^{2+}-Mn^{3+} exchange slowly (e_g electron transferred). A second factor in this difference in rates may be the greater steric availability of the t_{2g} orbitals, whereas the e_g orbitals are shielded by the ligands.

The reduction of various complexes of Co(III) has offered a number of effects which are best explained in terms of crystal field theory. The change in oxidation state between Co(II) and Co(III) is usually slow because the former has normally a high-spin $(t_{2g})^5(e_g)^2$ configuration and the

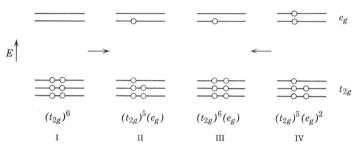

Fig. 6.10 Electronic distribution for the ground states, I and IV, of low-spin cobaltic and high-spin cobaltous complexes. Excitation to a high-spin cobaltic and a low-spin cobaltous state, II and III, is also shown.

latter a low-spin $(t_{2g})^6$ configuration. No simple addition or removal of an electron can convert one of these configurations into the other. It would appear necessary either to excite one of the oxidation states before reaction can occur, or else form both of the products in an excited state. Figure 6.10 shows the ground and excited states of the d^6 and d^7 configurations. The possible reaction paths are

$$I + III \rightarrow III + I$$
$$II + IV \rightarrow IV + II \qquad (145)$$
$$I + IV \rightarrow II + III$$

Promotion to an excited state of one reactant seems much more economical than to form the products both in higher electronic states. In any case the promotional energy is part of the activation energy for the electron exchange process and should show up as a slow rate of exchange. The magnitude of $10Dq$ should affect the promotion energies, the promotion energy for $I \rightarrow II$ increasing with $10Dq$, but that of $IV \rightarrow III$ decreasing with $10Dq$.

Indeed it is found that, if the ligands are arranged in order of increasing crystal field strength, $H_2O <$ oxalate $<$ EDTA $<$ $NH_3 <$ en $<$ phen, exchange between Co(II)-Co(III) is fastest at either end and very slow in the middle.[194] Thus $Co(H_2O)_6^{2+}$-$Co(H_2O)_6^{3+}$ exchanges very rapidly. The explanation is that diamagnetic $Co(H_2O)_6^{3+}$ is easily excited to paramagnetic $Co(H_2O)_6^{3+}$ because of the low crystal field of water.[195] $Co(phen)_3^{2+}$-$Co(phen)_3^{3+}$ exchanges some 10^5 times as rapidly as $Co(en)_3^{2+}$-$Co(en)_3^{3+}$. This is explained by assuming that high-spin Co(II) can easily become low-spin Co(II) because of the large crystal field strength of phenanthroline.[195] It is also possible that the unsaturated nature of the ligands in the phen case allows easier electron transfer. Electron transfer should be very rapid between CoF_6^{4-}-CoF_6^{3-} and $Co(diars)_3^{2+}$-$Co(diars)_3^{3+}$. In the first case both complexes are of high spin, and in the second both the o-phenylene-bis(dimethylarsine) complexes are low spin.[197]

The effect of the crystal field of X^{n-} on the rates of reduction of $Co(NH_3)_5X^{3-n}$ shows a more regular behavior. The plot of the activation energy for reduction at the dropping mercury electrode against $10Dq$ is linear.[198] Since Fig. 6.4 shows a linear relationship between log k_{DME} and the logarithms of the rate constants for several other outer-sphere electron transfers, these are probably also linear functions of $10Dq$. As the crystal field strength of X^{n-} diminishes, the rate of reduction increases. This could mean that excitation of the type I → II is required before the act of electron transfer.[198]

The correlation with $10Dq$ may be partly fortuitous, and the real correlation may be with the strength of the bond, Co-X. Since reduction will result in a lengthening of this bond, some increase in the Co-X bond distance will occur before reaction. The weaker the bond, the easier such a change will be. As discussed earlier (p. 170), the value of Dq rather accidentally parallels the bond strength except in a few cases. One is OH^-, which has a low crystal field strength[199] but a high bond strength. The data on $Co(NH_3)_5OH^{2+}$ show that it is hard to reduce in an outer-sphere process [see the $Ru(NH_3)_6^{2+}$ entry in Table 6.4]. This fact correlates better with the bond strength than with Dq. It may be mentioned that $Co(NH_3)_5OH^{2+}$ is also hard to reduce at the dropping mercury electrode.[200]

The effect of the second ligand, Y, on the rate of reduction of cis- and trans-$Co(NH_3)_4XY$ has also been studied. The crystal field strength of Y seems important for trans complexes when a bridged mechanism is operating. Orgel, who first discussed redox reactions in terms of crystal field theory, suggested that the electron in a bridged mechanism would appear in the e_g orbital directed towards the ligands X and Y.[201] Since this would be an antibonding orbital, the added electron would cause an increase in the metal-ligand distances, M-X and M-Y. A low crystal field for the trans ligand Y would allow this increase in bond distances to occur more easily.

Table 6.9   Rates of reduction by chromous ion and by ferrous ion of some cobalt(III) ammine complexes at 25°C

Complex	$k, M^{-1} \sec^{-1}$	Reference
a. Cr^{2+} reductant		
$Co(NH_3)_5OAc^{2+}$	0.18	173
cis-$Co(NH_3)_4(OAc)_2^+$	$\sim$30	202
$trans$-$Co(NH_3)_4(OAc)_2^+$	15	202
$Co(NH_3)_5N_3^{2+}$	0.0087	104a
cis-$Co(NH_3)_4(N_3)_2^+$	0.185	203
$trans$-$Co(NH_3)_4(N_3)_2^+$	0.073	203
cis-$Co(NH_3)_4(H_2O)N_3^+$	0.355	203
$trans$-$Co(NH_3)_4(H_2O)N_3^+$	24	203
cis-$Co(en)_2(H_2O)OH^{2+}$	7.9×10^5	204
$trans$-$Co(en)_2(H_2O)OH^{2+}$	2.6×10^6	204
b. Fe^{2+} reductant		
$trans$-$Co(en)_2NH_3Cl^{2+}$	6.6×10^{-5}	205
cis-$Co(en)_2NH_3Cl^{2+}$	1.8×10^{-5}	205
$trans$-$Co(en)_2NCSCl^+$	1.3×10^{-4}	205
cis-$Co(en)_2NCSCl^+$	1.7×10^{-4}	205
$trans$-$Co(en)_2Cl_2^+$	3.2×10^{-2}	205
cis-$Co(en)_2Cl_2^+$	1.6×10^{-3}	205
$trans$-$Co(en)_2BrCl^+$	3.6×10^{-2}	205
$trans$-$Co(en)_2H_2OCl^{2+}$	2.4×10^{-1}	205
cis-$Co(en)_2H_2OCl^{2+}$	4.6×10^{-4}	205
$trans$-$Co(en)_2N_3Cl^{2+}$	6.2×10^{-2}	205

Some rate data for reduction by Cr^{2+} have been gathered together in Table 6.9. The rate is larger for $trans$-$Co(NH_3)_4(OAc)_2^+$ than for $Co(NH_3)_5OAc^{2+}$. This is in the predicted direction, since the crystal field strength of acetate is less than that of ammine. The even larger rate increase for cis-$Co(NH_3)_4(OAc)^{2+}$ has been explained by a double-bridge mechanism,[202b] since the product is largely $Cr(H_2O)_4(OAc)_2^+$. The rate is somewhat larger for $trans$-$Co(en)_2(H_2O)OH^{2+}$ than for the cis isomer.[204] Presumably the hydroxo is the bridging group, and $trans$ water should be more reactive than $trans$ amine.

The azido complexes do not quite fit since the rates increase in the order $trans$-$NH_3 < N_3^- < H_2O$, whereas the crystal field strengths are $NH_3 > H_2O > N_3^-$. This again shows that it is the strength of the bond which is important, not the value of $10Dq$. The bond strength order would be azido greater than water, but less than ammine. It may also be noted that protonation of a *trans* group, such as azido or acetato, speeds up the rate of reduction.[202b,203] This is logically explained by the weaker binding of HOAc or HN_3, compared to their anions.

As shown also in Table 6.9, reduction of *trans*-Co(en)$_2$XCl$^+$ by Fe(II) follows the rate sequence X = H_2O > Br$^-$ > Cl$^-$ > SCN$^-$ > NH$_3$, with Co(en)$_2$H$_2$OCl^{2+} reacting some 10^4 times faster than Co(en)$_2$NH$_3$Cl^{2+}.[205] This is the order of increasing ligand bond strengths, as well as increasing ligand field strengths. For *cis*-Co(en)$_2$XCl$^+$ the spread in rates is only 10^2, with the order Cl$^-$ > H_2O > SCN$^-$ > NH$_3$. As predicted by Orgel,[201] it is the inert ligand in the *trans* position which has the greatest effect. One may also note that the rates with Fe(II) as a reductant run much lower than with Cr(II) as the reductant. This is the result of a difference of 1.2 volts in the potentials of the two redox complexes, Cr(II)/Cr(III) and Fe(II)/Fe(III).

The Hydrated Electron

It has often been spectulated as to whether an electron can be transferred over long distances through a suitably oriented solvent, such as water held fixed by hydrogen bridges. The evidence at present is not very convincing that such processes occur.[206] Another possibility is that some reducing agents act by giving up an electron to the solvent, followed by a rapid reaction of the solvated electron with the oxidizing agent. This has been suggested for the mechanism of oxidation of Ru(II) by water in acidic media.[207] The stoichiometry is

$$2Ru^{2+} + 2H^+ \rightarrow 2Ru^{3+} + H_2 \qquad (146)$$

The rate is given by the equation

$$\text{Rate} = k[Ru^{2+}] \qquad (147)$$

with $k = 2.5 \times 10^{-5}$ sec^{-1} for the disappearance of Ru(II). The proposed mechanism is

$$Ru^{2+} \xrightarrow{\ k\ } Ru^{3+} + e^-(aq) \qquad (148)$$

$$e^-(aq) + H^+ \rightarrow H \qquad (149)$$

$$2H \rightarrow H_2 \qquad (150)$$

with the first step being rate determining.

The identification of the hydrated electron[208] and studies of its properties[209] enable us to decide unambiguously on the feasibility of such a mechanism. The hydrated electron is formed in secondary processes whenever ionizing radiation passes through water. About 10^{-11} sec is needed to thermally equilibrate the electron and to polarize the medium surrounding it. After this short period of time it is possible to measure the rate of reaction of the electron with many oxidizing agents.

Most conveniently the technique of pulse radiolysis is used in which a burst of ionizing radiation, of about 1 μsec duration, produces the electrons. The disappearance of the electron can then be followed by spectrophotometry, the absorption spectrum having a strong maximum at 7200 A in water. The lifetime of the electron even in fairly pure water is only a few hundred microseconds. A common mode of decay is reaction 149 which has[210] a second-order rate constant of 2.3×10^{10} M^{-1} sec^{-1}. Thus in acid solution hydrogen atom is the dominant reducing species in radiation chemistry, but in neutral or alkaline solution the hydrated electron is dominant. The OH radical is also produced in the radiation step

$$H_2O \rightsquigarrow H^+ + \cdot OH + e^-(aq) \tag{151}$$

Methyl alcohol is often added to convert the hydroxyl radical to the unreactive $HOCH_2\cdot$ radical.

Table 6.10 shows the rate constants for the reaction of a number of metal complexes with the hydrated electron. The reactions are presumed to be

$$ML_n{}^q + e^-(aq) \rightarrow ML_n{}^{q-1} \tag{152}$$

In only one or two cases, however, have the immediate products of reaction been identified. Since the standard electrode potential of the electron has been estimated as 2.7 volts,[211,223]

$$e^-(aq) + H^+ = \tfrac{1}{2}H_2(g)$$
$$\Delta E^0 = 2.7 \text{ volts} \tag{153}$$

most reactions of the type 152 are strongly exothermic. This means that the products will be formed in highly excited states, often in excited electronic states. In other cases, such as in the reaction of Zn^{2+}, an unknown valence state, Zn^+, is postulated.[212] The spectra and kinetic properties of such unusual species have been measured in some cases.

The rate constants in Table 6.10 are all quite large (small rate constants could not be measured in any case). They are often near the limit of diffusion control. Equations 59 and 60 may be used to calculate the expected rate constants for reaction between a negative electron and variously charged complexes. The diffusion constant of the electron has been determined[218] as 4.4×10^{-5} cm^2 sec^{-1}. A constant value of σ, the distance of closest approach, equal to 5.5 A may be chosen. This gives values of the rate constant k from 59 and 60 as follows:

$$M^{3+} + e^-(aq) \qquad k = 7.2 \times 10^{10} \ M^{-1} sec^{-1}$$
$$M^0 + e^-(aq) \qquad k = 2.4 \times 10^{10} \tag{154}$$
$$M^{3-} + e^-(aq) \qquad k = 1.6 \times 10^9$$

Table 6.10 Rate constants for reaction of hydrated electrons with some metal ion complexes at 25°C

$$ML_n{}^q + e^-(aq) \rightarrow ML_n{}^{q-1}$$

Complex	$k, M^{-1}\,sec^{-1}$	Reference
$Mn(H_2O)_6{}^{2+}$	7.7×10^7	213
$Fe(H_2O)_6{}^{2+}$	3.5×10^8	213
$Co(H_2O)_6{}^{2+}$	1.2×10^{10}	213
$Ni(H_2O)_6{}^{2+}$	2.2×10^{10}	213
$Cu(H_2O)_6{}^{2+}$	3.0×10^{10}	213
$Zn(H_2O)_6{}^{2+}$	1.5×10^9	213
$Eu(H_2O)_n{}^{3+}$	6.1×10^{10}	214
$Yb(H_2O)_n{}^{3+}$	4.3×10^{10}	214
$Sm(H_2O)_n{}^{3+}$	2.5×10^{10}	214
$Nd(H_2O)_n{}^{3+}$	5.9×10^8	214
$Pr(H_2O)_n{}^{3+}$	2.9×10^8	214
$Gd(H_2O)_n{}^{3+}$	5.5×10^8	214
$La(H_2O)_n{}^{3+}$	3.4×10^8	214
$Al(H_2O)_6{}^{3+}$	2.0×10^9	215
$Cr(H_2O)_6{}^{3+}$	6.0×10^{10}	215
$Co(NH_3)_6{}^{3+}$	9.0×10^{10}	213
$Rh(NH_3)_6{}^{3+}$	7.9×10^{10}	216
$Ir(NH_3)_6{}^{3+}$	1.3×10^{10}	216
$Ru(NH_3)_6{}^{3+}$	7.4×10^{10}	216
$Os(NH_3)_6{}^{3+}$	7.2×10^{10}	216
$Co(dipy)_3{}^{3+}$	8.3×10^{10}	216
$Co(NH_3)_5Cl^{2+}$	5.4×10^{10}	213
$trans\text{-}Coen_2Cl_2{}^+$	3.2×10^{10}	213
$cis\text{-}Coen_2(NCS)_2{}^+$	6.9×10^{10}	217
$Co(CN)_6{}^{3-}$	2.7×10^9	213
$Co(ox)_3{}^{3-}$	1.2×10^{10}	213
$Co(NO_2)_6{}^{3-}$	5.8×10^{10}	213
$Cr(en)_3{}^{3+}$	5.3×10^{10}	217
$cis\text{-}Cr(en)_2Cl_2{}^+$	7.1×10^{10}	217
$cis\text{-}Cr(en)_2(NCS)_2{}^+$	4.2×10^{10}	217
$cis\text{-}Cr(ox)_2(H_2O)_2{}^-$	1.3×10^{10}	217
$Cr(EDTA)^-$	2.6×10^{10}	217
$Cr(ox)_3{}^{3-}$	1.8×10^{10}	217
$Cr(CN)_6{}^{3-}$	1.5×10^{10}	215
$Cr(H_2O)_2(OH)_4{}^-$	2.0×10^8	215

A few of the constants in Table 6.10 are less than the predicted values. These correspond to the cases where the required potential for reaction is large enough so that reaction does not occur at every collision. Examples are some of the rare earth ions, where only Eu(III), Sm(III), and Yb(III) have rates that are encounter controlled. These also are the only three that have known divalent states. The rate constants for the divalent ions of the series from Mn(II) to Zn(II) show the same trend as the second ionization potentials of these elements in the gaseous state,

$$M^+(g) \rightarrow M^{2+}(g) + e \tag{155}$$

Thus the low rate for Mn(II) means that reduction to Mn(I) is harder than for any other ion in the series.

The plus three complexes of cobalt and chromium show the expected rates for diffusion control. The minus three complexes do not decrease in rate as much as predicted. There are two possible explanations. One is that electron transfer occurs at distances as large as 15–20 A, rather than the 5.5 A assumed. The other is that there is an interaction between the polarizable, or soft, electron and the polarizable anions. Such an interaction, which might be simple polarization energy, van der Waals attraction, or electron correlation, would lower the electrostatic repulsion and increase the encounter rate constant.

From a consideration of the effect of ligands on the rates with a number of complexes, Anbar and Hart[215] concluded that the efficacy of reaction with $e^-(aq)$ increases along the series $OH^- < CN^- < NH_3 < H_2O < F^- < Cl^- < Br^- < I^-$. This is the same order as found in the reduction of $Co(NH_3)_5X^{3-n}$ either by the D.M.E. or by outer-sphere electron transfer. The same explanation, ease of rearrangement of the metal-ligand bonds, seems to apply. This also might account for the decreasing rate of reduction along the series $Co(NH_3)_6{}^{3+} > Rh(NH_3)_6{}^{3+} > Ir(NH_3)_6{}^{3+}$. The C.F.S.E. would increase along this series, and rearrangement would become difficult. The same trend is again found in the rates of reduction at the D.M.E.

Marcus[219] has developed a theory for the reaction of the hydrated electron with metal complexes which is very similar to the Marcus-Hush theory for electron transfer in general. It applies only for non-diffusion control. The pertinent equations are

$$k = 10^{11}e^{-\Delta G^{\ddagger}/RT} \ M^{-1} \ \text{sec}^{-1}$$

$$\Delta G^{\ddagger} = w + \frac{\lambda}{4}\left(1 + \frac{\Delta G^0 - w}{\lambda}\right)^2$$

$$w = \frac{Ze^2}{dD} \tag{156}$$

$$\lambda = \lambda_M + \lambda_e$$

The work term, w, is small. The reorganization energy, λ, is large. The value of λ_M for the metal complex may be estimated from the exchange reaction of the metal complex. Its value is 1 or 2 electron volts. The reorganization energy of the electron, λ_e, is difficult to assess because the wave function, or state, of the electron in solution is not known. The value of λ_e seems to be about 1 ev. ΔG^0 is a corrected standard free energy change for the solution in question. The conclusion from equations 156 is that reactions will become slow if the E^0 of the metal complex becomes about 2 volts. This agrees well with the limited data available in this potential range (see the rare earth ions in Table 6.10).

Finally we can answer the question as to whether equations 148–150 can represent a reasonable mechanism for the oxidation of Ru^{2+}. The answer is no, as can be seen by examining the equilibrium

$$Ru^{2+} \underset{k_2}{\overset{k_1}{\rightleftharpoons}} Ru^{3+} + e^-(aq) \tag{157}$$

The potential difference can be calculated as $\Delta E^0 \sim -3$ volt although the Ru^{2+}/Ru^{3+} couple is not accurately known. The equilibrium constant can then be estimated as about 10^{-49} for 157. Since we also have $k_1/k_2 = K_{eq}$, and since k_2 cannot be any larger than $10^{11}\ M^{-1}\ sec^{-1}$ for a diffusion-controlled reaction, the maximum value of k_1 is $10^{-38}\ sec^{-1}$. This means that the postulated mechanism can safely be ruled out. However, reducing agents with potentials up near 2.5 volts, such as sodium metal, might very well react by ejecting electrons into the solvent. There is, in fact, both spectral and kinetic evidence that this happens.[224]

References

For recent reviews see H. Taube, *Advan. Inorg. Chem. Radiochem.*, **1**, 1 (1959); J. Halpern, *Quart. Rev. (London)*, **15**, 207 (1961); N. Sutin, *Ann. Rev. Nucl. Sci.*, **12**, 285 (1962); *Mechanisms of Electron Transfer*, W. L. Reynolds and R. W. Lumry, Ronald Press, New York, 1966.

1. J. O. Edwards, *Chem. Revs.*, **50**, 455 (1952).
2. H. Taube *Advan. Inorg. Chem. Radiochem.*, **1**, 1 (1959).
3. H. S. W. Massey and E. H. S. Burhop, *Electron and Ionic Impact Phenomena*, Oxford University Press, 1952.
4. J. B. Hasted, *Proc. Roy. Soc. (London)*, **A227**, 476 (1955).
5. (a) C. Zener, *Phys. Rev.*, **82**, 403 (1951). (b) H. Eyring, J. Walter, and G. E. Kimball, *Quantum Chemistry*, John Wiley and Sons, New York, 1944, Chap. 8.
6. E. F. Gurnee and J. L. Magee, *J. Chem. Phys.*, **26**, 1237 (1957).
7. W. F. Libby, *J. Phys. Chem.*, **56**, 863 (1952).
8. E. U. Condon, *Am. J. Phys.*, **15**, 365 (1947).
9. N. Sutin, *Ann. Rev. Nucl. Sci.*, **12**, 285 (1962).

10. R. Lafont, *Compt. rend.*, **244**, 1481 (1957).
11. G. Sartori, C. Furlani, and A. Damioni, *J. Inorg. Nucl. Chem.*, **8**, 119 (1958).
12. P. George and J. S. Griffith, *The Enzymes* (P. D. Boyer *et al.*, eds.), Academic Press, New York, 1959, Vol. 1, Chap. 8.
13. J. Weiss, *Proc. Roy. Soc.* (*London*), **A222**, 128 (1954).
14. R. J. Marcus, B. J. Zwolinski, and H. Eyring, *J. Phys.*, *Chem.*, **58**, 432 (1954); see also R. A. Marcus, *J. Chem. Phys.*, **24**, 970 (1956).
15. N. F. Mott and I. N. Sneddon, *Wave Mechanics and Its Applications*, Clarendon Press, Oxford, 1948.
16. Reference 5b, p. 355.
17. S. Glasstone, K. Laidler, and H. Eyring, *The Theory of Rate Processes*, McGraw-Hill Book Co., New York, 1941, p. 189.
18. K. J. Laidler, *Can. J. Chem.*, **37**, 138 (1959); K. J. Laidler and E. Sacher, *Trans. Faraday Soc.*, **59**, 396 (1963).
19. R. A. Marcus, (a) *J. Chem. Phys.*, **24**, 966, 979 (1956), and **26**, 867 (1947); (b) *Disc. Faraday Soc.*, **29**, 129 (1960).
20. N. S. Hush, (a) *Z. Elektrochem.*, **61**, 734 (1957); (b) *J. Chem. Phys.*, **28**, 962 (1958); (c) *Trans. Faraday Soc.*, **57**, 557 (1961).
21. A. A. Frost and R. G. Pearson, *Kinetics and Mechanism*, John Wiley and Sons, New York, 1961, p. 93.
22. Reference 21, p. 129.
23. L. E. Orgel, Tenth Solvay Conference, Brussels, 1956, p. 289.
24. H. Taube, *Record Chem. Progr. Kresge-Hooker Sci. Lib.*, **17**, 25 (1956).
25. H. Taube, H. Myers, and R. L. Rich, *J. Am. Chem. Soc.*, **75**, 4118 (1953); H. Taube and H. Myers, *ibid.*, **76**, 2103 (1954).
26. H. Taube, *J. Am. Chem. Soc.*, **77**, 4481 (1955).
27. H. Taube, *J. Am. Chem. Soc.*, **82**, 526 (1960).
28. A. E. Ogard and H. Taube, *J. Am. Chem. Soc.*, **80**, 1084 (1958).
29. H. Taube and E. L. King, *J. Am. Chem. Soc.*, **76**, 4053 (1954).
30. R. W. Dodson and N. Davidson, *J. Phys. Chem.*, **56**, 866 (1952).
31. W. L. Reynolds and R. Lumry, *J. Chem. Phys.*, **23**, 2560 (1955).
32. (a) A. G. Maddock, *Trans. Faraday Soc.*, **55**, 1268 (1959). (b) R. A. Horne and E. H. Axelrod, *J. Chem. Phys.*, **40**, 1518 (1964). (c) J. Menashi, W. L. Reynolds, and G. van Auken, *Inorg. Chem.*, **4**, 299 (1965).
33. J. Hudis and R. W. Dodson, *J. Am. Chem. Soc.*, **78**, 4053 (1956).
34. A. Zwickel and H. Taube, *J. Am. Chem. Soc.*, **31**, 1288 (1959).
35. N. Sutin, J. K. Rowley, and R. W. Dodson, *J. Phys. Chem.*, **65**, 1248 (1961).
36. D. R. Stranks in *Modern Coordination Chemistry* (J. Lewis and R. G. Wilkins, eds.), Interscience Publishers, New York, 1960, p. 78.
37. I. M. Klotz, J. Ayers, J. Y. C. Ho, M. G. Horowitz, and R. E. Heiney, *J. Am. Chem. Soc.*, **80**, 2132 (1958).
38. R. Stewart, *Oxidation Mechanisms: Applications to Organic Chemistry*, W. A. Benjamin, New York, 1964, W. A. Waters, *Mechanisms of Oxidation*, John Wiley and Sons, New York, 1964.
39. B. S. Thyagarajan, *Chem. Rev.*, **58**, 439 (1958).
40. For reviews see H. E. DeLaMare, J. K. Kochi, and F. F. Rust, *J. Am. Chem. Soc.*, **85**, 1437 (1963); R. M. Haines and W. A. Waters, *J. Chem. Soc.*, **1955**, 4256.
41. (a) E. Collinson, F. S. Dainton, B. Mile, S. Tazuke, and D. R. Smith, *Nature*, **198**, 26 (1963). (b) O. Bamford, A. Jenkins, and R. Johnson, *Proc. Roy. Soc.* (*London*), **A239**, 214 (1957).

42. J. K. Kochi and R. V. Subramanian, *J. Am. Chem. Soc.*, **87**, 4855 (1965).

43. A. Haim and H. Taube, *J. Am. Chem. Soc.*, **85**, 495 (1963).

44. A. Tobolsky and R. B. Mesrobian, *Organic Peroxides*, Interscience Publishers, New York, 1954, pp. 95 ff.

45. J. O. Edwards, *Peroxide Reaction Mechanisms*, Interscience Publishers, New York, New York, 1962.

46. F. Haber and J. Weiss, *Proc. Roy. Soc.* (*London*), **A147**, 332 (1934).

47. L. Michaelis, *Trans. Electrochem. Soc.*, **71**, 107 (1937).

48. A. M. Armstrong and J. Halpern, *Can. J. Chem.*, **35**, 1020 (1957); J. Halpern *ibid.*, **37**, 148 (1959).

49. F. H. Westheimer, *The Mechanism of Enzyme Action*, The Johns Hopkins Press, Baltimore, 1954, p. 321.

50. W. C. E. Higginson and J. W. Marshall, *J. Chem. Soc.*, **1957**, 447.

51. P. A. Shaffer, *J. Am. Chem. Soc.*, **55**, 2169 (1933); *J. Phys., Chem.*, **40**, 1021 (1936).

52. K. V. Krishnamurty and A. C. Wahl, *J. Am. Chem. Soc.*, **80**, 5921 (1958).

53. S. C. Furman and C. S. Garner, *J. Am. Chem. Soc.*, **74**, 2333 (1952).

54. W. C. E. Higginson, D. R. Rosseinsky, J. B. Stead, and A. G. Sykes, *Disc. Faraday Soc.*, **29**, 49 (1960).

55. A. Anderson and N. A. Bonner, *J. Am. Chem. Soc.*, **76**, 3826 (1954).

56. D. L. Ball and E. L. King, *J. Am. Chem. Soc.*, **80**, 1091 (1958).

57. Y. Chia and E. L. King, *Disc. Faraday Soc.*, **29**, 109 (1960).

58. A. D. Britt and W. M. Yen, *J. Am. Chem. Soc.*, **83**, 5416 (1961); O. E. Myers and J. C. Sheppard, *ibid.*, **83**, 4739 (1961).

59. J. Hudis and A. C. Wahl, *J. Am. Chem. Soc.*, **75**, 4153 (1953).

60. N. Sutin, J. K. Rowley, and R. W. Dodson, *J. Phys. Chem.*, **65**, 1248 (1961).

61. R. A. Horne, Doctoral dissertation, Columbia University, New York, 1955.

62. G. S. Laurence, *Trans. Faraday Soc.*, **53**, 1326 (1957).

63. D. Bunn, F. S. Dainton, and S. Duckworth, *Trans. Faraday Soc.*, **57**, 1131 (1961).

64. R. A. Horne, *J. Phys. Chem.*, **64**, 1512 (1960).

65. S. Fukushima and W. L. Reynolds, *Talanta*, **11**, 283 (1964); *Inorg. Chem.*, **2**, 176 (1963).

66. W. L. Reynolds, N. Liu, and J. Mickus, *J. Am. Chem. Soc.*, **83**, 1078 (1961).

67. M. H. Ford-Smith and N. Sutin, *J. Am. Chem. Soc.*, **83**, 1830 (1961).

68. N. Sutin and B. M. Gordon, *J. Am. Chem. Soc.*, **83**, 70 (1961).

69. C. F. Deck and A. C. Wahl, *J. Am. Chem. Soc.*, **76**, 4054 (1954).

70. B. M. Gordon, L. L. Williams, and N. Sutin, *J. Am. Chem. Soc.*, **83**, 2061 (1961).

71. M. W. Dietrich and A. C. Wahl, *J. Chem. Phys.*, **38**, 1591 (1963).

72. H. Diebler and N. Sutin, *J. Phys. Chem.*, **68**, 174 (1964).

73. W. L. Reynolds and R. Lumry, *J. Chem. Phys.*, **23**, 2560 (1955).

74. C. E. Johnson, *J. Am. Chem. Soc.*, **74**, 959 (1952).

75. E. Roig and R. W. Dodson, *J. Phys. Chem.*, **65**, 2175 (1961); S. W. Gilks and G. M. Waind, *Disc. Faraday Soc.*, **29**, 102 (1960).

76. W. G. Barb, J. H. Baxendale, P. George, and K. R. Hargrave, *Trans. Faraday Soc.*, **47**, 491 (1951).

77. J. H. Baxendale, H. R. Hardy, and L.·H. Sutcliffe, *Trans. Faraday Soc.*, **47**, 963 (1951).

78. J. H. Baxendale, *Kinetics and Mechanism of Inorganic Reactions in Solution*, The Chemical Society, London (Special Publication No. 1), 1954, p. 43.

79. B. R. Baker, F. Basolo, and H. M. Neuman, *J. Phys. Chem.*, **63**, 371 (1959).

80. D. R. Stranks, *Disc. Faraday Soc.*, **29**, 73 (1960).

81. F. P. Dwyer and A. M. Sargeson, *J. Phys. Chem.*, **65**, 1892 (1961).
82. D. R. Stranks, *Advances in the Chemistry of the Coordination Compounds* (S. Kirschner, ed.), The MacMillan Co., New York, 1961, p. 571.
83. H. M. McConnell and H. E. Weaver, *J. Chem. Phys.*, **25**, 307 (1956).
84. E. N. Sloth and C. S. Garner, *J. Am. Chem. Soc.*, **77**, 1440 (1955).
85. J. Halpern, R. J. Legare, and R. Lumry, *J. Am. Chem. Soc.*, **85**, 680 (1963).
86. P. Hurwitz and K. Kustin, *Inorg. Chem.*, **3**, 823 (1964).
87. R. J. Campion, N. Purdie, and N. Sutin, *J. Am. Chem. Soc.*, **85**, 3528 (1963).
88. R. J. Campion, N. Purdie, and N. Sutin, *Inorg. Chem.*, **3**, 1091 (1964).
89. J. C. Sullivan, D. Cohen, and J. C. Hindman, *J. Am. Chem. Soc.*, **79**, 3672 (1957).
90. T. K. Keenan, *J. Phys. Chem.*, **61**, 1117 (1957).
91. S. W. Rabideau and R. J. Kline, *J. Phys. Chem.*, **62**, 617 (1958).
92. See P. George and D. H. Irvin, *J. Chem. Soc.*, **1954**, 587, for a number of examples.
93. H. A. C. McKay, *Nature*, **142**, 997 (1938); G. Friedlander and J. W. Kennedy, *Nuclear and Radiochemistry*, John Wiley and Sons, New York, 1955.
94. R. J. Prestwood and A. C. Wahl, *J. Am. Chem. Soc.*, **71**, 3137 (1949).
95. F. P. Dwyer and E. C. Gyarfas, *Nature*, **166**, 1181 (1950).
96. Y. A. Im and D. H. Busch, *J. Am. Chem. Soc.*, **83**, 3357 (1961).
97. G. R. Bruce, R. E. Norberg, and S. I. Weissman, *J. Chem. Phys.*, **24**, 473 (1965).
98. S. I. Weissman and C. S. Garner, *J. Am. Chem. Soc.*, **78**, 1072 (1956).
99. See reference 21, pp. 268 ff., for a discussion.
100. P. Debye, *Trans. Electrochem. Soc.*, **82**, 265 (1942).
101 (a) W. Biltz. *Z. anorg. allgem. Chem.*, **164**, 246 (1927) (b) M. T. Barnett, B. M. Craven, H. C. Freeman, J. A. Ibers, and N. Kime, *Chem. Commun.*, **1966**, 307.
102. J. F. Endicott and H. Taube, *J. Am. Chem. Soc.*, **86**, 1686 (1964); *Inorg. Chem.*, **4**, 437 (1965).
103. A. M. Zwickel and H. Taube, *Disc. Faraday Soc.*, **29**, 42 (1960).
104. (a) J. P. Candlin, J. Halpern, and D. L. Trimm, *J. Am. Chem. Soc.*, **86**, 1019 (1964). (b) J. P. Candlin and J. Halpern, *Inorg. Chem.*, **4**, 766 (1965).
105. O. Gansow, Ph.D. thesis, Northwestern University, Evanston, Ill., 1966.
106. D. L. Ball and E. L. King, *J. Am. Chem. Soc.*, **80**, 1091 (1958).
107. J. H. Espenson, *Inorg. Chem.* **4**, 121 (1965).
108. G. Dulz and N. Sutin, *J. Am. Chem. Soc.*, **86**, 829 (1964).
109. (a) R. J. Campion, T. J. Conocchioli, and N. Sutin, *J. Am. Chem. Soc.*, **86**, 4591 (1964). (b) J. Menashi, S. Fukushima, and W. L. Reynolds, *Inorg. Chem.*, **3**, 1242 (1964).
110. (a) A. W. Adamson, *J. Am. Chem. Soc.*, **73**, 5170 (1951); W. Heiber, R. Nast, and C. Bartenstein, *Z. anorg. allgem. Chem.*, **272**, 32 (1953). (b) A. W. Adamson. *J. Am. Chem. Soc.*, **78**, 4260 (1965).
111. (a) J. P. Candlin, J. Halpern, and S. Nakamura, *J. Am. Chem. Soc.*, **85**, 2517 (1963). (b) J. Halpern and S. Nakamura, *Proceedings of the Eighth International Conference on Coordination Chemistry* (V. Gutmann, ed.), Springer-Verlag, Vienna, 1964, p. 271.
112. C. K. Jørgensen, *Inorg. Chem.*, **3**, 1201 (1964).
113. (a) J. L. Burmeister, *Inorg. Chem.*, **3**, 919 (1964). (b) J. L. Burmeister and D. Sutherland, *Chem. Commun.*, **9**, 175 (1965).
114. A. A. Vlček, *Advances in the Chemistry of the Coordination Compounds*, The Macmillan Co., New York, 1961, p. 289.
115. R. A. Marcus, *J. Phys. Chem.*, **67**, 853 (1963); *J. Chem. Phys.*, **43**, 679 (1965).
116. T. W. Newton and F. B. Baker, *Inorg. Chem.*, **3**, 569 (1964).

117. A. Haim and W. K. Wilmarth, *J. Am. Chem. Soc.*, **83**, 509 (1961).
118. A. Werner and A. Mylius, *Z. anorg. Chem.*, **16**, 1245 (1898); M. Ardon and R. A. Plane, *J. Am. Chem. Soc.*, **81**, 3197 (1959).
119. For recent discussions see M. L. Kremer, *Trans. Faraday Soc.*, **58**, 702 (1962), and **59**, 2535 (1963); V. A. Garten, *Aust. J. Chem.*, **15**, 719 (1962); P. Jones, R. Kitching M. L. Tobe, and W. F. K. Wynne-Jones, *Trans. Faraday Soc.*, **55**, 79 (1959).
120. P. George and D. H. Irvine, *J. Chem. Soc.*, **1954**, 587.
121. J. C. Sheppard and A. C. Wahl, *J. Am. Chem. Soc.*, **79**, 1020 (1957).
122. A. C. Wahl, *Z. Elektrochem.*, **60**, 90 (1960).
123. L. Gjertsen and A. C. Wahl, *J. Am. Chem. Soc.*, **81**, 1572 (1959).
124. M. Shporer, G. Ron, A. Loewenstein, and G. Navon, *Inorg. Chem.*, **4**, 362 (1965).
125. R. L. Ward and S. Weissman, *J. Am. Chem. Soc.*, **79**, 2086 (1957); S. Weissman and N. Hirota, *ibid.*, **86**, 2537 (1964).
126. A. C. Aten, J. Dieleman, and G. J. Hoijtink, *Disc. Faraday Soc.*, **29**, 182 (1960).
127. F. C. Adam and S. Weissman, *J. Am. Chem. Soc.*, **80**, 1518 (1958).
128. F. Klanberg, J. P. Hunt, and H. W. Dodgen, *Inorg. Chem.*, **2**, 139 (1963), review the evidence for perchlorate complexes.
129. (a) R. J. Prestwood and A. C. Wahl, *J. Am. Chem. Soc.*, **71**, 3137 (1949). (b) G. Harbottle and R. W. Dodson, *ibid.*, **73**, 2442 (1951). (v) S. W. Gilks and G. Nord-Waind, *Disc. Faraday Soc.*, **29**, 102 (1960).
130. G. Biedermann, *Arkiv Kemi*, **5**, 441 (1953).
131. E. Penna-Franca and R. W. Dodson, *J. Am. Chem. Soc.*, **77**, 2651 (1955).
132. G. Nord-Waind, *Symposium on Coordination Chemistry*, Tihany, Hungary, Sept. 1964, p. 441.
133. T. G. Spiro, *Inorg. Chem.*, **4**, 731 (1965).
134. L. G. Carpenter, M. H. Ford-Smith, R. P. Bell, and R. W. Dodson, *Disc. Faraday Soc.*, **29**, 92 (1960).
135. R. L. Burwell, Jr., and R. G. Pearson, *J. Phys. Chem.*, **70**, 300 (1966).
136. C. B. Amphlett, *Quart. Rev. (London)*, **8**, 219 (1954); C. L. Browne, R. P. Craig, and N. Davidson, *J. Am. Chem. Soc.*, **73**, 1946 (1951).
137. N. A. Bonner, *J. Am. Chem. Soc.*, **76**, 2611 (1954); H. M. Neumann, *ibid.*, **76**, 2611 (1954); H. M. Neumann and H. Brown, *ibid.*, **78**, 1843 (1956).
138. E. G. Myer and M. Kahn, *J. Am. Chem. Soc.*, **73**, 4950 (1951); E. G. Myer and A. Melnick, *J. Phys. Chem.*, **61**, 367 (1957).
139. F. B. Barker and M. Kahn, *J. Am. Chem. Soc.*, **78**, 1317 (1956).
140. W. E. Becker and R. E. Johnson, *J. Am. Chem. Soc.*, **79**, 5157 (1957).
141. Y. T. Chia and E. L. King, *Disc. Faraday Soc.*, **29**, 109 (1960).
142. R. Snellgrove and E. L. King, *J. Am. Chem. Soc.*, **84**, 4609 (1962).
143. F. Basolo, P. H. Wilks, R. G. Pearson, and R. G. Wilkins, *J. Inorg. Nucl. Chem.*, **6**, 161 (1958).
144. L. T. Cox, S. B. Collins, and D. S. Martin, *J. Inorg. Nucl. Chem.*, **17**, 383 (1961).
145. F. Basolo, M. L. Morris, and R. G. Pearson, *Disc. Faraday Soc.*, **29**, 80 (1960).
146. A. M. Rubinstein, *Compt. rend. URSS*, **28**, 55 (1940); *Izv. Plat.*, **20**, 53 (1947).
147. R. C. Johnson and F. Basolo, *J. Inorg. Nucl. Chem.*, **13**, 36 (1960).
148. H. R. Ellison, F. Basolo, and R. G. Pearson, *J. Am. Chem. Soc.*, **83**, 3943 (1961).
149. M. Delepine, *Bull. Soc. Chim. France*, **45**, 235 (1929); *Compt. rend.*, **236**, 559 (1953).
150. J. V. Rund, F. Basolo, and R. G. Pearson, *Inorg. Chem.*, **3**, 658 (1964).
151. R. D. Gillard, J. A. Osborn, R. B. Stockwell, and G. Wilkinson, *Proc. Chem. Soc.*, **1964**, 284.

152. W. R. Mason and R. C. Johnson, *Inorg. Chem.*, **4**, 1258 (1965).

153. R. L. Rich and H. Taube, *J. Am. Chem. Soc.*, **76**, 2608 (1954).

154. R. Dreyer, *Z. physik. Chem.* (*Frankfort*), **29**, 347 (1961); G. Schmidt and H. Herr, *Z. Naturforsch.*, **16a**, 748 (1961).

155. R. Dreyer, I. Dreyer, and D. Rettig, *Z. physik. Chem.* (*Leipzig*), **227**, 105 (1964).

156. K. G. Ashurst and W. C. E. Higginson, *J. Chem. Soc.*, **1953**, 3044.

157. W. C. E. Higginson, D. R. Rosseinsky, J. B. Stead, and A. G. Sykes, *Disc. Faraday Soc.*, **29**, 49 (1960).

158. J. Y. Tong and E. L. King, *J. Am. Chem. Soc.*, **82**, 3805 (1960).

159. J. H. Espenson, *J. Am. Chem. Soc.*, **85**, 5101 (1964).

160. J. H. Espenson and E. L. King, *J. Am. Chem. Soc.*, **85**, 3328 (1963).

161. N. Bailey and M. C. R. Symons, *J. Chem. Soc.*, **1957**, 203.

162. W. Klemm, *Angew. Chem.*, **66**, 468 (1954).

163. R. Woods, I. M. Kolthoff, and E. J. Meehan, *J. Am. Chem. Soc.*, **85**, 2385, 3334 (1963).

164. J. B. Kirwin, F. D. Peat, P. J. Proll, and L. H. Sutcliffe, *J. Phys. Chem.*, **67**, 1617, 2288 (1963).

165. B. M. Gordon and A. C. Wahl, *J. Am. Chem. Soc.*, **80**, 273 (1958).

166. D. Benson, P. J. Proll, L. H. Sutcliffe, and J. Walkley, *Disc. Faraday Soc.*, **29**, 60 (1960); J. Kochi, *J. Am. Chem. Soc.*, **87**, 1811, 3609 (1965).

167. W. C. E. Higginson, R. T. Leigh, and R. Nightingale, *J. Chem. Soc.*, **1962**, 435.

168. T. J. Conocchioli, E. J. Hamilton, Jr., and N. Sutin, *J. Am. Chem. Soc.*, **87**, 926 (1965).

169. J. Halpern and J. G. Smith, *Can. J. Chem.*, **34**, 1419 (1956).

170. J. H. Espenson and J. P. Birk, *Inorg. Chem.*, **4**, 527 (1965).

171. R. T. M. Fraser, *Inorg. Chem.*, **2**, 954 (1963).

172. R. T. M. Fraser, D. K. Sebera, and H. Taube, *J. Am. Chem. Soc.*, **8**, 1906 (1959); R. T. M. Fraser and H. Taube, *ibid.*, **81**, 5000, 5514 (1959).

173. D. K. Sebera and H. Taube, *J. Am. Chem. Soc.*, **83**, 1785 (1961).

174. H. Taube, *J. Am. Chem. Soc.*, **77**, 4481 (1955).

175. (a) E. S. Gould and H. Taube, *J. Am. Chem. Soc.*, **86**, 1318 (1964). (b) E. S. Gould, *ibid.*, **87**, 4730 (1965).

176. R. T. M. Fraser, *Advances in the Chemistry of the Coordination Compounds*, The Macmillan Co., New York, 1961, p. 287.

177. (a) R. D. Butler and H. Taube, *J. Am. Chem. Soc.*, **87**, 5597 (1965). (b) D. H. Hutchital and H. Taube, *Inorg. Chem.*, **4**, 1660 (1965).

178. J. P. Candlin and J. Halpern, *J. Am. Chem. Soc.*, **85**, 2518 (1963).

179. R. T. M. Fraser and H. Taube, (a) *J. Am. Chem. Soc.*, **83**, 2239 (1961); (b) *ibid.*, **83**, 2242 (1961).

180. (a) D. K. Sebera and H. Taube, *J. Am. Chem. Soc.*, **83**, 1785 (1961). (b) R. T. M. Fraser, *ibid.*, **83**, 564 (1961). (c) D. H. Hutchital and H. Taube, *ibid.*, **87**, 5371 (1965).

181. R. T. M. Fraser, *Inorg. Chem.*, **3**, 1561 (1964).

182. J. Halpern and L. E. Orgel, *Disc. Faraday Soc.*, **29**, 32 (1960).

183. P. V. Manning, R. C. Jarnagin, and M. Silver, *J. Phys. Chem.*, **68**, 265 (1964).

184. C. A. Coulson and H. C. Longuet-Higgins, *Proc. Roy. Soc.* (*London*), **A191**, 39 (1947).

185. G. Dulz and N. Sutin, *Inorg. Chem.*, **2**, 917 (1963).

186. P. G. Rasmussen and C. H. Brubaker, Jr., *Inorg. Chem.*, **3**, 977 (1964).

187. L. C. W. Baker and V. E. Simmons, *J. Am. Chem. Soc.*, **81**, 4744 (1959).

188. B. M. Gordon, L. L. Williams, and N. Sutin, *J. Am. Chem. Soc.*, **83**, 2061 (1961).

189. M. G. Adamson, F. S. Dainton, and P. Glentworth, *Trans. Faraday Soc.*, **61**, 689 (1965).

190. J. H. Espenson, *Inorg. Chem.*, **4**, 1025 (1965).

191. N. Sutin and B. M. Gordon, *J. Am. Chem. Soc.*, **83**, 70 (1961); see also N. Sutin and M. H. Ford-Smith, *ibid.*, **83**, 1830 (1961).

192. A. A. Vlček, *Collection Czech. Chem. Commun.*, **20**, 894 (1955); *Progr. Inorg. Chem.*, **5**, 211 (1963).

193. M. J. Aspray, D. R. Rosseinsky, and G. B. Shaw, *Chem. & Ind.*, **1963**, 911.

194. A. W. Adamson and K. S. Vorres, *J. Inorg. Nucl. Chem.*, **3**, 206 (1956).

195. H. L. Friedmann, J. P. Hunt, R. A. Plane, and H. Taube, *J. Am. Chem. Soc.*, **73** 4028 (1951).

196. B. R. Baker, F. Basolo, and H. M. Neumann, *J. Phys. Chem.*, **63**, 371 (1959).

197. H. F. Burstall and R. S. Nyholm, *J. Chem. Soc.*, **1952**, 3570.

198. A. A. Vlček, *Disc. Faraday Soc.*, **26**, 164 (1958).

199. The value of $10Dq$ is nearly the same for OH^- and for H_2O, according to W. E. Hatfield, J. F. Anders, and L. J. Rivela, *Inorg. Chem.*, **4**, 1088 (1965).

200. A. A. Vlček, private communication.

201. L. E. Orgel, reference 23.

202. (a) K. D. Kopple and R. R. Miller, *Proc. Chem. Soc.*, **1962**, 306. (b) R. T. M. Fraser, *J. Am. Chem. Soc.*, **85**, 1747 (1963).

203. A. Haim, *J. Am. Chem. Soc.*, **86**, 2352.

204. R. D. Cannon and J. E. Earley, *J. Am. Chem. Soc.*, **87**, 5264 (1965).

205. P. Benson and A. Haim, *J. Am. Chem. Soc.*, **87**, 3826 (1965).

206. See, however, F. S. Dainton and F. T. Jones, *Radiation Res.*, **17**, 388 (1962).

207. G. A. Rechnitz and H. A. Catherino, *Inorg. Chem.*, **4**, 112 (1965).

208. E. J. Hart and J. W. Boag, *J. Am. Chem. Soc.*, **84**, 4090 (1962).

209. For a review of the properties see L. M. Dorfman and M. S. Matheson, *Progr. Reaction Kinetics*, **3**, 239 (1965). For a brief account see E. J. Hart, *Science*, **146**, 19 (1964).

210. L. Dorfman and I. A. Taub, *J. Am. Chem. Soc.*, **85**, 2370 (1963).

211. J. H. Baxendale, *Radiation Res. Suppl.*, **4**, 139 (1964).

212. J. H. Baxendale, E. M. Fielden, and J. P. Keene, *Proc. Chem. Soc.*, **1963**, 242.

213. J. H. Baxendale *et al.*, *Nature*, **201**, 468 (1964).

214. J. K. Thomas, S. Gordon, and E. J. Hart, *J. Phys. Chem.*, **68**, 1254 (1964).

215. M. Anbar and E. J. Hart, *J. Phys. Chem.*, **69**, 973 (1965).

216. W. L. Waltz, unpublished results.

217. A. Szutka, J. Thomas, S. Gordon, and E. J. Hart, *J. Phys. Chem.*, **69**, 289 (1965).

218. K. Schmidt and W. Buck, private communication.

219. R. A. Marcus, *J. Chem. Phys.*, **43**, 3477 (1965).

220. J. H. Espenson and J. P. Birk, *J. Am. Chem. Soc.*, **87**, 3280 (1965).

221. J. Halpern and S. Nakamura, *J. Am. Chem. Soc.*, **87**, 3002 (1965).

222. J. K. Yandell and D. R. Stranks, *Exchange Reaction Symposium*, I.A.E.A., Brookhaven National Laboratory, October 1965.

223. E. J. Hart, S. Gordon, and E. M. Fielden, *J. Phys. Chem.*, **70**, 150 (1966).

224. J. Jortner and G. Stein, *Nature*, **175**, 893 (1955); G. Hughes and R. J. Roach, *Chem. Comm.*, **1965**, 600.

7

Reactions of Transition Metal Organometallics

One of the most important developments in chemistry in the last fifteen years has been the synthesis and study of many organometallic derivatives of the transition metals. This development began essentially with the discovery of ferrocene, $Fe(C_5H_5)_2$, in 1951,[1] and with the recognition of its sandwich-type structure.[2] There has been a great activity in this field, particularly in synthesis and in the theoretical interpretation of structures. There is also much interest in the reactions of these complexes, though mechanistic studies are still in their infancy. We can anticipate a great increase in such studies, however, because of the many unusual reactions and products and because of the commercial importance of some of these applications.

In this chapter we will consider the alkyls, aryls, and hydrides of the transition metals. In addition the carbonyls and the many complexes in which an unsaturated organic group is bound to a metal will be included. The compounds in the first group are examples of σ covalent bonding, and those in the second group are complexes held together by both σ and π bonding. All these systems have certain properties which makes it convenient to discuss them together. Between them, they constitute the organometallics of the transition elements.

Any theory of bonding of these compounds must explain several observations which are quite general.

1. Simple alkyls or hydrides, such as MR_n or MH_n, are not known or are very unstable. This situation contrasts with the non-transition elements.

2. Associated with an H^- or R^- ligand attached to a transition metal will be a number of other ligands which are almost always soft bases. Furthermore some of these must have π-bonding orbitals available for π back-bonding. Bonding to carbon in general, by either σ or π bonds, usually requires the presence of other soft ligands in the molecule.

3. The total number of valence electrons in the $(n-1)d$ and ns and np orbitals of the central metal adds up to eighteen in the great majority of

cases. This is Sidgwick's *effective atomic number rule*, whereby the metal atom takes up an electron configuration like the next noble gas. Occasionally a complex with sixteen valence electrons will be found and, very rarely, one with seventeen, less than sixteen, or more than eighteen.

4. The majority, but not all, of the organometallics of the transition elements are formed with the metal in a state of low or zero oxidation number. The oxidation number is often ambiguous in these compounds, because the ligands are frequently of the type that Jørgensen has called non-innocent ligands.[3] For example, ferrocene may be considered as made up of Fe^{2+} and two cyclopentadienyl ions, $C_5H_5^-$. Alternatively it may be regarded as composed of Fe^0 and two cyclopentadienyl radicals, $\cdot C_5H_5$. In either case we obtain eighteen valence electrons (6 + 12 or 8 + 10).

5. Many of the hydride and alkides are remarkably stable to air and moisture compared to the corresponding representative metal compounds.

The last observation provides good evidence for covalent bonding in the transition element cases. The non-transition metals show the characteristic reactions of ionic H^- and R^- and must have quite polar bonds. There is evidence that polarity is actually reversed for the transition elements. Thus $HCo(CO)_4$ and $H_2Fe(CO)_4$ ionize as acids

$$HCo(CO)_4 \rightleftharpoons H^+ + Co(CO)_4^- \tag{1}$$

in aqueous solution.[4] The dipole moment of $IrHCl_2(PEt_3)_3$ shows that the hydrogen is slightly positive.[5] Corresponding to the reverse of reaction 1, protons can be added to many organometallics to form hydrides[6]

$$H^+ + Fe(CO)_3C_4H_6 \rightarrow HFe(CO)_3C_4H_6^+ \tag{2}$$

In the same way many carbonium ions have been found to add as ligands to transition metal ions.[7]

Since σ covalent bonding for H^- and R^- ligands would necessarily put large amounts of negative charge on the metal atom, we can understand observations 1 and 2. The simple hydrides and alkides are unstable because of excess negative charge on the metal atom. The role of soft, particularly unsaturated ligands is simply to remove excess negative charge on the metal by π back-bonding. This is the original concept of Pauling, which he applied to metal carbonyls and cyanides.[8]

The low or zero oxidation state for the metal may be attributed to the circumstance of its being combined with a number of soft ligands with extensive electron donation to the metal. It is also an example of the principle which states that soft bases prefer to coordinate to soft acids. Hence the metal atom, to be soft, should be of low valence. The principle of symbiosis[9] is also found in that there is a clustering of soft ligands around the soft acid center.

The second important characteristic of the organometallics of the transition metals is the wide applicability of the E.A.N. rule, or the sixteen-electron rule in some cases. The latter compounds are almost always square planar in structure, whereas the former are tetrahedral, trigonal bipyramidal, or octahedral. The numbers 16 and 18 are clearly related to double occupancy of the eight stable valence orbitals of the planar structure, one ns, three np, and four $(n - 1)d$ orbitals, and the nine stable valence orbitals of the remaining structures, one ns, three np, and five $(n - 1)d$. Both σ and π-bonding possibilities are included.

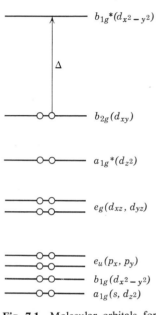

Fig. 7.1 Molecular orbitals for a square planar complex. The metal orbitals chiefly involved are shown in parentheses. The four lowest M.O.'s are the σ-bonding M.O.'s.

Thus the rule seems to be that maximum occupancy of all possible bonding orbitals exists. All σ orbitals are engaged in ligand to metal electron donation, and all π orbitals in metal to ligand back-bonding. Provided steric factors are not excessive, there is no reason not to have the maximum number of ligands possible. Furthermore, it would be a disadvantage to have any π-type orbitals on the metal empty. It has been shown[10] that this combination of σ and π bonding in the first transition series keeps the total potential function of the central metal atom very similar to that of the krypton atom itself.

We may also regard the factors stabilizing the organometallics in terms of ligand field theory. It is known that H^- and R^- have large ligand field strengths, at least in complexes of Pt(II).[11] Also soft ligands in general stand high in the spectrochemical series (p. 67). Hence ligand field stabilization energy should be a significant factor. The compound *trans*-$Pt(PEt_3)_2(CH_3)Cl$ may be considered a normal d^8 complex of Pt(II). It has a square planar structure.[12] Figure 7.1 shows the M.O. energy level scheme for this structure. The sixteen valence electrons are accommodated in the low-energy orbitals, and the high-energy b_{1g}^* orbital is avoided (derived from the metal $d_{x^2-y^2}$ orbital).

The octahedral structure of $Cr(CO)_6$ is similarly expected for the d^6 Cr(0) system, since the $(t_{2g})^6$ orbital configuration is so stable. The tetrahedral structure for the d^{10} central atom in $Ni(CO)_4$ is in agreement with the lack of C.F.S.E. to be found in any structure for a d^{10} atom. It might have been expected that Fe(0), a d^8 system, would form square planar Fe(CO)$_4$ instead of trigonal bipyramidal Fe(CO)$_5$. However, CO is a particularly strong π-bonding ligand. It has already been mentioned that a d^8 ion will become five coordinated with a trigonal bipyramid structure when π-bonding ligands are present. Four strong π bonds can be formed with this structure, but only three π bonds with the planar structure.

Chatt and Shaw[13] have used ligand field theory in a somewhat special way to account for the stability of hydride and alkide complexes. First, the preference of these molecules for planar or octahedral structures and the lack of tetrahedral structures indicate that C.F.S.E. is indeed important. Thus Co(C$_6$Cl$_5$)$_2$(PR$_3$)$_2$ is planar, whereas CoCl$_2$(PR$_3$)$_2$ is tetrahedral. Second, the energy gap labeled Δ in Fig. 7.1 should be as large as possible to enhance stability. Hence the accompanying ligands should be soft and consequently of high ligand field strength.

If Δ is large, an electron promotion from the b_{2g} to the $b_{1g}*$ orbital is unlikely. This will prevent the thermal liberation of R· or H· as a free radical or atom. Also if Δ is large, the loss of C.F.S.E. in a bimolecular substitution reaction will be large (Chapter 3). This will prevent hydrolytic decomposition. Support for the latter view is given by the observation that *ortho*-substituted aryl complexes, NiAr$_2$(PR$_3$)$_2$, are more stable than the phenyl complexes.[14] This is chiefly a result of steric hindrance to displacement reactions, though it may also be that Δ is larger for an *ortho*-substituted aryl group. For similar complexes the order of stability is always Pt > Pd > Ni, which is explicable in terms of the increased value of Δ in going from the first to third transition series.

A very important class of the organometallics of the transition metals consists of compounds in which an unsaturated molecule or radical is attached to a metal. Examples are known for olefinic, acetylenic, and aromatic unsaturation, and many other special types. The requirement is to have a group of carbon (or other) atoms which contain a π system of electrons. The class is extremely old, since Zeise's salt, KPtCl$_3$C$_2$H$_4$, has been known since 1828. Only in recent years have extensive studies and developments been made.

With a proper choice of stabilizing ligands, most of the transition metals will form complexes with unsaturated groups. Some metal ions will form them in aqueous solution with no other special ligands present. The most stable systems of this type are formed by d^{10} atoms and ions such as Cu(I), Ag(I), and Hg(II), and by d^8 atoms and ions such as Pd(II) and Pt(II). Gold would undoubtedly form such complexes in either its plus one or plus three oxidation states, but it is too easily reduced to the metal.

There is very little doubt that the unsaturated group is held to the metal by essentially a double bond, in which unsaturation electrons from the organic molecule form a σ coordinate bond to the metal and the metal in turn donates a pair of d electrons to the organic molecule through a π bond.[15] The best formulation of the bonds in such a system is that due to Dewar.[16] The problem is to form bonding orbitals from the set of atomic orbitals consisting of p orbitals on each carbon atom and an s orbital, or $(s + p)$ hybrid, and a d orbital, or $(d + p)$ hybrid, on the metal.

Figure 7.2 shows the atomic orbitals involved and the convenient way of representing the two lowest molecular orbitals that can be formed

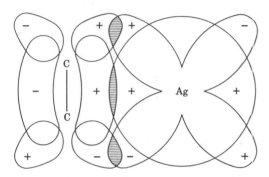

Fig. 7.2 The double bonding in a silver ion-olefin complex. From reference 16.

from them. From the criterion of matching signs for the wave functions in regions of overlap, it is clear that an s orbital on the metal will combine with the hybrid obtained by adding together the two carbon p orbitals. This is the bonding M.O. of the C-C double bond. The d orbital of the metal will combine with the hybrid obtained by changing the sign of one carbon p orbital and then adding. This corresponds to the antibonding M.O. of the double bond. Schematically the silver ion–ethylene complex may be represented by either Ia or Ib. If Ia is used, it must be remembered

that the bond between the metal and the olefin is more nearly a double bond. The bonding is obviously different from that of the complexes formed between unsaturated systems and such ions as H^+ and Al^{3+}, or generalized acids such as BF_3, $SnCl_4$, $TiCl_4$. These systems are of interest in that they are the intermediates in the cationic type of polymerization, but we shall not discuss them further here.[17]

The bonding of the silver ion to olefin is reasonably strong. Thus the heat of the reaction

$$C_2H_4(CCl_4) + Ag(H_2O)_n^+ \rightarrow AgC_2H_4(H_2O)_{n-1}^+ + H_2O \qquad (3)$$

is about 6 kcal exothermic.[18] Neglecting the differences in the heat of solution of the olefin in water and in carbon tetrachloride, this gives a figure for the metal ion–ethylene coordinate bond of between 20 kcal and 30 kcal.[19] The uncertainty lies in not knowing whether n is 6 or 4 in correcting for the hydration energy of the silver ion.

The importance of the d type of bonding from the metal is brought out by the fact that the stability of the platinum-olefin complexes decreases in the order $PtC_2H_4Cl_3^- \simeq PtC_2H_4ACl_2 > PtC_2H_4A_2Cl^+ > PtC_2H_4A_3^{2+}$, where A is a neutral ligand. Thus negative charge on the complex stabilizes the olefin portion in a way consistent with the concept of electron donation to the olefin. It is of interest to note that, for these square planar complexes of Pt(II), the C-C axis of ethylene is perpendicular to the plane of the ring. This minimizes the repulsion of the ethylene for the ligands *cis* to it and allows for π bonding from the metal.

The olefin complexes of Cu(I) are more stable than those of Ag(I) in agreement with the ease of oxidation of each metal to the divalent state. Likewise, Pt(II) complexes are more stable than those of Pd(II). Sometimes the complexes of the divalent cations are more stable than those of the monovalent ions; for example, Hg^{2+}-cyclohexene is more stable than Ag^+-cyclohexene.[20] This indicates a greater importance of the σ bond (olefin to metal bonding) than the π bond (metal to olefin bonding) in such cases.

Substitution of almost any kind on ethylene makes it a poorer coordinating species.[21] *cis* Olefins form more stable complexes than *trans* olefins. Acetylenes form slightly less stable complexes with silver ion than olefins do, but more stable than those of aromatic systems. The complexes of silver and of mercury with acetylenes can lose a proton, if a C-H bond is present, to form acetylides.

The bonding scheme for $Ag(C_2H_4)^+$ shown in Fig. 7.2 can be generalized into a theory for the bonding of other π organic systems to a central metal atom with d electrons.[22] Consider the π system stripped of all its electrons. The carbon (or other) atoms will be a set of points, usually in a plane. The molecular orbitals for this system can now be found by the usual Hückel approximation or some higher approximation.[23] We need only consider the symmetries of the resulting M.O.'s to understand the general bonding scheme to the metal. Atomic orbitals on the metal are now combined with the organic M.O.'s of the same symmetry to form new M.O.'s for the entire complex. These may be of overall σ, π, or δ symmetry and will form bonds of the same type.

Figure 7.3 shows schematically the M.O. wave functions for a number of simple examples of unsaturated ligands. For the open systems the sign and rough magnitude of the wave function are shown as a function of position along the carbon chain. For the cyclic systems only the sign of the wave

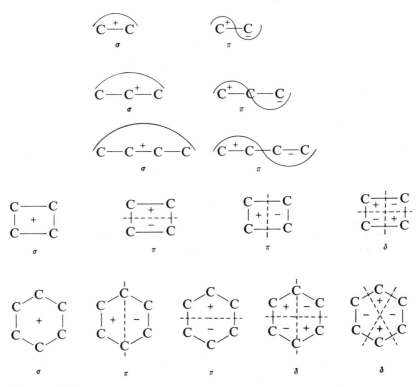

Fig. 7.3 The ligand molecular orbitals (for unsaturated organic ligands) that may be combined with metal orbitals to give bonds of the symmetry shown. Amplitude of wave function and mathematical sign shown for C_2H_4, C_3H_5 and C_4H_6. Sign only shown for C_4H_4 and C_6H_6.

function is given. In all cases the view is that seen from the nucleus of a metal atom to be bonded to the organic group.

In all cases the first M.O. shown, which is that of lowest energy, is of σ-type symmetry with respect to the metal-ligand axis. The next one or two orbitals, of higher energy, are of π-type symmetry. The next are the δ type and are usually so high in energy that their role in bonding is quite small. If the metal-ligand axis is the z axis, a σ-bonding orbital on the metal could be formed by a hybrid of s, d_{z^2}, and p_z orbitals. Also two π-type orbitals on the metal could be formed from a combination of d_{xz} and p_x, and of d_{yz} and p_y.

For example, the π-allyl complex $[PdC_3H_5Cl]_2$ has the structure[24]

(II)

The unit complex may be considered to be made up of Pd(II) with eight valence electrons, an allyl anion which contributes four electrons, and a chloride ion which contributes two electrons. The bridging chlorine brings the electron count up to sixteen. The allyl group is bound by one σ bond and one π bond to palladium. The σ bond is concentrated on the central carbon but extends over all three. The π bond is equally towards each of the end carbons.

One interesting result of the theory of such unsaturated hydrocarbon complexes of metals is that it was predicted[25] that the unknown cyclobutadiene could be prepared in the form of its complexes. A variety of such complexes has now been prepared, including $Ni(C_6H_5)_4C_4Br_2$, $Ni(CH_3)_4C_4Cl_2$, and $FeC_4H_4(CO)_3$.[26] The last-named compound appears to release unstable C_4H_4 upon low-temperature decomposition.[27]

Metal Carbonyls and Their Derivatives

The now classical discovery of $Ni(CO)_4$[28] in 1890 by Mond was followed almost immediately by the discovery of $Fe(CO)_5$.[29] This led to the development of the chemistry of metal carbonyls and subsequently to derivatives of metal carbonyls. There has been a continued interest[30] in these compounds, but in the past this was very modest compared with relatively recent activity.[31] The tremendous increase in interest in the metal carbonyls over the last decade has arisen partly as a result of the discovery of many novel transition metal organometallic compounds in which a metal carbonyl system forms an integral part of the structure. Also, a very practical stimulus is provided by the fact that metal carbonyls are often excellent catalysts for certain industrial processes.

The chemistry of the metal carbonyls and their derivatives is described in detail in several review articles on the subject.[30,31] It is sufficient here to give a brief general introduction before discussing the mechanisms of reaction of some of these systems. The known binary metal carbonyls and some of their physical properties are given in Table 7.1. The metals that form neutral binary metal carbonyls and those that form metal carbonyl halides are shown in Fig. 7.4.

Table 7.1   The binary metal carbonyls

V	VI	VII	VIII		
$V(CO)_6$ black, dec. 70°, sublimes *in vacuo*	$Cr(CO)_6$ colorless, sublimes	$Mn_2(CO)_{10}$ yellow, m.p. 155°, sublimes	$Fe(CO)_5$ yellow, m.p. −20°, b.p. 103°	$Co_2(CO)_8$ orange-red, m.p. 51°	$Ni(CO)_4$ colorless, m.p. −25°, b.p. 43°
	$Mo(CO)_6$ colorless sublimes	$Tc_2(CO)_{10}$ colorless, m.p. 160°	$Fe_2(CO)_9$ dec. 100°	$Co_4(CO)_{12}$ black, dec. 60°	
	$W(CO)_6$ colorless, sublimes	$Re_2(CO)_{10}$ colorless, m.p. 177° sublimes	$Fe_3(CO)_{12}$ green, dec. 140°	$Rh_2(CO)_8$? orange, m.p. 76°	
			$Ru(CO)_5$ colorless, m.p. −22°	$[Rh(CO)_3]_4$? red, sublimes	
			$Ru_3(CO)_{12}$ green, cryst.	$Rh_6(CO)_{16}$ black, dec. 200°	
			$Os(CO)_5$ colorless, m.p. −15°	$Ir_2(CO)_8$? yellow-green, sublimes	
			$Os_3(CO)_{12}$ yellow, m.p. 224°, sublimes	$[Ir(CO)_3]_4$? yellow, dec. 210°	

The metal carbonyls are prepared in a variety of ways. Only nickel, iron, and cobalt seem to react directly with carbon monoxide to give the carbonyls. Generally, carbonyls are prepared by the reduction of suitable salts or complexes of the metal in the presence of CO. In recent years several novel methods have been used to obtain in good yields some of the previously less accessible metal carbonyls.[32]

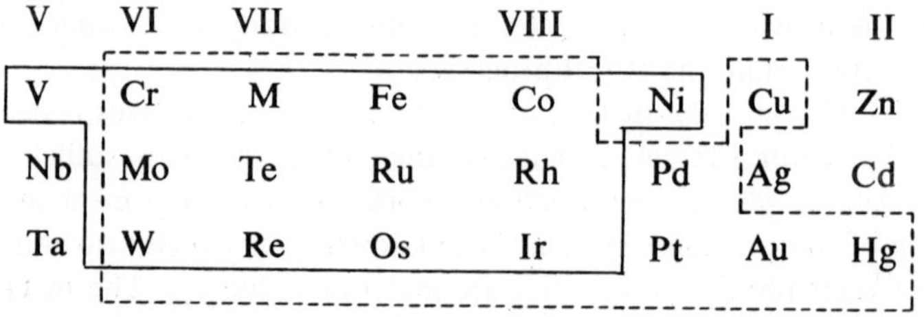

Fig. 7.4 ——— Encloses metals that form neutral binary metal carbonyls. – – – Encloses metals that form neutral and/or anionic metal carbonyl halides.

Metal carbonyls and their derivatives generally are diamagnetic and have an electronic structure that contains eighteen valence electrons surrounding the metal in accord with the Sidgwick effective atomic number (E.A.N.) rule. Thus nickel has ten valence electrons ($3d^8 + 4s^2$) and requires eight more to attain the "magic number" of eighteen. Since a molecule of CO contributes two electrons, it follows that four molecules are needed to give the stable compound $Ni(CO)_4$. The metal is also found to achieve its closed shell electronic structure in the more complicated carbonyls such as $Fe_3(CO)_{12}$[33] and $Co_4(CO)_{12}$,[34] in ionic carbonyls such as

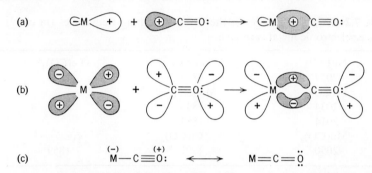

Fig. 7.5   Representation of M-C bonding in metal carbonyls by (a) and (b) the M.O. and (c) the V.B. theories. Shaded orbitals contain electrons; open oribtals are empty. The σ bonding is represented by (a), π bonding by (b), and the V.B. theory canonical structures by (c).

$Fe(CO)_4^{2-}$ and $Mn(CO)_6^+$,[35] and in substituted carbonyls such as $C_5H_5Rh(CO)_2$[36] and $MnNO(CO)_4$.[37] There are some exceptions; the one best known is $V(CO)_6$, which is a seventeen-electron system. As might be expected, the compound is readily reduced[38] to $V(CO)_6^-$. Other paramagnetic metal carbonyls include compounds such as $Cr(CO)_5I$,[39] $Mn(CO)_3(phen)$,[40] $Fe(CO)_2(diars)I$,[41] and $(C_5H_5Ni)_3(CO)_2$.[42]

The metal-carbon bond in metal carbonyls is believed to involve a σ bond resulting from donation of the lone electron pair on carbon to the metal and a π bond due to the back donation of electrons from the filled non-bonding d orbitals on the metal to the π antibonding orbitals of CO. This is illustrated in Fig. 7.5. The π bond not only has the effect of furnishing an additional bond but also increases the electron density on carbon, which then strengthens its σ-bond formation. This in turn increases the electron density on the metal and strengthens its π-bond formation. The net effect of mutual reinforcement, or synergic interactions between the two types of bonding, probably accounts for the major part of the M-C bond strength.

A significant consequence of the presence of electrons in the π^* orbital of CO is the reduction in the C-O bond order. The infrared spectra of these systems provide a most convenient and useful estimate of this. Whereas the C-O stretching frequency, ν_{CO}, of CO itself has a value of 2155 cm^{-1}, the corresponding frequencies of terminal metal carbonyl groups are much less and usually have values in the neighborhood of 2000 cm^{-1}.

One of the strongest effects upon this frequency value is that of charge on the metal carbonyl or oxidation state of the metal. Typical i.r. data are shown in Table 7.2 for three groups of isoelectronic and isostructural species. These show that as the negative charge increases, or the oxidation

Table 7.2   Effect of charge on the C—O stretching frequencies (in cm^{-1}) of some isoelectronic metal carbonyls

$Ni(CO)_4$	$Co(CO)_4^-$	$Fe(CO)_4^{2-}$ [a]
2057	1886	1786
$Fe(CO)_5$	$Mn(CO)_5^-$ [a]	
2034	1895	
2014	1863	
$Mn(CO)_6^+$	$Cr(CO)_6$	$V(CO)_6^-$ [b]
2090	1981	1859

[a] W. F. Edgell *et al.*, *J. Am. Chem. Soc.*, **82**, 1254 (1960).
[b] W. Beck and R. E. Nitzshmann, *Z. Naturforsch.*, **17b**, 577 (1962).

state of the metal decreases, there is an accompanying decrease in the value of ν_{CO}. Roughly, a unit of negative charge lowers ν_{CO} by about 100 cm^{-1}, whereas a unit of positive charge increases it by about the same amount. This result is readily explained on the basis of the proposed nature of the M-C bonding in these systems (Fig. 7.5). Thus the negative charge, or lower oxidation state of the metal, places a larger electron density on the metal, which means more metal to carbon π bonding and, as a result, a decrease in the C-O bond order. A positive charge on the metal carbonyl, or an increase in oxidation state of the metal, has the opposite effect, resulting in an increase of the C-O bond order relative to the neutral isoelectronic compound.

The replacement of CO with other ligands also has an effect on the C-O stretching frequencies of the remaining carbon monoxides in the substituted product. What happens is illustrated by the data collected in Table 7.3 for some molybdenum carbonyls. Except perhaps for PF_3, it appears that the replacement of CO with some other ligand is accompanied by a decrease in ν_{CO}. Considering that other ligands are generally stronger σ bonders and poorer π bonders than is CO, it follows that in systems containing other ligands the metal will be somewhat more negative and

Table 7.3 Effect of ligand on the C—O stretching frequencies (in cm^{-1}) and force constants (in mdynes/A) of molybdenum carbonyls

Compound	ν_{CO}	$F_{CO}^{t\ a}$	$F_{CO}^{c\ a}$
Mo(CO)$_6$	2120, 2022, 1990	...	16.52
Mo(CO)$_5$PCl$_3$	2095, 2001, 1987	16.38	16.46
Mo(CO)$_5$P(OC$_6$H$_5$)$_3$	2085, 1975, 1963	15.97	16.14
Mo(CO)$_5$P(OCH$_3$)$_3$	2080, 1967, 1995, 1950	15.62	16.02
Mo(CO)$_5$P(C$_6$H$_5$)$_3$	2078, 1951, 1990, 1951	15.57	15.99
Mo(CO)$_5$P(CH$_3$)$_3$	2071, 1952, 1943	15.61	15.87
cis-Mo(CO)$_4$[P(C$_6$H$_5$)$_3$]$_2$	2023, 1929, 1911, 1899	14.64	15.41
cis-Mo(CO)$_4$[P(CH$_3$)$_3$]$_2$	2019, 1920, 1903, 1893	14.82	15.33
trans-Mo(CO)$_4$[P(C$_6$H$_5$)$_3$]$_2$	1955, 1902	...	15.30
trans-Mo(CO)$_4$[P(CH$_3$)$_3$]$_2$	1893	...	15.23
cis-Mo(CO)$_3$(PF$_3$)$_3$	2090, 2055	16.98	...
cis-Mo(CO)$_3$[P(CH$_3$)$_3$]$_3$	1945, 1854	14.35	...
trans-Mo(CO)$_3$[P(CH$_3$)$_3$]$_3$	1961, 1854	13.95	14.85

From reference 43.

^{a} F_{CO}^t is the force constant for CO *trans* to the ligand, whereas F_{CO}^c is that for CO *cis* to the ligand (note *trans* to another CO). Units are millidynes/ angstrom.

have a greater tendency to π-bond with the remaining CO molecules. This net effect is smaller than but analogous to that of placing a negative charge on the system as described above.

Estimated force constants are also included in Table 7.3, and these provide a more convenient comparison than do the stretching frequencies of changes in the C-O bond orders with changes in the ligand. One important point is that the bond order of C-O in a given compound differs depending on whether it is *trans*, F_{CO}^t, or *cis*, F_{CO}^c, to the ligand. Values of F_{CO}^t are always lower than the corresponding F_{CO}^c values. This can be understood on the basis of the directional properties of the metal d orbitals used in π bonding. Since the ligand L is a weak π bonder compared to CO, it follows that CO *trans* to L has a major share of the metal d orbital electrons in competition with L (Fig. 7.6b). Hence there will be more M-C π bonding for this CO than for one *cis* to L but *trans* to another CO, and in competition with it for π bonding (Fig. 7.6a). Keep in mind that a larger M-C π-bond order means a smaller C-O bond order and a smaller force constant.

One other significant feature of the data in Table 7.3 is that the C-O force constants vary with changes in the nature of the ligand. For example, the values of F_{CO} for corresponding substituted metal carbonyls decrease in the order PF$_3$ > PCl$_3$ > P(OR)$_3$ > PR$_3$, which is believed to be the

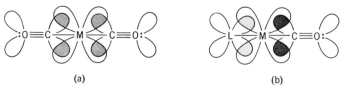

(a)   (b)

Fig. 7.6 Competition for π bonding in metal carbonyl derivatives such as $M(CO)_5L$. (a) The π bonding of CO molecules *cis* to L but *trans* to CO. (b) The π bonding of CO trans to weak π-bonding ligand L.

order of decreasing π-bonding tendency of these ligands. Many data of this type have been collected and discussed by several different investigators.[43] By making use of data from various sources, a "spectrochemical series" for π-bonding ligands has been compiled in Table 7.4. The best π-bonding ligands are NO, CO, and PF_3, whereas amines which cannot π-bond are at the end of the series. It may be of interest to note that the value of $F_{CO} = 16.98$ mdynes/A for *cis*-$Mo(CO)_3(PF_3)_3$, compared to a value of 16.52 for $Mo(CO)_6$, suggests that PF_3 is a better π bonder than is CO.

The most extensively measured physical property of the metal carbonyls and their derivatives is their i.r. spectra. These spectra provide information not only on the nature of the metal-carbon and metal-ligand bonding, but also on the structures of the compounds. One common application of the i.r. spectra is that of detecting the presence of bridging carbonyl groups,

$$M-\overset{\overset{\displaystyle O}{\|}}{C}-M.$$ The C-O stretching frequencies for such groups are at about 1850 cm^{-1}. Another application is that of evaluating the symmetry properties of a molecule, and thus its structure, on the basis of the number and

Table 7.4 A "spectrochemical series" for π bonding of ligands

NO	$As(OCH_3)_3$	$P(C_6H_5)_3$
CO	$PCl(OC_4H_9)_2$	$S(C_2H_5)_2$
PF_3	$As(OC_2H_5)_3$	$As(C_2H_5)_3$
$SbCl_3$	$P(OC_6H_5)_3$	$P(CH_3)_3$
$AsCl_3$	$PCl(C_6H_5)_2$	$P(C_2H_5)_3$
PCl_3	$p\text{-}CH_3OC_6H_4NC$	$o\text{-}C_6H_4[P(C_2H_5)_2]_2$
$PCl_2(OC_4H_9)$	$P(OCH_3)_3$	$P(NC_5H_{10})_3$
$PCl_2(OC_2H_5)$	$t\text{-}C_4H_9NC$	phen[a]
$PCl_2(C_6H_5)$	$As(NC_5H_{10})_3$	dien[a]
PBr_2CH_3	$As(C_6H_5)_3$	

From reference 44.

[a] phen = 1,10-phenanthroline. dien = diethylenetriamine.

relative intensities of the CO absorption bands.[45] In practice, however, the spectra are often complicated and the assignments of structure must be made with caution.

Substitution reactions of metal carbonyls occur fairly readily, but often it is extremely difficult to replace all of the carbon monoxides by other ligands. For example, the reaction of $Mo(CO)_6$ with excess $P(C_6H_5)_3$ yields $Mo(CO)_3(PPh_3)_3$ as the final substitution product, and a similar reaction of $Ni(CO)_4$ gives $Ni(CO)_2(PPh_3)_2$. Results of this type are interpreted on the basis of the π-bonding concept described above and are in qualitative agreement with the decrease in C—O stretching frequency with increased substitution. Thus, since the M-C π bonding, and presumably the bond strength, increase with substitution, it follows that each step in the replacement of CO from a metal carbonyl is of higher energy than the preceding step. This explanation is based on an assumption which is not necessarily valid: that there is a simple relationship between vibrational stretching frequencies and the strength of the bonds involved. It is well known that there is *no theoretical reason* why this should be so.[46] In terms of a potential energy versus nuclear coordinate diagram, the dissociation energy of a bond is given by the depth of the potential well (less the zero point energy). The force constant, which controls the frequencies for systems of fixed mass, is given by the curvature of the potential energy function. There is no obvious relationship between the two properties. However, for systems such as the metal carbonyls it appears that empirically the two quantities are related to each other.

Substitution by poorer π-bonding ligands then will decrease the lability of each successive CO ligand, making them harder to displace. However, with PF_3, a slightly better π bonder than CO, it is possible to replace all of the CO molecules of a metal carbonyl. The entire series of compounds $Fe(CO)_{5-n}(PF_3)_n$, where n has values of 1–5, and $Ni(CO)_{4-n}(PF_3)_n$, where n has values of 1–4, has been prepared.[47] The compounds $Cr(PF_3)_6$ and $Mo(PF_3)_6$ have also been obtained.[48]

Metal carbonyls undergo reactions other than substitution, such as redox,

$$V(CO)_6 + Na \rightarrow Na[V(CO)_6] \qquad (4)$$

$$Mn_2(CO)_{10} + Br_2 \rightarrow 2Mn(CO)_5Br \qquad (5)$$

disproportionation,

$$Co_2(CO)_8 + 6C_5H_5N \rightarrow [Co(C_5H_5N)_6][Co(CO)_4]_2 + 8CO \qquad (6)$$

and condensation,

$$2Fe(CO)_5 \xrightarrow{U.V.} Fe_2(CO)_9 + CO \qquad (7)$$

reactions. However, the kinetics and mechanism of these reactions have usually not been studied, and therefore the discussion that follows is limited to CO exchange and substitution reactions of metal carbonyls.

Carbon Monoxide Exchange

An appreciable amount of data is now available on the exchange of ^{14}CO with a variety of metal carbonyls. It is convenient to discuss this topic in terms of the three different classes of compounds, (1) metal carbonyls, (2) metal carbonyl halides, and (3) π-cyclopentadienyl metal carbonyls.

Metal Carbonyls.   The data in Table 7.5 refer to metal carbonyls and include also for comparison a few substituted metal carbonyls. The results provide information on the relative reactivities of these systems as a function of various changes in the carbonyl, such as coordination number, charge, extent of substitution, metal, and structure.

Because of the low solubility of CO gas in most solvents, the experimental technique used to measure the exchange of ^{14}CO with metal carbonyls in solution is rather troublesome. The usual procedure is to circulate the gas through the solution, kept at constant temperature, and have some device in the closed system to monitor the radioactivity of the gas as it changes with time.[49] The exchange data follow the McKay[50] equation and give linear plots of log $(A_0 - A_\infty/A - A_\infty)$ versus time, where A_0 is the initial radioactivity, A is the radioactivity at time t, and A_∞ is the radioactivity at equilibrium. The half-lives given in Table 7.5 are obtained from this first-order rate constant, k_{obs}, and are comparable only for the same experimental conditions. The rate constants given in this table are the true first or second-order rate constants, estimated from k_{obs} by means of the equation

$$k_{true} = k_{obs} \frac{xa^{1-\alpha}yb^{1-\beta}}{xa + yb} \tag{8}$$

In this equation a is the concentration of metal carbonyl, b is the concentration of CO in solution, x is the number of exchangeable CO's in the metal carbonyl, y is the ratio of total moles of CO in the enclosed system to moles of CO in solution, α represents the order in a, and β the order in b. The true rate constants are directly comparable in the usual manner and, unlike the k_{obs} or half-lives, are not a function of the total amount of CO used in the enclosed system.

The exchange of CO with the simplest first-row transition metal carbonyls in solution in the dark is extremely slow for $Cr(CO)_6$, $Mn_2(CO)_{10}$, and $Fe(CO)_5$, moderately slow for $V(CO)_6$, and very fast for $Co_2(CO)_8$ and $Ni(CO)_4$. Both $V(CO)_6$ and $Co_2(CO)_8$ are perhaps special cases, the former being paramagnetic[58] and the latter having two bridging carbon monoxides.[59] Thus $V(CO)_6$ may exchange more rapidly than $Cr(CO)_6$

Table 7.5 Exchange of carbon monoxide with some metal carbonyls

Compound	Temp., °C	Solvent	Conc., mM Compound	Conc., mM CO	Rate[a]	Ref.
$Ni(CO)_4$ [b]	0	toluene	51	4.1	7.8×10^{-4}	49
$Fe(CO)_5$ [c]	25	benzene	49	3.4	4 yr	51
$Cr(CO)_6$ [b]	117	gas phase	40	20	2×10^{-5}	52
$Mo(CO)_6$ [b]	116	gas phase	21	42	7.5×10^{-5}	53
$W(CO)_6$ [b]	142	gas phase	16	42	2.6×10^{-6}	53
$V(CO)_6$	10	heptane	22	2 atm	7 hr	54
$Co_2(CO)_8$ [b]	0	toluene	22	3.7	1.5×10^{-3}	49
$Mn_2(CO)_{10}$	25	benzene	11	2.1	10 yr	51
$Fe_3(CO)_{12}$	25	benzene	5.8	2.8	350 hr	51
$Co_4(CO)_{12}$	25	benzene	5.2	3.1	80 hr	51
$Co(CO)_4^-$	60	water	1	0.02	N.E. 20 hr	55
$Fe(CO)_4^{2-}$	60	water	1	0.02	N.E. 20 hr	55
$Mn(CO)_5^-$	40	water	1	0.02	N.E. 20 hr	55
$Re(CO)_5^-$	20	ether	1	0.22	N.E. 20 hr	55
$Mn(CO)_6^+$	30	acidic	0.75	0.22	N.E. 15 hr	55
$Re(CO)_6^+$	60	water	1	0.37	N.E. 60 hr	55
$CoNO(CO)_3$ [d]	25	benzene	28	1.8	19 hr	51
$Ni(CO)_3P(C_6H_5)_3$	25	toluene	14	1.6	1×10^{-3}	49
$Ni(CO)_2[P(C_6H_5)_3]_2$	25	benzene	14	6.4	1.4×10^{-5}	49
$Mo(CO)_n(CNC_6H_5)_{6-n}$	107	gas phase	10	3	slow	53
$Co_3(CO)_9CH$	40	toluene	52	6	9.5×10^{-7}	56
$Co_3(CO)_9CF$ [b]	40	toluene	52	6	1.1×10^{-5}	56
$Co_3(CO)_9CCl$ [b]	40	toluene	52	6	6.3×10^{-6}	56
$Co_3(CO)_9CBr$ [b]	40	toluene	52	6	3.7×10^{-6}	56
$Hg[Co(CO)_4]_2$ [b]	0	toluene	2.2	0.4	3.5×10^{-3}	57
$Cd[Co(CO)_4]_2$ [b]	−21	toluene	1.2	2.6	1.9×10^{-3}	57
$(CH_3)_3SnCo(CO)_4$	20	butyl ether	2.0		2×10^{-4}	57
$(C_6H_5)_3SnCo(CO)_4$	40	butyl ether	3.7	0.2	1×10^{-3}	57
$(C_6H_5)_3PAuCo(CO)_4$	20	butyl ether	3.2		2×10^{-3}	57
$CH_3COCo(CO)_4$	0	butyl ether	4.6		8.5×10^{-4}	57

[a] Values in 10^{-n} are for true first-order rate constants k in sec^{-1}. Values in hr and yr are for half-lives of exchange at these conditions, and values preceeded by N.E. mean no detectable exchange. See text and equation 8.

[b] Activation parameters for exchange as follows.
$Ni(CO)_4$: $\Delta H^{\ddagger}$, 12 kcal/mole; $\Delta S^{\ddagger}$, −26 eu. E_a for $M(CO)_6$: Cr, 39; Mo, 31; W, 40.
$Co_2(CO)_8$: $\Delta H^{\ddagger}$, 23; $\Delta S^{\ddagger}$, −13. E_a for $Co_3(CO)_9CX$: F, 15; Cl, 20; Br, 23.
$Hg[Co(CO)_4]_2$: $\Delta H^{\ddagger}$, 13; $\Delta S^{\ddagger}$, −24.
$Cd[Co(CO)_4]_2$: $\Delta H^{\ddagger}$, 11; $\Delta S^{\ddagger}$, −28.

[c] At −21° in 1,2-dichlorethane plus CF_3COOH $Kk_{eq} \sim 1$–4×10^{-2} M^{-1} sec^{-1} with $K_{eq} \ll 1$; see text.

[d] At 25° in toluene $k = 4 \times 10^{-6}$, reference 118.

because d^5 systems are generally more labile than d^6 and/or because the d^5 system has only five electrons to contribute in dative π bonding. The reactivity of $Co_2(CO)_8$, as will be discussed later, may be due to the ease with which the bridged structure can provide a low-energy path for exchange.

Except for these two compounds, it appears that the reactivity of the metal carbonyls is related to their coordination number: four-coordinated $Ni(CO)_4$ exchanges rapidly, whereas five- and six-coordinated $Fe(CO)_5$ and $Cr(CO)_6$ exchange very slowly. It is of interest to note that this same trend is observed for the exchange of cyanide ion with cyanometal complexes. For example, hexacyano systems such as $Cr(CN)_6^{3-}$, $Fe(CN)_6^{4-}$, and $Co(CN)_6^{3-}$ are slow to exchange, whereas tetracyano complexes such as $Ni(CN)_4^{2-}$, $Hg(CN)_4^{2-}$, and $Pd(CN)_4^{2-}$ undergo rapid exchange. This has been explained in terms of a low-energy bimolecular displacement path for the four-coordinated systems, this path not being as readily available to the six-coordinated complex.

This same explanation cannot account for the rapid CO exchange of $Ni(CO)_4$ compared with the slow exchange of $Cr(CO)_6$. Kinetic studies[49,52] show that in both cases the rate of exchange does not depend on the concentration of CO but is first order in metal carbonyl concentration. The simplest explanation of such a result is that exchange proceeds by a dissociation mechanism.

$$M(CO)_n \rightleftharpoons M(CO)_{n-1} + CO \qquad (9)$$

This suggests that the rate of exchange should parallel the M-C bond strength. The heats of combustion of $Cr(CO)_6$, $Fe(CO)_5$, and $Ni(CO)_4$ have been determined,[60] and the average M-C bond energies of these systems were estimated to be 27.1, 27.7, and 35.2 kcal, respectively. These values are inconsistent with the observation that the exchange of $Ni(CO)_4$ is fast, whereas that of $Fe(CO)_5$ and $Cr(CO)_6$ is extremely slow. It was suggested[49] that these bond energies are for the metals in their ground states, whereas in the exchange process the metals retain their low-spin electronic structures. Therefore, the average bond energies should be adjusted to values of 57, 60, and 44 kcal for $Cr(CO)_6$, $Fe(CO)_5$, and $Ni(CO)_4$, assuming valence states of d^6, d^8, and d^{10}, respectively. It is seen that the adjusted values are in agreement with the observed rates of CO exchange.

The estimated average bond energy of 44 kcal for the Ni-C bond in $Ni(CO)_4$ is much larger than the activation energy of 12 kcal. A value of 12 kcal was also estimated for the presumed (p. 547) thermal gas-phase dissociation of $Ni(CO)_4$ into $Ni(CO)_3$.[61] This was explained[49] by assuming that the energy required for the rupture of the first Ni-C bond is much smaller than the average bond energy. In support of this assumption is the chemical evidence that two CO's in $Ni(CO)_4$ are readily replaced to form $Ni(CO)_2L_2$, but the last two are much less reactive.

Not only is it difficult to understand the low activation energy for the exchange of CO with $Ni(CO)_4$, but also its negative entropy of activation, $\Delta S^{\ddagger} = -26$ eu, is not consistent with a simple dissociation mechanism. Such a process, with an increase in the number of particles in going from the ground to the transition state, is expected to have a positive entropy of activation. That the value is negative may be due to more extensive π bonding in $Ni(CO)_3$ compared to the tetracarbonyl and thus greater restriction of motion in the transition state relative to the ground state.

However, investigations[62,63] suggest that the exchange of CO with $Ni(CO)_4$ does not proceed by a simple dissociation mechanism. It has been observed that the rate of the reaction

$$Ni(CO)_4 + P(C_6H_5)_3 \rightarrow Ni(CO)_3P(C_6H_5)_3 + CO \qquad (10)$$

does not depend on the concentration of $P(C_6H_5)_3$. Such a result would support a dissociation mechanism for exchange, provided the rate and activation parameters for substitution were identical to that for exchange. In such a case the rate-determining step for both would be that of dissociation to form $Ni(CO)_3$. However, this is not the case, and reaction 10 in toluene has a rate constant of 4×10^{-4} sec^{-1} at $0°$ and activation parameters of $\Delta H^{\ddagger} = 21$ kcal/mole and $\Delta S^{\ddagger} = +2$ eu (compared with CO exchange values of $k = 8 \times 10^{-4}$, $\Delta H^{\ddagger} = 12$, $\Delta S^{\ddagger} = -26$). Similar results are obtained for the analogous reaction with $P(OCH_3)_3$, and it appeared that these substitution reactions proceed by a dissociation process. This means that some other low-energy path is also available for CO exchange with $Ni(CO)_4$, but not for its substitution reactions with these reagents.

Further study[62] shows that such an explanation of the substitution reaction proceeding by a dissociation mechanism and exchange by some other low-energy process is not correct. If it were correct, the rate of the dissociation process would increase more rapidly (because of its larger $\Delta H^{\ddagger}$) than the rate of exchange. Thus at some temperature exchange would take place by dissociation and the rates of substitution and exchange would be the same. What is found is that the rate of substitution can become greater than the rate of exchange. This means that the substitution reaction cannot be taking place by a simple dissociation process. Furthermore, in an experiment where both ^{14}CO and $P(OCH_3)_3$ are added to a solution of $Ni(CO)_4$ and both the rates of exchange and of substitution are monitored, the rate constants obtained are in good agreement with those found in separate experiments. This means that ^{14}CO and $P(OCH_3)_3$ do not compete for a common intermediate, but react by completely independent paths.

We are left with the very unusual situation that exchange and substitution are both first-order processes but neither one involves a simple dissociation mechanism. We can speculate that one path may involve a rearrangement of tetrahedral $Ni(CO)_4$ into a square planar form (p. 427) which then can readily undergo exchange but not substitution (or vice versa). Another independent path may involve a ligand migration (p. 580) to give an active intermediate which can undergo substitution but not exchange (or vice versa). The π bonding differences of CO and L may in part be responsible for their taking different reaction paths. It also appears that this type of behavior may be fairly general. For example, the rate of CO exchange with $Hg[Co(CO)_4]_2$ is first order and appears to proceed by a different mechanism from that of its reactions with different reagents to yield $Hg[CoL(CO)_3]_2$.[57] Similarly the rate of CO exchange with $CoNO(CO)_3$ is first order and faster than its rate of reaction with $As(C_6H_5)_3$ extrapolated to zero concentration of reagent (p. 574).

The data in Table 7.5 also show that, although the exchange of CO with $Ni(CO)_4$ is fast, exchange with the analogous anionic carbonyls $Co(CO)_4^-$ and $Fe(CO)_4^{2-}$ is very slow. This result is in agreement with the C-O stretching frequencies of the tetracarbonyls (Table 7.2), which show that $Ni(CO)_4$ has the highest value, suggesting that it has the least amount of M-C π bonding. Similarly, $CoNO(CO)_3$ and $Fe(NO)_2(CO)_2$ are slow to exchange CO, as compared to $Ni(CO)_4$, and here also the i.r. data suggest more M-C π bonding in the nitrosyl systems. Furthermore, substituted nickel carbonyls exchange CO more slowly than does the parent compound, as is illustrated by the relative rates of exchange for $Ni(CO)_4$: $Ni(CO)_3$-PPh_3 : $Ni(CO)_2(PPh_3)_2$ at 25° of approximately 420 : 70 : 1. Here also the decrease in rate of exchange parallels the increase in Ni-C π bonding.

The hexacarbonyls of the chromium triad show no detectable exchange of CO in solution at room temperature during a period of several days. However, at elevated temperatures in the gas phase exchange occurs at a measurable rate and has been studied in some detail.[52,53] The rate of exchange is independent of CO concentration, and it appears that exchange involves a dissociation process of the type represented by equation 9. A somewhat surprising result is that, of the three hexacarbonyls, $Mo(CO)_6$ is the fastest to exchange. It also has the lowest activation energy for exchange, and this is in agreement with the M-C and C-O stretching force constants:

	$Cr(CO)_6$	$Mo(CO)_6$	$W(CO)_6$
E_a, kcal/mole	39	31	40
F_{MC}, mdynes/A[64]	2.03	1.81	2.15
F_{CO}, mdynes/A[64]	17.87	18.12	17.70

Thus $Mo(CO)_6$ has the lowest F_{MC} value and the highest F_{CO} value, both implying less M-C π bonding for the molybdenum compound than for the other two. The M-C π bonding is seen to decrease in the order W-C > Cr-C > Mo-C. Why this should be the order of π bonding is not clear, but it should be remembered that this is a function of various factors, such as the spatial extention of the d orbitals, electronegativity of the metal, and screening efficiency of other outer electrons. It may be of interest to note that a similar disorder occurs in the $M(CN)_4^{2-}$ systems, where

$$F_{HgC} > F_{ZnC} > F_{CdC} {}^{65}$$

The i.r. spectrum of $Mn(CO)_6^+$, compared to that for $Cr(CO)_6$ (Table 7.2), suggests that the cationic species should be more reactive. The necessary data to test this prediction are not available. All that is known is that there is no detectable exchange of CO with $Mn(CO)_6^+$ at 30° in ether solution.[55] Similarly, there is no exchange for $Re(CO)_6^+$ at 60° in water solution over a period of 60 hr.

The mono-, di-, and trisubstituted phenylisonitrile derivatives of chromium and molybdenum carbonyls were studied at conditions comparable to those for the hexacarbonyls.[53] Quantitative data were not collected, but it was observed that the exchange of CO is slower with the substituted carbonyls than with the parent hexacarbonyls. This is again in agreement with an increase in substitution. The reverse is true for the rate of exchange of phenylisonitrile, which increases as more isonitrile groups are replaced by CO in the parent compound $Cr(CNC_6H_5)_6$. Thus, the half-life for exchange of phenylisonitrile with $Cr(CNC_6H_5)_6$ at 75° is 1.1 hr,[66] whereas for $Cr(CO)_3(CNC_6H_5)_3$ at 9° it is 5 min and for the tetra- and pentacarbonyls it is too short to measure. This is in accord with CO being a better π bonder than CNC_6H_5 (Table 7.4).

That the exchange of isonitrile is independent of its concentration supports a dissociation mechanism. It is of interest to note that the rate of exchange of isonitrile with $Cr(CNC_6H_5)_6$ is much faster than the rate of exchange of CO with $Cr(CO)_6$, indicating a greater Cr-C bond strength in the hexacarbonyl.

The other simple monomeric carbonyl that has been examined is $Fe(CO)_5$. Its rate of exchange in solution, in the dark and at room temperature, is extremely slow[51] (Table 7.5). However, upon the addition of acid the compound becomes very labile[67] (Table 7.5, footnote c). Its rate of CO exchange shows a dependence on acid concentration but not on CO concentration. The mechanism of this acid-catalyzed exchange is believed to involve a rapid acid-base equilibrium

$$Fe(CO)_5 + (CF_3COOH)_2 \overset{K}{\rightleftharpoons} Fe(CO)_5H^+, CF_3CO_2HO_2CCF_3^- \quad (11)$$

followed by a rate-determining dissociation step

$$Fe(CO)_5H^+, CF_3CO_2HO_2CCF_3^- \overset{k}{\rightleftharpoons} Fe(CO)_4H^+, CF_3CO_2HO_2CCF_3^- + CO \quad (12)$$

The experimentally observed rate constant is then equal to the product of the equilibrium constant and the rate constant, Kk. Studies[6,68] on the interaction of strong acids with several organometallic compounds have shown that metal-proton bonds are often formed. In the case of metal carbonyls the effect is to increase the C-O stretching frequency by as much as 140 cm^{-1}. This is analogous to the effect of charge on isoelectronic metal carbonyls (Table 7.2) and suggests a weaker M-C bond strength in the cationic protonated species. As a result the system is expected to be more labile.

Since $HFe(CO)_5^+$ and $HMn(CO)_5$ are isoelectronic (presumably also isostructural), it is of interest to note that the exchange rate of the latter is much slower than that of the cationic carbonyl. For example, in 1,2-dichloroethane solution at $-21°$ CO exchange with $HMn(CO)_5$ has a rate constant of $k = 2 \times 10^{-3} \text{ sec}^{-1}$, compared with $HFe(CO)_5^+$, which has a value of $Kk = 2 \times 10^{-2} M^{-1} \text{ sec}^{-1}$, where $K \ll 1$. This is consistent with the greater amount of back donation of the metal d orbital electrons expected from the lower nuclear charge in $HMn(CO)_5$.

All five CO's exchange at the same rate in $HMn(CO)_5$ in spite of its octahedral structure,[69] which makes one CO *trans* to hydrogen and hence different from the other four. It is possible that reversible loss and readdition of the proton occurs, randomizing all five CO ligands. The data on CO exchange in $HFe(CO)_5^+$ show some curvature, indicating two kinds of exchangeable CO. However, some decomposition also is found. In the case of $Fe(CO)_5$ it is known[70] from the ^{13}C n.m.r. spectrum that all five CO's are equivalent. As in PF_5 and other trigonal bipyramidal systems, a rapid intramolecular rearrangement takes place which scrambles the axial and equatorial groups.

One other point of interest is that the acid-catalyzed CO exchange of $Fe(CO)_4P(C_6H_5)_3$ (see footnote c, p. 541) is also extremely fast and only three CO's exchange. Presumably the axial CO *trans* to $P(C_6H_5)_3$ does not exchange under the conditions of this experiment. It would be of interest to know the ^{13}C n.m.r. spectrum of this compound to see whether intramolecular rearrangement is fast or slow. One thing certain is that some of these inert systems are very dramatically labilized by acid, and this property should be exploited in the synthesis of such compounds.

Photochemical reactions of metal carbonyls are common,[71] and a classical example is shown by the equation

$$2Fe(CO)_5 \overset{h\nu}{\longrightarrow} Fe_2(CO)_9 + CO \quad (13)$$

This reaction has been carried out in the presence of ^{14}CO in solution, and the radioactivity of the product dimer examined.[51] It was found that approximately one half a molecule of CO per $Fe_2(CO)_9$ was radioactive. This result is in accord with an earlier investigation[72] of the photochemical dimerization of $Fe(CO)_5$ in the gas phase at a wavelength of 400 mμ. It was observed in this study that the reaction proceeds with a quantum efficiency of two and that foreign gases such as Ar, N_2, and CO inhibit the dimerization. Presumably this inhibition is due to collision with and deactivation of the excited molecule $Fe(CO)_5^*$. The mechanism proposed for reaction 13 is that of photoexcitation of the carbonyl (14) followed by its reaction with a molecule of the carbonyl in the ground state (15).

$$Fe(CO)_5 \xrightarrow{k\nu} Fe(CO)_5^* \tag{14}$$

$$Fe(CO)_5^* + Fe(CO)_5 \rightarrow Fe_2(CO)_9 + CO \tag{15}$$

The incorporation of a half a mole of ^{14}CO into the product $Fe_2(CO)_9$ may perhaps be due to the exchange lability of the excited molecule $Fe(CO)_5^*$.

Investigations of the decomposition of $Ni(CO)_4$ by flash photolysis with high-intensity ultraviolet light gave results that were interpreted according to the reaction scheme shown by the equations[73]

$$Ni(CO)_4 + h\nu \rightarrow Ni(CO)_3 + CO \tag{16}$$

$$Ni(CO)_3 + h\nu \rightarrow Ni(CO)_2 + CO \tag{17}$$

$$Ni(CO)_2 \rightarrow solid\ products \tag{18}$$

Decomposition is strongly inhibited by added CO because of the reverse of reactions 16 and 17. It appears that $Ni(CO)_3$ is quite stable and is present in appreciable concentration after the photoflash but that it rapidly recombines with CO. The results also support a finite stability for $Ni(CO)_2$ and argue against the mechanism[61] proposed for the thermal decomposition of $Ni(CO)_4$, which involved the formation of $Ni(CO)_3$ and its decomposition to nickel and CO, rather than 18.*

Strohmeier[74] and his students have published a series of papers on the photochemistry of the reactions of $M(CO)_6$, where M = Cr, Mo, or W, and of $C_5H_5Mn(CO)_3$ with a variety of different nucleophiles. Their results show that at time zero the quantum yield of the photochemical primary step is equal to one and is independent of the substrate, the reagent, and the solvent. They propose that the primary step involves a dissociation

---

* Intermediates such as $Ni(CO)_3$ and $Ni(CO)_2$ cannot be detected in a mass spectroscopic study of the pyrolysis of $Ni(CO)_4$.[250]

mechanism with the formation of a carbonyl of lower coordination number:

$$M(CO)_6 \xrightarrow{h\nu} M(CO)_6{}^* \longrightarrow M(CO)_5 + CO \tag{19}$$

Spectroscopic evidence is now available for the existence of stable $M(CO)_5$ species in irradiated $1:4$ isopentanemethylcyclohexane glasses at $-180°$, containing originally $M(CO)_6$.[75] The pentacoordinated compounds have C_{4v} symmetry, but on warming the glass to $-160°C$ it softens and the i.r. spectrum of $Mo(CO)_5$ changes to D_{3h} symmetry. This suggests that the tetragonal pyramidal structure is formed initially in the solid glass because the molecule is unable to assume the more stable trigonal bipyramidal structure.

The structure of $Fe_3(CO)_{12}$ has been the subject of much speculation, and no less than six widely differing molecular models have been proposed since its discovery.[76] The structure of $[HFe_3(CO)_{11}]^-$ has been determined,[77] and on the basis of an analogy with this it was suggested that $Fe_3(CO)_{12}$ has the structure represented by

(III)

This structure† is in accord with x-ray, Mossbauer, and solid state i.r. studies.[76-78] The exchange of CO with $Fe_3(CO)_{12}$ also supports a structure containing two non-equivalent CO molecules.[51] The exchange data were interpreted in terms of six CO's exchanging rapidly and the other six not exchanging at all. On the basis of the presently presumed structure III, it would appear that a more plausible interpretation of the data is that the four terminal CO's on the unique iron exchange at a different rate from the other eight. In the discussion that follows we will see that the rate of exchange of bridging CO's and terminal CO's on the same metal atom may be the same.‡

† The structure has been established by x-ray diffraction studies [C. H. Wei and L. F. Dahl, *J. Am. Chem. Soc.*, **88**, 1821 (1966)].

‡ Non-rigid structures appear to exist for systems of this type [F. A. Cotton, *Inorg. Chem.*, **5**, 1083 (1966)].

Carbon monoxide exchange with bridged metal carbonyls has been most extensively investigated for the cobalt systems. The simplest such compound is $Co_2(CO)_8$ with the structure[59]

(IV)

where each of the cobalt atoms may be effectively regarded as being in a distorted octahedral environment, from which one ligand is "missing." In its place there is presumably a "bent"[79] Co-Co bond. The rate of ^{14}CO exchange with $Co_2(CO)_8$ is immeasurably rapid at room temperature in both light and dark.[51] At lower temperatures, it was possible to investigate the kinetics of exchange,[49] and this was found to follow the rate law given by

$$Rate = k[Co_2(CO)_8] \qquad (20)$$

Furthermore, the experiments showed that all eight CO's exchange at the same rate.

On this basis it was concluded that the mechanism of exchange may involve the opening of a carbonyl bridge as the rate-determining step, followed by rapid addition and the reverse random expulsion of CO according to

$$(21)$$

This process is in accord with the rate law 20 and the fact that all CO's exchange at the same rate. It is also supported by the observation that $Co_2(CO)_7(C_7H_8O_2)$ with one carbonyl bridge[59] (V) rapidly exchanges all seven CO's, whereas $Co_2(CO)_6(C_6H_5C_2C_6H_5)$ with no carbonyl bridge[70] (VI)

(V)   (VI)

does not exchange CO at these conditions.

In spite of this seemingly plausible interpretation of the mechanism of CO exchange with $Co_2(CO)_8$, it now appears that an alternative explanation is required. Subsequent to the exchange studies, Noack[81] has investigated the temperature dependence of the i.r. spectra of pentane solutions of $Co_2(CO)_8$ and has reached the conclusion that these contain two different species in rapid equilibrium:

$$(OC)_3Co \underset{C}{\overset{C}{\rightleftharpoons}} Co(CO)_3 \rightleftharpoons (OC)_4Co\text{—}Co(CO)_4 \qquad (22)$$

(VII)   (VIII)

At room temperature the solution contains 43% of VII and 57% of VIII, whereas at $-104°C$ there is 84% of VII and 16% of VIII at equilibrium, whence $\Delta H = -1.3$ kcal/mole and $\Delta S^0 = +5$ eu. The species VIII is assigned a non-carbonyl bridged structure because its i.r. spectrum is very similar to that of $Hg[Co(CO)_4]_2$, which is reported[82] to have a trigonal bipyramidal structure around each cobalt with the equatorial CO's in staggered positions:

(IX)

Since equilibrium 22 is established rapidly, all eight CO's are randomized. The non-reactivity of VI suggests that species VIII is the form that exchanges rapidly. This conclusion is also supported by the observation that other metal-metal bonded systems, such as $Hg[Co(CO)_4]_2$, $Cd[Co(CO)_4]_2$, $R_3SnCo(CO)_4$, and $(C_6H_5)_3PAuCo(CO)_4$, also undergo fairly rapid exchange at a rate independent of the CO concentration (Table 7.5). However, these compounds may react by a mechanism involving a ligand migration reaction to form $MCOCo(CO)_3$, which then can readily add ^{14}CO, resulting in exchange.[57] Studies[83] show that it is also possible to obtain the free radical monomer $Co(CO)_4$.

The tetranuclear cobalt carbonyl $Co_4(CO)_{12}$ has a structure[34]

(X)

in which the four cobalt atoms are at the corners of a tetrahedron; single carbonyl bridges are formed between three equivalent cobalt atoms, while the fourth is held only by Co-Co bonds. This compound exchanges CO much more slowly than does the dinuclear compound, and all twelve of the CO's exchange at the same rate.[51] Detailed kinetic studies have not been made on this system, but it has been observed that the reaction

$$2Co_2(CO)_8 \rightleftharpoons Co_4(CO)_{12} + 4CO \qquad (23)$$

takes place at elevated temperatures.[84] Such an equilibration can lead to the exchange of all CO's through the formation of $Co_2(CO)_8$ and its rapid exchange.§

There are some interesting results[56] on CO exchange with $Co_3(CO)_9CX$ (where X = H, F, Cl, Br), which has a structure[34,85] analogous to that of X. The essential difference is that the $Co(CO)_3$ group in X is replaced by CX, as is shown by XI. Carbon is at one of the corners of the tetrahedron and is σ bonded to each of the three cobalt atoms. The CO exchange of these compounds is somewhat slower than that of X, but the exchange rate remains first order in the metal carbonyl and zero order in CO concentration.

§ The equilibration of all CO's in $Co_4(CO)_{12}$ may take place instead by a facile internal rearrangement of the molecule caused by its steric non-rigidity [F. A. Cotton, *Inorg. Chem.*, **5**, 1083 (1966)].

The most significant result is that for XI only three CO's undergo exchange. An equilibrium of the type 22 leading to the exchange of all CO's is not possible in this system, although carbonyl bridge opening and closing

(XI) (XII)   (24)

may occur. The non-bridged structure (XII) has a set of three equivalent CO molecules (represented by *CO) and another set of six equivalent CO's. The experimental results suggest that the three *CO's exchange, perhaps by a dissociative mechanism.

Note that these three groups may be the ones situated in a position *trans* to C—X, and it is likely that C—X has a *trans* labilizing influence similar to that observed for CH_3 in Pt(II) systems.[11] Furthermore it is of interest that for changes in X the rates of exchange decrease in the order F > Cl > Br > H with the relative rates being 12:6.5:4:1, respectively. We will see in the discussion that follows on metal carbonyl halides that this order of reactivity parallels that for $Mn(CO)_5X$, where X is attached directly to the metal.

Metal Carbonyl Halides.   The exchange of CO with several metal carbonyl halides has been investigated, and some of the kinetic data are collected in Table 7.6. The six-coordinated compounds, including also $C_5H_5Fe(CO)_2X$, are much less labile than are the four-coordinated square planar systems. A comparison of the rates of exchange shows a decrease in the order Pt(II), Rh(I), Ir(I) carbonyl halides >> $Fe(CO)_4X_2$ > $Mn(CO)_5X$ > $C_5H_5Fe(CO)_2X$. The rapid rate of exchange for the square planar compounds is due to a low-energy bimolecular displacement path. The slow exchange of $C_5H_5Fe(CO)_2X$ suggests that these compounds behave more like six-coordinated systems than sterically accessible distorted tetrahedra.

The most extensively studied systems are the compounds of $Mn(CO)_5X$ and their derivatives. Three definite conclusions can be drawn from the exchange studies on $Mn(CO)_5X$: (1) the rate of CO exchange does not

Table 7.6   Exchange of carbon monoxide with some metal carbonyl halides

Compound	Temp., °C	Solvent	Conc., mM Compound	CO	Rate[a]	Ref.
$Mn(CO)_5Cl$	31.8	toluene	13	6.2	3×10^{-3}	87
$Mn(CO)_5Br$	31.8	toluene	17	6.2	1.1×10^{-4}	87
$Mn(CO)_5I$	31.8	toluene	17	6.2	1.3×10^{-5}	87
$Mn(CO)_5H$	−21	dichloro-ethane	...	...	2×10^{-3}	67
$Ph_3PAuMn(CO)_5$	20	butyl ether	1.9	...	N.E. 27 hr	57
$Mn(CO)_3(PPh_3)_2Cl$	20	benzene	0.5	0.07	17 min	55
$Mn(CO)_3(AsPh_3)_2Cl$	20	benzene	0.5	0.07	1.3 hr	55
$Mn(CO)_3(SbPh_3)_2Cl$	40	benzene	0.5	0.07	5.0 hr	55
$Mn(CO)_3(TePh_2)_2Cl$	30	benzene	2	0.3	20 min	55
$Mn(CO)_3(phen)Cl$	40	chloroform	1	0.15	N.E. 20 hr	55
$Fe(CO)_4Br_2$	20	CCl_4	12	0.3	1.7 hr	87
$Fe(CO)_4I_2$	31.8	CCl_4	14	1.5	7.5 hr	87
$C_5H_5Fe(CO)_2Cl$	31.8	toluene	33	0.3	1.9 hr	87
$C_5H_5Fe(CO)_2Br$	31.8	toluene	33	0.3	38 hr	87
$C_5H_5Fe(CO)_2I$	31.8	toluene	33	0.3	10^3 hr	87
$C_5H_5Fe(CO)_2CN$	31.8	toluene	33	0.3	2×10^3 hr	87
$Rh(PPh_3)_2COCl_3$	25	chloroform	2.5	...	3.4×10^{-5}	89
$Rh(PPh_3)_2COCl$	−30	chloroform	...	...	inst.	90
$Rh_2(CO)_4Cl_2$	−80	ethanol	...	...	4.0^b	90
$Rh(CO)_2(am)Cl^c$	−80	ethanol	...	...	2.0^b	90
$Ir(CO)_2(am)Cl^c$	−80	ethanol	...	...	2.0^b	90
$Pt_2(CO)_2Cl_4$	25	benzene	18	1.2	inst.	87

[a] Values in 10^{-n} are for true first-order rate constants k in sec^{-1}. Values in min and hr are for half-lives at these conditions, and "inst." means instantaneous or complete within the time of the first reading. See text and equation 8.
[b] Second-order rate constant k in $M^{-1} sec^{-1}$.
[c] am = p-toluidine or p-anisidine.

depend on the concentration of CO, (2) one CO exchanges more slowly than do the other four, and (3) the rate of CO exchange does depend on the ligand X. That four CO's exchange more rapidly than does the fifth is clearly shown in Fig. 7.7. This observation is significant because it can readily be explained on the basis of the current views of bonding in these systems. Thus each of the four CO's in the same plane is *trans* to another CO and must compete with it for a share in π bonding with the filled d orbitals on manganese (Fig. 7.6a), whereas the non-equivalent CO is *trans* to X, which is a much poorer π bonder (Fig. 7.6b).

That there is less Mn═C═O contribution to the bonding of the four *cis*-CO's is shown by the value of their CO stretching force constant:[43] 17.23 mdynes/A compared with 16.07 for the CO *trans* to bromine in $Mn(CO)_5Br$. This same conclusion, that the axial CO group is bonded more strongly to manganese than the other four CO groups, is also consistent with the interpretation of the electronic structures of $Mn(CO)_5X$

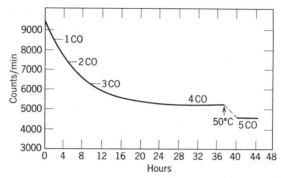

Fig. 7.7   Rate of CO exchange with Mn(CO)₅Br in toluene solution at 31.8°.

compounds in terms of the M.O. theory of bonding.[91] It should be mentioned that at higher temperatures all CO's were found[55] to exchange at about the same rate for Mn(CO)₅I. This is readily understood because the CO *trans* to iodine has a higher activation energy for exchange, and at some elevated temperature its rate of exchange will equal that for the other four CO's.‡

Since the rate of exchange does not depend on the concentration of CO, this suggests that exchange involves a dissociation mechanism. The structure of the five-coordinated species is not known, but it most probably is that of a trigonal bipyramid or tetragonal pyramid (Fig. 7.8). Whatever its structure, the results require that the less reactive CO retain its identity in this species and not become equivalent to the other three CO's.

It is significant that the ratio of rates of CO exchange for Mn(CO)₅X for X = I:Br:Cl is 1:8:200. The same reactivity trend with changes in halogen was also observed for the systems Fe(CO)₄X₂ and π-C₅H₅Fe-(CO)₂X (Table 7.6). This order of reactivity can be explained on the basis of the polarizability and/or electronegativity of the halide ions. Since the iodide ion is the most polarizable and least electronegative, it permits the largest amount of electron density on manganese. This in turn means that Mn=C=O makes its largest contribution to the bonding, and the resulting

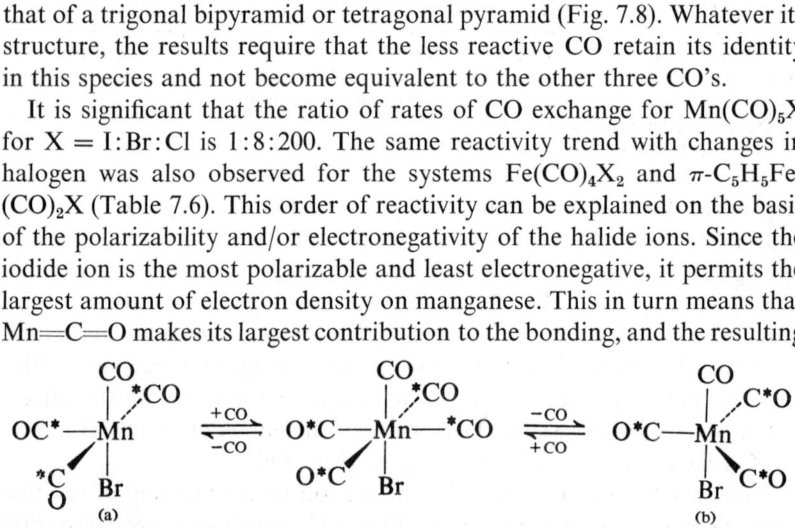

$$
\begin{array}{ccc}
\underset{\substack{| \\ *C \\ O}}{\overset{\substack{CO \\ |}}{OC^*\!-\!Mn}}\!\!\diagdown\!\!\overset{*CO}{}\!\!Br
&
\underset{-CO}{\overset{+CO}{\rightleftharpoons}}
&
\underset{\substack{| \\ O^*C}}{\overset{\substack{CO \\ |}}{O^*C\!-\!Mn}}\!\!\diagdown\!\!\overset{*CO}{}\!\!Br
\end{array}
$$

(a) $\underset{+CO}{\overset{-CO}{\rightleftharpoons}}$ (b)

Fig. 7.8   Dissociation mechanism for the CO exchange of the four more labile *CO's in Mn(CO)₅Br involving either a tetragonal pyramidal (a) or a trigonal bipyramidal (b) structure.

‡ Private communications from H. D. Kaesz and from J. Lewis suggest that all 5 CO's exchange at similar rates, also, at room temperature for all three halide compounds.

greater Mn-C bond strength causes a slower rate of CO exchange relative to the other halide systems. This explanation is supported by the i.r. spectra of these compounds which permit an estimate[43] of $F_{CO} = 17.24$: $17.23 : 17.10$ mdynes/A for X = Cl : Br : I. Likewise the slow CO exchange for $(C_6H_5)_3PAuMn(CO)_5$ is also consistent with its i.r. spectrum,[92] suggesting that the group $(C_6H_5)_3PAu$ allows a greater electron density on manganese than does iodine.

The hydride ion ligand in $HMn(CO)_5$ appears to be a special case because the i.r. spectrum[93] of this compound suggests that it should be inert whereas CO exchange is found to be extremely rapid. Furthermore, it appears that all five CO's exchange at the same rate. We can speculate that the hydrocarbonyl may be reacting by a different mechanism, the ligand migration process (see p. 580). Such a mechanism would allow a low-energy path for the addition of ^{14}CO as the hydride ion migrates to an adjacent position. Its return to the metal would be acompanied by a random loss or exchange of CO:

$$HMn(CO)_5 + CO \rightleftharpoons HCOMn(CO)_5 \qquad (25)$$

It does appear that the hydride ion has a pronounced labilizing influence on these systems; for example, $HCo(CO)_4$ is much more reactive than are other $LCo(CO)_4$ compounds.[94]

Substituted carbonyls of the type $Mn(CO)_3L_2X$ are expected to have a greater Mn-C bond strength and to exchange CO more slowly than the analogous $Mn(CO)_5X$, and this is what is found. Some caution is required in the interpretation of the rates of exchange of the substituted carbonyls, because there exists the possibility that this exchange may involve the prior replacement of one or more L groups by CO.

The rate of CO exchange with $Fe(CO)_4X_2$ does depend on the concentration of CO, and initially[87] this was said to be due to a bimolecular displacement process. Recent studies[88] show that the rate of exchange is inhibited by the presence of X_2, and furthermore that for $Fe(CO)_4Br_2$ the rate of CO exchange approximately equals that of exchange with Br_2.[95] For this reason it has been suggested[88] that the two types of exchange may involve the formation of the same active intermediate, $Fe(CO)_4$, for which both ^{14}CO and Br_2 must compete. This also agrees with the fact that all four CO's in cis-$Fe(CO)_4Br_2$ exchange at the same rate and with the observation that the irradiation of $Fe(CO)_5$ in a 1:4 isopentanemethyl-cyclohexane glass at $-180°$ gives a different species, perhaps $Fe(CO)_4$.[75]

The rates of exchange of CO with the square planar carbonyl halides of Pt(II), Rh(I), and Ir(I) (Table 7.6) are much too fast to measure by conventional techniques at room temperature.[87] However, at $-80°C$ in ethanol solution it was possible to study the kinetics of CO exchange with

$Rh_2(CO)_4Cl_2$ and with $M(CO)_2(am)Cl$, where $M = Rh(I)$ or $Ir(I)$ and am = p-toluidine or p-anisidine.[90] The results show that all of the CO's in these systems exchange at the same rate and that the rate depends on the concentration of CO.

There is little doubt that these systems are labile because of the ease with which they can expand their coordination number and allow for a

Table 7.7   Exchange of carbon monoxide with some π-cyclopentadienyl metal carbonyls

		Conc., mM		
Compound	Temp., °C	Compound	CO	Rate
$(C_5H_5)_2Ni_2(CO)_2$	25	21	2.8	6.1×10^{-2} [a]
$C_5H_5Co(CO)_2$	0	26	7.6	2.2×10^{-2} [a]
$C_5H_5Rh(CO)_2$	40	9.5	0.1	3 hr[b]
$(C_5H_5)_2Fe_2(CO)_4$	32	24	0.5	slow[c]
$C_5H_5Mn(CO)_3$	32	45	6	very slow[d]
$CH_3C_5H_4Mn(CO)_3$	32	66	6	very slow[d]
$(C_5H_5)_2Mo_2(CO)_6$	32	22	6	very slow[d]
$CH_3C_6H_5Cr(CO)_3$	25	45	5	very slow[d]
$C_5H_5V(CO)_4$	25	23	6	very slow[d]

From reference 98. Solvent toluene.

[a] Second-order rate constants, M^{-1} sec^{-1}. E_a for $(C_5H_5)_2Ni_2(CO)_2 \sim 20$ kcal/mloe, and for $C_5H_5Co(CO)_2 \sim 16$ kcal/mole.

[b] Half-life, from reference 100.

[c] Slight exchange with some decomposition in 4 days.

[d] No detectable exchange in 3 weeks.

low-energy displacement mechanism. Direct evidence of the formation of five-coordinated species is provided by the isolation of compounds such as $Ir(CO)_2(PPh_3)_2Cl$[96] and the Rh(I) and Ir(I) compounds $MCO(PPh_3)_3H$.[97] Also in agreement with this explanation is the observation[89] that the six-coordinated compound $RhCO(PPh_3)_2Cl_3$ exchanges CO slowly, although its i.r. spectrum suggests that the Rh-C bond strength is less than it is in the analogous labile compound $RhCO(PPh_3)_2Cl$.

π-Cyclopentadienyl Metal Carbonyls.   Kinetic data for CO exchange with some π-cyclopentadienyl metal carbonyls are collected in Table 7.7. The results show that, for the first-row transition metal compounds, only the nickel and cobalt compounds exchange rapidly. These are the only two that have been studied sufficiently to give information regarding the mechanism of exchange.[98] Since the rate of exchange depends on the concentration of CO, it appears that exchange takes place by an S_N2 mechanism. This may explain why $C_5H_5Co(CO)_2$ is labile, whereas $Fe(CO)_5$ is inert. Recall that these two compounds have a formal analogy, if we consider that one π-$C_5H_5^-$ group takes the place of three CO's. The compounds are somewhat analogous chemically in that some of their reactions are of the same type.[99] In the same manner we can consider that there is an analogy between $(C_5H_5)_2Ni_2(CO)_2$ and $Co_2(CO)_8$. However, here too the π-cyclopentadienyl system exchanges CO at a rate depending on its concentration, while there is no dependence on this for the cobalt carbonyl compound.

An explanation for these S_N2, rather than S_N1, mechanisms lies in the special nature of the π-C_5H_5 ligand. Though formally it is a six-electron donor forming three bonds, sterically it is much less than three single ligands. Furthermore it is highly polarizable and would respond to the approach of another ligand to the central metal atom. It could take back electronic charge or, in the limit, form one or two fewer bonds to the metal. This would open up the metal to nucleophilic attack, as is represented by the equation

$$(26)$$

Except for the π-cyclopentadienyl carbonyls of nickel, cobalt, and rhodium, the compounds in Table 7.7 are very inert to exchange. This is clearly related to the higher overall coordination number of these systems. There is probably a simple steric retardation of the bimolecular displacement path. Note that this is true not only of the π-C_5H_5 compounds but also of the π-toluene compound $CH_3C_6H_5Cr(CO)_3$. Although these systems are inert, compounds such as $C_5H_5Mn(CO)_3$ and $M(CO)_6$ are reactive under the influence of light.[71]

It is further of interest that in spite of there being no exhcange of CO with (arene)$Cr(CO)_3$, even at $140°$,[52] ^{14}C-benzene does exchange with $C_6H_6Cr(CO)_3$.[101] This exchange in heptane solution has a two-term rate law given by the equation

$$\text{Rate} = k_1[C_6H_6Cr(CO)_3]^2 + k_2[C_6H_6Cr(CO)_3][C_6H_6] \qquad (27)$$

It is suggested that the k_1 path, which is second order in substrate, results from a bimolecular displacement to generate $Cr(CO)_3$, which in turn rapidly combines with C_6H_6 in solution:

$$\text{(28)}$$

The other path, k_2, is believed to involve a bimolecular displacement process of the substrate with benzene, and also inversion of the configuration:

$$\text{(29)}$$

With the resolution of an optically active substituted (arene)$Cr(CO)_3$,[102] it should now be possible to test this mechanism of inversion for arene exchange.

This same investigation was made for the corresponding chlorobenzene and toluene compounds, as well as for the toluene compounds of the molybdenum and the tungsten tricarbonyls. The rate law for exchange is the same for all of these compounds, and some of the data are shown in Table 7.8. For the (arene)$Cr(CO)_3$'s the rate of arene exchange decreases in the order $C_6H_5Cl > C_6H_6 > C_6H_5CH_3$, which parallels the increasing order of electron density in the aromatic ring. For the toluene metal tricarbonyls the rates vary in the order $Cr < Mo > W$, which is similar to that found for the exchange of CO with $M(CO)_6$. Corresponding studies with the cycloheptatriene and the naphthalene chromium tricarbonyls gave a rate law similar to 27, except that the k_1 path is only first order in substrate. The authors[101] suggest that for some unknown reason these results might be caused by the fact that these compounds contain localized double bonds, rather than the delocalized systems of the benzene metal tricarbonyls.

Under certain conditions oxygen atoms in metal carbonyls undergo moderately fast exchange with the oxygen atoms in water. This is of interest

Table 7.8 Exchange of ^{14}C-arene with π-arenetricarbonylmetal(0) in heptane at 140°C

	$ClC_6H_5Cr(CO)_3$	$C_6H_6Cr(CO)_3$	$CH_3C_6H_5Cr(CO)_3$	$CH_3C_6H_5Mo(CO)_3$	$CH_3C_6H_5W(CO)_3$
k_1, M^{-1} sec^{-1}	3.7×10^{-5}	5.8×10^{-6}	2.2×10^{-6}	5.8×10^{-2}	5.8×10^{-4}
k_2, M^{-1} sec^{-1}	3.8×10^{-6}	6.1×10^{-7}	2.2×10^{-7}	3.0×10^{-4}	1.2×10^{-6}
E_{a1}, kcal	30	30	35	19	27
E_{a2}, kcal	30	25	32	13	26
$\Delta S^{\ddagger}_1$, eu	-1	-5	$+7$	-11	-3
$\Delta S^{\ddagger}_2$, eu	-6	-20	-6	-32	-13

From reference 101. See rate law 27 and the text for the meaning of k_1, k_2, etc.

because oxygen atoms in metal carbonyls are thermodynamically strongly bonded and are rarely considered as kinetically labile nuclei. However, it is found[103] that $Re(CO)_6{}^+$, dissolved in ^{18}O-water, is significantly enriched in ^{18}O within a matter of minutes. At 25°, exchange of all oxygen atoms in the carbonyl cation with those in the water is about 41% complete in half an hour. In contrast, there is no detectable evidence of such exchange between $Mo(CO)_6$ and water within a 75 hr period.

This difference between $Re(CO)_6{}^+$ and $Mo(CO)_6$ is a rather striking illustration of the activation of a ligand site in a metal complex by a formal positive charge. The effect of charge is analogous to that found for the alkaline hydrolysis of metal chelates derived from tropolone and β-diketones.[104] On the basis of analogy with these results it was suggested[103] that the nitrogen atoms in cationic metal cyanides may exchange with the nitrogen atoms in ammonia solutions, and that the oxygen atoms of metal nitrosyls may show lability with respect to water oxygen atoms in aqueous solutions. Also, activation of ligand sites toward electrophiles may be achieved in certain anionic complexes, and it is possible that a facile deuteration of the π-cyclopentadienyl ring takes place in some of its anionic metal compounds in acidic aqueous media. For a further discussion of some reactions of coordinated ligands see the section on this topic in the next chapter.

The exchange of oxygen with $Re(CO)_6{}^+$ must surely take place by an attack on a carbon atom by OH^- or H_2O to give intermediates of the type $(OC)_5ReCOOH$ or $(OC)_5ReC(OH)_2{}^+$, respectively. For example, a previous observation[35,105] had been made of the analogous reaction represented by the equilibrium

$$M(CO)_4L_2{}^+ + OR^- \underset{HX}{\overset{KOH}{\rightleftharpoons}} M(CO)_3L_2COOR \qquad (30)$$

where $M = Mn$, Re; $L = P(C_6H_5)_3$, 1,10-phenanthroline; $R = CH_3$, C_2H_5, C_5H_{11}, $CH_2C_6H_5$; and $X = Cl$, Br. No investigations have been made of the mechanisms of these reactions, but it appears that the forward reaction is analogous to an organic esterification process:

$$(31)$$

The reverse of this reaction may be analogous to the acid catalysis of ester hydrolysis:

$$(32)$$

Substitution Reactions

The replacement of CO in metal carbonyls by other ligands has been studied more extensively than has the CO exchange. One reason is that the substitution reactions are easier to follow experimentally. This is usually done by monitoring the i.r. spectrum of a reaction mixture in the CO stretching region or by measuring the rate of release of gaseous CO. It is apparent from the discussion in the previous section that examples are known of metal carbonyls which react at rates independent of the concentration and nature of the entering reagents and of others where these factors do affect the rate of reaction. Therefore it is convenient in this section to subdivide the substitution reactions into (1) first-order and (2) second-order reactions. The first-order reactions afford information on what factors affect the reactivities of different substrates, and the second-order reactions also provide information on what factors contribute to the nucleophilic strength of various reagents towards metal carbonyls.

First-Order Reactions. We shall consider first substitution reactions of the four-coordinated, tetrahedral nickel compounds. There has been a detailed study[106] of substitution reactions of nickel carbonyl derivatives, and some kinetic data are shown in Table 7.9. Also included in this table are some recent data on the reaction of $Ni(CO)_4$ with different ligands.[62,63] It is apparent that the rate of replacement of CO decreases in the order

Table 7.9 Rates of reaction of some nickel carbonyls at 25°C

$$Ni(CO)_2L_2 + L' \rightarrow Ni(CO)_2LL' + L$$

Compound	Solvent[a]	L'	k, sec^{-1}
$Ni(CO)_4$ [b]	T	$P(C_6H_5)_3$	4×10^{-4}
$Ni(CO)_4$ [c]	A	$P(OCH_3)_3$	3×10^{-4}
$Ni(CO)_3P(C_6H_5)_3$	A	$P(C_6H_5)_3$	1.3×10^{-3}
$Ni(CO)_3P(C_6H_5)_3$	C	$P(C_6H_5)_3$	5.7×10^{-4}
$Ni(CO)_2(PCl_3)_2$	C	$P(C_4H_5)_3$	$>1 \times 10^{-2}$
$Ni(CO)_2[P(C_2H_4CN)_3]_2$ [d]	A	$P(OC_6H_5)_3$	1.4×10^{-3}
$Ni(CO)_2(PPh_3)_2$	C	$P(C_4H_9)_3$	5.6×10^{-4}
$Ni(CO)_2[P(C_4H_9)_3]_2$	A	$P(C_2H_4CN)_3$	1.2×10^{-4}
$Ni(CO)_2[P(C_4H_9)_3]_2$	C	$P(C_6H_5)_3$	3.9×10^{-5}
$Ni(CO)_2[P(OC_2H_5)_3]_2$	C	$P(C_4H_9)_3$	$<1 \times 10^{-7}$
$Ni(CO)_2[P(OC_6H_5)_3]_2$	C	$P(C_4H_9)_3$	$<1 \times 10^{-7}$

From reference 106 except as specified in notes *b* and *c*.

[a] A = acetonitrile, C = cyclohexane, T = toluene.

[b] From reference 63. $\Delta H^{\ddagger} = 20$ kcal/mole, $\Delta S^{\ddagger} = +2$ eu in toluene, k at 0°.

[c] From reference 62. $\Delta H^{\ddagger} = 21$, $\Delta S^{\ddagger} = +2$, k at 0°.

[d] $\Delta H^{\ddagger} = 25.5$ and $\Delta S^{\ddagger} = +10.5$.

$Ni(CO)_4 > Ni(CO)_3L \gg Ni(CO)_2L_2$, where L groups are phosphines or phosphites. In fact, under the conditions of these experiments, the last two CO's are not replaced even in the presence of a large excess of reagent.

This is interpreted in terms of there being only two strong π bonds possible in a tetrahedral structure and these being largely localized on the remaining two CO's, thus producing a maximum Ni-C bond strength. The contribution of $Ni\!=\!C\!=\!O$ per CO is less, and the Ni-C bond strength is less, for the monosubstituted carbonyl and least for $Ni(CO)_4$, nicely paralleling the observed order of reactivity.

Most of the information in Table 7.9 deals with the replacement of phosphines and phosphites from $Ni(CO)_2L_2$. The results show that the rates of reaction do not depend on the reagent and that the effect of solvent is relatively small, all of which supports a non-polar dissociation mechanism. For changes in L the rates of reactions vary by approximately five orders of magnitude, decreasing in the order $PCl_3 \gg P(CH_2CH_2CN)_3 \sim P(C_6H_5)_3 > P(C_4H_9)_3 \gg P(OC_2H_5)_3 \sim P(OC_6H_5)_3$. This order closely parallels that of increasing basicity[107] of the ligands, with the exception of the two phosphite complexes. This suggests that the strength of the Ni-P bond is largely due to σ bonding, with π-bonding playing a minor role. Such a result is reasonable, keeping in mind that only two strong π bonds are possible and these are largely localized on the two CO's, which are much better π bonders than are the phosphorus ligands (see Table 7.4).

Although it appears that the replacement of L in $Ni(CO)_2L_2$ by L', where L and L' = phosphines or phosphites, takes place by a simple dissociation process, there is now a need for some caution here. For example, the reaction of $Ni(CO)_4$ to form $Ni(CO)_3L$, where L = $P(C_6H_5)_3$ or $P(OCH_3)_3$, is first order but does not seem to proceed by a dissociation mechanism (p. 543).

Heck[94,108] has investigated the kinetics of the reaction of cobalt carbonyl and many of its derivatives with triphenylphosphine. Some of the data reported for the acylcobalt tetracarbonyls (a) and the π-allylcobalt tricarbonyls (b) are summarized in Table 7.10. In both cases the rates are first order and it is presumed that the reactions proceed by a dissociation mechanism. For the acyl systems the results show that both steric and electronic factors have an effect on the rates of reaction. For example, the rates increase with changes in the acyl group in the order $CH_3CO < (CH_3)_2CHCO \ll (CH_3)_3CCO$. That this is predominately a steric effect is indicated by the fact that the addition of one methyl group to the acetyl compound has only about one-fortieth the effect of adding two methyl groups. This observation is also in accord with the steric acceleration generally found for dissociation reactions (p. 162).

Table 7.10   Rates of reaction of some acyl- and π-allylcobalt carbonyls at 0°C in diethyl ether solution

Compound	k, sec^{-1}	Relative Rate
(a) $RCOCo(CO)_4 + P(C_6H_5)_3 \rightarrow RCOCo(CO)_3P(C_6H_5)_3 + CO$		
$CH_3COCo(CO)_4$ [a]	1.0×10^{-3}	1.0
$(CH_3)_2CHCOCo(CO)_4$	2.1×10^{-3}	2.1
$(CH_3)_3CCOCo(CO)_4$	8.6×10^{-2}	86
$(CH_3)_2CHCH_2COCo(CO)_4$	1.2×10^{-3}	1.2
$CH_3OCH_2COCo(CO)_4$	2.8×10^{-4}	0.3
$CF_3COCo(CO)_4$	9.4×10^{-5}	0.1
$CH_3CH{=}CHCOCo(CO)_4$	6.2×10^{-2}	62
$C_6H_5COCo(CO)_4$	3.4×10^{-2}	34
$p\text{-}CH_3OC_6H_4COCo(CO)_4$	5.0×10^{-2}	50
$p\text{-}NO_2C_6H_4COCo(CO)_4$	1.7×10^{-2}	17
$2,4,6\text{-}(CH_3)_3C_6H_2COCo(CO)_4$	2.0×10^{-4}	0.02
(b) $\pi\text{-}C_3H_5Co(CO)_3 + P(C_6H_5)_3 \rightarrow \pi\text{-}C_3H_5Co(CO)_2P(C_6H_5)_3 + CO$		
$\pi\text{-}C_3H_5Co(CO)_3$ [b]	3.3×10^{-4}	1.0
$2\text{-}CH_3\text{-}\pi\text{-}C_3H_4Co(CO)_3$	2.8×10^{-3}	8.6
$2\text{-}Br\text{-}\pi\text{-}C_3H_4Co(CO)_3$	4.1×10^{-3}	12
$2\text{-}Cl\text{-}\pi\text{-}C_3H_4Co(CO)_3$	6.5×10^{-3}	20
$1\text{-}CH_3\text{-}\pi\text{-}C_3H_4Co(CO)_3$	1.8×10^{-4}	0.6
$1\text{-}Cl\text{-}\pi\text{-}C_3H_4Co(CO)_3$	9.4×10^{-5}	0.3

From reference 108.

[a] $\Delta H^{\ddagger} = 21$ kcal and $\Delta S^{\ddagger} = +3.4$ eu.

[b] $\Delta H^{\ddagger} = 23$ kcal and $\Delta S^{\ddagger} = +7.2$ eu.

Inductive effects are likewise important, as is shown by the CF_3CO compound, which reacts ten times slower than does the CH_3CO compound. The retardation in rate by electron-withdrawing substituents is not readily understood. In many cases, as discussed previously, the removal of electron density from the metal decreases the extent of M-C π bonding and also its bond strength, and this is accompanied by an increase in reactivity.

The relatively fast reaction of $CH_3CH{=}CHCOCo(CO)_4$ is attributed to its marked tendency to form the cyclic tricarbonyl shown by structure XIII in the equilibrium

$$CH_3CH{=}CHCOCo(CO)_4 \rightleftharpoons \underset{\text{(XIII)}}{CH_3CH} \overset{CH}{\underset{\underset{O}{\|}{C}}{-}} Co(CO)_3 \tag{33}$$

(p. 589). A similar interaction between cobalt and the aromatic ring may be responsible for the reactivity of the benzoylcobalt carbonyls. The much lower reactivity of the mesitoyl compound may be due to the methyl groups making it sterically difficult for the benzene ring to partially bond to the cobalt. Electron-withdrawing substituents on the phenyl group have a slight retardation effect on the rate of reaction.

The π-allyl cobalt carbonyls react in much the same manner as do the acetyl compounds, except that substituent effects on the rate appear to be smaller. That the 2-methyl derivative reacts faster than the parent π-allyl compound is in accord with the acetyl reactions, which increase in rate with added electron-releasing groups. However, there is also an increase in rate for the electron-withdrawing groups 2-bromo and 2-chloro. This cannot be due to steric acceleration because the rate of reaction of the bromo derivative is slower than that of the chloro compound. With the data available it can be concluded that substituent effects on the rates of reaction of these systems are small.

The kinetics of substitution reactions of several manganese carbonyl halides and the *cis-trans* isomerization[110] of a few of the product systems have been investigated.[109a,111] Some of the data reported are collected in Table 7.11, and these will be discussed in the order shown of (a) reactions of $Mn(CO)_5X$, (b) reactions of *cis*-$Mn(CO)_4LBr$, and (c) isomerization of *cis* → *trans*-$Mn(CO)_3L_2Br$. The assignment of structure was made on the basis of a group theoretical treatment[45] of the i.r. spectra of the compounds in the C-O stretching region, and the *cis* and *trans* designations for the disubstituted derivatives apply to structures XIV and XV, respectively.

(XIV) (*cis*)   (XV) (*trans*)   (XVI)

Structure XVI has not been reported and is not considered in the discussion that follows.

Substitution reactions of all of the manganese compounds that have been investigated proceed at a rate independent of the concentration and the nature of the reagent. Thus the rates of substitution (Table 7.11) and of CO exchange (Table 7.6) are the same, within experimental error, for the same compound. This implies that both substitution and exchange involve the same dissociation mechanism (Fig. 7.8). It was mentioned and discussed previously (p. 554) that the rates of reaction for $Mn(CO)_5X$ decrease in the order Cl > Br > I, and the activation energies are now seen to increase in the same order, which agrees with the interpretation that this represents

Table 7.11   Rates of reaction of some manganese carbonyl halides

(a) $Mn(CO)_5X + L \xrightarrow{40°} cis\text{-}Mn(CO)_4LX + CO$

X	L	Solvent	k, sec^{-1}
Cl	$P(C_6H_5)_3$	$CHCl_3$	2.7×10^{-3}
Cl [a]	$As(C_6H_5)_3$	$CHCl_3$	2.6×10^{-3}
Br	C_5H_5N	$CHCl_3$	3.3×10^{-4}
Br [a]	$As(C_6H_5)_3$	$CHCl_3$	3.3×10^{-4}
I [a]	$As(C_6H_5)_3$	$CHCl_3$	1.6×10^{-5}
I [b]	I	$CHCl_3$	1.5×10^{-5}
Br	$As(C_6H_5)_3$	C_6H_{12}	7.4×10^{-4}
Br	$As(C_6H_5)_3$	C_6H_6	4.1×10^{-4}
Br	$As(C_6H_5)_3$	$(CH_3)_2CO$	1.8×10^{-4}
Br	$As(C_6H_5)_3$	CH_3NO_2	1.2×10^{-4}

(b) $cis\text{-}Mn(CO)_4LBr + L' \xrightarrow{40°} cis\text{-}Mn(CO)_3LL'Br + CO$

L	L'	Solvent	k, sec^{-1}
$P(C_6H_5)_3$	$P(OC_4H_9)_3$	s-TCE	7.7×10^{-4}
$As(C_6H_5)_3$ [c]	$P(OC_4H_9)_3$	s-TCE	2.1×10^{-4}
$P(C_4H_9)_3$	$P(OC_4H_9)_3$	s-TCE	1.1×10^{-4}
$P(C_6H_5)_2Cl$	$P(OC_4H_9)_3$	s-TCE	1.1×10^{-4}
$P(OC_6H_5)_3$	$P(OC_4H_9)_3$	s-TCE	5.7×10^{-5}
$P(OC_6H_5)_3$	$P(OC_6H_5)_3$	s-TCE	4.8×10^{-5}
$Sb(C_6H_5)_3$	$P(OC_4H_9)_3$	s-TCE	5.1×10^{-5}
$P(C_6H_5)Cl_2$	$P(C_6H_5)Cl_2$	s-TCE	3.7×10^{-5}
$P(OC_4H_9)_3$	$P(OC_4H_9)_3$	s-TCE	3.5×10^{-5}
$P(OC_4H_9)_3$	$P(OC_4H_9)_3$	$CHCl_3$	5.3×10^{-5}
$P(OCH_2)_3CCH_3$	$P(OCH_2)_3CCH_3$	$CHCl_3$	4.4×10^{-6}
$As(C_6H_5)_3$	$P(OC_4H_9)_3$	$C_6H_5CH_3$	4.3×10^{-4}
$As(C_6H_5)_3$	$P(OC_4H_9)_3$	$C_6H_5NO_2$	2.8×10^{-4}
C_5H_5N	C_5H_5N	s-TCE	fast

(c) $cis\text{-}Mn(CO)_3L_2Br \xrightarrow{60°} trans\text{-}Mn(CO)_3L_2Br$

L	Solvent	k, sec^{-1}	E_a, kcal	$\Delta S^{\ddagger}$, eu
$P(C_6H_5)Cl_2$	s-TCE	3.0×10^{-4}	26.4	3.0
$P(OC_6H_5)_3$	s-TCE	1.7×10^{-4}	29.0	9.1
$P(OC_4H_9)_3$	s-TCE	3.5×10^{-5}	31.8	14
$P(OC_6H_5)_3$	$C_6H_5CH_3$	2.1×10^{-4}		
$P(OC_6H_5)_3$	$C_6H_5NO_2$	2.2×10^{-4}		

From references 109a, 110, and 111.
[a] E_a for X: Cl, 27.5 kcal/mole; Br, 30; I, 32. $\Delta S^{\ddagger}$ for X: Cl, 16 eu; Br, 19; I, 21.
[b] Temp., 39.2°C.
[c] $E_a = 30$; $\Delta S^{\ddagger} = 18$.

the order of increasing Mn—C bond strength. Also, the positive entropy of activation is expected for a dissociation process where the transition state is less restricted than the ground state. The effect of solvent on the rate of reaction is not large, but the rate does decrease with increasing dielectric strength of the solvent, suggesting that the transition state is less polar than the ground state.

Although the exchange of ^{14}CO with $Mn_2(CO)_{10}$ at room temperature is extremely slow, the carbonyl does react with ligands such as $P(C_6H_5)_3$ in solution at elevated temperatures. Initial studies[109b] indicated that the paramagnetic monomer $Mn(CO)_4P(C_6H_5)_3$ was produced, and subsequent research[109c] reported the formation of the dimer $[Mn(CO)_4P(C_6H_5)_3]_2$. Recent investigations[109d] show that $Mn_2(CO)_{10}$ reacts with $P(C_6H_5)_3$ to form $Mn_2(CO)_9P(C_6H_5)_3$, which in turn reacts to form $Mn_2(CO)_8[P(C_6H_5)_3]_2$. Kinetic data were collected for the replacement of CO by $P(C_6H_5)_3$, which is first order in the carbonyl concentration and zero order in phosphine.

The kinetic behavior of the monosubstituted compounds $Mn(CO)_4LBr$ [Table 7.11(b)] is much the same as that of the parent compound $Mn(CO)_5Br$. In fact, rates of reaction and the activation parameters are about the same for $Mn(CO)_4As(C_6H_5)_3Br$ and $Mn(CO)_5Br$. Although the rates of reaction are similar to the rate of the parent pentacarbonyl when L = phosphines or phosphites, the rates of reaction are much faster when L = pyridine or aniline. The rates of reaction for changes in L decrease in the order

$$C_5H_5N, \ C_6H_5NH_2 \gg P(C_6H_5)_3 > As(C_6H_5)_3 > P(C_4H_9)_3$$
$$\sim P(C_6H_5)_2Cl > P(OC_6H_5)_3 \sim SbP(C_5H_5)_3$$
$$> P(C_6H_5)Cl_2 \sim P(OC_4H_9)_3 > P(OCH_2)_3CCH_3.$$

It was suggested[109a] that the rates of reaction of the phosphine and phosphite derivatives increase with increasing bulkiness of the group, which is the usual behavior of steric acceleration for dissociation reactions. Although steric factors may be important in considerations of groups containing the same or very similar ligand atoms, it is apparent that they cannot account for the rapid reactions of the pyridine and aniline derivatives. These monosubstituted compounds react more rapidly than the parent pentacarbonyl, and its reaction with the amine reagents produces only the disubstituted product.

That the systems $Mn(CO)_4LBr$ containing L with nitrogen ligand atoms are more reactive than the phosphorus analogs is similar to the greater reactivity of $Mn(CO)_5Cl$ compared to $Mn(CO)_5I$. Thus the less electronegative and more polarizable P-type ligand renders the compound less reactive than does the corresponding N-type ligand. This order of reactivity does not parallel the π-bonding tendency of the groups, because the P-type ligands are better π bonders than the N-type and would be expected to leave less $Mn{=}C{=}O$ bonding for the reactive CO's. This would have the effect of weakening the bonding more in the phosphine complexes than in the amine complexes, contrary to what is observed.

The results can be interpreted if we consider the σ-bonding properties of L as being the more important. This has already been done for the

$Mn(CO)_5X$ systems (p. 554). An equivalent explanation may be given in terms of the symbiosis effect.[3] Thus a complex containing all soft ligands, such as CO or phosphorus donors and iodine, will be more stable than one containing a mixture of hard and soft ligands, such as amines or chlorine and CO. The unstable complex will dissociate more readily. The same behavior is found for $Cr(CO)_5X^-$ and $Cr(CO)_4$bipy, both of which are much more reactive than $Cr(CO)_6$ (pp. 569 and 570).

The kinetic product for the reaction of $Mn(CO)_4LBr$ with L to give $Mn(CO)_3L_2Br$ is usually the *cis* isomer. In most cases it rearranges to the thermodynamically stable *trans* form.[110] That the initial product is *cis* seems plausible because in $Mn(CO)_4LBr$ two of the CO's adjacent to L are *trans* to each other and presumably must share in the π bonding so that the Mn-C bond strength is weaker than for the two CO's *trans* to L and bromine, respectively. That the more stable isomer is the *trans* isomer is explained in terms of steric factors. For steric reasons the bulky ligands L give rise to a more stable compound if situated in remote (*trans*) positions to one another.

The rates of *cis* → *trans* isomerization[110] of $Mn(CO)_3L_2Br$ are given in Table 7.11c. In addition the rate of ligand interchange by the equation

$$cis\text{-}Mn(CO)_3[P(OC_6H_5)_3]_2Br + 2P(OC_4H_9)_3 \rightarrow$$

$$cis\text{-}Mn(CO)_3[P(OC_4H_9)_3]_2Br + 2P(OC_6H_5)_3 \quad (34)$$

is about ten times faster than the rate of *cis-trans* isomerization. The same rate of ligand interchange is found for $P(C_6H_5)_3$. In both cases the rate does not depend on the ligand concentration. This suggests that a dissociation process may provide a path for isomerization, with the five-coordinated intermediate returning to the *cis* isomer approximately eleven times for every twelve dissociations.

A probable mechanism is shown in Fig. 7.9a along with a plot of the energy-reaction profile (7.9b). The structure of the active intermediate(s) is not known, but a tetragonal pyramid (Fig. 7.9a, A) can readily permit ligand interchange without accompanying isomerization. However, if this form has time to generate a trigonal bipyramidal structure (Fig. 7.9a, B) before the ligand return, it then appears the ligand return could take place in the trigonal plane at a remote position from the bulky ligand already there and give rise to the *trans* isomer. This hypothesis is supported by the observation that the compounds containing the best π-bonding ligands have the lowest activation energies for isomerization, and it is just these ligands that are expected to have the greatest stabilizing influence of a trigonal bipyramidal structure (p. 374). Similar observations[112] have been made on the isomerization *cis* → *trans*-$Mo(CO)_4(PEt_3)_2$.

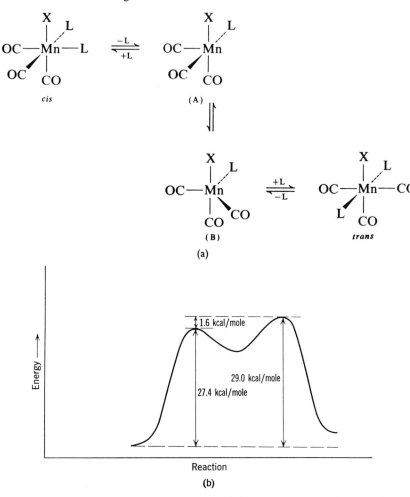

Fig. 7.9 Dissociation mechanism for the *cis-trans* isomerization of Mn(CO)$_3$L$_2$X. The activation parameters are given for Mn(CO)$_3$(PPh$_3$)$_2$Br.

Salts of the anions Mn(CO)$_4$X$_2^-$ and Cr(CO)$_5$X$^-$ have been prepared[113] by the reaction of the parent penta- or hexacarbonyl, respectively, with X$^-$. The anion Cr(CO)$_5$X$^-$ is isoelectronic and isostructural with Mn(CO)$_5$X, and it is of interest that the two systems are somewhat analogous in their reactions. Kinetic data[114] on the rates of reaction of M(CO)$_5$X$^-$ with different reagents to give M(CO)$_4$LX$^-$ are given in Table 7.12a. The rates of reaction do not depend on the reagent, and it appears that a dissociation mechanism similar to that for Mn(CO)$_5$X is followed. Not only is the mechanism the same, but also the rates are very similar for analogous

Table 7.12   Rates of reaction of some Group VI metal carbonyls

$$(a)^a \; M(CO)_5X^- + L \xrightarrow{\text{diglyme}} M(CO)_4LX^- + CO$$

M	X	Temp., °C	L	k, sec^{-1}
Cr	Cl	19.6	$P(C_6H_5)_3$	1.6×10^{-4}
Cr	Cl	19.6	$P(p\text{-}FC_6H_4)_3$	1.6×10^{-4}
Cr	Br	29.8	$P(C_6H_5)_3$	7.0×10^{-5}
Cr	I	29.8	$P(C_6H_5)_3$	slow
Mo	Cl	19.6	$P(C_6H_5)_3$	fast
Mo	Br	19.6	$P(C_6H_5)_3$	1.3×10^{-4}
Mo	I	29.8	$P(C_6H_5)_3$	1.1×10^{-4}
Mo	I	29.8	$P(p\text{-}ClC_6H_4)_3$	1.1×10^{-4}
W	Cl	29.8	$P(C_6H_5)_3$	1.7×10^{-4}

$$(b)^b \; M(CO)_4(\text{bipy}) + L \xrightarrow[47.9°]{s\text{-DCE}} cis\text{-}M(CO)_3L(\text{bipy}) + CO$$

M	L	k, sec^{-1}	$\Delta H^{\ddagger}$ kcal/mole	$\Delta S^{\ddagger}$ eu
Cr	$P(OC_2H_5)_3$	4.3×10^{-4}	24.3	1.9
Cr	$P(OCH_2)_3CCH_3$	4.4×10^{-4}	23.4	-1.1
Cr ^{c}	$P(OC_2H_5)_3$	1.8×10^{-4}	22.6	-5.4
Mo	$P(OC_2H_5)_3$	1.6×10^{-4}	24.6	0.5
Mo ^{c}	$P(OC_2H_5)_3$	7.8×10^{-4}	27.3	7.5
W ^{d}	$P(OC_2H_5)_3$	6.1×10^{-4}	26.1	-7.5

^{a} From reference 114.
^{b} From reference 115.
^{c} Chlorobenzene solvent.
^{d} Temp., 100°C.

$Cr(CO)_5X^-$ and $Mn(CO)_5X$ compounds. This is surprising if we consider π bonding only, since the anion is expected to have stronger π bonding because of the greater electronic charge on the metal.

Even more surprising is the greater reactivity of $M(CO)_5X^-$ compounds compared to the parent $M(CO)_6$ molecules. In these cases the i.r. spectra also seem to show that the metal-carbon bond strength is greater in the anion than in the neutral species. We can only conclude that σ bonding is also important for the binding of CO to metal atoms. Particularly in the anionic complexes, the σ bonding must be weakened to the point where CO is only loosely held. This does not necessarily disagree with the strong

π bonding indicated by the i.r. data. We must also bear in mind that there is no necessary theoretical requirement that force constants, even of bonds between the same atoms, be related to bond energies.

It will be noted that the rates of reaction are in the order $Mn(CO)_5X >$ $Mn(CO)_6^+$ and $Cr(CO)_5X^- > Cr(CO)_6$. The effect of the group X is to weaken the bonding compared to the parent hexacarbonyl. This has already been explained by the symbiosis effect, in which a hard ligand (X) confers instability to the remaining soft ligands (CO). In both series, $M(CO)_5X^-$ and $M(CO)_6$, the reactivities follow the order $Cr < Mo > W$.

Data[115] on the rate of reaction of $M(CO)_4(bipy)$ with L to yield *cis*-$M(CO)_3L(bipy)$ are given in Table 7.12b. Here, too, the rates of reaction are largely first order and are much faster than the rates of reaction by the metal hexacarbonyls. The explanation for this difference is the same as that given above for the greater reactivity of $M(CO)_5X^-$ compared to $M(CO)_6$. In addition to this first-order rate term the observed rate law for the reactions of the molybdenum and tungsten compounds contains a second-order term and is given by the equation

$$\text{Rate} = k_1 + k_2 \,[\text{reagent}]\,[\text{substrate}] \qquad (35)$$

Reaction path k_2 gives a mixture of *cis*-$M(CO)_3L(bipy)$ and *trans*-$M(CO)_4L_2$ as products. The rates of reaction by this path for different reagents increase in the order $P(OC_2H_5)_3 < P(OCH_2)_3CCH_3 < PO_3C_6H_9$, which is the order of basicity of these groups towards BH_3 and $B(CH_3)_3$.[116]

It is possible that reaction by this path takes place by means of a bimolecular displacement path, since seven-coordinated systems[117] such as $M(CO)_4I_3^-$ exist for molybdenum and tungsten but not for chromium. This path does not appear to be operative for the chromium compound. An alternative mechanism which involves the opening of the bipy chelate ring and addition of reagent would also be consistent with the first-order dependence on reagent. However, it does not appear that this is what happens because the same rate law is found for the reaction of $Mo(CO)_5py$ with $P(OCH_2)_3CCH_3$.[115a] Second-order kinetics, and presumably a bimolecular displacement mechanism, have also been observed for the reaction of $M(CO)_5X^-$, where $M = Cr$, Mo, W, with $P(C_6H_5)_3$ to give $M(CO)_5P(C_6H_5)_3$.[114] All of these second-order reactions, if verified, will be of interest because they will represent examples of little known bimolecular displacements in a six-coordinated system (see Chapter 3).

Recent investigations[115b] do not support a bimolecular displacement mechanism for the substitution reactions of some of these six-coordinated systems. For example, the replacement of CO in $Mo(CO)_6$ by a variety of phosphine and amine reagents proceeds with a rate constant of $k = 6 \times 10^{-5}\,\text{sec}^{-1}$ at $98°$ in *n*-decane-cyclohexane solution. The rates of reaction are first order in $Mo(CO)_6$ concentration and independent of nucleophile. With π-bonding type of reagents such as benzene, mesitylene, and norbornadiene, the rates of reaction are also independent of reagent concentration but vary for different reagents. These results are complicated by the experimental difficulty of the removal of CO without loss of $Mo(CO)_6$ at these high temperatures. Nevertheless, it is suggested that the reactions proceed by stepwise equilibria initiated by dissociation to $Mo(CO)_5$. ‖

Substitution reactions of $Fe(CO)_4X_2$ have also been investigated,[88] but unfortunately these appear to be rather complicated and do not permit a direct comparison with the corresponding $Mn(CO)_5X$ and $Cr(CO)_5X^-$ systems. The results do show that the reactions of $Fe(CO)_4X_2$ are much faster than those of the pentacarbonyls, and the rates of reaction to form $Fe(CO)_3LX_2$ do not depend on the reagent. However, the reaction does not appear to be a simple dissociation process because the rate of substitution is faster than the rate of CO exchange (p. 555) and the rate of substitution is inhibited by the presence of halogen. It is reassuring to find[88] that the monosubstituted derivatives $Fe(CO)_3LX_2$ react in a normal fashion by a dissociation mechanism and that the reactions are not inhibited by the presence of halogen. These systems behave as do the analogous $Mn(CO)_4LX$, except that the iron compounds react about 700 times faster, in accord with a weaker M-C bond strength for iron than for manganese.

Second-Order Reactions.   This section will describe the substitution reactions of $CoNO(CO)_3$, $Fe(NO)_2(CO)_2$, $\pi\text{-}C_5H_5Rh(CO)_2$, and (arene)-$Mo(CO)_3$. Considering first the nitrosyl carbonyls, we recall that the CO exchange with these compounds is slow (Table 7.5). However, the reaction of $CoNO(CO)_3$ with $P(C_6H_5)_3$ proceeds at a moderate rate and one that is first order in both substrate and reagent concentrations.[94] The same is true for the reactions of $Fe(NO)_2(CO)_2$; some of the kinetic data collected on the reactions of the cobalt[83,118] and iron[119] nitrosyl carbonyls are given in Table 7.13.

The results obtained clearly show that these compounds react by an S_N2 mechanism because the rates of CO exchange are slow compared to the rates of substitution. This raises the question of why these nitrosyl carbonyls do not react by a first order process as does their isoelectronic $Ni(CO)_4$. Two reasons can be offered for this. One is that the nuclear charge on the metal increases in these systems in the order $Fe < Co < Ni$

‖ The rate of reaction of $Mo(CO)_6$ with good nucleophiles such as $P(n\text{-}C_4H_9)_3$ at high reagent concentrations shows a dependence on its concentration. Rate law 35 applies, and it is believed that k_1 represents a dissociation path, whereas k_2 corresponds to a bimolecular displacement [R. J. Angelici and J. K. Graham, *J. Am. Chem. Soc.*, **88**, 3658 (1966)].

Table 7.13   Rates of reaction of $CoNO(CO)_3$ and of $Fe(NO)_2(CO)_2$ with various reagents in toluene at 25°C

$$CoNO(CO)_3 + L \xrightarrow{k_{Co}} CoNO(CO)_2L + CO$$

$$Fe(NO)_2(CO)_2 + L \xrightarrow{k_{Fe}} Fe(NO)_2COL + CO$$

		M^{-1}, sec^{-1}	
L	ΔH.N.P., mv.[a]	k_{Co}	k_{Fe}
$P(C_2H_5)_3$	111	2.2×10^{-1}	1.2×10^{-1}
$P(C_4H_9)_3$	131	9.2×10^{-2}	2.6×10^{-1}
$P(C_6H_5)(C_2H_5)_2$	300	4.6×10^{-2}	3.5×10^{-2}
$P(C_6H_{11})_3$	33	9.4×10^{-3}	2.4×10^{-2}
$P(C_6H_5)_2(C_2H_5)$	400^b	5.9×10^{-3}	5.3×10^{-3}
$P(C_6H_5)_2(C_4H_9)$	400^b	4.4×10^{-3}	
$P(p\text{-}CH_3OC_6H_4)_3$	439	$7.6 \times 10^{-3\,d}$	
$P(OC_4H_9)_3$	520^b	2.8×10^{-3}	6.3×10^{-3}
$P(OCH_3)_3$	520^b	1.8×10^{-3}	
$P(C_6H_5)_3{}^c$	573	1.0×10^{-3}	1.0×10^{-3}
$P(OCH_2)_3CCH_3$	650^b	6.5×10^{-4}	
$P(C_6H_5)_2Cl$	...	9.0×10^{-5}	
$P(OC_6H_5)_3{}^d$	875	3.4×10^{-5}	1.5×10^{-5}
$P(N(CH_3)_2)_3$	...	3.2×10^{-5}	
CNC_6H_{11}	...	7.2×10^{-3}	
$4\text{-}CH_3C_5H_4N$	200^b	$7.8 \times 10^{-5\,d}$	
C_5H_5N	286	3.9×10^{-5}	
$3\text{-}ClC_5H_4N$	450^b	4.5×10^{-6}	
$As(C_6H_5)_3$		very slow	very slow

From reference 118 for cobalt and 119 for iron.

[a] Difference in half-neutralization potential between L and N,N'-diphenyl guanidine in nitromethane.[83] The smaller ΔH.N.P., the more basic and perhaps more polarizable is L (see text).

[b] The ΔH.N.P. are estimated values.[118]

[c] For L = $P(C_6H_5)_3$, $k_{Co} = 2.4 \times 10^{-3}\,M^{-1}\,sec^{-1}$, $E_a = 15$ kcal, $\Delta S^{\ddagger} = -23$ eu; and for $L = P(OC_6H_5)_3$, $k_{Co} = 6.1 \times 10^{-5}$, $E_a = 17$, $\Delta S^{\ddagger} = -22$ in nitromethane.

[d] For nitromethane.

[or the oxidation states can be assigned as Fe(-II), Co(-I), Ni(0)]. Hence the extent of metal-carbon π bonding would decrease in the same order. This is supported by the i.r. data on force constants for the C–O stretching vibration. If the bond strength were determined largely by π bonding, the activation energy for a CO dissociation would be least for nickel and greatest for iron. Such a factor would reduce the chance of an S_N1 mechanism for iron and cobalt.

The second reason is related to the special properties of NO as a ligand, which increase the chance of an S_N2 mechanism for these same metals. The nitrosyl group in various complexes may be considered[120] as being NO^+, NO neutral, or NO^-. Thus NO is a highly polarizable ligand. Ordinarily in the nitrosyl carbonyls, NO is considered to have donated its odd electron to the metal to make up the E.A.N. of eighteen. Hence we have NO^+ for the normal state of the ligand. The approach of a ligand, with a lone pair of electrons, could cause a pair of electrons from the metal, or a metal-nitrogen bond, to concentrate on the ligand to form NO^-. This would make the metal more positive, perhaps with an empty bonding orbital, and facilitate nucleophilic attack. In valence bond terms the polarization may be written as shown by the equation

$$M = N = \overset{..}{\underset{..}{O}} \quad \xrightarrow{\;:L\;} \quad M - \overset{..}{N} = \overset{..}{\underset{..}{O}} \atop {\underset{L:L}{\uparrow}} \tag{36}$$

One point of extreme interest in the data in Table 7.13 is the information provided on the nucleophilic strengths of various reagents towards substrates of this type. A discussion of the factors that contribute to the strength of a nucleophile towards different substrates is given on pp. 138 and 396. Like Pt(II), the metals in metal carbonyls are believed to be class (b) or soft, because they are usually in a low oxidation state and contain very polarizable or soft ligands. It is therefore to be expected that the nucleophilic strength of a reagent will depend primarily on its polarizability, and its basicity (towards H^+) will play a minor role. As expected, phosphines are better reagents than amines towards both Pt(II) and metal carbonyl compounds.

Included in Table 7.13 are the half-neutralization potentials of some reagents, relative to N,N'-diphenyl guanidine taken as a standard, for titrations with perchloric acid in nitromethane.[107] This is a measure of the relative proton basicities of these reagents, and the L.F.E.R. plot (Fig. 7.10) shows that for the same donor-atom reagents, where steric factors are kept approximately constant, the free energy of activation decreases with increasing basicity of the reagent. However, for different donor-atom reagents, the basicity does not provide an estimate of nucleophilic strength. For example, at the same basicity, phosphines and phosphites are much better reagents than are pyridines, and the isonitriles are weak bases but very good nucleophiles. The linear plots in Fig. 7.10 may result from the fact that for analogous ligands, such as the phosphorus donors, a measure of basicity is in fact also a measure of polarizability. It seems that for these substrates the nucleophilic strength is largely determined by the polarizability of the reagent.

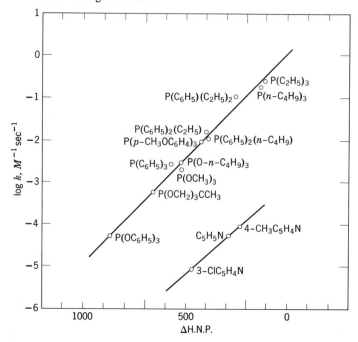

Fig. 7.10 The L.F.E.R. of the rate of reaction with the polarizability of the nucleophile for the reaction of $CoNO(CO)_3$ with different reagents in CH_3NO_2 solution at 25°. See text for meaning of ΔHNP.

However, it is not correct to conclude from this that the nucleophilic strength always increases with rising polarizability. In such a case $As(C_6H_5)_3$ would be a better reagent than $P(C_6H_5)_3$, which is contrary to the experimental results (Table 7.13). The same pattern is observed for the stability of complexes of class (b), or soft metals, which vary with changes in the ligand atom in the order $N \ll P > As > Sb$. Thus the arsines, compared to the phosphines, are always weaker bases, no matter what the reference acid is. Still the arsines will form many more stable complexes with soft acids than with hard acids; that is, they are relatively stronger to soft acids because of their polarizability.

The rate of reaction of $CoNO(CO)_3$ with $As(C_6H_5)_3$ follows rate law 35. One would expect the first-order path, given by k_1, to be a simple dissociation process. However, the rate of CO exchange, also first order, is some fifty times faster than the rate of first-order substitution by $As(C_6H_5)_3$. These results resemble those described earlier for the similar reactions of $Ni(CO)_4$ (p. 543).

The cobalt and the iron nitrosyl compounds show much the same behavior and react with a given nucleophile at approximately the same rate.¶ Also, for the cobalt compound, the solvent has only a small effect on its rate of reaction, and its enthalpies of activation are small and its entropies of activation negative. This is similar to the activation parameters obtained for the reactions of Pt(II) complexes (p. 404) and supports a bimolecular displacement process.

Although the replacement of one CO from these compounds is moderately fast, the replacement of a second CO

$$Fe(NO)_2COP(C_6H_5)_3 \xrightarrow{slow} Fe(NO)_2[P(C_6H_5)_3]_2 + CO \qquad (37)$$

is extremely slow. This appears to be the result of increased π bonding and greater Fe-C bond strength in the monosubstituted derivative relative to the parent compound. Advantage was taken of these properties to prepare a heterometal bridged carbonyl by the reaction of a mixture of $Fe(NO)_2(CO)_2$ and $CoNO(CO)_3$ with $(C_6H_5)_2PC_2H_4P(C_6H_5)_2$.[121] This is successful because, in spite of the favorable entropy effect for ring closure, the rate of chelation $(k_2^{40°} = 5.8 \times 10^{-5} \text{ sec}^{-1})$ is less than the rate of removal of the first CO $(k_1^{25°} = 5.1 \times 10^{-3} M^{-1} \text{ sec}^{-1})$ for the stepwise reaction represented by the equation

$$Fe(NO)_2(CO)_2 \xrightarrow{k_1} (NO)_2COFePPh_2C_2H_4PPh_2$$

$$\downarrow k_2$$

$$(NO)_2COFe \underset{P}{\overset{P}{\diagdown}} \overset{Ph_2}{\underset{Ph_2}{\diagup}} \overset{CH_2}{\underset{CH_2}{|}} \qquad (38)$$

This is contrary to the expected behavior of Werner complexes, for which usually $k_1 < k_2$ and only the formation of the chelate is observed. It follows that in the presence of excess metal carbonyl one prepares the symmetrical bridged carbonyl and in a mixture of two different metal carbonyls obtains also the heterometal bridged carbonyl. This results from the more rapid reaction of the monodentate carbonyl

$(NO)_2COFePPh_2C_2H_4PPh_2 + CoNO(CO)_3 \rightarrow$

$$(NO)_2(CO)FePPh_2C_2H_4Ph_2PCoNO(CO)_2 + CO \qquad (39)$$

rather than its chelate formation.

Very similar results to those described for the reactions of $CoNO(CO)_3$ and $Fe(NO)_2(CO)_2$ are obtained for the reaction of $C_5H_5Rh(CO)_2$ with various reagents.[100] Some of the kinetic data on the reactions of this compound, and the corresponding cobalt and iridium compounds, are

¶Recent studies show that $Mn(NO)_3CO$ reacts much faster (H. Wawersik, to be published).

Table 7.14 Rates of reaction of $\pi\text{-}C_5H_5M(CO)_2$ in toluene at 40°C

$$\pi\text{-}C_5H_5M(CO)_2 + L \rightarrow \pi\text{-}C_5H_5MCOL + CO$$

M	L	k, $M^{-1}\,sec^{-1}$
Co	$P(C_6H_5)_3$	3.1×10^{-5} [a]
Rh	$P(C_6H_5)_3$	3.0×10^{-4}
Ir	$P(C_6H_5)_3$	1.4×10^{-5} [a]
Rh	$P(C_2H_5)_3$	8.0×10^{-3}
Rh	$P(C_2H_5)_2C_6H_5$	4.3×10^{-3} [b]
Rh	$P(C_4H_9)_3$	3.3×10^{-3}
Rh	$P(p\text{-}CH_3OC_6H_4)_3$	5.6×10^{-4}
Rh	$P(OCH_2)_3CCH_3$	5.6×10^{-4}
Rh	$P(OC_4H_9)_3$	3.8×10^{-4} [c]
Rh	$P(C_6H_{11})_3$	7.7×10^{-5}
Rh	$P(OC_6H_5)_3$	7.3×10^{-5}
Rh	C_5H_5N	very slow
Rh	$As(C_6H_5)_3$	very slow

From reference 100.

[a] Assumed to be second order like rhodium.

[b] $\Delta H^\ddagger = 15$ kcal/mole, $\Delta S^\ddagger = -20$ eu. In tetrahydrofuran $k = 2.5 \times 10^{-3}$, $\Delta H^\ddagger = 13$, $\Delta S^\ddagger = -28$.

[c] $\Delta H^\ddagger = 18$, $\Delta S^\ddagger = -16$. In tetrahydrofuran $k = 2.2 \times 10^{-4}$, $\Delta H^\ddagger = 16$, $\Delta S^\ddagger = -23$.

collected in Table 7.14. The rates of reaction for the rhodium compound are second order, and the order of nucleophilic strength of different reagents is the same as that found for the nitrosyl carbonyls and, as far as the data go, the same as that for Pt(II) complexes. Thus rhodium in this substrate is a class (b) or soft metal, and the important feature of a good reagent is that it be highly polarizable or soft.

Steric factors seem to be less important in the reaction of the nitrosyl carbonyl compounds described above than in $\pi\text{-}C_5H_5Rh(CO)_2$, perhaps because of the size of the $\pi\text{-}C_5H_5$ group. This is shown by the low reactivity of the large nucleophile $P(C_6H_{11})_3$. That the $\pi\text{-}C_5H_5$ group, like NO, can make available a low-energy vacant orbital for nucleophilic attack was shown by equation 36. Finally, it is of interest to note that once again the enthalpies of activation are low, the entropies of activation are negative, and the rates of reaction of $\pi\text{-}C_5H_5M(CO)_2$ vary in the order Co < Rh > Ir. The order of reactivity for this triad parallels that for $M(CO)_6$,

$$Cr < Mo > W.$$

Cramer[122] has made the interesting discovery that ethylene in $\pi\text{-}C_5H_5Rh(C_2H_4)_2$ rotates with the coordination bond as its axis, with an energy barrier of 6 kcal. This can happen because the usual bonding shown by structure XVII for a π-C_2H_4 complex may also be achieved by making use of the filled d_{xy} metal orbital in the xy plane of a square planar complex. Such bonding would bring the C_2H_4 group into the xy plane, forming the transient structure XVIII, and providing a low-energy process for the rotation of coordinated π-C_2H_4 around the bond axis.

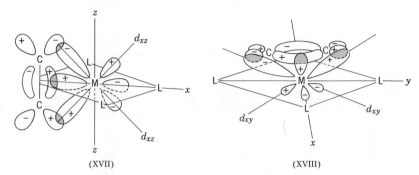

(XVII)   (XVIII)

Of interest to our present discussion is the experiment that was done in order to rule out an intermolecular process for rotation. This was accomplished by showing that there is no exchange between coordinated C_2H_4 in π-$C_5H_5Rh(C_2H_4)_2$ and C_2D_4 during 5 hr at 100°C, conditions far more rigorous than those required for the intramolecular rotation of the coordinated C_2H_4. These conditions are also far more rigorous than those required for the substitution reactions of π-$C_5H_5Rh(CO)_2$ and for its CO exchange. This means either that C_2H_4 is not as good a nucleophile as are the reagents used with the dicarbonyl or, more likely, that the C_2H_4 groups in π-$C_5H_5Rh(C_2H_4)_2$ offer more steric resistance to nucleophilic attack on rhodium than do the CO's in the dicarbonyl. It was also noted by means of n.m.r. techniques that the exchange of C_2H_4 with $Rh(acac)(C_2H_4)_2$ has an average lifetime of less than 10^{-4} sec at 25°. The rate of exchange is second order, being first order in the ethylene concentration. Since $Rh(acac)(C_2H_4)_2$ is a normal square planar d^8 system, such a result is expected. The mechanism would be an S_N2 displacement process. The π-$C_5H_5Rh(C_2H_4)_2$ is formally a d^{10} system and has one less vacant metal orbital available for adding a nucleophile.

The rates of reaction of (arene)$Mo(CO)_3$ with different reagents to yield cis-$MoL_3(CO)_3$ have been determined,[123] and some of the data are given in Table 7.15. The results can be summarized as follows: (1) the rates of reaction are second order, being first order in both the concentrations of the metal carbonyl and of the entering ligands; (2) the rates of reaction decrease for changes in arene in the order toluene $\simeq$ p-xylene > mesitylene; (3) the rates of reaction decrease for changes in reagent in the order $P(n\text{-}C_4H_9)_3 \gg PCl_2C_6H_5 > PCl_3$; and (4) the rates of reaction are about the same in the solvents n-heptane, chloroform, and s-tetrachloro-ethane.

Table 7.15 Rates of reaction of (arene)Mo(CO)$_3$ to form cis-MoL$_3$(CO)$_3$ in n-heptane solution at 25°C

Arene	L	$10^4 k, M^{-1} \sec^{-1}$
Mesitylene	PCl$_3$	1.4[a]
Mesitylene	PCl$_3$	3.2[b]
Mesitylene	PCl$_3$	2.5[c]
Mesitylene	PCl$_2$(C$_6$H$_5$)	2.8
Mesitylene	P(n-C$_4$H$_9$)$_3$	67
p-Xylene	PCl$_3$	4.2[d]
p-Xylene	PCl$_2$(C$_6$H$_5$)	8.3
p-Xylene	P(n-C$_4$H$_9$)$_3$	500
Toluene	PCl$_3$	3.2[e]
Toluene	PCl$_2$(C$_6$H$_5$)	8.4
Toluene	P(n-C$_4$H$_9$)$_3$	520

From reference 123.
[a] $\Delta H^{\ddagger} = 17$ kcal/mole, $\Delta S^{\ddagger} = -20$ eu.
[b] Chloroform solution.
[c] s-Tetrachloroethane solution.
[d] $\Delta H^{\ddagger} = 15$ kcal/mole; $\Delta S^{\ddagger} = -24$ eu.
[e] $\Delta H^{\ddagger} = 16$ kcal/mole; $\Delta S^{\ddagger} = -21$ eu.

That the rates of reaction are second order is consistent with the observations on the rates of arene exchange in these systems (p. 558). Also the mesitylene compound is the slowest to react in accord with the arene exchange studies. The striking difference is that exchange is very slow and requires temperatures of 100° or higher, whereas substitution reactions take place readily at room temperature. This means the phosphorus ligands used are much better reagents towards these substrates than are the arenes. That P(n-C$_4$H$_9$)$_3$ is a much better nucleophile than is PCl$_3$ is in agreement with the order of nucleophilic strength described above.

The reaction mechanism favored for the formation of cis-MoL$_3$(CO)$_3$ is shown in Fig. 7.11. There is some evidence[124] for the existence at low temperature of (arene)W(CO)$_5$ which is analogous to the postulated reactive intermediate (arene)MoL$_2$(CO)$_3$. In an alternative process there is a bimolecular displacement of arene to form MoL(CO)$_3$, which then reacts rapidly to form cis-MoL$_3$(CO)$_3$.

The Insertion or Ligand Migration Reaction

A large number of reactions with certain common features have been recognized for organometallic compounds and have been called *insertion reactions*.[125] The insertion reaction, in this sense, is the addition of the

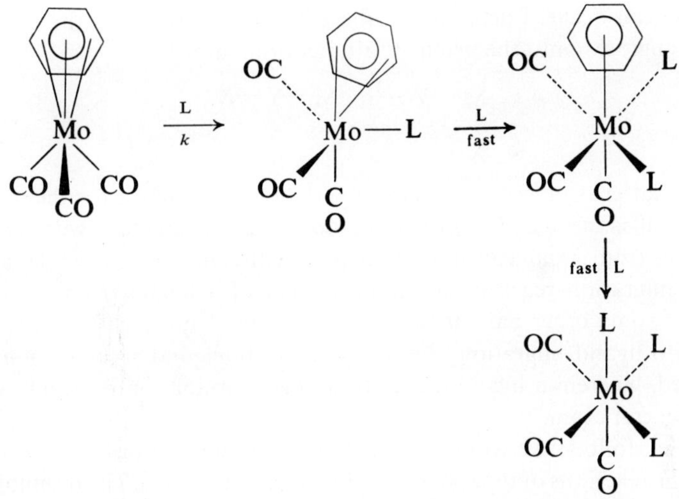

Fig. 7.11 Mechanism proposed for the reaction of (arene)Mo(CO)$_3$ to form *cis*-MoL$_3$(CO)$_3$.

organometallic, M—X, to an unsaturated molecule, :Y, to form a new complex with Y inserted between M and X.

$$M—X + :Y \rightarrow M—Y—X \qquad (40)$$

The molecule :Y may be CO, $\overset{\diagdown}{\underset{\diagup}{C}}=\overset{\diagup}{\underset{\diagdown}{C}}$, diene, acetylene, RCHO, RCN,

SO$_2$, O$_2$, or other unsaturated systems. The ligand X may be H$^-$, R$^-$, OR$^-$, NR$_2^-$ or NR$_3$, OH$^-$ or H$_2$O, halide ion, or another metal atom.

The name "insertion reaction," while describing accurately the overall result, may be mechanistically misleading. The label has been used for a long time to describe processes such as the reactions of oxygen or sulfur atoms, or methylene, CH$_2$, with C—H bonds:

$$\overset{\diagdown}{\underset{\diagup}{C}}—H + O \rightarrow \overset{\diagdown}{\underset{\diagup}{C}}—OH \qquad (41)$$

$$\overset{\diagdown}{\underset{\diagup}{C}}—H + :CH_2 \rightarrow \overset{\diagdown}{\underset{\diagup}{C}}—CH_3 \qquad (42)$$

These reactions are essentially of a free radical nature and probably occur by a collision of the two reactants, with insertion of the free atom between the C-H bond in a single activated process.[126] As we shall show, there is evidence that the group :Y must coordinate to the metal M before reaction can occur. Furthermore, there is evidence that it is the group X which migrates onto the group Y after coordination:

$$M{-}Y \longrightarrow M{-}Y{-}X \tag{43}$$

If the latter is indeed what happens, than a better name for the general reaction 40 is the *ligand migration reaction*. This is by analogy with familiar examples from organic chemistry such as methyl migration. We define the ligand migration reaction as the movement of a ligand from the metal atom to some other part of the same complex. Thus it will usually be a ligand to ligand migration. Simple isomerizations and racemizations are excluded, wherein a ligand moves to a new coordination position on the same central atom.

In what follows we will make the implicit assumption that most, if not all, of the reactions of type 40 follow the same mechanism. The resemblance of many of these reactions to each other and the possibility that they may have the same mechanism have been stressed by Halpern.[127] It must be borne in mind, however, that a variety of mechanisms may be operating.

The first convincing, and by now the most studied, example of reaction 40 is the so-called carbon monoxide insertion reaction. In 1957 Coffield and his co-workers showed that alkylmanganese pentacarbonyls will absorb CO reversibly to form acylmanganese pentacarbonyls:[128]

$$CH_3Mn(CO)_5 + {}^*CO \rightarrow CH_3COMn({}^*CO)_5 \tag{44}$$

It was further shown that if radioactive *CO is used, a coordinated, inactive CO is inserted rather than the incoming CO. In keeping with this observation it is also possible to use other ligands, L, such as amines[129] and phosphines[130,131] to cause the insertion reaction:

$$CH_3Mn(CO)_5 + L \rightarrow CH_3COMn(CO)_4L \tag{45}$$

In several non-hydroxylic solvents, such as tetrahydrofuran, the kinetics of reaction 44 have been studied and found to be first order in $CH_3Mn(CO)_5$ and first order in CO.[132] This suggests a nucleophilic attack by CO on the complex, accompanied by a rearrangement

$$CH_3Mn(CO)_5 + {}^*CO \rightarrow \underset{\substack{\\ H_3C}}{\overset{\substack{O \\ \| \\ C}}{\vdots}}Mn(CO)_4 \rightarrow \text{product} \tag{46}$$

$$^*CO$$

The stereochemistry of the labeled *CO with respect to the acetyl group is not known.

More extensive studies using a variety of nucleophiles show quite a different reaction mechanism to be important.[130] The kinetics of reaction 45 were determined as a function of the nature and concentration of L, using several different L's in various polar solvents. With L in considerable

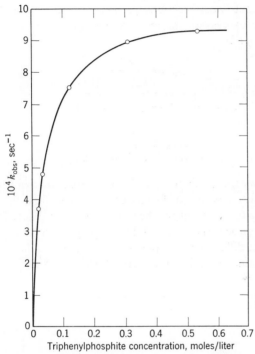

Fig. 7.12 Plot of the observed rate constant vs. phosphite concentration for the reaction of $CH_3Mn(CO)_5$ with triphenylphosphite in tetrahydrofuran.

excess over $CH_3Mn(CO)_5$ so that pseudo-first-order behavior was followed, the variation of the pseudo-first-order constant, k_{obs}, with the concentration of L in all cases followed the general pattern shown in Fig. 7.12.

At low values of [L] the order with respect to L appeared to be one. At high concentrations, the rate leveled off and k_{obs} became independent of [L]. Such a result can be explained by a two-stage mechanism which may be written as follows:

$$M \underset{k_{-1}}{\overset{k_1}{\rightleftharpoons}} M(S) \underset{k_{-2}}{\overset{k_2}{\rightleftharpoons}} ML \qquad (47)$$

The starting complex is designated as M, M(S) is a reactive intermediate, which may be solvated, and ML is the final product.

The steady state approximation may now be used for the concentration of M(S). This yields the rate equation

$$\text{Rate} = \frac{d[ML]}{dt} = k_2[L]\frac{k_1[M] + k_{-2}[ML]}{k_{-1} + k_2[L]} - k_{-2}[ML] \qquad (48)$$

It is assumed that only the rate step given by k_2 depends on the concentration of L. Since most reactions go well to completion, k_{-2} may be ignored and the expression for the observed first-order rate constant is given by the equation

$$k_{obs} = \frac{k_1 k_2[L]}{k_{-1} + k_2[L]} \qquad (49)$$

The test of this equation is the reciprocal plot.

$$\frac{1}{k_{obs}} = \frac{k_{-1}}{k_1 k_2}\left(\frac{1}{[L]}\right) + \frac{1}{k_1} \qquad (50)$$

Figure 7.13 shows $1/k_{obs}$ versus $1/[L]$ for the data shown in Fig. 7.12. The linearity confirms equation 50. The slope is $k_{-1}/k_1 k_2$, and the intercept is $1/k_1$. Since k_1 is a function only of the $CH_3Mn(CO)_5$ and not of L, a further test of the reaction sequence is possible. Keeping the solvent constant, we can use and treat different nucleophiles as in Fig. 7.13. The same value of k_1 should be found for all. Table 7.16 shows that this is so for three

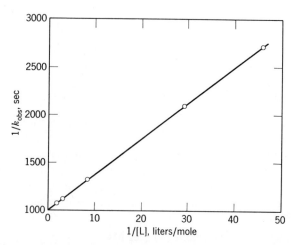

Fig. 7.13 Plot of the reciprocal of observed rate constant vs. the reciprocal of phosphite concentration for the reaction of $CH_3Mn(CO)_5$ with triphenylphosphite in tetrahydrofuran.

different L's in the solvent tetrahydrofuran. Also the ratio of rate constants k_{-1}/k_2 is given. This is an inverse measure of the relative reactivity of L for the reactive intermediate M(S).

Since the solubility of CO is small, it is quite possible that the second-order kinetics found for this reagent[132] also are given by equation 48 with $k_{-1} \gg k_2[L]$. That is, CO may be on the initial linear portion of a curve such as Fig. 7.12. This assumption of a common mechanism seems more plausible than the alternative that CO is a much better nucleophile than

Table 7.16   Rate constants for the reaction

$$L + CH_3Mn(CO)_5 \rightarrow CH_3COMn(CO)_4L$$

in tetrahydrofuran at 25.5°C

L	k_1, sec^{-1}	k_{-1}/k_2, M
cyclo-$C_6H_{11}NH_2$	9.8×10^{-4}	$\sim 3 \times 10^{-3}$
$(C_6H_5)_3P$	9.0×10^{-4}	5.1×10^{-3}
$(C_6H_5O)_3P$	9.9×10^{-4}	3.6×10^{-2}

From reference 130.

the others used.** A test can be made of the two explanations by studying the kinetics of CO at high pressures to see whether the same limiting rate is reached as for other nucleophiles.

The intermediate M(S) may reasonably be considered to be the acetyl complex, which either is five-coordinated or has a solvent molecule in the sixth coordination position. Thus the mechanism becomes

$$CH_3Mn(CO)_5 \underset{(S)}{\overset{(S)}{\rightleftharpoons}} CH_3COMn(CO)_4(S) \underset{L}{\overset{L}{\rightleftharpoons}} CH_3COMn(CO)L + (S) \quad (51)$$

Support for this intermediate comes from a study[131] of the rate of the reaction

$$CH_3COMn(CO)_5 + (C_6H_5)_3P \rightarrow CH_3COMn(CO)_4P(C_6H_5)_3 + CO \quad (52)$$

The rate is independent of the concentration of the phosphine. Furthermore the rate constant for 52 is the same as the first-order rate constant in the decarbonylation reaction, which is the reverse of reaction 44:

$$CH_3COMn(CO)_5 \rightarrow CH_3Mn(CO)_5 + CO \quad (53)$$

** It has been found that iodide ion reacts with $CH_3Mn(CO)_5$ at a rate exceeding that of the limiting value k_1. The rate also increases with [I$^-$] [F. Calderazzo and K. Noack, *J. Organomet. Chem.*, **4**, 250 (1965)].

This identity of rates, in the same solvent, strongly suggests that the loss of a coordinated CO molecule is rate determining for both reactions:

$$CH_3COMn(CO)_5 \xrightarrow{(S)} CH_3COMn(CO)_4(S) + CO \qquad (54)$$

The intermediate is the same as that of reaction 51. In the presence of excess phosphine it reacts to form $CH_3COMn(CO)_4P(C_6H_5)_3$. In the absence of a suitable ligand it rearranges to form $CH_3Mn(CO)_5$.

Some information on the role of the solvent in the insertion reaction may be obtained by studying the rate in various solvents of different

Table 7.17 Rate constants for the formation of the intermediate $CH_3COMn(CO_4)S$ in different solvents at 25.5°C

Solvent	$k, M^{-1} sec^{-1}$ [a]	Dielectric Constant
Dimethylformamide	$>1.0 \times 10^{-3}$	27
Methanol	2.6×10^{-4}	32
Bis(β-methoxyethyl)ether	1.6×10^{-4}	...
Nitromethane	8.9×10^{-5}	37
Tetrahydrofuran	7.9×10^{-5}	7.7
Bis(β-ethoxyethyl)ether	6.6×10^{-5}	5.7
Mesitylene	3.0×10^{-7}	2.2
n-Hexane	$<10^{-7}$	1.9
Cyclohexylamine	1.1×10^{-4} [b]	...
Cyclohexylamine	2.7×10^{-5} [c]	...

[a] Values of k_1 divided by molar concentration of solvent.
[b] Second-order rate constant in mesitylene.
[c] Second-order rate constant in n-hexane.

coordinating powers.[130] While it is not practicable to carry out the reaction in the gas phase, inert solvents such as n-hexane and mesitylene may be used. In these solvents the reactions become second order, being first order in the concentration of L. Also, in general, the rates increase in more polar solvents.[130,132] This suggests that the solvent does play an active role, and, if the solvent is non-coordinating, the nucleophile necessarily takes up its part.

Table 7.17 shows the limiting rate constant, k_1, reached in a number of solvents of varying polarity and coordinating ability. Actually the first-order constants have been divided by the concentration of the solvent in order to get a set of second-order rate constants. In this way they may be compared with some second-order constants found in inert solvents. The spread of values is moderate, about 10^4. This may be only a manifestation of a simple stabilization of a polar transition state by the more polar solvents. However, in well defined cases of very polar transition states, the effect on rate constants is surprisingly small in changing the solvent over a wide range.[133]

It is tempting to speculate that the mechanism is a solvent-assisted migration, similar to that postulated for many substitution reactions of octahedral complexes (Chapter 3). This would allow for a modest variation of the rate with the properties of the solvent. On the other hand, the substitution reactions of the manganese pentacarbonyl halides go faster in non-polar solvents (p. 565) than in polar ones:

$$Mn(CO)_5X + L \rightarrow Mn(CO)_4LX + CO \qquad (55)$$

Since an S_N1 mechanism is postulated, a five-coordinated intermediate is believed to be formed, $Mn(CO)_4X$. This does not seem to be strongly stabilized by the solvent, whereas the similar $CH_3COMn(CO)_4$ does seem to be stabilized. The reason for the difference is not clear. In any event, if solvent stabilization does involve coordination to the metal, the interaction is a weak one since no solvated intermediate or product can be detected.

The next question is to consider the stereochemistry of the transition state and of the final products in detail. Both *cis* and *trans* products, $CH_3COMn(CO)_4L$, have been identified, depending on the nature of L. However, this is not too informative since the starting material $CH_3Mn(CO)_5$ does not have sufficient stereochemical identification. The important question to be answered is whether it is a CO ligand that moves and "inserts" itself between the methyl group and the manganese, or whether a methyl group migrates from the manganese to a carbonyl group. A third possibility is that both the CO and CH_3 groups move in a cooperative manner.

Figure 7.14 shows that the question of which group moves is a meaningful one in the sense that it has an experimentally accessible answer. The figure illustrates the reverse of the CO insertion reaction, the decarbonylation reaction. By the principle of microscopic reversibility, it can be used to discuss forward and reverse reactions equally. It is necessary to use a substituted complex, *trans*-$CH_3COMn(CO)_4Z$, in order to possess a stereochemical marker. The assumption is made that this group remains fixed during the decarbonylation reaction.

The figure shows that movement of a CO group, reverse of insertion, would form *trans*-$CH_3Mn(CO)_4Z$, whereas methyl migration would form *cis*-$CH_3Mn(CO)_4Z$. The experimental observation is that

$$cis\text{-}CH_3Mn(CO)_4P(C_6H_5)_3$$

is formed by heating *trans*-$CH_3COMn(CO)_4P(C_6H_5)_3$.[134] This strongly indicates that methyl migration has occurred. However, other possibilities

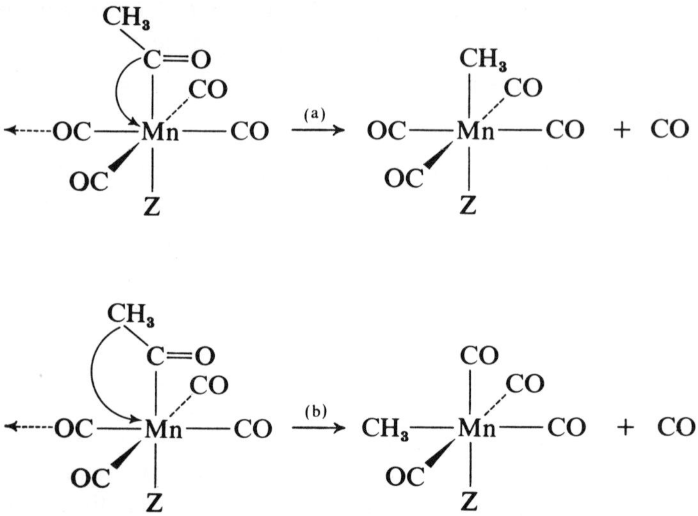

Fig. 7.14 Decarbonylation of *trans*-$CH_3COMn(CO)_4Z$: (a) by reverse of insertion, (b) by methyl migration.

exist. For example, it may be that *trans*-$CH_3Mn(CO)_4P(C_6H_5)_3$, which is unknown, is formed first and rapidly rearranges to the *cis* isomer. Also it is known[248] that *cis* and *trans*-$CH_3COMn(CO)_4P(C_6H_5)_3$ equilibrate in solution in times comparable to that needed for decarbonylation.

However, the simplest explanation is that methyl migration has occurred. Furthermore, a consideration of energetics suggests that this must be an easier path than CO insertion, since the CH_3 group is freer in the latter case, that is, less bonded in the transition state. In addition, alkyl migrations are well known in organic chemistry.

There is evidence that alkyl groups migrate rather extensively in some attempted insertion reactions. Thus $C_5H_5Mo(CO)_3C_2H_5$ reacts to give $[C_2H_5C_5H_4Mo(CO)_3]_2$ under insertion conditions.[135] The ethyl group has moved to the cyclopentadienyl ring. The alkyl group is not very free during the migration process since it has been shown that an optically active alkyl group, $\cdot$*R, in the insertion reaction of *RMn(CO)_5 gives a product *RCOMn(CO)_5 with essentially complete retention of activity and configuration.[136]

The rate of migration of various alkyl groups falls off in the order[137] $CH_3CH_2CH_2 \sim CH_3CH_2 > C_6H_5 > CH_3 > C_6H_5CH_2 \sim CF_3$. Thus the most stable carbanions, CF_3^- and $C_6H_5CH_2^-$, correspond to the groups that migrate most slowly. This may simply mean stronger metal-carbon bonding in these cases. If the alkyl group is never free, the question of whether it moves as a carbanion, a free radical, or a carbonium ion may not be a meaningful one. Any of these may be considered as a ligand in the compounds under consideration.

In the following sections we will discuss the probable mechanisms of other examples of the insertion reaction. It will be of interest to see whether the mechanism proposed for $CH_3Mn(CO)_5$ can be applied to other cases, particularly if the ligand X in reaction 40 is the moving group, rather than the unsaturated group :Y. Of course methylmanganese pentacarbonyl is a special case in that we start with :Y already coordinated. There is ample evidence in other CO insertion reactions that CO need not start out coordinated. Thus we have the examples[138,139]

$$RPtBr(PR_3)_2 + CO \rightarrow RCOPtBr(PR_3)_2 \qquad (56)$$

$$Hg(OAc)(OCH_3) + CO \rightarrow Hg(OAc)(COOCH_3) \qquad (57)$$

In reaction 57 a methoxide ion takes the role of R^- in the earlier cases.

In both 56 and 57 it is certainly possible, and seems almost inevitable, that coordination of CO occurs before migration of the ligand completes the reaction. The extremely rapid reactions at very low temperature ($-50°C$) of SO_2 with a number of organometallics, e.g.,[140]

$$C_5H_5Fe(CO)_2R + SO_2 \rightarrow C_5H_5Fe(CO)_2SO_2R \qquad (58)$$

are of interest in that SO_2 insertion occurs rather than CO insertion even though CO is already coordinated. In the case of π-C_5H_5 as a ligand, we can readily imagine that the central metal can rapidly coordinate SO_2 by expanding its coordination number. Alternatively, SO_2 can act as a nucleophile forcing the formation of $C_5H_5Fe(COR)(CO)(SO_2)$, which then rearranges to the final product.

The Oxo Reaction

A most important example of homogeneous catalysis is the so-called oxo or hydroformylation reaction.[141] The system, composed of cobalt salts, carbon monoxide, molecular hydrogen, and organic substrate, undergoes a variety of reactions in the liquid state. Some examples are

Hydroformylation $\quad \diagdown C = C \diagup + CO + H_2 \rightarrow \diagdown CH - \underset{\displaystyle |}{C} - \overset{\displaystyle H}{\underset{\displaystyle |}{C}} = O \qquad$ (59a)

Hydrogenation $\quad \diagdown C = C \diagup + H_2 \rightarrow \diagdown CH - CH \diagup \qquad$ (59b)

Homologation $\quad -CH_2OH + CO + 2H_2 \rightarrow -CH_2 - CH_2OH + H_2O$

$\hfill$ (59c)

Hydrogenolysis $\quad R_2CHOH + H_2 \rightarrow R_2CH_2 + H_2O \qquad$ (59d)

Temperatures are 90–200°C and pressures from 100 to 400 atms. It has been shown that dicobalt octacarbonyl and cobalt hydrocarbonyl are formed under the reaction conditions.[142] Furthermore, cobalt hydrocarbonyl plus the organic substrate will, at room temperature and pressure, give the same products as are formed in the oxo reaction. Hence it seems reasonably sure that $HCo(CO)_4$ is the active agent to consider in some of the reactions that occur.

This interesting substance was first prepared by Coleman and Blanchard.[143] It is an unstable liquid which decomposes according to the equation

$$2HCo(CO)_4 \rightarrow H_2 + Co_2(CO)_8 \tag{60}$$

The assumption is that formation of the hydrocarbonyl in the liquid state occurs by the reversal of 60. The anion, $Co(CO)_4^-$, is stable.

Dicobalt octacarbonyl has the bridge structure IV, evidence being presented for two kinds of CO groupings, a carbonyl type and a CO type. Since five of the coordination positions of cobalt are occupied by CO groups, the sixth position is still free, though the orbital corresponding to it contains a single electron. The two cobalt atoms are then close enough to couple the spins of the two electrons forming a metal-metal bond. It is this bond which would probably first be broken in forming $HCo(CO)_4$, a homolytic split of H_2 occurring.

In aqueous solution $HCo(CO)_4$ is a strong acid, being completely ionized in a saturated solution, 0.056 M.[144] In view of this it is remarkable that n.m.r. studies[145] show that the proton signal occurs at such a frequency as to indicate a hydride ion-like environment. The structure has not been completely determined, but by analogy with similar hydrides the hydrogen atom takes the role of a normal ligand. Thus the geometry is probably a distorted trigonal bipyramid with the hydrogen atom at one of the apical positions.

A kinetic study of the oxo reaction proper, which is the hydroformylation reaction, shows that it is first order in olefin and approximately first order in the amount of cobalt present.[146] The rate rises with increasing hydrogen pressure and falls with increasing CO pressure.[147] The reaction rate is virtually independent of the nature of the solvent, is faster for terminal olefins than for internal olefins, and is slowed down by chain branching in the olefin.[148] Olefins can be isomerized by the conditions of the oxo reaction.[149]

Because of the overall complexity of the oxo reaction, the mechanism is best approached by simpler studies of probable individual steps. For example, it is known[150] that alkylcobalt tetracarbonyls undergo the insertion reaction in a completely analogous fashion to alkylmanganese pentacarbonyls, except that the reaction is very much faster and is readily reversible.

$$RCo(CO)_4 + CO \rightleftharpoons RCOCo(CO)_4 \tag{61}$$

Because of the rapidity of this reaction, no detailed kinetic studies have been made, but it is likely that the mechanism is the same as for the manganese case.

As expected, other nucleophiles may be used to convert alkyl to acetyl derivatives:[151]

$$RCo(CO)_4 + PR_3 \rightarrow RCOCo(CO)_3PR_3 \tag{62}$$

Again the kinetics have not been studied. However, a study has been made of a closely related reaction,[152]

$$RCOCo(CO)_4 + PR_3 \rightarrow RCOCo(CO)_3PR_3 + CO \tag{63}$$

The rate is found to be first order and independent of the phosphine concentration (Table 7.10). This suggests a dissociation mechanism

$$RCOCo(CO)_4 \underset{k_{-1}}{\overset{k_1}{\rightleftharpoons}} RCOCo(CO)_3 + CO \tag{64}$$

$$RCOCo(CO)_3 + PR_3 \xrightarrow{k_2} RCOCo(CO)_3PR_3 \tag{65}$$

The steady state solution yields the rate equation

$$\text{Rate} = k_1[RCOCo(CO)_4] \frac{k_2[PR_3]}{k_{-1}[CO] + k_2[PR_3]} \tag{66}$$

The rate becomes first order when [CO] is small compared to [PR$_3$]. There is a prediction of inhibition of the rate at high CO concentrations. This has not been tested for the phosphine reaction, but inhibition is known for the reaction of acylcobalt tetracarbonyls with HCo(CO)$_4$, hydrogen, olefins, dienes, and acetylenes.[153] Thus the dissociation 64 is indicated for all of these reactions.

An interesting observation[108] is that the crotonyl complex reacts 62 times more rapidly than the acetyl complex. The double bond greatly facilitates the formation of the four-coordinated intermediate. The nature of the stabilization is indicated by the fact that the crotyl complex exists as an equilibrium mixture of two forms. The second form is a π-allyl complex formed by loss of CO (see equation 33). We may conclude that, in reactions in which a ligand is lost, stabilization by an external force such as the remote double bond or a solvent molecule can indeed be a factor, but not an overwhelming one.

We next consider the part which the olefin plays in hydroformylation. It is known that the insertion reaction occurs readily with cobalt hydrocarbonyl and olefins.[153]

$$HCo(CO)_4 + C_2H_4 \rightarrow C_2H_5Co(CO)_4. \tag{67}$$

The product is a normal, σ-bonded alkyl group. The further insertion reaction with alkylcobalt tetracarbonyl is slow and incomplete.

$$RCo(CO)_4 + C_2H_4 \overset{slow}{\rightleftharpoons} RCH_2CH_2Co(CO)_4 \tag{68}$$

If 1-pentene is used as the olefin, a mixture of 1- and 2-pentylcobalt tetracarbonyl is produced. Both the insertion reaction and the isomerization are inhibited by 1 atm pressure of CO, with 1-pentene as the solvent.

The inhibition agrees with a reversible dissociation mechanism with a coordinatively unsaturated tricarbonyl as an active intermediate.[153]

$$HCo(CO)_4 \rightleftharpoons HCo(CO)_3 + CO \tag{69}$$

The coordinative unsaturation allows the addition of olefin, presumably as a π-complex. This then undergoes a hydride ion migration reaction to give the alkyl derivative. Pickup of a CO molecule completes the process.

$$HCo(CO)_3 + C_2H_4 \rightleftharpoons HCo(CO)_3(C_2H_4) \tag{70}$$

$$HCo(CO)_3(C_2H_4) \rightarrow C_2H_5Co(CO)_3 \tag{71}$$

$$C_2H_5Co(CO)_3 + CO \rightarrow C_2H_5Co(CO)_4 \tag{72}$$

Another possibility is that the CO insertion reaction has occurred.

$$HCo(CO)_4 \rightarrow HCOCo(CO)_3 \tag{73}$$

Again an unsaturated species is formed which allows coordination of an olefin molecule. The inhibiting effect of CO could now arise from the reversible equilibrium

$$HCOCo(CO)_3(C_2H_4) \rightleftharpoons HCo(CO)_3(C_2H_4) + CO \tag{74}$$

It is also possible that inhibition by CO results from an equilibrium such as

$$HCo(CO)_3(C_2H_4) + CO \rightleftharpoons HCo(CO)_4 + C_2H_4 \tag{75}$$

Although the details are not known with any certainty, the important step is that of reaction 71. Here a hydride migration leads to an apparent ethylene insertion process. This migration step may be represented in more detail as follows:

Again the solvent may play a role in inducing the migration of hydride or in stabilizing the intermediate, which is shown as four coordinated. Although the intermediate geometries are not known, it is predicted that there is a *cis* addition to the double bond.

The formation of an alkylcobalt tetracarbonyl is followed by a CO insertion reaction, equation 61, under oxo conditions. The mechanism of reduction of the acyl carbonyl compound to aldehyde is not very well known. It may be H_2 or $HCo(CO)_4$ which functions as the reducing agent.[154] It is known that H_2 is a reducing agent without first forming $HCo(CO)_4$.[249] A very pertinent observation is that of Breslow and Heck,[150] who showed that while H_2 will reduce $CH_3COCo(CO)_4$ the reduction is completely inhibited by a high CO pressure. This suggests that it is $CH_3COCo(CO)_3$ which is being reduced.

$$CH_3COCo(CO)_4 \rightleftharpoons CH_3COCo(CO)_3 + CO \qquad (76)$$

The unsaturated species could react with H_2,

$$CH_3COCo(CO)_3 + H_2 \rightarrow CH_3CHOCoH(CO)_3 \rightarrow$$

$$CH_3CHO + HCo(CO)_3 \quad (77)$$

or with hydrocarbonyl,

$$CH_3COCo(CO)_3 + HCo(CO)_4 \rightarrow CH_3CHO + Co_2(CO)_7 \qquad (78)$$

The species $Co_2(CO)_7$ would regenerate $Co_2(CO)_8$ and eventually $HCo(CO)_4$.

Acetaldehyde and other aldehydes, being unsaturated, could also complex with the species $HCo(CO)_3$. This opens a path for their further reduction to alcohols. The original coordination may be as a π-complex. However, hydride ion migration could go to either the carbon or the oxygen end:

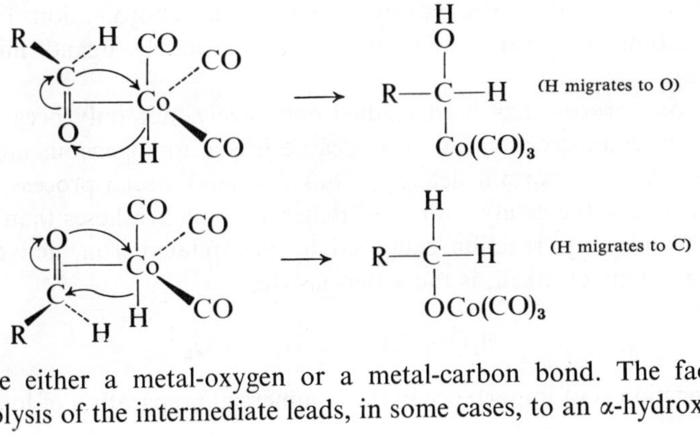

to give either a metal-oxygen or a metal-carbon bond. The fact that alcoholysis of the intermediate leads, in some cases, to an α-hydroxy ester suggests the formation of a metal-carbon bond.[155] An insertion reaction with CO occurs first.

$$RCHOHCo(CO)_4 + CO \rightarrow RCHOHCOCo(CO)_4 \qquad (79)$$

$$RCHOHCOCo(CO)_4 + R'OH \rightarrow RCHOHCOOR' + HCo(CO)_4 \qquad (80)$$

The reduction of propionaldehyde with hydrogen to propyl alcohol, using $Co_2(CO)_8$ catalyst, has been studied kinetically in toluene solution.[156] The rate law at 150°C is found to be

$$Rate = k[CH_3CH_2CHO][Co][H_2][CO]^{-2} \qquad (81)$$

where [Co] is the total cobalt concentration. The strong inhibition by CO is explained not only by the dissociation reaction to form $HCo(CO)_3$, but also by the requirement of coordinative unsaturation before H_2 can react.

$$HCo(CO)_4 \rightleftharpoons HCo(CO)_3 + CO \qquad (82)$$

$$HCo(CO)_3 + RCHO \rightleftharpoons RCHOHCo(CO)_3 \qquad (83)$$

$$RCHOHCo(CO)_3 + H_2 \rightarrow RCH_2OH + HCo(CO)_3 \qquad (84)$$

$$RCHOHCo(CO)_3 + CO \rightleftharpoons RCHOHCo(CO)_4 \qquad (85)$$

The species $RCHOHCo(CO)_4$ is assumed to be non-reactive towards H_2 or $HCo(CO)_4$. A similar mechanism has been proposed to account for the formation of hydrocarbons in the oxo process (reaction 59d).[157]

Although each of these studies is incomplete and involves much speculation, they can be put together to form a reasonable mechanism for the oxo reaction. The sequence is essentially that suggested by Breslow and Heck.[150] The important features are that coordinatively unsaturated, or solvated, species must be formed to coordinate unsaturated organic substrates. Reaction then proceeds by a series of such coordinations followed by insertion reactions, which are in fact probably ligand migration reactions.

The oxo process has been studied extensively, not only because it is important commercially, but also because it is a homogeneous model for the even more important heterogeneous Fischer-Tropsch process.[158] Iron is a more versatile catalyst for the Fischer-Tropsch syntheses than cobalt. For example, one reaction catalyzed by precipitated iron, activated by small amounts of alkali, is the water-gas shift

$$H_2O + CO \xrightarrow{Fe} H_2 + CO_2 \qquad (86)$$

This reaction is of importance in the commercial preparation of hydrogen.

A homogeneous model for the water-gas shift involves the use of iron pentacarbonyl as a catalyst.[159] When $Fe(CO)_5$ is treated with an aqueous solution of NaOH, the following reaction occurs:[160]

$$Fe(CO)_5 + 3NaOH \rightarrow NaHFe(CO)_4 + Na_2CO_3 + H_2O \qquad (87)$$

Thus the anion $HFe(CO)_4^-$ of iron hydrocarbonyl, $H_2Fe(CO)_4$, is formed. In stronger alkali $Fe(CO)_4^{2-}$ would be produced.[160] At high CO pressures an aqueous solution containing $HFe(CO)_4^-$ can catalyze the reaction of water and CO to form hydrogen and carbon dioxide, the water-gas shift reaction.

It has been shown that a dimer is formed from $HFe(CO)_4^-$, which can then lose hydrogen as molecular hydrogen:[161]

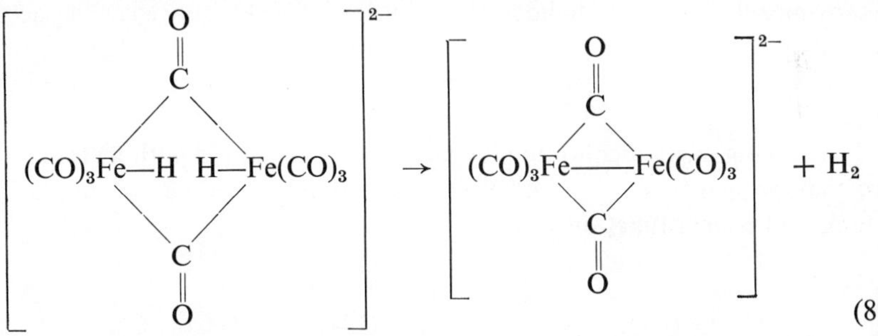

$$(88)$$

The anion $Fe_2(CO)_8^{2-}$ is presumably the species which can then split water and, in the presence of CO, regenerate the anion $H_2Fe_2(CO)_8^{2-}$. The analogy between these bridged species of iron and the cobalt compounds involved in the oxo reaction is striking. As might be expected, these iron compounds can also catalyze the oxo reaction.[161] However, the usual product, instead of being aldehyde, is alcohol.[162] This is reasonable in view of the expected great reducing properties of the species $H_2Fe_2(CO)_8^{2-}$.

A number of other reactions are analogous to the oxo process and presumably involve similar mechanisms. For example, olefins and acetylenes can be carboxylated or carboxyalkylated by carbon monoxide, water, or alcohol. The catalyst is nickel carbonyl, though cobalt carbonyls are also effective.[163] Reactions occur at low temperature (40°C):

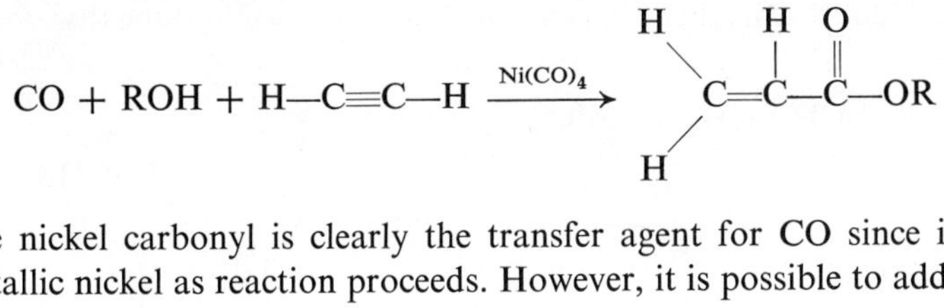

$$(89)$$

The nickel carbonyl is clearly the transfer agent for CO since it forms metallic nickel as reaction proceeds. However, it is possible to add acid to form salts of Ni(II) and hydrogen, and then to regenerate nickel carbonyl by CO under pressure.

$$5CO + NiCl_2 + H_2O \rightarrow Ni(CO)_4 + 2HCl + CO_2 \qquad (90)$$

It is possible to operate continuously so that the nickel carbonyl is a true catalyst.

The interesting fact that triphenylphosphine and iodide ion are activators for the nickel carbonyl[164] suggests that some CO must be replaced before further reaction. It has been suggested that traces of hydrogen halides are also activators in these reactions.[165]

$$HX + Ni(CO)_4 \rightarrow HNi(CO)_2X + 2CO \qquad (91)$$

The hydride would then add the olefin or acetylene to give an alkyl- or alkenylnickel dicarbonyl halide. The addition of CO would give the acyl derivative. Alkyl halides probably react in the same fashion as HX to give $RNi(CO)_2X$. This has been established for the case where R is an allyl group.[166]

The cleavage with alcohol to give an ester is more rapid with methoxide ion than with methyl alcohol.[163c] This is probably a simple nucleophilic attack on the acyl function.

$$\overset{\displaystyle O}{\overset{\displaystyle \|}{R-C}}-Co(CO)_4 + OCH_3^- \rightarrow \overset{\displaystyle O}{\overset{\displaystyle \|}{R-C}}-OCH_3 + Co(CO)_4^- \qquad (92)$$

The other product is the anion of cobalt hydrocarbonyl.

Palladium(II) chloride acts as a catalyst for the carbonylation of olefins, dienes, and allyl halides.[167] Esters are formed in alcohol solvent and acyl halides in non-hydroxylic solvents. Reduction of Pd(II) to palladium metal accompanies the reactions

$$C_2H_4 + PdCl_2 + CO \rightarrow ClCH_2CH_2COCl + Pd \qquad (93)$$

$$C_4H_6 + PdCl_2 + CO + C_2H_5OH \rightarrow$$
$$Pd + CH_3CH=CH-CH_2CO_2C_2H_5 \qquad (94)$$

Reaction 94 is not balanced since the solvent must be involved in the reduction stages. Although the mechanisms of these reactions are unknown, they probably involve olefin coordination, chloride ion migration, and CO insertion.[167] Butadiene is known[168] to form a chloromethyl π-allyl complex.

$$2CH_2=CH-CH=CH_2 + 2PdCl_2 \rightarrow$$

$$(95)$$

A number of reactions between the heavier transition metal halides and organic solvents occur in the presence of phosphines and arsines. These may be looked upon as reverse oxo reactions. Decarbonylation of the organic molecule occurs, and a metal carbonyl is produced. A hydride group is often attached to the metal atom as well. For example, Vaska[169] has shown the following reactions with high-boiling alcohols:

$$IrCl_3 + (C_6H_5)_3P + \text{alcohols} \rightarrow IrClCO[P(C_6H_5)_3]_2 \qquad (96)$$

$$\begin{array}{ll} RuCl_3 + (C_6H_5)_3P + \text{alcohols} \rightarrow RuHClCO[P(C_6H_5)_3]_3 & (97) \\ (OsCl_3) & (Os) \end{array}$$

It is very likely that the initial step is the formation of an alkoxide complex, since base assists the reaction.[170] Hydride transfer from RO^- to the metal produces an aldehyde, which is then the source of the carbonyl group. In the case of ethyl alcohol, methane is a known product as well.[170]

$$[Ru_2Cl_3(PR_3)_6]Cl + 2KOH + 2C_2H_5OH \rightarrow$$

$$2RuHClCO(PR_3)_3 + 2CH_4 + 2KCl + 2H_2O \quad (98)$$

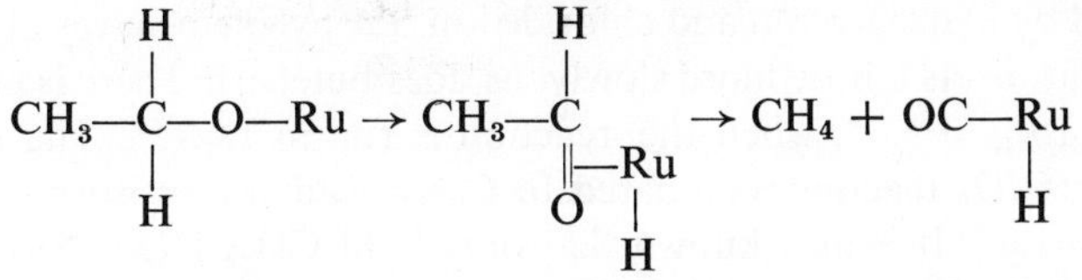

$$\underset{\underset{H}{|}}{\overset{\overset{H}{|}}{CH_3-C}}-O-Ru \rightarrow \underset{\underset{O}{\overset{\|}{}}\underset{|}{|}-Ru}{\overset{\overset{H}{|}}{CH_3-C}} \rightarrow CH_4 + \underset{\underset{H}{|}}{OC-Ru}$$

It is not clear whether the methane comes directly from the aldehyde or a $Ru-CH_3$ bond is formed first and then cleaved. Isotope labeling might answer this question.

A mixture of $RhCl_3$ and triphenylphosphine reacts with a variety of organic solvents to give $RhClCO(P(C_6H_5)_3)_2$.[171] In these cases, as in 96, reduction from the metal(III) to the metal(I) state occurs. Whereas cobalt carbonyl will catalyze the formation of dimethylformamide from CO and dimethylamine,[172]

$$CO + (CH_3)_2NH \xrightarrow{Co_2(CO)_8} HCON(CH_3)_2 \qquad (99)$$

a heavier metal, such as Rh(III), does just the reverse. The solvent dimethylformamide is torn apart to form the amine and the metal carbonyl.[171] The differences in behavior can be explained by the greater stability of the hydrides and carbonyls of the heavier transition metals. Thus, for the lighter metals, the hydrides and carbonyls are unstable enough to serve as intermediates for the formation of complex organic molecules. The heavier metals tend to break down complex organic species into coordinated carbonyl and hydride fragments. This is not always the case, however, since $RhCl_3[P(C_6H_5)_3]_3$ can be used as a hydroformylation catalyst under some conditions.[173]

The Wacker Process

Another commercially important example of the insertion reaction is the oxidation of ethylene to acetaldehyde by aqueous Pd(II) chloride (the Wacker process):[174]

$$PdCl_4^{2-} + C_2H_4 + H_2O \rightarrow CH_3CHO + Pd + 4Cl^- + 2H^+ \quad (100)$$

Since palladium metal is easily oxidized to Pd(II) by Cu(II), and since Cu(I) is easily oxidized by air to the cupric state, a true homogeneous catalytic process is established.

$$4Cl^- + Pd + 2Cu^{2+} \rightarrow PdCl_4^{2-} + 2Cu^+ \quad (101)$$

$$4Cu^+ + O_2 + 4H^+ \rightarrow 4Cu^{2+} + 2H_2O \quad (102)$$

Only ethylene and oxygen are consumed.

The kinetics of reaction 100 have been extensively studied.[175] The rate is first order in ethylene concentration and in the palladous ion, and is inhibited by hydrogen ion and chloride ion. Propylene behaves in the same way[176] but reacts a little more slowly, as does butene-1. There is an isotope effect, $k_H/k_D = 4.05$, when the reaction is run in D_2O.[177] The rate constant for C_2D_4 reacting, compared to C_2H_4, leads to an isotope effect of $k_H/k_D = 1.07$. It is also known that only light CH_3CHO is formed from C_2H_4 in D_2O.[177]

A detailed study[178] reveals that the rate law in HCl solution is given by

$$\text{Rate} = \frac{k[PdCl_3C_2H_4^-]}{[H^+][Cl^-]} \quad (103)$$

The equilibrium constants for both the reactions

$$PdCl_4^{2-} + C_2H_4 \rightleftharpoons PdCl_3C_2H_4^- + Cl^- \quad (104)$$

$$PdCl_3C_2H_4^- + H_2O \rightleftharpoons PdCl_2(C_2H_4)(H_2O) + Cl^- \quad (105)$$

have been measured. The inverse hydrogen ion dependence is attributed to the further equilibrium

$$PdCl_2(C_2H_4)(H_2O) \rightleftharpoons PdCl_2(C_2H_4)(OH)^- + H^+ \quad (106)$$

This agrees with the isotope effect in D_2O since weak acids containing deuterium as the acidic atom are weaker than their light hydrogen analogs by factors of the magnitude of 4, though the effect varies with the strength of the acid.[179]

Since all of the foregoing equilibria are labile, the slow step involves some reaction of $PdCl_2(C_2H_4)(OH)^-$. The most plausible reaction is the ligand migration of OH^- to the coordinated olefin, or the insertion reaction.[178]

$$\text{(107)}$$

$$\text{(108)}$$

Thus the rate-determining step is the insertion reaction or conversion of the π-bonded olefin to a σ-bonded β-hydroxyethyl ligand.[180] The breakdown into the final products is written as a fast step since otherwise the reaction of C_2D_4 should be much slower than that of C_2H_4. That is, the third hydrogen of the methyl group must come from a hydrogen atom migration from the β-carbon atom. A deuterium migration would be slower.

If acetic acid is used as a solvent, vinyl esters are formed.[181] The final breakdown step takes a different course in this case.

$$\rightarrow 2Cl^- + HOAc + Pd + H^+ + CH_2\!\!=\!\!CHOAc$$

$$\text{(109)}$$

The presence of the acylium ion, CH_3CO^+, instead of the proton on the terminal oxygen atom prevents the same kind of reaction as in water solvent.

In both solvents it is possible that the reverse of an insertion reaction occurs in the breakdown step. A hydride ion transfer to the metal would lead to formation of a Pd-H bond, which could decompose to palladium and a proton, followed by the loss of coordinated vinyl ester.

$$\longrightarrow Pd + H^+ + CH_2\!\!=\!\!CHOAc$$

$$\text{(110)}$$

Alternatively, in water the hydride ion might migrate again to carbon:

$$Pd\text{---}C\text{---}CH_3 \longrightarrow Pd + CH_3CHO + H^+ \tag{111}$$

There is evidence that quite free rotation of coordinated olefins does occur.[122,182] Such a rotation is needed for the second migration (p.577).

Other oxidizing metal ions such as Hg(II),[183] Pb(IV),[184] and Tl(III)[185] will produce carbonyl compounds from olefins. In those cases glycols are formed as well. The rate of the reaction

$$Tl^{3+} + C_2H_4 \xrightarrow{H_2O} CH_3CHO + C_2H_4(OH)_2 + Tl^+ \tag{112}$$

is first order in the concentrations of Tl(III) and of ethylene.[186] It is strongly accelerated by increasing salt concentration, the effect being related to changes in the activity of water. Presumably more complexing between the metal ion and the olefin occurs at lower water activity.[187] The yields of aldehyde and glycol are about equal at low salt concentration, but less glycol is formed at high salt concentrations. Acidity does not affect the rate. Alkyl substitution on the olefin greatly increases the rate.

The information is best explained by a mechanism in which a π complex is rapidly formed and a slow insertion reaction occurs in which water is the migrating ligand.[186]

$$CH_2\text{=}CH_2 + Tl^{3+} \underset{OH_2}{\rightleftharpoons} \begin{matrix} CH_2 \\ \| \\ CH_2 \end{matrix} Tl^{3+} \xrightarrow{slow} H^+ + HOCH_2CH_2Tl^{2+} \tag{113}$$

The hydroxyethyl complex then decomposes in two ways: by a hydrogen atom migration, as in the palladium reaction, to give CH_3CHO, and by attack of a water molecule to give glycol.

$$TlCH_2CH_2OH^{2+} \begin{cases} Tl^+ + CH_3CHO + H^+ \\ \xrightarrow{H_2O} Tl^+ + CH_2OHCH_2OH + H^+ \end{cases} \tag{114}$$

The nature of the products and their stereochemistry, when cyclohexene is oxidized by Tl(III) in acetic acid, suggests that an acetoxonium ion is an intermediate in this case.[188]

$$\text{cyclohexene} + \text{Tl(III)} \xrightarrow{\text{HOAc}} \text{acetoxonium intermediate} + \text{Tl(I)} \longrightarrow \text{products} \quad (115)$$

This may be regarded as a carbonium ion stabilized by a neighboring group. By analogy ethylene in water might sometimes form the hydroxy-stabilized carbonium ion, which is simply the oxonium ion of ethylene oxide.

$$\text{TlCH}_2\text{CH}_2\text{OH}^{2+} \rightarrow \text{Tl}^+ + \overset{\overset{\textstyle H}{\textstyle O}}{\text{CH}_2 \diagup \diagdown \text{CH}_2^+} \quad (116)$$

This would rapidly yield ethylene glycol. Branched-chain olefins do not behave in this way, however, since the products are not those expected from an oxide.

In contrast to the Wacker process, in which branching of the olefin slows down the rate slightly, putting alkyl groups on ethylene speeds up the rate of oxidation by Tl(III). Thus propylene reacts 150 times as fast as ethylene, and isobutene reacts 1000 times as fast.[186] This suggests that the rate-determining step develops a large amount of carbonium ion character in the coordinated olefin group. Thus the hydroxyalkyl group formed in reaction 113 is to be considered as a β-hydroxycarbonium ion coordinated to Tl(I).

Hydration of Acetylenes

In contrast to the oxidation of olefins brought about by certain metal ions, the characteristic reaction of acetylenes is hydration.[189]

$$R\text{—}C\equiv C\text{—}R' \xrightarrow{M^+} R\text{—}\overset{\overset{\textstyle O}{\textstyle \|}}{C}\text{—}CH_2\text{—}R' \quad (117)$$

An important commercial application is the hydration of acetylene itself to acetaldehyde, catalyzed by Hg(II) salts in acid solutions.

$$H\text{—}C\equiv C\text{—}H + H_2O \xrightarrow{\text{Hg(II)}} CH_3CHO \quad (118)$$

Acetylenes, like olefins, form complexes with many class (b) metal ions such as Ag(I) and Hg(II). Such a π complex is usually considered to be the reactive species for the hydration reaction. The slow step is the addition of water to the complexed acetylene.

It is known that both hydrogen atoms of the added water molecule wind up in the methyl group of the aldehyde.[190] A plausible mechanism is a ligand migration reaction in which water is the migrating ligand. This is followed by an acid cleavage.

$$\text{(structure)} \longrightarrow \text{Hg}^{-}\!\!\begin{matrix}H & H \\ | & | \\ C\!\!=\!\!C-OH^+ \\ \diagdown H^+\end{matrix} \longrightarrow Hg^{2+} + CH_2\!\!=\!\!CHOH \longrightarrow$$

$$Hg^{2+} + CH_3CHO \quad (119)$$

Vinyl alcohol would then rearrange to aldehyde. While a bis-acetylene complex has been found to be formed in the case of phenylacetylene and mercuric perchlorate,[191] it is probable that a mono complex is adequate for the hydration step.

What is not known is whether it is coordinated water or free water which attacks the unsaturated molecule. Only by analogy does one assume that it is coordinated water (the insertion reaction). Mercury salts of anions which coordinate poorly, such as ClO_4^-, BF_4^-, NO_3^-, and RSO_3^-, are good catalysts. Salts of Cl^-, OAc^-, and HPO_4^{2-} are poor catalysts.[192] This shows the need for at least some coordination sites to be free on the metal ion.

Olefins are not so susceptible to hydration by metal ion catalysis as are the acetylenes. Hydration of olefins by simple acid catalysis is, of course, well known. The usual reaction with mercuric ion is the addition to form a stable organomercury compound, e.g.,[193]

$$C_2H_4 + HgX_2 \rightarrow XHgCH_2CH_2X \quad (120)$$

where X = OAc^-, Cl, OH^-, etc. Both *cis* and *trans* addition can be found for substituted olefins.[194] It seems likely that a π complex of the olefin is formed first, and that a *trans* adduct is due to attack by an external X^- group and a *cis* product to the ligand migration reaction.[195]

Ruthenium(III) chloride is a catalyst for the hydration of acetylenic compounds.[196] The rate law is

$$\text{Rate} = k[C_2H_2][Ru(III)] \quad (121)$$

but k varies with the concentration of HCl, a maximum value being reached at about 4 M HCl, as shown in Fig. 7.15. Furthermore it is $[Cl^-]$ which affects the rate and not $[H^+]$, since the latter may be varied, at

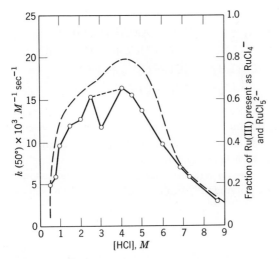

Fig. 7.15 Dependence of the rate constant (—○—) and of the concentration of Ru(III) chloride complexes (– – – –) on the HCl concentration: reference 2.

constant chloride concentration, without affecting k. There is, in fact, a good correlation of the rate with the sum of the concentrations of the two species $Ru(H_2O)_2Cl_4^-$ and $Ru(H_2O)Cl_5^{2-}$, as shown in Fig. 7.15.

This suggests that these two species are the most effective catalysts and that $RuCl_6^{3-}$, in particular, is not a catalyst. Thus at least one water molecule in the coordination shell is needed for catalytic activity.[196] The rate-determining step may be the formation of a π-acetylene complex by loss of another Cl^-.

$$Ru(H_2O)Cl_5^{2-} + C_2H_2 \rightarrow Ru(C_2H_2)(H_2O)Cl_4^- + Cl^- \qquad (122)$$

This is followed by a rapid ligand migration. The lower chloro complexes, such as $Ru(H_2O)_5Cl^{2+}$, are substitution inert and hence are not good catalysts since they would lose Cl^- or H_2O only slowly.

Olefin Polymerization

The polymerization of olefins by catalysts of the Ziegler-Natta type represents a most important example of the insertion reaction.[197] High-molecular-weight polyethylene can be obtained at low pressures of ethylene, for example. The catalysts are formed from an organometallic of a non-transition element and some compound of a transition element. The most familiar example is the original Ziegler catalyst formed from $TiCl_4$ and aluminum trialkyls.[198] These components react in a way that is not completely understood but may involve the following steps:

$$TiCl_4 + Al(C_2H_5)_3 \rightarrow Al(C_2H_5)_2Cl + TiCl_3C_2H_5 \qquad (123)$$

$$TiCl_3C_2H_5 \rightarrow HCl + C_2H_4 + TiCl_2 \qquad (124)$$

$$TiCl_3C_2H_5 + HCl \rightarrow C_2H_6 + TiCl_4 \qquad (125)$$

$$TiCl_2 + TiCl_4 \rightarrow 2TiCl_3 \qquad (126)$$

In the inert hydrocarbon solvents used, an insoluble mixed halide-alkyl complex of aluminum and titanium is formed of variable composition. This material is the active catalyst for the polymerization of ethylene, presumably acting as a heterogeneous catalyst.

Natta and his co-workers have had remarkable success in the production of stereospecific polymers.[199] For example, olefins like propylene have been

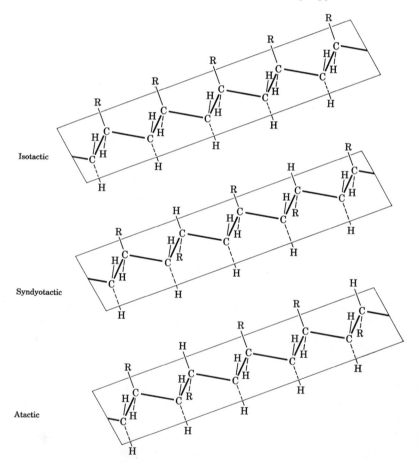

Fig. 7.16 Different types of polymers.

polymerized in such a way as to yield long linear head-to-tail chains consisting of sequences of monomeric units having the same steric structure. These polymers, which are called *isotactic* polymers, crystallize easily, whereas those with monomeric units of different steric arrangement phased at random do not crystallize well. These latter polymers are called *atactic*. Polymers of regular, alternating structure, called *syndyotactic* polymers, are also known (Fig. 7.16).

Though some free radicals are produced in forming the catalyst, the bulk of the polymerization certainly seems to be an anionic process. For example, with a constant supply of olefin a constant rate of polymerization can be obtained, showing that the catalyst is not used up as it would be in a radical-initiated process. The mechanism for both the initiation and propagation steps probably involves addition of a carbanion to an adsorbed olefin molecule. In spite of many studies, the details of the mechanism are still not known, partly because a variety of catalysts has been used and partly because the reactions are heterogeneous.

It seems quite certain that stereoregular polymers are only formed as a result of the structural features of the solid catalyst. Soluble catalysts such as those derived from VCl_3-$Sn(C_6H_5)_4$-$AlBr_3$ and $(C_2H_5)_2TiCl_2$-$(CH_3)_2AlCl$ are effective in causing polymerization of ethylene but are not useful for stereospecific polymerization of α-olefins.[200,201]

A mechanism due to Cossee[202] seems very reasonable in view of the experimental facts known and by analogy to other insertion reactions. The active site on the catalyst surface is a metal ion which is essentially octahedrally coordinated and which has a growing polymer chain, R, at one position, and one position vacant or occupied only by solvent. The other sites are occupied by halide ions, for example, in $TiCl_3$. The olefin is coordinated to the vacant site, and an insertion reaction occurs by a rate-determining migration of the group R.

A new vacant site, also on the surface, has now been created so that another molecule of olefin can be adsorbed. The chain can continue to grow by switching back and forth between the two sites. Termination would occur by a reverse insertion reaction in which a hydride ion shift to the metal occurred.

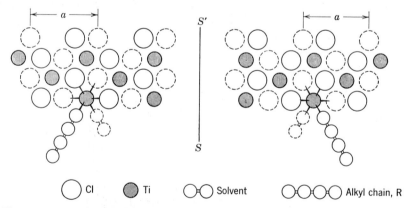

$+$ catalyst site

Cossee's theory also stresses the point that the metal-alkyl bond should not be too stable. In effect this means that the coligands, X, should not be too soft.

The layer-lattice structure of the transition metal halides is ideally suited to provide two or three surface coordination sites. Figure 7.17 shows the layer-lattice structure with active sites containing an R group and a co-ordinated solvent molecule. It can be seen that these sites correspond to rigid complexes of the type *cis*-TiCl$_4$AB. Hence they exist as a racemic mixture of asymmetric sites. The adsorption of an α-olefin can occur in two ways to give essentially diastereomeric systems of different energy.[203] If one form is favored sufficiently, an isotactic polymer is formed.

Non-transition metal alkyls will catalyze the polymerization of olefins, but usually to materials of low molecular weight. Examples are the aluminum,[204] gallium, beryllium, and indium[205] alkyl growth reactions.

○ Cl   ● Ti   ○─○ Solvent   ○─○─○─○ Alkyl chain, R

Fig. 7.17 Formation of TiCl$_4$RS on the border of the basal plane of TiCl$_3$ ($a = 6.12$ A) gives rise to enantiomorphous centers. *SS'* defines a plane separating two enantiomorphs.

Lithium alkyls are effective, particularly for the polymerization of dienes.[206] These reactions are presumably examples of the insertion reactions of olefins. In the insertion reaction of R_2AlH, there is evidence for *cis* addition to the olefin, as required by a mechanism in which the olefin is first coordinated to the metal.[207]

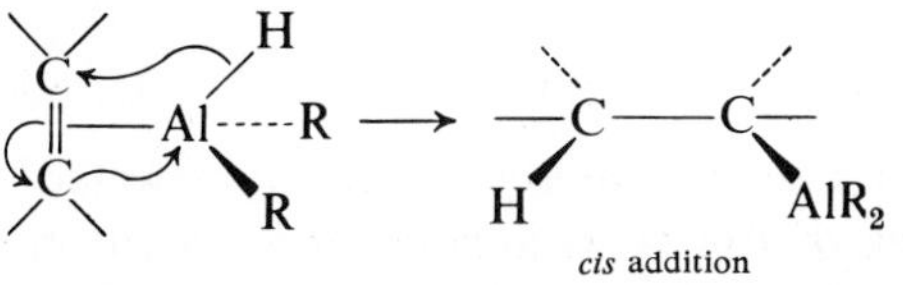

cis addition

The same *cis* addition is found in the hydroboration reaction.[208]

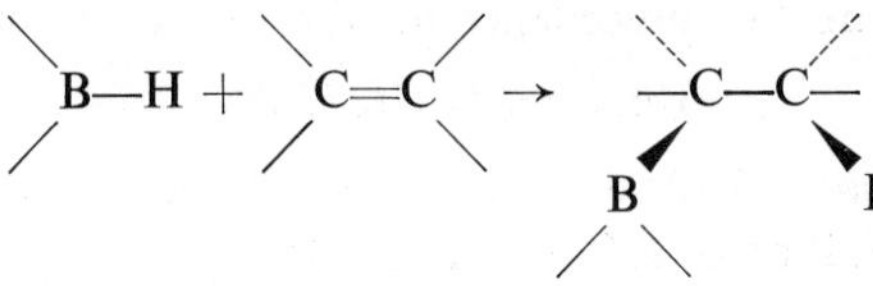

This important reaction does not lead to polymerization but seems to be mechanistically related, as does the aluminum alkyl reaction. In the latter case more olefin can be inserted and a longer-chain alkyl grown.

A recent surprising development has been the discovery that many olefins and diolefins can be polymerized, or dimerized, in aqueous or alcoholic solution. The catalysts are salts of Group VIII metals. The first example was Rh(III) chloride or nitrate, which polymerizes butadiene to crystalline *trans*-1,4-polybutadiene.[209] Salts of Pd(II), Ir(III), Ru(III), and Co(II) are also effective.[210] Some of these same metal ions will isomerize linear olefins as well.[211]

These observations are remarkable in relation to the systems described earlier, which are quite sensitive to the presence of protic solvents, M-R functions being readily hydrolyzed to give R-H. Also Rh(III) and Ir(III) are so inert to substitution reactions that it is, at first glance, hard to see how mechanisms of the insertion type can be operating. The latter difficulty is removed by the observation that Rh(III) is reduced to Rh(I) in the presence of ethylene.[212]

$$2RhCl_3 + 6C_2H_4 + 2H_2O \rightarrow [Rh(C_2H_4)_2Cl]_2 + 2CH_3CHO + 4HCl$$

(127)

Rhodium(I) complexes will be sufficiently labile.

A detailed study has been made by Cramer of the mechanism of ethylene dimerization by Rh(III) in ethyl alcohol.[213] A mixture of 1-butene and 2-butene is obtained in 99 % yield with practically no higher hydrocarbons.[214] Pressures of 1–100 atm of ethylene are used. There is an induction period of about 30 min, at 40°C, in which the added $RhCl_3$ (0.1 mole %) is converted to the soluble precursor of the dimer of equation 127, $Rh(C_2H_4)_2Cl_2.^-$ This substance may be considered the true catalyst.

The next stage of reaction happens rapidly in excess HCl. It is the addition of HCl to the planar Rh(I) complex to form an octahedral Rh(III) complex.

$$Rh(C_2H_4)_2Cl_2^- + H^+ + Cl^- + S \rightarrow Rh(C_2H_4)(C_2H_5)Cl_3S^- \quad (128)$$

Here S stands for a solvent molecule, alcohol or water. The evidence for the ethyl complex of Rh(III) is indirect. It is based on n.m.r. studies in solution and on the isolation of a compound, $Cs_2[C_2H_5RhCl_3H_2O]_2$, formed upon the removal of ethylene by pumping.

There is a great deal of precedence for the formation of

$$Rh(C_2H_4)(C_2H_5)Cl_3S^-,$$

if it is assumed that a hydrido complex is its precursor. The hydride is formed by the addition of HCl to $Rh(C_2H_4)_2Cl_2^-$. This is followed by an insertion reaction.

$$Rh(C_2H_4)_2Cl_2^- + H^+ + Cl^- \rightarrow Rh(C_2H_4)_2HCl_3^- \xrightarrow{\ S\ }$$
$$Rh(C_2H_4)(C_2H_5)Cl_3S^- \quad (129)$$

The oxidation of Rh(I) to Rh(III) is, in part, only formal since it arises because a proton is added to the metal and then arbitrarily called a hydride ion:

$$Rh(I) + H^+ \rightarrow Rh(III) + H^- \quad (130)$$

However, the increase in coordination number from four to (probably) six is also evidence that a d^8 system has become a d^6 system.

Many examples are now known of various covalent molecules being added to d^8 complexes, four or five coordinated, to produce six-coordinated d^6 complexes. Examples of molecules added are hydrogen, halogens, hydrogen halides, carboxylic acids, sulfonyl halides, mercaptans, mercuric halides, alkyl halides, oxygen, and others.[215] The addition of HCl is well documented, e.g.,[216]

$$IrCl(CO)[P(C_6H_5)_3]_2 + HCl \rightarrow Ir(CO)H[P(C_6H_5)_3]_2Cl_2 \quad (131)$$

The prototype of such additions to d^8 complexes would be the oxidation of Pt(II) to Pt(IV), e.g.,

$$Pt(en)_2^{2+} + Cl_2 \rightarrow trans\text{-}Pt(en)_2Cl_2^{2+} \quad (132)$$

Until recently it was assumed that these reactions always led to the formation of an octahedral product with the added fragments being above and below the plane and hence *trans* to each other. Several examples are now known of *cis* addition as well.[217,244]

The rate-controlling step in the ethylene dimerization reaction is normally the rearrangement of the ethyl complex into a butyl complex.[213]

$$Rh(C_2H_4)(C_2H_5)Cl_3S^- \xrightarrow[S]{slow} RhC_4H_9Cl_3S_2^- \qquad (133)$$

This presumably occurs by an alkyl migration reaction. The butyl complex, by a reverse hydride migration, splits off olefin, followed by loss of HCl to form another Rh(I) complex:

$$CH_3CH_2CH_2CH_2RhCl_3S_2^- \rightarrow (CH_3CH_2CHCH_2)RhHCl_3S^- \qquad (134)$$

$$(CH_3CH_2CHCH_2)RhHCl_3S^- \rightarrow CH_3CH_2CH{=}CH_2 + H^+$$

$$+ Cl^- + RhCl_2S_2^- \qquad (135)$$

The Rh(I) complex would rapidly pick up ethylene to regenerate the catalyst, $Rh(C_2H_4)_2Cl_2^-$.

The evidence for reaction 133 being the slow step is twofold. First of all, all of the other postulated steps may be directly observed to be much faster. Second, if the rate of dimerization is measured as a function of the concentrations of H^+, Cl^-, and C_2H_4, the same behavior is found. The rate is first order in each of these components at low concentration and becomes independent of the concentration at high concentration. For chloride ion, the rate goes to zero at ratios of Cl/Rh of less than 3.

These experiments suggest the composition of $Rh(C_2H_4)(C_2H_5)Cl_3S^-$ as being the composition of the transition state as well. When all components to form it are in excess (with respect to rhodium), then the rearrangement of $Rh(C_2H_4)(C_2H_5)Cl_3S^-$ is rate determining. At low ethylene pressures, it decomposes reversibly as follows:

$$Rh(C_2H_4)(C_2H_5)Cl_3S^- \rightleftharpoons C_2H_4 + Rh(C_2H_5)Cl_3S_2^- \qquad (136)$$

Hence the rate is first order in ethylene, which maintains the reactive form.

Isomerization of the 1-butene, predicted by the mechanism, to 2-butene has been demonstrated[218a] and accounts for the product distribution. For each molecule of 1-butene isomerized, one atom of Rh(I) is oxidized to Rh(III) and then is reduced back to Rh(I). Hence isomerization probably involves a hydride ion migration to coordinated olefin, followed by a reverse hydride migration.

The rhodium is in the trivalent state, as before, because of HCl addition. A mixture of *cis* and *trans*-2-butene is formed. Deuterium-labeling experiments support the mechanism shown, but not the alternate π-allyl mechanism (see below).

The mechanism of isomerization of olefins by transition metal complexes has been discussed at length.[218b] There are two processes which have received support. One is the hydride migration and its reverse as shown above. The other is the formation of a π-allyl complex as an intermediate. In this case an M-H bond is formed by abstracting a hydrogen from the olefin. An example is shown for iron carbonyl, which is a catalyst.

$$RCH_2CH{=}CH_2 + Fe(CO)_5 \longrightarrow \underset{RCH \quad CH_2}{\overset{CH}{\diagup \diagdown}}\!\!-\!\!\overset{H}{\underset{}{\mid}}\!\!Fe(CO)_3 \longrightarrow$$

$$RCH{=}CH{-}CH_3 + \text{iron carbonyl species} \quad (137)$$

The π-allyl intermediate allows for a 1,3-hydrogen atom shift since the two terminal carbon atoms of the allyl system become equivalent.

Acetylene Condensations

Acetylenes may also be polymerized by catalysts of the Ziegler type.[219] However, molecular weights are low, and cyclizations are common. More typical of acetylene behavior are the aromatic cyclizations, catalyzed by various transition metal complexes, discovered by Reppe.[220] Acetylene, in non-aqueous solvents and under the influence of nickel complexes, such as $Ni(CN)_2$ or $Ni(acac)_2$, cyclizes to cyclooctatetraene (COT).[221]

$$4C_2H_2 \xrightarrow{\text{Ni(CN)}_2} C_8H_8 \qquad (138)$$

A study of the effect of various ligands on the yield of COT strongly suggests that 4 moles of coordinated acetylene form COT directly.[222] Figure 7.18a shows how four molecules may be positioned to yield the stable conformer of the product. If triphenylphosphine is added, 1 mole/ mole of catalyst, there is complete inhibition of the formation of COT. Instead benzene is formed in good yield. Figure 7.18b indicates how blocking one coordination site by a good ligand will lead to this result. A bidentate inhibitor, such as *o*-phenanthroline, will prevent the formation of both COT and benzene (Fig. 7.18c).

The compound $Ni(CO)_4$, activated by triphenylphosphine, is also a good catalyst for the conversion of acetylenes to benzenes.[223] The catalyst in this case appears to be $Ni(CO)_2[P(C_6H_5)_3]_2$.[166] It would appear that these condensation reactions of acetylenic molecules are not mechanistically the same as the insertion reactions of olefins.

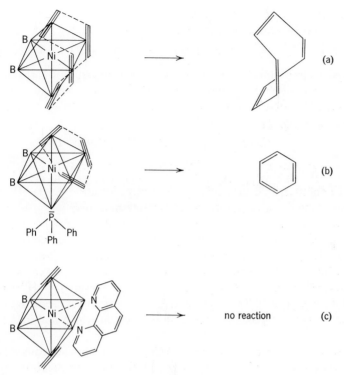

Fig. 7.18 Mechanism of acetylene condensation on a Ni(II) catalyst. From reference 222.

Very similar is the condensation of disubstituted acetylenes to form substituted benzenes, catalyzed by chromium triphenyl in tetrahydrofuran solution.[224] The replacement of three coordinated tetrahydrofuran molecules by dimethylacetylene leads to an arrangement which can easily form hexamethylbenzene:

$$2CH_3 - C \equiv C - CH_3 \xrightarrow{Cr(C_6H_5)_3(THF)_3} C_6(CH_3)_6 \qquad (139)$$

Homogeneous Catalytic Hydrogenation

A number of examples of the metal ion activation of molecular hydrogen in solution have been reported.[224] Following earlier observations by Ipatieff, the first example studied was that of Calvin.[225] He showed that, in quinoline solution, Cu(I) salts of organic acids catalyze the reduction by dissolved hydrogen of Cu(II) salts and benzoquinone. The details of this reaction have been elucidated in subsequent papers.[226]

It is found that the reaction is homogeneous, is independent of the concentration of the oxidizing agent, and follows the rate law

$$\text{Rate} = k[\text{Cu A}]^2[\text{H}_2] \tag{140}$$

where A^- is the anion of the organic acid. The interpretation is that molecular hydrogen is split by a dimer of Cu(I), or in a termolecular process to a hydride-like species which is a very active reducing agent. A schematic mechanism would be

$$2\text{Cu(I)} + \text{H}_2 \rightleftharpoons 2\text{Cu(I)} \cdot \text{H} \text{ or } [\text{Cu(I)} \cdot \text{H}]_2 \tag{141}$$

$$\text{Cu(I)} \cdot \text{H} + \text{Cu(II)} \xrightarrow{\text{fast}} 2\text{Cu(I)} + \text{H}^+ \tag{142}$$

with the splitting rate determining. The representation $\text{Cu(I)} \cdot \text{H}$ is not intended to be a complete formula of the intermediate.

In the absence of an oxidizing agent the reversibility of 141 is shown by the ability of the system to catalyze the *ortho-para*hydrogen conversion[227] and the exchange of deuterium isotope with a hydrogen donor in solution.[228] The activation energy for the splitting of H_2 is 13.0 kcal when A^- is acetate.[226d] As expected, D_2 reacts somewhat slower than H_2 with an activation energy of 13.7 kcal. In general the system is very sensitive to the presence of various possible ligands in the system which may deactivate Cu(I).

In a similar fashion it is found[229] that Cu^{2+} and Hg^{2+} in aqueous solution can catalyze the reduction by hydrogen of a number of oxidizing agents such as Cr(VI).

A detailed study of the activation of H_2 by $\text{Cu(H}_2\text{O)}_6^{2+}$ in HClO_4 solution reveals that the kinetic order of Cu(II) changes from one to two as the acidity increases.[230] At the same time a decrease in rate is observed. The following mechanism can account for these facts:

$$\text{Cu}^{2+} + \text{H}_2 \underset{k_2}{\overset{k_1}{\rightleftharpoons}} \text{CuH}^+ + \text{H}^+ \tag{143}$$

$$\text{CuH}^+ + \text{Cu}^{2+} \xrightarrow{k_3} 2\text{Cu}^+ + \text{H}^+ \tag{144}$$

$$2\text{Cu}^+ + \text{substrate} \xrightarrow{\text{fast}} \text{products} + 2\text{Cu}^{2+} \tag{145}$$

Application of the steady state method, assuming CuH^+ a reactive intermediate, gives the rate equation:

$$\text{Rate} = \frac{k_1 k_3[\text{H}_2][\text{Cu}^{2+}]^2}{k_3[\text{Cu}^{2+}] + k_2[\text{H}^+]} \tag{146}$$

The ratio of k_2/k_3 was found to be 0.25 at 110°C. This mechanism can explain a number of phenomena such as the effect of the nature of the solvent and of added anions on the rates and kinetic orders. Thus the proton and the metal ion will be stabilized to varying degrees by the solvent or by anions. Competition of these stabilized forms for CuH$^+$ determines the characteristics observed. In aqueous solution the effect of various complexing agents is shown in Table 7.18.

It can be seen that the more basic simple anions produce high rates of reduction of the substrates such as Cr$_2$O$_7^{2-}$, IO$_3^-$, Ce^{4+}. This can be attributed to the stabilization of the hydrogen ion, so that k_2 is diminished. Chelating agents such as glycine, however, are inhibitors for the catalytic

Table 7.18 Effect of complexing agents on the catalytic activity of Cu^{2+} in aqueous solution

Ligand	Relative Activity	Ligand	Relative Activity
Butyrate	150	Chloride	2.5
Propionate	150	Perchlorate	1.0
Acetate	120	Glycine	0.5
Sulfate	6.5	Ethylenediamine	0.1

Data from reference 230.

reaction because Cu(II) ion is now most stabilized, and k_3 and/or k_1 is diminished. Very similar results are obtained for the activation of H$_2$ by Ag$^+$.[231]

The rate law for the latter case is more complex.[232] When Cr(VI) is the oxidizing agent, the rate is

$$\text{Rate} = \frac{k_1 k_3 [H_2][Ag^+]^2}{k_3[Ag^+] + k_2[H^+]} + k_4[H_2][Ag^+]^2 \qquad (147)$$

Apparently there is both a heterolytic path, analogous to Cu^{2+},

$$Ag^+ + H_2 \rightleftharpoons AgH + H^+ \qquad (148)$$

and a homolytic path, analogous to Cu$^+$,

$$2Ag^+ + H_2 \rightarrow 2AgH^+ \qquad (149)$$

The reversibility of reaction 148 has been demonstrated by H$_2$-D$_2$O exchange.[231]

A fairly straightforward calculation can be made of the energies required for heterolytic and homolytic splitting of H$_2$ in water:

$$H_2(aq) \rightarrow 2H \cdot (aq) \qquad (150)$$

Splitting into free atoms requires about 100 kcal, whereas the ionic splitting

$$H_2(aq) \rightarrow H^+(aq) + H^-(aq) \qquad (151)$$

requires only about 33 kcal. These figures are based on heats of hydration for the proton of -260 kcal, for hydride ion of -108 kcal, and for H_2 of -2 kcal. Consequently, unless two hydrogen atoms can simultaneously be accepted by some species in solution, the ionic splitting should be favored in solvents of high polarity.

Coordination of either H^+ or H^- would facilitate the reaction.

$$M^+ + H\!-\!H + B \rightarrow MH + BH^+ \qquad (152)$$

It has been shown that a strong base can split H_2 into H^- and H^+. Thus, if B is hydroxide ion or amide ion, a metal ion is not needed to cleave the hydrogen molecule.[233] The cleavage is proved by deuterium isotope exchange and by *ortho-para*hydrogen conversion. Reaction would be most effective if a metal ion and a base acted cooperatively. There is a remarkable activation of Ag(I) by fluoride ion in hydrogenation reactions. The rate constant increases by a factor of 10^4 if F^- is incorporated into the transition state.[234] This suggests a cooperative effect such as

In addition to the simple metal ions, a number of complexes of the transition metals have been reported to activate molecular hydrogen. Table 7.19 shows several examples, together with the supposed intermediates and, when known, stable analogs of these intermediates. It can be seen that the

Table 7.19   Hydrogen activating complexes

Electron Configuration	Metal Ion	Catalytic Complex	Postulated Hydride Intermediate	Stable Analog
d^5	Ru(III)	$RuCl_6^{3-}$	$HRuCl_5^{3-}$	
d^6	Ru(II)	$RuCl_n^{2-n}$	$HRuCl_{n-1}^{2-n}$	$HRuCl(Et_2PC_2H_4PEt_2)_2$
				$HRuCl(CO)(PPh_3)_3$
	Rh(III)	$RhCl_6^{3-}$	$HRhCl_5^{3-}$	$HRhCl(trien)^+$
d^7	Co(II)	$Co(CN)_5^{3-}$	$HCo(CN)_5^{3-}$ [a]	
d^8	Pd(II)	$PdCl_4^{2-}$	$HPdCl_3^{2-}$	$HPdCl(PEt_3)_2$
	Pt(II)	$PtCl_2$-$SnCl_2$	?	$HPtCl(PEt_3)_2$
	Ir(I)	$IrCl(CO)(PPh_3)_2$	$H_2IrCl(CO)(PPh_3)_2$ [a]	
	Rh(I)	$RhCl(PPh_3)_3$[b]	$H_2RhCl(PPh_3)_3$	
d^9	Cu(II)	Cu^{2+}(aq)	CuH^+	
d^{10}	Cu(I)	$CuOOCR$	CuH^+, CuH	
	Ag(I)	Ag^+(aq)	AgH^+ AgH	
	Hg(II)	Hg^{2+}(aq)	?	

[a] Stable species. From reference 224a except as specified in note b.
[b] Reference 245.

active metal ions are in the latter parts of the transition series, containing 5–10 d orbital electrons. This is a factor which will help stabilize hydride intermediates. Of course, it is not desirable that these hydrides be too stable. This will lower their reactivity and prevent them from being useful catalysts. Some mechanistic details of the way in which the complexes of Table 7.19 catalyze hydrogenation reactions are known. This information is largely due to the work of Halpern and his students.

In HCl solution Ru(III) will catalyze the oxidation of H_2 by oxidants such as Ru(IV) and Fe(III).[235] Isotope exchange between D_2 and H_2O will occur in the absence of an oxidant. A heterolytic splitting mechanism has been proposed:

$$H_2 + RuCl_6^{3-} \underset{slow}{\rightleftharpoons} H^+ + Cl^- + HRuCl_5^{3-} \quad (153)$$

$$HRuCl_5^{3-} + 2Fe(III) + Cl^- \xrightarrow{fast} RuCl_6^{3-} + 2Fe(II) + H^+ \quad (154)$$

A more interesting example is provided by Ru(II), which, in HCl solution, will cause the hydrogenation of activated olefinic compounds such as maleic and fumaric acid.[236] A Ru(II)-olefin complex is formed first which is then hydrogenated in a slow step.

$$Rate = k[Ru(II)\text{-olefin}][H_2] \quad (155)$$

Reduction of fumaric acid with D_2 in H_2O yields undeuterated succinic acid. The hydrogen which enters the double bond comes from the solvent. Furthermore, reduction with H_2 or D_2 in D_2O yields chiefly $(\pm)$-2,3-dideuterosuccinic acid. This means the addition of hydrogen is *cis*. A mechanism which explains these observations is shown in Fig. 7.19.[236] This mechanism resembles that proposed by Burwell *et al.* for the heterogeneous hydrogenation of olefins on chromium oxide gel.[237]

Although unsubstituted olefins such as ethylene are not hydrogenated under these conditions, they do form complexes. The complexes with Ru(II) cause D_2-H_2O exchange at about the same rate as the fumaric acid complex undergoes hydrogenation. A study has been made of the rate of formation of the ethylene complex.[238] The rate law is

$$Rate = \frac{k_1 k_2 [RuCl_n][C_2H_4]}{k_{-1}[Cl^-] + k_2[C_2H_4]} \quad (156)$$

This suggests a mechanism in which dissociation of a chloro complex of Ru(II), $RuCl_n$, is rate determining. A species is formed which reacts competitively with either ethylene or chloride ion.

$$RuCl_n \underset{k_{-1}}{\overset{k_1}{\rightleftharpoons}} RuCl_{n-1} + Cl^- \quad (157)$$

$$RuCl_{n-1} + C_2H_4 \xrightarrow{k_2} RuCl_{n-1}(C_2H_4) \quad (158)$$

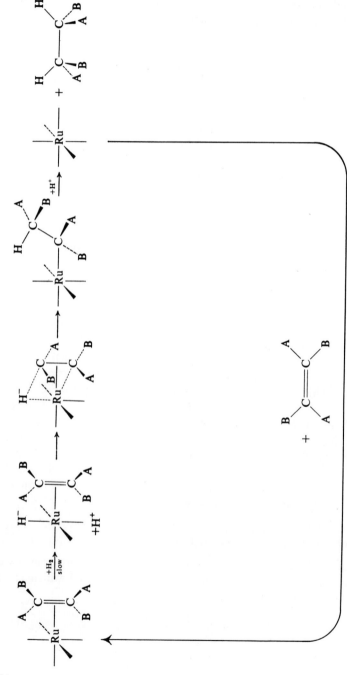

Fig. 7.19 Mechanism for the hydrogenation of olefins catalyzed by ruthenium(II). From reference 236.

The species designated as $RuCl_{n-1}$ may be of reduced coordination number, or it may simply be an aquo complex.

The reversible uptake of H_2 by aqueous solutions of $Co(CN)_5^{3-}$ provides another example of homolytic splitting.[239]

$$2Co(CN)_5^{3-} + H_2 \rightleftharpoons 2HCo(CN)_5^{3-} \tag{159}$$

As expected, the rate law shows[240]

$$\text{Rate} = k[H_2][Co(CN)_5^{3-}]^2 \tag{160}$$

The equilibrium constant has also been determined:[240] $K = 1.6 \times 10^5 \ M^{-1}$ at $25°C$; $\Delta H = -11.2$ kcal/mole; $\Delta S° = -15$ eu. The H-Co bond energy thus works out to be 57 kcal/mole (compare equation 150).

The ion $Co(CN)_5^{3-}$ is a homogeneous catalyst for the hydrogenation of a variety of substrates, including conjugated diolefins such as butadiene and styrene.[241] The proposed mechanism is 159 followed by

$$HCo(CN)_5^{3-} + C_4H_6 \rightarrow (C_4H_7)Co(CN)_5^{3-} \tag{161}$$

$$C_4H_7Co(CN)_5^{3-} + HCo(CN)_5^{3-} \rightarrow C_4H_8 + 2Co(CN)_5^{3-} \tag{162}$$

The proposed intermediate $(C_4H_7)Co(CN)_5^{3-}$ has also been prepared[242] by the reaction of crotyl bromide with $Co(CN)_5^{3-}$. Studies using n.m.r. show it to be a σ-bonded butenyl complex, which rearranges by loss of CN^- to form a π-allyl complex. Other examples of this kind of equilibration are known.[243]

$$CH_3-CH{=}CH-CH_2-Co(CN)_5^{3-} \rightleftharpoons$$
$$\text{or}$$
$$H_2C{=}CH-CH-Co(CN)_5^{3-}$$
$$\qquad\qquad\qquad | $$
$$\qquad\qquad\quad CH_3$$

At low CN^- concentrations the product of hydrogenation is *trans*-2-butene, and at high $[CN^-]$ the product is 1-butene. This suggests that the σ-bonded complex cleaves to give 1-butene and the π-bonded complex yields 2-butene.

A third method by which a coordination complex may activate molecular hydrogen is now well substantiated. This is the addition of both atoms of hydrogen to a single metal atom. The first example known has already been mentioned.[216]

$$H_2 + IrCl(CO)[P(C_6H_5)_3]_2 \xrightarrow{\text{benzene}} IrH_2Cl(CO)[P(C_6H_5)_3]_2 \tag{163}$$

It corresponds to a formal oxidation of Ir(I) to Ir(III). An interesting point is that the addition appears to give a *cis*-dihydro arrangement.[244]

$$\phi_3P-\underset{\underset{O}{\overset{|}{C}}}{\overset{\overset{\displaystyle Cl}{|}}{Ir}}-P\phi_3 + H_2 \rightarrow \phi_3P-\underset{\underset{\underset{O}{C}}{\overset{|}{\underset{\nearrow}{\quad}}}}{\overset{\overset{\displaystyle H}{|}}{Ir}}\overset{Cl}{\underset{H}{\cdots}}-P\phi_3$$

The compound $IrCl(CO)(P(C_6H_5)_3)_2$ also reacts reversibly to form olefin complexes. It, as well as its rhodium analog, will cause catalytic hydrogenation of ethylene when a mixture of C_2H_4 and H_2 is added.[244] Acetylene is hydrogenated as well, and $RhCl[P(C_6H_5)_3]_3$ is also a catalyst.[245]

The trigonal bipyramidal d^8 complex, $IrH(CO)[P(C_6H_5)_3]_3$, is an even more efficient catalyst for the hydrogenation of ethylene.[246] Ambient conditions may be used. Continuous conversion of $C_2H_4 + H_2$ to C_2H_6 goes on at a total gas pressure of 800 mm. Both H_2 and C_2H_4 react reversibly to form new complexes with the iridium complex. It appears that a seven-coordinated species is formed, since two atoms of hydrogen are added with no loss of the original ligands.

A special mechanism may be operating for catalysis by monohydrides.[246] A periodic expansion and contraction of the coordination is postulated, e.g.,

$$Os-H + C_2H_4 \rightleftharpoons Os-C_2H_5 \tag{164}$$

$$Os-C_2H_5 + H_2 \rightleftharpoons H-\underset{\underset{H}{|}}{Os}-C_2H_5 \tag{165}$$

$$H-\underset{\underset{H}{|}}{Os}-C_2H_5 \rightarrow H-Os + C_2H_6 \tag{166}$$

The other ligands bound to osmium are not shown. Reaction 164 would proceed by ethylene π-complex formation, followed by hydride ion migration.

It has also been reported[247] that a number of soluble Ziegler-type catalysts are capable of causing hydrogenation of olefins. Typically the catalyst consists of an aluminum trialkyl and some complex of Co(II), Fe(III), Mn(II), Ni(II), Ru(III), and other metal ions. It is supposed that hydrogen cleaves an alkyl-transition metal bond to give a hydride.

$$RMX_2 + H_2 \rightarrow HMX_2 + RH \tag{167}$$

$$HMX_2 + \underset{\diagup}{\overset{\diagdown}{C}}=\underset{\diagdown}{\overset{\diagup}{C}} \rightarrow R'MX_2, \text{ etc.} \tag{168}$$

In the formation of RH from an alkyl-metal bond it is not clear whether molecular hydrogen causes cleavage directly as written in 167. Alternatively an M-H function might be the cleaving agent. This could happen by the group acting as a simple proton donor.

References

General references for this chapter include *Organometallic Chemistry* (H. Zeiss, ed.) Reinhold Publishing Corp., New York, 1960; *Organo-Metallic Compounds* by G. E. Coates, John Wiley and Sons, New York, 2nd ed., 1961; *Metall-π-Komplexe mit di- und oligoolefinischen Liganden* by E. O. Fischer and H. Werner, Verlag Chemie, Weinheim/Bergstr., 1963; *Advances in Organometallic Chemistry* (F. G. A. Stone and R. West, eds.), Academic Press, New York, 1964, and succeeding years.

1. T. J. Kealy and P. L. Pauson, *Nature*, **168**, 1039 (1951); S. A. Miller, J. A. Tebboth and J. F. Tremaine, *J. Chem. Soc.*, **1952**, 632.
2. G. Wilkinson, M. Rosenblum, M. C. Whiting, and R. B. Woodward, *J. Am. Chem. Soc.*, **74**, 2125 (1952).
3. C. K. Jørgensen, Symposium on SHAB, CERI, Geneva, 1965.
4. H. W. Sternberg, I. Wender, R. A. Friedel, and M. Orchin, *J. Am. Chem. Soc.*, **75**, 2717 (1953); P. Krumholz and H. M. A. Stettiner, *ibid.*, **71**, 3035 (1949).
5. J. Chatt, Tilden Lecture, *Proc. Chem. Soc.*, **1962**, 318.
6. G. Wilkinson, *Advances in the Chemistry of the Coordination Compounds*, The Macmillan Co., New York, 1961, p. 50.
7. H. J. Dauben and L. R. Honnen, *J. Am. Chem. Soc.*, **80**, 5570 (1958); J. E. Mahler and R. Pettit, *ibid.*, **84**, 1511 (1962); M. L. H. Green and P. L. I. Nagy, *J. Chem. Soc.*, **1963**, 189.
8. L. Pauling, *Nature of the Chemical Bond*, Cornell University Press, Ithaca, N.Y., 1939, p. 231.
9. C. K. Jørgensen, *Inorg. Chem.*, **3**, 1201 (1964).
10. D. P. Craig and G. Doggett, *J. Chem. Soc.*, **1963**, 4189.
11. J. Chatt and R. G. Hayter, *J. Chem. Soc.*, **1961**, 772.
12. J. Chatt and B. L. Shaw, *J. Chem. Soc.*, **1959**, 705
13. References 5 and 12; also J. Chatt and B. L. Shaw, *J. Chem. Soc.*, **1961**, 285.
14. J. Chatt and B. L. Shaw, *J. Chem. Soc.*, **1960**, 1718.
15. J. Chatt, *Nature*, **177**, 852 (1956).
16. M. J. S. Dewar, *Bull. soc. chim. France*, **18**, C79 (1951).
17. See *Cationic Polymerization* (P. H. Plesch, ed.), Hefner and Sons, Cambridge, 1953.
18. S. Winstein and H. J. Lucas, *J. Am. Chem. Soc.*, **60**, 836 (1938).
19. D. D. Eley in reference 17, p. 6.
20. H. J. Lucas, F. R. Hepner, and S. Winstein, *J. Am. Chem. Soc.*, **61**, 3102 (1939).
21. J. C. Traynham and J. R. Olechowski, *J. Am. Chem. Soc.*, **81**, 571 (1939).
22. For a review see L. E. Orgel, *An Introduction to Transition Metal Chemistry*, John Wiley and Sons, New York, 1960, Chap. 10.
23. See J. D. Roberts, *Notes on Molecular Orbital Calculations*, W. A. Benjamin, New York, 1962; A. Streitwieser, Jr., *Molecular Orbital Theory for Organic Chemists*, John Wiley and Sons, New York, 1961.
24. J. M. Rowe, *Proc. Chem. Soc.*, **1962**, 66.

25. H. C. Longuet-Higgins and L. E. Orgel, *J. Chem. Soc.*, **1956**, 1969.

26. R. Criegee and G. Schröder, *Ann.*, **623**, 1 (1959); H. H. Freedman, *J. Am. Chem. Soc.*, **83**, 2194 (1961); G. F. Emerson, L. Watts, and R. Pettit, *ibid.*, **87**, 131 (1965).

27. L. Watts, J. D. Fitzpatrick, and R. Pettit, *J. Am. Chem. Soc.*, **87**, 3253 (1965).

28. L. C. Mond, C. Langer, and F. Quinke, *J. Chem. Soc.*, **57**, 749 (1890); P. Gilmont and A. A. Blanchard, *Inorg. Syn.*, **2**, 242 (1946).

29. L. C. Mond and F. Quinke, *Chem. News.* **63**, 301 (1981); L. C. Mond and C. Langer, *J. Chem. Soc.*, **1891**, 1090; M. Berthelot, *Compt. rend.*, **112**, 1343 (1891).

30. W. Hieber, *Z. Elektrochem.*, **43**, 390 (1937); A. A. Blanchard, *Chem. Rev.*, **21**, 3 (1937); J. S. Anderson, *Quart. Rev. (London)*, **1**, 331 (1947); J. W. Cable and R. K. Sheline, *Chem. Rev.*, **56**, 1 (1956).

31. J. Chatt, P. L. Pauson, and L. M. Venanzi, in *Organometallic Chemistry* (H. Zeiss, ed.), Reinhold Publishing Corp., New York, 1961, Chap. 10. E. W. Abel, *Quart. Rev. (London)*, **17**, 133 (1963).

32. J. C. Hileman in *Preparative Inorganic Reactions* (W. L. Jolly ed.), Interscience Publishers, New York, Vol. I, 1964, Chap. 4.

33. J. Dewar and H. O. Jones, *Proc. Roy. Soc. (London)*, **A79**, 66 (1906).

34. P. Coradini, *J. Chem. Phys.*, **31**, 1676 (1959); C. H. Wei and L. F. Dahl, *J. Am. Chem. Soc.* **88**, 1821 (1966).

35. W. Hieber and T. Kruck, *Z. Naturforsch.*, **16b**, 709 (1961).

36. E. O. Fischer and K. Bittler, *Z. Naturforsch.*, **16b**, 225 (1961).

37. P. M. Treichel, E. Pitcher, R. B. King, and F. G. A. Stone, *J. Am. Chem. Soc.*, **83** 2593 (1961).

38. R. Ercoli, F. Calderazzo, and A. Alberola, *J. Am. Chem. Soc.*, **82**, 2966 (1960).

39. V. H. Behrens and H. Zizlsperger, *Z. Naturforsch.*, **16b**, 349 (1961).

40. W. Hieber and W. Schrapp, *Z. Naturforsch.*, **15b**, 271 (1960).

41. H. L. Nigam, R. S. Nyholm, and R. Roa, *J. Chem. Soc.*, **1959**, 1397.

42. E. O. Fischer and C. Palm, *Chem. Ber.*, **91**, 1725 (1958).

43. M. Bigorgne, *J. Organometal. Chem.*, **1**, 101 (1963); F. A. Cotton and C. S. Kraihanzel, *J. Am. Chem. Soc.*, **84**, 4432 (1962), and *Inorg. Chem.*, **2**, 533 (1963); F. A. Cotton, *ibid.*, **3**, 702 (1964); G. R. Dobson, *ibid.*, **4**, 1673 (1965).

44. W. D. Horrocks and R. C. Taylor, *Inorg. Chem.*, **2**, 723 (1963).

45. L. E. Orgel, *Inorg. Chem.*, **1**, 982 (1962).

46. See, for example, K. Nakamato, *Infrared Spectra of Inorganic and Coordination Compounds*, John Wiley and Sons, New York, 1963, pp. 8–10.

47. R. J. Clark, *Inorg. Chem.* **3**, 1395 (1964); R. J. Clark and E. O. Brimm, *ibid.*, **4**, 651 (1965).

48. T. Kruck, *Z. Naturforsch.*, **19b**, 165 (1964).

49. F. Basolo and A. Wojcicki, *J. Am. Chem. Soc.*, **83**, 520 (1961).

50. H. A. McKay, *Nature*, **142**, 997 (1938).

51. D. F. Keeley and R. E. Johnson, *Inorg. Nucl. Chem.*, **11**, 33 (1959).

52. G. Pajaro, F. Calderazzo, and R. Ercoli, *Gazz. Chim. Ital.*, **90**, 1486 (1960).

53. G. Cetini and O. Gambino, *Atti Accad. Sci. Torino*, **97**, 757, 1189, 1197 (1963).

54. G. Pajaro, F. Calderazzo, and R. Ercoli, private communication.

55. W. Hieber and K. Wollmann, *Chem. Ber.*, **95**, 1552 (1962).

56. G. Cetini, R. Ercoli, O. Gambino, and G. Vaglio, *Atti Accad. Sci. Torino*, **99**, 1 (1965).

57. S. Breitschaft and F. Basolo, *J. Am. Chem. Soc.*, **88**, 2702 (1966).

58. R. Ercoli, F. Calderazzo, and A. Alberola, *J. Am. Chem. Soc.*, **82**, 2966 (1960).

59. O. S. Mills and G. Robinson, *Proc. Chem. Soc.*, **1959**, 156; G. G. Sumner, H. P. Kbeg, and L. E. Alexander, *Acta Cryst.*, **17**, 732 (1964).

60. F. A. Cotton, A. K. Fischer, and G. Wilkinson, *J. Am. Chem. Soc.*, **81**, 800 (1959).
61. A. P. Garrett and H. W. Thompson, *J. Chem. Soc.*, **1934**, 1817, 1822; C. E. H. Bawn, *Trans. Faraday Soc.*, **31**, 440 (1935).
62. L. R. Kangas, R. F. Heck, P. M. Henry, S. Breitschaft, E. M. Thorsteinson, and F. Basolo, *J. Am. Chem. Soc.*, **88**, 2334 (1966).
63. R. J. Angelici, private communication.
64. L. H. Jones in *Theory and Structure of Complex Compounds* (J. Jezowska-Trzebiatowska, ed.), Pergamon Press, London, 1964, pp. 45–53.
65. L. H. Jones, *Spectrochim. Acta*, **17**, 188 (1961).
66. G. Cetini and O. Gambino, *Ann. Chem.*, **53**, 236 (1963).
67. F. Basolo, A. T. Brault, and A. J. Poë, *J. Chem. Soc.*, **1964**, 676.
68. A. Davison, W. McFarlane, L. Pratt, and G. Wilkinson, *J. Chem. Soc.*, **1962**, 3653.
69. S. J. LaPlaca and J. A. Ibers, *J. Am. Chem. Soc.*, **86**, 2288 (1964).
70. R. Bramley, B. N. Figgis, and R. S. Nyholm, *Trans. Faraday Soc.*, **58**, 1893 (1962).
71. E. O. Fischer, H. P. Kogler, and P. Kuzel, *Chem. Ber.*, **93**, 3006 (1960); W. Strohmeier and K. Gerlack, *Z. Naturforsch.*, **16b**, 413 (1960); and later papers by E. O. Fischer and by W. Strohmeier.
72. G. Eyber, *Z. Physik. Chem.*, **144A**, 1 (1929).
73. A. B. Callear, *Proc. Roy. Chem. Soc.*, **265A**, 71, 88 (1962).
74. W. Strohmeier and D. V. Hobe, *Chem. Ber.*, **94**, 761 (1961); W. Strohmeier, D. V. Hobe, G. Schoenauer, and H. Laporte, *Z. Naturforsch.*, **17b**, 502 (1962).
75. I. W. Stolz, G. R. Dobson, and R. K. Sheline, *J. Am. Chem. Soc.*, **85**, 1013 (1963).
76. L. F. Dahl and K. E. Rundle, *J. Chem. Phys.*, **26**, 1751 (1957); **27**, 323 (1957); G. R. Dobson and R. K. Sheline, *Inorg. Chem.*, **2**, 1313 (1963), and references therein.
77. L. F. Dahl and J. F. Blount, *Inorg. Chem.*, **4**, 1373 (1965).
78. M. Kalvins, U. Zahn, P. Kienle, and H. Eicher, *Z. Naturforsch.*, **17a**, 494 (1962); R. H. Herber, W. R. Kingston, and G. K. Wertheim, *Inorg. Chem.*, **2**, 153 (1963); E. Fluck, W. Kerler, and W. Neuwirth, *Angew. Chem. Intern. Ed. Engl.*, **2**, 277 (1963).
79. L. F. Dahl, C. Martell, and D. L. Wampler, *J. Am. Chem. Soc.*, **83**, 1761 (1961).
80. W. G. Sly, *J. Am. Chem. Soc.*, **81**, 18 (1959).
81. K. Noack, *Spectrochim. Acta*, **19**, 1925 (1963); *Helvet. Chim. Acta*, **47**, 1064 (1964).
82. H. Stammreich, K. Kawoi, O. Sala, and P. Krumholz, *J. Chem. Phys.*, **35**, 2175 (1961).
83. H. J. Keller and H. Wawersik, *Z. Naturforsch.*, **20**, 938 (1965).
84. R. Ercoli and F. Barbieri-Hermitte, *Atti Accad. Nazl. Lincei*, **16**, 249 (1954).
85. P. W. Sutton and L. F. Dahl, private communication, 1965.
86. F. Basolo, J. Chatt, H. B. Gray, R. G. Pearson, and B. L. Shaw, *J. Chem. Soc.*, **1961**, 2207.
87. A. Wojcicki and F. Basolo, *J. Am. Chem. Soc.*, **83**, 525 (1961).
88. I. A. Cohen and F. Basolo, *J. Inorg. Nucl. Chem.*, **28**, 511 (1966).
89. A. T. Brault, E. M. Thorsteinson, and F. Basolo, *Inorg. Chem.*, **3**, 770 (1964).
90. A. Wojcicki and H. B. Gray, *Proc. Chem. Soc.*, **1960**, 358; *Abstracts of the 141st National Meeting of the American Chemical Society*, Washington, D.C., March 1962, p. 32M.
91. H. B. Gray, E. Billig, A. Wojcicki, and M. Farona, *Can. J. Chem.*, **41**, 1281 (1963); H. B. Gray, I. Bernal, and E. Billig, *J. Am. Chem. Soc.*, **84**, 3404 (1962).
92. A. S. Kasenally, J. Lewis, A. R. Manning, J. R. Miller, R. S. Nyholm, and M. H. B. Stiddard, *J. Chem. Soc.*, **1965**, 3409.
93. W. E. Wilson, *Z. Naturforsch.*, **13b**, 349 (1958).

94. R. F. Heck, *J. Am. Chem. Soc.*, **85**, 657 (1963).
95. W. Hieber and K. Wollmann, *Chem. Ber.*, **94**, 305 (1961).
96. M. Angaletta, *Gazz. Chim. Ital.*, **89**, 2359; 1021 (1960).
97. S. S. Bath and L. Vaska, *J. Am. Chem. Soc.*, **85**, 3500 (1963).
98. A. Wojcicki and F. Basolo, *J. Inorg. Nucl. Chem.*, **17**, 77 (1961).
99. R. B. King, P. M. Treichel, and F. G. A. Stone, *J. Am. Chem. Soc.*, **83**, 3593, 3600 (1961).
100. H. G. Schuster-Woldan and F. Basolo, *J. Am. Chem. Soc.*, **88**, 1657 (1966).
101. W. Strohmeier and H. Mittnacht, *Z. Physik. Chem.*, **29**, 339 (1961); and **34**, 82 (1962); W. Strohmeier and R. Muller, *ibid.*, **40**, 85 (1964).
102. A. Mandelbaum, Z. Neuwirth, and M. Cois, *Inorg. Chem.*, **2**, 902 (1963).
103. E. L. Muetterties, *Inorg. Chem.*, **4**, 1841 (1965).
104. E. L. Muetterties and C. M. Wright, *J. Am. Chem. Soc.*, **86**, 5132 (1964); **87**, 21 (1965).
105. (a) T. Kruck and K. Noack, *Chem. Ber.*, **97**, 1693 (1964). (b) L. Malatesta, G. Caglio and M. Angoletta, *J. Chem. Soc.* 6974 (1965).
106. L. S. Meriwether and M. L. Fiene, *J. Am. Chem. Soc.*, **81**, 4200 (1959).
107. C. A. Streuli, *Anal. Chem.*, **31**, 1652 (1959); **32**, 985 (1960).
108. R. F. Heck, *J. Am. Chem. Soc.*, **85**, 651, 655 (1963).
109. (a) R. J. Angelici and F. Basolo, *J. Am. Chem. Soc.*, **84**, 2495 (1962); *Inorg. Chem.*, **2**, 728 (1963). (b) W. Hieber and W. Freyer, *Chem. Ber.*, **92**, 1765 (1959). (c) A. G. Osborne and M. H. B. Stiddard, *J. Chem. Soc.*, **1964**, 634. (d) H. Wawersik and F. Basolo, *Chem. Comm.* 366 (1966).
110. R. J. Angelici, F. Basolo, and A. J. Poë, *J. Am. Chem. Soc.*, **85**, 2215 (1963).
111. R. J. Angelici, *Inorg. Chem.*, **3**, 1099 (1964).
112. R. Poilblanc and M. Bigorgne, *Bull. soc. chim.*, 1301 (1962).
113. W. Hieber and W. Schropp, Jr., *Z. Naturforsch.*, **14b**, 460 (1959); E. W. Abel and I. S. Butler, *J. Chem. Soc.*, **1964**, 434; R. J. Angelici, *Inorg. Chem.* **3**, 1099 (1964); E. W. Abel, I. S. Butler, and J. G. Reid, *J. Chem. Soc.*, **1963**, 2068; A. Wojcicki and M. F. Farona, *J. Inorg. Nucl. Chem.*, **26**, 2289 (1964).
114. P. Barrett, Doctorate thesis, University of Toronto, Toronto, Canada, 1965.
115. (a) R. J. Angelici and J. K. Graham, *J. Am. Chem. Soc.*, **87**, 5586, 5590 (1965), (b) D. A. Brown, J. N. Gogan, and H. Sloan, *J. Chem. Soc.*, **1965**, 6873; H. Werner. *J. Organometal. Chem.*, 5, 100 (1966); H. Werner and R. Prinz, *ibid.*, **5**, 79 (1966).
116. C. W. Heitsch and J. G. Verkade, *Inorg. Chem.*, **1**, 863 (1962); **2**, 512 (1963).
117. R. B. King, *Inorg. Chem.*, **3**, 1039 (1964).
118. E. M. Thorsteinson and F. Basolo, *J. Am. Chem. Soc.*, **88**, 3929 (1966).
119. D. Morris, private communication.
120. B. Jezowska-Trzebiatowska and J. Ziolkowski, *Chem. Zvesti*, **19**, 177 (1965) and references therein.
121. R. J. Mawby, D. Morris, E. M. Thorsteinson, and F. Basolo. *Inorg. Chem.*, **5**, 27 (1966).
122. R. Cramer, *J. Am. Chem. Soc.*, **86**, 217 (1964).
123. F. Zingales, A. Chiesa, and F. Basolo, *J. Am. Chem. Soc.*, **88**, 2707 (1966).
124. I. W. Stolz, H. Haas, and R. K. Sheline, *J. Am. Chem. Soc.*, **87**, 716 (1965).
125. For a review of examples see R. F. Heck, *Advan. Chem. Ser.*, **49**, 181 (1965).
126. H. E. Gunning *et al.*, *J. Am. Chem. Soc.*, **86**, 4243 (1964); J. Hine, *Divalent Carbon*, Ronald Press, New York, 1964.
127. J. Halpern, B. R. James, and A. L. W. Kemp, *J. Am. Chem. Soc.*, **83**, 4097 (1961).
128. T. H. Coffield, J. Kozikowski, and R. N. Closson, *J. Org. Chem.*, **22**, 598 (1957); *Spec. Publ. Chem. Soc.* No. 13, p. 126 (1959).

129. K. A. Keblys and A. H. Filbey, *J. Am. Chem. Soc.*, **82,** 4204 (1960); F. Calderazzo, *Inorg. Chem.*, **4,** 293 (1965).

130. R. J. Mawby, F. Basolo, and R. G. Pearson, *J. Am. Chem. Soc.*, **86,** 3994 (1964).

131. F. Calderazzo and F. A. Cotton, *Chim. ind. (Milan)*, **46,** 1165 (1964).

132. F. Calderazzo and F. A. Cotton, *Inorg. Chem.*, **1,** 30 (1962).

133. R. E. Pincock, *J. Am. Chem. Soc.*, **86,** 1820 (1964); R. G. Pearson, *J. Chem. Phys.*, **20,** 1478 (1952).

134. R. J. Mawby, F. Basolo, and R. G. Pearson, *J. Am. Chem. Soc.*, **86,** 5043 (1964).

135. J. A. McCleverty and G. Wilkinson, *J. Chem. Soc.*, **1963,** 4096.

136. F. Calderazzo, private communication.

137. F. Calderazzo and F. A. Cotton, *Proceedings of the Seventh International Conference on Coordination Chemistry*, Stockholm, 1962, p. 296.

138. G. Booth and J. Chatt, *Proc. Chem. Soc.*, **1961,** 67.

139. W. Schoeller, W. Schrauth, and W. Essens, *Ber.*, **46,** 2864 (1913); A. C. Harkness and J. Halpern, *J. Am. Chem. Soc.*, **83,** 1258 (1961).

140. J. P. Bibler and A. Wojcicki, *J. Am. Chem. Soc.*, **88,** 4862 (1966).

141. For reviews see I. Wender *et al.*, *U.S. Bur. Mines. Bull.* Washington, D. C. 1962; C. W. Bird, *Chem. Rev.*, **62,** 283 (1962).

142. I. Wender, H. W. Sternberg, and M. Orchin, *J. Am. Chem. Soc.*, **75,** 3041 (1953); M. Orchin, L. Kirch, and I. Goldfarb, *ibid.*, **78,** 5450 (1956).

143. G. W. Coleman and A. A. Blanchard, *J. Am. Chem. Soc.*, **58,** 2160 (1936); W. Heiber and H. Schulten, *Z. anorg. allgem. Chem.*, **232,** 29 (1937).

144. H. W. Sternberg, I. Wender, R. A. Friedel, and M. Orchin, *J. Am. Chem. Soc.*, **75,** 2717 (1953).

145. R. A. Friedel, I. Wender, S. L. Shufler, and H. W. Sternberg, *J. Am. Chem. Soc.*, **77,** 3951 (1955).

146. G. Natta and R. Ercoli, *Chim. ind. (Milan)*, **34,** 503 (1952).

147. G. Natta, R. Ercoli, S. Castellano, and P. H. Barbieri, *J. Am. Chem. Soc.*, **76,** 4049 (1954).

148. I. Wender, S. Metlin, S. Ergun, H. W. Sternberg, and H. Greenfield, *J. Am. Chem. Soc.*, **78,** 5401 (1956).

149. M. Johnson, *J. Chem. Soc.*, **1963,** 4859; R. W. Goetz and M. Orchin. *J. Am. Chem. Soc.*, **85,** 1549 (1963).

150. (a) D. S. Breslow and R. F. Heck *Chem. & Ind.*, **17,** 467 (1960). (b) *J. Am. Chem. Soc.*, **83,** 4023 (1961); **84,** 2499 (1962).

151. R. F. Heck and D. S. Breslow, *J. Am. Chem. Soc.*, **82,** 4438 (1960); R. F. Heck, *ibid.*, **85,** 1220 (1963).

152. R. F. Heck, *J. Am. Chem. Soc.*, **85,** 651 (1963).

153. R. F. Heck, *J. Am. Chem. Soc.*, **86,** 5138 (1964).

154. C. L. Aldridge and H. B. Jonassen, *J. Am. Chem. Soc.*, **85,** 886 (1963).

155. S. K. Bhattacharyya, *Actes de Deuxieme Congres International de Catalyse*, Editions Technip, Paris, 1961, p. 2401.

156. L. Marko, *Proc. Chem. Soc.*, **1962,** 67.

157. L. Marko, *Chem & Ind.*, **1962,** 260.

158. H. H. Storch, N. Golumbic, and R. B. Anderson, *The Fischer-Tropsch and Related Syntheses*, John Wiley and Sons, New York, 1951.

159. J. W. Reppe, *Ann.*, **582,** 121 (1953); W. Hieber and F. Leutert, *Z. anorg. allgem. Chem.*, **204,** 145 (1932).

160. P. Krumholz and H. M. A. Stettiner, *J. Am. Chem. Soc.*, **71,** 3035 (1949).

161. H. W. Sternberg, R. Markby, and I. Wender, *J. Am. Chem. Soc.*, **79,** 6116 (1957); W. Hieber and G. Brendel, *Z. anorg. allgem. Chem.*, **289,** 324 (1957).

162. J. W. Reppe and H. Vetter, *Ann.*, **582**, 133 (1953).
163. (a) J. W. Reppe and H. Kroper, *Ann.*, **582**, 38 (1953). (b) J. W. Copenhaver and M. H. Bigelow, *Acetylene and Carbon Monoxide Chemistry*, Reinhold Publishing Corp., New York, 1949. (c) R. F. Heck and D. S. Breslow, *J. Am. Chem. Soc.*, **85**, 2779 (1963).
164. J. D. Rose and F. S. Statham, *J. Chem. Soc.*, **1950**, 69.
165. R. F. Heck, *J. Am. Chem. Soc.*, **85**, 2013 (1963).
166. E. O. Fischer and G. Burger, *Chem. Ber.*, **94**, 2409 (1961); *Z. Naturforsch.*, **16b**, 77 (1961).
167. J. Tsuji, J. Kiji, S. Imamura, and M. Morikawa, *J. Am. Chem. Soc.*, **86**, 4350 (1964); J. Tsuji, M. Morikawa, and J. Kiji, *ibid.*, **86**, 4851 (1964); J. Tsuji and S. Hosaka, *ibid.*, **87**, 4075 (1965).
168. B. L. Shaw, *Chem. & Ind.*, **1962**, 1190.
169. L. Vaska, *Z. Naturforsch.*, **15b**, 56 (1960); L. Vaska and J. W. DiLuzio, *J. Am. Chem. Soc.*, **83**, 1262, 2784 (1961).
170. J. Chatt and B. L. Shaw, *Chem. & Ind.*, **1960**, 931, and **1961**, 290; J. Chatt, B. L. Shaw, and A. E. Field, *J. Chem. Soc.*, **1960**, 3466.
171. A. A. Vlček and A. Rusina, *Nature*, **206**, 295 (1965).
172. H. W. Sternberg, I. Wender, R. A. Friedel, and M. Orchin, *J. Am. Chem. Soc.*, **75**, 3148 (1953); H. W. Sternberg and I. Wender, *Spec. Publ. Chem. Soc.* No. 13, p. 35 (1959).
173. J. A. Osborn, G. Wilkinson, and J. F. Young, *J. Chem. Soc.*, **1966A**, 1711.
174. (a) J. Smidt *et al.*, *Angew. Chem.*, **71**, 176 (1959). (b) J. Smidt *et al.*, *Angew. Chem. Intern. Ed. Engl.*, **1**, 80 (1962). (c) A. Aguilo, *Advances in Organometallic Chemistry* (F. G. A. Stone and R. West, eds.), Academic Press, N.Y., Vol. 5, 1967.
175. M. N. Vargaftik, I. I. Moiseev, and Y. K. Sirkiv, *Dokl. Akad. Nauk SSSR*, **147**, 399 (1962); *Izv. Akad. Nauk SSSR Otd. Khim. Nauk*, 1147 (1963).
176. T. Dozono and T. Shiba, *Bull. Japan. Petrol. Inst.*, **5**, 8 (1963).
177. I. I. Moiseev, M. N. Vargaftik, and Y. K. Sirkin, *Izv. Akad. Nauk SSSR Otd. Khim. Nauk*, 1143 (1963).
178. P. M. Henry, *J. Am. Chem. Soc.*, **86**, 3246 (1964).
179. C. K. Rule and V. K. Lamer, *J. Am. Chem. Soc.*, **60**, 1974 (1938).
180. J. Chatt, L. M. Valarino, and L. M. Venanzi, *J. Chem. Soc.*, **1957**, 3413.
181. I. I. Moiseev, M. N. Vargaftik, and Y. K. Syrkin, *Dokl. Akad. Nauk SSR*, **133**, 377 (1960); E. W. Stern and M. L. Spector, *Proc. Chem. Soc.*, **1961**, 370; E. W. Stern, *ibid.*, **1963**, 111.
182. R. Cramer, *Inorg. Chem.*, **4**, 445 (1965).
183. G. F. Wright, *Ann. N.Y. Acad. Sci.*, **65**, 436 (1957).
184. R. Criegee, *Angew. Chem.*, **70**, 173 (1958).
185. R. R. Grinstead, *J. Org. Chem.*, **26**, 238 (1963).
186. P. M. Henry, *J. Am. Chem. Soc.*, **87**, 990, 4423 (1965).
187. B. B. Baker, *Inorg. Chem.*, **3**, 200 (1964).
188. C. A. Anderson and S. Winstein, *J. Org. Chem.*, **28**, 605 (1963).
189. For a review see reference 44b and also M. Miogue, N. M. Hung, and V. Q. Yen, *Ann. Chim.*, **8**, 157 (1963).
190. A. F. Redasheva and I. P. Samchenko, *Dokl. Akad. Nauk SSSR*, **133**, 1340 (1960).
191. W. L. Budde and R. E. Dessy, *J. Am. Chem. Soc.*, **85**, 3964 (1963).
192. R. R. Vogt and J. A. Nieuwland, *J. Am. Chem. Soc.*, **43**, 2071 (1921).
193. J. Chatt, *Chem. Rev.*, **48**, 7 (1951).
194. T. G. Traylor and A. W. Baker, *Tetrahedron Letters*, **19**, 14 (1959); M. M. Anderson and P. M. Henry, *Chem. & Ind.*, **1961**, 2053.

195. G. Ward and P. M. Henry, private communication.
196. J. Halpern, B. R. James, and A. L. W. Kemp, *J. Am. Chem. Soc.*, **83**, 4097 (1961).
197. For reviews see J. K. Stille, *Chem. Rev.*, **58**, 541 (1958); A. D. Ketley and F. X. Worber, *Science*, **145**, 667 (1964); F. Dawans and P. Teyssie, *Bull. soc., chim. France*, **10**, 2376 (1963).
198. K. Ziegler, E. Holzkamp, H. Breil, and H. Martin, *Angew. Chem.*, **67**, 541 (1955).
199. G. Natta, *Atti accad. naz. Lincei*, 8, **14**, 61 (1955); G. Natta, P. Pino, G. Mazzanti, and P. Longhi, *Gazz. Chim. Ital.*, **87**, 549 (1957).
200. W. L. Carrick *et al.*, *J. Am. Chem. Soc.*, **82**, 1502 (1960); J. C. Chien, *ibid.*, **81**, 86 (1959).
201. E. J. Arlman, *J. Catalysis*, **3**, 89 (1964); *J. Polymer Sci.*, **62**, 830 (1962).
202. P. Cossee, *Tetrahedron Letters*, **17**, 12, 17 (1960); *J. Catalysis*, **3**, 80 (1964); E. J. Arlman and P. Cossee, *ibid.*, **3**, 99 (1964).
203. G. Natta, *Angew. Chem.*, **68**, 393 (1956).
204. K. Ziegler, *Angew. Chem.*, **64**, 323 (1952); **68**, 721 (1956).
205. K. Ziegler and H. G. Gellert, U.S. Patent 2,699,453 (1955).
206. K. Ziegler, F. Crossman, H. Kleiner, and O. Shafter, *Ann.*, **473**, 1 (1929); H. Sinn and F. Patat, *Angew. Chem. Intern. Ed. Engl.*, **3**, 93 (1964).
207. G. Wilke and H. Muller, *Ann.*, **618**, 267 (1958).
208. H. C. Brown, *Hydroboration*, W. A. Benjamin, New York, 1962, p. 14.
209. R. E. Rinehart, H. P. Smith, H. S. Witt, and H. Romeyn, Jr., *J. Am. Chem. Soc.*, **83**, 4864 (1961); **84**, 4145 (1962).
210. A. J. Canale, W. A. Hewett, T. M. Shryne, and E. A. Youngman, *Chem. & Ind.*, **1962**, 1054; A. J. Canale and W. A. Hewett, *J. Polymer Sci.*, Pt. B, **2**, 1041 (1964).
211. J. F. Harrod and A. J. Chalk, *J. Am. Chem. Soc.*, **86**, 1776 (1964).
212. R. Cramer, *Inorg. Chem.*, **1**, 722 (1962).
213. R. Cramer, *J. Am. Chem. Soc.*, **87**, 4717 (1965).
214. T. Alderson, E. L. Jenner, and R. V. Lindsey, *J. Am. Chem. Soc.*, **87**, 5638 (1965).
215. James P. Collman and W. R. Roper, *J. Am. Chem. Soc.*, **87**, 4008 (1965).
216. L. Vaska and J. W. DiLuzio, *J. Am. Chem. Soc.*, **83**, 2784 (1961); **84**, 679 (1962).
217. J. A. Ibers and S. J. LaPlaca, *Proceedings of the Eighth International Conference on Coordination Chemistry*, Vienna, 1964, p. 95.
218. (a) R. Cramer, *J. Am. Chem. Soc.*, **88**, 2272 (1966). (b) M. Orchin, in *Advances in Catalysis* (D. D. Eley, H. Pines, and P. D. Weisz, eds.), Academic Press, New York, Vol. 16, 1966.
219. N. Gaylord and H. F. Mark, *Linear and Stereoregular Polymers*, Interscience Publishers, New York, 1959, p. 219.
220. J. W. Reppe, *Acetylene Chemistry*, P. B. Report 18852-S, Chas. A. Mayer and Co., New York, 1949; G. Wilke, *Proc. R. A. Welch Foundation Conf. IX. organometallic compounds* (W. O. Milligan, ed.), Houston, Texas, 1965, Ch.7; also reference 224b.
221. J. W. Reppe *et al.*, *Ann.*, **560**, 1 (1948).
222. G. N. Schrauzer and S. Eichler, *Chem. Ber.*, **85**, 550 (1962).
223. J. W. Reppe and W. J. Schweckendieck, *Ann.*, **560**, 104 (1948).
224. For reviews see (a) J. Halpern, *Proceedings of the Third International Congress on Catalysis*, Amsterdam, 1964, Interscience Publishers, New York, Vol. 1, 1965, p. 146. (b) J. Halpern, *Ann. Rev. Phys. Chem.* **16**, 103 (1965).
225. M. Calvin, *Trans. Faraday Soc.*, **34**, 1181 (1938).
226. (a) M. Calvin, *J. Am. Chem. Soc.*, **61**, 2230 (1939). (b) W. K. Wilmarth, M. K. Barsh, and S. S. Dharmotti, *ibid.*, **74**, 5035 (1952). (c) M. Calvin and W. K.

Wilmarth, *ibid.*, **78**, 1301 (1956). (d) W. K. Wilmarth and M. K. Barsh, *ibid.*, **78**, 1305 (1956).

227. W. K. Wilmarth and M. K. Barsh, *J. Am. Chem. Soc.*, **75**, 2237 (1953).

228. S. Weller and G. A. Mills, *J. Am. Chem. Soc.*, **75**, 769 (1953); L. W. Wright and S. Weller, *ibid.*, **76**, 3345 (1954).

229. A. H. Webster and J. Halpern, *J. Phys. Chem.*, **60**, 280 (1956); O. J. Korinek and J. Halpern, *ibid.*, **60**, 285 (1956).

230. J. Halpern and E. Peters, *J. Chem. Phys.*, **23**, 605 (1955); E. Peters and J. Halpern, *J. Phys. Chem.*, **59**, 793 (1955); J. Halpern, E. R. McGregor, and E. Peters, *ibid.*, **60**, 1455 (1956).

231. J. Halpern and J. B. Milne, *Proceedings of the Second International Congress on Catalysis*, Paris, 1960, Editors Technip, Paris, Vol. 1, 1961, p. 445.

232. A. H. Webster and J. Halpern, *J. Phys. Chem.*, **61**, 1239 (1957); J. Halpern, *Advan. Catalysis*, **9**, 302 (1957).

233. K. Wirtz and K. F. Bonhoeffer, *Z. physik. Chem.*, **177A**, 1 (1936); W. K. Wilmarth, J. C. Dayton, and J. M. Fluornoy, *J. Am. Chem. Soc.*, **75**, 4549 4553 (1953); J. M. Fluornoy and W. K. Wilmarth, *ibid.*, **83**, 2257 (1961).

234. M. T. Beck, I. Gemesi, and J. Farkas, *Nature*, **197**, 73 (1963).

235. J. F. Harrod, S. Ciccone. and J. Halpern *Can. J. Chem.*, **39**, 1372 (1961); U. Schindewolf, *Ber. Bunsenges.*, **67**, 219 (1963).

236. J. Halpern, J. F. Harrod, and B. R. James, *J. Am. Chem. Soc.*, **83**, 753 (1961); **88**, 5150 (1966).

237. R. L. Burwell, Jr., A. B. Littlewood, M. Cardew, G. Pass, and C. T. H. Stoddart, *J. Am. Chem. Soc.*, **82**, 6272 (1960).

238. J. Halpern and B. R. James, *Can. J. Chem.* **44**, 495 (1966).

239. N. K. King and M. E. Winfield, *J. Am. Chem. Soc.*, **80**, 2060 (1958); **83**, 3366 (1961).

240. B. DeVries, *J. Catalysis*, **1**, 489 (1962).

241. J. Kwiatek, I. L. Mador, and J. K. Seyler, *Advan. Chem. Ser.* **37**, 201 (1963).

242. J. Kwiatek and J. K. Seyler, *Proceedings of the Eighth International Conference on Coordination Chemistry*, Vienna, 1964, Springer-Verlag, p. 308.

243. W. R. McClellan *et al.*, *J. Am. Chem. Soc.*, **83**, 1601 (1961).

244. L. Vaska and R. E. Rhodes, *J. Am. Chem. Soc.*, **87**, 4470 (1965).

245. F. H. Jardine, J. A. Osborn, G. Wilkinson, and J. F. Young, *Chem. & Ind.*, **1965**, 560; *Chem. Commun.*, **1965**, 131.

246. L. Vaska, *Inorg. Nucl. Chem. Letters*, **1**, 89 (1965).

247. M. F. Sloan, A. S. Matlock, and D. S. Breslow, *J. Am. Chem. Soc.*, **85**, 4014 (1963).

248. C. S. Kraihanzel and P. K. Maples, *J. Am. Chem. Soc.*, **87**, 5267 (1965).

249. R. F. Hesh, *Advances in Organometallic Chemistry* (F. G. A. Stone and R. West, eds.), Academic Press, N.Y., Vol. 4, 1966, p. 254.

250. S. M. Schildcrout, G. A. Pressley, Jr., and F. E. Stafford, *J. Am. Chem. Soc.*, in press.

8

Metal Ion Catalysis : Photochemistry

Metal Ion Catalysis of Organic Reactions

A very large number of reactions are known in which coordination compounds, or rather the metal ions which form coordination compounds, act as catalysts. At the end of the reaction the metal ion can be recovered, though possibly in a changed oxidation state and coordinated with different groups from the original ones. However, these are secondary effects, and the efficiency of very small amounts of the metal ion justifies the use of the term catalyst. It will be seen to be characteristic of these reactions that intermediate coordination compounds are formed which undergo further reaction. In some cases the metal ion is consumed stoichiometrically in the reaction, and a more rigorous terminology in these instances would be "metal ion promotion" rather than "metal ion catalysis," but the latter is continually used.

A brief survey is given here of metal ion catalysis of organic reactions under two broad classifications: (1) acid-base reactions and (2) redox reactions. The first will discuss the acid catalysis by metal ions of hydrolysis reactions, carboxylation and decarboxylation reactions, elimination reactions, transaminations, and aldol condensations. The discussion of redox reactions will be limited to autoxidation of organic compounds with some mention being made of synthetic oxygen-carriers. The last section provides a few examples of reactions of coordinated ligands, in particular the template process for the synthesis of macrocyclic ligands.

A large amount of research has been done on metal ion catalysis, particularly in the borderline disciplines of inorganic-organic chemistry and inorganic chemistry-biochemistry. About all we can hope to do here is give a few examples that permit a discussion of some of the basic principles involved. Fortunately, several excellent reviews have been written on the subject, and the reader wanting a more complete coverage is referred to these, e.g., acid-base reactions,[1] redox reactions,[2] and reactions of coordinated ligands.[3] No doubt the most important and interesting examples of such reactions are to be found in biological systems. However, such systems are beyond the scope of our discussion, but again there are excellent reviews[4] of metal ion catalysis in biological systems. Many of the simple examples that will be described here may be considered as models for biological cases.

Acid-Base Reactions

The activity of metal ions in acid-catalyzed reactions comes about in a very straightforward manner. Thus, reactions that are catalyzed by hydrogen ion or other acids are also generally catalyzed by metal ions, which are themselves Lewis acids. In fact, even reactions that are catalyzed only by hydrogen ion and not by acids such as acetic acid molecules (specific catalysis) will still be catalyzed by metal ions. This is so because hydrogen ion and metal ions are acids of the same type. However, as we shall see in the discussions that follow, metal ions may have many advantages over hydrogen ion. Metal ions usually have a positive charge greater than one, can readily form metal chelates, and may be considered as super-acids that can exist in neutral solution.

There are a number of ways in which acid catalysis may occur.[1] For the reactions of interest to us here, the major effect may be considered to be that of the acid adding on to a substrate in such a way as to drain electrons toward the site of attachment. This then facilitates reaction at some other part of the substrate, and the greater the "electron sink" efficiency of the acid, the more effective it will be as a catalyst.

Hydrolysis Reactions. Surely the most extensively studied organic (or inorganic) reaction is the hydrolysis, or solvolysis, of a variety of different organic compounds. The classical example of ester hydrolysis, which is both acid and base catalyzed, has been the subject of extensive investigations. The classical ^{18}O experiments of Bender[5] have helped in the elucidation of the mechanism of ester hydrolysis, and it is now generally agreed that the acid catalysis, of interest here, takes place by the series of equilibria shown by the scheme

$$
\begin{array}{ccccc}
\overset{O}{\underset{\|}{R-C-OR'}} & \underset{\xrightarrow{H^+}}{\rightleftharpoons} & \overset{OH}{\underset{|}{R-\overset{+}{C}-OR'}} & \underset{\xrightarrow{H_2O}}{\rightleftharpoons} & \overset{OH}{\underset{\underset{\overset{|}{OH_2^+}}{|}}{R-C-OR'}} \\
\end{array}
$$

$$\updownarrow$$

$$OH$$

$$
RCO_2H \xrightarrow{-H^+} RCO_2H_2^+ + R'OH \rightleftharpoons R-\underset{\underset{OH}{|}}{\overset{\overset{OH}{|}}{C}}-\overset{+}{O}HR'
\tag{1}
$$

It is apparent that the replacement of H^+ in this scheme by M^{n+} may give rise to an analogous form of metal ion catalysis. This does in fact happen, but what is observed in practice is that for such simple esters H^+ is a more efficient catalyst than is M^{n+}. The reason is that the proton brings a higher positive charge density on the substrate than does a much larger metal ion, even if its oxidation state is greater than one. Metal ions tend to become more catalytically active in substrates containing other functional groups in appropriate positions to permit chelation with the metal ion.

For example, in 1951 Kroll[6] discovered that metal ions effectively catalyze the hydrolysis of amino acid esters. This is undoubtedly due to the presence of the amine group, which coordinates to the metal ion and greatly enhances its coordination to the carbonyl oxygen of the carboxyl group by chelation. There is now direct evidence[7] of this type of chelation in the solid state for the $1:1$ complexes of certain amino acid esters with the halides of Cu^{2+}, Ni^{2+}, and Cd^{2+}, as shown by

$$
\begin{array}{ccc}
\text{ROC}=\!=\!\text{O} & & \text{Cl} \\
| & \diagdown \;\; \diagup & \\
| & \text{Cu} & \\
| & \diagup \;\; \diagdown & \\
\text{CH}_2\!-\!\text{N} & & \text{Cl} \\
& \text{H}_2 & \\
& \text{(I)} &
\end{array}
$$

The hydrolysis of amino acid ester complexes with Co^{2+}, Cu^{2+}, Mn^{2+}, Ca^{2+}, and Mg^{2+} is extremely rapid, even at pH 7–8, where the amino ester itself is stable. When the concentration of metal ion is raised, the rate of hydrolysis increases, reaching a maximal value at a metal ion/ester ratio of unity, indicating that the most active species is a complex containing one metal ion and one ester molecule. Furthermore, the effectiveness of the metal ion as a catalyst rises with its increasing tendency to form complexes. For example,[6] at the experimental conditions of $pH = 7.9$, $24.5°C$, and M^{2+} = glycine methyl ester = 0.016 M, the observed rate constants (k_{obs}, sec^{-1}) decrease in the following order:

$$Cu^{2+} \;(4.3 \times 10^{-2}) > Co^{2+} \;(1.6 \times 10^{-2}) > Mn^{2+} \;(3.5 \times 10^{-3})$$
$$> Ca^{2+} \;(7 \times 10^{-4}).$$

Keep in mind that under these conditions without the metal ion the glycine methyl ester does not hydrolyze. It is also of interest to note that Cu^{2+} is much more effective than either H^+ or OH^- for the catalysis of the hydrolysis of phenylalanine ethyl ester.[8]

This much greater effectiveness of Cu^{2+} relative to OH^- and H^+ for the catalyzed hydrolysis of phenylalanine ethyl ester cannot be due solely to the electrostatic effect of an attack of OH^- on a positively charged α-amino ester. The introduction of a positive charge, two atoms from the carbonyl group of an ester, usually increases the rate constant of alkaline hydrolysis by a factor of 10^3, whereas there is a difference of approximately 10^6 between the Cu^{2+} and OH^- rates of hydrolysis of phenylalanine ethyl ester. Furthermore, the reaction cannot be due to attack by a water molecule on a positively charged α-amino acid ester, because the rate of acid hydrolysis in model systems is very small. Thus, it seems reasonable to postulate that the rapid hydrolysis of α-amino acid esters as catalyzed by Cu^{2+} is due to a direct interaction of the metal ion with the reaction center, the ester group.

In support of this are structures of the type shown by I. Likewise, carbonyl oxygen exchange experiments accompanying the Cu^{2+}-catalyzed hydrolysis of phenylalanine ethyl ester-carbonyl-^{18}O suggest a mechanism very analogous to that of H^+-catalyzed ester hydrolysis (1).

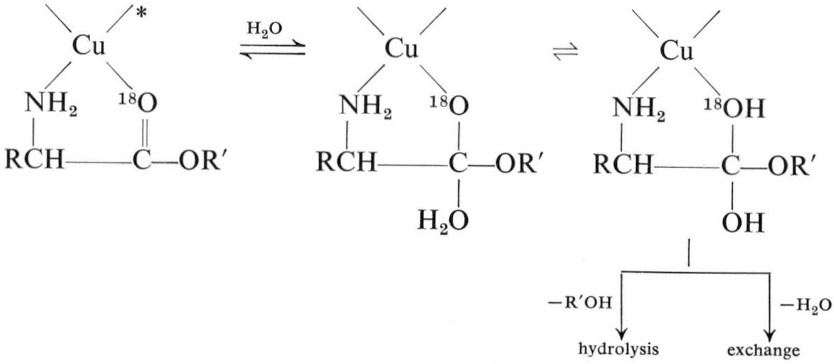

$$(2)$$

Additional evidence that the metal ion catalysis of amino acid esters is due to a direct interaction of the metal ion with the reaction center is furnished by the investigations of Alexander and Busch.[9] They prepared bis(ethylenediamine)cobalt(III) complexes of the type represented by II in the scheme

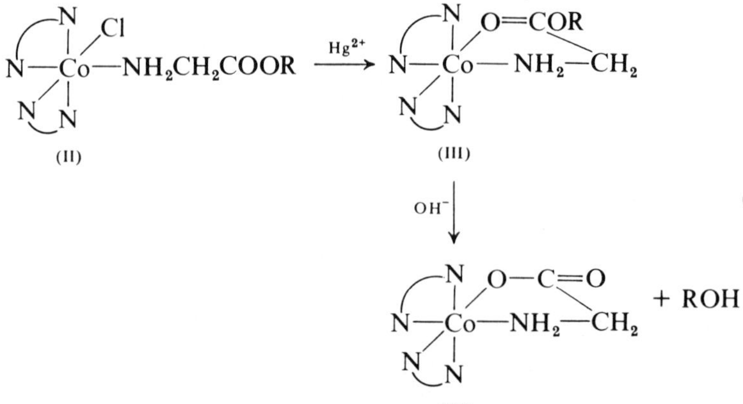

(II)   (III)

$$(3)$$

(IV)

* Representations of this type are used throughout, and it is understood that the "open" coordination positions, $\overset{\diagdown\diagup}{Cu}$, are occupied by solvent or other ligands.

and found that the rate of ester hydrolysis is very small, but the addition of Hg^{2+} to remove the coordinated Cl^- greatly enhances the rate of ester hydrolysis. Direct evidence for the existence of intermediate III was obtained by examining the i.r. spectrum of a reaction mixture which shows initially the characteristic amino acid ester carbonyl band at 1740 cm^{-1}. Upon the addition of Hg^{2+} this band rapidly disappears, and a new one forms at 1610 cm^{-1} (presumably that of III) which slowly diminishes in intensity as a band at 1640 cm^{-1} appears; this band is the one known for the glycinato product, IV.

Related to this is the prior observation of Collman and Buckingham[10] that hydrolytic cleavage of N-terminal peptide bonds is smoothly accomplished by the complex $Co(trien)H_2O(OH)^{2+}$. The N-terminal amino acid residue is selectively hydrolyzed and simultaneously converted into the inert Co(III) complex, as shown by the equation

$$Co(trien)H_2O(OH)^{2+} + H_2NCHRCNHP \overset{O}{\underset{\|}{}} \rightarrow$$
$$Co(trien)(H_2NCHRCOO)^{2+} + H_2NP \quad (4)$$

The reaction takes place rapidly in aqueous solution at $65°$ and pH 7–8. Although stoichiometric rather than catalytic, this process is perhaps the best model at present for the *in vitro* action of *exo*metal peptidases. The reaction may also prove useful as a method of sequential peptide analysis and for stepwise degradation of natural peptides.

Specific examples of reaction 4 are given by the equations

$$Co(trien)H_2O(OH)^{2+} + gly\text{---}gly\text{---}gly \xrightarrow[\substack{65° \\ 12 \text{ min}}]{pH\ 7.5} Co(trien)(gly)^{2+} + gly\text{-}gly$$
$$\substack{0.03\ M \qquad\qquad\qquad 0.03\ M}$$

$$(5)$$

$$Co(trien)H_2O(OH)^{2+} + gly\text{---}phe \xrightarrow[\substack{65° \\ 25 \text{ min}}]{pH\ 7.5} Co(trien)(gly)^{2+} + phe$$
$$\substack{0.01\ M \qquad\qquad 0.02\ M}$$

$$(6)$$

$$Co(trien)H_2O(OH)^{2+} + phe\text{---}gly \xrightarrow[\substack{65° \\ 25 \text{ min}}]{pH\ 7.5} Co(trien)(phe)^{2+} + gly \quad (7)$$
$$\substack{0.01\ M \qquad\qquad 0.02\ M}$$

where gly is the glycine residue and phe is phenylalanine. The first step in these reactions is surely the replacement of coordinated water by the amino group of the polypeptide. Assuming that then mechanism 3 is followed, the carbonyl oxygen of the β-amide group is coordinated and this promotes hydrolysis to yield the observed products. Alternatively the coordinated hydroxyl group may attack the peptide carboxyl carbon through a five-ring intermediate, the complex acting both as a template (p. 650) and a buffered source of hydroxide ion. It should be mentioned that metal-bearing enzymes, such as leucine amino peptidase,[11] catalyze the hydrolysis of N-terminal peptide bonds through a process involving chelation between the enzyme, the substrate, and the metal ion. Likewise, divalent metal ions have also been shown to accelerate the hydrolysis of peptides.[12]

Alkaline hydrolysis of the half ethyl esters of oxalic, malonic, adipic, and sebacic acids has been studied[13] in the presence of the ions Li^+, Na^+, K^+, Tl^+, Ca^{2+}, Ba^{2+}, and $Co(NH_3)_6^{3+}$. The multivalent ions and Tl^+ catalyze the hydrolysis of the oxalate and malonate esters, and the alkali-metal ions have only a small negative salt effect on the rates of reaction of the adipate and sebacate esters. The catalytic effects are attributed to activated complexes having the structures shown by V and VI. These structures

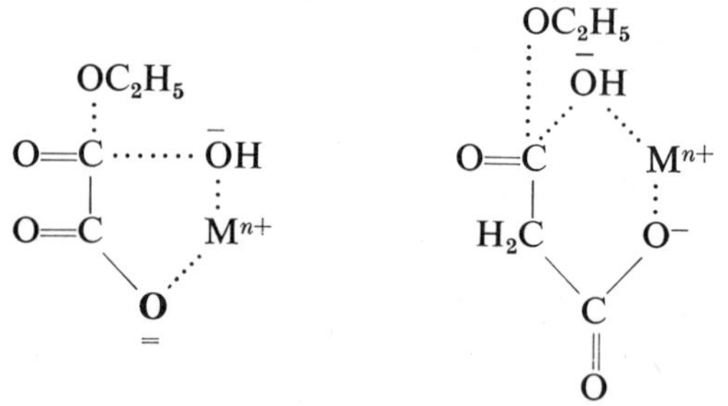

(V)   (VI)

are similar to those postulated for the metal ion-catalyzed hydrolysis of α-amino acid esters. The greater effect found for oxalate ion is in line with the greater stability of the oxalato complexes. Since the inert complex $Co(NH_3)_6^{3+}$ is catalytically active, it appears that the formation of an outer-sphere complex may be sufficient to promote hydrolysis.

From this discussion it is clear that the hydrolysis of esters other than carboxylic acid esters may well be susceptible to metal ion catalysis. Brief mention will be made here of only two additional examples, both of which have been studied in considerable detail. First, it has been known for several years[14] that thiol esters are rapidly cleaved in the presence of Hg^{2+}. Acetyl coenzyme A[15] and acetoacetyl coenzyme A[16] undergo almost instantaneous hydrolysis in essentially neutral solutions to give Hg(II) mercaptides. Chelation with Hg^{2+} may occur in these systems, but it does not appear to be essential because Hg^{2+} also cleaves simple thio esters containing no secondary ligand groups. Presumably the strong coordination of the sulfur atom with Hg^{2+} is sufficient driving force for this reaction.

Extensive investigations have been made of the metal ion catalysis of the hydrolysis of phosphate esters. In general monosubstituted phosphate esters, $ROPO_3^{2-}$, are stable towards hydrolysis in alkaline solution. This may in part be due to the negative charge which retards attack by the nucleophile OH⁻. Divalent metal ions such as Mg^{2+} and Cu^{2+} will neutralize this charge and so catalyze the reaction. In addition the metal ions chelate with the phosphate oxygens to provide a further driving force for reaction.

The hydroxides of La^{3+}, Ce^{4+}, and Th^{4+} promote the hydrolysis of α-glycerylphosphate in the pH range 7–10.[17] It was suggested that the reaction could be regarded as a model for the metal ion-promoted alkaline phosphatases which cleave phosphate esters[18] at a pH of 9. Further study[19] shows that the model reaction indeed resembles the enzymatic reaction in that cleavage occurs exclusively at the P-O bond and with complete retention of stereochemical configuration. The reaction does not take place readily unless the phosphate ester is substituted in the β position, so that the hydrolysis of ethylphosphate is not greatly promoted by $La(OH)_3$ gel, but the hydrolyses of β-methoxyethyl-, β-hydroxyethyl-, and β-amino-ethylphosphates are strongly catalyzed at pH 8.5. For the β-methoxy-ethylphosphate, it is suggested that the activated complex may have the structure shown by

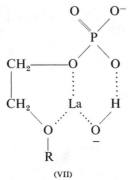

(VII)

In addition to the hydrolysis of monoesters of phosphoric acid, the hydrolysis of diesters of phosphoric acid is also metal ion catalyzed.[20] Sarin, isopropylmethylphosphonylfluoridate, and analogous compounds have been extensively studied (p. 440). Martell[21] and his students report that for such substrates Cu(II) chelates of diamines have the greatest catalytic activity, although certain chelates of VO(IV), ZrO(IV), and $MO_2(VI)$ are also quite active. They suggest a mechanism involving interaction between Sarin, the diaquo Cu(II) chelate, and hydroxide ion.

A very closely related reaction is the hydrolysis of condensed phosphates catalyzed by metal ions.[22] The cleavage of pyrophosphate to orthophosphate

$$P_2O_7^{2-} + H_2O \rightarrow 2HPO_4^{2-} \tag{8}$$

is not catalyzed, but the hydrolysis of higher polyphosphates is.[23] This suggests that VIII is stabilized to hydrolysis, but IX is activated. Attack by water occurs at the terminal, uncomplexed phosphorus in IX.

(VIII)   (IX)

Metal ion catalysis of hydrolysis reactions of compounds other than esters is known. Mention was made earlier of the hydrolysis of amides, reaction 4. Both metal ion catalysis and retardation have been observed for the hydrolysis of Schiff bases. Thus Eichhorn and Bailar[24] found that Schiff bases are easily hydrolyzed if made part of a chelate system of the type shown in

$$\xrightarrow{\text{H}_2\text{O}} \text{2RCHO} + \qquad (9)$$

However, if the aldehyde moiety is coordinated to the metal ion as in the structure

(X)

cleavage of the Schiff base is retarded.[25] Although the electron displacement responsible for the weakening of the C-N bond is present in both complexes, the difference in behavior is attributed to the fact that removal of the aldehyde in 9 leaves the chelate ring intact, whereas the removal of salicylaldehyde from X converts a two-ring chelate to a one-ring chelate. The resultant loss of chelate stabilization more than offsets the electron withdrawal effect.

Transamination. These reactions are reminiscent of those discovered by Pfeiffer,[26] in which Cu(II) and Ni(II) chelates of Schiff bases formed from salicylaldehyde and esters of optically active α-amino acids were shown to undergo rapid racemization, ester exchange, and oxidative deamination. The racemization and deamination are understandable in terms of the prototropic tautomerism of these aldimine systems:

$$\underset{\substack{| \\ RCHCO_2^-}}{NH_2} + \underset{\substack{\| \\ R'CCO_2^-}}{O} + M^{2+} \underset{+H_2O}{\overset{-H_2O}{\rightleftharpoons}} \quad (10)$$

$$\underset{\substack{\| \\ RCCO_2^-}}{O} + \underset{\substack{| \\ R'CHCO_2^-}}{NH_2} + M^{2+} \underset{+H_2O}{\overset{-H_2O}{\rightleftharpoons}} \quad (11)$$

Hydrolysis of the new tautomer will now lead to transamination (11). This mechanism appears to be responsible for the reaction of α-amino acids in the presence of pyridoxal and metal ions and similarly those which are catalyzed in biological systems by pyridoxal phosphate proteins.[27]

Aldol Condensations. Related to the metal ion-pyridoxal reactions is a group of aldol condensations catalyzed by multivalent metal ions. For example, in basic solution (pH 11 at 100°C) diglycinatocopper(II) readily condenses either with formaldehyde to form the Cu(II) complex of serine or with acetaldehyde to produce Cu(II) complexes of threonine and allo-threonine:[28]

$$(12)$$

Presumably the catalytic activity of the metal ion is due to the polarization of the C-H bond sufficiently to facilitate the formation of an enolate ion. The effectiveness of the metal ion is markedly improved[29] in the system Co(en)$_2$gly^{2+}, perhaps because of the +2 charge instead of a zero charge for 12. Studies using n.m.r. show that in this complex the glycine C—H hydrogens rapidly exchange with deuterium in alkaline solution.[30]

Bromination. In any reaction, such as the one just described, where the cleavage of a C-H bond is important, the introduction of a metal ion into the molecule in the proper position should facilitate the reaction. Another example is furnished by the work of Pedersen[31] on the bromination of ethyl acetoacetate catalyzed by Cu^{2+}:

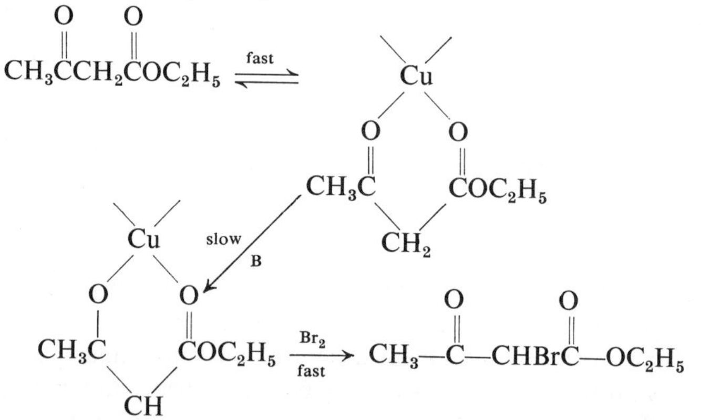

$$
\begin{array}{c}
\underset{\substack{\parallel \\ O}}{CH_3C}\underset{\substack{\parallel \\ O}}{CH_2C}OC_2H_5 \xrightleftharpoons[\text{fast}]{}
\end{array}
$$

(13)

Here B is any base in solution, and the resulting enolate reacts rapidly with bromine. The effect of Cu^{2+} is quite pronounced; 0.007 M Cu^{2+} causes a doubling of the rate. Only a small amount of the metal complex is formed, and the rate of reaction depends on its concentration or, in other words, on the stability of the metal complex. This is borne out by the observation that the rates of bromination parallel the complex stabilities, which decrease in the order

$$Cu^{2+} > Ni^{2+} > La^{3+} > Zn^{2+} > Pb^{2+} >$$

$$Mn^{2+} > Cd^{2+} > Ca^{2+} > Ba^{2+} > H^+$$

Decarboxylation. Whenever a β-keto acid decarboxylates, the CO_2 leaves behind a pair of electrons. If the decarboxylation is to proceed at a practical rate, the pair of electrons left on the rest of the molecule must be stabilized in some fashion. It is clear that a metal ion properly situated in he substrate may behave as an "electron sink" to assist the reaction, and accordingly the decarboxylation of a number of β-keto acids is susceptible to metal ion catalysis. Kinetic studies show that the mechanism of reaction is probably that represented by

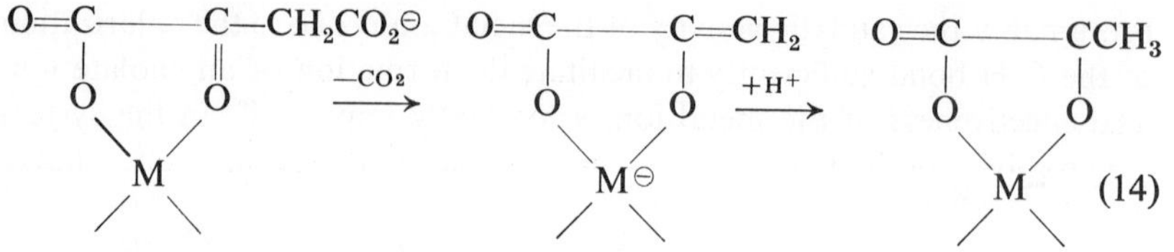

(14)

Good correlation exists between catalytic efficiency and complex-forming ability of the metal, the order in the former being $Al^{3+} > Fe^{3+} > Cu^{2+} > Fe^{2+} > Zn^{2+} > Mg^{2+} > Mn^{2+} > Ca^{2+}$. In some cases metal ions inhibit the decarboxylation reactions, and one reason suggested[33] for this is that the metal ion may also coordinate with the otherwise labile carboxyl group and prevent its departure in the form of CO_2.

Carboxylation. Metal ions will not catalyze the decarboxylation of monocarboxylic acids, presumably because metal ion coordination is more stable with the ground state than with the transition state. However, a reversal of this argument suggests that metal ions may catalyze the carboxylation of substances containing active hydrogens, since the metal ion complex should be more stable in the transition state than in the ground state. The ground state might be a metal methylcarbonate or, as was found to be effective, magnesium methoxide. Both aliphatic nitro compounds

$$Mg(OCH_3)_2 + CH_3NO_2 + CO_2 \rightarrow Mg \begin{matrix} O-C \overset{O}{\diagdown} \\ \diagdown \\ O-N \overset{\diagup O}{\diagdown} O \end{matrix} CH + 2CH_3OH \quad (15)$$

and ketones

$$Mg(OCH_3)_2 + R-\overset{O}{\underset{\|}{C}}-R' + CO_2 \rightarrow Mg \begin{matrix} O-C \overset{\diagup O}{} \\ \diagdown \\ O-C \overset{\diagdown}{R} \end{matrix} CR' + 2CH_3OH \quad (16)$$

can be carboxylated by this method, an excellent organic synthetic tool and an interesting catalytic phenomenon.[34]

Conclusion. Having just described several specific examples of metal ion catalysis of organic reactions, we find it worth while to recapitulate the role of the metal ion in these systems. No doubt the most important factor in most cases is that the metal ion coordinates with the substrate in some strategic position and removes electron density from an atom subject to nucleophilic attack in the reaction process. This is also done effectively by a proton in the corresponding acid-catalyzed reactions. A metal ion, however, is superior to a proton on several grounds. A metal ion can introduce a multiple positive charge into the substrate, whereas a proton can introduce only a single positive charge. Furthermore, a metal ion can operate in a neutral solution and can coordinate to several donor atoms, whereas a proton must operate in acid solution and can only coordinate with one donor atom.

In listing the ways in which metal ions may promote organic reactions, the requirement that the metal ion be suitably positioned within the substrate molecule must be emphasized. Chelation of the metal ion with the substrate appears to be a usual requirement of metal ion catalysis, which means that the substrate must contain a donor atom near the reactive center in order to permit chelation. The effectiveness of catalysis of a series

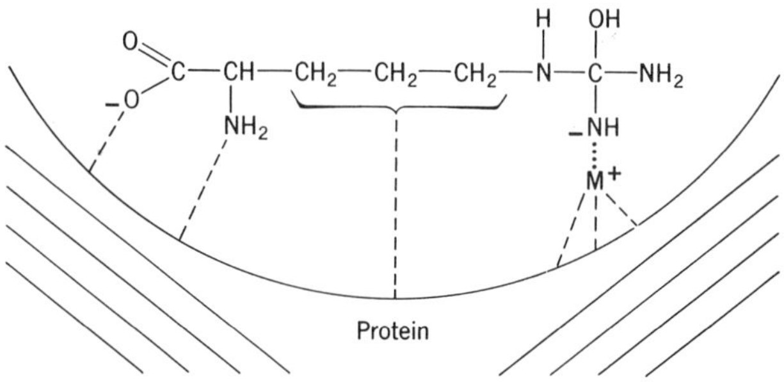

Fig. 8.1   Schematic representation of metal-stabilized activated state in enzymatic hydrolysis of arginine. From reference 33.

of metal ions usually parallels their formation constants for complexation with the same or related chelating agents. This indicates that the metal ion complex must stabilize the transition state for reaction. If it were to stabilize the ground state, then it follows that the presence of the metal ion would retard the reaction (see VIII and X).

Since metal ions have a large coordination number, it is possible to form not only a metal ion complex with the substrate but also a metal ion complex with both the substrate and the reagent. Hence the metal ion can serve as a central collection point for both components of a bimolecular reaction, and presumably assist the reaction by making its entropy of activation more positive. For example, Klotz[35] has found that small organic molecules not ordinarily bound to proteins form strong complexes if suitable metal ions are present, and suggests that this accounts for the role of metal ions in the action of hydrolytic enzymes (Fig. 8.1).

Redox Reactions

The role played by complexes in the previous case of acid-catalyzed reactions was purely that of a generalized acid and depended on complex-forming ability. Except for this ability there was no distinction between transition, inner transition, and representative elements. The second kind of catalytic behavior to be discussed is confined almost entirely to the transition elements since the key feature is the ability of the metal ion to exist in solution in more than one oxidation state. Ability to complex plays a secondary, but still necessary, role.

If a given oxidizing agent and reducing agent have the proper redox potentials (or standard free energies) to react with each other, the reaction may still be slow. This is particularly true of organic reducing agents. In such a case a metallic ion of variable valence may greatly accelerate the rate by providing an easier reaction path. Essentially alternate reactions of the ion with an oxidizing agent and a reducing agent occur.

Generally this will involve complexing of the metal ion with the other reagents. Such coordination often greatly increases the ease with which an electron transfer can occur.[36] An example is the catalytic effect of Mn(III) on the reaction between chlorine and oxalate ion. The key step is the internal oxidation-reduction of $MnC_2O_4^+$, followed by reaction with chlorine.[37]

$$MnC_2O_4^+ \rightarrow Mn^{2+} + CO_2 + CO_2^- \tag{17}$$

$$CO_2^- + Cl_2 \rightarrow CO_2 + Cl + Cl^- \tag{18}$$

$$Cl + Mn^{2+} \rightarrow Cl^- + Mn^{3+} \tag{19}$$

Trivalent manganese is again free to react with oxalate ion.

Autoxidation of Organic Substances. The term autoxidation is used to denote the reaction of oxidizable materials with molecular oxygen unaccompanied by the phenomena of flame and high temperature. The reaction takes place slowly, homogeneously in the case of liquids, is inhibited by easily oxidized materials such as phenols, aromatic amines, and secondary alcohols, and is greatly accelerated by the presence of small amounts of metal ions from the transition series.

The reaction is an undesirable one in many cases, such as the deterioration of edible fats, lubricating oils, and high polymers like rubber. It is desirable in the hardening of drying oils, the oxidation of reactive impurities (such as mercaptans) in mixtures, and particularly in the industrially important air oxidation of hydrocarbons to more valuable intermediates.

That it is the metals of variable valence that are effective in these reactions has long been known. Thus copper, cobalt, iron, manganese, and nickel salts are good catalysts, whereas aluminum, magnesium, zinc, and lead salts are inactive or very poor catalysts. Since metals used in the construction of equipment can form their ions by corrosion, the latter metals may be preferable to the former for many cases where oxidizable materials contact the equipment. If oxidation is desired, the usual practice is to add the metal in the form of a salt of ill-defined constitution such as naphthenate, resinate, or stearate for reasons of solubility in the organic phase.

To illustrate autoxidation generally, a discussion of the oxidation of hydrocarbons will be given.[38] Cobalt(II) salts are the preferred catalysts, and small amounts of organic peroxides or hydroperoxides are usually added to prevent the induction period which is otherwise encountered.[39] The reaction may go at room temperature or up to 150°C or so. Pressure may be atmospheric or higher. Only a small amount of dissolved oxygen is actually reacting, but this is sufficient if a reservoir in the gas phase is available. The reaction is slow with saturated hydrocarbons, but unsaturation greatly activates it, as do most negative groups.

The start of the reaction coincides with the oxidation of Co(II) to Co(III). Starting with Co(III) may eliminate the need for added peroxides.[40] The major initial product is hydroperoxides, later accompanied by peroxides, alcohols, ketones, and carboxylic acids. The rate of the reaction expressed as $-dO_2/dt$ is generally independent of the oxygen pressure or concentration and may be between first and second order in the hydrocarbon and between zero and first order in the catalyst concentration. Under steady state conditions, the rate should depend on the square root of the catalyst concentration.[41]

The essential steps appear to be those of the following free radical chain mechanism (RH is the hydrocarbon):

$$Co^{2+} + ROOH \rightarrow Co^{3+} + OH^- + RO \cdot \tag{20}$$

$$Co^{3+} + ROOH \rightarrow Co^{2+} + H^+ + ROO \cdot \tag{21}$$

$$ROO \cdot + RH \rightarrow ROOH + R \cdot \tag{22}$$

$$R \cdot + O_2 \rightarrow ROO \cdot \tag{23}$$

$$RO \cdot + RH \rightarrow ROH + R \cdot \tag{24}$$

$$2ROO \cdot \rightarrow \text{inactive products} \tag{25}$$

and other chain-terminating steps involving the combination of free radicals.[42] Equations 20 and 21 represent initiating steps which also perpetuate the catalyst. Reactions 22 and 23 are the main chain-carrying steps leading to hydroperoxide. Some of the hydroperoxide is used up to regenerate the catalyst. Further oxidation and decomposition of the hydroperoxide and alcohol, ROH, can occur, so that too much oxidation leads to a reduced yield of the hydroperoxide.

Reactions 21 and 23 are generally fast and do not influence the overall rate, which depends chiefly on 22 and on the relative rates of chain initiation in 21 and the various chain-breaking steps. Because of the complicated mechanism the observed rate equation can take on various forms, depending on the hydrocarbon and the experimental conditions.

The reactions involving the metal ion usually entail prior coordination of the metal and the hydroperoxide. The role of the catalyst in both forming and decomposing hydroperoxide was first clearly pointed out by Ivanov.[42] Since the rate of the chain-initiating step depends on the product of metal ion and peroxide, and since peroxide is destroyed by metal ion in two ways, it is possible that the rate becomes independent of metal ion concentration after a point. Further, a reaction such as

$$Co^{2+} + ROO\cdot \rightarrow CoOOR^{2+} \tag{26}$$

essentially the reverse of 21, could become a chain-interrupting step at higher metal ion concentrations.

The effect of inhibitors, such as β-naphthol, is to break the chains by combining with the active free radicals in some as yet not completely specified manner.[44] The chains must be very long as judged by the influence of minute amounts of inhibitor. Some inhibitors simply retard the reaction, reducing the overall rate. Others completely stop it until they are themselves used up. This leads to induction periods of varying duration.

There are other ways in which the metal ion can enter into the reaction. For example, Co(III), if not strongly complexed, as the aquo ion or in acetic acid, will oxidize directly many organic molecules,[44] e.g.,

$$Co^{3+} + RCHO \rightarrow Co^{2+} + RCO + H^+ \tag{27}$$

Also Co(II) probably forms an addition product with oxygen molecule,

$$Co^{2+} + O_2 \rightarrow CoO_2^{2+} \tag{28}$$

the addition product being a free radical. The stability and fate of such an adduct depend on the environment, particularly on the other ligands surrounding the Co(II). For a brief account of synthetic oxygen-carriers see the discussion starting on p. 641.

Radical Reactions with Metal Ions.   Peroxides and hydroperoxides are used as convenient sources of free radicals, particularly to initiate polymerization reactions.[45] Metal ion catalysis of their decomposition is common. As discussed earlier in Chapter 7, a variety of reactions is possible between organic free radicals and metal ions. For example, Cu(II) carboxylates in benzene solution catalyze the decomposition of n-valeryl peroxide according to[46]

$$(n\text{-}C_4H_9CO_2)_2 \xrightarrow{\text{Cu(RCOO)}_2} C_4H_8 + CO_2 + n\text{-}C_4H_9COOH \tag{29}$$

With $CuCl_2$ the reaction product is the alkyl chloride

$$(n\text{-}C_4H_9CO_2)_2 \xrightarrow{\text{CuCl}_2} n\text{-}C_4H_9Cl + CO_2 + CuCl + n\text{-}C_4H_9COOH \tag{30}$$

In both cases a butyl free radical is assumed to be an intermediate. It either is oxidized to olefin or carries out an atom transfer type of reduction of $CuCl_2$.

Organometallic compounds of some stability have been detected in the reactions of organic halides with aqueous Cr(II).[47] For example, the stoichiometry of the reaction of benzyl chloride with Cr^{2+} is given by

$$C_6H_5CH_2Cl + 2Cr^{2+} + H^+ \rightarrow C_6H_5CH_3 + Cr(H_2O)_6{}^{3+} + Cr(H_2O)_5Cl^{2+} \tag{31}$$

A detailed kinetic study of this reaction affords good evidence in support of the scheme shown by the equations

$$C_6H_5CH_2Cl + Cr^{2+} \xrightarrow{\text{slow}} C_6H_5CH_2 \cdots Cl \cdots Cr(H_2O)_5$$
$$\Big\downarrow \text{fast} \tag{32}$$
$$C_6H_5CH_2\cdot + ClCr(H_2O)_5{}^{2+}$$

$$C_6H_5CH_2\cdot + Cr^{2+} \xrightarrow{\text{fast}} C_6H_5CH_2Cr(H_2O)_5{}^{2+} \tag{33}$$

$$C_6H_5CH_2Cr(H_2O)_5{}^{2+} + H_3O^+ \longrightarrow C_6H_5CH_3 + Cr(H_2O)_6{}^{3+} \tag{34}$$

The relative rates of reaction 32 for $C_6H_5CH_2X$ decrease in the order $I^- > Br^- > Cl^- = 555:124:1$. This is the same order as that observed for the reduction of $Co(NH_3)_5X^{2+}$ with Cr(II) (see p. 482). The formation of $C_6H_5CH_2Cr(H_2O)_5{}^{2+}$ is established by observing the absorption spectra of these reaction mixtures, all of which give the same transient spectrum with absorption bands at 360, 297, 274, and 243 mμ. The same spectrum is obtained by the decomposition of α,α-dimethyl-β-phenethyl hydroperoxide with chromous ion. The rate of formation and disappearance of $C_6H_5CH_2Cr(H_2O)_5{}^{2+}$ is shown in Fig. 8.2 for the reaction of $C_6H_5CH_2Cl$ with an acid solution of $Cr(ClO_4)_2$. The same reaction has been used[48]

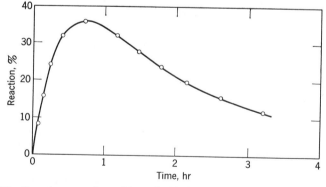

Fig. 8.2 Complete reaction of benzyl chloride with Cr(II) at 41°. Formation and disappearance of $C_6H_5CH_2Cr(H_2O)_5{}^{2+}$. From reference 47.

for the synthesis of a new series of stable organopentacyanocobalt(III) anions:

$$RX + Co^{(II)}(CN)_5^{3-} \rightarrow RCo^{(III)}(CN)_5^{3-} + XCo^{(III)}(CN)_5^{3-} \quad (35)$$

It is obvious that these organometallic reactions are of the same type as the inner-sphere redox mechanisms for inorganic reactions described in Chapter 6.

Synthetic Oxygen Carriers. For autoxidations of hydrocarbons, the exact role(s) of the metal ions in their catalysis remains somewhat open to speculation. One possible function of the metal ion is to form an addition product with oxygen as is represented by equation 28; this product, being a free radical, may enter into reaction with the organic substrates.

A compound capable of adding molecular oxygen and giving it up reversibly

$$\text{Compound} + O_2 \rightleftharpoons \text{Compound} \cdot (O_2) \quad (36)$$

is called an *oxygen-carrying compound*. There are several well known naturally occurring[49] or synthetic[50] compounds of this type. A transition metal is present in all such compounds and plays a major role in the oxygen-carrying properties of these systems.

There are three principal forms of blood with O_2-carrying molecules. By far the most common is red blood, in which the O_2-carrying component contains iron inside a heme group (which in turn is attached to a protein). Lobsters and crabs have blue blood which is due to hemocyanin, a copper compound, and the violet color of certain marine worms is caused by an iron (but non-heme-containing) protein, hemerythrin. These biological systems carry oxygen to a series of catalysts that are oxidized by oxygen. There is a variety of such catalysts, and they are also coordination compounds, such as the cytochromes and the copper oxidases. Naturally, there is considerable interest in these systems, but as yet a detailed understanding of the mechanism of these reactions is not available. However, it is known that the metal is the active site for the reversible attachment of oxygen, and this is of interest in our discussion here of synthetic O_2-carriers. Cobalt[51] and iridium[52] O_2-carriers have been synthesized. There is a suggestion[53] that the anion $Cl_5ReOReCl_5^{4-}$ may combine reversibly with O_2, and similar claims are made for the dimethylglyoxime complexes of Fe(II)[54] and Ni(II).[55] It now appears certain that Mn(II)-phthalocyanine does not have O_2-carrying properties.[56]

We shall next consider specific examples of O_2-carriers of cobalt and of iridium. However, it may first be of help to have some background information on the air oxidation of Co(II) complexes. The brown salts obtained by air oxidation of ammonical solutions of Co(II) salts, called oxocobaltiates by Fremy,[57] were shown by Werner and Mylius[58] to contain the diamagnetic cation $(H_3N)_5CoO_2Co(NH_3)_5^{4+}$. Salts of the green paramagnetic ion $(H_3N)_5CoO_2Co(NH_3)_5^{5+}$ are prepared similarly, or more efficiently by oxidation with H_2O_2.[59] These two classes, diamagnetic and paramagnetic, of dinuclear Co-O_2 compounds are fairly common. For example, the reaction of air with a solution of Co(II)-CN$^-$ at 0° gives the brown diamagnetic anion[60] $(NC)_5CoO_2Co(CN)_5^{6-}$, which on oxidation with bromine in alkaline solution gives the red paramagnetic ion $(NC)_5CoO_2$-$Co(CN)_5^{5-}$. The diamagnetic compounds have formulas that can be expressed in terms of two Co(III) atoms connected by a peroxide ion, e.g., $Co^{(III)}$—O_2^{2-}—$Co^{(III)}$.

Werner formulated the paramagnetic, usually green, systems as containing two non-equivalent cobalt atoms, e.g., Co^{III}—O_2^{2-}—Co^{IV}. However, we can hardly expect two cobalt atoms which appear to be in equivalent environments to have different oxidation states. Modern M.O. theory predicts that the odd electron is in an orbital which extends over both cobalt atoms and both oxygen atoms. If the orbital were heavily concentrated on the oxygen atoms, this would justify labeling each cobalt as Co(III) and the two oxygen atoms as a superoxide group, O_2^-. The hyperfine structure of the e.s.r. spectrum definitely establishes that both cobalts are equivalent and that the odd electron spends a great deal of its time near a cobalt nucleus.[61]

Vlček,[62] on the basis of theoretical considerations, suggested that O_2 is π bonded to the cobalt atoms and that, therefore, the O_2 group lies with

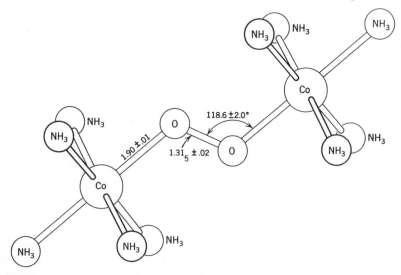

Fig. 8.3 Structure of the cation in the salt $[(NH_3)_5CoO_2Co(NH_3)_5]SO_4(HSO_4)_3$. From reference 64.

its axis perpendicular to the Co-Co axis. This prediction seemed to be supported[63] by x-ray analysis of the structure of $[(NH_3)_5CoO_2Co(NH_3)_5]$-$(NO_3)_5$, but recent studies[64] suggest that this determination is not reliable and the correct structure is that shown in Fig. 8.3 for the cation in $[(NH_3)_5$-$CoO_2Co(NH_3)_5]SO_4(HSO_4)_3$. Thus, the bridging oxygen group is not perpendicular to the Co-Co axis. Each of the oxygen atoms appears to be σ bonded to one of the cobalt atoms, resulting in the staggered arrangement shown. These four atoms are almost coplanar; in contrast to H_2O_2, there is only a small dihedral angle at the O-O bond. The O—O distance (1.31 A) is only slightly longer than that found in superoxides (1.28 A) and is much shorter than that in most peroxides (1.48 A). Therefore, it appears that the oxygen bridging group is more nearly a superoxide (O_2^-), though the e.s.r. measurements show that the unpaired electron is sometimes found on the cobalt atoms.[61] X-ray studies[65] also show the same staggered structure for $[Co—O_2—Co]^{4+}$ in $[(NH_3)_5CoO_2Co(NH_3)_5](SCN)_4$.

One point of particular significance is that these oxygen-bridged complexes with the staggered structure for $[Co—O_2—Co]^{4\ or\ 5+}$ are not O_2-carriers. The oxygen is firmly held, and therefore the takeup of molecular oxygen in these systems is not reversible. We shall see later that the iridium O_2-carrier has a structure that may be considered trigonal bipyramidal (see Fig. 8.4), containing a π-bonded O_2. Unfortunately this is as yet the only

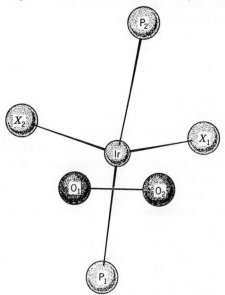

Fig. 8.4   A perspective drawing of the $O_2IrCl(CO)(P[C_6H_5]_3)_2$ molecule. Phenyl rings are not shown. X_1 and X_2 refer to the disordered positions of CO and Cl. From reference 72.

O_2-carrier for which the structure has been determined, and it is only speculative to suggest that all such systems must contain π-bonded O_2. In the discussion that follows we will arbitrarily assume that either this π-bonded structure or a weakly σ-bonded structure (Fig. 8.3) is necessary for an efficient O_2-carrier.

Certain cobalt chelates can behave as O_2-carriers. Among chelates with Schiff bases, two types

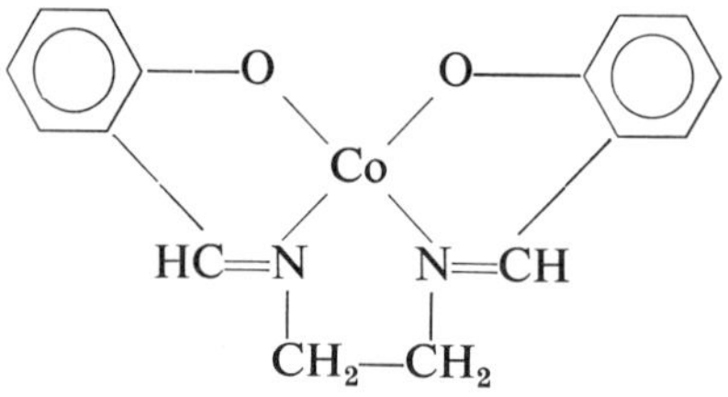

(XI)

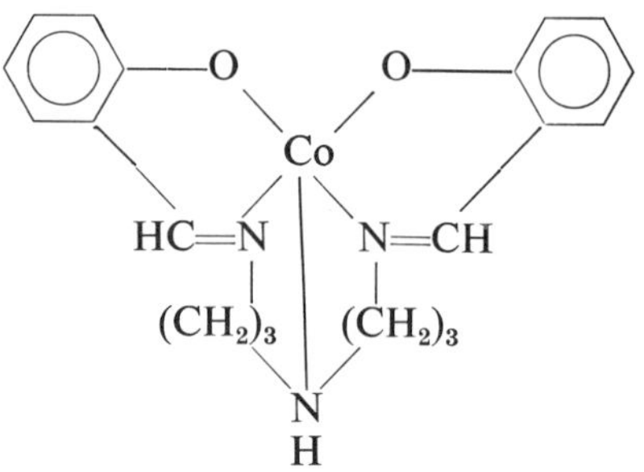

(XII)

of complexes are known to be able to reversibly carry oxygen both in the solid state and in solution.[50] During World War II these complexes were investigated as a means of isolating pure oxygen from air.[67] For several months during this period the U.S. Navy produced oxygen in this way aboard a destroyer tender for welding and cutting. The cost of producing oxygen by this means did not exceed that of cylinder oxygen, but the process was discontinued because of a shortage of cobalt.

Complexes of the type XII have magnetic moments close to 3.8 B.M., corresponding to three unpaired electrons per mole. The compounds absorb 1 mole of O_2 per mole of cobalt, and the magnetic moment decreases to a value near that for one unpaired electron per mole. Complexes of type XI have paramagnetic susceptibilities corresponding to the presence of one unpaired electron. These absorb up to half a mole of O_2 per mole of cobalt, accompanied by a decrease in the paramagnetism. When the solid compound XI was cycled (oxygenation at room temperature and deoxygenation at 80–100°C), it was found to deteriorate to 70% of its original activity after 300 cycles.[50] In quinoline solution, the oxygenation was reversible for only a few cycles.

It was suggested[51b] that the oxygenated form of XI has a binuclear bridged structure in which a molecule of oxygen and a molecule of water are held in the bridge,

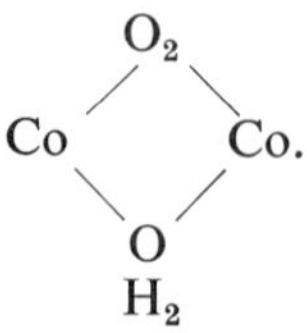

$$Co \overset{\displaystyle O_2}{\underset{\displaystyle \underset{H_2}{O}}{\diamond}} Co.$$

This structure seems to be generally

accepted in recent review articles,[50,67] and the compound is quoted as the only one known to contain a bridging water molecule of this type. The evidence given for this bridged compound, however, is indirect and very speculative. It was further suggested that on recycling the O_2-carrying capacity of the compound deteriorates because of the gradual loss of water and removal of the active bridging site.

Studies[68] have been made in an attempt to obtain direct evidence for the coordinated water in these compounds, and the results strongly suggest that such a molecule of water is not present. Some of the evidence is as follows: (1) the i.r. spectra of the unoxygenated and the oxygenated compounds show no absorptions in the 3300 and 1600 cm^{-1} regions expected for water; (2) the preparation of XI in D_2O gave a compound with an i.r. spectrum identical to that prepared in H_2O; (3) the thermogravimetric analysis of XI showed no stable phase attributable to loss of water and no weight loss until about 240°, at which point decomposition of the compound begins; (4) a small sample of the O_2-carrier was refluxed with pyridine, and three-quarters of the pyridine was distilled, which would presumably remove any coordinated water. Pyridine was then removed at 170° under reduced pressure, and the residue, XI, was an active O_2-carrier.

It therefore appears that coordinated water is not necessary and that its bridged complex is not essential for O_2-carrying properties. x-Ray studies[51] show that molecules of XI are square planar and stacked parallel in the crystal. Inactive forms of XI have been prepared, but these can be activated by the pyridine treatment described above. Apparently, the inactive isomer has a crystal structure which does not allow access of the O_2 molecules. Whenever the pyridine (or water) has been removed from its adduct, a more open structure remains, which will allow reaction with O_2. Deterioration on repeated recyclization is presumably due to irreversible oxidation. A plausible structure for the oxygenated form of the chelate is either

(XIII)   or   (XIV)

Structure XIII is similar to that of Fig. 8.3 for a compound that is not an O_2-carrier. However, if the σ-bonded Co—O is sufficiently weak in XIII, such a structure may lead to easily reversible addition-subtraction of molecular oxygen. Structure XIV is a possibility because it resembles that of Fig. 8.4, but it should be noted that bridged π-bonded systems of this type have no known analogy with other π complexes. For this reason and because of the known σ-bonded bridged structure (Fig. 8.3), structure XIII would now be favored over XIV. The π-bonded structure may be correct for the 1:1 adduct for XII:O_2, and it is known that these complexes react with NO on a mole for mole basis.[69]

At about the same time that this work on the Schiff base chelates of cobalt was in progress there appeared in the literature results on the O_2-carrying properties of bis(histidine)cobalt(II), and a large number of complexes of other α- and β-amino acids.[70] The compounds are prepared by dissolving histidine, its derivatives, glycylglycine, or amino acids in water at a particular pH and then adding a solution of $CoCl_2$. All the physical measurements on oxygenation were made on these aqueous solutions, although it was possible to isolate some of the oxygenated chelates as solids. The oxygenated compounds have a ratio of one O_2 per 2 moles of cobalt.

The Cu(II) and Ni(II) derivatives of histidine are unchanged in the presence of O_2, whereas the Fe(II) chelate is irreversibly oxidized to Fe(III). In the series Fe(II), Co(II), Ni(II), Cu(II), the oxidation potentials steadily decrease, and presumably this trend is emphasized by chelation with histidine. This would cause Fe(II) to be oxidized but would not increase sufficiently the oxidation potentials of Ni(II) and Cu(II). However, Co(II) is in an intermediate position, and this appears to permit an equilibrium between the oxygenated form and the free chelate and free oxygen, but not to cause the permanent oxidation of Co(II) to Co(III).

Neither the structure of bis(histidine)cobalt(II) nor that of its oxygenated form is as yet known. On the basis of the fact that there are two cobalt atoms per oxygen molecule and that the oxygenated compound is diamagnetic, two bridged structures have been proposed for it.[50] These structures correspond to structures XIII and XIV. Infrared studies[71] support such a bridged structure, but what is required is an x-ray study.

Vaska's[52] observation that Ir(PPh$_3$)$_2$COCl behaves as an O_2-carrier is a most significant discovery because this provides us with a simple system that can be studied in considerable detail and can serve as a model for more complicated O_2-carriers. The structure of the oxygenated compound Ir(PPh$_3$)$_2$COCl(O_2) was determined[72] by x-ray studies and is shown in Fig. 8.4. The structure may be regarded as six-coordinated with the ligands CO, Cl, and the two oxygen atoms of the O_2 molecule in the basal plane with iridium; above and below this basal plane are the two phosphorus atoms of the P(C$_6$H$_5$)$_3$ groups. Alternatively the structure can be considered to be five coordinated, with one coordination position directed toward the center of the two oxygen atoms of the O_2 molecule and the structure being trigonal bipyramidal.

The significant results regarding the oxygen attachment to iridium are: (1) the two oxygen atoms are equivalent and equidistant from the iridium, (2) the O-O bond length of 1.30 ± 0.03 A is longer than in molecular O_2 (1.20 A) and significantly shorter than in O_2^{2-} (1.48 A). The equivalence of the oxygen atoms is consistent with the suggested π bonding[73] of molecular O_2 to the iron in oxyhemoglobin, which differs from the earlier ideas of Pauling.[74] That the O-O distance is very nearly that for O_2^- is perhaps misleading, because then the iridium is formally Ir(II) and yet the compound is diamagnetic. If this were an Ir(II) compound, it would be a low-spin d^5 system and would be paramagnetic.

The parent compound $Ir(PPh_3)_2COCl$ does not react with O_2 as a solid, but in benzene solution it takes up 1 mole of O_2 per iridium and the color changes from yellow to red. The oxygenated solid is quite stable at room temperature in an atmosphere of O_2 in the dark, though an irreversible photochemical oxidation takes place in the light. The O_2 may be removed in solution at low pressure, but the solid loses O_2 only slowly in vacuum. Molecular weight determinations show that it is monomeric in benzene or chloroform solutions, and treatment with acid yields H_2O_2. Its i.r. spectrum has a band at 860 cm^{-1}, which is a frequency associated with a coordinated peroxy group, and the CO stretching frequency drops on oxygenation. On the basis of all of these observations along with the fact that this compound adds reversibly other molecules such as H_2, HCl, and Cl_2 (p. 14), it appears that the mechanism for O_2 cyclization is represented by the equilibrium

$$
\begin{array}{c}
\overset{\displaystyle O}{\underset{\displaystyle}{C}} \\
\text{P}\diagdown \; | \diagup \\
\text{Ir} \quad + \quad \overset{O}{\underset{O}{\|}} \;\rightleftharpoons\; \text{Ir}\!-\!\overset{O}{\underset{O}{\|}} \\
\text{P}\diagup \; | \\
\text{Cl}
\end{array}
\qquad (37)
$$

In this representation the $P(C_6H_5)_3$ groups are in front and behind the plane of the paper.

In conclusion it would appear that the most important factor in considering whether or not a system will function as an O_2-carrier is the ease with which electron transfer occurs from the metal to the O_2 ligand. In the reversible combination between O_2 and a complex of an oxidizable metal, there is the possibility of the redox equilibria shown by

$$
M^{n+} + O_2 \underset{}{\overset{\text{add.}}{\rightleftharpoons}} M^{n+}(O_2) \xrightarrow{\text{oxid.}} M^{2+n+}(O_2^{2-}) \qquad (38)
$$

If a molecule is to be an efficient O_2-carrier, then the addition step must take place and the oxidation step must be prevented. This is surely the function of the ligand in hemoglobin and of the multidentate ligands in the Co(II) chelates. Similarly the electron acceptor properties of CO and of $P(C_6H_5)_3$ in $Ir(PPh_3)_2COCl$ stabilize the lower oxidation state of iridium and so make possible the reversible addition to and removal of O_2 from Ir(I) without the interference of the irreversible oxidation. The principles involved in O_2-carriers now appears to be fairly well understood, and it should be possible to design and prepare better synthetic O_2-carriers. These advances also bring us closer to a better understanding of O_2-carriers in biological systems.†

Reactions of Coordinated Ligands

The metal ion catalysis of organic reactions clearly involves reactions of coordinated ligands, as was discussed in the previous section and in the last portion of Chapter 7. In this section we will describe a few examples of stoichiometric reactions of coordinated ligands, with particular attention paid to the influence of the metal on the reaction. For example, an entirely new area of aromatic chemistry was made possible with the discovery of ferrocene and the synthesis of other π-cyclopentadienyl metal compounds. These systems undergo electrophilic (and free radical) substitution reactions on the π-cyclopentadienyl rings typical of aromatic reactions, and a great deal of work has been done in this area. This topic will not be discussed here, but the interested reader is referred to the several reviews written on the subject.[75]

However, one point regarding reactions of π-cyclopentadienyl metal complexes is unique and should be mentioned. This is the fact that carbonium ions adjacent to metallocene systems possess unusual stability. Two examples will be given. First it was observed[76] that the solvolyses of α-methylmetallocenyl-carbinyl acetates proceed by a carbonium ion mechanism, and that these acetates hydrolyze with rates greater than even triphenylmethyl (trityl) acetate. The relative rates of solvolysis, and therefore the carbonium ion stabilities, increase in this order: trityl:Fe:Ru: Os = 0.15:1.00:1.4:5.4, where iron, ruthenium, and osmium are the metals in the π-cyclopentadienyl metal compounds. This order for carbonium ion stabilization for the metal systems is found to parallel that for the strength of intramolecular hydrogen bonds of the metals to the carbinols, but is the reverse of that observed for reactivity of the parent metallocene toward acetylation. This supports an explanation of a greater amount of overlap

---

† Metal complexes of molecular nitrogen have been reported[130] and nitrogen fixation at room temperature has been achieved.[131]

between the filled metal orbital and the vacant p orbital of the carbonium ion with increasing atomic number of the metal.

Second, it was found[77] that vinylmetallocenes are extraordinarily reactive towards the addition of weak acids such as HN_3 and $HC_2H_3O_2$ across the double bond. It was postulated that the mechanism of addition involves the intermediate formation of α-metallocenylcarbonium ion (XV) as shown by the equations‡

(39)

(XV)

Again the rates of reaction increase with increasing atomic number of the metal in the relative order $Fe < Ru < Os = 1.00:1.2:4.6$.

Aromatic Ligands. The effect of coordination on electrophilic substitution reactions of aromatic ligands such as aniline and pyridine has been discussed,[78] and it appears that the pattern of reactivity is similar to that of the free ligand. However, the rates of reaction do differ between the free and the coordinated (metal or proton) ligand. As expected, coordination which removes electron density from the aromatic ligand reduces its reactivity to electrophilic attack. The point of interest is to compare the reactivity of a protonated ligand with that coordinated to a metal. An example of this is provided by the nitration of 1,10-phenanthroline. The recommended conditions[79] for its nitration require mixtures of nitric acid and oleum at a temperature of 170°C. In contrast the complex $Co(phen)_3^{3+}$ is readily nitrated in concentrated sulfuric acid at 80°, and a 70% yield of the 5-nitro-1,10-phenanthroline is isolated after treatment of the nitrated complex with EDTA. Estimates were made[80] of the second-order constants for nitration at 100°C in 98% H_2SO_4; H_2phen^{2+}, 5.7×10^{-5} M^{-1} sec^{-1}; $Co(phen)_3^{3+}$, 2.7×10^{-3}; $Fe(phen)_3^{3+}$, 4.2×10^{-3}. It is not yet known whether this difference in reactivity derives simply from the difference in the effective charge on the nitrogen atoms or whether there is, in addition, an important degree of π electron donation from the filled t_{2g} orbitals of the metals.

‡ It now appears that neighboring d orbital participation is unimportant and that resonance stabilization of the carbonium ion is responsible [T. T. Tidwell and T. G. Traylor, *J. Am. Chem. Soc.*, **88**, 3442 (1966)].

Quasiaromatic Ligands. Extensive investigations have been made on the reactions of the quasiaromatic metal chelates $M(acac)_3$, where $M =$ Cr(III), Co(III), Rh(III), and acac is the acetylacetonate anion. The results of these studies are reviewed by Collman.[81] Electrophilic substitution reactions take place at the central carbon of the chelate rings as represented by

These reactions include halogenation, nitration, thiocyanation, acylation, formylation, chloromethylation, and aminomethylation. One, two, or all three of the chelate rings can be substituted, except in acylation and formylation, which do not yield the trisubstituted chelates.

The mechanism of reaction appears to be that represented by 40, although no kinetic studies have as yet been reported. The best evidence in support of this mechanism is the observation that, when optically active metal chelates are used, the reactions take place without racemization. This suggests, but does not require (see p. 316), that reactions occur without the chelate rings having to open and close.

An example of the anomalous chemical properties often exhibited by functional groups on these chelate rings is the unusually facile displacement of several groups from these rings under electrophilic conditions. Thus the acetyl groups in the acetylated chelates are readily displaced under nitration, chlorination, bromination, and thiocyanogenation conditions:

The cleavage of C-C bonds under such mild conditions has few classical analogies.

Template Reactions. Biological systems such as metal porphyrins are very complex, and the *in vivo* reactions leading to their synthesis are still largely a mystery. However, it does seem plausible that the metal ion may serve as a central point of organization at some stage of the process to bring together in a particular manner certain portions of the complicated molecular system. Surely the function of the metal in many synthetic reactions is known to be that of bringing together the reactants in a specific fashion in a multistep process. Such a process is referred to as a *template reaction*.[82] For example, it is common knowledge that the synthesis of metal-containing phthalocyanines is generally easier than the synthesis of the free base, almost certainly because the metal ion directs the course of the reaction.

Curtis[83] discovered that $Ni(en)_3{}^{2+}$ reacts with dry acetone

$$Ni(en)_3{}^{2+} + CH_3COCH_3 \rightarrow \text{(XVI)} \tag{42}$$

in a sealed tube at about 100°C and in the presence of anhydrous $CaSO_4$ to form a quadridentate macrocyclic Ni(II) chelate (XVI). This reaction has been extended to include other metals, amines, ketones, and also aldehydes so that a variety of different macrocyclic compounds has been prepared. Very little is known about the mechanism of this reaction, but the rate is accelerated by base and retarded by water. It would appear that the first stages of the reaction may involve a series of condensation reactions

$$Ni(en)_3{}^{2+} + CH_3COCH_3 \rightleftharpoons \text{(XVII)} + H_2O \tag{43}$$

to form the Schiff base complex (XVII). Equilibrium 43 is readily reversed if the water produced by the reactions is not removed. The overall reaction also generates 1 mole of ethylenediamine, which can serve as the base in the reaction

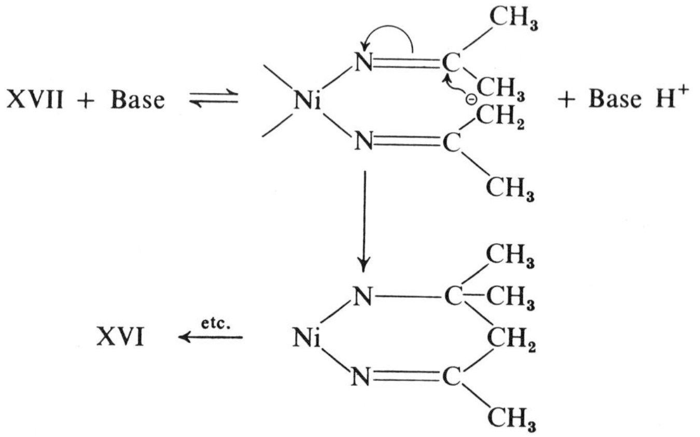

$$XVII + Base \rightleftharpoons \text{(structure)} + Base\ H^+ \tag{44}$$

XVI $\xleftarrow{\text{etc.}}$ (structure)

This total reaction process may depend on the orientation influence of the metal. It is of interest that the complex (XVI) can be readily reduced[84] to give the chelate of the saturated amine, which then reacts with CN^- to form the free quadridentate macrocyclic amine

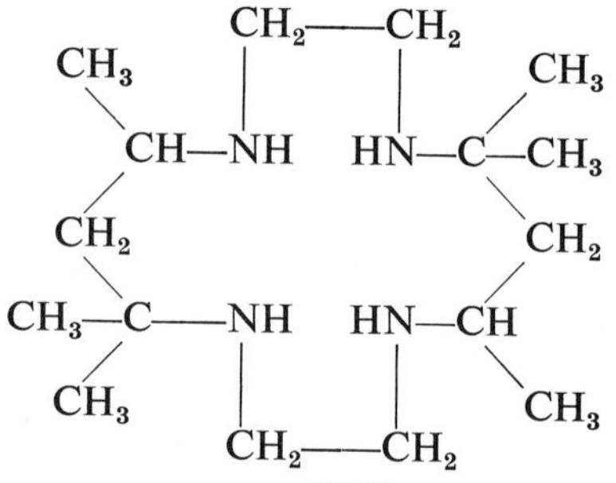

(XVIII)

Attempts to prepare the Schiff base

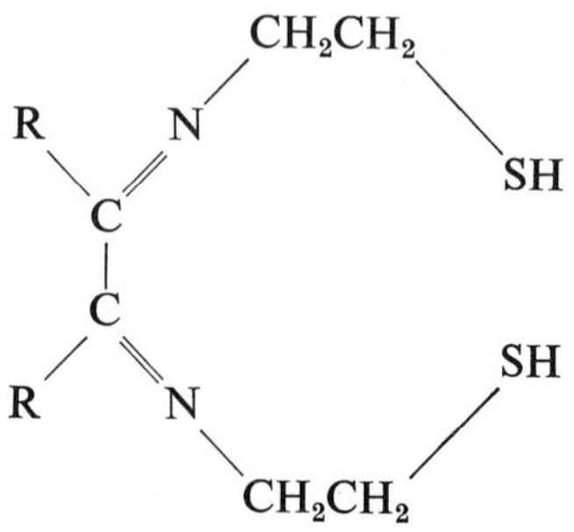

(XIX)

by the reaction of $NH_2CH_2CH_2SH$ with α-diketones were not successful because the amine and the mercapto groups behave as competitive nucleophiles, and this usually results in the formation of thiazolines and thiazoles. However, in the presence of Ni^{2+} a yield in excess of 70% of the desired Schiff base is obtained:[85]

$$R\!-\!\overset{\overset{\displaystyle O}{\|}}{C}\!-\!\overset{\overset{\displaystyle O}{\|}}{C}\!-\!R + 2NH_2CH_2CH_2SH + Ni^{2+} \rightarrow$$

$$+ 2H_3O^+ \quad (45)$$

(XX)

From the manner of synthesis it may be concluded that the metal ion mediates the condensation reaction between the α-diketone and β-mercaptoethylamine. The principal effect of Ni^{2+} is to produce that possible reaction product which is best suited to form a stable complex.

With the two sulfur atoms in *cis* positions in XX, it should be possible to close this chelate ring by reacting it with an appropriate difunctional molecule:

$$(46)$$

This has been done by the reaction of XX, with α,α'-dibromo-o-xylene.[85] Another example[86] of a cyclization reaction of a different type is that between *bis*(dimethylglyoxamato)nickel(II) and boron trihalide:

$$Ni(DMG)_2 + BX_3 \rightarrow$$

$$(47)$$

Even quinquidentate and sexadentate macrocyclic chelate groups have been prepared.[87] With Fe^{2+} used as the template metal ion, 2,6-diacetyl-pyridine condenses with triethylenetetramine to give the quinquidentate and with tetraethylenepentaamine to give the sexadentate chelate compounds, respectively.

Applications of template reactions should prove very useful in the total synthesis of certain natural products. This concept has already met with success in the synthesis of corrin.[88] Its two halves were synthesized separately and then cyclized to give corrin by using a Ni(II) template. Woodward's[89] elegant synthesis of chlorophyll, however, did not include the use of a metal coordination sphere as a template during the cyclization of the porphyrin. Also, it has been shown that the Schiff base precursor of XVIII can be prepared from $enHClO_4$ and acetone without any added metal ion.[132]

Photochemistry of Complex Ions

Most of the complexes, including aquo ions, of the transition metals show two distinct kinds of absorption of light. The first kind occurs chiefly in the visible, though it may extend to the infrared and ultraviolet regions, and consists of one or more moderately well defined bands of low intensity. Molar extinction coefficients are of the order of 0.1–100. The second kind of absorption occurs chiefly in the ultraviolet, though it may extend to the visible, and has much higher intensity, the molar extinction coefficients being of the order of 1000–10,000. One or more bands may be found, or often only a steadily increasing absorption with decreasing wavelength so that the maximum is not accessible. Figure 8.5 shows some typical spectra, those of two *luteo* cobalt(III) ions.

The visible, weak absorption is due to transitions involving only electrons on the central metal atom, chiefly the electrons which can be associated with orbitals formed from the d orbitals of the isolated metal atom. These may be called d-d transitions. Their occurrence is responsible for the usual colors associated with complex ions. With the work of Ilse and Hartmann[90] as a beginning a rather satisfactory understanding of d-d spectra has been developed by using crystal field theory.[91] The most important point is that absorption of a quantum of light removes an electron from a low-energy orbital and puts it into a higher-energy orbital.

In an octahedral complex, this usually means promoting an electron from a non-bonding t_{2g} orbital to an antibonding $e_g{}^*$ orbital. The effect should be to weaken the bonding of the ligands to the metal. Hence it is predicted that various substitution, isomerization, and racemization processes will occur easily in the photoexcited states.

The intense absorption in the ultraviolet region mentioned earlier is of the so-called "charge transfer" type.[92] The term refers to the characteristic feature that when light is absorbed an electron is transferred from one definite part of the system to another. Such spectra are characteristic of associated pairs of molecules, where we can identify a charge-donating group and a charge-accepting group, or, alternatively, a Lewis base and a Lewis acid, or a reductant and an oxidant. The theory of light absorption by such complexes has been developed by Mulliken.[93] The intensity of

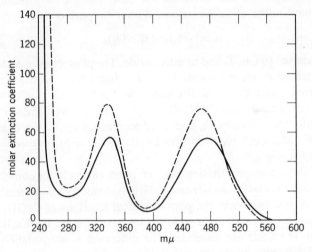

Fig. 8.5 Visible and near-ultraviolet absorption spectra of $Co(NH_3)_6^{3+}$ (solid line) and $Co(en)_3^{3+}$ (dashed line) in aqueous solution.

absorption is due to the absence of hindering selection rules and to the large change in polarity accompanying the transition from the ground state to the excited state. In the case of d-d bands, the intensity is low because the transitions are parity forbidden and sometimes spin forbidden as well.

In the case of complex ions it is not always clear in which direction the charge transfer has occurred. It has been suggested[94] that in the case of easily oxidized cations (or easily reduced ligands) the electron transfer of lowest energy is from cation to ligand:

$$M—L \xrightarrow{h\nu} M^+—L^- \tag{48}$$

In the reverse case of easily reduced cation (or easily oxidized ligand) the transfer is in the opposite direction:

$$M—L \xrightarrow{h\nu} M^-—L^+ \tag{49}$$

Because the metal ion of a complex is usually already positive with respect to the ligand, it is expected that electron transfer from the ligand to the metal will be much more common. This is supported by the evidence (see below).

The charge transfer process is clearly a photochemical oxidation-reduction reaction. It is expected, then, that irradiation of complexes with light in the charge transfer regions of their spectra will cause chemical change.

This has long been known to be the case, though only recently has detailed quantitative work been done. Burger[95] reported that

$$[Co(NH_3)_5NO](NO_3)_3$$

was decomposed to Co(II) and to nitric oxide. The photolysis of $K_3M(CN)_6$ was reported to produce cyanogen and a reduced form of the metal ion and occurred more easily in the order $Mn > Fe > Cr > Co$.[96] Metal oxalates such as $Fe(C_2O_4)_3^{3-}$, $Co(C_2O_4)_3^{3-}$, and the well known uranyl oxalate actinometer yield CO_2 and a reduced metal ion.[97] The complexes $Co(NH_3)_5I^{2+}$ and $Co(NH_3)_5N_3^{2+}$ give Co(II) and I_2 or N_2, respectively, on exposure to sunlight.[98]

Most of the recent quantitative work on photochemistry of complex ions has dealt with the stable Co(III) and Cr(III) systems. The two metals differ markedly in their behavior; the photochemical reactions of Co(III) can be either substitution reactions or redox reactions, whereas for Cr(III) only substitution reactions are observed. The difference is presumably due to the greater difficulty of reducing Cr(III) to Cr(II), compared to reducing Co(III) to Co(II).

Table 8.1 summarizes photochemical data on a number of Co(III) complexes. Quantum yields and products at wavelengths in the visible and in the ultraviolet are shown. The nature of the products is a function of the wavelength of light employed. Light of 550 mμ, which excites the d-d bands, produces more aquation than 370 mμ light, which excites the charge transfer bands. However, the ease of oxidation of the attached ligands is even more important. Thus $Co(NH_3)_5I^{2+}$ yields 100% reduction to Co(II) at both wavelengths, and $Co(NH_3)_5Cl^{2+}$ gives 100% aquation.

For the series $Co(CN)_5X^{3-}$, the quantum yields for hydrolysis decrease in the order $I > CN > Br > Cl$. This is not the order of the spectrochemical series or of coordinate bond strengths, as might be expected if the primary act were dissociation into ions. Instead the order is that of decreasing ease of oxidation. This suggests that the primary act is one of homolytic bond breaking, even though the final products correspond to aquation and not reduction. Also the absorption of light is largely of the d-d type in these cases.

Table 8.1 Photochemical reactions of some cobalt(III) complexes

Complex	Wavelength Irrad., $m\mu$	Product	Quantum Yield, %
$Co(NH_3)_6^{3+}$	370	no reaction	...
$Co(NH_3)_5Cl^{2+}$	370	$Co(NH_3)_5H_2O^{3+}$	0.011
	550	$Co(NH_3)_5H_2O^{3+}$	0.001
$Co(NH_3)_5I^{2+}$	370	$Co(II), I_2$	0.66
	550	$Co(II), I_2$	0.10
$Co(NH_3)_5NCS^{2-}$	370	$Co(NH_3)_5H_2O^{3+}/Co(II) = 0.47$	0.045
	550	$Co(NH_3)_5H_2O^{3+}/Co(II) = 4.1$	6.7×10^{-4}
$Co(NH_3)_5SO_4^{+}$	370	no reaction	...
$Co(NH_3)_5NO_2^{2+}$	370	$Co(NH_3)_5H_2O^{3+}/Co(II) = 0.54$	1.0
$Co(NH_3)_5Br^{2+}$	370	$Co(NH_3)_5H_2O^{3+}/Co(II) = 1.0$	0.21
	550	$Co(NH_3)_5H_2O^{3+}$	0.001
$Co(NH_3)_5N_3^{2+}$	370	$Co(II)$	0.44
	550	$Co(II)$	0.011
$Co(CN)_6^{3-}$	370	$Co(CN)_5H_2O^{2-}$	0.9
$Co(CN)_5Cl^{3-}$	370	$Co(CN)_5H_2O^{2-}$	0.3
$Co(CN)_5Br^{3-}$	370	$Co(CN)_5H_2O^{2-}$	0.7
$Co(CN)_5I^{3-}$	370	$Co(CN)_5H_2O^{2-}$	0.95
	550	$Co(CN)_5H_2O^{2-}$	0.7
$Co(C_2O_4)_3^{3-}$	370	$Co(II), CO_2$	1.0
	550	$Co(II), CO_2$	0.007
$(-)\text{-}Co(C_2O_4)_3^{3-}$	550	no photoracemization	...

Data from references 99 and 100.

Adamson and Sporer have accordingly proposed[99] a three-stage mechanism in which the first stage is homolytic bond breaking, but with the products remaining associated.

$$M^{(III)}A_5X + h\nu \to \to M^{(II)}A_5 \cdot X \tag{50}$$

The double arrow indicates that there may be intervening states between the primary excited state and the state in which bond breaking occurs.

The species $M^{(II)}A_5 \cdot X$ is a common precursor which can react in one of two ways: it can return to the ground state,

$$M^{(II)}A_5 \cdot X \to M^{(III)}A_5X \tag{51}$$

or it can react with the solvent water,

$$M^{(II)}A_5 \cdot X + H_2O \to M^{(II)}A_5H_2O \cdot X \tag{52}$$

The species formed in 52 may be a Co(II) complex with an X· radical in the second coordination sphere. This can react in one of two ways. If electron transfer from the metal to X is favorable energetically, aquation will result.

$$M^{(II)}A_5H_2O \cdot X \rightarrow M^{(III)}A_5H_2O + X^- \tag{53}$$

If X is not a good electron acceptor, a redox reaction will occur.

$$M^{(II)}A_5H_2O \cdot X \rightarrow M^{(II)}A_5H_2O + X \cdot \tag{54}$$

The free radical X· may react in various ways. The products have not always been identified, though it appears that simple recombination to form I_2 is found for iodine atoms. Alternatively, there may be reactions such as[101]

$$Co(NH_3)_5I^{2+} + I \cdot \rightarrow Co(II) + 5NH_3 + I_2 \tag{55}$$

Since NH_3 would be oxidized by free bromine, $Co(NH_3)_5Br^{2+}$ does not give Br_2. However, by using the technique of flash photolysis, it has been possible to detect both iodine atoms and bromine atoms in the photolysis of the corresponding pentaammine halides.[102]

The sequence of reactions 50 to 54 seems quite reasonable. The reversal reaction 51 would account for the fact that quantum yields, ϕ, are usually less than unity. The quantum yields for various products are functions of the temperature. They may increase or decrease with rising temperature; this must be interpreted in terms of different activation energies for reactions 51–54.

The chief objection to the mechanism is that it does not account for the variations in yields of the several products with wavelength that is observed in some cases. It is assumed that the probability of reaction 51 occurring does increase as the amount of excitation energy decreases. This would account for the general fall-off of the quantum yield as the wavelength of light increases but should not influence the relative probabilities of reactions 53 and 54. Because of the small quantum yields at 550 mμ, it is also possible that sometimes the chemical reaction which occurs is due to excitation by the tail of the charge transfer bond. This would agree with a common intermediate irrespective of the wavelength used.

It seems likely that for some Co(III) complexes, at least, different intermediates exist for oxidation-reduction and aquation. Changes to very energetic radiation certainly cause changes in the mechanism. Short-wavelength light of 2537 A will cause photodecomposition of most Co(III) complexes.[103] Even $Co(NH_3)_6^{3+}$ and $Co(en)_3^{3+}$, which are unaffected by light in the near ultraviolet, are decomposed. The decomposition products of $Co(en)_3^{3+}$ include Co(II), NH_3, and formaldehyde.[104] The quantum yields can be functions of the pH, suggesting that protolytic equilibria are involved as well.

Table 8.2 shows some photochemical data for Cr(III) ammine and aquo complexes. As already noted, reduction to Cr(II) does not seem to occur, and only substitution or racemization is found. Also the quantum yields are remarkably insensitive to the wavelength of light used, at least in the 300–700 mμ region. The quantum yield increases with rising temperature. Apparent activation energies run as high as 14 kcal.[105,106]

Table 8.2 Photochemical reactions of some chromium(III) complexes

Complex	Wavelength Irrad., mμ	Product	Quantum yield, ϕ
$Cr(H_2O)_6^{3+}$	254	^{18}O exchange	0.03
	540–730	^{18}O exchange	0.02
$Cr(NH_3)_6^{3+}$	254	$Cr(NH_3)_5H_2O^{3+}$	0.49
	320–600	$Cr(NH_3)_5H_2O^{3+}$	0.32
$Cr(NH_3)_5H_2O^{3+}$	320–600	$Cr(NH_3)_4(H_2O)_2^{3+}$	0.25
$Cr(NH_3)_4(H_2O)_2^{3+}$	320–700	$Cr(NH_3)_3(H_2O)_3^{3+}$	0.16
$Cr(NH_3)_3(H_2O)_3^{3+}$	320–700	$Cr(NH_3)_2(H_2O)_4^{3+}$	0.014
$Cr(NH_3)_2(H_2O)_4^{3+}$	320–700	$Cr(NH_3)(H_2O)_5^{3+}$	0.0018
$Cr(NH_3)_5NCS^{2+}$	560	$Cr(NH_3)_5H_2O^{3+}$	0.013
	360	$Cr(NH_3)_5H_2O^{3+}$	0.018
$Cr(NH_3)_5H_2O^{3+}$	560	$Cr(NH_3)_5NCS^{2+}$	0.075
$Cr(H_2O)_6^{3+}$	575	$Cr(H_2O)_5NCS^{2+}$	0.002
	400	$Cr(H_2O)_5NCS^{2+}$	0.0024
$Cr(H_2O)_5NCS^{2+}$	575	$Cr(H_2O)_6^{3+}$	0.0001
	400	$Cr(H_2O)_6^{3+}$	0.003
$Cr(H_2O)_6^{3+}$	370	$Cr(H_2O)_5Cl^{2+}$	0.006
$(+)-Cr(C_2O_4)_3^{3-}$		racemization	0.045

Data from references 99, 105, and 107.

Such high activation energies for a photochemical reaction can only be explained if some process following photoactivation is an activated process, that is, requires a large thermal energy before it can happen. This in turn means the process must be relatively slow. Assuming a normal frequency factor for a unimolecular reaction,

$$k = 10^{13}e^{-(14,000/RT)} = 10^3 \text{ sec}^{-1} \tag{56}$$

We have just completed the argument which shows that an intermediate lasting as long as a millisecond or so is needed to account for the effect of temperature on ϕ. This needed long-lived intermediate has been postulated to be the excited doublet state, ^2E_g, by some investigators.[105,108]

To understand the reasoning behind this proposal, we must examine the energy level scheme of a typical octahedral Cr(III) complex shown in Fig. 8.6. The ground electronic state is the high-spin $^4A_{2g}$, with the d electron configuration $(t_{2g})^3$. There are three spin-allowed (quartet) excited states. For ammine and aquo ligands the first two produce absorption bands in the regions of 500 and 350 mμ, respectively, very similarly to Fig. 8.5. The third allowed band is often hidden in the intense charge transfer region, since it is very high in energy.

In addition there is a spin-forbidden transition to the doublet state in which the electron configuration is still $(t_{2g})^3$, but two electrons are paired

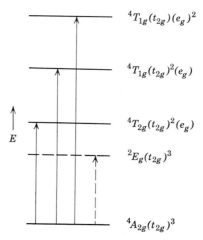

$^4T_{1g}(t_{2g})(e_g)^2$

$^4T_{1g}(t_{2g})^2(e_g)$

$^4T_{2g}(t_{2g})^2(e_g)$

E

$^2E_g(t_{2g})^3$

$^4A_{2g}(t_{2g})^3$

Fig. 8.6 Electronic energy levels for a Cr(III) octahedral complex. The spin-forbidden transition is shown as a dashed arrow, and the allowed transitions as full arrows.

in a single d orbital. This leaves one t_{2g} orbital entirely vacant. According to theory (see Chapter 3), this empty, low-lying orbital will allow very facile reaction by either S_N1 or S_N2 mechanisms. There is no crystal field activation energy, compared to the substantial C.F.A.E. of the ground state. The spin-forbidden band appears with a very sharp spike, in the region of 600 mμ. It is usually only a small increment to the tail of the band at 500 mμ.

Schläfer[109] has estimated the radiative lifetimes of the various excited states from the widths of the absorption bands. This is an example of the Heisenberg uncertainty principle in which a broad line (large ΔE) corresponds to a short lifetime (small Δt), and vice versa. The results are that the excited quartet states will revert to the ground state in times of the order of 10^{-6} to 10^{-7} sec. The spin-forbidden transition from ^2E_g to the ground state has a lifetime of about 10^{-3} to 10^{-4} sec, however. Actually collisional deactivation will cause the two higher quartet states to drop to the lowest excited quartet state, $^4T_{2g}$, in 10^{-10} to 10^{-11} sec with no emission of radiation. The main path for transition from the $^4T_{2g}$ state to the ground state is also non-radiative in nature since fluorescence is not observed.

A radiationless transition from $^4T_{2g}$ to ^2E_g also takes place in a time of about 10^{-7} to 10^{-8} sec.[109] Hence photochemical excitation to any of the quartet states will cause some population of the metastable doublet state. Since this is long-lived and labile, it can be the necessary intermediate for chemical reaction. It will be noted in Table 8.2 that the quantum yield for the aquoammines falls steadily from $Cr(NH_3)_6^{3+}$ to $Cr(H_2O)_6^{3+}$. This decline is explained in the doublet theory by the small spacing between the ^2E_g and $^4T_{2g}$ states in the case of the aquo complex (about 7 kcal).[107] Thermal excitation could cause the ^2E_g state to pass back to the $^4T_{2g}$ state and thence to the $^4A_{2g}$ state, so that ϕ would be reduced. The larger spacing for $Cr(NH_3)_6^{3+}$ would prevent this leakage mechanism.

An alternative theory has been proposed in which Jahn-Teller distorted quartet states are the reactive intermediates.[110] The distorted state would have some metal ligand distances lengthened and hence would be labile (cf. Cu^{2+} and Cr^{2+}). Furthermore its radiative lifetime would be long because its geometry is so different from that of the non-distorted ground state. Irradiation at 650 mμ, which should excite the ^2E_g state, does not[110] lead to a quantum yield of unity, as reported earlier.[107] This result is not really evidence one way or the other, since most of the light absorbed at this wavelength still is causing excitation to the $^4T_{1g}$ state.

The photolysis of the trioxalates of trivalent metal ions has been extensively studied, the ferric oxalate system forming a convenient actinometer.[111]

$$2Fe(C_2O_4)_3^{3-} \xrightarrow{h\nu} 2Fe(C_2O_4)_2^{2-} + C_2O_4^{2-} + 2CO_2 \qquad (57)$$

Figure 8.7 shows the primary quantum yield as a function of wavelength for Fe(III), Mn(III), Co(III), and Cr(III).[112] The $Cr(C_2O_4)_3^{3-}$ does not display any photodecomposition, though optically active $Cr(C_2O_4)_3^{3-}$ does show a fairly efficient photoracemization.[113] Racemization by light has been observed for a number of complex ions.[114]

The mechanism proposed for the redox decomposition postulates the formation of an oxalate radical ion.[111,115]

$$M(C_2O_4)_3^{3-} + h\nu \rightarrow M(C_2O_4)_2^{2-} + C_2O_4^- \qquad (58)$$

$$C_2O_4^- + M(C_2O_4)_3^{3-} \rightarrow 2CO_2 + M(C_2O_4)_2^{2-} + C_2O_4^{2-} \qquad (59)$$

The primary quantum yield is thus half that of the M(II) complex formed. The quantum yield is seen in Fig. 8.7 to be constant in the charge transfer region and to fall off in the d-d band region. Any excess energy at short

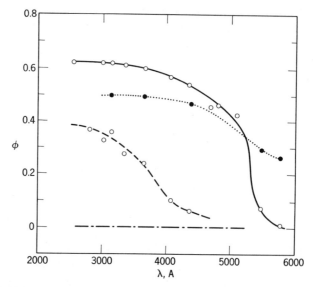

Fig. 8.7 Primary quantum yield action spectra: ———, $Fe(C_2O_4)_3{}^{3-}$; ·······, $Mn(C_2O_4)_3{}^{3-}$; − − − −, $Co(C_2O_4)_3{}^{3-}$; − ·− · −, $Cr(C_2O_4)_3{}^{3-}$.

wavelengths is thus lost by degradative (collisional) processes. For the three metal ions that are reduced, the region of fall-off of ϕ matches the region of minimum absorption between the charge transfer and d-d bands. It is assumed that absorption at the energy of the d-d band still can lead to excitation of the charge transfer type, but with low probability.[112] The competing process is degradation of the absorbed energy. Cage recombination of the radical and $M(C_2O_4)_2{}^{2-}$ could also lower ϕ at low energies.

It was mentioned on p. 237 that substitution reactions of Pt(IV) complexes are often light sensitive. In the case of the halide complex, the action of light leads to exchange with labeled halide ion in solution.

$$PtCl_6{}^{2-} + {}^*Cl^- \rightleftharpoons Pt{}^*Cl_6{}^{2-} + Cl^- \qquad (60)$$

The assumption is that the primary photochemical act was formation of Pt(III) and chlorine atom.[116]

$$PtCl_6{}^{2-} + h\nu \rightarrow PtCl_5{}^{2-} + Cl \qquad (61)$$

It was expected that Pt(III), a d^7 system, would be labile and undergo rapid exchange. A chain reaction could also be established by atom transfer.

$$PtCl_5{}^{2-} + {}^*Cl^- \rightarrow Pt{}^*Cl_5{}^{2-} + Cl^- \qquad (62)$$

$$Pt{}^*Cl_5{}^{2-} + PtCl_6{}^{2-} \rightarrow Pt{}^*Cl_6{}^{2-} + PtCl_5{}^{2-} \qquad (63)$$

The complex $PtBr_6^{2-}$ behaves in a similar way.[102] Photoacceleration of exchange with labeled bromide ion occurs with a very high quantum yield ($\phi \gg 1$), as expected for a chain reaction. However, flash photolysis does not indicate any formation of bromine atoms. Since an oxidizing species is formed on irradiation, it has been proposed that the primary act is as follows:[102]

$$PtBr_6^{2-} + h\nu \rightarrow PtBr_4^{2-} + Br_2 \tag{64}$$

To account for the rapid exchange, it is also supposed that $PtBr_4^{2-}$ does not have the normal planar structure but is distorted in some way. This would be logical if a *cis* pair of bromine atoms were removed from the original octahedral structure. It follows that $PtBr_4^{2-}$ must also be a chain carrier,

$$Pt^*Br_4^{2-} + PtBr_6^{2-} \rightarrow Pt^*Br_6^{2-} + PtBr_4^{2-} \tag{65}$$

to account for the high quantum efficiency.

Some work has also been reported on photochemical reactions of planar d^8 complexes. For example, both *cis-* and *trans-*$Pt(P(C_2H_5)_3)_2Cl_2$ are photochemically isomerized to a photoequilibrium mixture.[117]

$$cis\text{-}Pt(P(C_2H_5)_3)_2Cl_2 \xrightleftharpoons{h\nu} trans\text{-}Pt(P(C_2H_5)_3)_2Cl_2 \tag{66}$$

Normally the isomerization is very slow and requires some free phosphine to occur.[118]

In the isomerization 66, it is the *d-d* bands which are active. The quantum yield is about 0.01. The postulated mechanism is the formation of an excited triplet state. It is known that some of the *d-d* bands are singlet-triplet transitions for Pt(II), but there is still confusion as to the exact assignment.[119]

The triplet state is capable of relatively easy conversion to a tetrahedral structure, at least compared to the ground singlet state. This may be seen by comparing the C.F.S.E. of the following four systems (see p. 69):

	Singlet	Triplet
Square planar	$24.56Dq$	$14.56Dq$
Tetrahedral	$3.56Dq$	$3.56Dq$

The C.F.A.E. would be $10Dq$ units less for conformational isomerization in the triplet state than in the singlet state. Once a tetrahedral structure is achieved, isomerization is sure to follow upon return to the planar configuration.

Although this is an attractive mechanism, it is also possible that photochemical excitation causes substitution, releasing a phosphine ligand into solution. The phosphine would then cause isomerization as previously proposed (p. 426).

Both *trans*-Pd(gly)$_2$ and *trans*-Pt(gly)$_2$ undergo decomposition upon irradiation in the charge transfer region.[120] The *cis* isomer of Pt(gly)$_2$ is converted into the *trans* isomer upon irradiation in the *d-d* band region. The *trans* isomer is not affected in this region,

$$cis\text{-}Pt(gly)_2 + h\nu \rightarrow trans\text{-}Pt(gly)_2 \tag{67}$$

probably because it is the stable form. The quantum yield of 67 is 0.12 at 254 mμ and 0.13 at 313 mμ.

Again it is proposed that the excited *cis*-triplet state assumes a tetrahedral configuration to give the more stable *trans*-triplet state with the planar structure. Since the quantum yield is the same at two wavelengths, and since at least one of these must be a singlet-singlet excitation, the primary excitation need not be to a triplet state. In the case of these glycinate complexes, it is also possible that the mechanism actually is one of solvolysis, which would release free glycine. However, this seems rather unlikely since the reported rate of thermal isomerization, which requires free glycine, seems much too slow.[121]

A brief discussion of some photolytically induced reactions of metal carbonyls and related compounds has already been given on pp. 547. These are usually substitution reactions of one kind or another.

Photooxidation

A number of metal ions in a reduced state are oxidized by the action of ultraviolet light in aqueous solution. At the same time the solvent is reduced. One possible mechanism is that a hydrogen atom is detached from a coordinated water molecule:

$$M(H_2O)_6^{2+} + h\nu \rightarrow M(H_2O)_5OH^{2+} + H \tag{68}$$

There is a linear correlation between the oxidation potential of the M^{2+}/M^{3+} couple and the energy of the long wavelength limit of the light which will cause photooxidation.[122]

Species such as Fe(CN)$_6^{4-}$ also undergo a photochemical oxidation even though no coordinated water is present. The mechanism here has been clearly demonstrated by the detection of the hydrated electron by means of its characteristic absorption spectrum.[123]

$$Fe(CN)_6^{4-} + h\nu \rightarrow Fe(CN)_6^{3-} + e^-(aq) \tag{69}$$

The quantum yield of reaction 69 at 254 mμ is 0.66.[124] It is assumed that some of the electrons that are ejected recombine with the ferricyanide ion before either can escape from the solvent cage that surrounds them at the instant of formation. This is called *geminate recombination* or, more simply, the *cage effect*.

A number of anions are assumed to eject electrons on irradiation.[125] Various radicals or radical anions are formed as the other product, e.g.,

$$OH^- + h\nu \rightarrow HO\cdot + e^-(aq) \tag{70}$$

$$SO_4^{2-} + h\nu \rightarrow SO_4^{\overline{}} + e^-(aq) \tag{71}$$

A convenient source of the NO_3 radical is a $Ce(NO_3)_4$ solution which is irradiated.[126] Since a complex, $Ce(NO_3)_6^{2-}$, is the chief component present, it is likely that a simple charge transfer process is involved, possibly

$$Ce(NO_3)_6^{2-} + h\nu \rightarrow Ce(NO_3)_4^- + NO_3^- + NO_3\cdot \tag{72}$$

The oxidation of metal ions shown in reaction 68 may also occur in two steps: photoemission of an electron, followed by reaction of the electron with hydrogen ion to form the hydrogen atom. A transfer mechanism for aquo ions has also been proposed.[127]

$$Ce(H_2O)^{3+} + h\nu \rightarrow Ce^{4+}, H_2O^- \tag{73}$$

$$Ce^{4+}, H_2O^- + H^+ \rightarrow Ce^{4+} + H_2O + H \tag{74}$$

Thus the electron is shown as localized on one of the coordinated water molecules.

Although spectroscopists have been most interested in the *d-d* bands of metal complexes, it is clear that the charge transfer bands are potentially of much greater chemical interest. Considerable understanding of the possible chemical consequences of absorption in the charge transfer region is given by the concept of optical electronegativity.[128] Jørgensen has shown that the wave numbers of the bands can be predicted by the equation

$$\tilde{\nu} = 30[X_{opt}(L) - X_{opt}(M)] \tag{75}$$

where the X values are optical electronegativities of the ligand, L, and the metal, M, respectively. The wave numbers are given in thousands of reciprocal centimeters (cm^{-1}) or kilokaysers. A correction should be made to $\tilde{\nu}$ for spin-pairing effects. Equations for making these corrections are available, but the changes they cause are not large.[128]

Table 8.3 shows a number of optical electronegativities deduced from spectra. It will be noted that different values are needed for the lower *d* orbitals (t_{2g}) and the upper *d* orbitals (e_g) of octahedral complexes. The difference between them for a given metal ion, multiplied by 30,000 cm^{-1}, should give the $10Dq$ values of the *d-d* spectra. Similarly for the ligands, different electronegativities for π and σ orbitals are listed.

Table 8.3 Optical electronegativities of central atoms and ligands
Values given in parentheses are for full subshells and are derived from the otherwise known values of $10Dq$.

Electron Configuration	Central Atom	Lower Subshell	Upper Subshell	Ligand	π	σ
$3d^3$	Cr(III)	1.8	1.0–1.3	CN^-	...	2.8
$3d^5$	Fe(III)	2.1–2.5	...	cyclopentadienide	2.3?	...
$3d^6$	Co(III)	(2.4)	1.6–1.9	NH_3	...	3.3
$3d^7$	Co(II)	(2.1)	1.9	diethylenetriamine	...	3.2
$3d^8$	Ni(II)	(2.3)	2.1	o-phenanthroline	2.6	...
$3d^9$	Cu(II)	(2.6)	2.3	H_2O	3.5	...
$4d^0$	Mo(VI)	2.1	...	acetylacetonate	2.7	...
$4d^3$	Mo(III)	1.7	1.1	$EDTA^{4-}$	3.3?	...
	Tc(IV)	2.2	1.4	$SO_4{}^{2-}$	3.2	...
$4d^4$	Ru(IV)	2.4	1.6	F^-	3.9	4.4
$4d^5$	Ru(III)	2.1	1.1–1.5	R_3P	...	2.6
	Rh(IV)	2.6	...	R_2S	2.9	...
$4d^6$	Rh(III)	(2.3)	1.3–1.7	$(C_2H_5O)_2PS_2{}^-$	2.7	...
	Pd(IV)	(2.7)	1.9	$(C_2H_5)_2NCS_2{}^-$	2.6?	...
$4d^8$	Pd(II)	(2.4)	1.7	Cl^-	3.0	3.5
$4f^2$	Nd(IV)	2.45	—	R_3As	...	2.5
$4f^5$	Sm(III)	0.95	...	$(C_2H_5O)_2PSe_2{}^-$	2.6	...
$4f^6$	Eu(III)	1.1	...	Br^-	2.8	3.3
$4f^8$	Dy(IV)	3.55	...	I^-	2.5	3.0
$4f^{12}$	Tm(III)	1.6	...			
$4f^{13}$	Yb(III)	1.75	...			
$5d^0$	W(VI)	2.0	...			
$5d^2$	Os(VI)	2.6	...			
$5d^3$	Re(IV)	2.0	1.1			
	Ir(VI)	2.9	...			
$5d^4$	Os(IV)	2.2	1.3			
	Pt(VI)	3.2	...			
$5d^5$	Os(III)	1.9	1.1			
	Ir(IV)	2.35	1.5			
$5d^6$	Ir(III)	(2.25)	1.3–1.5			
	Pt(IV)	(2.6)	1.6–1.7			
$5d^8$	Au(III)	(2.8)	1.8			
$5f^2$	U(IV)	1.5	...			
$5f^3$	Np(IV)	1.75	...			
$5f^4$	Pu(IV)	2.05	...			

From reference 129.

It will be noted that σ electrons are held more tightly than π electrons. Also the electronegativity of a metal ion increases with its oxidation state. A ligand of low electronegativity will easily transfer an electron to a metal ion of high electronegativity, and $\tilde{\nu}$ will be small. If the electronegativities are inverted, electron transfer in the opposite direction is expected. Actually the only cases of electron transfer from the metal to the ligand that are indicated by spectroscopic evidence involve aromatic heterocyclic ligands. These include o-phenanthroline, dipyridyl, acetylacetone, and others. The cyanide ion and carbon monoxide ligands are also probable examples.[129]

References

1. M. L. Bender, *Advan. Chem. Ser.*, **37**, 19 (1963); R. W. Hay, *Rev. Pure Appl. Chem.*, **13**, 157 (1963); A. E. Martell, *Advan. Chem. Ser.*, **37**, 161 (1963); M. M. Jones and W. A. Connar, *Ind. Eng. Chem.*, **55**, 15 (1963); M. T. Beck, *Rec. Chem. Progr.*, **27**, 37 (1966).
2. W. A. Waters, *Mechanisms of Oxidation of Organic Compounds*, Methuen and Co., London, 1964; R. Stewart, *Oxidation Mechanisms*, W. A. Benjamin, New York, 1964.
3. M. L. Tobe, *Sci. Progr.*, **XLIX**, 475 (1961); D. H. Busch, *Advan. Chem. Ser.*, **37**, 1 (1963).
4. R. J. P. Williams, *Biol. Rev. Cambridge Phil. Soc.*, **28**, 381 (1953); G. L. Eichhorn, *Advan. Chem. Ser.*, **37**, 37 (1963); F. P. Dwyer in *Chelating Agents and Metal Chelates* (F. P. Dwyer and D. P. Mellor, eds.), Academic Press, New York, 1964, pp. 335–378; also A. Shulman and F. P. Dwyer, *op. cit.*, pp. 383–435.
5. M. L. Bender, *J. Am. Chem. Soc.*, **73**, 1626 (1951).
6. H. Kroll, *J. Am. Chem. Soc.*, **74**, 2036 (1952).
7. M. P. Springer and C. Curran, *Inorg. Chem.*, **2**, 1270 (1963).
8. M. L. Bender and B. W. Turnquest, *J. Am. Chem. Soc.*, **77**, 4271 (1955); **79**, 1889 (1957).
9. M. D. Alexander and D. H. Busch, *J. Am. Chem. Soc.*, **88**, 1130 (1966).
10. J. P. Collman and D. A. Buckingham, *J. Am. Chem. Soc.*, **85**, 3039 (1963).
11. E. L. Smith and R. L. Hill, *The Enzymes*, Vol. 4 (P. D. Bayer, H. Lardy, and K. Myrback, eds.), Academic Press, New York, 1960, p. 37.
12. L. Meriwether and F. H. Westheimer, *J. Am. Chem. Soc.*, **78**, 5119 (1956).
13. J. I. Hoppe and J. E. Prue, *J. Chem. Soc.*, **1957**, 1775.
14. G. Sachs, *Ber.* **54**, 1849 (1921).
15. F. Lynch, E. Reichert, and L. Rueff, *Ann.*, **574**, 14 (1951).
16. J. R. Stern, *J. Biol. Chem.*, **221**, 33 (1956).
17. E. Bamann and M. Meisenheimer, *Ber.*, **71**, 1711 (1938); E. Bamann, F. Fischler, and H. Trapmann, *Biochem. Z.*, **325**, 413 (1951).
18. A. Lehninger, *Physiol. Rev.*, **30**, 393 (1950).
19. W. W. Butcher and F. H. Westheimer, *J. Am. Chem. Soc.*, **77**, 2420 (1955).
20. F. Smith, G. I. Drummond, and H. G. Khorana, *J. Am. Chem. Soc.*, **83**, 698 (1961).
21. R. L. Gustafson, S. Chaberek, and A. E. Martell, *J. Am. Chem. Soc.*, **85**, 598 (1963) and references therein.
22. J. Van Wazer, *Phosphorus and Its Compounds*, Interscience Publishers, New York, 1958, Vol. I, pp. 457, 653.
23. J. M. Rainey, M. M. Jones, and W. L. Lockhart, *J. Inorg. Nucl. Chem.*, **26**, 1415 (1964); E. Thilo, *Advan. Inorg. Chem. Radiochemistry*, **4**, 31 (1962).
24. G. L. Eichhorn and J. C. Bailar, Jr., *J. Am. Chem. Soc.*, **75**, 2905 (1953).
25. G. L. Eichhorn and I. M. Trachtenberg, *J. Am. Chem. Soc.*, **76**, 5183 (1954); G. L. Eichhorn and N. D. Marchand, *ibid.*, **78**, 2688 (1956); G. L. Eichhorn, *Federation Proc.*, **20**, 40 (1961).
26. P. Pfeiffer, W. Offermann, and H. Werner, *J. prakt. Chem.*, **159**, 313 (1941).
27. D. E. Metzler, M. Ikawa, and E. E. Snell, *J. Am. Chem. Soc.*, **76**, 648 (1954); E. E. Snell, *Vitamins Hormones*, **16**, 77 (1958); D. L. Leussing and E. M. Hanna, *J. Am. Chem. Soc.*, **88**, 693, 697 (1966).

28. S. Akabori, T. Otani, R. Marshall, M. Winitz, and J. P. Greenstein, *Arch. Biochem. Biophys.*, **83**, 1 (1959).
29. M. Murakami and K. Takahashi, *Bull. Chem. Soc. Japan.* **32**, 308 (1959).
30. D. H. Williams and D. H. Busch, *J. Am. Chem. Soc.*, **87**, 4644 (1965).
31. K. Pedersen, *Acta Chem. Scand.*, **2**, 252, 385 (1948).
32. A. Kornberg, S. Ochoa, and A. H. Mehler, *J. Biol. Chem.*, **174**, 159 (1948); J. E. Prue, *J. Chem. Soc.*, **1952**, 2331; E. Gelles and R. W. Hay, **1958**, 3673; E. Gelles and A. Salama, *ibid.*, **1958**, 3684, 3689.
33. J. F. Speck, *J. Biol. Chem.*, **178**, 315 (1949).
34. M. Stiles, *J. Am. Chem. Soc.*, **81**, 2598 (1959); M. Stiles and H. L. Finkheimer, *ibid.*, **81**, 505 (1959).
35. I. M. Klotz and W. C. Loh Ming, *J. Am. Chem. Soc.*, **76**, 805 (1954).
36. F. R. Duke, *J. Am. Chem. Soc.*, **69**, 3054 (1947); F. R. Duke and A. A. Forist, *ibid.*, **71**, 2790 (1949).
37. H. Taube, *J. Am. Chem. Soc.*, **69**, 1418 (1947), and **70**, 1216 (1948); F. R. Duke, *ibid.*, **69**, 2885 (1947).
38. For a general review see G. A. Russell, *J. Am. Chem. Soc.*, **79**, 3871 (1957); *J. Chem. Educ.*, **36**, 111 (1959).
39. J. P. Wibaut and A. Strong, *Koninkl. Ned. Akad. Wetenschap. Proc.*, **B54**, 102 (1951).
40. R. Lombard and L. Rammert, *Bull. soc. chim. France*, **23**, 36 (1956).
41. For recent quantitative rate studies see H. Boardman, *J. Am. Chem. Soc.*, **84**, 1376 (1962).
42. K. I. Ivanov, V. K. Savinova, and E. G. Mikhailova, *Compt. rend acad. sci. URSS*, **25**, 34, 40 (1939).
43. See H. S. Blanchard, *J. Am. Chem. Soc.*, **82**, 2014 (1960), for example.
44. C. E. H. Bawn, *Disc. Faraday Soc.*, **14**, 181 (1953).
45. See, for example, F. A. Bovey, I. M. Kolthoff, A. I. Medalia, and E. J. Meehan, *Emulsion Polymerization*, Interscience Publishers, New York, 1955.
46. J. K. Kochi and R. D. Gilliam, *J. Am. Chem. Soc.*, **86**, 5251 (1964).
47. (a) F. A. L. Anet and E. LeBlanc, *J. Am. Chem. Soc.*, **79**, 2649 (1957). (b) J. K. Kochi and D. D. Davis, *ibid.*, **86**, 5264 (1964).
48. J. Halpern and J. P. Maher, *J. Am. Chem. Soc.*, **86**, 2311 (1964); **87**, 5361 (1965).
49. C. Manwell, *Ann. Rev. Physiol.*, **22**, 191 (1960).
50. L. H. Vogt, H. M. Faigenbaum, and S. E. Wiberley, *Chem. Rev.*, **63**, 269 (1963); J. A. Connor and E. A. V. Ebsworth, *Advan. Inorg. Chem. Radiochem.*, **6**, 279 (1964).
51. (a) A. E. Martell and M. Calvin, *Chemistry of the Metal Chelate Compounds*, Prentice-Hall, Englewood Cliffs, N.J., 1952. (b) H. Diehl and C. C. Hoch, *Inorg. Syn.*, **3**, 196 (1950).
52. L. Vaska, *Science*, **140**, 809 (1963).
53. B. Jezowska-Trzebiatowska and B. Przywarska, *Memoirs of the Sixteenth Congress of the International Union of Pure and Applied Chemistry*, Paris, 1958, p. 843.
54. J. F. Drake and R. J. P. Williams, *Nature*, **182**, 1084 (1958).
55. J. Selbin and J. H. Junkin, *J. Am. Chem. Soc.*, **82**, 1057 (1960).
56. G. Engelsma, Y. Yamamoto, E. Markman, and M. Calvin, *J. Phys. Chem.*, **66**, 2517 (1962).
57. E. Fremy, *Ann. Chem.*, **83**, 227 (1952).
58. A. Werner and A. Mylius, *Z. anorg. Chem.*, **16**, 245 (1898).
59. K. Gleu and K. Rehm, *Z. anorg. allgem. Chem.*, **237**, 79 (1938).
60. A. Haim and W. K. Wilmarth, *J. Am. Chem. Soc.*, **83**, 509 (1961).
61. G. L. Goodman, H. L. Hecht, and J. A. Weil, *Advan. Chem. Ser.*, **36**, 90 (1962).

62. A. A. Vlček, *Trans. Faraday Soc.*, **56**, 1137 (1960).

63. N. G. Vannerberg and C. Brosset, *Acta Cryst.*, **16**, 247 (1963).

64. W. P. Schaefer and R. E. Marsh, *J. Am. Chem. Soc.*, **88**, 178 (1966).

65. N. G. Vannerberg, *Acta Cryst.*, **18**, 449 (1965).

66. P. Pfeiffer, E. Brieth, E. Lubbe, and T. Tsumaki, *Ann. Chem.*, **503**, 84 (1933); T. Tsumaki, *Bull. Chem. Soc. Japan*, **13**, 252 (1938); M. Calvin, R. H. Bailes, and W. K. Wilmarth, *J. Am. Chem. Soc.*, **68**, 2254 (1946).

67. R. F. Steward, P. A. Estep, and J. J. S. Sebastian, *U.S. Bur. Mines Inform. Circ.* No. 7906 (1959).

68. P. C. Hewlett and L. F. Larkworthy, *J. Chem. Soc.*, **1965**, 882.

69. A. Earnshaw, P. C. Hewlett, and L. F. Larkworthy, *J. Chem. Soc.*, **1965**, 4718.

70. D. Burk, J. Z. Hearon, L. Caroline, and A. L. Schade, *J. biol. Chem.*, **165**, 723 (1946); J. Z. Hearon and D. Burk, *J. Natl. Cancer Inst.*, **9**, 337 (1949); L. Michaelis, *Arch. Biochem.*, **14**, 17 (1947).

71. Y. Sano and H. Tanabe, *J. Inorg. Nucl. Chem.*, **25**, 11 (1963).

72. J. A. Ibers and S. J. LaPlaca, *Science*, **145**, 920 (1964); *J. Am. Chem. Soc.*, **87**, 2581 (1965).

73. J. S. Griffith, *Proc. Roy. Soc. (London)*, **A235**, 23 (1956).

74. L. Pauling, "Hemoglobin," *Sir Joseph Barcroft Memorial Symposium*, Butterworths, London, 1949, p. 57.

75. P. L. Pauson, *Organometallic Chemistry* (H. Zeiss, ed.), Reinhold Publishing Corp., New York, 1960, Chap. 7; M. D. Rausch, *Advan. Chem. Ser.*, **37**, 4 (1963).

76. E. A. Hill and J. H. Richards, *J. Am. Chem. Soc.*, **83**, 3840, 4216 (1961).

77. G. R. Buell, W. E. McEwen, and J. Kleinberg, *J. Am. Chem. Soc.*, **84**, 40 (1962).

78. M. M. Jones, *Advan. Chem. Ser.*, **37**, 116 (1963).

79. G. F. Smith and F. W. Cagle, *J. Org. Chem.*, **12**, 781 (1947).

80. A. F. Richards, J. H. Ridd, and M. L. Tobe, *Chem. & Ind.*, **1963**, 1727.

81. J. P. Collman, *Advan. Chem. Ser.*, **37**, 78 (1963).

82. D. H. Busch, *Record Chem. Progr.*, **25**, 107 (1964).

83. N. F. Curtis, *J. Chem. Soc.*, **1960**, 4409; M. M. Blight and N. F. Curtis, *ibid.*, **1962**, 1204, 3016; D. A. House and N. F. Curtis, *J. Am. Chem. Soc.*, **84**, 3248 (1962); and **86**, 223, 1331 (1964).

84. N. F. Curtis, *J. Chem. Soc.*, **1964**, 2644.

85. M. C. Thompson and D. H. Busch, *J. Am. Chem. Soc.*, **86**, 312, 3651 (1964).

86. G. N. Schrauzer, *Ber.*, **95**, 1483 (1962); F. Umland and D. Thierig, *Angew. Chem.*, **74**, 388 (1962).

87. J. D. Curry and D. H. Busch, *J. Am. Chem. Soc.*, **86**, 592 (1964).

88. A. Eschenmoser, R. Scheffold, E. Bertele, M. Pesaro, and H. Gschwind, *Proc. Roy. Soc. (London)*, **288**, 306 (1965).

89. R. B. Woodward, *Pure Appl. Chem.*, **2**, 383 (1964).

90. F. E. Ilse and H. Hartmann, *Z. physik. Chem.*, **197**, 239 (1951); *Z. Naturforsch.*, **6a**, 751 (1951).

91. For detailed discussions see B. N. Figgis, *Introduction to Ligand Fields*, Interscience Publishers, New York, 1965; C. J. Ballhausen, *Introduction to Ligand Field Theory*, McGraw-Hill Book Co., New York, 1962; T. M. Dunn, D. S. McClure, and R. G. Pearson, *Some Aspects of Crystal Field Theory*, Harper and Row, New York, 1965.

92. L. E. Orgel, *Quart. Rev. (London)*, **8**, 452 (1954).

93. R. S. Mulliken, *J. Am. Chem. Soc.*, **74**, 811 (1952); *J. Phys. Chem.*, **56**, 801 (1952); *J. Chim. Phys.*, **61**, 20 (1964).

94. E. Rabinowitch, *Rev. Mod. Phys.*, **14**, 112 (1942.)

95. O. K. H. Burger, *Proc. Chem. Soc.*, **27**, 160 (1911).
96. R. Schwartz and H. Weiss, *Ber.* **58B**, 746 (1925); R. Schwartz and K. Tede, *ibid.*, **60B**, 69 (1927).
97. J. Vranek, *Z. Elektrochem.*, **23**, 336 (1939); C. A. Parker, *Proc. Roy. Soc. (London)*, **220**, 104 (1952).
98. M. Linhard and M. Wiegel, *Z. anorg. allgem. Chem.*, **266**, 49, 73 (1951); M. Linhard and H. Flygare, *ibid.*, **262**, 328 (1950).
99. A. W. Adamson and A. H. Sporer, *J. Am. Chem. Soc.*, **80**, 3865 (1958).
100. A. W. Adamson, *Disc. Faraday Soc.*, **29**, 163 (1960).
101. A. Haim and H. Taube, *J. Am. Chem. Soc.*, **85**, 495 (1963).
102. S. A. Penkett and A. W. Adamson, *J. Am. Chem. Soc.*, **87**, 2514 (1965).
103. J. F. Endicott and M. Z. Hoffman, *J. Am. Chem. Soc.*, **87**, 3348 (1964); V. Bolzani, V. Carassiti, L. Moggi, and N. Sabbatini, *Inorg. Chem.*, **4**, 1247 (1965).
104. D. Klein and C. W. Moeller, *Inorg. Chem.*, **4**, 394 (1965).
105. R. A. Plane and J. P. Hunt, *J. Am. Chem. Soc.*, **79**, 3343 (1957).
106. A. W. Adamson, *J. Inorg. Nucl. Chem.*, **13**, 275 (1960).
107. M. R. Edelson and R. A. Plane, *J. Phys. Chem.*, **63**, 327 (1959); *Inorg. Chem.*, **3**, 231 (1964).
108. H. L. Schläfer, *Z. phys. Chem.*, **11**, 5 (1957); *Z. Elektrochem.*, **64**, 886 (1960).
109. H. L. Schläfer, *J. Phys. Chem.*, **69**, 2201 (1965).
110. E. E. Wegner and A. W. Adamson, *J. Am. Chem. Soc.*, **88**, 394 (1966).
111. C. A. Parker, *Trans. Faraday Soc.*, **50**, 1213 (1954); C. A. Parker and C. G. Hatchard, *J. Phys. Chem.*, **63**, 22 (1959).
112. G. B. Porter, J. G. W. Doering, and S. Karanka, *J. Am. Chem. Soc.*, **84**, 4027 (1962).
113. S. T. Spees and A. W. Adamson, *Inorg. Chem.*, **1**, 531 (1962).
114. Reference 24 and F. P. Dwyer, I. K. Reid, and F. L. Garvan, *J. Am. Chem. Soc.*, **83**, 1285 (1961).
115. T. B. Copestake and N. Uri, *Proc. Roy. Soc. (London)*, **A228**, 252 (1955).
116. R. L. Rich and H. Taube, *J. Am. Chem. Soc.*, **76**, 2608 (1954).
117. P. Haake and T. A. Hylton, *J. Am. Chem. Soc.*, **84**, 3774 (1962).
118. J. Chatt and R. G. Wilkins, *J. Chem. Soc.*, **1952**, 273.
119. H. B. Gray and C. J. Ballhausen, *J. Am. Chem. Soc.*, **85**, 260 (1963); D. S. Martin and C. A. Lenhardt, *Inorg. Chem.*, **3**, 1368 (1964).
120. V. Balzani, V. Carassiti, L. Moggi, and F. Scandola, *Inorg. Chem.*, **4**, 1243 (1965).
121. L. M. Volshtein and I. O. Volodima, *Zh. Neorgan. Khim.*, **7**, 2685 (1962).
122. F. S. Dainton, *J. Chem. Soc.*, **1952**, 1533.
123. M. S. Matheson, W. A. Mulac, and J. Rabini, *J. Phys. Chem.*, **67**, 2613 (1963).
124. F. S. Dainton and P. L. Airey, *Nature*, **207**, 119 (1965).
125. F. S. Dainton and D. G. L. James, *J. Chim. Phys.*, **48**, 1 (1951); J. Jortner, M. Ottolenghi, and G. Stein, *J. Phys. Chem.*, **68**, 247 (1964).
126. T. W. Martin, R. E. Rummel, and R. C. Gross, *J. Am. Chem. Soc.*, **86**, 2595 (1964).
127. F. Hussain and R. G. W. Norrish, *Proc. Roy. Soc. (London)*, **275A**, 161 (1963).
128. C. K. Jørgensen, *Orbitals in Atoms and Molecules*, Academic Press, New York, 1962; C. K. Jørgensen, *Mol. Phys.*, **6**, 43 (1963).
129. C. K. Jørgensen, *Essays in Coordination Chemistry*, Birkhauser Verlag, Basel, 1964.
130. A. D. Allen and C. V. Senoff, *Chem. Comm.* 621 (1965); J. P. Collman and J. W. Kang, *J. Am. Chem. Soc.* **88**, 3459 (1966).
131. M. E. Volp'in and V. B. Shur, *Nature*, **209**, 1236 (1966); H. Brintzinger, *J. Am. Chem. Soc.* **88**, 4305, 4307 (1966).
132. N. F. Curtis and R. W. Hay, *Chem. Comm.* 524 (1966).

Author Index

Subject Index

(Because of their frequency of occurrence, complexes of Co, Cr, and Pt are not indexed)